ANNUAL REVIEW OF PHYSIOLOGY

EDITORIAL COMMITTEE (1985)

ANNUAL REVIEW OF PHYSIOLOGY

VOLUME 47, 1985

ROBERT M. BERNE, *Editor*

University of Virginia Medical School

JOSEPH F. HOFFMAN, *Associate Editor*

Yale University School of Medicine

ANNUAL REVIEWS INC.   4139 EL CAMINO WAY   PALO ALTO, CALIFORNIA 94306 USA

ANNUAL REVIEWS INC.
Palo Alto, California, USA

International Standard Serial Number: 0066-4278
International Standard Book Number: 0-8243-0347-4
Library of Congress Catalog Card Number: 39-15404

Typesetting by Kachina Typesetting Inc., Tempe, Arizona; John Olson, President Typesetting coordinator, Janis Hoffman

PRINTED AND BOUND IN THE UNITED STATES OF AMERICA

PREFACE

The purpose of a preface is usually to present the goals of the book and the course of action taken to achieve those goals. It also recognizes and thanks the individuals who have made the book possible. Since sectionalization of the *Annual Review of Physiology* (ARP) (see prefaces to Volumes 42 and 43), the introductory comments of the section editors now serve these purposes. In these introductions, each section editor has indicated the central theme of his section and the manner in which the component reviews relate to each other.

Therefore I would like to depart from the customary preface format and dedicate this volume to the late Julius H. Comroe, Jr., a former editor of ARP and one of the most outstanding and influential physiologists of our times. Dr. Comroe made many contributions to physiology as an investigator, author, teacher, critic, editor, and defender of the pursuit of basic science. He was the founder and for 16 years the director of the Cardiovascular Research Institute (CVRI) of the University of California at San Francisco. His intellectual and scientific leadership was instrumental in making the CVRI a meeting place for basic science and clinical research, both of the highest caliber. His devotion to critical thinking and scientific rigor inspired an entire generation of physician investigators who began their research careers at the CVRI.

One of Dr. Comroe's most important contributions was his careful tracing of the bits and pieces of basic science that eventually led to breakthroughs in the understanding and treatment of disease. He explained this process of information transfer to government officials, the public, and his fellow scientists in the clearest terms. His spoken and written words on this subject, lucid, precise, and spiced with subtle humor, will always be remembered because of the great impact they had in encouraging support for biomedical research.

As editor of ARP, Julius Comroe was imaginative, innovative, skillful, and perseverant. He generated new ideas for ARP, laying the groundwork for the sectionalization of the volume, for example. Implementation of the new format was undertaken during the editorship of Isidore S. Edelman, a colleague of Comroe's whom Julius had originally recruited to the editorial board. In Dr. Edelman's preface to Volume 41 of ARP, he wrote: "A special debt of gratitude is owed to J. H. Comroe, Jr., who, during his tenure as Editor, began to explore new ways for the *Annual Review of Physiology* to fulfill its responsibilities." In the preface to Volume 44, Edelman wrote that Comroe's "leadership and foresight played a key role in the evolution of ARP during the last decade."

In recognition of his numerous important and lasting contributions, and particularly of his role in the enhancement of ARP, this volume is dedicated to the memory of Julius H. Comroe, Jr.

ROBERT M. BERNE
EDITOR

Annual Review of Physiology
Volume 47, 1985

CONTENTS

OTHER REVIEWS OF INTEREST TO PHYSIOLOGISTS

From the *Annual Review of Biochemistry,* Volume 54 (1985):

Chemical Probes of Mitochondrial ATP Synthesis and Translocation, P. V. Vignais, Joel Lunardi

The Mitochondrial Oxidative Phosphorylation System, Youssef Hatefi

The Membrane Skeleton of Human Erythrocytes and Its Implications for More Complex Cells, Vann Bennett

Cell Adhesion and the Molecular Process of Morphogenesis, Gerald M. Edelman

Growth Hormone Releasing Factors, Roger Guillemin, Nicholas Ling, Peter Bohlen, Fred Esch, Fusun Zeytin, Andrew Baird, and William Wehrenberg

Receptors and Phosphoinositide-Generated Second Messengers, Lowell E. Hokin

From the *Annual Review of Medicine,* Volume 36 (1985):

The Electrophysiology of Acute Myocardial Ischemia, Harry A. Fozzard and Jonathon Makielski

Beta-Adrenergic Blocking Drugs, Alan S. Nies and John G. Gerber

Pathophysiology of Myocardial Reperfusion, Keith A. A. Fox, Burton E. Sobel, and Steven R. Bergmann

Current Concepts of the Molecular Mechanism of Insulin Action, C. Ronald Kahn

Hormonal Regulation of Glomerular Filtration, Valentina Kon and Iekuni Ichikawa

Pathophysiology and Treatment of Sleep Apnea, David H. Ingbar and Bernard Gee

From the *Annual Review of Neuroscience,* Volume 8 (1985):

The Primate Premotor Cortex: Past, Present, and Preparatory, Steven P. Wise

Adenosine As a Neuromodulator, Solomon H. Snyder

Applications of Monoclonal Antibodies to Neuroscience Research, Karen L. Valentino, Janet Winter, and Louis F. Reichardt

Central Pattern Generators for Locomotion, with Special Reference to Vertebrates, Sten Grillner and Peter Wallén

Real-Time Optical Mapping of Neuronal Activity: From Single Growth Cones to the Intact Mammalian Brain, Amiram Grinvald

Brainstem Control of Saccadic Eye Movements, A. F. Fuchs, C. R. S. Kaneko, and C. A. Scudder

Phototransduction in Vertebrate Rods, E. A. Schwartz

Mobility and Localization of Proteins in Excitable Membranes, Mu-ming Poo

Spatial Frequency Analysis in the Visual System, Robert Shapley and Peter Lennie

Postnatal Development of Vision in Human and Nonhuman Primates, Ronald G. Boothe, Velma Dobson, and Davida Y. Teller

Horace W. Davenport

Ann. Rev. Physiol. 1985. 47:1-14

THE APOLOGY OF A SECOND-CLASS MAN

Horace W. Davenport

Department of Physiology, The University of Michigan, Ann Arbor, Michigan 48109

INTRODUCTION

I was once a member of the Editorial Committee of the *Annual Review of Physiology,* so when the Black Spot arrived, I knew how I had been chosen.

SCENE: *A conference room. The editorial committee is in session.*

Chairman: . . . So it is agreed that this year we will do gating potentials in the left bundle for the heart section, and next year we will do gating potentials in the right bundle. Now, how about the prefatory chapter? You will remember that last year we wanted X, but he turned us down. We had Y and Z in reserve, and Y did a fine job. How about Z this year?

Committee Member A: Z doesn't really deserve it. We ought to get someone else. How about Davenport?

Committee Member B: Who's he?

Committee Member A: The stomach man, you know. Been at Michigan for fifty years.

Committee Member C: I thought he was dead.

Committee Member A: He was going strong writing history when I was in Ann Arbor last month. He can always be relied upon to say something amusing. We ought to get him before it's too late.

Committee Member D: I agree.

Chairman: So we'll ask Davenport. Now for the kidney section. I suggest that this year we do the first three cells of the descending loop . . .

First, I must explain my title. The word *Apology* is an allusion to Colley Cibber's *Apology for His Life*. He was a second-class dramatist and poet

1

0066-4278/85/0315-0001$02.00

although he may have been a first-class actor, and this autobiographical essay is more like his *Apology* than like Cardinal Newman's *Apologia pro Vita sua.*

In 1937 the Examiners of Oxford University put me firmly in the Second Class in the Final Honour School of Animal Physiology. I have since lived much of my life among first-class men, and when I compare myself with Wallace Fenn or W. A. H. Rushton, for example, I know the Examiners were right. The question I shall try to answer here is, How can a second-class man accomplish anything that deserves to be commemorated in a prefatory chapter? Because there are so many more second-class men than first-class ones, perhaps the answer will encourage some of the younger ones.

After my sophomore year at the California Institute of Technology I never intended to be anything but an academic. An academic's obligations are teaching, service, and research; I shall take them up in that order.

TEACHING—AND OTHER WAYS OF LEARNING

To teach physiology, I first had to learn some. When I went to Oxford in 1935 as a Rhodes Scholar I was headed toward biochemistry—I knew no physiology. In those days Oxford had no independent School of Biochemistry, so I was required to read for the Animal Physiology School, which was three fourths physiology and one fourth biochemistry. My tutor at Balliol College parceled out the subject in one-week bits and assigned me an essay on each bit. When I had a physiological topic I read *Starling* and *Physiological Reviews,* and then a monograph if a recent one were applicable. Then I skimmed some of the primary literature. Thus I learned classical mammalian physiology with a good foundation of general physiology. It was an inefficient way to learn, and I would have done better if I had first been through the kind of survey course—a sort of physiological Chaucer to Browning—that I later taught.

The other quarter of the Animal Physiology School was devoted to biochemistry as taught at Oxford by Professor R. A. Peters. He had isolated what he then called aneurin. We now call it thiamin. He had found that aneurin is a cofactor in the decarboxylation of pyruvate, and consequently he was the first man to know the function of a vitamin. I introduced myself to him. He was kind to me and allowed me to do a little research on vitamin C in his laboratory during the summer vacation. I knew about vitamin C, for I had worked on it with Henry Borsook at Caltech, and I spent the six-week spring vacation of 1936 in a library in Munich reading all that had been published about it. One day in 1937 I got an urgent call: Would I please see Professor Peters at once? He had agreed to write an Annual Review on the water-soluble vitamins. The manuscript was already overdue, and he had just remembered that vitamin C is water-soluble. Would I help? I wrote a draft in less than two weeks, and Professor Peters revised it. Thus the 1938 volume of *Annual Review of*

Biochemistry contains an article on *The Vitamin B Complex* by R. A. Peters & J. R. O'Brien and one on *Vitamin C* by R. A. Peters & H. W. Davenport. When I last saw the professor, by then Sir Rudolph Peters and the inventor of British Anti-Lewisite, at the centenary meeting of the British Physiological Society in Cambridge in 1976, he said it had been a jolly good review. He also said that because he was 87 he would have to give up his laboratory the next year.

I was privileged to take the laboratory courses that had been developed in England beginning about 1860. When William Sharpey started to teach physiology at University College London, his only practical work was histology. In that tradition, histology was part of the physiology course at Oxford. We stained our own sections and examined muscle spindles that had been prepared by C. S. Sherrington. In 1870 Michael Foster had added work with frog heart, nerve, and muscle to the University College practical course in physiology, and John Burdon Sanderson brought Michael Foster's laboratory teaching to Oxford when he became professor of physiology there. Consequently, I spent the Saturday mornings of two terms in the "Frog Jumps" laboratory, measuring refractory periods and demonstrating decrementless conduction. Determination of the strength-duration relationship had been added in the 1920s, and I learned to use a Keith Lucas spring rheotome to obtain the data used in calculating chronaxie.

Sherrington had started a mammalian laboratory for students when he was in Liverpool, and he transferred it to Oxford in 1913. When I took that laboratory course, a young Demonstrator named Jack Eccles showed me how to make a Langendorff heart preparation by perfusing an isolated heart's coronary vessels by way of the aorta. The grand climax of the mammalian experiments was the demonstration of ipsalateral flexion and crossed extension in a decorticated cat. Carl Pfaffmann and I did that together, but when I was asked in the Practical Examination for Schools to "Demonstrate as many reflexes as possible," I was able to make that rather tricky preparation all by myself.

There was a surprising amount of human physiology. I learned to analyze my own gastric juice and to record the A, C, and V waves in the jugular vein by means of a Mackenzie polygraph. Douglas and Priestley themselves taught me how to collect alveolar air and analyze it with a Haldane apparatus. The questions I was asked on that part of the final practical examination were to determine total, free, and combined acid in a sample of gastric juice and to measure the energy cost of walking four miles an hour. For the latter I put on a Douglas bag and a nose clip and walked around the parks with a stopwatch in my hand. Then I measured and analyzed my expired air, with F. J. W. Roughton as external examiner looking over my shoulder. I had learned the equations used in the Haldane open-circuit method, and I made the appropriate calculations.

When Cuthbert Bazett gave me my first job as a physiologist in 1941, an instructorship at the University of Pennsylvania, I was of course expected to teach physiology although I had no experience as a teacher or as a physiologist. I really learned something about physiology and the technique of teaching in the student laboratory on the English model that Bazett had provided for dental and medical students.

Two years later I had the exciting experience of teaching under Eugene Landis when he revised the teaching of physiology at Harvard. He added a good bit more human physiology, so I learned about the distribution of skin temperature over the body and its changes when the body is cooled and warmed, about circulatory changes occurring when one stands on a tilt table, and about responses of blood flow through the hand to emotional stress.

In those days youngsters did what they were told. At Pennsylvania in 1941, for the first time in 40 years A. N. Richards was too busy to teach renal physiology, and I was told to do it. I started with Arthur Cushny and discovered what Richards himself and E. K. Marshall and Homer Smith had done. Those dreadful lecture rooms at Penn were entered from both the first and second floors, and the second floor door was directly opposite Vice-president Richards's office. One day while I was lecturing in my loud, self-confident voice about Homer Smith and the wonders of renal clearance I was horrified to see Richards standing in the upper door listening to me.

At Harvard I was told to teach endocrinology in both lecture and laboratory, and I had to work up all branches of that enormous subject. I remember with particular pleasure discovering the work of Fuller Albright. For the laboratory I learned to pancreatectomize a cat, to follow the estrous cycle of a rat with vaginal smears, and to measure the salt appetite of an adrenalectomized rat. When we did the Ascheim-Zondek pregnancy test, using urine I had obtained at the Women's Hospital, a couple of students, for some mysterious reason, brought samples from home.

When I went to Utah in 1945 as head of the Department of Physiology I had the responsibility of teaching the entire course, so I learned about backward and forward failure and critical closing pressure. I knew the prewar Krogh-Barcroft-Haldane respiratory physiology, but I had to learn the Fenn-Rahn-Otis-Pappenheimer kind in order to teach it. I taught acid-base physiology, as I had learned it at Harvard, to anyone who would stand still long enough. I even taught anesthesiology residents how to measure plasma carbon dioxide with a Van Slyke apparatus. Naturally, I wrote down what I taught, and the result was my book *The ABC of Acid-Base Chemistry*. An immense amount of teaching experience went into the six editions of that book. It sold over 140,000 copies in the American editions and heaven only knows how many in French, German, Spanish, Italian, Portugese, Japanese, and Korean. When I say that it has been called a "pedagogical classic" I also say that there is a point beyond which modesty becomes affectation.

It has always been difficult to teach gastrointestinal physiology in the student laboratory. Frank Brooks solved the problem at Pennsylvania by assembling a kennel of chronically prepared dogs, but I never tried that. At Harvard, Eugene Landis gave me the task of devising and supervising an exercise on the radiology of the esophagus and stomach, quite appropriate for W. B. Cannon's old department. When I became associated with gastrointestinal physiologists because of my work on acid secretion, publishers nagged me to write a chapter. I always refused, reasoning that because I had no training in gastrointestinal physiology, I did not know enough.

When I later joined the Editorial Committee of the *Annual Review of Physiology*, I was asked to write about the digestive tract for the volume. I thought that as a committee member I couldn't refuse, although I learned that others didn't have the same delicate conscience. I wrote the review, and when I had finished I thought I might know enough to write an introductory text for the Year Book series that was being planned by Julius Comroe & Robert Pitts. For two years I went to the medical library every weekday evening from 7 to 9. I read and read about some topic until I knew enough to write straight off a summary of it. Then I wrote a chapter of what became my *Physiology of the Digestive Tract*. For 20 years I felt obligated to keep up with the rapidly proliferating literature on the subject in order to prepare four more editions. It was a great relief to stop!

I greatly enjoyed teaching, particularly laboratory and small group teaching, and I miss doing it. Physiology has advanced far beyond me, but the heart still beats and the blood still carries oxygen and carbon dioxide. I would like once more to be allowed to shepherd a few students through the answer to such questions as: "A man puts out four liters of urine a day. Describe in *logical order* how you would determine the cause." That question, however, reveals the nature of my teaching; it was spoon-feeding. A really first-class teacher stimulates his students to do original work and to learn on their own. Benjamin Jowett of Balliol was such a teacher; no student dared face him unless he had done the best of which he was capable. My students, on the contrary, came to me with their mouths open, ready to be fed the pap I had so artfully prepared, and I knew exactly the angle to hold the spoon. My teaching was a useful and economical method of transferring information, but it was definitely second class.

I regret what has happened to the teaching of physiology in many schools. One need only to look back to the teaching sessions of the American Physiological Society to know that in my day teachers of physiology took their job seriously. A couple of hundred persons went to the fall meetings in Madison, Wisconsin, a day early to hear Julius Comroe and his team tell the story that was eventually published as *The Lung*. Later I participated in three such sessions, one on gastroenterology, one on acid-base balance, and one on laboratory methods—for which I hauled a plethysmograph from Ann Arbor to Urbana,

Illinois. In medical schools and colleges teachers invented new ways and refined old ones, and, assisted by the Society's teaching committee, they discussed their experiences with each other. But around 1970, several things went wrong.

Students who had been through the new secondary science curriculum revolted against science as they revolted against everything else. All they wanted was a few hints on how to be humane doctors, and they refused to attend laboratory sessions. Research interests of the faculty drifted away from the whole animal and its organs to bits and pieces of cells. Lectures were given by relays of specialists who never listened to each other. "Curriculum reform" emasculated the basic science departments in medical schools and took away time for laboratory work. Teaching laboratories and small-group conferences disappeared.

The purpose of the teaching laboratory in medical schools was never to teach the scientific method. The first question asked when a laboratory exercise was planned was "Will it work?" That meant "Will it give the expected results?" The laboratory's purpose was to give the student a first-hand, quantitative knowledge of how the circulation, the respiration, and the rest work. A few years ago I taught most of a physiology course for medical students, and as I did so I thought over and over again how much the students were missing by not having laboratory work. They had never seen a triple response, felt ischemic pain, measured partial pressures in alveolar air during hyperventilation, or seen the bottom fall out of the diastolic pressure as a man is about to faint. Students are not the only losers. A young faculty member, such as I once was, is deprived of the opportunity to learn the core of physiology by teaching it. He may know a lot about down-regulation of glucose receptors, but he hasn't the faintest idea what happens to his circulation when he attempts to expire on a closed glottis while defecating.

SERVICE

I learned about the service obligations of an academic when, at the age of 32, I leaped from instructor at Harvard to professor and head of the Department of Physiology at Utah. Utah's College of Medicine had been a two-year school, and it had been told to get better or quit. It was getting better in a spectacular way, for those in authority had decided to bring in outsiders, men devoted to research, and to staff the clinical departments with full-time men. Louis Goodman, Mark Nickerson, George Sayers, Tom Dougherty, Leo Samuels, Max Wintrobe, and Hans Hecht, plus some pediatricians and obstetricians each with a Ph.D. in a basic science, were early members of the faculty. The university itself was being transformed by a physicist president who was impressed by the quality of the medical faculty and who was raising the quality of the university by persuading Mormon scientists like Henry Eyring to return to Zion.

I learned much more than I taught, and one way was by serving on many university and medical school committees. It is customary to complain of the time that committees waste, but I have found that, given a good dean or a good president, they are the best way of involving the faculty in the management of an academic institution. With good will on the part of its members, a committee can eventually reach a consensus that is often better than the original opinions brought to it, and at the end all members are committed to implementing the consensus. In committees I learned how to cooperate for the good of the institution, that you don't have to like a man to get along with him, and that the most effective form of selfishness is conspicuous unselfishness. I also learned how to deal with the Department of Buildings and Grounds and that a liberal application of soft soap helps to get the best out of the Purchasing Department. I made mistakes, but when I went to The University of Michigan as chairman eleven years later I knew exactly what I wanted to do and how to do it.

A chairman's job is to provide the atmosphere in which good men, and I use the word *men* in a neutral sense, can do good work. First, one must find the men. In recruiting I looked for *demonstrated promise*. It was a well-defined type. The man I looked for was Phi Beta Kappa from Haverford or Princeton. If he had an M.D., he was Alpha Omega Alpha from Columbia or Hopkins, but if I needed a neurophysiologist he was from the University of Washington in Seattle. He had interned at Cornell or Barnes Hospital, and he had done his national service at the N. I. H. Then followed the regulation two years in Copenhagen. If he had a Ph.D., it was from Chicago or the University of Illinois in Urbana, and he had comparable postdoctoral experience. He had published four or five papers, but he hadn't yet found himself. When he visited the department to give his seminar, I talked to him a few minutes about the job, and I told him that his full-time salary would not depend upon grant support. Then I sent him on a day-long tour of the department so that others could judge him and he could discover what they thought of the man in the front office. When he accepted the offer, I did little more than provide start-up facilities and some encouragement. After a period of quite respectable fumbling, he suddenly took off on his own with stopped flow, the role of carnitine, single-cell activity in the hippocampus, or the protective function of fever. Then the department had a man of *demonstrated performance*.

In one disasterous experience I learned it is futile to try to keep a man after he has decided to accept another job. Instead, I practiced preventive maintenance so that when one assistant professor told me he was tempted by an offer from a place with better computer facilities I was able to tell him that the week before I had proposed his promotion. He stayed, and later, by saying yes to a proposal and writing a couple of letters, I was able to advance his career materially. I did the same with others, saying yes at the right time and occasionally no, giving them teaching assignments they wanted, relieving them of teaching altogether when it seemed appropriate, proposing them for Career Development Awards, Markle Scholarships, university distinctions, and for what raises the dean allowed. The result was a stable department and a dozen or so who owe me a good bit. Whether they were happy I don't know, for I avoided personal relations. There were, of course, a few who didn't like me and who left in a cloud of acrimony. I didn't like them either, but I tried not to let that affect my behavior toward them.

Research always came first, and in that as in many other ways I tried to set an example. For years I got to work about 6:30 A.M. to work in my laboratory. If someone wanted a paper signed, he had to bring it to the room in the animal quarters where I was working with my dogs. Teaching did not suffer: it was done well at all levels. Good scientists are, in general, good teachers one way or another—science and teaching being expressions of superior qualities. Of the many ways we taught, formally and informally, I am proudest of Physiology 101–102, the course for undergraduate college students that showed them what every educated person ought to know about his own body. Through no fault of my own I had done a bad job with college teaching at Utah, and when I went to Michigan I determined to do it right. I hired a little dynamo named Virginia McMurray from Smith College whose mission in life was to spread the gospel of physiology. Within a year, working through the Extension Division, she knew more persons in Michigan than did the governor, Soapy Williams. When she left to get married, a woman from Goucher and Pennsylvania came to teach the one-term course.

In 1962–63 I was away on sabbatical leave, and the department's secretary was inexperienced. When word came from the Office of the Registrar that Physiology 101–102 was oversubscribed in advanced registration, she said: "My, my, how interesting," and threw the notice away. So when Madeline Fusco went to meet the class the first day, she found 500 students milling around in the hall. When I returned I took the problem to Vice-president Heyns, who said it was the kind of problem he liked to solve. He gave me another instructorship to be filled by a postdoctoral fellow, James Sherman, so that the course could be repeated a second term. The purpose of the course was to teach college students what they ought to know about their own bodies. A short time later Arthur Vander and Dorothy Luciano, out of missionary zeal, pitched in to help teach it. For 15 years it was second only to art history as the most popular course in the university. The Vander-Sherman-Luciano textbook, *Human Physiology,* was derived from the course, so many are familiar with the course's content.

Unlike many a first-class man who has built a monolithic department and has driven his staff to do wonders for him, I was totally incapable of dominating mine. Each member had his own independent program, and he took on one or another department job because he wanted to. A succession of men took charge of the graduate program, and all I had to do was sign the training grant application once a year. Because I was distressed by my own spoon-feeding, I was particularly proud of the rigorous course in general physiology taught by John Jacquez; when his class session was over, the blackboard was covered with integral and differential equations. Those who taught Physiology 101–102 used it to train graduate students as teachers, and they used it to recruit college students for their laboratories. Consequently, the department was always full of youngsters I didn't know. Some of them remained with us when they became medical students, so they had six or so years of research experience by the time they graduated. David Bohr scrutinized the records of students on admission to medical school, and promising ones received offers of research assistantships before their classes began. Many continued in the department for the next four years. Their presence is symbolized to me by my encounter, on the hottest Saturday afternoon one summer, with a medical student in a scrub shirt and shorts repeatedly measuring the cardiac output of a hypertensive rat by the thermal dilution method. As a result of such dedication, our department had almost a monopoly on the Borden awards for student research, and three members of one medical class are now professors of physiology at very good universities—not a random event.

RESEARCH

Is it possible to accomplish something significant in research without good luck? Certainly, I have been Fortune's favorite, although it never seemed so at the time. When my father died, my mother chose to live within what turned out to be commuting distance to Caltech. Had we lived ten miles farther away, I could not have afforded the daily journey during the Depression. Luck gave me the oportunity to serve as Henry Borsook's unpaid research assistant in the summer between my junior and senior years. I learned much more than biochemistry from Borsook: how to cook an omelet and what Cézanne had been up to, among much else.

In the spring of 1941 I was in my second postdoctoral year as a Sterling Fellow at Yale. I was desperate for a job, having haughtily turned down the University of Chicago's offer of an instructorship at $2,000 a year. At the federation meetings in the Stevens Hotel in Chicago my current chief, C. N. H. Long, went through a door just as Cuthbert Bazett of Pennsylvania was about to go through it in the other direction. Bazett said: "Hugh, do you know anyone who wants a job?" Hugh Long replied: "Yes, that tall man over there." Bazett had hired an Englishman who suddenly couldn't come to the States because of the war, so he hired me almost on the spot. Bazett was an Oxonian; I was an

Oxonian and therefore obviously qualified. So I became a physiologist. Ten seconds either way for Long or Bazett going through that door, and I would have remained a biochemist. Considering the postwar explosion in biochemistry and my inability to learn new methods, that was the luckiest thing that ever happened to me. Otherwise, I might now be an embittered associate professor in some intellectual backwater.

As I was about to return to Pasadena from Oxford in June of 1938, I discussed gastric secretion of acid with my supervisor, David Fisher. He said acid secretion might result from a sort of chloride shift, and therefore there might be carbonic anhydrase in the gastric mucosa. I said, "Pooh, pooh," for Meldrum & Roughton had failed to find carbonic anhydrase anywhere but in erythrocytes. Nevertheless, Fisher persuaded me to look, and of course I found it there. The next autumn as a graduate student at Caltech I used a version of the Linderstrøm-Lang method to determine the cellular locus of the enzyme. I punched out cylinders of gastric mucosa and sliced them on a freezing microtome. I measured the enzyme content and counted the oxyntic, or parietal, cells in alternate slices, and I found a surprisingly good correlation between enzyme content and oxyntic cell count. I held my breath for the next 20 years until others using different methods confirmed that carbonic anhydrase is indeed in the oxyntic cells. Henry Borsook, who must have been anxious to get rid of a student who was not working on his favorite problems, saw to it that I got my Ph.D. at the end of the year.

I desperately wanted carbonic anhydrase to be in the oxyntic cells and nowhere else in the mucosa. However, my data eventually convinced me that it must be in the surface epithelial cells as well. That taught me that no matter how hard I tried, I couldn't cook my data to get the results I wanted. I have often had the same experience since, and always the "wrong" result turned out to be better than the "right" one. It was fortunate I didn't leave carbonic anhydrase to be discovered in the surface cells by someone else, for bicarbonate secretion has turned out to be an important function of those cells.

That work and some papers I published in my first postdoctoral year, papers that turned out to have good data and ludicrously wrong conclusions, got me off to a flying start. Carbonic anhydrase was a fashionable subject, the prostaglandin of its day, and in addition my work was the first to provide any solid evidence, as contrasted with wild speculation, relating to the mechanism of acid secretion. As a result, I became known as a coming man. In my first paper on gastric carbonic anhydrase I had said as clearly as I could that hydration of carbon dioxide and subsequent ionization of carbonic acid could not possibly be the driving force behind the secretion of HCl at 150 mN. Others who had not paid attention erected a "Carbonic Anhydrase Theory of Acid Secretion" and fastened it on me. After an unhappy postdoctoral year at Yale—in which I failed to inhibit acid secretion with sulfanilamide, the one carbonic anhydrase inhibitor then available—I wrote a brief editorial for *Gastroenterology* called *In Memoriam: The Carbonic Anhydrase Theory of Gastric Acid Secretion*. *Gastroenterology* printed the title in suitably mournful Gothic type, and at once I earned a tremendous reputation for scientific integrity. I was amazed, for I had thought that the object of research is to learn the truth, not to provide ammunition for someone dying in the last ditch while defending an untenable theory.

There is no point in describing my next 20 years of research on the mechanism of acid secretion. I worked hard and accomplished nothing, chiefly because I didn't know enough cell biology. There wasn't much cell biology of the right kind in those days, but I didn't have the ingenuity to invent it. A few years ago I met George Sachs, the man who has come nearest to succeeding where I failed, and I am proud of the fact that I was delighted by his accomplishment rather than jealous. By 1962 I was at a dead end, and I decided to quit research altogether. The University of Michigan owed me one term's sabbatical leave. A grant from the U.S.P.H.S. paid my salary for a second term away from Ann Arbor. For a last fling at research I spent the year 1962-63 working under Charlie Code at the Mayo Clinic. I told Code to treat me like a postdoctoral fellow and to give me a research problem. He had a versatile and productive research program, and from among his many problems he asked me to explain the effect of eugenol on the gastric mucosa.

Franklin Hollander had found that eugenol, the active ingredient of clove oil and the only thing in gastroenterology that smells good, stimulates secretion of mucus by the gastric mucosa. Charlie Code, in his quest for the elusive inhibitor *gastrone* that might be a component of mucus, had bathed a dog's Heidenhain pouch with a suspension of eugenol. Acid secretion did seem to be inhibited, for immediately subsequent stimulation of the pouch with histamine caused a flow of juice that was low in acid and high in sodium. Code was too cautious to conclude that he had demonstrated an effect of gastrone, and he put the results aside until I came to the clinic. He asked me: Does eugenol affect the acid-secreting mechanism, or is there another explanation?

The pieces of the answer were all in place; all Charlie and I had to do was put them together. Years before, Code had done pioneer work on the impermeability of the gastric mucosa, and he had coined the descriptive term the gastric mucosal barrier. Juice collected from an intact Heidenhain pouch is high in acid and low in sodium, for the reason that the barrier prevents back diffusion of secreted acid into the mucosa and diffusion of sodium from mucosal interstitial fluid into the juice. Franklin Hollander had found that repeated application of eugenol to the gastric mucosa causes the mucosa to shed a "sero-sanguinous" fluid, but he hadn't quite recognized the implications of that fact. Therefore, after the barrier is broken by eugenol, acid should disappear from the juice by back diffusion, and sodium from the interstitial fluid should replace it. This could be tested by putting a buffer in the eugenol-treated pouch to trap the secreted acid before it had a chance to diffuse away.

It was easy enough to show that our idea was right. Charlie Code prepared the dogs, provided advice and technical assistance, and guided me through the splendid facilities of the clinic. Each morning I worked with one of the dogs, irrigating her pouch with test solutions for five consecutive 30-min periods, and gradually working through the elaborate protocol of controls and crucial experiments we had planned. By 5 P.M. I had finished the day's analyses and radioactive counting and could calculate the net and unidirectional fluxes. Toward the end Code had a postdoctoral fellow make the appropriate potential-difference measurements. Charlie wrote the paper and saw it through the clinic's meticulous section of publications. Mort Grossman, then the editor of *Gastroenterology,* said the paper would revolutionize the physiology of the stomach. It may not have done quite that, but, together with a little paper I published before the big one was in print, it did stir up the animals.

The work described in the little paper was done in my last few weeks in Rochester when I tackled the problem of the nature of the gastric mucosal barrier. It ought to be penetrated by un-ionized, fat-soluble, short-chain fatty acids but not by the same acids in the ionized state. I demonstrated that this is true for acetic, propionic, and butyric acids. I used acetic acid, because I knew it precipitates mucus, and even then I was worrying about the role of mucus on the surface of the stomach. I didn't use acids having longer chains, for the clinic's stock room didn't have any. Later, Code did an elegant set of experiments with longer chains, increasing their length until he ran out of water solubility.

While I was doing those experiments I read a preposterous paper by a gastroscopist describing the inflamed gastric mucosa lying beneath a fleck of aspirin on its surface. From his discussion, one would have thought that the fleck of aspirin was giving off some sort of malignant ray. I knew that Adrian Hogben and his friends at the N. I. H. had shown that aspirin, or acetylsalicylic acid, is absorbed from an acid solution in the stomach but that its ionized form, acetylsalicylate, is not absorbed from a neutral solution. I also knew that the clinical world was having one of its recurrent spasms of concern about gastric bleeding induced by aspirin. It ought to be amusing, I thought, to show that aspirin, like acetic acid, breaks the barrier. I sent to the drug store for some aspirin.

I did the crucial experiment first. I irrigated a Heidenhain pouch in a preliminary test period with 100 mN HCl to show that its barrier was intact. Very little acid disappeared from the test solution, and little sodium entered it. Then I irrigated the pouch with a solution of aspirin in 100 mN HCl. As I expected, aspirin entered the mucosa, broke the barrier, and greatly increased fluxes of H^+ and Na^+. In addition, the unexpected occurred: the pouch bled furiously and shed a large volume of fluid. Although the isotopic data showed that the permeability to Na^+ had greatly increased, my titrations showed that there was almost as much acid in the fluid within the pouch at the end of the period of incubation as there had been at the beginning. I couldn't believe that a gastric mucosa highly permeable to Na^+ was impermeable to H^+. It looked as though acid diffusing into the mucosa had stimulated the mucosa to secrete acid.

The appropriate control for that experiment was first to test the pouch with 100 mN HCl to demonstrate that the barrier was intact and then to irrigate it with the same concentration of aspirin in neutral solution. When I attempted to do that a few days later using the same dog, I found that her pouch bled during the initial period of irrigation with acid. It had not healed adequately. I debated whether to continue, and fortunately I did. When I irrigated the pouch with aspirin in neutral solution, the bleeding stopped. It took me 16 busy years to work out the implications of those two experiments.

Although I did use a flame photometer and a primitive counter, I could have done most of the work with a little glassware and an old-fashioned block comparator. I did have one enormously valuable resource: about five or six self-starting graduate students and postdoctoral fellows. Soon after I returned to Ann Arbor, Leonard Johnson—"Rusty" to everyone—came to work with me for the summer. I told him to borrow a smooth-muscle bath from David Bohr and to measure histamine. He came back a week later and told me he couldn't make the method work. I bought two airplane tickets and took Rusty to Rochester, Minnesota, where Charlie Code's assistant, Joe Kennedy, taught Rusty how to do it in one day. Thereafter Rusty took off on his own, and by the time he left me he was well on his way to becoming the best Ph.D. gastroenterologist under 40. In a similar fashion others did original work while they were nominally my students. In my more cheerful moments I think that my spoon-feeding of undergraduates is more than offset by my treatment of the others. I simply pointed them in the right direction and cheered them on.

I did my research solely to solve scientific puzzles, but because of its nature I published in clinical journals. Orthodox physiologists, like Committee Members B and C, had no idea what I was doing. That was not true of clinicians, particularly the surgeons who had to deal with gastric ulcers and with exsanguinating hemorrhages in their intensive care units. They immediately picked up the idea of the gastric mucosal barrier and the consequences of breaking it. A clinician's first paper would begin: "Davenport has shown that . . ." His second would begin: "We have shown that." His third paper would omit my name from its bibliography, a vastly amusing example of the fate of most scientists. Nevertheless, I know quite well that a substantial number of very good clinical scientists who are doing progressive work are my scientific children.

Having written this *Apology*, I must try to answer the question I posed at its beginning. If I have done nothing first class, I can say that I have been useful. My teaching, and in particular my *ABC of Acid-Base Chemistry,* has raised the general level of understanding some fraction of a millimeter. My work as a department chairman has helped the institutions and the faculties I have served. The applications of the results of my research have had some small impact on the quality of patient care. That is, I suppose, as much as a second-class man can hope for.

COMPARATIVE PHYSIOLOGY: RHYTHMICITY IN LIVING SYSTEMS

Introduction, James E. Heath, *Section Editor*

Biological systems produce regular rhythmic responses, varying from a few milliseconds to annual cycles. The chapters prepared here address both the generation of such signals and their significance to animal behavior and adaptation.

At the base of all rhythms lie the spontaneously depolarizing cells, pacemakers, that, like the escapement of a mechanical clock, generate all other rhythmic activity. Dr. Connor reviews the factors developing and modulating rhythmicity of cells.

Drs. Selverston & Moulins consider endogenously active networks underlying central pattern generation. When pacemakers or bursting cells are combined with other neurons in network circuits, new and longer rhythms result. These program generators underlie locomotor and other repetitive patterns and may bridge to even longer periods.

Dr. Turek summarizes research that indicates that circadian rhythms arise from neural networks. These networks may contain multiple subnets or be driven by pacemaker cells. Thus, daily rhythms could be initiated by the mechanisms described in either of the first two chapters.

Dr. Farner takes up annual rhythmicity. Such rhythms seem to be adjusted or tuned by fixed geophysical signals, notably the regular progress of varying day length with season. Photoperiodicity resets an annual clock, but does not

15

describe the clock itself. The clock, whatever its underlying neural organization, is further finely tuned by other environmental signals such as temperature, food availability, and so on to optimize the reproductive success of the animal.

Few areas in biology have yielded as begrudgingly to research effort as rhythmicity. Progress has been bedeviled by comprehensive but uninformative mathematical models, subtle experimental artifacts, and even chicanery. These reviews demonstrate that study of rhythmicity of timing systems has shed these burdens and is accelerating toward comprehensive explication. Increasingly, experimental design of all behavioral and physiological biology must take serious account of the endogenous rhythms of organisms.

Ann. Rev. Physiol. 1985. 47:17–28

NEURAL PACEMAKERS AND RHYTHMICITY

John A. Connor

AT&T Bell Laboratories, Murray Hill, New Jersey 07974

INTRODUCTION

This review will draw on material gathered both from nerve cells and from other types of secretory cells that display excitability characteristics similar to those of neurons. Indeed, in view of the similarities, it may be profitable to regard many types of secretory cells as neurons with vanishingly short axons and dendrites. I will emphasize the possible mechanisms linking the internal state of the cell to rhythmic electrical activity, predominantly a membrane phenomena. This seems a sensible relationship to bring out because, in the broad sense, rhythmic neurons are a component of control loops in which the output of an effector organ is modulated by neural firing. With the obvious exception of stretch receptors and the like, where it is probable that the primary stimulus input directly alters membrane properties (cf. 99), many environmental factors (for neurons) have their strongest effects on cytoplasmic conditions or levels of cytoplasmic second messengers, raising the question of how these changes are coupled to the cell membrane.

At the present there is no particular difficulty in generating periodic electrical discharge in computer simulations based upon experimentally defined membrane conductances. The characteristic frequencies of these discharges lie in the millisecond-to-minute range, depending upon which parameters are used in the simulations and from what preparation they were derived. Data for these simulations have come exclusively from invertebrate neurons, which are much more amenable to the voltage-clamp analysis necessary to describe membrane conductances than are neurons from vertebrates.

The data base of longest standing is the one derived from the squid giant axon by Hodgkin & Huxley (51). A number of investigators demonstrated that this set of conductances (or in more modern terminology, the Na and delayed K-ion

17

0066-4278/85/0315-0017$02.00

channels) comprises a system that generates rhythmic action potential firing when given a constant current input (35, 53, 103). The frequency range of firing is rather narrow, 80–130 impulses per second using parameters appropriate to 18°C, as is the frequency range of the squid giant axon under the conditions appropriate to repetitive firing activity. Experiments have subsequently been carried out on other types of neurons, molluscan central neurons and crustacean walking leg axons, that exhibit repetitive firing over a broad frequency range, maximum frequency $\geqslant$ 50-fold the minimum frequency. These studies demonstrated the presence and importance of an additional type of membrane ion channel over the two types present in squid giant axons (22, 26, 27, 47). This set of ion channels, the A-current channels, although selective for K^+, differed in most other important characteristics from the squid-axon type-K channel, being activated at subthreshold voltages, having a rapid transient time course, and being blocked by different pharmacological agents. The effect of these ion channels is to bring down the low end of the repetitive firing range to rates that are typically less than 2–5% of the maximum rate. The absolute firing rates depend upon the relaxation rates of the membrane conductances, and these parameters depend strongly upon the preparation studied. For example, the activation and inactivation time constants of Na current in squid or crustacean axon are approximately ten-fold faster (at a given temperature) than the corresponding current in gastropod central neurons (a fortuitous event given that microelectrode voltage clamps that must be used with cell bodies are far slower than the axial wire or sucrose gap techniques used on axons). The characteristic relaxations of the A current are also much more rapid in the crustacean axons than in molluscan cell bodies. Consequently, the range of measured and simulated firing frequencies spans the range 2–400 Hz (spikes sec^{-1}), while that for the central neurons runs about 0.3–15 Hz (28, 29, 88). Thus wide differences in rhythmic frequencies are generated by the same basic conductance mechanisms. The details of how the three conductances interact in a uniformly polarized cell membrane to generate repetitive firing have been reviewed elsewhere (21).

It is worth noting that the A-current channels and their involvement in rhythmic behavior are not a peculiar curiosity of invertebrate neurons. The presence of these channels has been demonstrated in neurons from several areas of the mammalian brain and spinal cord (7, 46, 54, 55) as well as in neurons from vertebrate sympathetic ganglia (2, 36, 37). In most of these preparations the voltage dependence and the relative size of the A current are sufficient to guarantee it an important function in rhythmic discharge, but particulars of the necessary voltage-clamp analysis are lacking.

Historically, information has developed almost in parallel about a second type of system capable of generating oscillatory voltage patterns. This is a two-conductance system made up of voltage-gated Ca channels (cf. review

108) and a class of potassium channel that requires the presence of appreciable Ca^{2+} at the inner surface of the membrane in order to be opened (81, 83). Normally cytoplasmic free Ca is held at a very low level, in the vicinity of 100 nm, in neurons (6). These potassium channels are also voltage-dependent, having an increasing frequency of opening at a given $[Ca^{2+}]$ for more positive voltages (cf. 87). As a variety of data from patch-clamp studies accumulates, the possibility has been raised that there are two different types of Ca-activated K channels having very different unitary conductances. The channel commonly observed has a conductance of around 200 ps, while the other channel, described in snail neurons (78) and vertebrate red cells (48), has a conductance of approximately 20 ps. It is unclear at present what other differences these K channels might show. Possibly the existence of two channel types can explain some of the reported differences in pharmacology, such as blocking or non-blocking of the channel by tetraethylammonium (cf. 3, 4, 23, 43).

Generally Ca and Ca-activated K channels are found nested in the same membrane with Na channels, delayed-rectifier K channels, and A-current channels (cf. 1), but there is at least one neural example where these two conductances appear to dominate membrane behavior (41). It is commonly thought that oscillatory behavior is brought about because Ca influx is regenerative, and during a depolarization, which may or may not be assisted by Na entry, an excess of Ca^{2+} accumulates near the inner surface of the membrane. The Ca^{2+} accumulation gradually activates potassium current flow, which repolarizes the membrane (cf. 18, 42, 82). Oscillation frequency and amplitude are therefore dependent upon the calcium handling (diffusion, buffering, and uptake) characteristics of the cytoplasm as well as membrane conductance characteristics.

Several investigators have made computational studies using four or five conductance models in order to simulate uniform repetitive activity and also the rhythmic, grouped discharge of action potentials (bursting) characteristic of *Aplysia* neuron R-15 and other molluscan neurons. Byrne and his colleagues (13–15, 100) have analyzed conductance changes in the motoneurons mediating the inking response of *Aplysia*. A four-conductance model—Na, delayed K, A current, and Ca—successfully predicts the delayed-onset firing characteristics of these neurons. Plant (93), developing on an earlier model of burst firing based upon a four-conductance system (94), has incorporated Ca conductance and Ca-activated K conductance in further simulations of burst-firing behavior.

In a simulation study of burst firing more closely data based, Smith & Thompson (see 102) have analyzed a six-conductance model derived from voltage-clamp experiments on burst-firing neurons *Tritonia diomedia*. The sixth element is a conductance that generates a *depolarizing after-potential* (DAP) when a spike is fired. The DAP conductance is characteristic of the burst-firing neurons of mollusks (105) and in this model is the key element in causing action-potential discharge to be grouped into bursts rather than uniformly distributed in time. As the other studies have shown, however, the DAP conductance is not essential for one to simulate burst discharge using a reasonable set of membrane conductance. It is not surprising in a system of the complexity of a four-to-six–conductance mesh that similar behaviors can be generated by differing combinations of parameters.

As better data have been gathered from vertebrate neurons under more isolated conditions than whole brain (e.g. brain slices and dispersed cultures), it has become evident that the ion conductance profile of higher animals is every bit as complex as that of the invertebrates (cf. 71). This was not always the conventional wisdom. In studies particularly of interest to this review, Llinas and his colleagues have examined properties of central neurons in brain slices from guinea pig (54, 55, 73–77). These neurons display oscillatory electrical behavior both in vivo and in vitro that may be linked in some way to physiological tremor (cf. 72). Some of these neurons exhibit two types of calcium conductance mechanisms. The first, a high-threshold, slowly (or noninactivating) mechanism, is similar to the extensively described Ca conductance in invertebrate neurons and secretory cells (34). Inactivation of this channel may be brought about by intracellular Ca^{2+} accumulation, as proposed by Eckert and his colleagues (cf. 33). The second, a low-threshold, rapidly inactivating mechanism, has drawn little attention until recently. There are preliminary reports describing a low-threshold Ca conductance of similar properties in dorsal root ganglion cells (86) and GH3 cells (80), as well as a more complete description in snail neurons (11, 12).

In the mammalian CNS neurons, the high-threshold channels sometimes appear to be localized to the dendrites while the low-threshold channels are somatic, providing a spatial component to activation as well as simple voltage-dependent differences. These neurons also display Na channels, delayed-rectifier K channels, Ca-activated K channels, and, in the case of the thalamic neurons, A-current K channels. These central neurons are then a very complex mosaic that has not been analyzed in sufficient detail to permit modeling studies, but convincing arguments have been made that this interacting conductance ensemble can account for the observed 5–15 Hz oscillations that take the form of repetitive spiking or subthreshold oscillations in these neural populations without recourse to special circuit interconnections (55, 77).

FACTORS REGULATING STEADY PACEMAKER CURRENT

Many nerve-cell membranes may then be looked at as naturally oscillatory circuits, needing only a steady driving input to make them fire rhythmically. It therefore is reasonable to assume that a search for factors that can provide and modulate such steady driving input should occupy much of the future research in the area. It is worthwhile to point out a contrasting view summarized in an excellent review by Rapp & Berridge, (96). In the modeling studies done to date the driving input has been derived from constant input current or from arbitrary adjustments of conductance parameters that give rise to a steady or time-varying inward current in the subthreshold voltage region.

cAMP

The two general types of intracellular second messengers to receive significant attention as of this writing are the cyclic nucleotides (cAMP and cGMP) and calcium ion. There are undoubtably others as important; however, as is custom-ary, our general ignorance constrains the field of view. In this regard I call attention to recent reports of ATP-dependent modulation of membrane con-ductance both from inside heart cells (85) and outside neurons (110). Also, Chaplain has suggested for a number of years that factors linked to glycolysis are important in controlling membrane conductances (10, 20). Cyclic nu-cleotide concentrations, primarily cAMP, are elevated in response to certain neurotransmitters in a wide variety of neurons from both vertebrates and invertebrates. Information as to the specific brain locations and amounts has accumulated rapidly since the availability of efficient radioimmunoassay kits for both cAMP and cGMP. This literature is summarized in several recent reviews (45, 97, 98). The literature on the consequences of cAMP (or cGMP) for membrane conductance is less extensive at present; however, one is able to extract certain neuron-specific trends in the available data (see also 63).

The clearest, most widespread action of cAMP is to generate an increase in sodium conductance that mirrors the time course of internal cAMP elevation. This effect has been examined in a variety of identifiable neurons from mollusks: *Helix* (5, 104), *Aplysia,* several species of the Dorids, *Limax* (24, 25, 50), and *Pleurobranchea* (44). In all of these studies cAMP was injected directly into the neuron, avoiding many of the potential complications intro-duced by bath application of phosphodiesterase inhibitors or cAMP analogs, although generally the effects are consistent in these different types of experi-ments. In one set of experiments the injected dose of cAMP was quantified by coinjection of a tracer dye (25). It was shown that tonic action potential discharge could be induced in quiescent neurons by injected amounts of cAMP on the order of 50 μM in cells of *Aplysia* and *Archidoris.* Larger injected amounts produced intense action-potential discharge, and some neurons after multiple injections showed a tendency to generate a patterned burst discharge (dissimilar to the widely described parabolic burst discharge of *Aplysia* R-15). At this time no one has successfully addressed the question of relating injected amounts of cAMP to actual cellular concentration changes because the substance is hydrolyzed rapidly, and, in large neurons, diffusion times are appreciable. Rapid hydrolysis has been inferred from the fact that the phosphodiesterase inhibitor isobutylmethylxanthine (IBMX) prolongs the duration of current flow and increases the current amplitude induced by cAMP injections of a given size (5, 25). In some neurons, among them R2 of *Aplysia,* IBMX (10^{-4}–10^{-3} M) produces repetitive discharge, or inward voltage clamp current (25). This effect is probably caused by elevation of cAMP from endogenous sources, shown to be a two-fold to three-fold increase over the approximately 20-μm resting level in these neurons (19, 66). This is roughly the same range as the injection experiments have shown to be necessary for induction of firing and indicates that the induced changes in excitability occur at physiologically reasonable levels of cAMP.

In other neurons, molluscan and vertebrate, cAMP suppresses potassium conductance (30, 79, 101), and in some of these systems leads to maintained pacemaker discharge. The clearest example of this effect occurs in the bag-cell neurons of *Aplysia,* the set of "command" neurons that trigger egg laying (62, 64). In these cells, elevation of cAMP by applying an analog externally induces a period of discharge lasting up to half an hour (56) in the normally, quiescent cells of the intact ganglion. Kaczmarek & Strumwasser (58) have shown that a similar behavior is preserved in dispersed cultures of the bag cells, indicating that the oscillations are an intrinsic cellular property although the extensive circuit interconnections of the neurons in the intact ganglion must certainly influence the electrical discharge in vivo. Voltage-clamp studies on the bag-cell neurons in culture (59) have convincingly demonstrated decreased K conductance but have failed as yet to sort out which types of K channels are most affected. Presumably the excitatory drive must come from Na or Ca channels normally open at subthreshold voltages whose currents are substantially counterbalanced by the potassium current suppressed by cAMP.

A very different effect of cAMP has been reported in the normally spontaneous neuron, R15, of *Aplysia.* It was shown some years ago in this preparation that elevation of cAMP induces a delayed *increase* in K-current that slows the repetitive burst discharge characteristic of this neuron (31, 32, 65, 66, 107). More recent studies (8, 106) have identified the channels responsible for this action as the anomalous rectifier channels, a type of channel not mentioned in the preceding discussion. These studies have for the most part employed external application of lipid-soluble cAMP analogs. Pellmar, working with the RB cluster neurons of *Aplysia,* has described cAMP-mediated increases in calcium current (90, 91).

cGMP

Studies on the effects of cGMP are less numerous and include a relatively high-density area in phototransduction (17, 38, 84, 109). As with cAMP, there is no one clear effect. Levitan & Norman (67) report a depolarization and lengthening of burst period in *Aplysia* R15 resulting from exposure to cGMP analogs. In other studies the effects of intracellular injections of cGMP were very similar to those of cAMP in a variety of neurons tested, from *Archidoris*, *Aplysia* (not including R15), and other gastropod species (24, 25). In these neurons cGMP induced a tonic Na influx as described above. A similar phenomenon apparently occurs in the vertebrate rod outer segment (78a).

With regard to factors that increase internal levels of cAMP, one usually thinks exclusively of neurotransmitters or circulating hormones. In the bag-cell example, peptides from the atrial gland set off the cAMP-mediated electrical discharge (49). In *Aplysia* R2 and R15, one external factor is apparently serotonin (19, 65, 68). Serotonin also regulates the frequency of oscillatory transepithelial potential in the salivary gland of the blowfly (95), and in this case also it is thought that the control is achieved through cAMP and, in addition, Ca^{2+} levels in the cytoplasm. However, other systemic signals may also be effective. For example, the data of Calhoon & Gillette (16) indicate that cAMP phosphodiesterase in *Pleurobranchea* neurons has peak activity at pH 7.5 and falls off steeply to either side. If adenylate cyclase activity is relatively insensitive to pH (or at least a monotonic function), a shift of intracellular pH will cause cytoplasmic cAMP to rise. pH signaling can occur in the ventral white neuron of *Pleurobranchea*, where a rise in intracellular pH of 0.2–0.3 unit evokes discharge similar in most respects to the discharge induced by cAMP elevation (39).

Intracellular Ca

Since the description of calcium-activated potassium conductance by Meech and its subsequent appearance almost everywhere (cf. 83, 92), calcium has been thought of as primarily an inhibitory factor. This is because a small Ca influx into most cells gives rise to a much larger K efflux (cf. 3, 9, 23, 57, 70). With the discovery of the Ca-activated monovalent cation channel by patch-clamp techniques in heart (20a), neuroblastoma (111), and pancreatic acininar cells (92), a partial revision may be in order. These channels show very little discrimination between Na and K and are highly permeable to all the alkali metal ions (111). Unlike Ca-activated K channels, there is very little voltage sensitivity to channel opening. The reversal potential for current through these channels is in the neighborhood of 0 mV under physiological conditions, making its effect excitatory.

A channel of this type, but not necessarily permeable only to monovalents, could account for several recent observations in standard neuron preparations. Hofmeier & Lux (52) demonstrated that brief pressure injections of $CaCl_2$ (100 ms) induced, first, an inward current that persisted for 10–15 sec, and then a delayed outward current. This current was accompanied by decreased membrane conductance and had a reversal potential between -20 and $+20$ mV. The authors ascribed differences in methodology as the cause of the differences between their findings and earlier results of others that showed only outward current in response to Ca injections (cf. 43, 81).

Lewis (69) recently published a careful study examining spike after-potentials or currents (DAPs and DACs) in *Aplysia* R15. His findings are similar to the Hofmeier & Lux study, in that, a brief period of Ca entry—in this case an action potential—is followd by a biphasic current transient. The transient consists of an inward current that persists for about 1 sec and is followed by a longer-lasting outward current. Both currents are blocked by treatments that stop Ca entry during the action potential or subthreshold depolarizations (external Mn^{2+}, 0 Ca^{2+}) or buffering internal $[Ca^{2+}]$ changes due to influx (internal EGTA). It has been an experimental problem for a number of years to determine whether the channels that generated the DAC also generate the slow inward current (or vice versa) that around threshold gives many neurons a negative-slope resistance I-V relationship (cf. 1, 40, 105). This is certainly not true in general because there is a strong negative-slope region in many neurons, but no DAC (cf. 89). Lewis has taken a conservative view of his data, noting that the differences did not necessarily imply different mechanisms. In a preliminary report, Kramer & Zucker (61) concluded that the DAC and slow inward current (which is carried primarily by Ca^{2+} in the *Aplysia* neurons they studied) are carried by different sets of ion channels.

In certain neurons then, possibly a large number, elevating internal Ca^{2+} has an excitatory effect (activates inward current). At present it is not known what the relative activation levels of Ca are for the inward and outward current carrying channels, nor what other factors may be involved in activating, inactivating, or deactivating the different channels.

Literature Cited

1. Adams, D. J., Smith, S. J., Thompson, S. H. 1980. Ionic currents in molluscan soma. *Ann. Rev. Neurosci.* 3:141–67
2. Adams, P. R., Brown, D. A., Constanti, A. 1982. M-currents and other potassium currents in bullfrog sympathetic neurones. *J. Physiol.* 330:537–72
3. Ahmed, Z., Connor, J. A. 1979. Measurement of calcium influx under voltage clamp in molluscan neurons using the metallochromic dye Arsenazo III. *J. Physiol.* 286:61–82
4. Akaike, N., Brown, A. M., Dahl, G., Higashi, H., Isenberg, G., et al. 1983. Voltage-dependent activation of potassium current in *Helix* neurones by endogenous cellular calcium. *J. Physiol.* 334:309–24
5. Aldenhoff, J. B., Hofmeier, G., Lux, H. D., Swandulla, D. 1983. Stimulation of a sodium influx by cAMP in *Helix* neurons. *Brain Res.* 276:289–96
6. Alvarez-Leefmans, F. J., Rink, T. J., Tsien, R. Y. 1981. Free calcium ions in neurones of *Helix Aspersa* measured with ion-selective micro-electrodes. *J. Physiol.* 315:531–48
7. Barrett, J. N., Crill, W. E. 1972. Voltage clamp analysis of conductances underlying cat motoneuron action potentials. *Fed. Proc.* 31:305
8. Benson, J. A., Levitan, I. B. 1983. Serotonin increases an anomalously rectifying K^+ current in the *Aplysia* neuron R15. *Proc. Natl. Acad. Sci. USA* 80:3522–25
9. Bernardo, L. S., Prince, D. A. 1982.

Dopamine modulates a Ca^{2+}-activated potassium conductance in mammalian hippocampal pyramidal cells. *Nature* 297:76–78

10. Both, R., Finger, W., Chaplain, R. A. 1976. Model predictions of the zonic mechanisms underlying the beating and bursting pacemaker characteristics of molluscan neurons. *Biol. Cybernetics* 23:1–11

11. Brown, A. M., Camerer, H., Kunze, D. L., Lux, H. D. 1982. Similarity of unitary Ca^{2+} currents in three different species. *Nature* 299:156–58

12. Brown, A. M., Morimoto, K., Tsuda, Y., Wilson, D. L. 1981. Calcium current-dependent and voltage-dependent inactivation of calcium channels in *Helix aspersa*. *J. Physiol.* 320:193–218

13. Byrne, J. H. 1980. Quantitative aspects of ionic conductance mechanisms contribution to firing pattern of motor cells mediating inking behavior in *Aplysia californica*. *J. Neurophysiol.* 43:651–68

14. Byrne, J. H. 1980. Analysis of ionic conductance mechanisms in motor cells mediating inking behavior in *Aplysia californica*. *J. Neurophysiol.* 43:630–50

15. Byrne, J. H., Shapiro, E., Dieringer, N., Koester, J. 1979. Biophysical mechanisms contribution to inking behavior in *Aplysia*. *J. Neurophysiol.* 42:1233–50

16. Calhoon, R. D., Gillette, R. 1983. Ca^{2+}-activated and pH-sensitive cyclic AMP phosphodiesterase in the nervous system of the mullusc pleurobranchaea. *Brain Res.* 271:371–74

17. Capovilla, M., Cervetto, L., Toree, V. 1982. Antagonism between steady light and phosphodiesterase inhibitors on the kinectics of rod photoresponses. *Proc. Natl. Acad. Sci. USA* 79:6698–702

18. Carnevale, N. T., Wachtel, H. 1980. Two reciprocating current components underlying slow oscillations in *Aplysia* bursting neurons. *Brain Res.* 2:45–68

19. Cedar, H., Schwartz, J. H. 1972. Cyclic adenosine monophosphate in the nervous system of *Aplysia californica*. II. Effects of serotonin and dopamine. *J. Gen. Physiol.* 60:570–87

20. Chaplain, R. A. 1979. Metabolic control of neuronal pacemaker activity and the rhythmic organization of central nervous functions. *J. Exp. Biol.* 81:113–30

20a. Colquhoun, D., Neher, E., Reuter, H., Stevens, C. F. 1981. Inward current channels activated by intracellular Ca in cultured cardiac cells. *Nature* 294:752–54

21. Connor, J. A. 1982. Mechanisms of pacemaker discharge in invertebrate neurons. In *Cellular Pacemakers*, ed. D.

O. Carpenter, pp. 187–217. New York: Wiley

22. Connor, J. A. 1975. Neural repetitive firing: A comparative study of membrane properties of crustacean walking leg axons. *J. Neurophysiol.* 38:922–32

23. Connor, J. A. 1979. Calcium current in molluscan neurones: Measurement under conditions which maximize its visibility. *J. Physiol.* 286:41–60

24. Connor, J. A., Hockberger, P. E. 1982. Direct measurements of cAMP effects on membrane conductance, intracellular Ca^{2+}, and pH in molluscan neurons. In *Conditioning: Representation of Involved Neural Functions*, ed. C. D. Woody, pp. 179–96. New York: Plenum

25. Connor, J. A., Hockberger, P. 1984. A novel membrane sodium current induced by injection of cyclic nucleotides into gastropod neurons. *J. Physiol.* 354:139–62

26. Connor, J. A., Stevens, C. F. 1971. Inward and delayed outward membrane currents in isolated neural somata under voltage clamp. *J. Physiol.* 213:1–20

27. Connor, J. A., Stevens, C. F. 1971. Voltage clamp studies of a transient outward membrane current in gastropod neural somata. *J. Physiol.* 213:21–30

28. Connor, J. A., Stevens, C. F. 1971. Prediction of repetitive firing behavior from voltage clamp data on an isolated neurone soma. *J. Physiol.* 213:31–53

29. Connor, J. A., Walter, D., McKnown, R. 1977. Neural repetitive firing: Modifications of the Hodgkin-Huxley axon suggested by experimental results from crustacean axons. *Biophys. J.* 18:81–102

30. Deterre, P., Paupardin-Tritsch, D., Bockaert, J., Gerschenfeld, H. M. 1982. cAMP-mediated decrease in K^+ conductance evoked by serotonin and dopamine in the same neuron: A biochemical and physiological single-cell study. *Proc. Natl. Acad. Sci. USA* 79:7934–38

31. Drake, P. F., Treistman, S. N. 1980. Alteration of neuronal activity in response to cyclic nucleotide agents in *Aplysia*. *J. Neurobiol.* 11(5):471–82

32. Drummond, A. H., Benson, J. A., Levitan, I. B. 1980. Serotonin-induced hyperpolarization of an identified *Aplysia* neuron is mediated by cyclic AMP. *Proc. Natl. Acad. Sci. USA* 77(8):5013–17

33. Eckert, R., Chad, J. 1984. Inactivation of Ca channels. *Prog. Biophys. Mol. Biol.* In press

34. Fenwick, E. M., Marty, A., Neher, E. 1982. Sodium and calcium channels in bovine chromaffin cells. *J. Physiol.* 331:599–635

35. Fitzhugh, R., Antosiewicz, H. A. 1959. Automatic computation of nerve excita-

tion. Detailed corrections and additions. *J. Soc. Indust. Appl. Math.* 7:458–77

36. Freschi, J. E. 1982. Effect of serum-free medium on growth and differentiation on sympathetic neurons in culture. *Dev. Brain Res.* 4:455–64

37. Freschi, J. E. 1983. Membrane currents of cultures rat sympathetic neurons under voltage clamp. *J. Neurophysiol.* 50:1460–78

38. George, J. S., Hagins, W. A. 1983. Control of Ca^{2+} in rod outer segment disks by light and cyclic GMP. *Nature* 303:344–48

39. Gillette, R. 1983. Intracellular alkalinization potentiates slow inward current and prolonged bursting in a molluscan neuron. *J. Neurophysiol.* 49(2):509–15

40. Gola, M. 1976. Electrical properties of bursting pacemaker neurones. *Neurobiology of Invertebrates, Gastropoda Brain. Tihany 1975*, pp. 381–423

41. Gola, M. 1985. Electrical behavioral correlates of calcium and potassium currents in molluscan nerve cells. In *Model Neural Networks and Behavior*, ed. A. Selverston. New York: Plenum. In press

42. Gorman, A. L. F., Hermann, A., Thomas, M. V. 1982. Ionic requirements for membrane oscillations and their dependence on the calcium concentration in a molluscan pacemaker neuron. *J. Physiol.* 327:185–217

43. Gorman, A. L. F., Hermann, A. 1979. Internal effects of divalent cations on potassium permeability in molluscan neurons. *J. Physiol.* 296:393–410

44. Green, D. J., Gillette, R. 1983. Patch- and voltage-clamp analysis of cyclic AMP-simulated inward current underlying neurone bursting. *Nature* 306:784–85

45. Greengard, P. 1979. Cyclic nucleotides, phosphorylated proteins, and the nervous system. *Fed. Proc.* 38:2208–17

46. Gustafson, B., Galvan, M., Grafe, P., Wigstrom, H. 1982. A transient outward current in a mammalian central neuron blocked by 4-aminopysidine. *Nature* 299:252–54

47. Hagiwara, S., Kusano, K., Saito, N. 1961. Membrane changes of *Onchidium* nerve cell in potassium-rich media. *J. Physiol.* 155:470–89

48. Hamill, O. P. 1981. Potassium channel currents in human red blood-cells. *J. Physiol.* 319:97–98

49. Heller, E., Kaczmarek, L. K., Hunkapiller, M. W., Hood, L. E., Strumwasser, F. 1980. Purification and primary structure of two neuroactive peptides that cause bag cell after-discharge in peptidergic neurites. *Proc. Natl. Acad. Sci. USA* 75:5200–54

50. Hockberger, P., Connor, J. A. 1983. Intracellular calcium measurements with Arsenazo III during cyclic AMP injections into molluscan neurons. *Science* 219:869–71

51. Hodgkin, A. L., Huxley, A. F. 1952. A quantitative description of membrane current and its application to conduction and excitation in nerve. *J. Physiol.* 117:500–44

52. Hofmeier, G., Lux, H. D. 1981. The time courses of intracellular free calcium and related electrical effects after injection of $CaCl_2$ into neurons of the snail, Helix pomatia. *Pfluegers Arch.* 319:242–51

53. Huxley, A. F. 1959. Ion movements during nerve activity. *Ann. NY Acad. Sci.* 81:221–46

54. Jahnsen, H., Llinas, R. 1984. Electrophysiological properties of guinea-pig thalamic neurones: an in vitro study. *J. Physiol.* 349:205–26

55. Jahnsen, H., Llinas, R. 1984. Ionic basis for the electroresponsiveness and oscillatory properties of guinea-pig thalamic neurones in vitro. *J. Physiol.* 349:227–48

56. Kaczmarek, L. K., Jennings, K., Strumwasser, F. 1978. Neurotransmitter modulation, phosphodiesterase inhibitor effects, and cAMP correlates of after discharge in peptidergic neurites. *Proc. Natl. Acad. Sci. USA* 75:5200–4

57. Kaczmarek, L. K., Kauer, J. A. 1983. Calcium entry causes a prolonged refractory period in peptidergic neurons of *Aplysia*. *J. Neurosci.* 3:2230–39

58. Kaczmarek, L. K., Strumwasser, F. 1981. The expression of long lasting after discharge by isolated *Aplysia* bag cell neurons. *J. Neurosci.* 11(6):626–34

59. Kaczmarek, L. K., Strumwasser, F. 1984. A voltage clamp analysis of currents underlying cyclic-AMP induced membrane modulation in isolated peptidergic neurons of *Aplysia*. *J. Neurophysiol.* 52:340–49

60. Kononenko, N. I., Kostyuk, P. G., Shcherbatko, A. D. 1983. The effect of intracellular cAMP injections on stationary membrane conductance and voltage- and time-dependent ionic currents in identified snail neurons. *Brain Res.* 268:321–38

61. Kramer, R. H., Zucker, R. S. 1984. Calcium-activated slow inward current in *Aplysia* bursting pacemaker neurons. *Biophys. J.* 45:264a (Abstr.)

62. Kupfermann, I. 1970. Stimulation of egg laying by extracts of neuroendocrine cells

(bag cells) of abdominal ganglion of *Aplysia*. *J. Neurophysiol.* 33:877–81

63. Kupfermann, I. 1980. Role of cyclic nucleotides in excitable cells. *Ann. Rev. Physiol.* 42:629–41

64. Kupfermann, I., Kandel, E. R. 1970. Electrophysiological properties and functional interconnections of two symmetrical neurosecretory clusters (bag cells) in abdominal ganglion of *Aplysia*. *J. Neurophysiol.* 33:865–76

65. Lemos, J. R., Novak-Hofer, I., Levitan, I. B. 1982. Serotonin alters the phosphorylation of specific proteins inside a single living nerve cell. *Nature* 298:64–65

66. Levitan, I. B. 1978. Adenylate cyclase in isolated Helix and *Aplysia* neuronal cell bodies: stimulation by serotonin and peptide-containing extract. *Brain Res.* 154:404–8

67. Levitan, I. B., Norman, J. 1980. Different effects of cAMP and cGMP derivatives on the activity of an identified neuron: Biochemical and electrophysiological analysis. *Brain Res.* 187:415–29

68. Levitan, I. B., Drummond, A. H. 1980. Neuronal serotonin receptors and cyclic AMP. Biochemical pharmacological and electrophysiological analysis. *Neurotransmitters and Their Receptors*, ed. U. Littauer et al, pp. 163–75. London: John Wiley & Sons

69. Lewis, D. L. 1984. Spike after currents in R15 of *Aplysia*: their relationship to slow inward current and calcium influx. *J. Neurophysiol.* 51:387–403

70. Lewis, D. L., Wilson, W. A. 1982. Calcium influx and potassium current during early adaptation in *Aplysia* giant neurons. *J. Neurophysiol.* 48:202–16

71. Llinas, R. 1984. Comparative electrobiology of mammalian central neurons. In *Brain Slices*, ed. Raymond Dingledine, pp. 7–24. New York: Plenum

72. Llinas, R. Rebound excitation as the physiological basis for tremor: A biophysical study of the oscillatory properties of mammalian central neurons in vitro. *Int. Neurol Symp. Tremor*, ed. L. J. Findley, R. Capildeo. New York: Macmillan. In press

73. Llinas, R., Greenfield, S. A., Jahnsen, H. 1984. Electrophysiology of pars compacta cells in the in vitro substantia nigra—a possible mechanism for dendritic release. *Brain Res.* 294:127–32

74. Llinas, R., Jahnsen, H. 1982. Electrophysiology of mammalian thalamic neurons in vitro. *Nature* 297(5865):406–8

75. Llinas, R., Sugimori, M. 1979. Calcium conductances in purkinje cell dendrites:

Their role in development and integration. *Development and Chemical Specificity of Neurons*, ed. Cuenod, Kreutzberg, Bloom, pp. 323–34. Amsterdam: Elsevier

76. Llinas, R., Yarom, Y. 1981. Properties and distribution of ionic conductances generating electroresponsiveness of mammalian inferior olivary neurones in vitro. *J. Physiol.* 315:569–84

77. Llinas, R., Yarom, Y. 1981. Electrophysiology of mammalian inferior olivary neurones in vitro, different types of voltage-dependent ionic conductances. *J. Physiol.* 315:549–67

78. Lux, H. D., Neher, E., Marty, A. 1981. Single channel activity associated with calcium-dependent outward current in *Helix pomatia*. *Pfluegers Arch.* 389:293–95

78a. MacLeish, P. R., Schwartz, E. A., Tachibana, M. 1983. Control of the generator current in solitary rods of the *Ambystoma Tigrinum* retina. *J. Physiol.* 348:645–64

79. Madison, D. V., Nicoll, R. A. 1982. Dual action of norepinephrine in hippocampus *Soc. Neurosci. Abstr.* 8:922

80. Matteson, D. R., Armstrong, C. M. 1984. Evidence for two types of Ca channels in Gh 3 cells. *Biophys. J.* 45:36a

81. Meech, R. W. 1974. The sensitivity of *Helix Aspersa* neurons to injected calcium ions. *J. Physiol.* 237:259–77

82. Meech, R. W. 1979. Membrane potential oscillations in molluscan "burster" neurons. *J. Exp. Biol.* 81:93–112

83. Meech, R. W. 1978. Calcium-dependent potassium activities in nervous tissues. *Ann. Rev. Biophys. Bioeng.* 7:1–18

84. Meyertholen, E. P., Wilson, M. J., Ostroy, S. E. 1980. Removing bicarbonate CO_2 reduces the cGMP concentration of the verterate photoreceptor to the levels normally observed on illumination. *Biochem. Biophys. Res. Commun.* 96:785–92

85. Noma, A. 1983. ATP-regulated K^+ channels in cardiac muscle. *Nature* 305:147–48

86. Nowycky, M. C., Fox, A. C., Tsien, R. W. 1984. Two components of calcium channel current in chick dorsal root ganglion cells. *Biophys. J.* 45:36a (Abstr.)

87. Pallotta, B. S., Magleby, K. L., Barrett, J. N. 1981. Single channel recordings of Ca^{2+}-activated K^+ currents in rat muscle cell culture. *Nature* 291:471–74

88. Partridge, L. D., Connor, J. A. 1978. A mechanism for minimizing temperature effects on repetitive firing frequency. *Am. J. Physiol.* 235:c155–61

89. Partridge, L. D., Thompson, S. R.,

Smith, S. J., Connor, J. A. 1979. Current-voltage relationships of repetitively firing neurons. *Brain Res.* 164:69–79

90. Pellmar, T. C. 1981. Ionic mechanism of a voltage-dependent current elicited by cyclic AMP. *Cell Molec. Neurobiol.* 1:87–97

91. Pellmar, T. C. 1984. Enhancement of inward current by serotonin in neurons of *Aplysia. J. Neurobiol.* 15:13–25

92. Petersen, O. H., Maruyama, Y. 1984. Calcium-activated potassium channels and their role in secretion. *Nature* 307:693–96

93. Plant, R. E. 1978. The effects of calcium on bursting neurons, a modeling study. *Biophys. J.* 217–37

94. Plant, R. E., Kim, M. 1976. Mathematical description of a bursting pacemaker neuron by a modification of the Hodgskin-Huxley equations. *Biophys. J.* 16:227–44

95. Rapp, P. E., Berridge, M. J. 1981. The control of transepithelial potential oscillations in the salivary gland of *Calliphora Erythrocephal. J. Exp. Biol.* 93:119–32

96. Rapp, P. E., Berridge, M. J. 1977. Oscillations in calcium-cyclin AMP control loops from the basis of pacemaker activity and other high frequency biological rhythms. *J. Theor. Biol.* 66:497–525

97. Rasmussen, H. 1981. Calcium and cAMP as Synarchic Messengers. New York: Wiley-Interscience

98. Rodnight, R. 1979. Cyclic nucleotides as second messengers in synaptic transmission. *Int. Rev. Biochem.* 26:1–80

99. Sachs, F., Guharay, F. 1984. Stretch-activated single ion-channel currents in tissue-cultured embryonic chick skeletal muscle. *J. Physiol.* 352:685–701

100. Shapiro, E., Koester, J., Byrne, J. H. 1979. *Aplysia* Ink Release: Central locus for selective sensitivity to long-duration stimuli. *J. Neurophysiol.* 42:1223–32

101. Siegelbaum, S., Camardo, J., Kandel, E. 1982. Serotonin and cAMP close single K^+ channels in *Aplysia* sensory neurons. *Nature* 299:413–17

102. Smith, S. J., Zucker, R. S. 1980. A equorin response facilitation and intracellular calcium accumulation in molluscan neurons. *J. Physiol.* 300:167–96

103. Stein, R. B. 1967. The frequency of nerve action potentials generated by applied currents. *Proc. R. Soc. London Ser. B* 167:64–86

104. Swandulla, D., Lux, R. D. 1984. Changes in ionic conductances induced by cAMP in *Helix* neurons. *Brain Res.* 305:115–22

105. Thompson, S. H., Smith, S. J. 1976. Depolarizing after-potentials and burst production in molluscan neurons. *J. Neurophysiol.* 39:153–61

106. Treistman, S. M. 1981. Effect of adenosine 3', 5'-monophosphate on neuronal pacemaker activity: A voltage clamp analysis. *Science* 211:59–61

107. Treistman, S. N., Drake, P. F. 1979. The effects of cyclic nucleotide agents on neurons in *Aplysia. Brain Res.* 168:643–47

108. Tsien, R. W. 1983. Calcium channels in excitable cell membranes. *Ann. Rev. Physiol.* 45:41–58

109. Yamazaki, A., Bartucca, F., Ting, A. Bitensky, M. W. 1982. Reciprocal effects of an inhibitory factor on catalytic activity and noncatalytic cGMP binding sites of rod phosphodiesterase. *Proc. Natl. Acad. Sci. USA* 79:3702–6

110. Yatani, A., Tsuda, Y., Akaike, N., Brown, A. M. 1982. Nanomolar concentrations of extracellular ATP activate membrane Ca channels in snail neurones. *Nature* 296:169–71

111. Yellen, G. 1982. Single Ca^{2+} activated nonselective cation channels in neuroblastoma. *Nature* 296:357–59

Ann. Rev. Physiol. 1985. 47:29–48

OSCILLATORY NEURAL NETWORKS

Allen I. Selverston

Department of Biology, University of California, San Diego, La Jolla, California 92093

Maurice Moulins

C. N. R. S. and Université de Bordeaux I, Arcachon, France

INTRODUCTION

Oscillatory neural networks are ensembles of neurons responsible for a wide variety of periodic behavior patterns. Much of what is known about the neuronal basis of rhythmic behaviors has come from the analysis of oscillatory neural networks in invertebrates. With invertebrates it is possible to identify component cells and synapses and work with them repeatedly; this review will be restricted to only these systems. The kind of networks we will be discussing are those capable of generating oscillatory activity without requiring some sensory input, although many do require some form of tonic excitation. Such networks are commonly referred to as central pattern generators (CPGs), and the goal of most efforts towards their analysis has been to try to explain their operation in terms of the cellular and synaptic properties of the neurons involved. To fully consider oscillatory networks, it will not only be necessary to examine their mechanisms when completely isolated but also when under the influence of neuromodulatory pathways.

There has been considerable progress since neuronal oscillators were last reviewed (20, 38, 39). Several are now known in enough detail that a reasonable explanation of their mechanisms can be put forward, and many others are far enough along that at least an idea of some components of their total mechanism can be suggested.

In this review we will first consider the possible ways in which neuronal oscillators may work, then, after stating the criteria used to identify network

29

0066-4278/85/0315-0029$02.00

oscillators, give several examples of some that have been worked out in the most detail. We will then point out some of the cellular and synaptic properties that are most important to the successful functioning of oscillators and conclude with some new information relative to their control and plasticity.

TYPES OF OSCILLATORY NETWORKS

There are two ways that neuronal oscillators could work: one or more cells embedded in a network would have the property of endogenous bursting (cell-driven oscillators), or else the network itself would produce bursts as a result of synaptic interactions (network oscillators).

If a cell can be completely isolated from any synaptic input as well as from bloodborne substances (2), and the cell is still able to produce bursting pacemaker potentials, it can be considered a true endogenous burster. The most important feature of this cell is that it contains the intrinsic conductances necessary to produce slow waves of potential (28, 90). Superimposed upon these conductances may be the voltage-sensitive conductances necessary to generate spikes, and in these cases the cell will burst periodically. In some cases, neuromodulatory inputs or humoral agents are necessary to unmask the conductances inducing the slow waves of potential (4, 48, 51). Such cells can be termed conditional bursters.

When neurons with intrinsic burstiness are connected with excitatory or inhibitory synapses to other neurons, complex phase relationships among a large number of cells can be established.

In circuits without endogenous bursters, oscillatory activity can be generated as a function of the connections alone. Such circuits fall into two main categories, those with predominantly inhibitory connections only and those made up of both excitatory and inhibitory connections. One example of the latter type appears to be emerging from recent work on the locust-flight CPG.

Perhaps no system has had more importance as an impetus for the detailed cellular study of neuronal oscillators than the locust-flight motor-pattern generator. As a result of Wilson's demonstration that the basic flight motor pattern could be produced without sensory feedback (91), the idea that invertebrate central-pattern generators might serve as good models for the unit analysis of oscillatory networks became firmly entrenched. The locust CPG, however, has been remarkably refractive to intracellular analysis, and until recently (65), virtually nothing has been known about this network. Despite the fact that the details of the oscillator have remained elusive, an enormous amount of information is available regarding the role of sensory feedback. Interestingly, many investigators now feel that sensory feedback serves a larger role than just increasing the frequency of the CPG output, as was originally postulated (91, 92). Recent work has shown that phasic sensory input can both entrain the CPG (87) as well as reset it (3, 34).

This is not to say that a flight-motor CPG does not exist and have powerful effects on the wing-muscle motor neurons, but that the real flight motor may be made up of both central and peripheral components, i.e. the sensory feedback may be part of the oscillator (1, 86). Whether this is the case or not, dual intracellular recordings from interneurons in the flight-pattern generator have now been made (65) and reveal a network that has interneurons able to both drive motor neurons and participate in pattern formation. No endogenously bursty cells have as yet been found, and the pattern appears to be the result of the many excitatory and inhibitory synaptic interactions.

Most of the networks that have been described are made up of predominantly inhibitory synapses. Several types of such networks are particularly noteworthy. Reciprocal inhibition has been suggested for some time to be the driving mechanism behind alternate bursting (6, 93). Such networks require a source of tonic excitatory drive, as well as some form of fatigue (such as accommodation) so that firing on the active side can be terminated.

A second form of inhibitory network known as recurrent cyclic inhibition has been described to account for leech swimming (21, 37, 75). This mechanism would permit more phases than the two seen with reciprocal inhibition and in addition does not require that fatigue properties be present. The principal evidence put forward to support this type of mechanism being the basis for leech swimming was that the Stent-Friesen circuit (20) could produce bursts in the correct phase relationships when modeled with electronic neuromimes (21). The data that was modeled, however, was unfortunately very weak—in most cases monosynapticity was not proven and virtually nothing was known about the synaptic parameters or the intrinsic properties of the cells involved. Nevertheless, this oscillator now appears in some introductory textbooks, unfortunately, as an example of a neuronal network oscillator whose detailed mechanism has been explained (12, 71).

The predictions that derive from the Friesen-Stent model have recently been tested both by a series of ingenious lesion experiments and the findings of a swim-initiating neuron (85). These experiments have demonstrated that a single ganglion can, contrary to the model, produce the swimming rhythm. The cells that had originally been described do have properties that would suggest that they are part of the oscillator circuit, and they probably do play some role in pattern generation. But because these new results cannot be explained by the Stent-Friesen circuit, it should be considered at best incomplete and probably conceptually incorrect.

The third class of oscillator also appears to be of a hybrid form—those in which the oscillatory pattern is generated by both bursty cells and network interactions (mixed oscillators). These, in fact, may turn out to be the most predominant form, and because each mechanism would tend to reinforce the other, these networks would be both more robust and reliable.

An example of such a mixed oscillator is the feeding CPG of the snail

Lymnaea. The rhythmic output of this system is due mainly to the endogenous capabilities of neurons in the N1 group to oscillate (66). The actual pattern, however, appears to be due to the properties of the inhibitory connections between the N1 group and the N2 and N3 groups, but the details of the connections and the mechanism involved have not yet been worked out.

EXAMPLES OF OSCILLATING NEURAL NETWORKS

In order to understand in mechanistic terms how a neural network can produce a rhythmic-patterned output, it is necessary to explain at least qualitatively: (*a*) What is the source of the rhythmicity? (That is, why do the neurons display cyclic activity?) and (*b*) How is the pattern produced? (That is, what determines the sequence of firing of the neurons in one cycle?) To answer these two questions, several criteria must be fulfilled:

1   Identification of the Neurons in the Network

First, all of the neurons active during the rhythm must be considered. Second, it is necessary to distinguish those which are directly participating in the genesis of the rhythm from those which are only driven. There is not always a decisive test that makes this distinction. Nevertheless, if an evoked transient perturbation in the activity of one neuron resets the overall rhythm, this neuron is likely to be an element of the rhythm generator. It can also be a neuron that has access to, but is not part of, the rhythm generator (see 38). When possible, the identification can be confirmed by photoinactivation of the cell (47), which must result in a measurable and irreversible alteration of the rhythm if the cell is an important part of the oscillator.

Because a systematic search of a ganglion is the only way of finding such cells, and because some ganglia contain thousands of cells, knowing whether or not one has identified all of the cells in an oscillatory network remains one of the most persistent problems.

2   Determination of the Synaptic Relationships Between the Neurons

This is critical, and many circuits are misunderstood only because the wiring diagram has not been completely worked out. Monosynapticity must be demonstrated, and this requires simultaneous intracellular recordings from the pre- and postsynaptic neurons. Moreover, several tests for monosynpaticity should be used concurrently to avoid errors (see 5, 12). Note that when the presynaptic neuron is nonspiking, monosynapticity is almost impossible to demonstrate.

3   Characterization of the Intrinsic Properties of the Elements and of the Synapses

In cell-driven oscillators, the individual properties of the neurons play the major role. It is also clear, however, that even in network-driven oscillators the intrinsic properties of at least some neurons can play an important role either in the process of rhythm generation or in the organization of the pattern (22). Finally, in any circuit, knowledge of the individual synapses in more or less quantitative terms (e.g. strength, time course, facilatory properties) is essential.

At the present time, there are only a few circuits for which most of these criteria have been successfully met; these will be considered next.

THE LOBSTER CARDIAC GANGLION: A CELL-DRIVEN OSCILLATOR

One of the smallest neuronal networks capable of generating coordinated oscillatory activity is the nine-celled cardiac ganglion of the lobster. This system produces bursts of motor impulses that drive the heart muscle at a frequency of 20–50 per minute. The ganglion consists of five motor neurons (cells 1–5), sometimes called large cells, and four interneurons (cells 6–9), which are referred to as small cells. All of the cells in the ganglion are connected to each other with nonrectifying electrotonic synapses so that during oscillatory activity they all tend to fire at about the same time. The four small cells are posteriorly located and have axons confined to the ganglion. These axons run anteriorly in the ganglionic trunk and make electrotonic connections as well as chemical excitatory synapses onto processes of the large cells within the ganglionic neuropil (for review see 31).

There is general agreement that both large and small cells are able to show endogenous bursting but that the primary control comes from the small cells (19, 43, 77, 81). Recent work has shed considerable light on the problem of how the small cells are able to provide this control, particularly with regard to cycle period and burst duration. Two types of conductance mechanisms appear to be involved: one that causes the production of pacemaker potentials, and the other that leads to the production of a regenerative depolarizing potential (78–80). This latter potential is termed a driver potential and has properties similar to those of the plateau potentials found in lobster stomatogastric neurons (67, 68). Cells with this property will not burst spontaneously but do have the capability of bursting as a result of some depolarizing input. This capability means that a population of such cells can form complex phase relationships, something that spontaneous bursters cannot. Because only the small cells have the conductances necessary to generate pacemaker potentials, these serve as the trigger for producing driver potentials and subsequent bursts.

The smaller cells fire first, and the EPSPs that they put onto the large cells trigger driver potentials and bursts in them. The slow driver potentials have a longer plateau (duration) in the small cells than in the large ones. There are also a greater number of spikes and a higher rate of firing in the small cells, due to lower thresholds and less accommodation. It appears that in normal circumstances the cardiac burst is initiated in the small cells, which produce coordinated but not absolutely synchronized action potentials leading to the production of EPSPs in the large cells. This triggers a burst in the large cells that is synchronized by their electrotonic connections. If spikes from the small cells are blocked by means of a ligature, the reduced synaptic input shortens the large cell burst, but they continue to produce coordinated bursting as a result of electrotonic conduction. If this is also removed, there is now some question as to whether or not the large cells can generate bursts (78).

The principal role of the EPSPs is to increase burst duration, this being the only deficit produced when spikes are blocked with TTX. One notes in this system the crucial role played by the extensive electrotonic interconnectivity in terms of coordinating the oscillations.

TRITONIA SWIM OSCILLATOR: A NETWORK OSCILLATOR

The sea slug, *Tritonia diomedia,* escapes from predators by a series of dorsal and ventral flexion movements termed swimming (36, 89). During the swim, dorsal flexion neurons (DFN) and ventral flexion neurons (VFN) fire antagonist bursts of impulses to the dorsal and ventral musculature (88).

Complete isolation of the ganglion containing both the pattern-generating interneurons and motor neurons does not prevent the production of alternating bursts in the motor nerves when an appropriate input nerve is electrically stimulated (15, 16).

Four groups of premotor interneurons have been found that appear to be responsible for generating the pattern (23–26, 76). Recordings made from these interneurons in isolated brain preparations during "fictive" swimming have the following characteristics:

1. Alternating bursts occur between the dorsal swim interneurons (DSI) and two classes of ventral swim interneurons (VSI-A and VSI-B).
2. The third class of interneuron termed cerebral cell 2 (C2), fire after the DSI burst and continue through the initiation of the VSI bursts.
3. All of the bursts are superimposed onto a prolonged depolarizing ramp that declines as the swim progresses but is initially responsible for maintaining the swim activity (41).

The four classes of interneurons have been demonstrated to be part of the swim CPG by showing that current pulses that advance or delay their bursting can reset the entire motor pattern (25, 27). Monosynapticity has been demonstrated not only between the interneurons making up the CPG (26), but also between the interneurons and the dorsal and ventral flexion motor neurons (25, 35).

The principal synaptic mechanism underlying the swim oscillator appears to be reciprocal inhibition paralleled by delayed excitation (24). Note from Figure 1 that the oscillator consists of two sides, the DSI and the VSI. Synergists within these groups are coupled by reciprocal excitation. However, the two sides themselves are coupled via reciprocal inhibition. The monosynpatic inhibitory pathway from DSI to VSI is paralleled by a delayed excitatory pathway via the C2 interneuron. The mechanism underlying the oscillations emanating from this network can be described as follows:

1. The swim cycle begins when the DSI interneurons are depolarized and begin to fire.
2. When the DSIs fire, they inhibit the VSIs and excite C2.
3. C2 fires simultaneously with the DSIs for a short period, but although the VSIs are being inhibited by the DSIs, they are also receiving excitation from C2 that eventually causes them to start firing.
4. Once VSI starts firing, it inhibits both the DSIs and the C2, thus terminating their bursts.
5. Now VSI is no longer receiving any excitation from C2 and its spike frequency declines, releasing the DSIs from inhibition and starting the cycle over again.

The oscillation will continue as long as the ramp depolarization is sufficient to make the DSIs fire at a high enough frequency, following their release from inhibition, to bring C2 to threshold. Crucial for the operation of this network is a delay between the onset of inhibition and the onset of excitation to

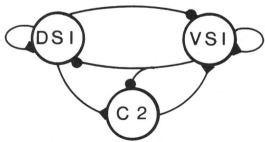

Figure 1 The neuronal network for generating the swim motor pattern in *Tritonia diomedea* consists of three types of cells. The dorsal swim interneuron *(DSI)* and the ventral swim interneuron *(VSI)* are premotor to the dorsal and ventral flexor muscles. The *C2* interneuron plays a complex role in the generation of the pattern because it is excited by *DSI* and inhibited by *VSI*. Excitatory synapses are represented in this and subsequent figures by *triangles,* while inhibitory synapses are represented by *circles.*

the VSI. Two separate mechanisms, one for each class of *VSI*, appear to be involved. VSI-A receives a dual-action inhibitory-excitatory synapse from C2 (27), so that although its initial effect is inhibitory, it changes to excitation after a delay of 1–1.5 seconds. VSI-B, on the other hand, shows a delayed response to C2 excitation as a result of having a fast transient potassium current ("A current" of Connor & Stevens, 13), activated by depolarization. This current keeps the membrane from becoming depolarized by the EPSPs from C2. The A current inactivates after a few seconds, allowing the VSI-B neurons to fire.

This circuit is an excellent example of a network oscillator: the pattern emerges from the network as a whole, no single cell being capable of producing bursts. The network relies on both synaptic interactions and the intrinsic membrane properties of the individual neurons to generate the motor pattern.

LEECH HEARTBEAT: A MIXED OSCILLATOR

The circuit that controls the leech heartbeat is probably one of the best examples of a mixed oscillator. Leech circulation is governed by two longitudinal vessels that constrict with a period of 10–30 seconds. The rhythmic constrictions are driven by segmental pairs of motor neurons [HE cells of Thompson & Stent, (82)] that innervate the parietal muscles of the left and right heart tubes in the corresponding segment. Each heart tube has two different contraction patterns: (*a*) a peristaltic pattern with a longitudinal wave of constriction going forward and corresponding to successive bursts of spikes in the HE cells from posterior to anterior on the corresponding side; and (*b*) a nonperistaltic pattern with an almost synchronous constriction of all the regions of the tube, corresponding to synchronous bursts of HE cells on the corresponding side.

When one heart tube behaves in a peristaltic mode, the other behaves in a nonperistaltic mode. Approximately, every 50 cycles, the two heart tubes trade roles (11, 83).

After isolation of the ventral nerve cord, recordings from the vascular motor nerves show a fictive heart beat with the pattern described above (8). This demonstrates the presence of a heartbeat CPG within the CNS. The corresponding circuit is one of the best known, with almost all of the participating neurons and synapses identified. There is a set of segmental interneurons, the HN cells, and each ganglion from the first and the seventh contains a bilateral pair. All of the HN cells project posteriorly and inhibit the ipsilateral HE cells. The HN cells produce bursts of impulses with the heartbeat rhythm, which are interrupted by barrages of IPSPs coming from other HN cells (Figure 2*A*) (11, 84). Recent work has elucidated the main mechanisms involved (8, 58–60).

We first consider the timing of the heartbeat, i.e. the rhythm generator. A perturbation imposed on any of the HN1 to HN4 neurons in the circuit resets the phase of the oscillation in the whole network (60). Conversely, the same test

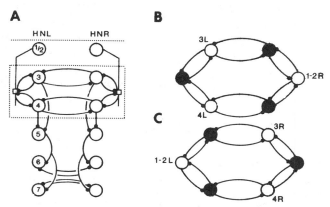

Figure 2   The neuronal network for generating the heartbeat motor pattern in the leech is made up of seven pairs of bilaterally organized *HN* cells. The numbers (shown only on the *left side*) represent the segmental ganglion each pair is found in. The timing oscillator *(A)* is located in the third and fourth ganglion; the *small boxes* represent the spike-initiating zones of HN1 and HN2. The more posterior HN cells are driven by this oscillator. The changes in coordination modes are represented in *B* and *C*, where the *clear circles* represent firing and the *filled circles* represent silent cells. See text for details.

applied to any other neuron fails to reset the rhythm. This suggests that the eight HN interneurons form the circuit for the heartbeat rhythm. Because the HN cells of the first two ganglia (HN1 and HN2) have their spike-initiating zones in the fourth ganglion, a preparation containing only the third and fourth ganglion can still produce the pattern.

The circuit for G3 and G4 is a closed loop of six elements connected by reciprocal inhibition. In such a loop there are two functionally stable states: In the first, HN3L, HN1–2R, and HN4L are firing, and the other intercalated elements remain silent (Figure 2B). In the second, HN3R, HN4R, and HN1-2L are firing and the others are silent (Figure 2C). One burst of spikes in the three elements corresponding to the first stable state is always followed by one burst of spikes in the three elements corresponding to the second stable state. Considering only the HN3 and HN4 neurons (Figures 2B, and 2C) that serve as the output of the rhythm generator to the rest of the circuit, then in one of the segments (either segment 3 or 4), when one neuron fires, the other is silent, and in successive segments (segments 3 and 4), the ipsilateral neurons are either firing or are silent at the same time. Switching from one state to the other occurs when an inactive HN3 (Figure 2B) or an inactive HN4 (Figure 2C) starts to recover from inhibition. The ability to recover is probably governed by the endogenous regenerative properties of these cells, which can oscillate when synaptic inhibition is blocked (9, 10).

The timing of the pattern appears to be governed by a separate mechanism.

The circuit just described is able to generate the heartbeat rhythm, but cannot be responsible directly for the two patterns displayed by the whole circuit or for the regular switch that occurs between these two patterns for a given heart tube.

With regard to the latter point, it is known that it is the behavior of the two HN5 cells that determines the pattern (8). Depending upon the particular relationship, each HN5 bursts in antiphase with the ipsilateral HN3–HN4 interneurons. Moreover, each HN5 cell can be silenced by additional tonic inhibitory input, which remains from 20 to 50 cycles, the left and right HN5 being alternatively inhibited. When one HN5 cell is active, the other is silent and the heart tube ipsilateral to the active HN5 displays nonperistaltic behavior while the heart tube ipsilateral to the inactive HN5 displays peristaltic behavior. The existence of a switching oscillator, able to alternatively remove the spiking activity of each HN5, must be postulated and remains to be identified.

Returning to the first point, the wiring diagram (Figure 2A) shows that on the side ipsilateral to an HN5 active cell, all the interneurons that govern the HE motor neurons (e.g. HN3, 4, 6, and 7) are bursting in phase (and HN5 in antiphase). On this side, all the HE motor neurons produce synchronous bursts of spikes and the heart tube displays a nonperistaltic behavior. Conversely, on the side contralateral to an active HN5, the HN6 and 7 fire roughly in antiphase with the HN3 and HN4 cells. On this side, and proceeding rearwards along the nerve cord, there is a blending of inhibitory inputs at different phases onto the motor neurons, and the heart tube displays a peristaltic behavior. The analysis of the heartbeat-pattern generator provides a remarkable example of how a circuit displaying complex metastable coordination can be worked out.

LOBSTER PYLORIC SYSTEM

Neuronal oscillators in the lobster stomatogastric ganglion produce two rhythmic motor patterns that control the striated musculature of the stomach (70). Although the patterns are quite variable in vivo (18, 62), an isolated preparation consisting of the stomatogastric, the esophageal, and the paired commissural ganglia will produce extremely regular and robust oscillatory activity for many hours. The stomatogastric ganglion contains only 30 neurons, 14 of which comprise the pyloric oscillator.

The oscillatory properties are derived mainly from the synaptic interactions and intrinsic cellular properties of motor neurons, although there is one interneuron. When the principal input nerve to the stomatogastric ganglion (the stomatogastric nerve) is cut or blocked, the pyloric rhythm ceases or is greatly slowed down, depending on the species. This suggests the requirement for factors extrinsic to the stomatogastric ganglion are necessary for maintenance of the oscillation, although it is clear that these factors need not contain phasic timing information.

The pyloric neurons produce a three-phase cycle (Figure 3*A*) with one dilator phase (PD, AB) and two successive constrictor phases (LP, PY). The highly simplified version of the circuit (Figure 3*B*) is derived from older results (32, 44, 45) to which results obtained with the new cell photoinactivation technique (47) have been added (17, 49, 69).

Utilization of this technique has resulted in a qualitative explanation of the pyloric oscillatory mechanisms (69). The main features are:

1. When the inputs to the stomatogastric ganglion are intact, all of the pyloric cells show an intrinsic bursting capacity even if synaptically isolated from other cells.
2. If the PD and AB cells are removed from the network, the remaining cells will continue to oscillate as long as the inputs from the commissurals are intact. If the inputs are blocked, all oscillation ceases.
3. Tonic stimulation of the reduced network on the ganglion side of the stomatogastric nerve block turns on the oscillator, which continues to operate for several minutes after the end of the stimulating volley. It is clear, therefore, that the PD-AB cells are not necessary for the production of oscillatory activity as long as the inputs to the ganglion are intact. It has also been demonstrated, using the photoinactivation technique, that PD and AB cells have quite different physiological characteristics. Although the PD and AB cells are strongly coupled to each other, they do not make the same sets of connections of the LP and VD cells. Where they do make the same sets of connections, each may produce PSPs with different time courses, and in fact each uses different transmitters (17).

The presence of the inputs from the commissural ganglia confers at least two special properties: burstiness and the ability to generate plateau potentials (68).

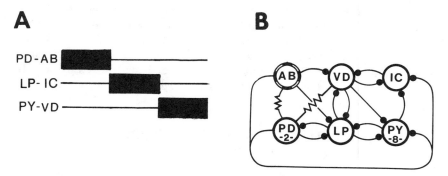

Figure 3   *(A)* The three-phase burst pattern of the pyloric system is shown schematically. The period in a combined preparation is approximately 0.5 seconds. *(B)* The neuronal network for generating the pyloric pattern; *circles* represent inhibitory synapses and the *resistors* represent electrotonic connections.

However, in ganglia that have been isolated and in which the AB cell has been photoinactivated, minimal reciprocal inhibitory subsets of the pyloric network can still produce alternate bursting (49). This is the first demonstration of a real "half-center" oscillator in a biological system and shows that patterned activity can be generated through the interconnection of neurons that would otherwise fire tonically.

The actual mechanism for the generation of the oscillatory pattern can be described when the ganglion is connected via the stomatogastric nerve to the commissural and esophageal ganglia as follows:

1. The VD-to-LP and the PD-to-LP cell pairs oscillate out of phase, due to their reciprocal inhibitory synaptic connections and their input-induced burstiness. If AB were not present, the VD and the LP would fire at about the same time.

2. The PDs put strong inhibition onto the PY and IC cells, causing them to be inhibited during the time of the PD bursts. However, both the LP cell and the IC cell recover before the PY cells, which have a built-in rebound delay (32). The delay explains why the rhythm occurs in three phases.

3. The AB cell not only puts strong synapses onto all of the other cells of the network, it is also strongly coupled to the PD cells so that in the intact network PD and AB always fire together. Under these conditions, VD will also be strongly inhibited by AB, overcoming the weak electrotonic connection to PD. Because VD is also inhibited by LP and IC, it will be constrained to fire during the PY period.

4. The AB cell also acts as the overall frequency controller for the network. As well as shutting off the other cells, rebound from AB's strong inhibitory drive acts to accelerate the progression of bursts within the pattern.

The existence of the pyloric pattern derives from both the oscillatory properties of the individual neurons in combination with the multiple reciprocally inhibitory interactions within the network. The phase relationships are a result of the synaptic connectivity, the relative synaptic strengths, postinhibitory rebound, rebound delay and the kinetics of the plateau, and bursting pacemaker potential mechanisms. The overall cycle frequency is determined by the AB cell both as a result of its oscillatory behavior and the strong synapses it makes with the other cells.

SPECIAL CELLULAR AND SYNAPTIC PROPERTIES OF OSCILLATORY NETWORK NEURONS

What are the most important cellular and synaptic properties involved in the production of oscillatory patterns? Although every known property may play some role (7), the examples just discussed have shown the following to be most crucial:

1   Bursting Pacemaker Potentials (BPPs)

In many oscillatory networks there are cells with regenerative bursting properties (see J. Connor, this volume) that are essential for the genesis of the rhythm and/or the organization of the pattern (8, 48, 78). One important point, however, is illustrated by the oscillatory neurons in the stomatogastric circuit. Here it has been shown that the ability to generate BPPs can require synaptic inputs that are inducing or unmasking the cyclical conductance changes that govern the oscillations of the membranes (48, 51, 54). Although this may be a means for turning an oscillatory circuit on and off, it also shows that the isolation that is necessary to work out a circuit can result in the loss of fundamental properties necessary to understand how the circuit works.

2   Plateau Potentials (or Driver Potentials)

Neurons able to develop plateau potentials are not endogenous bursters because they normally do not develop any pacemaker potentials. Nevertheless, if some input drives their membrane potential to a given threshold, they develop a plateau potential (68) or driver potentials (78) that can be directly compared to the second phase of the membrane trajectory of an endogenous burster. The ability of a neuron to produce plateau potentials is unmasked by tonic inputs in some cases (53, 67, 68). This input is also able to continuously control the kinetics of the regenerative jumps of potential that start or terminate a burst of spikes (14). Using this mechanism, the input can continuously control the phase at which the neuron delivers a burst of spikes in the cycle (50, 53). These results are important from two points of view. First, they show that the pattern can be continuously controlled by the tonic discharge of an extrinsic input. Second, they demonstrate that the modulation of the output may occur via changes in the intrinsic properties of the elements, properties that must now be considered in a dynamic perspective.

3   Postinhibitory Rebound (PIR)

With the large number of inhibitory synapses present in oscillatory networks, PIR becomes an important parameter. The termination of inhibition can, as a result of PIR alone, cause a burst of spikes in the postsynaptic cell. Modeling studies have shown it to be important in maintaining the alternate firing pattern of reciprocally inhibitory networks (57). The kinetics of the PIR determines the time at which a postsynaptic cell starts firing, so that two cells receiving the same inhibition can fire afterwards at two different phases if they have different rebound kinetics (32).

4   Repetitive Firing Properties (Frequency Adaptation)

Spike-frequency adaptation (55) is an intrinsic property of a neuron that can have important implications in shaping the pattern of oscillatory activity. For example, in *Tritonia,* some neurons respond to constant depolarization with a decelerating burst, whereas others respond with an accelerating burst (24, 25). This means that in one case a burst can stop before the end of the underlying synaptic drive and in another case can start long after the beginning of the drive (i.e. excitation can be delayed). Delayed excitation—caused by the development of a transient potassium conductance (A current) in some *Tritonia* cells—is a property that, as noted, can greatly affect phase relationships (22).

5   Graded Transmitter Release

This may be common in oscillatory circuits. This form of transmission has been described for the lobster pyloric generator (29, 61) as well as the cardiac oscillator (78). It has also been implicated in other oscillatory networks that are less completely known, such as the cockroach walking system (56), the lobster scaphagnothite (gill-bailer system) (46, 72), and the crayfish swimmeret system (33).

CONTROL OF OSCILLATORY NETWORKS

No oscillatory networks exist free of controlling inputs, but an exhaustive treatment of the elements that can be involved in this control, such as command fibers (40), coordinating fibers (74), and phasic sensory feedback (30), is beyond the scope of this review. However, some new data are especially germane to the general concept of neuronal network oscillators and must be considered.

Higher Order Oscillators

Included in the concept of CPGs was the premise that they were free of control by higher order oscillators located "upstream" (see 30). Recently, however, several examples of possible "master" oscillators have been documented.

The best example is found in the lobster pyloric system. In *Homarus* two pyloric oscillators have been identified, one in the stomatogastric ganglion (the pyloric CPG) and one in the higher order commissural ganglion (the commissural pyloric oscillator, CPO) (64). The oscillatory behavior of the CPO is determined by an endogenous burster neuron (CP). This neuron delivers cyclical monosynaptic excitation to the PD-AB group of the pyloric CPG and as a result entrains the entire pyloric rhythm. According to the instantaneous sensibility of the PD-AB group, the CPG can be entrained with different ratios of coordination (1:1, 1:2, 1:3 and so on) (50). Although not directly demonstrated, the CPO could also entrain each neuron of the pyloric CPG with a coordination mode that was a function of its instantaneous sensibility to the input. In other words, the CPO would be acting as a master oscillator controlling the frequency of the CPG as a whole as well as the frequency of each neuron in the CPG.

Recently described neuromodulatory inputs acting on the regenerative properties of all the neurons of the pyloric CPG can be responsible for the instantaneous sensitivity of the neurons to CPO inputs (14).

A comparable situation has now been described for the *Homarus* gastric CPG (63), where another higher order oscillator has been identified in the commissural ganglia. It is interesting to note that this oscillator (the CGO) receives phasic input from the CPO and strong phasic input from a proprioceptor associated with a gastric muscle (A. J. Simmers & M. Moulins, unpublished observations). This means that such a higher order oscillator can act as an interface between the CPG and several inputs capable of modifying it.

Finally, a similar independent high order oscillatory interneuron has also been described in the snail feeding system (66). This neuron (termed SO) monosynaptically excites a group of putative CPG interneurons and as a result is able to control the frequency of CPG activity.

Modulatory Inputs

Describing oscillatory circuits in terms of wiring diagrams and cell properties can allow us to understand how a circuit works, but they do not offer any explanation of the flexibility encountered in the intact animal. While sensory feedback can account for immediate, cycle-by-cycle flexibility, evidence is now accumulating that suggests that neuromodulatory mechanisms can be the origin of a more fundamental type of flexibility.

Recently it has been shown that the *Homarus* pyloric pattern can be completely modified by the tonic discharge of an identified interneuron (APM) (53). This cell appears to act monosynaptically on all the neurons of the oscillator and causes changes in phase relationships, the duration of bursts for several of the neurons, the firing frequency within the bursts, and the frequency of the rhythm itself. The efficacy of the synapses inside the network and the efficacy of the extrinsic inputs (such as the CPO) are modified in such a way that a new pattern appears (52). It has now been shown (14) that all of the modifications arise due to changes in the regenerative properties of the pyloric cells. In other words, the circuit is itself flexible in terms of its expression, and the control over this flexibility is insured by the control over the intrinsic properties of the cells (50).

Similar changes in synaptic efficacy have now been obtained by application of several neurotransmitters or neuromodulatory substances (42). It can be surmised that there are probably several neuromodulatory pathways acting in parallel and differentially on the pyloric neurons and able to "shape" the pyloric pattern in such a way that the pyloric CPG can produce a large repertoire of motor patterns. Although drastic, the effects of APM are only a small example of what can be produced using such mechanism in a small network.

Finally, the possibilities of "rewiring" neural circuits can be considered as a means by which a functional circuit can be specified from within the context of a larger network. In the network that produces swimming in *Tritonia*, Getting has suggested that two different circuits can be specified, depending upon the strength of the swim-initiating stimulus.

It may be difficult before long to consider a particular network as forming the basis for the generation of an oscillatory motor pattern. Future research may show that in these complex systems, extrinsic influences may be able to continuously rewire and rebuild circuits and that the idea of a specific fixed circuit should be abandoned.

SUMMARY

Despite the fact that a large number of neuronal oscillators have been described, there are only a few good examples that illustrate how they operate at the cellular level. For most, there is some isolated information about different aspects of the oscillator network, but too little to explain the whole mechanism. Two quite remarkable features do seem to be emerging from ongoing studies, however. One is that there are very few generalizable features common to neural oscillators. Many utilize reciprocal inhibitory circuits and endogenous burst-generating currents to some extent. All that have been well worked out utilize a combination of both cellular and network properties, but little else in the way of common mechanism is noteworthy.

Perhaps the most interesting aspect of recent work is the ability of a particular oscillator to produce a large repertoire of different outputs. This is separate and in addition to changes occurring via phasic sensory feedback. It is in fact a radical functional "rewiring" of the network in response to neuromodulators. The CPG circuits represent only the most basic form of a given pattern.

Finally, concerning the role of sensory feedback in generating oscillatory patterns, the concept of the CPG as a group of neurons able to produce oscillatory patterns without any sensory feedback is, in our opinion, still valid. There is no doubt that some oscillators may be quite weak when isolated, but they can still produce bursts with firing sequences similar to those seen in vivo. The fact that sensory feedback can both control and enhance the oscillations has never been in doubt. Similarly, entrainment of the pattern by sensory feedback does not mean that the receptor is part of the generator, only that it has access to it (as do command and coordinating fibers). The real question remains: Can a group of cells produce an oscillatory pattern without phasic sensory input? We must answer this affirmatively even for the insect-flight motor CPG, while emphasizing the fact that for this system sensory feedback plays a larger role than in most other CPGs. Most neural oscillators will probably fall on some continuum between those like insect flight, which need and use a large amount of phasic feedback, and those that can oscillate in a near-normal manner without it.

Literature Cited

1. Altman, J. 1982. The role of sensory inputs in insect flight motor pattern generation. *Trends Neurosci.* 5:257–60
2. Alving, R. O. 1968. Spontaneous activity in isolated somata of *Aplysia* pacemaker neurons. *J. Gen. Physiol.* 45:29–45
3. Bacon, J., Mohl, B. 1983. The tritocerebral commissure giant (TCG) wind sensitive interneurons in the locust. I. Its activity in straight flight. *J. Comp. Physiol.* 150:439–52
4. Barker, J. L. 1977. Physiological roles of peptides in the nervous system. In *Peptides in Neurobiology*, ed. H. Gainer, pp. 295–343. New York: Plenum
5. Berry, M. S., Penreath, V. W. 1976. Criteria for distinguishing between monosynaptic and polysynaptic transmission. *Brain Res.* 105:1–20
6. Brown, T. A. 1911. The intrinsic factors in the act of progression in the mammal. *Proc. R. Soc. London Ser. B.* 84:308–19
7. Bullock, T. H. 1977. *Introduction to Nervous Systems*. San Francisco: Freeman
8. Calabrese, R. L., Peterson, E. 1983. Neural control of heartbeat in the leech, *Hirudo medicinalis. S. E. B. Symposia* 37:195–221
9. Calabrese, R. L. 1979. Neural generation of the peristaltic and non-peristaltic heartbeat coordination modes in the leech, *Hirudo medicinalis. Am. Zool.* 19:87–102
10. Calabrese, R. L. 1979. The roles of endogenous membrane properties and synaptic interaction in generating the heartbeat rhythm of the leech, *Hirudo medicinalis. J. Exp. Biol.* 82:163–76
11. Calabrese, R. L. 1977. The neural control of alternate heartbeat coordination states in the leech *Hirudo medicinalis. J. Comp. Physiol.* 122:111–43
12. Camhi, J. M. 1984. *Neuroethology*. Sunderland, MA: Sinauer Assoc.
13. Connor, J. A., Stevens, C. F. 1971. Voltage clamp studies of a transient outward current in gastropod neural somata. *J. Neurophysiol.* 213:21–30
14. Dickinson, P. S., Nagy, F. 1983. Control of a central pattern generator by an identified modulatory interneuron in crustacea. II. Induction and modification of plateau properties in pyloric neurones. *J. Exp. Biol.* 105:59–82
15. Dorsett, D. A., Willows, A. O. D., Hoyle, G. 1973. The neuronal basis of behavior in *Tritonia*. IV. The central origin of a fixed action pattern demonstrated in the isolated brain. *J. Neurobiol.* 4: 287–300
16. Dorsett, D. A., Willows, A. O. D., Hoyle, G. 1969. Centrally generated nerve impulse sequences determining swimming behavior in *Tritonia*. *Nature* 244:711–12
17. Eisen, J. S., Marder, E. 1982. Mechanisms underlying pattern generation in lobster stomatogastric ganglion as determined by selective inactivation of identified neurons. III. Synaptic connections of electrically coupled pyloric neurons. *J. Neurophysiol.* 48:1392–415
18. Fleischer, A. S. 1982. The effect of eyestalk hormones on the gastric mill in the intact lobster, *Panulirus interruptus. J. Comp. Physiol.* 141:363–68
19. Friesen, W. O. 1975. Synaptic interactions in the cardiac ganglion of the spiny lobster, *Panulirus interruptus. J. Comp. Physiol.* 101A:191–205
20. Friesen, W. O., Stent, G. S. 1978. Neural circuits for generating rhythmic movements. *Ann. Rev. Biophys. Bioeng.* 7:37–61
21. Friesen, W. O., Stent, G. S. 1977. Generation of a locomotory rhythm by a neural network with recurrent cyclic inhibition. *Biol. Cyber.* 28:27–40
22. Getting, P. A. 1983. Neural control of swimming in *Tritonia*. In *Symposia of the Society for Experimental Biology*, 37:89–128. Cambridge Univ. Press
23. Getting, P. A. 1977. Neuronal organization of escape swimming in *Tritonia*. *J. Comp. Physiol.* 121:325–42
24. Getting, P. A. 1983. Mechanisms of pattern generation underlying swimming in *Tritonia*. II. Network reconstruction. *J. Neurophysiol.* 46:64–79
25. Getting, P. A. 1983. Mechanisms of pattern generation underlying swimming in *Tritonia*. III. Intrinsic and synaptic mechanisms for delayed excitation. *J. Neurophysiol.* 49:1036–50
26. Getting, P. A. 1981. Mechanisms of pattern generation underlying swimming in *Tritonia*. I. Neuronal network formed by monosynaptic connections. *J. Neurophysiol.* 46:65–79
27. Getting, P. A., Lennard, P. R., Hume, R. I. 1980. Central pattern generator mediating swimming in *Tritonia*. I. Identification and synaptic interactions. *J. Neurophysiol.* 44:151–64
28. Gola, M. 1974. Neurones a ondes-salves des mollusques. Variations cycliques lentes des conductances ioniques. *Pfluegers Arch.* 352:17–36

29. Graubard, K., Raper, J. A., Hartline, D. K. 1980. Graded synaptic transmission between spiking neurons. *Proc. Natl. Acad. Sci. USA* 77:1392–415

30. Grillner, S. 1977. On the neural control of movement—a comparison of different basic rhythmic behaviors. In *Function and Formation of Neural Systems,* ed. G. S. Stent, pp. 197–224. Berlin: Dahlem Konferenzen

31. Hartline, D. K. 1979. Integrative neurophysiology of the lobster cardiac ganglion. *Am. Zool.* 19:53–65

32. Hartline, D. K., Gassie, D. V. Jr. 1979. Pattern generation in the lobster *(Panulirus)* stomatogastric ganglion. I. Pyloric neuron kinetics and synaptic interactions. *Biol. Cybern.* 33:209–22

33. Heitler, W. J. 1983. The control of rhythmic limb movements in crustacea. *S. E. B. Symposia* 37:351–82

34. Horsmann, U., Heinzel, H. G., Wendler, G. 1983. The phasic influence of self-generated air current modulations on the locust flight motor. *J. Comp. Physiol.* 150:427–38

35. Hume, R. I., Getting, P. A. 1982. Motor organization of *Tritonia* swimming. II. Synaptic drive to flexion neurons from premotor interneurons. *J. Neurophysiol.* 47:75–90

36. Hume, R. I., Getting, P. A., Del Beccaro, M. A. 1982. Motor organization of *Tritonia* swimming. I. Quantitative analysis of swim behavior and flexion neuron firing patterns. *J. Neurophysiol.* 47:60–74

37. Kling, U., Szekely, G. 1968. Simulation of rhythmic nervous activities. I. Function of networks with cyclic inhibitions. *Kybernetik* 5:89–103

38. Kristan, W. B. Jr. 1977. Neural control of movement. See. Ref. 30, pp. 329–54

39. Kristan, W. B. Jr. 1980. Generation of rhythmic motor patterns. In *Information Processing in the Nervous System,* ed. H. M. Pinsker, W. D. Willis, Jr., pp. 241–61 New York: Raven

40. Kupferman, I., Weiss, K. R. 1978. The command neuron concept. *Behav. Brain Sci.* 1:3–10

41. Lennard, P. R., Getting, P. A., Hume, R. I. 1980. Central pattern generator mediating swimming in *Tritonia*. II. Initiation, maintenance, and termination. *J. Neurophysiol.* 44:165–73

42. Marder, K. 1984. Mechanisms underlying neurotransmitter modulation of a neuronal circuit. *Trends Neurosci.* 7:48–53

43. Mayeri, E. 1973. Functional organization of the cardiac ganglion of the lobster *Homarus americanus. J. Gen. Physiol.* 62:448–72

44. Maynard, D. M., Selverston, A. I. 1975. Organization of the stomatogastric ganglion of the spiny lobster. IV. The pyloric system. *J. Comp. Physiol.* 100:161–82

45. Maynard, D. M. 1972. Simpler networks. *Ann. NY Acad. Sci.* 193:59–72

46. Mendelson, M. 1971. Oscillator neurons in crustacean ganglia. *Science* 171:1170–73

47. Miller, J. P., Selverston, A. I. 1979. Rapid killing of single neurons by illumination of intracellularly injected dye. *Science* 206:702–4

48. Miller, J. P., Selverston, A. I. 1982. Mechanisms underlying pattern generation in the lobster stomatogastric ganglion as determined by selective inactivation of identified neurons. II. Oscillatory properties of pyloric neurons. *J. Neurophysiol.* 48:1378–91

49. Miller, J. P., Selverston, A. I. 1982. Mechanisms underlying pattern generation in lobster stomatogastric ganglion as determined by selective inactivation of identified neurons. IV. Network properties of pyloric system. *J. Neurophysiol.* 48:1416–32

50. Moulins, M., Nagy, F. 1983. Control of integration by extrinsic inputs in the crustacean pyloric circuit. *J. Physiol.* 78:755–64

51. Moulins, M., Cournil, I. 1982. All-or-none control of the bursting properties of the pacemaker neurons of the lobster pyloric pattern generator. *J. Neurobiol.* 13:447–58

52. Nagy, F., Dickinson, P. S. 1983. Control of a central pattern generator by an identified modulatory interneuron in crustacea. I. Modulation of the pyloric motor output. *J. Exp. Biol.* 105:33–58

53. Nagy, F., Dickinson, P. S., Moulins, M. 1981. Modulatory effects of a single neuron on the activity of the pyloric pattern generator in crustacea. *Neurosci. Lett.* 23:167–73

54. Nagy, F., Benson, J. A., Moulins, M. 1984. Stimulation of muscarinic receptors induces Ca-dependent bursting activity in stomatogastric neurones. *Neurosci. Lett.* In press

55. Partridge, L. D., Stevens, C. F. 1976. A mechanism for spike frequency adaptation. *J. Physiol.* 256:313–33

56. Pearson, K. G., Fourtner, C. R. 1975. Nonspiking interneurons in walking system of the cockroach. *J. Neurophysiol.* 38:33–52

57. Perkel, D. M., Mulloney, B. 1974. Motor pattern production in reciprocally

inhibitory neurons exhibiting post-inhibitory rebound. *Science* 185:181–83

58. Peterson, E. L. 1983. Generation and coordination of the heartbeat timing oscillation in the medicinal leech. I. Oscillatory neuronal circuits in ganglia. *J. Neurophysiol.* 49:611–26

59. Peterson, E. L. 1983. Generation and coordination of the heartbeat timing oscillator in the medicinal leech. II. The timer as a system of two coupled oscillators. *J. Neurophysiol.* 49:627–38

60. Peterson, E. L., Calabrese, R. L. 1982. Dynamic analysis of a rhythmic neural circuit in the leech *Hilrudo medicinalis*. *J. Neurophysiol.* 47:256–71

61. Raper, J. A. 1979. Non-impulse mediated synaptic transmission during the generation of a cyclic motor program. *Science* 205:304–6

62. Rezer, E., Moulins, M. 1983. Expression of the crustacean pyloric pattern generator in the intact animal. *J. Comp. Physiol.* 153:17–28

63. Robertson, R. M., Moulins, M. 1984. Oscillatory command input to the motor pattern generators of the crustacean stomatogastric ganglion. II. The gastric rhythm. *J. Comp. Physiol.* 154:473–91

64. Robertson, R. M., Moulins, M. 1981. Oscillatory command input to the pattern generators of the crustacean stomatogastric ganglion. I. The pyloric rhythm. *J. Comp. Physiol.* 143:453–63

65. Robertson, R. M., Pearson, K. G. 1983. Interneurons in the flight system of the locust: Distribution, connections, and resetting properties. *J. Comp. Neurol.* 215:33–50

66. Rose, R. M., Benjamin, P. R. 1981. Interneuronal control of feeding in the pond snail *Lymnase stagnalis*. II. The interneuronal mechanisms generating feeding cycles. *J. Exp. Biol.* 92:202–28

67. Russell, D. F., Hartline, D. K. 1982. Slow active potentials and bursting motor patterns in pyloric network of the lobster, *Panulirus interruptus*. *J. Neurophysiol.* 48:914–37

68. Russell, D. F., Hartline, D. K. 1978. Bursting neural networks: A reexamination. *Science* 200:453–56

69. Selverston, A. I., Miller, J. P. 1980. Mechanisms underlying pattern generation in lobster stomatogastric ganglion as determined by selective inactivation of identified neurons. I. Pyloric system. *J. Neurophysiol.* 44:1102–21

70. Selverston, A. I., Russell, D. F., Miller, J. P., King, D. G. 1976. The stomatogastric nervous system: Structure and function of a small neural network. *Prog. Neurobiol.* 7:215–290

71. Shepherd, G. M. 1983. *Neurobiology*. Oxford Univ Press

72. Simmers, A. J., Bush, B. M. H. 1983. Central nervous mechanisms controlling rhythmic burst generation in the ventilatory motor neurones of *Carcinus maenas*. *J. Comp. Physiol.* 150:1–21

73. Deleted in proof

74. Stein, P. S. F. 1974. Neural control of interappendage phase during locomotion. *Am. Zool.* 14:1003–6

75. Szekely, G. 1965. Logical network for controlling limb movements in *Urodela*. *Acta Physiol. Acad. Sci.* 27:285–89

76. Taghert, P. H., Willows, A. O. D. 1978. Control of a fixed action pattern by single, central neurons in the marine mollusc, *Tritonia diomedea J. Comp. Physiol.* 123:253–59

77. Tameyasu, T. 1976. Intracellular potentials in the small cells and cellular interactions in the cardiac ganglion of the lobster *Panulirus japonicus*. *Comp. Biochem. Physiol.* 54A:191–96

78. Tazaki, K., Cooke, I. M. 1983. Neuronal mechanisms underlying rhythmic bursts in crustacean cardiac ganglia. *S. E. B. Symposia* 37:129–57

79. Tazaki, K., Cooke, I. M. 1983. Topographical localization of function in the cardiac ganglion of the crab, *Portunus sanguinolentus*. *J. Comp. Physiol.* 151: 311–28

80. Tazaki, K., Cooke, I. M. 1983. Separation of neuronal sites of driver potential and impulse generation by ligaturing in the cardiac ganglion of the lobster, *Homarus americanus*. *J. Comp. Physiol.* 151:329–46

81. Tazaki, K., Cooke, I. M. 1979. Isolation and characterization of slow, depolarizing responses, of cardiac ganglion neurons in the crab, *Portunus sanguinolentus*. *J. Neurophysiol.* 42:1000–21

82. Thompson, W. J., Stent, G. S. 1976. Neuronal control of heartbeat in the medicinal leech. I. Generation of the vascular constriction rhythm by heart motor neurons. *J. Comp. Physiol.* 111: 261–79

83. Thompson, W. J., Stent, G. S. 1976. Neuronal control of heartbeat in the medicinal leech. II. Inter-segmental coordination of heart motor neuron activity by heart neurons. *J. Comp. Physiol.* 111:281–307

84. Thompson, W. J., Stent, G. S. 1976. Neuronal control of heartbeat in the

medicinal leech. III. Synaptic relations of the heart interneurons. *J. Comp. Physiol.* 111:309–33

85. Weeks, J. C. 1981. The neuronal basis of leech swimming: Separation of swim initiation, pattern generation, and intersegmental coordination by selective lesions. *J. Neurophysiol.* 45:698–723

86. Wendler, G. 1983. The locust flight system: Functional aspects of sensory input and methods of investigation. In *Biona Report 2, Physiology and Biophysics of Insect Flight,* ed. W. Nachtigall, pp. 113–25. Stuttgart: Gastav Fischer Verlag

87. Wendler, G. 1974. The influence of proprioceptive feedback on lobster flight coordination. *J. Comp. Physiol.* 88:173–200

88. Willows, A. O. D. 1971. Giant brain cells in molluscs. *Sci. Am.* 224:68–75

89. Willows, A. O. D. 1967. Behavioral acts elicited by stimulation of single, identifiable brain cells. *Science* 157:570–74

90. Wilson, W. A., Wachtel, H. 1974. Negative resistance characteristic essential for the maintenance of slow oscillations in bursting neurons. *Science* 186:932–34

91. Wilson, D. M., Wyman, R. J. 1965. Motor output patterns during random and rhythmic stimulation of locust thoracic ganglia. *Biophys. J.* 5:121–43

92. Wilson, D. M., Gettrup, E. 1963. A stretch reflex controlling wingbeat frequency in grasshoppers. *J. Exp. Biol.* 40:171–85

93. Wilson, D. M., Waldron, I. M. 1968. Models for the generation of the motor output pattern in flying locusts. *Proc. IEEE* 56:1058–64

Ann. Rev. Physiol. 1985. 47:49–64

CIRCADIAN NEURAL RHYTHMS IN MAMMALS

Fred W. Turek

Department of Neurobiology and Physiology, Northwestern University, Evanston, Illinois 60201

INTRODUCTION

Only in the last few decades has the study of circadian rhythms attracted the interest of a large number of life scientists. This is somewhat surprising in view of the fact that the vast majority of biochemical, physiological, and behavioral phenomena show profound diurnal fluctuations. In nature these diurnal rhythms are normally synchronized with 24-hour environmental rhythms such as the light-dark cycle. However, even under constant environmental conditions in a laboratory setting, most diurnal variations persist (50a). This finding, along with other experimental evidence, has demonstrated that these diurnal fluctuations are endogenous rhythms and are driven by an internal biological clock (50a). These rhythms are referred to as "circadian" rhythms—from the Latin *circa diem,* meaning about a day, because their period under constant conditions is close to, but rarely exactly, 24 hours.

A primary objective of circadian rhythm researchers over the past two decades has been to identify and localize biological clocks in living tissue. Various experimental findings suggest that the circadian system in multicellular animals consists of more than a single circadian oscillator. Support for this hypothesis includes the observation that isolated glands and pieces of tissue can continue to show circadian oscillations in culture (72) and the fact that various rhythms within a single organism sometimes free-run with different circadian periods during exposure to constant environmental conditions (3, 37, 74). Despite the data indicating that the circadian system is multioscillatory in nature, there is a good deal of evidence to suggest that within a given species, a small number of specific neural structures serve as "driving" or "master" circadian pacemakers regulating many different circadian rhythms.

49

0066-4278/85/0315-0049$02.00

The search for circadian pacemakers in both invertebrates and vertebrates has focused mainly on the nervous system. A variety of experimental approaches have been utilized to localize circadian clocks in the brain of silkmoths, the optic lobes of cockroaches, the eyes of molluscs, the pineal gland of birds, and the hypothalamus of birds and mammals (6, 15, 33, 35, 43, 72, 73). Despite the diversity of systems that are being studied, similar questions are being addressed by neurobiologists examining the nature of the circadian clock in various species. These include: How is neural tissue organized to generate circadian signals? How are neural oscillators coupled to the circadian rhythms they drive? How do environmental agents, particularly the light-dark cycle, entrain or synchronize endogenous circadian pacemakers?

The observation that destruction of the bilaterally paired suprachiasmatic nucleus (SCN) of the hypothalamus could abolish the circadian rhythms of drinking behavior, locomotor activity, and adrenal corticosterone secretion in rats (36, 68) gave mammalian circadian biologists a neural structure on which to focus their attention. Indeed, the vast majority of studies on circadian neural rhythms in mammals are centered on the SCN. Therefore, this review will focus primarily on what is known about the neurobiology of the SCN. Although a great deal of information about the anatomy, neurophysiology, and neurochemistry of the SCN has been obtained over the last decade, the reader should be aware that the key question—how are circadian rhythms generated—remains unanswered. Indeed, it is not even clear at what level of organization the search for the physiological mechanisms involved in the generation of circadian signals should be carried out. The generation of circadian signals may depend upon the interaction of a large number of neurons within a specific neural structure such as the SCN. Alternatively, circadian rhythmicity may be a property of individual cells within a pacemaker, and the interactions between these cells may serve only to achieve overall synchronization.

SUPRACHIASMATIC NUCLEUS

Lesion Studies

Many diverse circadian rhythms are totally abolished or severely disrupted following bilateral destruction of the SCN in both rats and hamsters maintained under constant darkness or constant light (35, 73). Neonatal ablation of the SCN in rats permanently eliminates the circadian rhythms of locomotor activity and drinking behavior, suggesting that other regions of the brain do not have the capacity to reorganize and take over the function of the SCN (39). Other studies (see below) have demonstrated that circadian oscillations are intrinsic to the SCN region, indicating that lesions of the SCN do not simply disrupt the efferent connections of a circadian pacemaker located elsewhere in the brain. However, there is also some experimental evidence in rodents to suggest that the entire system for generating 24-hr rhythms does not reside exclusively within the SCN. Following total destruction of the SCN, some hamsters continue to show diurnal as well as ultradian (8- or 12-hr) periods of activity, and entrainment to a light-dark cycle, although abnormal, is still observed sometimes (55). Furthermore, in both rats and hamsters, a restricted feeding regime can act as a Zeitgeber (synchronizing agent) in SCN-lesioned animals, suggesting that at least some diurnal temporal organization can be produced outside of the SCN region (24, 66). Nevertheless, a circadian pacemaker(s) in the rodent SCN is clearly responsible for coordinating a large variety of circadian rhythms, and it appears that this region of the hypothalamus is at or near the top of a hierarchy of circadian clocks.

Studies involving the lesioning of a single SCN have demonstrated that a single SCN is sufficient for the expression of circadian rhythmicity (48). Both in birds and hamsters, ablation of a single SCN generally induces a small change in the free-running period of the locomotor activity rhythm, but the rhythm is clearly maintained (13, 49, 71). Thus, each SCN has the capacity to maintain circadian rhythmicity, although under normal conditions there is an interaction between the bilaterally paired nuclei in the generation of the circadian rhythm of activity. In both invertebrates and vertebrates, bilaterally paired circadian pacemakers have been localized within the nervous system (6, 33, 43). However, it is not clear if each SCN contains a single circadian oscillator or if each SCN is organized as a pacemaker composed of many oscillatory units.

Few extensive studies have been carried out on the role of the SCN in the circadian organization of nonrodent mammals. The fact that a direct retinal projection to the SCN [a pathway by which light information reaches the rodent SCN, (see below)] is common to all mammals (34, 35) suggests that the SCN regulates circadian rhythmicity in all mammalian species. Indeed, in the few studies that have been carried out in primates, SCN ablation was also found to disrupt circadian rhythmicity (2, 16, 51). However, while SCN ablation induces a severe disruption of the daily melatonin and drinking rhythms in rhesus and squirrel monkeys, respectively, these same lesions have little effect on the circadian rhythms of cortisol and core body temperature (16, 51).

The fact that SCN lesions only affect certain circadian rhythms in primates has led to the hypothesis that two major circadian pacemakers are functional in the primate brain and that different circadian clocks are responsible for the regulation of different circadian functions (37, 38). However, this hypothesis has been challenged by the results of a recent study indicating that destruction of SCN tissue renders primates more sensitive to environmental disturbances (17). Although the drinking rhythm of squirrel monkeys is not normally entrainable by auditory cues, entrainment does occur following partial destruction of the SCN. Thus, destruction of SCN tissue may render primates more sensitive to the entraining effects of nonphotic environmental cues (e.g. feeding, noise, temperature, and social cues). Following destruction of SCN tissue, some rhythms may be more sensitive to these environmental disturbances than others and thus persist while other rhythms are abolished. It is particularly interesting to note that the "free-running" period of the temperature rhythm in SCN-lesioned squirrel monkeys maintained in constant light, as reported by Fuller and his colleagues (16), was very close to 24 hr in length, suggesting that this rhythm may have been entrained by periodic noise in the laboratory. The maintenance of a diurnal cortisol rhythm in SCN-lesioned rhesus monkeys may also have been due to the fixed time of daily care and food delivery (51). The fact that the rhythmic increase in cortisol occurred 4–6 hr prior to the onset of daily care and food delivery in SCN-lesioned animals exposed to diurnal lighting, constant light, or constant darkness strongly suggests that this laboratory disturbance was indeed responsible for the occurrence of this diurnal rhythm. Similar reports of diurnal rhythms in rats persisting after total SCN ablation (41, 70) may also have been due to laboratory disturbances, because there is some suggestion that rats are more sensitive to environmental signals following SCN destruction (53). It is likely that a variety of external inputs influence the circadian system and that at least some external stimuli may bypass the circadian pacemaker(s) itself. These interactions need to be understood to adequately define the role of the SCN in the regulation of different circadian rhythms. To conclude that a major circadian pacemaker resides outside of the SCN, one must show the existence of a free-running circadian rhythm with a period clearly different from 24 hr following total SCN destruction.

Intrinsic Oscillations

If the SCN does indeed function as a biological clock, then it should be possible to demonstrate that biological oscillations are intrinsic to the SCN itself. Inouye & Kawamura (26, 27) have demonstrated that a circadian rhythm in multiple-unit activity is observed in many different brain regions of freely moving rats. Importantly, a knife cut that isolates the SCN region from the rest of the brain abolishes circadian rhythmicity outside of the hypothalamic island while clear rhythmicity in multiple-unit activity persists within the island (Figure 1).

Multiple-unit activity within the hypothalamic island containing the SCN can be entrained by light-dark cycles and phase-shifted by light pulses if the retino-hypothalamic tract (RHT) is not destroyed (27). Inouye (25) has recently demonstrated that the immediate response of SCN neurons to a 1-hr light pulse is constant across a 24-hr day, even though there is a phase-dependent shift in SCN neural activity to 1-hr light pulses. Thus, while the direct effect of a light stimulus at the input side of the SCN shows no circadian variation, the output of the processing within the SCN does show circadian variation. Taken

MOTOR ACTIVITY

MUA

RETICULAR FORMATION

10⁴
5-

ISLAND(SCN)

10⁴
5-

21   9   21   9   21   9   21   9   21

Figure 1 Simultaneous recording of *motor activity* and *multiple-unit activity (MUA)* from the reticular formation and inside a hypothalamic island containing the *suprachiasmatic nucleus (SCN)*. The rat was housed in constant darkness. The abscissa represents real clock time in hours. The recordings began five days after hypothalamic isolation. Motor activity was detected by a wire attached to the animal and is plotted in 10-min bins. The height of the bar is proportional to the total motor activity for each 10-min period. Multiple-unit discharges are plotted in 5-min bins. While motor activity and multiple-unit activity of the reticular formation normally show circadian fluctuations, following the neural isolation of the SCN from the rest of the brain, these rhythms are abolished. In contrast, multiple-unit activity within the island containing the SCN continues to exhibit a clear circadian rhythm. (Reproduced with permission from S. T. Inouye, unpublished results).

together these results indicate that tissue within the SCN region is capable of generating circadian neural rhythms and these neural rhythms receive synchronizing information from the light-dark environment via the RHT. Furthermore, an endogenous circadian pacemaker(s) within the SCN drives other neural rhythms throughout the brain.

Additional evidence that neural tissue within the SCN region is capable of generating circadian neural signals has been obtained from in vitro studies. Three different laboratories have reported that single SCN cells in hypothalamic slice preparations show changes in neural activity synchronized to the light-dark cycle to which the animals were previously exposed (18, 19, 65). Exposure to constant darkness, or blinding, prior to the preparation of the hypothalamic slice decreases the normally high discharge rate of neurons during the day in the ventrolateral part of the SCN but has no effect on the discharge rate of neurons in the dorsomedial part of the SCN (64). This suggests that circadian neural activity may be intrinsic to the dorsomedial SCN, whereas diurnal changes in neural activity in the ventrolateral region may reflect changes in the light-dark environment. It should be noted, however, that in these in vitro studies recordings from individual cells have only been made for a few hours and the hypothalamic slice preparations have only been maintained long enough to observe a single diurnal cycle.

Schwartz and his colleagues (59), using the ^{14}C-labeled deoxyglucose technique to measure glucose utilization, have demonstrated that SCN metabolic activity in vivo was endogenously rhythmic in the rat, cat, and monkey. In both diurnal and nocturnal species, SCN metabolic activity is high during the subjective day and low during the subjective night. Higher metabolism during the subjective day is consistent with the finding that multiple-unit activity is also highest during the subjective day in nocturnal rats as well as diurnal chipmunks (27, 58). A circadian rhythm in glucose utilization was recently demonstrated in the SCN of fetal rats (24–36 hr before birth). The mother, through an unknown internal temporal cue, synchronizes the fetal circadian system to her own circadian clock, which in turn is usually entrained by the external light-dark cycle (52). Interestingly, although the fetal SCN shows a clear circadian rhythm in metabolic activity, the SCN is poorly developed and contains few synapses at this stage of development (30). Indeed, although a circadian metabolic rhythm in the SCN is apparent prior to birth, it is not until between days 11 and 14 postnatally that a clear diurnal rhythm in the firing rate of SCN neurons is observed in hypothalamic slice preparations (62). However, this apparent delay in the development of the neural rhythm relative to the metabolic rhythm may be due simply to the inability to detect low-amplitude diurnal neural rhythms in the hypothalamic slice preparation.

Anatomy

The establishment of a functional role for the SCN in the regulation of circadian rhythms has stimulated neurobiologists to study the intrinsic anatomy of the SCN and its afferent and efferent connections. The mechanisms by which circadian signals are generated in the SCN region and relayed to other neural and/or endocrine systems directly responsible for the expression of rhythms remain, however, unknown.

Lydic et al (32) found a wide variation in the size and three-dimensional geometry of the SCN in five species: rat, hamster, cat, rhesus, and squirrel monkey. In rodents, the SCN is oval in shape, whereas the outline of the SCN is irregular in the cat and monkey. In all species, however, the suprachiasmatic nuclei are bilaterally symmetrical and are located near the third ventricle and dorsal to the optic chiasm. Attempts to determine the exact size of the SCN are complicated by the fact that it is difficult to differentiate SCN from non-SCN cells, particularly in the dorsolateral and anterior SCN regions, where the boundary tends to fade gradually into the surrounding hypothalamus (76). The lack of clear anatomical differentiation between SCN and non-SCN tissue cautions against trying to assign a physiological role to a given group of cells. It may well be that tissue separate from the SCN, as tentatively defined by anatomical studies, also plays a role in the generation of circadian rhythms.

This possibility should be taken into account in trying to interpret the results from studies involving lesions of the SCN.

In rats, each SCN is estimated to contain about 8000 neurons (76). The neurons tend to be tightly packed and are among the smallest found in the brain, although there is variation in cell size. SCN cells tend to have a simple dendritic arborization with relatively small dendritic fields usually confined to the SCN, although dendrites of SCN cells can extend into other regions of the hypothalamus or optic chiasm (76). Examination of synapses within the SCN by electron microscopy indicates that a number of synaptic properties are sexually dimorphic (21), but the functional significance of these differences remains unknown (21).

Because the light-dark cycle is the primary synchronizing agent for many of the circadian rhythms regulated by the SCN, extensive studies have been carried out to determine how photic information reaches the SCN. In mammals, both blinding and bilateral transection of the fibers between the retina and the optic chiasm totally abolishes the entrainment of circadian rhythms by light (56). This is not a trivial finding, because extraretinal photoreceptors play a major role in mediating the effects of light on the circadian system in non-mammalian vertebrates (75). The retinal receptors that are involved in entrainment by light in mammals are not known.

Several lines of evidence suggest that the part of the optic system responsible for conveying information to circadian oscillators is morphologically and physiologically distinct from the visual system that deals with perceptional and pattern information. There is some indication that a specific morphological class of retinal ganglion cells may be responsible for conveying nonvisual information to the circadian system (45, 47). In both rats and hamsters, various circadian rhythms can still be entrained by light-dark cycles even after transection of all visual pathways beyond the optic chiasm (35). A direct retino-hypothalamic tract (RHT), which terminates in the SCN of mammals (35), is sufficient for the entrainment of circadian rhythms by light. Nevertheless, lesions of the lateral geniculate nucleus, as well as the primary and accessory optic tracts, have been shown to modify the entrainment response to light (56), indicating that light-dark information can reach the SCN by pathways other than the RHT.

The functional importance of the various retinal inputs into the SCN are not known. Previous attempts to examine the role of the RHT, lateral geniculate nucleus, and optic tracts in entrainment have been confined to only a few species (primarily the rat and hamster), and, even in these species, only a limited series of experiments have been carried out. It is not known what aspects of entrainment are controlled by the various visual inputs or whether the same neural pathways mediate the various effects of light on circadian rhythms in different mammalian species. Of primary importance is the determination of the effects on entrainment of transecting the RHT while the remaining visual inputs are left intact. Perhaps this experiment will be feasible on a larger mammal, where the RHT can be cut without extensive damage to SCN tissue or other visual inputs.

In addition to projections from the retina and the lateral geniculate nucleus, the SCN also receives inputs from a variety of other neural structures. Pickard (46), using horseradish peroxidase as a retrograde tracer molecule, mapped a number of afferent connections to the SCN in the golden hamster. A large number of neural inputs from the septum, hypothalamus, thalamus, hippocampus, and midbrain have now been established. It appears that these inputs are not necessary for the generation of circadian rhythms within the SCN, because knife cuts isolating the SCN region from all neural inputs do not abolish its circadian rhythm of multiple-unit activity (see above). Nevertheless, these inputs may play an important role in the modulation of circadian rhythms. The projections between the bilateral suprachiasmatic nuclei may be of particular significance for the coupling of circadian oscillators (46).

Efferent projections are found to leave the SCN via ventrocaudal, lateral, dorsal, and rostral pathways, with many of these projections terminating in other hypothalamic nuclei as well as in the thalamus and midbrain (4, 67, 69). There is now good evidence that different circadian rhythms are regulated by different SCN efferents. For example, lesions of the paraventricular nucleus, which receives a monosynaptic projection from the SCN (69), abolish the inhibitory effects of short days on the reproductive system (a response that depends upon a circadian clock) as well as the diurnal rhythms in pineal melatonin and N-acetyltransferase activity, but do not interfere with the circadian rhythm of locomotor activity in rodents (5, 28, 50).

Neurochemistry

Three general approaches have been used to elucidate the neurochemical events associated with the function of the SCN. First, a number of studies have attempted to identify the neuropeptides and/or neurotransmitters that are present in the SCN region. Second, various pharmacological agents have been administered either peripherally into the central nervous system or directly into the SCN to determine their effects on circadian rhythms regulated by the SCN. Finally, in a limited number of preliminary studies, the response of SCN neurons to pharmacological manipulations has been examined. As discussed below, the findings from these studies have laid the foundation for the eventual development of a coherent picture of the neurochemical events associated with the entrainment, generation, and expression of circadian rhythms.

A number of neuropeptides and neurotransmitters have now been found within the SCN. They include vasoactive intestinal peptide (VIP), vasopressin, somatostatin, serotonin, corticotropin-releasing factor, and avian pancreatic polypeptide (APP) (35, 44). In addition, choline acetyltransferase and cholinergic receptors have been localized within the SCN (7, 60), suggesting that acetylcholine acts as a neurotransmitter in this region. Some substances (e.g. vasopressin, VIP) are found primarily in the cell bodies of the SCN, indicating that they may play a role in the interneurons and/or efferent projections, whereas other substances (e.g. serotonin, APP) are found primarily in axons leading from afferent projections to the SCN (35). The distributional specificity of peptides and neurotransmitters indicates there is a specificity of function within the SCN (35). In addition to spatial variations, temporal differences in neurochemical activity may exist within the SCN, as evidenced by the recent finding that the concentration of cyclic AMP (a second messenger involved in hormone action and catecholaminergic neurotransmission) shows a circadian rhythm within the SCN of rats (40).

The precise role of the various neurochemicals found in the SCN region in (a) relaying information to the SCN, (b) integrating neural activity within the SCN, and/or (c) relaying circadian information to other neural centers is not known. However, there is now strong evidence to suggest that acetylcholine and an APP-like substance are involved in relaying light-dark information to the SCN. The acute administration of a cholinergic agonist, carbachol, into the cerebrospinal fluid can mimic the phase-shifting effects of light on both the circadian rhythm of wheelrunning activity in mice, and pineal serotonin N-acetyltransferase activity in rats (78, 79). Indeed, the phase-response curve of the locomotor-activity rhythm in the hamster to carbachol, administered intraventricularly at different circadian times, is similar to the phase-response curve obtained for 1-hr light pulses (Figure 2). Furthermore, the daily administration of carbachol to hamsters can entrain the circadian rhythm of locomotor activity in a manner similar to daily light pulses, and nighttime injections of carbachol can mimic the effects of light pulses and prevent short-day induced testicular regression, an event that depends upon a circadian clock to measure day length (9–11). These results suggest that acetylcholine may be involved in relaying light information from the retina to the SCN and/or the integration of light information within the SCN itself. Interestingly, the administration of APP or neuropeptide Y [a peptide with a structural sequence similar to APP and which cross-reacts with antibodies raised to APP (36a)] at various circadian times to hamsters free running in constant light has been found to phase shift the rhythm of wheel-running behavior in a manner similar to the presentation of dark pulses (1). The only known source of APP immunoreactivity in the SCN is from a projection from the ventral region of the lateral geniculate nucleus (vLGN) (8), indicating that an APP-like substance may relay information about the light-dark cycle from the vLGN to the SCN. Both acetylcholine and an APP-like substance may play a functional role in the entrainment of the circadian system by the light-dark cycle.

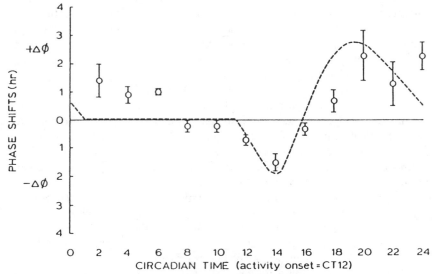

Figure 2   The *open circles* depict the response of the free-running circadian rhythm of locomotor activity to intraventricular injections of carbachol administered to hamsters exposed to constant darkness. Each *point* represents the mean response (± SEM), averaged over a 2-hr bin of circadian time, of 3–4 animals injected with carbachol. A point above the *solid line* indicates an advance (+Δø) in the onset of activity, while a point below this line indicates a dealy (–Δø) in the onset of activity. For comparative purposes, the phase-response curve to 1-hr light pulses is represented by the *dashed line* (14). [(Reproduced with permission from D. J. Earnest, (9).]

A few investigators have attempted to elucidate the neurochemistry of the SCN by monitoring the electrical activity of individual SCN neurons following the iontophoretic application of amino acids, peptides, and/or neurotransmitters to the SCN region in either anesthetized rats (20, 42) or a hypothalamic slice preparation (31, 61). Monoamines appear to inhibit SCN activity under both in vitro and in vivo conditions, whereas acetylcholine was found to be inhibitory under in vitro but stimulatory under in vivo conditions. Although the data are too sparse to draw any firm conclusions about the functional significance of the results obtained from these studies, the effects of two substances in particular, serotonin and acetylcholine, invite speculation. The iontophoretic application of serotonin, as well as stimulation of the dorsal raphe nucleus, a major serotonergic projection to the SCN, both act to suppress the firing of SCN cells (20), indicating that a serotonergic inhibition of SCN neuronal activity may be involved in the modulation of pacemaker function. In contrast to serotonin, the iontophoretic application of acetylcholine in an in vivo preparation (but not in vitro) increases the firing rate of SCN neurons (42). Furthermore, the majority of cells that are excited by optic nerve stimulation are also excited by acetylcholine. Interestingly, electrical stimulation of the

SCN (57), the presentation of a light pulse (14), and the administration of the cholinergic agonist, carbachol (Figure 2)—experimental procedures that can be expected to increase SCN neural activity—all have similar phase-shifting effects on the rhythm of wheel-running activity in hamsters.

OTHER CIRCADIAN CENTERS

Both entrained and free-running circadian rhythms have been observed in many animals following the reported total destruction of SCN tissue. These results suggest that neural tissue outside of the SCN region may be capable of generating circadian signals. However, it is not clear if prolonged self-sustained circadian rhythms can persist in the absence of periodic environmental cues in mammals devoid of any SCN tissue. In the few reported cases where circadian rhythms have been reported to exist under constant environmental conditions, there has usually been some methodological problem that did not preclude the possibility that 24-hr periodic signals from the environment (e.g. feeding, noise, temperature) were responsible for the expression of rhythmicity (see above and Ref. 12 for further discussion).

Less ambiguity surrounds the interpretation of the results from experiments in which SCN-lesioned animals were exposed to periodic fluctuations in the external environment; diurnal rhythms clearly persist in some SCN-lesioned animals in the presence of an entraining agent. Abnormal, but persistent, entrainment of the locomotor activity rhythm to a light-dark cycle has been observed in hamsters with complete SCN lesions (55). The presence of direct retinal projections to hypothalamic regions outside of the SCN (47, 54) is consistent with the idea that light-dark information may influence other areas in the hypothalamus besides the SCN. In addition, the periodic presentation of food on a circadian basis can entrain various circadian rhythms in SCN-lesioned rats (66). Interestingly, restricted feeding does not entrain a circadian rhythm in neural activity within the SCN under either in vivo or in vitro conditions (23, 63), further supporting the hypothesis that entrainment by food does not involve the SCN. In contrast to the effects of SCN lesions, lesions of the ventromedial hypothalamus (VMH) do eliminate the entraining effects of a restricted daily feeding schedule (22, 29), suggesting that the VMH may serve as a second circadian pacemaker in the mammalian brain. However, whether the VMH contains a self-sustained circadian oscillator has recently been questioned by Inouye (24). Although a daily rhythm in multiple-unit activity was present in the VMH of food-restricted rats with SCN lesions, no rhythm in VMH neural activity was apparent during ad-lib feeding in these animals. In contrast, lesions of the VMH had no effect on SCN neural rhythms. Inouye was not able to find any indication of a self-sustained circadian neural oscillator within the VMH.

SUMMARY

A number of different experimental findings indicate that endogenous circadian neural rhythms are generated within the SCN region of mammals. Rhythmic neural signals from the SCN directly, or indirectly, appear to regulate many, if not all, biochemical, physiological, and behavioral circadian rhythms. The circadian system in mammals is referred to as being "multioscillatory" in nature, although this term is often used to mean different things. The SCN itself may contain many circadian neural oscillators and the coordinated output of these multioscillators may regulate circadian rhythms. The term multioscillatory is also used to indicate the presence of anatomically distinct oscillators. However, the location and properties of circadian pacemakers that may lie outside of the SCN region remain unknown. Indeed, there is no conclusive evidence that circadian rhythms can be generated over a prolonged period of time in the absence of the SCN in mammals maintained under constant environmental conditions. Whereas the SCN appears capable of generating circadian neural signals indefinitely in the absence of any 24-hr fluctuations in the external environment, other components of the circadian system may function as damped oscillators (i.e. persist for only a few cycles in the absence of a periodic input) and/or only emit diurnal rhythms in the presence of rhythmic input from either the external (e.g. light-dark cycle) and/or internal (e.g. SCN) environment. On a conceptual as well as a physiological level, our understanding of the organization of the mammalian circadian system remains limited at the present time. Unfortunately, the limitations on our understanding of the circadian system are not always fully appreciated, and quite often a hypothesis based on limited experimental data is treated as fact. The study of the circadian system is still in the early stages of development, and further progress in elucidating the physiological mechanisms underlying the generation and expression of circadian rhythms may require new ways of looking at old problems as well as new experimental approaches.

One final comment should be made concerning the importance of an increased understanding of circadian rhythms for human health. Because the study of the physiology of the circadian system is still in its early stages of development, little is known about the importance of the normal functioning of the circadian system for the health and well-being of the organism. Recent studies in humans suggest that disorders within the circadian system itself may be involved in the etiology of at least some forms of mental illness (77). In view of the fact that most, if not all, physiological systems are influenced by circadian neural signals, a better understanding of the neurobiology of the circadian system in mammals should prove to be extremely important in the treatment, diagnosis, and understanding of numerous mental and physical disorders in humans.

ACKNOWLEDGMENTS

I am extremely grateful to Drs. Shin-ichi Inouye and Eve Van Cauter for their criticism and the suggestions they made for changing an earlier draft of this manuscript. This paper is dedicated to Dr. Colin S. Pittendrigh on the occasion of his sixty-fifth birthday.

Literature Cited

1. Albers, H. E., Ferris, C. F., Leeman, S. E., Goldman, B. D. 1984. Avian pancreatic polypeptide phase shifts hamster circadian rhythms when microinjected into the suprachiasmatic region. *Science* 223:833–35
2. Albers, H. E., Lydic, R., Gander, P. H., Moore-Ede, M. C. 1981. Gradual decay of circadian drinking organization following lesions of the suprachiasmatic nuclei in primates. *Neurosci. Lett.* 27: 119–24
3. Ashcoff, J., Wever, R. 1981. The circadian system of man. In *Handbook of Behavioral Neurobiology*, Vol. 4, *Biological Rhythms*, ed. J. Ashchoff, pp. 311–48. New York: Plenum
4. Berk, M. L., Finkelstein, J. A. 1981. An autoradiographic determination of the efferent projections of the suprachiasmatic nucleus of the hypothalamus. *Brain Res.* 226:1–13
5. Bittman, E. L., Lehman, M. N., Winans, S. S. 1983. Lesions of the hypothalamic paraventricular nucleus block the influence of photoperiod on gonadal regression and pineal melatonin in male hamsters. *Neurosci. Abstr.* 9:318
6. Block, G. D., Wallace, S. F. 1982. Localization of a circadian pacemaker in the eye of a mollusc, Bulla. *Science* 217:155–57
7. Brownstein, M., Kobayashi, R., Palkovits, M., Saavedra, J. M. 1975. Choline acetyltransferase levels in diencephalic nuclei of the rat. *J. Neurochem.* 24:35–38
8. Card, J. P., Moore, R. Y. 1982. Ventral lateral geniculate nucleus efferents to the rat suprachiasmatic nucleus exhibit avian pancreatic polypeptidelike immunoreactivity. *J. Comp. Neurol.* 206:390–96
9. Earnest, D. J. 1984. *Photic control of circadian rhythms and reproduction in the golden hamster.* Ph.D. dissertation. Northwestern Univ. 181 pp.
10. Earnest, D. J., Turek, F. W. 1983. Effect of one-second light pulses on testicular function and locomotor activity in the golden hamster. *Biol. Reprod.* 28:557–65
11. Earnest, D. J., Turek, F. W. 1983. Role for acetylcholine in mediating effects of light on reproduction. *Science* 219:77–79
12. Eastman, C. I., Mistlberger, R. E., Rechtschaffen, A. 1984. Suprachiasmatic nuclei lesions eliminate circadian temperature and sleep rhythms in the rat. *Physiol. Behav.* 32:357–68
13. Ebihara, S., Kawamura, H. 1981. The role of the pineal organ and the suprachiasmatic nucleus in the control of circadian locomotor rhythms in the Java sparrow, *Padda oryzivora*. *J. Comp. Physiol.* 141:207–14
14. Ellis, G. B., McKlveen, R. E., Turek, F. W. 1982. Dark pulses affect the circadian rhythm of activity in hamsters kept in constant light. *Am. J. Physiol.* 242:R44–R50
15. Eskin, A., Takahashi, J. S. 1983. Adenylate cyclase activation shifts the phase of a circadian pacemaker. *Science* 220:82–84
16. Fuller, C. A., Lydic, R., Sulzman, F. M., Albers, H. E., Tepper, B., Moore-Ede, M. C. 1981. Circadian rhythm of body temperature persists after suprachiasmatic lesions in the squirrel monkey. *Am. J. Physiol.* 241:R385–R391
17. Fuller, C. A., Lydic, R., Sulzman, F. M., Albers, H. E., Tepper, B., Moore-Ede, M. C. 1983. Auditory entrainment of primate drinking rhythms following partial suprachiasmatic nuclei lesions. *Physiol. Behav.* 31:573–76
18. Green, D. J., Gillette, R. 1982. Circadian rhythm of firing rate recorded from single cells in the rat suprachiasmatic brain slice. *Brain Res.* 245:198–200
19. Groos, G., Hendriks, J. 1982. Circadian rhythms in electrical discharge of rat suprachiasmatic neurones recorded *in vitro*. *Neurosci. Lett.* 34:283–88
20. Groos, G., Mason, R., Meijer, J. 1983. Electrical and pharmacological properties of the suprachiasmatic nuclei. *Fed. Proc.* 42:2790–95
21. Güldner, F. H. 1982. Sexual dimorphisms of axo-spine synapses and postsynaptic density material in the supra-

chiasmatic nucleus of the rat. *Neurosci. Lett.* 28:145–50

22. Inouye, S. T. 1982. Ventromedial hypothalamic lesions eliminate anticipatory activities of restricted daily feeding schedules in the rat. *Brain Res.* 250:183–87

23. Inouye, S. T. 1982. Restricted daily feeding does not entrain circadian rhythms of the suprachiasmatic nucleus in the rat. *Brain Res.* 232:194–99

24. Inouye, S. T. 1983. Does the ventromedial hypothalamic nucleus contain a self-sustained circadian oscillator associated with periodic feedings? *Brain Res.* 279:53–63

25. Inouye, S. T. 1984. Light responsiveness of the suprachiasmatic nucleus within the island with the retino-hypothalamic tract spared. *Brain Res.* 294:263–68

26. Inouye, S. T., Kawamura, H. 1979. Persistence of circadian rhythmicity in a mammalian hypothalamic "island" containing the suprachiasmatic nucleus. *Proc. Natl. Acad. Sci. USA* 76:5962–66

27. Inouye, S. T., Kawamura, H. 1982. Characteristics of a circadian pacemaker in the suprachiasmatic nucleus. *J. Comp. Physiol.* 146:153–60

28. Klein, D. C., Smoot, R. Weller, J. L., Higa, E., Markey, S. P., et al. 1983. Lesions of the paraventricular nucleus area of the hypothalamus disrupt the suprachiasmatic–spinal cord circuit in the melatonin rhythm generating system. *Brain Res. Bull.* 10:647–52

29. Krieger, D. T. 1980. Ventromedial hypothalamic lesions abolish food-shifed circadian adrenal and temperature rhythmicity. *Endocrinology* 106:649–54

30. Lenn, N. J., Beebe, B., Moore, R. Y. 1977. Postnatal development of the suprachiasmatic hypothalamic nucleus of the rat. *Cell Tissue Res.* 178:463–75

31. Liou, S. Y., Shibata, S., Yamakawa, U., Ueki, S. 1983. Inhibitory and excitatory effects of histamine on suprachiasmatic neurons in rat hypothalamic slice preparation. *Neurosci. Lett.* 41:109–13

32. Lydic, R., Albers, H. E., Tepper, B., Moore-Ede, M. C. 1982. Three-dimensional structure of the mammalian suprachiasmatic nuclei: A comparative study of five species. *J. Comp. Neurol.* 204:225–37

33. Menaker, M., Takahashi, J. S., Eskin, A. 1978. The physiology of circadian pacemakers. *Ann. Rev. Physiol.* 40:501–26

34. Moore, R. Y. 1982. The suprachiasmatic nucleus and the organization of a circadian system. *Trends Neurosci.* 5:404–7

35. Moore, R. Y. 1983. Organization and function of a central nervous system circadian oscillator: the suprachiasmatic hypothalamic nucleus. *Fed. Proc.* 42:2783–89

36. Moore, R. Y., Eichler, V. B. 1972. Loss of a circadian adrenal corticosterone rhythm following suprachiasmatic lesions in the rat. *Brain Res.* 42:201–6

36a. Moore, R. Y., Gustafson, E. L., Card, J. P. 1984. Identical immunoreactivity of afferents to the rat suprachiasmatic nucleus with antisera against avian pancreatic polypeptide, molluscan cardioexcitatory peptide, and neuropeptide Y. *Cell Tissue Res.* 236:41–46

37. Moore-Ede, M. C. 1983. The circadian timing system in mammals: two pacemakers preside over many secondary oscillators. *Fed. Proc.* 42:2802–8

38. Moore-Ede, M. C., Czeisler, C. A., Richardson, G. S. 1983. Circadian timekeeping in health and disease. I. Basic properties of circadian pacemakers. *New England J. Med.* 309:469–76

39. Mosko, S. S., Moore, R. Y. 1979. Neonatal suprachiasmatic nucleus lesions: Effects on the development of circadian rhythms in the rat. *Brain Res.* 164:17–38

40. Murakami, M., Takahashi, K. 1983. Circadian rhythm of adenosine-3',5'-monophosphate content in suprachiasmatic nucleus (SCN) and ventromedial hypothalamus (VMH) in the rat. *Brain Res.* 276:297–304

41. Nakayama, T., Arai, S., Yamamoto, K. 1979. Body temperature rhythm and its central mechanism. In *Biological Rhythms and Their Central Mechanism,* ed. M. Suda, O. Hayaishi, H. Nakagawa, pp. 395–403. Amsterdam: Elsevier/North Holland Biomed.

42. Nishino, H., Koizumi, K. 1977. Responses of neurons in the suprachiasmatic nuclei of the hypothalamus to putative transmitters. *Brain Res.* 120:167–72

43. Page, T. L. 1982. Transplantation of the cockroach circadian pacemaker. *Science* 216:73–75

44. Palkovits, M., Brownstein, M. J., Vale, W. 1983. Corticotropin releasing factor (CRF) immunoreactivity in hypothalamic and extrahypothalamic nuclei of sheep brain. *Neuroendocrinology* 37:302–5

45. Pickard, G. E. 1980. Morphological characteristics of retinal ganglion cells projecting to the suprachiasmatic nucleus: a horseradish peroxidase study. *Brain Res.* 183:458–65

46. Pickard, G. E. 1982. The afferent connections of the suprachiasmatic nucleus of the golden hamster with emphasis on

the retinohypothalamic projection. *J. Comp. Neurol.* 211:65–83

47. Pickard, G. E., Silverman, A. J. 1981. Direct retinal projections to the hypothalamus, piriform cortex, and accessory optic nuclei in the golden hamster as demonstrated by a sensitive anterograde horseradish peroxidase technique. *J. Comp. Neurol.* 196:155–72

48. Pickard, G. E., Turek, F. W. 1982. Splitting of the circadian rhythm of activity is abolished by unilateral lesions of the suprachiasmatic nuclei. *Science* 215:1119–21

49. Pickard, G. E., Turek, F. W. 1983. The suprachiasmatic nuclei: two circadian clocks? *Brain Res.* 268:201–10

50. Pickard, G. E., Turek, F. W. 1983. The hypothalamic paraventricular nucleus mediates the photoperiodic control of reproduction but not the effects of light on the circadian rhythm of activity. *Neurosci. Lett.* 43:67–72

50a. Pittendrigh, C. S. 1981. Circadian systems: General perspective. In *Handbook of Behavioral Neurobiology, Biological Rhythms,* ed. J. Aschoff, 4:57–80. New York: Plenum

51. Reppert, S. M., Perlow, M. J., Ungerleider, L. G., Mishkin, M., Tamarkin, L., et al. 1981. Effects of damage to the suprachiasmatic area of the anterior hypothalamus on the daily melatonin and cortisol rhythms in the rhesus monkey. *J. Neurosci.* 1:1414–25

52. Reppert, S. M., Schwartz, W. J. 1983. Maternal coordination of the fetal biological clock in utero. *Science* 220:969–71

53. Richter, C. P. 1978. "Dark-active" rat transformed into "light-active" rat by destruction of 24-hr clock: function of 24-hr clock and synchronizers. *Proc. Natl. Acad. Sci. USA* 75:6276–80

54. Riley, J. N., Card, J. P., Moore, R. Y. 1981. A retinal projection to the lateral hypothalamus in the rat. *Cell Tissue Res.* 214:257–69

55. Rusak, B. 1977. The role of the suprachiasmatic nuclei in the generation of circadian rhythms in the golden hamster. *J. Comp. Physiol.* 118:145–64

56. Rusak, B., Boulos, Z. 1981. Pathways for photic entrainment of mammalian circadian rhythms. *Photochemistry* 34:267–73

57. Rusak, B., Groos, G. 1982. Suprachiasmatic stimulation phase shifts rodent circadian rhythms. *Science* 215:1407–9

58. Sato, T., Kawamura, H. 1984. Circadian rhythms in multiple unit activity within and outside the suprachiasmatic nucleus

in the diurnal chipmunk *(Eutamias sibiricus). J. Neural Res.* In press

59. Schwartz, W. J., Reppert, S. M., Eagan, S. M., Moore-Ede, M. C. 1983. *In vivo* metabolic activity of the suprachiasmatic nuclei: a comparative study. *Brain Res.* 274:184–87

60. Segal, M., Dudai, Y., Amsterdam, A. 1978. Distribution of an α-bungarotoxin-binding cholinergic nicotinic receptor in rat brain. *Brain Res.* 148:105–19

61. Shibata, S., Liou, S. Y., Ueki, S. 1983. Different effects of amino acids, acetylcholine and monoamines on neuronal activity of suprachiasmatic nucleus in rat pups and adults. *Neurosci. Lett.* 39:187–92

62. Shibata, S., Liou, S. Y., Ueki, S. 1983. Development of the circadian rhythm of neuronal activity in suprachiasmatic nucleus of rat hypothalamic slices. *Neurosci. Lett.* 43:231–34

63. Shibata, S., Liou, S. Y., Ueki, S., Oomura, Y. 1983. Effects of restricted feeding on single neuron activity of suprachiasmatic neurons in rat hypothalamic slice preparation. *Physiol. Behav.* 31:523–28

64. Shibata, S., Liou, S. Y., Ueki, S., Oomura, Y. 1984. Influence of environmental light-dark cycle and enucleation on activity of suprachiasmatic neurons in slice preparations. *Brain Res.* In press

65. Shibata, S., Oomura, Y., Kita, H., Hattori, K. 1982. Circadian rhythmic changes of neuronal activity in the suprachiasmatic nucleus of the rat hypothalamic slice. *Brain Res.* 247:154–58

66. Stephan, F. K. 1981. Limits of entrainment to periodic feeding in rats with suprachiasmatic lesions. *J. Comp. Physiol.* 143:401–10

67. Stephan, F. K., Berkley, K. J., Moss, R. L. 1981. Efferent connections of the rat suprachiasmatic nucleus. *Neurosci.* 6:2625–41

68. Stephan, F. K., Zucker, I. 1972. Circadian rhythms in drinking behavior and locomotor activity of rats are eliminated by hypothalamic lesions. *Proc. Natl. Acad. Sci. USA* 69:1583–86

69. Swanson, L. W., Cowan, W. M. 1975. The efferent connections of the suprachiasmatic nucleus of the hypothalamus. *J. Comp. Neurol.* 160:1–12

70. Szafarczyk, A., Ixart, G., Alanso, G., Malaval, F., Nouguier-Soule, J., Assenmacher, I. 1981. Neural control of circadian rhythms in plasma ACTH, plasma corticosterone and motor activity. *J. Physiol.* 77:969–76

71. Takahashi, J. S., Menaker, M. 1982. Role of the suprachiasmatic nuclei in the

circadian system of the house sparrow, *Passer domesticus. J. Neurosci.* 2:815–28

72. Takahashi, J. S., Zatz, M. 1982. Regulation of circadian rhythmicity. *Science* 217:1104–11

73. Turek, F. W. 1983. Neurobiology of circadian rhythms in mammals. *BioScience* 33:439–44

74. Turek, F. W., Earnest, D. J., Swann, J. 1982. Splitting of the circadian rhythm of activity in hamsters. In *Vertebrate Circadian Systems*, eds. J. Aschoff, S. Daan, G. Groos, pp. 203–14. Berlin: Springer-Verlag

75. Underwood, H., Groos, G. 1982. Vertebrate circadian rhythms: Retinal and extraretinal photoreception. *Experientia* 38:1013–21

76. Van den Pol, A. N. 1980. The hypothalamic suprachiasmatic nucleus of rat: intrinsic anatomy. *J. Comp. Neurol.* 191:661–702

77. Wehr, T. A., Sack. D., Rosenthal, N., Duncan, W., Gillin, J. C. 1983. Circadian rhythm disturbances in manic-depressive illness. *Fed. Proc.* 42:2809–14

78. Zatz, M. 1979. Photoentrainment, pharmacology, and phase shifts of the circadian rhythm in the rat pineal. *Fed. Proc.* 38:2596–601

79. Zatz, M., Herkenham, M. A. 1981. Intraventricular carbachol mimics the phase-shifting effect of light on the circadian rhythm of wheel-running activity. *Brain Res.* 212:234–38

Ann. Rev. Physiol. 1985. 47:65–82

ANNUAL RHYTHMS

Donald S. Farner

Department of Zoology, University of Washington, Seattle, Washington 98195

HISTORICAL ASPECTS

Empirical knowledge of annual cycles in plants and animals is ancient. The survival of mankind in annually seasonal climates has depended on culturally transmitted information on procurement of periodically available food and other necessities. Contemporary agriculture and fisheries remain extensively dependent thereon. With the emergence of western science, annual cycles became of interest to naturalists, who drew inductive conclusions from field observations. This approach, which still persists, has produced a prodigious literature that provides few insights into the mechanisms underlying annual cycles. Notably exceptional was the recognition by Baker (4) of ultimate and proximal "causes" of annual cycles. The former are annually periodic environmental cycles that have selected heritable mechanisms of adaptive annual cycles. The latter are the annually periodic changes in the environment that induce internal adjustments in the individual so that its cycle is appropriately phased therewith. The proximal "causes" of Baker have also been designated as *predictive information* (38). For many species the source of predictive information is the annual photocycle.

The entry of experimental biology into the investigation of annual cycles occurred between 1925 and 1930, with demonstrations of photoperiodism in plants, insects, and birds. During the ensuing three decades these stimulated a plethora of investigations on divers species, with increasing attention to characterization of photoperiodic mechanisms (reviewed in 20, 35).

The concept of endogenous annual rhythms is not only ancient but also prevailed in intuitive interpretations of naturalists well into the twentieth century. In 1955, Aschoff (1) proposed that annual cycles are expressions of self-sustained endogenous rhythms that are entrained by an environmental Zeitgeber with a period of one year. According to this hypothesis, the role of photoperiodic control systems is the entrainment of these endogenous cycles

65

0066-4278/85/0315-0065$02.00

into adaptively phased annual cycles (e.g. 1, 2, 11, 12, 64–66). During the ensuing decades considerable support for this hypothesis was obtained from a variety of species (reviewed in 10, 21, 38, 48, 62, 64–66, 126).

This support for the hypothesis of Aschoff, in light of an abundance of evidence of the effectiveness of nonseasonal photoperiodic induction of gonadal development and of other functions, led to unfortunate arguments as to whether the annual photocycle functions generally as a Zeitgeber or an obligate driver. Because of multiple solutions in evolution, a plausible explanation is that both occur with variation in relative importance among species. Furthermore, it may well be that the evolution of natural periods of about one year, but without self-sustaining rhythms, in control systems was the first and more common adaptation (50). It has been argued that endogenous circannual rhythms provide adaptive protection against atmospherically induced vagaries in real day length. But the well-established "carry-over effect" in photoperiodic control systems (46), together with persistent circadian effects, may be equally effective.

Despite very extensive experimental evidence for the role of the annual photocycle in the control of annual cycles, especially in many avian species (reviewed in 27–29, 31, 47, 49, 77, 93, 119, 126), many field biologists were reluctant to accept its primary role therein. The diverse reasons therefor included well-established correlations between year-to-year differences in the phenologic development of the vernal season and the onset of reproductive function. Although modifying and essential supplementary environmental information has long been recognized by investigators of photoperiodic control systems in birds (e.g. 17, 36, 75), it is only recently that empirical (e.g. 9, 24, 25, 109, 116, 117, 120, 131, 133, 134) and experimental (e.g. 87, 88, 132) endocrine investigations on feral avian species under natural conditions have begun to resolve these differences. Results of these investigations and those of laboratory experiments demonstrate the role of modifying and essential supplemental information on circulating levels of gonadotropins and sex hormones once elevated activity of the hypothalamo-hypophysio-gonadal axis has been induced and sustained by long days. Thus for many species of birds that inhabit regions with significant changes in day length, some arc of the annual photocycle, acting either as a driver or a Zeitgeber, induces the development of the reproductive system to a near-functional state somewhat in advance of the mean optimal time for production of young. Thereafter, the time of onset of the reproductive effort is finely adjusted by other environmental information, including that from interactions between mates.

Although data obtained under natural conditions are sparse, it appears that the scheme described above holds for at least some species of mammals. However, among others, there are complications of duration of estrous cycles and the number thereof per season, duration of gestation, delayed implantation in some species, and hibernation in some species. Thus, in mammals, optimum time for breeding and birth of young is somewhat more complex than for birds (e.g. 73, 74, 82, 137).

DEFINITIONS, PERSPECTIVES, AND DELIMITATIONS
Terminology

In 1959 Halberg (69), recognizing that diel rhythms in organisms under natural conditions rarely have periods of precisely 24 hours, proposed therefor the term *circadian,* without connotation of etiology. Analogously, *circannual* was introduced for periods of approximately one year (70). Sources of variance under natural conditions were logically attributed to environmental effects, underlying endogenous rhythms with periods that differ somewhat from one year, errors in internal control and response systems, and errors in measurement. Accordingly, if the cycle is derived in part from an endogenous rhythm with a period of approximately one year, the observed period under constant conditions will be different from that observed under natural conditions.

Circannual rhythm, however, has also acquired a more rigorous sense as a designation for self-sustained endogenous cycles with periods of approximately one year under "constant" conditions (e.g. 2, 3, 10–14, 26, 48, 57–68, 79, 97, 98). Nevertheless, *circannual rhythm* in the original sense of Halberg is very widely used, especially in investigations on human cycles, primarily because of the marked increase in medical interest in these cycles. However, for this review I accept the more rigorous definition (e.g. 21), but with reservations concerning the definition of "constant" conditions. Unfortunately *circannual rhythm* retains some usage for observations on cycles of feral species under natural conditions. For such, however, rigor in communication would be better served by the simple designation of annual cycle with recognition of sources of variance, as indicated above by Halberg et al (70).

For demonstrations of self-sustained circannual rhythms, there remains the question of physiologically rigorous definition of constant conditions. To exclude effects of periodic changes in the environment, one must assume a priori that intensity and quality of light and other conditions must be held rigorously constant. With respect to light, strictly constant conditions exist only in continuous darkness (e.g. 7) or in continuous light of unvarying quality and intensity (e.g. 8, 18, 99, 122). Most reports, however, have been based on the assumption that repetitive photoregimes of $nL(24 - n)D$ constitute "constant conditions," an assumption that has been tested infrequently (18, 19, 99, 122). Whereas in *C. lateralis* (99) the periods of cycles under LL or DD were similar with that under 12L 12D (12 hr light followed by 12 hr dark), and in *Lonchura punctulata* the cycles under 12L 12D and LL were also similar (18), those for *Heteropneustis fossilis* (122) suggest caution in assuming that constant photoregimes of the class $nL(24 - n)D$ are adequate for demonstration of endogenous circannual rhythms. Furthermore, n as a variable in regimes of $nL(24 - n)D$ is by no means trivial in the conspicuous annual rhythm in testicular size of *Zonotrichia leucophrys gambelii*. For example, males held for 3.5–5 years on 8L 16D, 12L 12D, or 20L 4D, respectively, gave strikingly different results (45; D. S. Farner & R. A. Lewis, unpublished observations). Those on 8L 16D displayed no significant testicular development. Predictably (51, 112), those under 20L 4D underwent one immediate cycle of development and regression and then remained at minimal size for 3–4 years. However, those subjected to 12L 12D underwent "cycles" in testicular weight with periods substantially less than one year and generally with progressively decreasing amplitude and period. Significantly these birds failed to undergo postnuptial molt and periodic development of photorefractoriness, both normal components of the annual cycle of this species (133).

Entwined with both the problems of the reality and the demonstration of endogenous circannual rhythms is the question of "permissive" conditions under which overt expression thereof can be demonstrated (e.g. 2). This arises by analogy with overt expressions of circadian rhythms, which in some cases can be suppressed even though the rhythm of the pacemaker continues. However, the extent to which this analogy is valid remains to be ascertained. Whether the nature of apparent circannual pacemaker systems bear useful resemblance to the emerging comprehension of circadian pacemakers (e.g. 86, 91, 101) remains an open question. Although hypotheses of "permissive" conditions are both logical and heuristic, they require caution. Pressed to the limit, they reject all negative evidence with the argument that "permissive" conditions were not provided.

Perspectives

Understanding of the physiologic basis of annual cycles has been beclouded by diverse perspectives of investigators. Among these is the above-cited bemusement with the question of the role of the annual photocycle as Zeitgeber or driver, a special case of frequent assumption of a common mechanism with only minor species-specific modifications, which overlooks the evidence that mid and high latitudes have been invaded at different times by different species. Thus, functions of control systems, even with similar elements, may represent independent adaptations to the more sharply periodic environments of these latitudes (e.g. 36, 39, 43, 48). Whatever the mode of generation of an annual cycle, few species can escape the necessity of adjustment to the year-by-year variations in the optimal time for the production of young. As noted above, investigations on the mechanisms that alter the temporal course of the annual cycle to conform with the season at hand have developed only recently.

Perspectives and hypotheses concerning circannual cycles have frequently been developed through observation of one or a few overt functions in a single species. Among such functions are reproduction, migration, molt, shedding of antlers, changes in body mass, metabolism, and hibernation. In this review a dominant perspective is the primacy of control of the reproductive cycle, the primary target of natural selection. Thus control systems have been evolved such that young are produced at optimal or near-optimal times for the survival of young and parents (e.g. 1, 4, 36, 75, 76). Especially in smaller homeotherms, other circannually periodic functions that are ergonically or temporally incompatible with reproductive function are phased so that they do not overlap therewith (e.g. 36, 40, 133).

Unlike progress in investigation of pacemakers of circadian rhythms, there is scant evidence of such for circannual rhythms. However, investigations on *Sturnus vulgaris* (2, 59, 66) and on sylviinine warblers (13, 66) on changes in phase relationships among overt circannual cycles under different "constant" photoperiodic regimes have yielded results that suggest multiple circannual systems, which could be coupled with modifiable phase relationships to a pacemaker. However, other possible bases for generation of circannual rhythms have been suggested (34, 61, 65–67, 92).

Delimitations

Because of its modest length in relation to a large and diverse literature, I restrict the remainder of this review largely to selected feral species of birds and mammals for which there is some evidence of endogenous circannual rhythms and/or photoperiodic control systems. Because my perspective is one of comparative physiology with strong elements of evolutionary biology, I largely exclude consideration of those domesticated species, including *Homo sapiens,* that have responded extensively to artificial selection. I assume arbitrarily that circannual cycles occur only in species in which lifespan of a significant fraction of individuals exceeds one year.

Among birds, photoperiodic control of reproduction and/or other annual functions has been reported for about 60 species, although meaningful quantitative characterizations and endocrine correlates have been provided for fewer than 10. The situation in mammals is even more modest. Among animals in general, endogenous circannual rhythms have been described in more than 40 species if one accepts repeated photoregimes of $nL(24 - n)D$ as "constant" conditions insofar as light is concerned. But, as noted above, in only a few species have such cycles been described under DD or LL. Albeit with misgivings, in the following discussion I leave open the question of whether constant light or constant dark are prerequisite for the demonstration of circannual rhythms (see 2 for discussion).

ANNUAL RHYTHMS: A SPECTRUM OF RELATIVE ROLES OF ENDOGENOUS CIRCANNUAL RHYTHMS AND PHOTOPERIODIC CONTROL SYSTEMS?

General

Despite difficulties in comparison of circannual rhythms among species observed under different conditions in different laboratories, they obviously share to varying degrees the formal properties of oscillating systems (e.g. 2, 21, 65, 123), which, however, contribute only modestly to their etiology. Possible bases thereof have been the subject of several hypothetical discussions (e.g. 2, 34, 48, 50, 65–67, 83, 85, 92, 126, 133).

Vertebrate photoperiodic control systems, whether they function as Zeitgebers or drivers, and despite their apparent multiplicity of evolutionary origin, share at least some common organs, hormones, and functions (reviewed in 47, 52, 53, 73, 74). With the exception of mammals, the photoreceptors, as first demonstrated in birds by Benoit (6) and now confirmed in several other species (reviewed in 5, 41, 96), are encephalic—largely if not exclusively hypothalamic—whereas those of mammals are retinal. This difference may not be profound because the pertinent mammalian retinal receptors may be nonvisual (86), which raises the possibility that they may be homologous with those of other vertebrates.

Among the photoperiodic avian species thus far studied, reproductive function is generally induced by long days (reviewed in 39, 41, 119), although *Lonchura punctulata* is a clear exception (18, 19). The same appears to be true for small photoperiodic species of mammals with short gestation periods; in species with long gestation periods, gonadal function is induced by short days of autumn or early winter (reviewed in 57, 73, 74, 82, 106, 107). Although measurement of daylength in some species of insects is effected by hour-glass mechanisms, only mechanisms with circadian components have as yet been demonstrated in photoperiodic species of birds and mammals. However, disagreement has emerged concerning the nature of the circadian components. Most investigators (reviewed in 33, 41, 47, 52, 53) have interpreted their results in terms of a refinement (103) of the external coincidence model of Bünning (16). More recently, Pittendrigh (100–102) has persuasively suggested an internal-coincidence system in which changes in day length, by alteration in phase relationship between two or more endogenous circadian oscillators, induce the photoperiodic response.

In photoperiodic species, substantially more attention has been given to the mechanisms that induce seasonal reproduction than to those that terminate it. In birds, at least two mechanisms of termination have been demonstrated (reviewed in 75, 93, 126): (*a*) decrease in activity of hypothalamo-hypophysio-gonadal axis because of shorter days; and (*b*) development of photorefractoriness as a "delayed" response to long days. Of these, the better known is the latter, in which some element of the control system becomes insensitive to long days so that the functions of both the gametogenic and endocrine gonads regress to minimal levels. Recovery from photorefractoriness generally requires exposure to short days. Natural termination of reproduction by short days appears to occur in some nonmigratory species that produce more than one clutch per season.

There appear to be no unequivocally established cases of the development of long-day photorefractoriness among the photoperiodic species of mammals. Among the species that breed in the spring and/or summer, termination of reproductive function appears to be an inhibitory effect of shorter days of late summer and autumn, or a phase of an endogenous circannual cycle entrained by the annual photocycle, as possibly in *Mustelo putorius furo* (71).

In at least three species of small rodents (*Mesocricetus auratus, Phodopus sungorus,* and *Peromiscus leucopus*), seasonal recrudescence of the gonads occurs independently of day length in late winter; termination of gonadal function is induced by the shorter days of autumn with mediation through the antigonadal effect of the pineal gland through melatonin, whereafter the control system becomes refractory to short days, This short-day refractoriness is terminated under natural conditions by long days, but also terminates spontaneously under prolonged exposure to short days, or in blinded animals (reviewed in 74, 105, 107, 108). At least in *M. auratus,* regression of the gonads can be prevented or reversed by long days (e.g. 121). Gonads of pinealectomized subjects remain constantly functional. However, it has become increasingly clear that the roles of the pineal gland and melatonin are considerably more complex (e.g. 74, 125). Among some lagomorphs, termination of gonadal function in both sexes is also induced by the shorter days of late summer and autumn (e.g. 23).

Selected Cases

Presented here are cases of species that have been sufficiently investigated to provide at least some, although seldomly conclusive, information on the basic nature of their annual reproductive cycles and associated functions. This selection involves problems of comparability, not only of differences among species and of experimental conditions, but even more extensively of perspectives, objectives, and methods of investigators.

GOLDEN-MANTLED GROUND SQUIRREL   *Spermophilus lateralis* is the most extensively studied vertebrate species for which there is very strong evidence for truly endogenous circannual rhythms. Most investigations have assumed that photoregimes of nL(24 − *n*)D constitute "constant" conditions (e.g. 71,

81, 98, 135). However, because it has been demonstrated that a circannual cycle in hibernation occurs in LL, DD and in blinded animals (99), and because the reproductive cycle maintains a definite phase angle therewith (e.g. 136), one may assume that both are overt expressions of a central circannual oscillator. However, it seems clear that the cycle in body mass, and hence hibernation, is not dependent on the cycle of gonadal functions in either sex. Circannual cycles in body mass and reproductive function are apparently independent of circadian temporal organization. Although under natural conditions the cycles of this species are annual, the Zeitgeber therefor is not yet clear (e.g. 5, 80).

WOODCHUCK   Although critical experiments under LL or DD have not been accomplished with *Marmota monax,* the accumulated evidence suggests very strongly that annual cycles in hibernation and body weight reflect an endogenous circannual rhythm entrained by the annual photocycle (21, 22).

SIKA DEER   In *Cervus nippon* there is an apparent circannual cycle in shedding of antlers with a period of somewhat less than one year (reviewed in 57, 58). Under natural conditions this cycle is entrained by the annual photocycle with a rather constant phase angle to that of rut. The cycle in shedding of antlers persists in photoregimes of $nL(24 - n)D$ for several values of n, but not for $n = 12$. Apparently it has not been examined under LL or DD.

AIRSAC CATFISH   As noted above, there is a circannual cycle in ovarian function in *Heteropneustes fossilis.* Under constant temperature in LL, its period is distinctly shorter than its natural cycle, whereas in DD it is not distinctly different from one year (reviewed in 122). It is probable that the Zeitgeber is the annual photocycle, with local conditions providing information for fine adjustment to the onset of the monsoon season.

SYLVIINE WARBLERS   Extensive observations have been made on the cycles of body weight, Zugunruhe (migratory unrest), molt, and testicular size in several species of this group subjected to "constant" conditions of repeated daily photocycles of 10L 14D to 18L 6D (reviewed in 2, 11, 13, 48, 60, 62, 64–67). These cycles, especially among long-distance migrants, are relatively uniform, with periods generally of less than one year, with persistence for as many as nine cycles (11, 13). However, among these species there are differences in persistence of cycles. For example, on 12L 12D *Phylloscopus trochilus* sustained at least three cycles, whereas in *Ph. collybita* only a single cycle occurred (60). To my knowledge, none of these species have been studied under LL or DD.

EUROPEAN STARLING   Extensive early investigations by Bissonnette and his colleagues (reviewed in 17) indicated that *Sturnus vulgaris* is a typical photoperiodic species in which long days induce development of the reproductive system and eventually cause cessation of reproductive function through induction of photorefractoriness. However, subsequent investigations by Schwab and colleagues (e.g. 110, 113–115) and Gwinner and colleagues (e.g. reviews: 2, 63, 65–67) reveal a much more complex system. Testicular development occurs in DD (111), but circannual rhythms have apparently not been demonstrated thereunder. Testicular development occurs under all regimes of $nL(24 - n)D$ tested and in LL. But only with $n > 12.5$ and in LL does photorefractoriness, a natural component of the annual cycle, develop and persist (68, 113). It is possible that the "cycles" in photoregimes with $n < 12.5$ reflect the effects of intermittent negative gonadal feedback, as in *Zonotrichia leucophrys gambelii* subjected to 12D 12L (45, 91). By use of reduced "annual" environmental photocycles with natural amplitude in day length, Gwinner (63) has produced five cycles in molt and testicular size in one calendar year and has suggested that these cycles are the result of entrainment of an endogenous circannual rhythm by the annual environmental photocycle. The development of photorefractoriness appears to be dependent on some minimal plasma level of thyroid hormone, which may be induced photoperiodically, and is associated with a photoperiodically induced increase in circulating levels of prolactin (54, 55, 130). The development of photorefractoriness appears to be independent of circulating levels of gonadotropins and androgens, as is the case also in *Z. l. gambelii*. Despite the extensive investigations, it remains unclear as to whether the annual environmental photocycle functions as a Zeitgeber or driver, a problem that may prove to be largely semantic.

WHITE-CROWNED SPARROW   *Zonotrichia leucophrys gambelii* is one of the most extensively studied photoperiodic species and the most extensively investigated with respect to assessment of laboratory-obtained results under field conditions (reviewed in 40, 133). Under photoregimes of $nL(20 - n)D$ in which $n > 12$ hr and in LL, gonadal development proceeds at a logarithmic rate, as a positive function of n. Photorefractoriness, also induced by long days, becomes effective after maximum gonadal development; coupled therewith are reductions in plasma levels of gonadotropins, regression of the gonads, postnuptial molt, change from territorial to flock behavior, and preparation for late-summer migration (89, 90). Termination of photorefractoriness induced by long days, except in extremely rare cases, requires exposure to short days. When n is < 12 hr, testicular growth and development is very slow; when $n < 8$ hr and in DD, it is undetectable. On 12L 12D, several "cycles" of testicular growth and regression occur with generally decreasing period and amplitude (32, 45, 90), most probably the result of intermittent negative gonadal feedback. These "cycles" are "unnatural" in that they are not accompanied by development of photorefractoriness and postnuptial-type molt. Measurement of duration of long days in induction of development of gonads, photorefractoriness, and associated events, and of short days in termination of photorefractoriness, is most parsimoniously explained by an external-coincidence model. For the congeneric white-throated sparrow, *Z. albicollis,* however, an internal-coincidence model, based on photoperiodically induced changes in the phase angle between diel cycles in circulating corticosterone and prolactin, has been proposed to control the annual cycle (83, 84). Combined field and laboratory investigations, including endocrine studies, on *Z. l. gambelli* have shown convincingly that whereas long days are essential for the induction and maintenance of gonadal development, final functional state,—especially in females—requires additional environmental information, which also provides the basis for fine temporal adjustment to the phenologic course of the season.

CHAFFINCH   Extensively investigated by Dolnik and colleagues (reviewed in 27–29, 31, 126), the control of annual cycles has many similarities with that of *Z. l. gambelii.* Long days induce development of the reproductive system and, more slowly, that of photorefractoriness and the late-summer events coupled therewith. The rate of testicular growth is a positive function of day length. As in *Z. l. gambelii,* postnuptial molt, once underway, is accelerated by shorter days (30, 31, 94, 95). Although the available data appear to be rationalizable by an external-coincidence model, Dolnik (29) has also proposed an internal-coincidence model therefor: however, his specific model requires that testicular growth occur on day lengths of less than 6 hr, which, to my knowledge, has not been tested. He (26) has also suggested from experiments with young and adult chaffinches held for 19–24 months in either 12L 12D or 20L 4D that there is an endogenous circannual component in the mechanism that controls the annual cycle. Because these experiments were not under truly constant conditions and because there were conspicuous differences in the "cycles" in fat deposition, molt, and gonadal activity between groups on 20L 4D and 12L 12D, with no gonadal activity in the former during the second year, the suggested endogenous circannual component requires further investigation.

HOUSE SPARROW   *Passer domesticus,* a nonmigratory species that has been closely associated with evolving human culture for several millennia, displays many of the characteristics of photoperiodic species, but understandably with greater variance under both natural and experimental conditions (reviewed in 43, 50, 93). Photorefractoriness, to which the postnuptial molt is coupled, develops as a delayed effect of long days, apparently involving thyroid hormone (127), as in *Sturnus vulgaris.* Unlike most photoperiodic species, some males eventually recover from photorefractoriness in long days (R. S.

Donham, M. C. Moore & D. S. Farner, unpublished observations). This and occasional growth of testes in DD have been suggested to indicate an endogenous circannual component in the system that controls testicular function. However, because these cases are both sporadic and irregular, much more information is needed. Males of this species, somewhat like those of *S. vulgaris,* also undergo development on very short days (reviewed in 42). Although this and most other photoperiodic responses can be rationalized by an external-coincidence model (42), results of two investigations suggest that internal coincidence may be involved: (*a*) In a generally overlooked communication, Vaugien & Vaugien (128) reported that once testicular growth is photoperiodically induced, it can continue for 1–2 months after transfer to DD. (*b*) Males undergoing photoperiodically induced testicular growth undergo more rapid regression when changed to 8L 16D than to DD (44). In summary, the available evidence for this species offers no convincing evidence for a role of an endogenous circannual cycle in testicular function. Measurement of day length in photoperiodically induced testicular development may involve both external and internal coincidence as redundant functions, although the latter may be more probable.

GOLDEN HAMSTER   *Mesocricetus auratus* has become the most widely investigated photoperiodic mammalian species (reviewed in 33, 73, 74, 78, 105–108, 124, 137). Gonadal development is induced and maintained by long days. Day length is apparently measured by a system containing a circadian component, the performance of which can be rationalized by an external-coincidence model. Gonadal regression is induced by short days, to which the control system eventually becomes refractory. This short-day refractoriness eventually terminates spontaneously under either short or long days. Short-day refractoriness, which can be mimicked with exogenous melatonin, can also be caused to occur experimentally without gonadal regression (129). Intimately involved in the photoperiodic control system is the pineal gland, melatonin, and possibly other pineal hormones, because short-day induced gonadal regression is blocked by pinealectomy or by severance of its sympathetic innervation. The system is actually more complex because, under some conditions, melatonin can induce gonadal effects and because of steroid and circadian effects on the hypothalamo-hypophysial system (reviewed in 74, 124). Little is known about effects of domestication and laboratory conditions on the control system as compared with natural populations. There are no strong indications of endogenous circannual rhythms.

FERRET   Since the demonstration in 1932 (15) that long days induce development of the reproductive function of both sexes of *Mustela furo,* investigations, which have proceeded at a modest pace (reviewed in 72), have revealed that properties of its photoperiodic control system, including the role of the pineal gland, are generally similar to those of other "long-day" mammals. This is doubtless a further example of evolutionary convergence. However, there is a long-day photorefractoriness similar to that of photoperiodic species of birds (123). The demonstration that females, held on 8L 6D during winter and spring, come into estrus at approximately the normal time raises the possibility of an endogenous circannual component in the control system.

DOMESTIC SHEEP   Although this review has been intentionally oriented towards natural species, it seems desirable to note briefly the very extensive literature on breeds of *Ovis aries*. Collectively, this, including recent sophisticated endocrine investigations (reviewed in e.g. 56, 82), indicate that the original stock and at least some of the contemporary breeds are short-day photoperiodic mammals. The periods of rut and of estrous cycles are induced by the shorter days of autumn, thus permitting young to be born during favorable conditions in spring. Unfortunately the available information does not resolve the question as to whether the shorter days of autumn function as a Zeitgeber for endogenous circannual rhythms or a driver for the control system, although there appears to be a circadian element in its biochronometric component. It seems probable that the short-day system of this species exemplifies those of other temperate-zone ungulates (see Sika deer above; also reviewed in 82).

ZEBRA FINCH   Natural populations of *Poephila guttata castanotis* inhabit aseasonal arid regions of Australia in which they become reproductively active immediately after rainstorms (reviewed in 76, 118). I include this species in this review as an example of the great flexibility of the control systems in higher vertebrates to selective pressure in evolution and as an admonition to overzealous narrow categorization of the bases of control systems. The young are fed primarily on fresh soft seeds of grasses that develop after a rain. During dry periods the reproductive systems remain partially developed, thus reducing the time required to reach functional status once subjected to the appropriate predictive information. It has long been suspected (e.g. 37) that some change associated with rain, possibly improvement of internal water economy, constitutes the appropriate predictive information. A series of recent experiments (104) has confirmed that such an improvement of water economy, entirely independent of daylength and with no obvious endogenous circannual component, provides the necessary predictive information. As suggested by Immelmann (75), this may be reinforced and synchronized by group stimulation.

SUMMARY

The diverse but highly fragmentary information on generation of annual cycles in reproduction and associated functions in higher vertebrates can be rationalized only as multiple evolutionary adaptations to survival in annually periodic environments. At one extreme are control systems in which endogenous circannual rhythms are entrained by the annual photocycle. At the other extreme are systems for which the annual photocycle serves as a driver. The latter may have natural periods of about one year that do not generate endogenous rhythms. Intermediate systems certainly exist. Especially among birds and small mammals, control systems use additional environmental information for final temporal adjustment to the phenologic development of the season at hand. Primarily for reasons of parsimony, most investigators have rationalized observations on measurement of day length by external-coincidence models. However, it may well be that internal-coincidence models are more appropriate, although the possibility of both types as redundant elements should not be precluded.

ACKNOWLEDGMENT

Some cited, but unpublished, information was obtained from investigations supported by the National Science Foundation.

Literature Cited

1. Aschoff, J. 1955. Jahresperiodik der Fortpflanzung bei Warmblütern. *Stud. Gen.* 8:742–66
2. Aschoff, J. 1980. Biological clocks in birds. *Acta XVII Congr. Int. Ornithol.,* pp. 113–36. Berlin: Deutsche Ornithologen-Gesellschaft
3. Assenmacher, I. 1974. External and internal components of the mechanism controlling reproduction in drakes. In *Circannual Clocks,* ed. E. T. Pengelley, pp. 197–248. New York: Academic. 523 pp.
4. Baker, J. R. 1938. The evolution of the breeding season. In *Evolution,* ed. G. R. de Beer, pp. 161–77. Oxford: Oxford Univ. Press. 351 pp.
5. Barnes, B. M. 1983. *The reproductive endocrinology of the golden-mantled ground squirrel Spermophilus saturatus.* PhD dissertation. Seattle: Univ. Wash. 71 pp.
6. Benoit, J. 1935. Stimulation par la lumière artificielle du développment testiculaire chez des Canards aveuglés par énucléation des globes oculaires. *C. R. Soc. Biol.* 120:136–39
7. Benoit, J., Assenmacher, I., Brard, E. 1955. Évolution testiculaire du Canard domestique maintenu a l'obscurité totale pendant une longue durée. *C. R. Acad. Sci. Paris* 241:251–53
8. Benoit, J., Assenmacher, I., Brard, E. 1959. Action d'un éclairement permanent prolongé sur l'évolution testiculaire du Canard pékin. *Arch. Anat. Microsc. Morphol. Exp.* 48:5–12
9. Berry, H. H., Millar, R. P., Louw, G. N. 1979. Environmental clues influencing the breeding biology and circulating levels of various hormones and triglycerides in the cape cormorant. *Comp. Biochem. Physiol.* A 62:879–84
10. Berthold, P. 1974. Endogene Jahresperiodik. Konstanz: Universitätsverlag. 46 pp.
11. Berthold, P. 1978. Circannuale Rhythmik: Freilaufende selbsterregte Periodik mit lebenslanger Wirksamkeit bei Vögeln. *Naturwissenschaften* 65:546
12. Berthold, P. 1979. Innere Jahreskalender—Grundlage der Orientierung bei Tieren. *Biol. Unserer Zeit* 9:1–8
13. Berthold, P. 1980. Die endogene Steuerung der Jahresperodik: Eine kurze Übersicht. See Ref. 2, pp. 473–84
14. Berthold, P, Gwinner, E., Klein, H. 1972. Circannuale Periodik bei Grasmücken. II. Periodik der Gonadengrösse bei *Sylvia atricapilla* und *S. borin* unter verschiedenen konstanten Bedingungen. *J. Ornithol.* 113:407–17
15. Bissonnette, T. H. 1932. Modification of mammalian sexual cycles: reactions of ferrets of both sexes to electric light added after dark in November and December. *Proc. R. Soc. London Ser. B* 110:322–36
16. Bünning, E. 1960. Circadian rhythms and the time measurement in photo-

periodism. *Cold Spring Harbor Symp. Quant. Biol.* 25:249–56

17. Burger, J. W. 1949. A review of experimental investigations on seasonal reproduction in birds. *Wilson Bull.* 61:211–30

18. Chandola, A., Bhatt, D., Pathak, V. K. 1983. Environmental manipulation of seasonal reproduction in spotted munia *Lonchura punctulata.* In *Avian Endocrinology,* ed. S. Mikimi, K. Homma, M. Wada, pp. 229–42. Tokyo: Japan Sci. Soc. and Berlin: Springer-Verlag. 334 pp.

19. Chandola, A., Pathak, V. K., Bhatt, D. 1982. Evidence for an endogenous circannual component in the control of the annual gonadal cycle in munia. *J. Interdisc. Cycle Res.* 13:281–86

20. Danilevskii, A. S. 1961. *Fotoperiodizm i Sezonnoe Razvitie Nasekomykh.* Leningrad: Izdatelstvo LYG. 243 pp.

21. Davis, D. E. 1976. Hibernation and circannual rhythms of food consumption in marmots and ground squirrels. *Quart. Rev. Biol.* 51:477–514

22. Davis, D. E., Finnie, E. P. 1975. Entrainment of circannual rhythm in weight of woodchucks. *J. Mammal.* 56:199–203

23. Davis, G. J., Meyer, R. K. 1972. The effect of daylength on pituitary FSH and LH and gonadal development of snowshoe hares. *Biol. Reprod.* 6:246–49

24. Dawson, A. 1983. Plasma gonadal steroid levels in wild starlings *(Sturnus vulgaris)* during the annual cycle and in relation to the stages of breeding. *Gen. Comp. Endocrinol.* 49:286–94

25. Dawson, A., Goldsmith, A. R. 1982. Prolactin and gonadotropin secretion in wild starlings *(Sturnus vulgaris)* during the annual cycle and in relation to nesting, incubation, and rearing young. *Gen. Comp. Endocrinol.* 48:213–21

26. Dolnik, V. R. 1974. Okologodovaya tsiklichnost migratsionnovo otlozheniya zhira, polovoi aktivnosti i linki pri postoyannykh fotoperiodakh u zyablika. *(Fringilla coelebs). Zh. Obsch. Biol.* 34:543–55

27. Dolnik, V. R. 1975. *Migratsionnoe Sostoyanie Ptits.* Moscow: Izdatelstvo NAUKA. 398 pp.

28. Dolnik, V. R. 1975. Fotoperiodicheskii kontrol sezonnykh tsiklov beca tela, linki i polovoi aktivnosti u zyablikov *(Fringilla coelebs). Zool. Zh.* 54:1048–56

29. Dolnik, V. R. 1976. Fotoperiodizm u ptits. In *Fotoperiodizm Zhivotnykh i Rastenii,* ed. V. A. Zaslavsky, pp. 47–81. Leningrad: Akad. Nauk SSSR. 211 pp.

30. Dolnik, V. R. 1980. Regulyatsiya okon-

chaniya linki i nachala osennei migratsii u molodykh zyablikov *(Fringilla coelebs). Zool. Zh.* 49:91–98

31. Dolnik, V. R. 1982. *Populyatsionaya Ekologiya Zyablika.* Leningrad: NAUK. 301 pp.

32. Donham, R. S., Moore, M. C., Farner, D. S. 1983. Physiological basis of repeated testicular cycles on twelve-hour days (12L 12D) in white-crowned sparrows, *Zonotrichia leucophrys gambelii. Physiol. Zool.* 56:302–7

33. Elliott, J. A. 1976. Circadian rhythms and photoperiodic time measurement in mammals. *Fed. Proc.* 35:239–46

34. Enright, J. T. 1970. Ecological aspects of endogenous rhythmicity. *Ann. Rev. Ecol. Syst.* 1:221–38

35. Farner, D. S. 1961. Comparative physiology: Photoperiodicity. *Ann. Rev. Physiol.* 23:71–96

36. Farner, D. S. 1964. The photoperiodic control of reproductive cycles in birds. *Am. Sci.* 52:137–56

37. Farner, D. S. 1967. Control of avian reproductive cycles. *Proc. XIV Int. Ornithol. Cong.* pp. 107–33

38. Farner, D. S. 1970. Predictive functions in the control of annual cycles. *Environ. Res.* 3:119–31

39. Farner, D. S. 1975. Photoperiodic controls in the secretion of gonadotropins in birds. *Am. Zool.* 15(Suppl.):117–35

40. Farner, D. S. 1980. The regulation of the annual cycle of the white-crowned sparrow. *Zonotrichia leucophrys gambelii.* See Ref. 2, pp. 71–82

41. Farner, D. S. 1980. Endogenous periodic functions in the control of reproductive cycles. In *Neural and Endocrine Aspects of Biological Rhythms in Birds,* ed. Y. Tanabe, K. Tanaka, T. Ookawa, pp. 123–47. Tokyo: Japan Sci. Soc. and Berlin: Springer-Verlag. 373 pp.

42. Farner, D. S., Donham, R. S., Lewis, R. A., Mattocks, P. W., Darden, T. R., Smith, J. P. 1977. The circadian component in the photoperiodic mechanism of the house sparrow, *Passer domesticus. Physiol. Zool.* 50:247–68

43. Farner, D. S., Donham, R. S., Matt, K. S., Mattocks, P. W., Moore, M. C., Wingfield, J. C. 1983. The nature of photorefractoriness. See Ref. 18, pp. 149–66

44. Farner, D. S., Donham, R. S., Moore, M. C. 1981. Induction of testicular development in house sparrows, *Passer domesticus,* and white-crowned sparrows, *Zonotrichia leucophrys gambelii,* with very long days and continuous light. *Physiol. Zool.* 54:372–78

45. Farner, D. S., Donham, R. S., Moore,

M. C., Lewis, R. A. 1980. The temporal relationship between the cycle of testicular development and molt in the white-crowned sparrow, *Zonotrichia leucophrys gambelii. Auk* 97:63–75

46. Farner, D. S., Follett, B. K. 1966. Light and other factors affecting avian reproduction. *J. An. Sci.* 25(Suppl.):90–115

47. Farner, D. S., Follett, B. K. 1979. Reproductive periodicity in birds. In *Hormones and Evolution,* ed. J. W. Barrington, 2:829–72. London: Academic. 989 pp.

48. Farner, D. S., Gwinner, E. 1980. Photoperiodicity, circannual and reproductive cycle. In *Avian Endocrinology,* ed. A. Epple, M. H. Stetson, pp. 331–66. New York: Academic. 577 pp.

49. Farner, D. S., Lewis, R. A. 1971. Photoperiodism and reproductive cycles in birds. *Photophysiology* 6:325–70

50. Farner, D. S., Lewis, R. A. 1973. Field and experimental studies of the annual cycles of white-crowned sparrows. *J. Reprod. Fert.* 19:35–50 (Suppl.)

51. Farner, D. S., Wilson, A. C. 1957. A quantitative examination of testicular growth in the white-crowned sparrow. *Biol. Bull.* 113:254–67

52. Follett, B. K. 1978. Photoperiodism and seasonal breeding in birds and mammals. In *Control of Ovulation,* ed. G. E. Lamming, D. B. Creighton, pp. 267–293. London: Butterworths

53. Follett, B. K. 1982. Physiology of photoperiodic time measurement. In *Vertebrate Circadian Systems,* ed. J. Aschoff, S. Daan, G. A. Gross, pp. 268–75. Berlin: Springer-Verlag. 363 pp.

54. Goldsmith, A. R., Nicholls, T. J. 1984. Prolactin is associated with the development of photorefractoriness in intact, castrated and testosterone-implanted starlings *(Sturnus vulgaris). Gen. Comp. Endocrinol.* 54:247–55

55. Goldsmith, A. R., Nicholls, T. J. 1984. Thyroidectomy prevents the development of photorefractoriness and the associated rise in plasma prolactin in starlings. *Gen. Comp Endocrinol.* 54:256–63

56. Goodman, R. L., Karsch, F. J. 1980. Control of seasonal breeding in the ewe: Importance of changes in response to sex-steroid feed. *Prog. Reprod. Biol.* 5:134–54

57. Goss, R. J. 1983. *Deer Antlers: Regeneration, Function, and Evolution.* New York: Academic. 316 pp.

58. Goss, R. J., Dinsmore, C. E., Grimes, N. G., Rosen, J. K. 1974. Expression and suppression of the circannual antler growth in deer. See Ref. 3, pp. 393–421

59. Gwinner, E. 1967. Circannuale Periodik der Mauser und der Zugunruhe bei einem Vogel. *Naturwissenschaften* 54:447

60. Gwinner, E. 1971. A comparative study of circannual rhythms in warblers. In *Biochronometry,* ed. M. Menaker, pp. 405–27. Washington DC: Natl. Acad. Sci. USA. 622 pp.

61. Gwinner, E. 1973. Circannual rhythms in birds: Their interactions with circadian rhythms and environmental photoperiod. *J. Reprod. Fertil.* 19:51–65 (Suppl.)

62. Gwinner, E. 1975. Circadian and circannual rhythms in birds. In *Avian Biology,* ed. D. S. Farner, J. R. King, 5:221–85. New York: Academic. 523 pp.

63. Gwinner, E. 1977. Photoperiodic synchronization of circannual rhythms in the European starling *(Sturnus vulgaris). Naturwissenschaften* 64:44

64. Gwinner, E. 1977. Circannual rhythms in bird migration. *Ann. Rev. Ecol. Syst.* 8:381–405

65. Gwinner, E. 1981. Circannual systems. In *Handbook of Behavioral Neurobiology, Biological Rhythms,* ed. J. Aschoff, 4:391–410. New York: Plenum. 563 pp.

66. Gwinner, E. 1981. Circannuale Rhythm bei Tieren und ihre photoperiodische Synchronisation. *Naturwissenschaften* 68:542–51

67. Gwinner, E. 1981. Circannual rhythms: Their dependence on the circadian system. In *Biological Clocks in Seasonal Reproductive Cycles,* ed. B. K. Follett, D. E. Follett, pp. 153–69. Bristol: Wright. 292 pp.

68. Gwinner, E., Wozniak, J. 1982. Circannual rhythms in European starlings: Why do they stop under long photoperiods? *J. Comp. Physiol. A* 146:419–21

69. Halberg, F. 1959. Physiologic 24-hour periodicity: General and procedural considerations with reference to the adrenal cycle. *Z. Vitam. Horm. Fermentforsch.* 10:225–96

70. Halberg, F., Engeli, M., Hamburger, C., Hillman, D. 1965. Spectral resolution of low-frequency, small-amplitude rhythms in excreted 17-ketosteroids; probable androgen-induced circaseptan desynchronization. *Acta Endocrinol.* 103:5–54 (Suppl.)

71. Heller, H. C., Poulson, T. L. 1970. Circannian rhythms. II. Endogenous and exogenous factors controlling reproduction and hibernation in chipmunks *(Eutamias)* and ground squirrels *(Spermophilus). Comp. Biochem. Physiol.* 33:357–83

72. Herbert, J., Klinowska, M. 1978. Day length and annual reproductive cycle in the ferret *(Mustela furo):* The role of the pineal body. In *Environmental Endocri-*

nology, ed. I. Assenmacher, D. S. Farner, pp. 87–93. Berlin: Springer-Verlag. 334 pp.

73. Hoffmann, K. 1978. Annuale Periodik bei Säugern und ihre photoperiodische Steuerung. *Arz. Forsch.* 10a:1836–42

74. Hoffmann, K. 1981. Photoperiodism in vertebrates. See Ref. 65, pp. 449–73

75. Immelmann, K. 1963. Tierische Jahresperiodik in ökologischer Sicht. *Zool. Jahrb. Abt. Syst. Oekol.* 91:91–200

76. Immelmann, K. 1967. Periodische Vorgänge in der Fortpflanzung tierischer Organismen. *Stud. Gen.* 20:15–33

77. Jallageas, M., Assenmacher, I. 1981. Influence des facteurs externes sur le cycle annuel du fonctionnement testiculaire des oiseaux. *Bull. Soc. Zool. Fr.* 106:341–48

78. Johnson, L. Y., Reiter, R. J. 1978. The pineal gland and its effects on mammalian reproduction. *Prog. Reprod. Biol.* 4:116–56

79. Joy, J. E., Mrosovsky, N. 1982. Circannual cycles of molt in ground squirrels. *Can. J. Zool.* 60:3227–31

80. Kenagy, G. J. 1981. Interrelation of endogenous annual rhythms of reproduction and hibernation in the golden-mantled ground squirrels *Spermophilus lateralis. Compar. Physiol.* 134:333–40

81. Licht, P., Zucker, I., Hubbard, G., Boshes, M. 1982. Circannual rhythms of plasma testosterone and luteinizing hormone levels in golden-mantled ground squirrels *(Spermophilus lateralis). Biol. Reprod.* 27:411–18

82. Lincoln, G. A., Short, R. V. 1980. Seasonal breeding: Nature's contraceptive. *Recent Prog. Horm. Res.* 36:1–43

83. Meier, A. H., Ferrell, B. R. 1978. Avian endocrinology. In *Chemical Zoology*, ed. A. H. Brush. 10:214–71. New York: Academic. 436 pp.

84. Meier, A. H., Ferrell, B. R., Miller, L. J. 1980. Circadian component of the circannual mechanism in the white-throated sparrow. See Ref. 2, pp. 458–62

85. Menaker, M. 1974. Circannual rhythms in circadian perspective. See Ref. 3, pp. 507–20

86. Menaker, M. 1982. The search for principles of physiological organization in vertebrate circadian systems. See Ref. 53, pp. 1–12

87. Moore, M. C. 1982. Hormonal response of free-living male white-crowned sparrows to experimental manipulation of female sexual behavior. *Horm. Behav.* 16:323–29

88. Moore, M. C. 1983. Effect of female sexual displays on the endocrine physiology and behaviour of male white-crowned sparrows, *Zonotrichia leucophrys. J. Zool.* 199:137–48

89. Moore, M. C., Donham, R. S., Farner, D. S. 1982. Physiological preparation for autumnal migration in white-crowned sparrows. *Condor* 84:410–19

90. Moore, M. C., Schwabl, H., Farner, D. S. 1983. Biochronometry of testicular regression in white-crowned sparrows. *J. Comp. Physiol.* 153(A):489–94

91. Moore-Ede, M. C., Sulzman, F. M., Fuller, C. A. 1982. *The Clocks That Time Us.* Cambridge: Harvard Univ. 448 pp.

92. Mrosovsky, N. 1978. Circannual cycles in hibernators. In *Strategies in Cold,* ed. L. C. H. Wang, J. W. Hudson, pp. 21–65. New York: Academic. 715 pp.

93. Murton, R. K., Westwood, N. J. 1977. *Avian Breeding Cycles.* Oxford: Clarendon Press. 595 pp.

94. Noskov, G. A. 1975. Linka zyablika. *Zool. Zh.* 54:413–24

95. Noskov, G. A. 1977. Linka zyablika *(Fringilla coelebs).* II. Fotoperiodicheskaya regulyatsiya i mesto godovom tsikle. *Zool. Zh.* 61:1676–86

96. Oliver, J., Baylé, J. F. 1982. Brain photoreceptors for the photo-induced testicular response in birds. *Experientia* 38:1021–29

97. Pengelley, E. T., Asmundson, S. J. 1970. The effect of light on the free-running circannual rhythm of the golden-mantled ground squirrel. *Comp. Biochem. Physiol.* 32:155–60

98. Pengelley, E. T., Asmundson, S. J. 1974. Circannual rhythmicity in hibernating mammals. See Ref. 3, pp. 95–160

99. Pengelley, E. T., Asmundson, S. J., Barnes, B., Aloia, R. C. 1976. Relationship of light intensity and photoperiod to circannual rhythmicity in the hibernating ground squirrel, *Citellus lateralis. Comp. Biochem. Physiol.* 53A:273–77

100. Pittendrigh, C. S. 1974. Circadian oscillations in cells and the circadian organization of multicellular systems. In *The Neurosciences Third Study Program,* ed. F. O. Schmitt, F. G. Worden, pp. 437–58. Cambridge: MIT Press. 1107 pp.

101. Pittendrigh, C. S. 1981. Circadian systems: General perspective. See Ref. 74, pp. 57–80

102. Pittendrigh, C. S., Daan, S. 1976. A functional analysis of circadian pacemakers in nocturnal rodents. V. Pacemaker structure: A clock for all seasons. *J. Comp. Physiol.* 106(A):333–55

103. Pittendrigh, C. S., Minis, D. H. 1964. The entrainment of circadian oscillations by light and their role as photoperiodic clocks. *Am. Nat.* 98:261–94

104. Priedkalns, J., Oksche, A., Vleck, C., Bennett, R. K. 1984. The response of the hypothalamo-gonadal system to environmental factors in the zebra finch *(Poephila guttata castanotis):* Structural and functional studies. *Cell Tissue Res.* In press

105. Reiter, R. J. 1974. Circannual reproductive rhythms in mammals related to photoperiod and pineal function. *Chronobiologia* 1:365–95

106. Reiter, R. J. 1978. Interaction of photoperiod, pineal and seasonal reproduction as exemplified by findings on the hamster. *Prog. Reprod. Biol.* 4:169–90

107. Reiter, R. J. 1981. Seasonal reproduction: An expedient and essential artifice. *Prog. Reprod. Biol.* 5:1–4

108. Reiter, R. J. 1983. The pineal gland: An intermediary between the environment and the endocrine system. *Psychoneuroendocrinology* 8:31–40

109. Runfeld, S., Wingfield, J. C. 1984. Experimentally prolonged sexual activity in female sparrows delays termination of reproductive activity in their untreated mates. *Anim. Behav.* In press

110. Rutledge, J. T. 1974. Circannual rhythms of reproduction in male European starlings. See Ref. 3, pp. 297–345

111. Rutledge, J. T., Schwab, R. G. 1974. Testicular metamorphosis in starlings *(Sturnus vulgaris)* in the absence of daily photostimulation. *J. Exp. Zool.* 187:71–76

112. Sansum, E. L., King, J. R. 1976. Long-term effects of constant photoperiods on testicular cycles of white-crowned sparrows *(Zonotrichia leucophrys gambelii).* *Physiol. Zool.* 49:407–16

113. Schwab, R. G. 1971. Circannian testicular periodicity in the European starling in the absence of photoperiodic change. See Ref. 60, pp. 428–47

114. Schwab, R. G. 1980. Ahemeral light regimes test the photoperiodic threshhold of the European starling *(Sturnus vulgaris).* *Int. J. Biometeor.* 24:83–88

115. Schwab, R. G., Rutledge, J. T. 1975. Stable daily light regimes as inductive factors of endogenous cycles in the European starling, *Sturnus vulgaris. Int. J. Biometeor.* 19:219–31

116. Schwabl, H., Benziger-Schwabl, I., Farner, D. S. 1984. Relationship between migratory disposition and plasma levels of gonadotropins and steroid hormones in the European blackbird. *Naturwissenschaften.* 71:329–31

117. Schwabl, H., Wingfield, J. C., Farner, D. S. 1984. Endocrine correlates of autumnal behavior in sedentary and migratory individuals of a partially migratory population of the European blackbird *(Turdus merula).* *Auk* 101:499–507

118. Serventy, D. L. 1971. Biology of desert birds. See Ref. 62, pp. 287–339

119. Sharp, P. L. 1983. Hypothalamic control of gonadotropin secretion in birds. In *Progress in Nonmammalian Brain Research,* ed. G. Nisticó, L. Bolis, 3:123–76. Boca Raton, FL: CRC Press. 245 pp.

120. Silverin, B., Goldsmith, A. R. 1983. Reproductive endocrinology of free-living pied flycatchers *(Ficedula hypoleuca):* prolactin and FSH secretion in relation to incubation and clutch size. *J. Zool.* 200:119–30

121. Stetson, M. H., Watson-Whitmire, M., Matt, K. S. 1977. Termination of photorefractoriness in golden hamsters. *J. Exp. Zool.* 202:81–88

122. Sundararaj, B. I., Varsal, S., Halberg, F. 1982. Circannual rhythmic ovarian recrudescence in the catfish *Heteropneustes fossilis* (Bloch). *Adv. Biosci.* 41:319–37

123. Thorpe, P. A., Herbert, J. 1976. Studies on the duration of the breeding season and photorefractoriness in female ferrets pinealectomized or treated with melatonin. *J. Endocrinol.* 70:255–62

124. Turek, F. W., Campbell, C. S. 1979. Photoperiodic regulation of neuroendocrine-gonadal activity. *Biol. Reprod.* 20:32–50

125. Turek, F. W., Losee, S. H. 1978. Melatonin-induced testicular growth in golden hamsters maintained on short days. *Biol. Reprod.* 18:299–305

126. Tyshchenko, V. P., Goryshina, T. K., Dolnik, V. R. 1980. Sezionnye ritmy. In *Problemy Kosmicheskoi Biologii,* ed. V. N. Chernigvoskovo, pp. 238–88. Moscow: Izdatelstvo NAUK. 318 pp.

127. Vaugien, L. 1954. Influence de l'obscuration temporaire sur la durée de la phase réfractaire du cycle sexuel du Moineau domestique. *Bull. Biol. Fr. Belg.* 88:294–309

128. Vaugien, M., Vaugien, L. 1961. Le Moineau domestique peut dévelloper son activité sexuelle et la maintenir dans l'obscurité complète. *C. R. Acad. Sci.* 253:2762–64

129. Watson-Whitmyre, M., Stetson, M. H. 1984. Induction of photorefractoriness in the absence of gonadal regression. *Biol. Reprod.* 1:165 (Suppl. 30)

130. Wieselthier, A. S., van Tienhoven, A. 1972. The effect of thyroidectomy on testicular size and on the photorefractory period in the starling, *Sturnus vulgaris. J. Exp. Zool.* 179:331–38

131. Wingfield, J. C. 1984. Environmental and endocrine control in the song spar-

row, *Melospiza melodia*. I. Temporal organization of the breeding cycle. *Gen. Comp. Endocrinol.* In press

132. Wingfield, J. C. 1984. II. Agonistic interactions as environmental information stimulating secretions of testosterone. *Gen. Comp. Endocrinol.* In press

133. Wingfield, J. C., Farner, D. S. 1980. Control of seasonal reproduction in temperate-zone birds. *Prog. Reprod. Biol.* 5:62–101

134. Wingfield, J. C., Newman, A. L., Hunt, G. L. Jr., Farner, D. S. 1982. Endocrine aspects of female-female pairing in the western gull *(Larus occidentalis wymani)*. *Anim. Behav.* 30:9–22

135. Zucker, I., Boshes, M. 1982. Circannual body weight rhythms of ground squirrels: Role of gonadal hormones. *Am. J. Physiol.* 243:R546–51

136. Zucker, I., Boshes, M., Dark, J. 1983. Suprachiasmatic nuclei influence circannual and circadian rhythms of ground squirrels. *Am. J. Physiol.* 244:R472–80

137. Zucker, I., Johnston, P. G., Frost, D. 1980. Comparative, physiological and biochronometric analyses of rodent reproductive cycles. *Prog. Reprod. Biol.* 5:102–33

RENAL AND ELECTROLYTE PHYSIOLOGY

Introduction, Carl W. Gottschalk, *Section Editor*

The theme of this year's section on Renal Physiology is transport of metabolic substrates in the proximal tubule. Because proximal tubular transport accounts for the bulk of the reabsorptive work of the kidney, it is logical to focus on this portion of the uriniferous tubule. The authors discuss both the transport of the major metabolic substrates and the support of transport and other cell functions by these substrates. The presentations have a strong biochemical orientation, and the results of newer studies on membrane vesicles are emphasized.

As Dr. Mandel points out, substrates entering proximal tubular cells from the luminal or basolateral side face three possibilities: transepithelial transport, oxidation to CO_2, and interconversion to another substrate. He discusses the various methods for studying substrate metabolism in the kidney and the major results that have been obtained.

Drs. Schafer & Williams present the more recent findings relating to the mechanism of proximal tubular transport of metabolic substrates, especially glucose and amino acids. They also discuss the varying transport characteristics of organic solute transport along the proximal tubule, interactions with the transport of salt and water, and maintenance of normal epithelial cell volume and function.

Carboxylic acids in plasma are filtered at the glomerulus and reabsorbed in the proximal tubule. Dr. Wright summarizes the work on carboxylic acid transport in membrane vesicles, where it is possible to examine membrane transport in the absence of metabolism. He describes the several Na-cotransport systems that have been uncovered.

Drs. Schoolwerth & LaNoue discuss the role of transport of metabolic substrates in renal mitochondria. They emphasize that specialized transporters are required to maintain the steady flow of metabolites into and out of the mitochondrial matrix space. The chemical characteristics and physiological significance of the mitochrondrial transporters are described with emphasis on those transporters relevant to renal metabolism.

Ann. Rev. Physiol. 1985. 47:85–101

METABOLIC SUBSTRATES, CELLULAR ENERGY PRODUCTION, AND THE REGULATION OF PROXIMAL TUBULAR TRANSPORT

Lazaro J. Mandel

Department of Physiology, Duke University Medical Center, Box 3709, Durham, North Carolina 27710

INTRODUCTION

Proximal tubular transport accounts for about 70% of the reabsorptive work of the kidney (35, 42). The tubular cells use a variety of metabolic substrates to provide the energy needed for these transport processes (15). The actual substrates that are metabolized depend on the substrate mix present in the extracellular environment, on hormonal influences, and on the metabolic state (e.g. acid-base) of the animal.

Substrates may enter the proximal tubular cells either through the luminal side, from the glomerular filtrate, or through the basolateral side, from the blood. The proximal tubules reabsorb most of the metabolic substrates from the filtrate, and these are, therefore, potentially available to be metabolized for energy (15). Transporters for glucose, lactate, Krebs cycle intermediates, and amino acids have been identified in brush border membranes (72). Some evidence indicates that basolateral transporters also exist for some of these (34, 56). Fatty acids, which are mostly bound to albumin, are not filtered and therefore may enter through the basolateral side in vivo (15).

Substrates entering the proximal tubular cells face three possibilities: (*a*) transepithelial transport; (*b*) oxidation to CO_2; and (*c*) interconversion to another substrate.

0066-4278/85/0315-0085$02.00

Each of these possible fates is discussed for the major metabolic substrates utilized by proximal renal tubules. The brevity of this review does not permit a comprehensive treatment of all substrates, all metabolic pathways, and all the extensive work that has been performed in renal substrate metabolism. Only the major substrates and major pathways are described and representative experiments cited. For a more detailed review, the reader can consult Cohen & Kamm (15).

METHODS USED TO STUDY SUBSTRATE METABOLISM IN THE KIDNEY

Several methods have been used to study renal substrate metabolism. A short description of these methods follows, with an evaluation of their advantages and disadvantages in the study of proximal metabolism and function.

In Vivo Techniques

Injections of ^{14}C-labeled substrates into the renal artery or intravenous infusion have allowed the identification of substrates metabolized by the kidney in vivo. This technique has been useful in the quantitation of substrate uptake by the kidney but not for quantitation of the metabolism of these substrates. The rate of substrate decarboxylation cannot be inferred directly from the rate of [14]CO_2 production, because the specific activity of the substrate inside the cells is unknown. Furthermore, label dilution can occur by the metabolism of endogenous substrates and/or label exchange with other metabolic intermediates. Another limitation of this technique is the inability to provide segmental information, an important limitation in light of the metabolic diversity encountered in the various nephron segments (15).

The Perfused Kidney

The main advantage of the perfused kidney over the in vivo preparation is the ability to control the perfusate. Single labeled substrates can be introduced, their metabolism monitored, and their support for renal function measured. Again, their total uptake by the kidney can be quantitated but the quantitation of the metabolism of each substrate must be interpreted with caution, due to the same limitations noted above. Although some experimental maneuvers have been used to attempt a separation between proximal and distal tubular function with this preparation (16, 22), in general, limited segmental information can be obtained.

Tissue Slices

The ease of obtaining cortical tissue slices has made this preparation very popular. Extensive characterization of the cortical metabolic pathways has been performed using this preparation (15, 69). Both qualitative and quantitative studies have been performed in slices to study the contribution of endogenous and exogenous substrates to renal metabolism. Individual labeled substrates can be introduced in the bathing medium, their specific activity within the cells measured, and the metabolic fate of the ^{14}C label identified. Quantitative information can be obtained in this manner regarding the metabolic fluxes of each added substrate either individually or in the presence of other substrates. By comparing these fluxes to the overall oxygen consumption and CO_2 production rates of the slices, the contributions of each substrate to cortical metabolism have been evaluated (69).

There are, however, several important limitations in the use of slices (15, 42): (a) Cortical slices have a heterogeneous population of cell types, although the majority of cells are proximal; (b) The tubular lumens are largely closed, and therefore slices perform little transepithelial active transport; and (c) The geometry of a cortical slice is such that the high rate of oxygen consumption leads to areas of anoxia and probably substrate limitation. These disadvantages limit the usefulness of slices in the evaluation of the metabolic support of transport.

Tubule Suspensions

Fairly homogeneous suspensions of proximal tubules (85–90%) with open lumens may be obtained by collagenase perfusion of the kidney in situ, followed by dispersion and purification (3, 67). The open lumens imply that transepithelial transport occurs and the short tubular segments ensure that diffusional limitations do not impede metabolism or transport. Therefore, this preparation possesses the metabolic advantages of cortical slices without the disadvantages described above. However, an important limitation is that transepithelial transport cannot be measured directly in this preparation. This limitation can be partially overcome by using ouabain-sensitive oxygen consumption as an indirect measure of active sodium transport (32, 42). In the whole kidney, the rate of sodium reabsorption is directly proportional to the oxygen consumption rate (15, 42). Similarly, the (Na^+, K^+)-ATPase activity, measured by the rate of active potassium transport from the bathing solution into proximal tubules, is proportional to the oxygen consumption rate (32). Therefore, the ouabain-sensitive oxygen consumption provides a fairly good quantitative measure of the transport work performed by the tubules.

Cell Suspensions

Preparations of cell suspensions possess the same advantages as the tubule suspensions compared to slices. Otherwise, they differ from suspensions in the preparation time (usually longer) and in that some of the epithelial asymmetry is absent owing to the lack of tight junctions (65).

Microdissected Tubular Segments

The use of isolated perfused tubules has enabled the characterization of transport properties of many nephron segments (12). This preparation is ideal for the evaluation of the metabolic support for transport of individual substrates and the sidedness of this action (13). Microperfusion in situ has also been used to measure transport properties of individual nephron segments and their metabolic support (21). Unfortunately, other metabolic parameters are more difficult to measure due to the small cellular mass of single perfused tubules (about 0.1 μg protein per tubule).

The rate of $^{14}CO_2$ production from ^{14}C-labeled substrates has been measured in groups of microdissected unperfused tubules (36); however, these suffer from the same problems of quantitation as the perfused kidney studies described earlier. Microdissection of kidney segments has been used to investigate the distribution of enzymes (66) and hormonal action (45) along the length of the nephron. These studies have provided important information concerning nephron heterogeneity of metabolic pathways, but no simultaneous measurement of transport could be obtained.

Membrane Vesicles

Excellent preparations exist of brush border and basolateral membrane vesicles (72) derived from proximal tubules. These have been used to characterize the properties of the various transport systems residing at each membrane, including the transport of metabolic substrates (34, 72). However, because the membranes are separated from the cells, the relationship to metabolism cannot be obtained.

Isolated Mitochondria and Cytosol

Isolated mitochondria and microsomal preparations have been used extensively to establish the pathways and control of cellular metabolism in numerous tissues (40). In the past few years, techniques have evolved to permit the rapid separation of mitochondrial and cytosolic fractions in liver (1) and in kidney (26) to evaluate their individual contents of metabolic intermediates. Because metabolic compartmentation seems to be an important element in the effects of numerous substrates, this separation technique holds great promise for future investigations.

OUTLINE OF THE MAIN PATHWAYS FOR SUBSTRATE METABOLISM

The main pathways involved in the metabolism of the major substrates utilized by mammalian proximal tubules are described below in outline form. The main oxidative pathways are shown in Figure 1, whereas the main pathways for

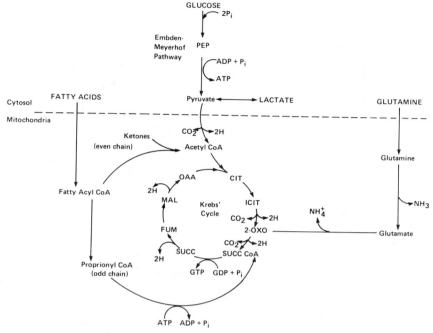

Figure 1   Schematic diagram of the main oxidative pathways of mammalian proximal tubules. Abbreviations are as follows: *ATP* and *GTP* = adenosine and guanosine triphosphate; *ADP* and *GDP* = adenosine and guanosine diphosphate; P_i = inorganic phosphate; *PEP* = phosphoenolpyruvate; *CIT* = citrate; *ICIT* = isocitrate; *2-OXO* = 2 oxoglutarate; *SUCC* = succinate; *SUCC CoA* = succinyl CoA; *FUM* = fumarate; *MAL* = malate; *OAA* = oxaloacetate.

substrate interconversions are shown in Figure 2. These schematic diagrams are intended for reference purposes only and, as such, they do not describe all the pathways involved.

Glucose is mainly oxidized by the glycolytic (Embden-Meyerhof) pathway to pyruvate. Under anaerobic conditions, the end product of glycolysis is lactate. In the presence of oxygen, pyruvate enters the mitochondria, where it is converted to acetyl CoA and is metabolized to CO_2 by the Krebs cycle. Glucose can also be partially oxidized by the hexose monophosphate shunt (not shown in Figure 1).

The other major substrates used by the proximal tubules are metabolized aerobically by entering the Krebs cycle through a variety of routes, as shown in Figure 1. Oxidation by the Krebs cycle produces CO_2 and reducing equivalents (2H), which are subsequently oxidized by the respiratory chain. Lactate is oxidized through pyruvate and acetyl CoA, combining with oxaloacetate (OAA) to form citrate. Fatty acids react with acetyl CoA and then enter the

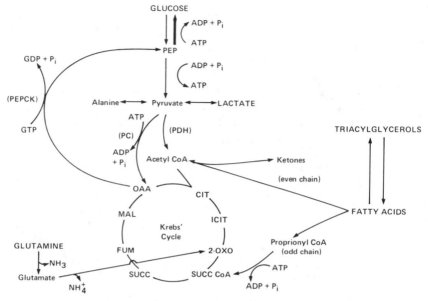

Figure 2 Schematic diagram of the main pathways for substrate interconversions in mammalian proximal tubules. Abbreviations are as in Figure 1. In addition, enzymes in parentheses are as follows: *PDH* = pyruvate dehydrogenase; *PC* = pyruvate carboxylase; *PEPCK* = phosphoenolpyruvate carboxykinase.

mitochondria through special carnitine-linked carriers. In a series of lipolytic steps, even chain-length fatty acids are broken down to acetyl CoA; and odd chain-length fatty acids are catabolized to both acetyl CoA and propionyl CoA, and the latter enters the Krebs cycle through succinyl CoA. Ketones readily enter into the mitochondria, where they can be converted into acetyl CoA and oxidized by the Krebs cycle. Glutamine enters the mitochondria through a specific carrier, is deamidinated to glutamate and converted to 2-oxoglutarate (also known as α-ketoglutarate), and oxidized by the Krebs cycle. The conversion of glutamine to 2-oxoglutarate yields 2 mol NH_3 per mol glutamine, and this is the main source of the ammonia secreted by the kidney during acidosis (51). Other amino acids are not oxidized to any extent by proximal tubules; rather, they seem to be involved in substrate interconversion reactions, as described below. Reabsorbed Krebs cycle intermediates can enter the mitochondria directly or indirectly and be metabolized to CO_2, as long as a source of acetyl CoA is present.

The proximal tubule does not store glycogen to any great extent (39, 46), and therefore the synthesis and degradation of glycogen do not contribute significantly to carbohydrate metabolism in this tissue. On the other hand, glucose is the end product of numerous substrate interconversion reactions. As shown in Figure 2, glucose can be synthesized from a variety of substrates. From lactate, gluconeogenesis proceeds through pyruvate-OAA-PEP and a reversal of glycolysis to glucose. The rate-limiting enzymes are pyruvate carboxylase (PC) and phosphoenolpyruvate kinase (PEPCK); both are energy-requiring, and both are activated by acetyl CoA. Ketones and even chain-length fatty acids are not themselves converted to glucose, but they activate gluconeogenesis from other substrates (especially lactate) by increasing the acetyl CoA levels. All of the Krebs cycle intermediates may be converted to glucose through OAA and the PEPCK pathway. Similarly, glutamine is gluconeogenic as a result of its conversion to 2-oxoglutarate and passage through the Krebs cycle to OAA.

The proximal tubule contains stored triacylglycerols that undergo continual synthesis and degradation (15, 70). Thus, fatty acids taken up from the extracellular fluid can be either oxidized or converted into triacylglycerols. The latter are in turn catabolized to provide fatty acids for oxidation and energy production. Fatty acids can also be converted into ketones and vice-versa.

There are numerous other substrate interconversion reactions that have been described for the kidney and other tissues. Their description is beyond the scope of this review.

SUPPORT OF CELLULAR FUNCTION BY INDIVIDUAL METABOLIC SUBSTRATES

Endogenous Substrates

Proximal tubular function is considerably decreased in the absence of exogenously added substrates. In various preparations of proximal tubules, endogenous substrates could only support about 50% of tubular function (13, 21, 69; S. P. Soltoff, M. Chamberlin, L. J. Mandel, unpublished observations). In the perfused rat kidney, endogenous substrates support the reabsorption of only 45% of the filtered Na (20), but the proportion of proximal inhibition of renal function could not be determined.

The main endogenous substrates of the kidney cortex seem to be long-chain lipids (triacylglycerols) and glycogen. Wirthenson & Guder (70) measured 68 μmol/g protein of fatty-acid equivalents in saturated triacylglycerols in freshly prepared proximal tubules from starved rats. Lee et al (39) measured 18 mg/g wet weight of saponifiable lipids in cortex slices from the rabbit. In the former study, incubation without substrates caused this content to decrease by 30% in 30 min, an amount that is fully capable of accounting for most of the observed oxygen consumption of 15–20 μmol/min/g protein (69) for 30 min. Other evidence suggesting that fats serve as the main endogenous metabolic substrate are: (a) the low respiratory quotient of 0.80 observed in the absence of substrates (69), and (b) addition of 2-tetradecylglycidic acid (TDGA), a specific and irreversible inhibitor of fatty-acid oxidation, reduces renal function by an additional 50% of the already inhibited state found with no substrates in the perfused rat kidney (20) and in rabbit proximal tubules in suspension (S. P. Soltoff, M. Chamberlin, L. J. Mandel, unpublished observations).

Approximately 1 μmol/g wet weight ($\sim$ 4 μmol/g protein of glycogen, in glucose equivalents) has been found in the rat renal cortex (46), and about twice that in rabbit renal cortex (39). However, it is unclear how much of that glycogen is present in proximal tubules, because some reports suggest that most of the cortical glycogen is located in the collecting ducts (48). Nevertheless, the oxidation of this amount of glycogen would not be sufficient to support the tissue oxygen consumption and energy requirements for more than a few minutes. Even less energy would be obtained if the glycogen were consumed anaerobically.

Glucose

The proximal tubules normally reabsorb virtually all of the filtered glucose but metabolize less than 1% of the glucose load (15). Although the enzymes necessary for glucose metabolism by the Embden-Meyerhof pathway are present in proximal tubules (66), their activities are much lower in proximal tubules (about 1 pmol/mm/min for hexokinase) as compared to more distal segments (4–6 pmol/mm/min for hexokinase). Glucose oxidation has been reported to contribute 10–25% of the total measured oxygen consumption in the dog kidney in vivo (15) as well as cortical renal slice preparations from the rabbit (39) and the rat (69). Due to the heterogeneity of each of these preparations, it is difficult to evaluate the actual quantitative contribution of glucose oxidation to proximal tubular function. The observed percentages probably represent maximal values for proximal glucose oxidation, due to the higher activity of glycolytic enzymes in the more distal segments also present in each of these preparations. In isolated single-nephron segments of the rat, $^{14}CO_2$ formation from glucose is barely measurable (36). In proximal tubule suspensions from the rabbit, glucose as the sole substrate could only maintain 60% of the respiration obtained with a full substrate complement (32), barely above the rate obtained with endogenous substrates. These results would suggest that glucose does not supply much of the metabolic energy required for normal proximal tubular function.

The main metabolic fates of glucose are the production of CO_2 and lactate (Figure 1). In proximal tubules, the activity of the hexose monophosphate shunt appears to be minimal, because little difference is found in the rates of $^{14}CO_2$ formation from 6- vs 1-labeled ^{14}C-glucose (36, 39). Under aerobic conditions, most of the metabolized glucose appears as CO_2, with little lactate production (15). Under anaerobic conditions, glucose utilization increases and there is an increased production of lactate (46). However, this process only provides minimal support for the energetic needs of proximal tubules, because ATP levels rapidly fall at least 85% during anoxia (2, 23, 46). In this regard, it is important to note that the rate of glucose oxidation in the kidney cortex is actually slightly higher than that in liver (39). The overall metabolic rate of the proximal tubule is so much larger than that of the liver (15) that such a glycolytic rate can only provide a small percentage of the energetic requirements of the kidney.

Despite the relatively small role that glucose oxidation plays in the total supply of energy to proximal tubules, the addition of glucose to various renal preparations produces significant improvements in function. Specifically, in the perfused rat kidney, glucose addition increases glomerular filtration rate (GFR) and the percentage of reabsorbed Na from the filtered load (22, 53). These effects of glucose are most likely due to a combination of: (*a*) a direct metabolic effect on the glomerular cells, modulating GFR (16); (*b*) distal metabolic effects of glucose that increase distal Na reabsorption (16); and (*c*) increased cotransport of glucose with Na to increase proximal reabsorption (13). Along these lines, a study by Gullans et al (31) recently found that the primary action of glucose in proximal tubules appears to be through stimulation of Na entry by cotransport rather than through direct action as a metabolic substrate.

Under aerobic conditions, addition of several substrates can inhibit glucose oxidation (39) and lead to gluconeogenesis (15, 46). Proximal tubules contain relatively large concentrations (66) of the rate-limiting enzymes for gluconeogenesis PC and PEPCK ($\sim$ 4 pmol/mm/min). As described below, proximal tubules produce glucose at a significant rate, and this is one of the end products in the metabolism of many substrates.

Lactate

Lactate is one of the main metabolic substrates oxidized by proximal tubules. Lactate uptake and metabolism has been observed in various kidney preparations from the dog, rat, and rabbit (9, 15, 16, 17, 36, 69). In the in vivo dog kidney, lactate cellular uptake is linearly dependent on blood lactate concentration (15, 19). Lactate oxidation has been calculated to provide about 22% of total renal QO_2 in acidosis and 47% in alkalosis (15). In rat cortical slices, lactate added as the sole substrate supplied 30% of the respiratory fuel (69). Lactate addition to the perfused rat kidney was able to support the reabsorption of 85–90% of the filtered sodium (9, 16). In isolated perfused proximal tubules from the rabbit, the use of glucose, lactate, and alanine (GLA) as metabolic substrates maintained fluid transport at the same rate as serum in the bathing medium (28). Because alanine (see below) and glucose are not good metabolic fuels in this renal segment, most of the energy is derived from the lactate in the GLA substrates. In a suspension of proximal tubules from the rabbit, the GLA substrate mixture provided adequate metabolic support for the tubules under normal conditions (32). However, when the respiratory system was stressed by addition of nystatin (a polyene antibiotic that increases the ionic permeability of the plasma membrane, thereby causing increased (Na^+, K^+)-ATPase turnover due to the increase in intracellular Na), GLA could only support 71% of maximal respiration (32).

The main metabolic fates of lactate are oxidation to CO_2 and conversion to glucose. Much of lactate oxidation seems to occur in the proximal tubules (15), because transport systems for lactate have been identified at the plasma membranes of this segment (6, 7). When added as sole substrate, some lactate appears in both end products (16, 17, 28, 69). In the presence of added fatty acids, lactate uptake and oxidation are inhibited (9), causing a conversion of most metabolized lactate into glucose (27, 28, 69). Therefore, it is unclear how important lactate is as a metabolic fuel for proximal function in vivo when fatty acids are normally present in the blood; under these conditions, its function may be mainly as principal gluconeogenic substrate.

Fatty Acids and Ketones

In blood, most fatty acids are bound to albumin and are therefore not filtered by the kidney. Entry into the tubular cells proceeds in vivo through the basolateral side. Some fatty acids utilize the organic acid pathway (4, 63), but, given the high lipid solubility of free fatty acids, most entry does not require specific proteinaceous transport pathways. Studies with the in vivo dog kidney have found a rapid uptake of ^{14}C-palmitate that is proportional to the blood palmitate concentration (5, 19, 24). However, the actual contribution of fatty-acid oxidation to the renal QO_2 has been difficult to estimate in vivo, due to label dilution by the high endogenous lipid content of the kidney (15). Only 5–10% of the label was found in [14]CO_2, most of it appearing in di- and triglycerides, phospholipids, and cholesterol esters (5, 15). Similarly, in slices from rabbit (39) and rat renal cortex (69), only about 25% of the ^{14}C from palmitate or oleate uptake appeared as [14]CO_2, whereas most of the label appeared in triglycerides and free fatty acids (69). In single proximal tubules from the rat kidney, [14]CO_2 formation from ^{14}C-palmitate was also low (36), possibly reflecting the same problems with label dilution. The amount of label dilution may vary among species and also appears to be a function of fatty-acid concentration, as seen by the distribution of label from ^{14}C-oleate in a suspension of rat proximal tubules (71). In contrast to the in vivo dog kidney, uptake was saturated in proximal tubules at about 0.6 mM oleate (Figure 3), which is within the normal range found in blood (19). Furthermore, at low concentrations, most of the oleate taken up by the tubules was converted to CO_2, whereas the percentage oxidized decreased with increasing fatty-acid concentration (Figure 3).

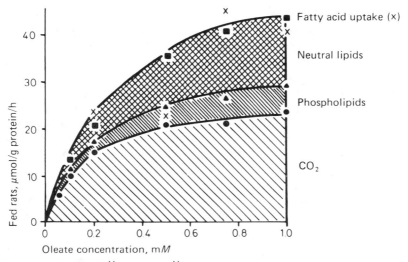

Figure 3 Distribution of ^{14}C-label from ^{14}C-oleate uptake as a function of oleate concentration in rat proximal tubules. Reproduced with permission from (71).

Based on the rate of $^{14}CO_2$ formation for the in vivo dog kidney and the high respiratory quotient (RQ) found in this tissue (14), Cohen & Kamm (15) concluded that the oxidation of fatty acids does not support a major portion of total renal work in vivo. However, studies from other laboratories found a low RQ for the kidney cortex (18, 33, 69), suggesting extensive oxidation of fatty acids in cortical segments. Furthermore, inhibitors of fatty acid oxidation caused a profound depression in renal function in the intact dog kidney (37, 64). Weidemann & Krebs (69) calculated that exogenous oleate metabolism could account for up to 50% of the QO_2, whereas the oxidation of endogenous fats could provide respiratory fuel for the other 50% of respiration in cortical slices from the rat kidney.

The oxidation of shorter-chain fatty acids seems to proceed at a faster rate than that of oleate and palmitate. Octanoate infused into the in vivo dog kidney is rapidly decarboxylated, producing large amounts of $^{14}CO_2$ (24). Similarly, more than 50% of ^{14}C-butyrate metabolized by rat kidney cortex slices appears as $^{14}CO_2$ (69), most of the rest being converted to acetoacetate. Based on these results, Weidemann & Krebs (69) calculated that either acetoacetate or butyrate could provide up to 80% of the cortical respiratory fuel. In suspensions of proximal rabbit renal tubules, valerate, butyrate, and acetoacetate are able to be metabolized at a sufficiently rapid rate to support respiration at close to 100% of the respiratory capacity of the tubular mitochondria when the (Na^+,K^+)-ATPase activity is stimulated by addition of nystatin (32). Therefore, a variety of studies using cortical preparations have demonstrated that fatty acids and ketones constitute the major source of metabolic energy in these segments (71).

Krebs Cycle Intermediates

The proximal tubules reabsorb Krebs cycle intermediates through Na-dependent transport systems identified at the brush border membranes (72). In addition, basolateral transport systems have also been identified (34). Most of these intermediates can be transported directly into the mitochondria, others after interconversion (38). Within the mitochondrial matrix they can be utilized as respiratory fuel for the Krebs cycle. The intermediate 2-oxoglutarate has been shown to be an excellent metabolic substrate for various kidney preparations (20, 43). Similarly, succinate, malate, and oxaloacetate have been shown to increase the rate of fluid reabsorption from rat renal proximal tubules (43). Klein et al (36) found that citrate, 2-oxoglutarate, succinate, and malate are decarboxylated to CO_2 at significant rates in single rat proximal tubules.

The metabolism of citrate has received special attention because its excretion in the urine is highly dependent on the acid-base status of the animal and because the kidney is important in the regulation of plasma citrate levels (15, 59). In various mammalian species, the kidney metabolizes not only all the reabsorbed citrate but also some taken up through the peritubular side (59). The major end products of citrate metabolism are CO_2 and glucose, but the proportion of each of these could vary with metabolic and hormonal status. It has been estimated that citrate provides 10–15% of the respiratory fuel of the kidney (8, 15, 47, 59). Mitochondrial citrate metabolism increases dramatically with decreased pH and bicarbonate concentration and, conversely, decreases when pH and bicarbonate concentration rise, as shown in Figure 4. A rise in pH of only 0.3 units inhibits citrate oxidation by almost 50% (57). Simpson & Hager (60) found that the mitochondrial accumulation of citrate, 2-oxoglutarate, malate, and glutamate was strongly dependent on pH in a bicarbonate medium, being significantly larger at low- than at high-bicarbonate concentrations.

Amino Acids

At normal blood concentrations of amino acids, the kidney is involved in the metabolism of glutamine, alanine, glycine, serine, and arginine (15). At higher blood concentrations, the kidney has the potential for metabolism of most other amino acids. The filtered amino acids essentially undergo complete reabsorption by the proximal tubules, where they can be potentially metabolized (44). In addition, certain amino acids are taken up by the peritubular side in proximal as well as distal segments (15, 56).

The main amino acid metabolized by proximal tubules is glutamine, which is an important respiratory fuel in this segment, as determined in tubule suspensions (27), single isolated tubules (36), and isolated mitochondria (54, 58). During metabolic acidosis, most of the glutamine is metabolized to NH_3 and 2-oxoglutarate, which is subsequently converted to CO_2 or glucose. Not surprisingly, the gluconeogenic rate and the rate of ammonia production from

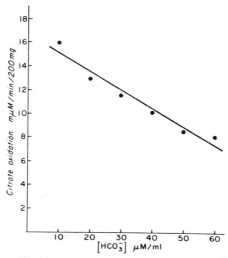

Figure 4   Citrate oxidation rate as a function of bicarbonate cencentration in the bathing medium in renal cortex slices. Reproduced with permission from (57).

glutamine are closely linked (15). The control of glutamine uptake and metabolism by acid-base status may involve changes in phosphate-dependent glutaminase activity (15) and the ΔpH across the inner mitochondrial membrane (58). Its discussion is beyond the scope of this review, but is treated in detail in one of the other reviews in this section (38).

Other amino acids do not serve as important metabolic fuels for the kidney, although the role of alanine is still unclear (15, 44). The kidney synthesizes alanine and other amino acids in significant amounts and can, therefore, influence their whole body homeostasis. These topics have been reviewed in detail elsewhere (15, 44).

INTERACTIONS AMONG METABOLIC SUBSTRATES

Of the substrates normally present in arterial blood, the dog kidney utilizes—at significant rates—glucose, lactate, palmitate, citrate, and glutamine (15). The uptake of each substrate into renal cells in vivo appears to be proportional to their respective concentration in blood (4, 19). The uptake rate of most substrates greatly exceeds their oxidation rate (4, 15, 17, 19). This is due to the multiple metabolic fates of each of the substrates, which include not only oxidation but also interconversion.

Similarly, in various cortical preparations, the uptake of each substrate generally exceeds the oxidation rate, because substrate interconversions occur at a significant rate (27, 69–71). The rates of each of these processes for particular substrates have been shown to depend on the presence of other substrates. For example, as described earlier, the oxidation of lactate is greatly inhibited by the presence of fatty acids, most of the lactate being instead converted into glucose (27, 28, 69). Similarly, ketones, oleate and lactate inhibit glutamine uptake, metabolism, and the rate of ammonia formation (25, 27, 68). In contrast, glutamine increases lactate uptake and, furthermore, lactate and glutamine increase oleate uptake and incorporation into triglycerides (27). These and other observations demonstrate that substrate interactions occur extensively in proximal tubules. Therefore, the proportion of each substrate used as respiratory fuel cannot be directly ascertained through uptake studies, requiring instead detailed experiments accounting for the fate of all the metabolized ^{14}C (27, 69, 71). These types of investigations indicate that fatty acids are the preferred fuel oxidized by proximal tubules, even in the presence of other metabolic substrates (27, 69, 71).

The substrate mix normally present in vivo provides the kidney with ample oxidizable substrate to maintain its cellular ATP levels. Even a minimal substrate mix, containing glucose, lactate, and alanine is sufficient to maintain normal ATP levels (32) and fluid absorption (28) in proximal tubules. Addition of other substrates does not alter the fluid absorption rate (28), and the ATP levels either remain unchanged (28) or increase slightly (11). However, addition of fatty acids or succinate produce dramatic alterations in other parameters, namely large increases in the rates of gluconeogenesis (28), phosphate reabsorption (29), and triglyceride formation from fatty acids (27, 70). The mechanisms involved in these alterations have been studied extensively for gluconeogenesis (15, 69) and triglyceride synthesis (27, 70); however, the interactions among the various metabolic pathways are complex and incompletely understood (28). Studies in liver have shown that particular metabolic substrates can affect the whole metabolic profile of the cells, which include levels of intermediate metabolic products, enzymes, cofactors, redox state, and intracellular compartmentation (11, 52, 55).

The dependence of the various proximal transport processes on metabolism is complex and difficult to understand, especially when only a single metabolic factor is considered. For example, the dependence on total cellular ATP is variable. Graded inhibition of ATP levels elicits greater inhibition in transepithelial phosphate transport than in fluid or glucose transport (30) in proximal tubules. Similarly, gluconeogenesis shows a steep dependence on ATP, but this is in turn affected by the metabolic substrate present (28). The aforementioned increase in phosphate transport upon addition of fatty acids or succinate cannot be attributed solely to the concurrent small increase in ATP (29). Therefore, it is quite possible that a number of factors closely associated with cellular metabolism affect each of these processes differentially. Some of the factors that have been considered to alter membrane permeability in a number of epithelial tissues are: cyclic AMP (49), energy metabolism (41, 50), calcium concentration (62), pH (10), and others. More subtle effects are obtained by alterations in compartmentation of metabolic intermediates within the various intracellular organelles (1, 11).

The overall picture that emerges from these considerations is that metabolic substrates provide not just the respiratory fuel to produce ATP, but also affect an array of metabolic variables that can control a variety of cellular processes. This multitude of potential variables makes the study of the regulation of active tubular transport by metabolic substrates one of the most interesting but difficult areas of epithelial transport.

ACKNOWLEDGMENTS

The author wishes to thank Drs. M. E. Chamberlin, S. P. Soltoff, and R. Schnellmann for critically reading the manuscript and Ms. E. Holmes for the typing. This work was supported in part by NIH Grant AM 26816.

Literature Cited

1. Akerboom, T. P. M., Bookelman, H., Zuurendonk, P. R., van der Meer, R., Tager, J. M. 1978. Intramitochondrial and extramitochondrial concentrations of adenine nucleotides and inorganic phosphate in isolated hepatocytes from fasted rats. *Eur. J. Biochem.* 84:413–20
2. Balaban, R. S., Mandel, L. J., Soltoff, S., Storey, J. M. 1980. Coupling of Na-K-ATPase activity to aerobic respiratory rate in isolated cortical tubules from the rabbit kidney. *Proc. Natl. Acad. Sci. USA* 77:447–51
3. Balaban, R. S., Soltoff, S., Storey, J. M., Mandel, L. J. 1980. Improved renal cortical tubule suspension: Spectrophotometric study of O_2 delivery. *Am. J. Physiol.* 238:F50–59
4. Barac-Nieto, M., Cohen, J. J. 1968. Nonesterified fatty acid uptake by dog kidney: effects of probenecid and chlorothiazide. *Am. J. Physiol.* 215:98–107
5. Barac-Nieto, M., Cohen, J. J. 1971. The metabolic fates of palmitate in the dog kidney in vivo. Evidence for incomplete oxidation. *Nephron* 8:488–99
6. Barac-Nieto, M., Kinne, R., Murer, H. 1980. Lactate sodium cotransport in rat renal brush border membranes. *Am. J. Physiol.* 239:F496–506
7. Barac-Nieto, M., Murer, H., Kinne, R. 1982. Asymmetry in the transport of lactate by basolateral and brush border membranes of rat kidney cortex. *Pfluegers Arch.* 392:366–71
8. Baruch, S. B., Burich, R. L., Eun, C. E.,

King, V. F. 1975. Renal metabolism of citrate. *Med. Clin. North Am.* 59:569–82
9. Baverel, G., Bonnard, M., de Castanet, E. D'A., Pellet, M. 1978. Lactate and pyruvate metabolism in isolated renal tubules of normal dogs. *Kidney Int.* 14:567–75
10. Biagi, B., Kubota, T., Sohtell, M., Giebisch, G. 1981. Intracellular potentials in rabbit proximal tubules perfused in vitro. *Am. J. Physiol.* 240:F200–10
11. Brazy, P. C., Mandel, L. J., Gullans, S. R., Soltoff, S. P. 1984. Interactions between phosphate and oxidative metabolism in proximal renal tubules. *Am. J. Physiol.* In press
12. Burg, M. B. 1982. Introduction: background and development of microperfusion technique. *Kidney Int.* 22:417–24
13. Burg, M., Patlak, C., Green, N., Villey, D. 1976. Organic solutes in fluid absorption by renal proximal convoluted tubules. *Am. J. Physiol.* 231(2):627–37
14. Cohen, J. J. 1960. High respiratory quotient of dog kidney in vivo. *Am. J. Physiol.* 199:560–68
15. Cohen, J. J., Kamm, D. E. 1981. Renal metabolism: relation to renal function. In *The Kidney*, ed. B. M. Brenner, F. C. Rector, pp. 144–248. Philadelphia: Saunders. 2nd ed.
16. Cohen, J. J., Kook, Y. J., Little, J. R. 1977. Substrate-limited function and metabolism of the isolated perfused rat kidney: Effects of lactate and glucose. *J. Physiol.* 266:103–21

17. Cohen, J. J., Merkens, L. S., Peterson, O. W. 1980. Relation of Na$^+$ reabsorption to utilization of O$_2$ and lactate in the perfused rat kidney. *Am. J. Physiol.* 238:F415–27

18. Dickens, F., Simer, F. 1930. The metabolism of normal and tumor tissue. II. The respiratory quotient, and the relationship of respiration to glycolysis. *Biochem. J.* 24:1301–26

19. Dies, F., Herrera, J., Matos, M., Avelar, E., Ramos, G. 1970. Substrate uptake by the dog kidney in vivo. *Am. J. Physiol.* 218:405–10

20. Fonteles, M. C., Cohen, J. J., Black, A. J., Wertheim, S. J. 1983. Support of kidney function by long-chain fatty acids derived from renal tissue. *Am. J. Physiol.* 244:F235–46

21. Forster, J., Steels, P. S., Boulpaep, E. L. 1980. Organic substrate effects on and heterogeneity of Necturus proximal tubule function. *Kidney Int.* 17:479–90

22. Frega, N. S., Weinberg, J. M., Ross, B. D., Leaf, A. 1977. Stimulation of sodium transport by glucose in the perfused rat kidney. *Am. J. Physiol.* 233(3):F235–40

23. Gerlach, E., Bader, W., Schwoerer, W. 1961. Uber den Stoffwechsel saureroslicher Phosphor-verbindungen in der Rattenniere. *Arch. Ges. Physiol.* 272:407–33

24. Gold, M., Spitzer, J. J. 1964. Metabolism of free fatty acids by myocardium and kidney. *Am. J. Physiol.* 206(1):153–58

25. Goldstein, L., Solomon, R. J., Perlman, D. F., McLaughlin, P. M., Taylor, M. A. 1982. Ketone body effects on glutamine metabolism in isolated kidneys and mitochondria. *Am. J. Physiol.* 243: F181–87

26. Guder, W. G., Purschel, S. 1980. The intracellular compartmentation of metabolites in isolated kidney cortex tubules. *Int. J. Biochem.* 12:63–67

27. Guder, W. G., Wirthensohn, G. 1979. Metabolism of isolated kidney tubules: Interactions between lactate, glutamine, and oleate metabolism. *Eur. J. Biochem.* 99:577–84

28. Gullans, S. R., Brazy, P. C., Dennis, V. W., Mandel, L. J. 1984. Interactions between gluconeogenesis and sodium transport in rabbit proximal tubule. *Am. J. Physiol.* 246(15):F859–69

29. Gullans, S. R., Brazy, P. C., Mandel, L. J., Dennis, V. W. 1984. Stimulation of phosphate transport in the proximal tubule by metabolic substrates. *Am. J. Physiol.* In press

30. Gullans, S. R., Brazy, P. C., Soltoff, S. P., Dennis, V. W., Mandel, L. J. 1982. Metabolic inhibitors: Effects on metabolism and transport in the proximal tubule. *Am. J. Physiol.* 243(12):F133–40

31. Gullans, S. R., Harris, S. I., Mandel, L. J. 1984. Glucose-dependent respiration in suspensions of rabbit cortical tubules. *J. Memb. Biol.* 78:257–62

32. Harris, S. I., Balaban, R. S., Barrett, L., Mandel, L. J. 1981. Mitochondrial respiratory capacity and Na$^+$- and K$^+$-dependent adenosine triphosphatase-mediated ion transport in the intact renal cell. *J. Biol. Chem.* 256:10319–28

33. Hohenegger, M., Wittmann, G., Dahlheim, H. 1973. Oxidation of fatty acids by different zones of the rat kidney. *Pfluegers Arch.* 341:105–12

34. Jørgensen, K. E., Kragh-Hansen, U., Røigaard-Petersen, H., Iqbal Sheikh, M. 1983. Citrate uptake by basolateral and luminal membrane vesicles from rabbit kidney cortex. *Am. J. Physiol.* 244: F686–95

35. Kinne, R. 1979. Metabolic correlates of tubular transport. In *Membrane Transport in Biology,* ed. G. Giebisch, D. C. Tosteson, H. H. Ussing, 4B:529–62. Berlin: Springer-Verlag

36. Klein, K. L., Wang, M.-S., Torikai, S., Davidson, W. D., Kurokawa, K. 1981. Substrate oxidation by isolated single-nephron segments of the rat. *Kidney Int.* 20:29–35

37. Kleinman, J. G., Mandelbaum, J., Levin, M. L. 1973. Renal functional effects of 4-pentenoic acid, an inhibitor of fatty acid oxidation. *Am. J. Physiol.* 224(1):95–101

38. LaNoue, K. F., Schoolwerth, A. 1985. Transport of metabolic substrates in renal mitochondria. *Ann. Rev. Physiol.* 47: 143-71

39. Lee, J. B., Vance, V. K., Cahill, G. F. Jr. 1962. Metabolism of ^{14}C-labeled substrates by rabbit kidney cortex and medulla. *Am. J. Physiol.* 203(1):27–36

40. Lehninger, A. L. 1975. *Biochemistry.* New York: Worth. 2nd ed.

41. Lipton, P., Edelman, I. S. 1971. Effects of aldosterone and vasopressin on electrolytes of toad bladder epithelial cells. *Am. J. Physiol.* 221:733–41

42. Mandel, L. J., Balaban, R. S. 1981. Stoichiometry and coupling of active transport to oxidative metabolism in epithelial tissues. *Am. J. Physiol.* 240: F357–71

43. Maude, D. L. 1970. Effects of substrates and inhibitors of the tricarboxylic acid cycle on proximal tubular fluid transport in vitro. *Biochim. Biophys. Acta* 215: 216–19

44. Mitch, W. E., Chesney, R. W. 1983. Amino acid metabolism by the kidney. *Mineral Electrolyte Metab.* 9:190–202

45. Morel, F. 1981. Sites of hormone action in the mammalian nephron. *Am. J. Physiol.* 240:F159–64

46. Needleman, P., Passonneau, J. V., Lowry, O. H. 1968. Distribution of glucose and related metabolites in rat kidney. *Am. J. Physiol.* 215:655–59

47. Nieth, H., Schollmeyer, P. 1966. Substrate-utilization of the human kidney. *Nature* 209:1244–45

48. Oliver, J. 1944. New directions in renal morphology: a method, its results, and its future. *Harvey Lectures* 40:102

49. Orloff, J., Handler, J. S. 1967. The role of adenosine 3',5'-phosphate in the action of antidiuretic hormone. *Am. J. Med.* 42:757

50. Palmer, L. G., Edelman, I. S., Lindemann, B. 1980. Current-voltage analysis of apical sodium transport in toad urinary bladder: effects of inhibitors of transport and metabolism. *J. Membr. Biol.* 57:59–71

51. Pitts, R. F. 1966. The renal metabolism of ammonia. *Physiologist* 9:97

52. Rabkin, M., Blum, J. J. 1984. Quantitative analysis of intermediary metabolism in hepatocytes incubated in the presence and absence of glucagon with a mixture containing glucose, ribose, fructose, alanine, and acetate. *Biochem. J.* In press

53. Ross, B. D., Epstein, F. H., Leaf, A. 1973. Sodium reabsorption in the perfused rat kidney. *Am. J. Physiol.* 225(5):1165–71

54. Schoolwerth, A. C., LaNoue, K. F. 1980. The role of microcompartmentation in the regulation of glutamate metabolism by rat kidney mitochondria. *J. Biol. Chem.* 255:3403–11

55. Sies, E. A., Brocks, D. G., Lattke, H. K., Wieland, O. H. 1977. Effect of glucagon on metabolite compartmentation in isolated rat liver cells during gluconeogenesis from lactate. *Biochem. J.* 166:225–35

56. Silverman, M., Vinay, P., Shinobu, L., Gougoux, A., Lemieux, G. 1981. Luminal and antiluminal transport of glutamine in dog kidney: Effect of metabolic acidosis. *Kidney Int.* 20:359–65

57. Simpson, D. P. 1967. Regulation of renal citrate metabolism by bicarbonate ion and pH: observations in tissue slices and mitochondria. *J. Clin. Invest.* 46:225–38

58. Simpson, D. P. 1980. Modulation of glutamine transport and metabolism in mitochondria from dog renal cortex. Influence of pH and bicarbonate. *J. Biol. Chem.* 255:7123–28

59. Simpson, D. P. 1983. Citrate excretion: a window on real metabolism. *Am. J. Physiol.* 244:F223–34

60. Simpson, D. P., Hager, S. R. 1979. pH and bicarbonate effects on mitochondrial anion accumulation. Proposed mechanism for changes in renal metabolite levels in acute acid-base disturbances. *J. Clin. Invest.* 63:704–12

61. Deleted in proof

62. Taylor, A., Windhager, E. E. 1979. Possible role of cytosolic calcium and Na-Ca exchange in regulation of transepithelial sodium transport. *Am. J. Physiol.* 236:F505–12

63. Trimble, M. E. 1982. Long chain fatty acid transport by the perfused rat kidney. *Renal Physiol.* 5:136–42

64. Trimble, M. E., Bowman, R. H. 1973. Renal Na$^+$ and K$^+$ transport: effects of glucose, palmitate, and α-bromopalmitate. *Am. J. Physiol.* 225:1057–62

65. Vandewalle, A., Kopfer-Hobelsberger, B., Heidrich, H-G. 1982. Cortical cell populations from rabbit kidney isolated by free-flow electrophoresis: characterization by measurement of hormone-sensitive adenylate cyclase. *J. Cell Biol.* 92:505–13

66. Vandewalle, A., Wirthensohn, G., Heidrich, H-G., Guder, W. G. 1981. Distribution of hexokinase and phosphoenolpyruvate carboxykinase along the rabbit nephron. *Am. J. Physiol.* 240:F492–500

67. Vinay, P., Gougoux, A., Lemieux, G. 1981. Isolation of a pure suspension of rat proximal tubules. *Am. J. Physiol.* 241:F403–11

68. Vinay, P., Lemieux, G., Cartiers, P., Ahmall, M. 1976. Effect of fatty acids on renal ammoniagenesis in in vivo and in vitro studies. *Am. J. Physiol.* 231:880–87

69. Weidemann, M. J., Krebs, H. A. 1969. The fuel of respiration of rat kidney cortex. *Biochem. J.* 112:149–66

70. Wirthensohn, G., Guder, W. G. 1980. Triacylglycerol metabolism in isolated rat kidney cortex tubules. *Biochem. J.* 186:317–24

71. Wirthensohn, G., Guder, W. G. 1983. Renal lipid metabolism. *Mineral Electrolyte Metab.* 9:203–11

72. Wright, E., 1985. Transport of metabolic intermediates across renal brush border membrane vesicles. *Ann. Rev. Physiol.* 47:127-41

Ann. Rev. Physiol. 1985. 47:103–25

TRANSPORT OF METABOLIC SUBSTRATES BY THE PROXIMAL NEPHRON

James A. Schafer and James C. Williams, Jr.

Nephrology Research and Training Center, Departments of Physiology and Biophysics, and Medicine, University of Alabama in Birmingham, Birmingham, Alabama 35294

INTRODUCTION

Given the high filtered load of metabolic substrates in the mammal, a considerable amount of energy must be expended in their tubular reabsorption, and the rate of transport must be great enough to ensure nearly complete recovery even at rapid flow rates. Most reabsorbed organic solutes are transported against a concentration gradient from the tubular lumen into proximal tubular cells by cotransport with Na^+ down its electrochemical potential gradient, and they move by facilitated but passive mechanisms from the cell to the interstitial space. Organic solutes for which there are no reabsorptive mechanisms are generally secreted, but the secretion process, although it may also derive energy from the Na^+ electrochemical potential gradient, appears to have a low specificity in order to accommodate a wide variety of solutes that include the by-products of metabolism and foreign substances.

In this review, we concentrate on the more recent findings related to these mechanisms. The reader is referred to previous reviews that provide a fuller historical perspective to the study of transport mechanisms for organic solutes in the proximal tubule (41, 69, 93, 102, 107, 110, 117, 128–130, 144, 145). Because of the considerable recent progress in determining the molecular mechanisms involved in glucose absorption, this process is the focus of the greater part of this article, in which we examine the specificity, kinetics, energetics, and attempts at isolation and reconstitution of the glucose transporter. [In this same volume, E. M. Wright also examines similar mechanisms that are involved in the reabsorption of mono- and dicarboxylic acids (155).]

0066-4278/85/0315-0103$02.00

103

Although the major emphasis of recent research has clearly been on the molecular mechanisms of organic solute transport, it has become clear that these membrane-localized processes have consequences that must be examined in the wider context of the epithelial cells themselves and the overall operation of the proximal nephron. In the final section, we discuss organic solute transport in the context of regional specialization, effects on salt and water absorption, glomerulotubular balance, and the regulation of normal cell volume and composition in the proximal nephron.

GLUCOSE TRANSPORT

General Principles

Early studies using both in vitro slices of renal cortex (74) and micropuncture (146) demonstrated that the active transport of sugars was dependent on Na^+, and it was generally assumed that a secondary active uptake of the sugar might be driven by the inward-directed Na^+ electrochemical potential gradient, as in the small intestine (24). Active uptake of the sugar into tubular cells from the lumen was demonstrated in the classic studies of Tune & Burg (135). Both the proximal convoluted and proximal straight tubule actively absorb glucose, and in the former segment the intracellular glucose concentration was found to be higher than the extracellular.

In early studies with brush border membrane vesicles, it was shown that entry of D-glucose was accelerated by the presence of Na^+, and that when an inward-directed Na^+ concentration gradient was initially present glucose could be transiently accumulated to concentrations in excess of the extravesicular concentration (the so-called "overshoot") (3, 12, 19, 70). Examination of basolateral membrane vesicles from rabbit renal cortex also showed a stereo-specific uptake of D-glucose, but in this case there was only marginal acceleration in the presence of Na^+, with no overshoot (70, 132). In addition, the brush border membrane site was found to be inhibited by pholorizin at low concentrations, whereas the basolateral membrane site was much less sensitive to phlorizin but more sensitive to inhibition by phloretin (70).

Specificity

The specificities of both the luminal and the basolateral glucose transporters as determined in isolated membrane preparations generally confirm those suggested by cortical slice data (73), microperfusion (115, 146), and multiple indicator–dilution methods in vivo (131). The Na^+-dependent system in the brush border transports the D-stereoisomers of glucose, galactose, and α- or β-methyl-D-glucoside, but 2-deoxy-D-glucose is only poorly transported, although the latter is still debated for some species (131). The specificity pattern for the glucose carrier is the same as observed for the intestinal carrier and is consistent with minimum requirements for a pyranose ring with hydroxyls in the glucose configuration at the C2 and C3 positions (3, 67, 131).

The basolateral membrane system has been examined in far less detail than the luminal, largely because of the greater difficulties in obtaining a high-yield preparation of pure membranes. However, all data at present indicate that this system shares most of the characteristics of the passive, facilitated glucose transport mechanism observed in a variety of cells including the erythrocyte, adipocyte, and muscle. Data from isolated mammalian tubules (73), multiple indicator–dilution in vivo (131), as well as basolateral membrane vesicles (131, 132) have shown that the system is shared by 2-deoxy-D-glucose and D-glucose, but has a poor affinity for α-methyl-D-glucoside. These results have been interpreted to indicate a requirement for a hydroxyl in the C1 position of a pyranose ring, but not a C2 hydroxyl.

Electrogenicity

The ability of an inward-directed Na^+ concentration gradient to drive glucose accumulation into brush border membranes requires that Na^+ be cotransported with the sugar, as demonstrated by an increased $^{22}Na^+$ flux associated with the transport of D-glucose (13, 14, 70). Furthermore, Hilden & Sacktor (50) showed that a large inward-directed gradient of D-glucose could drive a transient accumulation of $^{22}Na^+$ in brush border membrane vesicles. The system could operate in an electroneutral fashion in which the Na^+ is accompanied by a cotransported anion, or the carrier could transport net charge. If the carrier transfers positive charge (e.g. Na^+) inward or the equivalent of negative charge outward, then the sugar-uptake process could be energized by the membrane voltage as well as the Na^+ concentration gradient, i.e. by the potential energy inherent in the total Na^+ electrochemical potential gradient.

Charge transfer during sugar uptake in the intact epithelial cell would be expected to cause depolarization of the normal, cell-negative luminal membrane voltage. This effect was first demonstrated using intracellular microelectrodes in the newt proximal tubule (87), and in the rat proximal convoluted tubule Frömter and his collaborators (38, 115) demonstrated that the depolarization was due to an increase in the apical membrane conductance due to the enhancement of Na^+ entry by cotransport with the sugar. By using the magnitude of the apical membrane depolarization as an index of the rate of sugar-Na^+ cotransport with varying perfusate compositions in both the lumen and peritubular capillary network, Samarzija et al (115) were also able to confirm the specificity and kinetics of the transporter that had been observed in previous studies (146).

In brush border membrane vesicles, charge transfer with sugar uptake would produce a transient polarization of the vesicle with the intravesicular space positive, and this voltage would tend to limit the entry of sugar and Na^+ to the rate at which an anion could enter by a parallel pathway. In early studies it was shown that the rate of sugar-Na^+ entry was accelerated by the presence of more lipid permeant anions such as thiocyanate and retarded by the less permeant sulfate or isethionate (12, 70).

The electrogenic nature of the pump has also been demonstrated in brush border membrane vesicles by the effect of transmembrane voltage on the uptake process. By loading vesicles with K^+ and suspending them in a low-K^+ medium in the presence of the K^+-selective ionophore valinomycin, the resulting K^+ diffusion potential renders the vesicle interior negative relative to the medium in a manner similar to the generation of the normal membrane potential in the epithelial cell. Using this technique, Beck & Sacktor (12, 13) demonstrated that Na^+-dependent D-glucose uptake was greatly accelerated, and a transient accumulation of the sugar could be produced even when there was no transmembrane Na^+ concentration gradient. As expected, when the K^+ concentration gradient was reversed so as to produce an inside-positive voltage, uptake was retarded (13). An inside-negative voltage established by an outward-directed H^+ gradient in the presence of a protonophore also accelerated D-glucose entry in the same way as did the K^+ gradient in the presence of valinomycin (23). Both findings were entirely consistent with earlier studies on the glucose transporter in intestinal mucosa (95).

More recently it has been possible to measure membrane voltage changes associated with sugar transport in membrane vesicles using dyes of the carbocyanine type, which change their fluorescence or absorbance in association with changes in voltage (11). As noted by Wright (154), the use of these dyes has shown that all Na^+-dependent transport processes for neutral solutes are electrogenic. In particular, it has been found that the uptake of D-glucose into renal or intestinal brush border membrane vesicles results in a polarization of the membrane voltage with the intravesicular space positive (14, 79, 122, 154). The presence of more permeant anions reduces the extent of the hyperpolarization, and equal K^+ concentrations on both sides of the vesicle membrane in the presence of valinomycin prevents the voltage development, because the high K^+ conductance "short-circuits" the electrogenic transporter.

Stoichiometry and Kinetics

In their early studies of glucose transport in isolated perfused proximal tubules, Tune & Burg (135) observed that the maximal rate of D-glucose absorption by the convoluted segments was about ten-fold greater than that of the straight. These studies were extended by Barfuss & Schafer (7) using kinetic analysis of transepithelial glucose transport in the rabbit proximal nephrons. They demonstrated a high maximal transport rate (J_{max}) and a relatively high Michaelis constant (K_m) in the proximal convoluted tubule, but these parameters were significantly decreased in the early and late segments of the proximal straight tubule. Given these observations, Turner & Moran (139) isolated rabbit brush border membrane vesicles from both the outer cortex, where proximal convoluted tubules predominate, and from the outer medulla, where the S_3 segment of the proximal tubule but no convoluted segments are located. Their results showed that each vesicle preparation exhibited stereospecific D-glucose uptake, but the cortical transporter had a K_m of 6.0 mM, whereas that from the medulla had a K_m of 0.35 mM. In subsequent studies Turner & Moran (140, 141) showed that the cortical system had a Na^+-to-glucose (or phlorizin binding) stoichiometry of 1:1, whereas the medullary transporter had a 2:1 stoichiometry. The high- and low-affinity transporters have also been observed in mixed renal cortical and intestinal vesicle preparations (64, 142). [It is interesting to note that the $LLC-PK_1$ line of cultured epithelial cells, which were originally derived from pig kidney cortex, exhibits a 2:1 Na^+-to-glucose stoichiometry (92).]

The Na^+-to-glucose stoichiometry is of more than academic interest because it determines the maximal concentration gradient against which net glucose transport into the proximal tubule cell can occur. From a thermodynamic standpoint, the rate of energy expenditure required to transport glucose must be less than the rate of energy dissipation by Na^+ entry into the cell down its electrochemical potential gradient. Based on these thermodynamic considerations, if one assumes, for example, a typical intracellular Na^+ concentration of 10 mM and a luminal membrane voltage of -70 mV, the maximal glucose concentration ratio (cell-to-lumen) would be ~ 200 with a stoichiometry of 1:1 but $\sim 40,000$ with a stoichiometry of 2:1 (116, 141). Although these represent maximal theoretical glucose gradients, it is clear that the luminal glucose concentration could be reduced to nearly zero by the higher stoichiometry system.

The kinetics of glucose, phlorizin, and Na^+ interactions both in transport and binding to membrane vesicles have been analyzed in an attempt to describe the molecular details of the mechanisms. Although the transport site exhibits the characteristics classically ascribed to a membrane carrier molecule, including trans-stimulation of transport, the possibility of a large protein translocating across the membrane has been widely discounted. Alternatively, carrier-like behavior could be produced if a portion of the transporter were to relocate during transport and thus make the binding sites for glucose and Na^+ alternately available to one or the other side of the membrane (138). From analyses of the kinetics of transport and binding, it has been proposed that the transport site may act like a gated channel in which there are binding sites for Na^+ and the sugar (55, 66, 134). The model assumes that access to the transport sites would be regulated by movement of the gate portion of the molecule. Because of apparent directional asymmetry in the kinetics of transport activation by Na^+

and glucose, Hopfer & Groseclose (55) proposed that the transporter in both intestinal and renal brush border vesicles involves an ordered binding of Na^+ followed by glucose at the external membrane face, with Na^+ release before glucose at the inner surface. However, Turner and his associates (137, 138, 143) have argued that all of the effects can be explained by a model with random binding of the substrates. Despite this controversy, most investigators now agree that the Na^+-glucose-carrier complex transports the substrates in an electrically silent manner, and that the electrogenicity of the glucose transporter is the consequence of an "effective" negative-charge movement associated with the realignment of the carrier site after Na^+ and glucose have been released (2, 21, 52, 66, 99, 137, 143). This effective charge transfer might not involve the actual movement of a charged portion of the transport molecule through the membrane, but rather electrical events associated with the movement of, for example, a polar gate segment (134).

Purification and Reconstitution

Isolation and purification of the glucose-transport protein, a step crucial to study of its chemical and conformational characteristics, would also permit incorporation of the transporter into artificial lipid bilayer membranes in which its characteristics could be studied under well-defined conditions. In order to isolate and reconstitute the carrier, the membrane proteins are extracted using a detergent, separated chromatographically, and then fractions are analyzed for glucose-transport activity after incorporation into liposomes. By this procedure, with luck, the activity of the transporter incorporated can be increased several-fold above that observed in intact brush border membrane vesicles.

The first attempts to isolate the Na^+-dependent glucose transporter from renal brush border membranes produced a system that exhibited D-glucose specificity, with an overshoot accumulation of the sugar driven by an inward-directed Na^+ concentration gradient. Furthermore, the magnitude of the transport rate and the overshoot were proportional to the amount of protein incorporated (25, 34, 68, 100). However, as shown later, the protein incorporated was not exclusively the glucose-transport protein (76, 86). Thus in order to avoid the complications of possible parallel transport pathways, further purification of the extracted protein was sought (57, 71, 84, 123). The purified transporter reconstituted in liposomes made from pure lipids also exhibits all of the characteristics of the intact brush border vesicles (29, 77).

Although reconstitution and kinetic examination of the carrier molecule are important steps in defining the transport process, they provide less information concerning how the activity of this transporter may be regulated in the intact cell. Given the potential of cell culture techniques to select mutants with varying expression of transport and other biochemical activities, this methodology may provide essential information relating to the mechanisms involved in directing the Na^+-dependent glucose carrier to the luminal membrane and regulating its activity. It has been found that the LLC-PK$_1$ cell line, which was derived from porcine renal cortex, exhibits Na^+-dependent, active glucose uptake (see 94 for a recent review). Thus, examination and genetic manipulation of this system is becoming an important approach to the study of the active epithelial glucose transporter.

AMINO ACID TRANSPORT

Stop-flow (17), micropuncture (31, 147), and in vivo microperfusion studies (129) have shown clearly that all amino acids examined are actively absorbed in the early regions of the proximal tubule. It has been widely assumed from tissue uptake studies (106) that amino acids are absorbed by active transport across the luminal membrane followed by passive exit across the basolateral membrane. This hypothesis has been confirmed in the intact epithelium using perfusion of isolated segments of both convoluted and straight proximal tubules. In these experiments, it was shown that in the complete absence of amino acid in the bathing solution, amino acid is accumulated in the cell to concentrations higher than those in the luminal perfusate (5, 117, 118). The active step in the luminal membrane has been examined in considerably more detail using isolated brush border membrane vesicles. At least for the neutral amino acids, these studies have largely confirmed the conclusions reached for D-glucose transport, i.e. the neutral amino acids (preferentially the L-stereoisomers) are actively accumulated by an electrogenic cotransport with Na^+ so that the active uptake is driven by both the concentration and voltage components of the Na^+ electrochemical potential gradient (33, 35, 46, 89, 132, 145). With all of the neutral amino acids tested, an overshoot in the intravesicular concentration could be driven by either an inward-directed Na^+ concentration gradient or an inside-negative voltage. As discussed in greater detail below, the Na^+ dependency and electrogenicity of the mechanisms for acidic and basic amino acids are more complex. As described above for glucose, depolarization of the luminal membrane voltage following the luminal application of amino acids can be seen in electrophysiologic studies (58). Extensive intracellular voltage studies by Samarzija & Frömter (112–114) in the rat proximal tubule, using double-perfusion micropuncture techniques to control both the luminal and peritubular medium compositions, have confirmed the existence of at least five distinct transport sites in the luminal membrane as found in vesicle studies.

Neutral Amino Acids

Samarzija & Frömter (112) have shown that the luminal membrane is depolarized in rat proximal tubules by all of the neutral amino acids and that the magnitude of the depolarization is related to the luminal amino acid concentration in the manner predicted by Michaelis-Menten kinetics. By testing combinations of amino acids in the lumen, these investigators identified three neutral amino acid systems: one for all neutral amino acids except cystine, one for proline and hydroxy-proline, and one for the β-amino acids. Results in microperfused rat proximal tubules confirm the three systems but suggest that cystine shares a site with neutral amino acids (112, 129, 148, 149). Studies in brush border membrane vesicles show that cystine can cross this membrane either by the general neutral amino acid system or by the basic amino acid system (16).

There has been controversy regarding whether glycine shares the imino acid system or has an independent transport system. McNamara et al (89) observed high- and low-affinity transport systems that transport both L-proline and glycine, but Hammerman & Sacktor (46, 47) have found that glycine and L-proline were accumulated into brush border vesicles by separate, high-affinity systems with no indication of a low-affinity system. The discrepancy in these reports may relate to the manner in which competition for a common transport site is assessed. As in most classical competition studies, McNamara et al (89) measured the extent to which the presence of one amino acid diminished the transport of the other and used this as an index of the extent to which they shared a common transport site. However, because both amino acids depend on Na^+ cotransport for uptake, apparent competition can occur because the "competing" amino acid drives Na^+ into the vesicle, reducing or reversing the Na^+ electrochemical potential gradient (47, 117). A more direct indication that two solutes share a common transport site is the presence of accelerative exchange diffusion, i.e. acceleration of the uptake or exit of one amino acid by the presence of the second amino acid on the other (trans) side of the membrane. This method indicated no interaction between L-proline and glycine and supported the existence of a transport site specific to glycine (47). Other studies with brush border membrane vesicles also indicate that there are additional sites that transport dipeptides intact, although this process has not been demonstrated to be active (39).

Basic Amino Acids

Although a separate mechanism for the transport of basic amino acids (and to some extent cystine) has been identified in the brush border (45, 113, 133), there is still disagreement over whether the active transport of these cationic amino acids is driven exclusively by the membrane voltage or by the total Na^+ electrochemical potential gradient. The absorption of dibasic amino acids requires the presence of luminal Na^+ (113) and electrophysiological measurements show that dibasic amino acids depolarize the luminal membrane only in the presence of Na^+ (113). On the other hand, there is abundant evidence from brush border vesicle studies that basic amino acids can be accumulated even in the absence of Na^+ but in the presence of an inside-negative voltage produced either by a K^+ gradient in the presence of valinomycin or by a H^+ gradient in the presence of a protonophore (20, 45, 61, 133). In addition, although an inward-directed NaCl gradient drives accumulation of L-ornithine or L-arginine, an equivalent accumulation can be produced by chloride salts of several cations (61, 83).

The study of the basic amino acids using vesicle methodology is complicated by the fact that these amino acids exhibit exceptionally high binding to the vesicles (61, 133). In addition, even in the absence of Na^+, the basic amino acids exhibit rapid exchange diffusion in cortical slices (127) as well as membrane vesicles (45). At present a reasonable interpretation of the data is that there is a single transport system for basic amino acids that can operate either in the presence of Na^+ (45)—in which case the total Na^+ electrochemical potential gradient may contribute to uptake, as suggested by Hilden & Sacktor (51)—or in the absence of Na^+—in which case the accumulation of the cationic amino acid is driven only by the membrane voltage (45). In the latter case, the Na^+ site on the carrier may be satisfied by the basic group on the amino acid as first proposed from cortical slice data (37, 45).

Acidic Amino Acids

Uptake of these amino acids into brush border membrane vesicles is Na^+-dependent, and active accumulation of either aspartate or glutamate can be produced by an outward-directed K^+ gradient (18, 96, 109, 111, 124), although whether the process is electrogenic or not is unclear. [It is interesting that K^+ countertransport was the hypothesis originally advanced by Riggs et al (104) to explain active amino acid accumulation in Ehrlich ascites tumor cells.] Burckhardt et al (18) found that the uptake of L-glutamate was dependent on the transmembrane voltage only in the presence of K^+, and, using carbocyanine dyes, they observed net inward positive-charge movement. On the basis of these observations, Murer et al (96) proposed that the negatively charged amino acid was transported inward together with three Na^+ ions, with one K^+ returning. Thus the carrier cycle would give a net entry of one positive charge. On the other hand, Schneider et al (125) could find no evidence for electrogenicity even in the presence of K^+. More recently, Nelson et al (97) have shown that Na^+-dependent glutamate accumulation could also be stimulated by an outward-directed proton gradient, as previously suggested by Schneider & Sacktor (124). However, a low intravesicular pH tended to reduce the stimulation of uptake induced by intravesicular K^+, which suggested to the authors that H^+ could compete for the internal K^+ site (124). Although the weight of the evidence from brush border vesicles tends to support an electroneutral carrier cycle, electrophysiological studies in the in vivo rat proximal tubule have shown a Na^+-dependent depolarization of the luminal membrane in the presence of acidic amino acids in the lumen (114). Thus the question is at present unresolved.

Basolateral Membrane Transport Sites

Less is known about the mechanisms of amino acid transport across the basolateral membrane; however, results from isolated perfused tubule techniques have demonstrated that at least glycine and L-cystine are accumulated actively into the proximal straight tubule from the peritubular environment, and Na^+-dependence of this uptake was demonstrated in the case of glycine (10, 118). This mechanism may subserve primarily the maintenance of cellular amino acid pools necessary for metabolism (91, 117), because the uptake of amino acids from the lumen is limited by low luminal concentrations in the late proximal tubule. Therefore, basolateral uptake may not be related to the pathways that mediate amino acid efflux from the cell in net transepithelial absorption, although this point has not been examined directly. [It is again interesting to note that the Na^+-dependent active accumulation of neutral amino acids in the cultured LLC-PK$_1$ cell line is associated exclusively with their basolateral membranes! (101)]

In isolated basolateral membrane vesicles, the transport of various amino acids is saturable and exhibits relatively little Na^+ dependence (132), although Mircheff et al (91) have shown Na^+-dependent uptake of L-alanine in basolateral vesicles from rat intestine. In agreement with the former results, Samarzija & Frömter (112) found very little Na^+-dependent depolarization of the basolateral membrane when neutral or basic amino acids were added to the peritubular perfusate, but they could examine only the proximal convoluted tubule, whereas the active basolateral accumulation has been reported to occur in the straight segment (10, 22). In contrast to the studies of Samarzija & Frömter (113), in basolateral membrane vesicles it appears that there are both high- and low-affinity Na^+-dependent systems for basic amino acid exit and that they may also mediate cystine movement (103).

The transport of acidic amino acids across the peritubular membrane may be quite different from that of the neutral and basic amino acids. An inward-directed Na^+ gradient in basolateral membrane vesicles has been shown to drive an overshoot in the L-glutamate concentration, and this overshoot is further enhanced by an outward-directed K^+ gradient (111). In addition, Samarzija & Frömter (114) have shown that there is a Na^+-dependent depolarization of the basolateral membrane in the intact proximal tubule. Both studies indicate that acidic amino acids are probably actively accumulated across the basolateral membrane under normal conditions. The presence of active transport at both membrane surfaces may explain the high intracellular levels observed for the acidic amino acids as well as high luminal concentrations under stopped-flow conditions (22, 98).

SECRETION OF ORGANIC IONS

The proximal tubule has been shown to transport a remarkably wide variety of organic ions, of both natural and artificial origin. Some of these transport mechanisms, such as those described above for amino acids, show great specificity for the class of molecule that is transported. Other mechanisms, however, are responsible for the relatively nonspecific secretory transport of an array of organic ions, including many pharmaceutical agents as well as metabolic products. In general, it appears that a single system may be responsible for the tubular secretion of organic anions (researched primarily through studies using para-aminohippurate, or PAH). Another single system may be responsible for the secretion of cations (researched using tetraethylammonium, TEA, or N-methylnicotinomide, NMN). Recently, studies with membrane vesicles obtained from renal cortex have shed considerable light on the mechanisms underlying each of these systems, as discussed below.

Anion Transport

Studies using the stilbene anion exchange inhibitors [4,-acetamido-4'-isothiocyano-2,2' stilbene disulfonate (SITS) or 4,4'diidothiocyano-2,2'-stilbene disulfonate (DIDS)] first suggested that organic anion secretion might involve ion exchange–type transport systems (27, 78). This idea has been extensively investigated in studies using membrane vesicles and isolated tubules, with the conclusion that secretion of PAH is mediated at *both* basolateral and apical membranes by anion exchange systems. We will first consider the properties of the basolateral transport system.

As described in a recent review by Ross & Holohan (107), movement of PAH into the cell across the basolateral membrane is probably mediated by a system that combines PAH and Na^+ cotransport inward in exchange for exit of an anion. Although uptake of labeled PAH into basolateral membrane vesicles is stimulated by preloading the vesicles with unlabeled PAH (56, 63), overshoot of PAH accumulation is not observed. Similarly, uptake of PAH can be stimulated by the presence of an out-to-in Na^+ gradient (15, 72), but again, overshoot is not seen. If, however, the Na^+ gradient is imposed on anion-loaded vesicles, overshoot is observed, using either PAH-loaded vesicles from the rat (63) or OH^--loaded vesicles from rabbit (32). The mechanism proposed by Kasher et al (63) to explain these results is that of Na-coupled entry of PAH linked to exit of a counter-anion. Kasher et al (63) also presented data to suggest that there may be a coupling of two Na^+ to one PAH molecule that is transported. However, further evidence supporting this stoichiometry, as well as studies examining the question of whether or not a net transfer of charge occurs, have not yet been reported.

The specificity of the proposed Na-stimulated anion exchange mechanism has not been tested. Recently, however, Löw & Burckhardt (85) reported an anion exchanger in rat renal basolateral membrane that appears to handle PAH as well as sulfate, chloride, bicarbonate, thiosulfate, phosphate, formate, acetate, pyruvate, lactate, and oxalate. Transport was measured using only sulfate uptake, but all these anions showed probenecid-inhibitable trans-stimulation of sulfate uptake. Each anion also showed cis-inhibition of sulfate uptake, when uptake was driven by a Na gradient (out $\rightarrow$ in), a pH (or OH⁻) gradient (in $\rightarrow$ out), or a PAH gradient (in $\rightarrow$ out). If this system were identical to the PAH systems studied by Kasher et al (63) and Eveloff (32), it appears that a wide variety of anions could be transported across the basolateral membrane via the PAH secretory pathway.

This low specificity is also observed for the apical PAH-anion exchanger studied using vesicles from brush border membranes. Kahn et al (62) have shown an anion exchanger in rat brush border vesicles that transports PAH, urate, OH⁻, or bicarbonate. The exchange is sensitive to probenecid and unaffected by Na^+ gradients. Guggino et al (43) report a similar system in dog brush border vesicles but in addition show that the exchanger handles chloride as well as several carboxylic and small-chain fatty acids.

Thus, it appears that PAH secretion may occur by a mechanism something like the following: uptake of PAH into the cell occurs in the basolateral membrane, accompanied by uptake of Na^+ and in exchange for an intracellular anion. The intracellular anion might be bicarbonate, chloride, or an anion that is absorbed apically through a specific pathway (such as lactate). Movement of PAH across the apical membrane occurs in exchange for a luminal anion, such as chloride, urate, or lactate. In general, such a nonspecific anion transport system would lead to net secretion of any anion for which a specific apical uptake mechanism did *not* exist. Thus, we can see how the kidney can carry out enhanced excretion of a wide variety of foreign anions, such as pharmaceuticals, using a nonspecific system of secretion, without also losing valuable anion metabolites, for which there are specific absorption systems in the apical membrane.

Although the data cited above suggest that the secretory system for organic anions is the same in all species studied, we know that this is probably not the case. Work with snake tubules suggests that urate and PAH are secreted through separate systems (26), while the tubules of the rabbit (150) or the pig (121) apparently secrete these related anions via the same system. It may be that there are a series of anion exchangers in the proximal tubule with differing but overlapping specificities (150). In addition, it is clear that the apparent localization of the PAH secretory system to the pars recta [as in the rabbit (136)] is not seen in the pig, in which maximum PAH secretion is found in the pars convoluta (121).

Cation Transport

The renal organic cation secretory system has been recently reviewed by Rennick (102) and Ross & Holohan (107). In general, it is clear that although entry of the cation across the basolateral membrane may be a passive process, transport from the negative cell interior into the lumen of the tubule must be active. Again, it appears that entry of N-methyl-nicotinamide (NMN) probably occurs via a cation exchanger in the basolateral membrane (53). Exit of NMN across brush border membranes appears also to be mediated by a cation exchanger, driven by antiport with luminal H^+, which is in high concentration in the lumen of the proximal tubule due to the presence of an Na^+/H^+ exchange mechanism in the brush border membrane (108). In support of this hypothesis, Holohan & Ross (54) showed that uphill accumulation of NMN in brush border vesicles could be driven by a H^+ gradient, and McKinney (88) found that acetazolamide (an inhibitor of H^+ secretion) or luminal amiloride (an inhibitor of Na^+/H^+ exchange) reduced the rate of secretion of procainamide, an organic cation, in isolated, perfused rabbit tubules. It is also interesting to note that catecholamines, which are secreted via the NMN system (82), are recovered into synaptic vesicles via a proton-exchange system (1). Thus, the secretion of organic cations via a cation/proton exchange system is an attractive hypothesis, but as pointed out by McKinney (88), much work on characterization of this mechanism remains to be done.

RELATION OF ORGANIC SOLUTE TRANSPORT TO THE INTEGRATED FUNCTION OF THE PROXIMAL NEPHRON

When discussing the details of organic solute transport in isolated membrane systems it is easy to lose sight of the overall function of these processes as well as their integration with the other functions of the proximal tubule. It has become apparent that the transport characteristics of sugar and amino acid transport change with location along the nephron and that these changes are important to the conservation of metabolic substrates. However, organic-solute transport also impinges on other functions of the proximal nephron, including the reabsorption of salt and water and the maintenance of normal epithelial cell volume and composition.

Importance of Varying Transport Characteristics Along the Proximal Nephron

From recent studies in isolated rabbit tubules, specialization in the transport characteristics for glucose and amino acids along the proximal nephron have been demonstrated (5, 7). Both the transport capacity (J_{max}) and the Michaelis constant (K_m) are significantly greater in the proximal convoluted tubule than in the early or late segments of the proximal straight tubule, and the backleak permeability (which probably relates to the relatively nonspecific permeability of the paracellular pathway) decreases from the convoluted to the straight segment (5, 7). This arrangement is ideally suited to the absorption of large amounts of organic solutes in the early proximal tubule, where the load from glomerular filtration is high. On the other hand, the nearly complete reabsorption of amino acids and sugars depends upon the presence of a high-affinity system in concert with a low passive backleak permeability in the late proximal tubule. In the case of glucose, cystine, and glycine, we have demonstrated quantitatively that the transport characteristics of the late proximal tubule permit the load of these solutes delivered to the loop of Henle to be reduced to no more than that present in the final urine; that is, the proximal nephron can account for the normal total renal reabsorption (5, 7, 10, 118). The minimal luminal concentration of an actively transported solute will be uniquely determined by the kinetic characteristics of the active transport system and the permeability of the backleak pathway that shunts that system (5–7, 17). Thus it is easily understood that amino acidurias and glucosurias can result from increased nonspecific backleak or a deficiency in the low-capacity high-affinity system, as well as from the more commonly assumed deficiency in the high-capacity absorption system.

Effect on Salt and Water Absorption

From studies in isolated tubule segments it has been recognized that maximal rates of volume absorption are dependent on the presence of preferentially absorbed solutes, including amino acids and glucose in the luminal perfusate (19, 151). In the early proximal convoluted tubule, it is likely that a large fraction of the transepithelial osmotic gradient associated with volume absorption is due to the preferential absorption of these solutes (8, 9). This effect has been attributed not only to the increased absorption of solutes with potentially higher reflection coefficients (8, 9, 119), but also to the acceleration of luminal Na^+ entry by the organic solutes. Thus, increases in the filtered load of organic solutes can accelerate volume absorption directly and could be responsible for the increase in absolute proximal tubule salt and water absorption with increased filtration rate, i.e. glomerulotubular balance. According to conservative theoretical calculations, the effect of increased delivery of these preferentially absorbed solutes could account for only ~30% of ideal glomerulotubular balance, but nonetheless would certainly contribute to this regulatory mechanism (6).

On the other hand, there is an unexplained difference in the response of the in vivo proximal nephron and the in vitro perfused preparation to changes in perfusion rate. Several investigators have observed that volume and glucose absorption increase in parallel with increased luminal perfusion rate in vivo (28, 48, 75). In contrast, in the isolated perfused proximal straight tubule, there is no increase in volume absorption with perfusion rate (120). In the proximal convoluted tubule a modest correlation between volume absorption and flow is found, but only as perfusion rates are decreased below 8 nl min^{-1} (60), and in this situation there is depletion of preferentially absorbed solutes along the perfused segment (6, 60). Although glucose absorption increases with increased perfusion rate at low perfusate glucose concentrations (7, 135), this effect can be attributed entirely to the effect of axial flow on the average luminal glucose concentration and not to any increase in the intrinsic glucose-transport capacity (6, 7). However, in the in vivo rat proximal tubule, glucose transport is enhanced by increased perfusion rate, with no significant change in the average luminal glucose concentration, thus implying that the transport process itself is augmented in some way by increased axial flow (75).

There is also a direct correlation of the absorption of salt and organic solutes independent of glomerular filtration rate (GFR). It has been shown that volume expansion reduces salt, water, and glucose absorption in spite of an increase in GFR (49, 81, 105, 152). On the other hand, salt and water retention caused, for example, by an AV fistula or the initial response to hyperoncotic albumin solutions, produces increased absorption of both salt and glucose (4, 65). The mechanisms involved in these correlations of salt and glucose absorption, independent of filtered load, are probably indications of important physiologic processes that are as yet unexplained.

Effects of Organic-Solute Transport on Cell Volume and Composition

It is clear that the movement of glucose and amino acids into proximal tubule cells is accompanied by at least equimolar amounts of Na^+. Given the higher stoichiometries and more rapid transport rates observed for some of the dicarboxylic acids (155), the entry of Na^+ associated with organic solute absorption may be considerable, especially in the early proximal nephron. Because luminal Na^+ entry and thus Na^+ accessibility to the basolateral (Na^+,K^+)-ATPase appears to be rate-limiting to transepithelial salt and water transport, the stimulatory effect of organic solute delivery on volume absorption is easily understood. On the other hand, rapid Na^+ entry, and its potential variability with changes in the rate of organic solute delivery, require that the cell be able to regulate rapidly its intracellular solute composition. One may calculate that the rate of transepithelial Na^+ transport is sufficient to turn over the intracellular glucose, amino acid, and Na^+ pools several times a minute. Considering that the cell must resist swelling at least to prevent occlusion of the lumen, and that most cells probably "prefer" to have a normal ratio of Na^+ to K^+, mechanisms must be present to match transepithelial transport to luminal entry, as discussed by Schultz (126).

Most studies that address this problem have been carried out in amphibian epithelia, due to the larger cell size that permits easier use of intracellular voltage and ion-specific electrodes. In the Necturus small intestine, sugar transport is associated with a dramatic depolarization of the luminal membrane due to the associated increase in Na^+ conductance, but this is followed by a repolarization due to an increased conductance of the basolateral membrane (44). Using K^+-selective microelectrodes, this adaptation appears to result from a specific increase in the K^+ conductance of the basolateral membrane (42). Similarly, in the Necturus proximal tubule, although glucose depolarizes the apical membrane, there is no change in intracellular Na^+ or K^+ activities (30). These results indicate that the cell compensates for the increased Na^+ entry by a stimulation of basolateral K^+ conductance and a parallel increase in basolateral pump activity so that total cell solute content and thus volume remain constant. On the other hand, in the rat proximal convoluted tubule, the application of luminal glucose or amino acids results in a stable increase in the luminal membrane Na^+ conductance and an indefinite depolarization (30, 112–115). However, in his analysis of the electrical data, Frömter (38) was forced to assume that there was no change in the basolateral membrane conductance because it was not feasible to measure the individual membrane resistances directly. In addition, Burg et al (19) observed that proximal tubule cells show a definite volume increase when organic solutes are added to the luminal perfusate, in spite of an increase in basolateral pumping as demonstrated by the increased volume absorption. These results would indicate that the mammalian proximal tubule cell does not exhibit a complete compensation for the increase in luminal solute entry, and a new steady state with increased total intracellular solute must be achieved.

Adaptive Changes in Organic-Solute Transport

From the classical descriptions of sugar and amino acid transport as T_m-limited systems, one gains the impression of an invariant transport capacity of the proximal nephron for each solute. However, there is emerging evidence, both on the level of the organ itself and on the level of the cell and membranes, that substantive adaptation of transport can occur. Certainly, changes in the transport capacity of surviving nephrons have long been identified as a response to nephron loss or contralateral nephrectomy. Increases in the single-nephron transport maximum for glucose have been demonstrated to be a part of this response (80). In addition, development of increased renal amino acid absorption is associated with growth in the neonate (59, 90).

More acute effects on organic solute absorption have also been demonstrated in the adult animal with normal renal function. For example, administration of testosterone has also been shown to stimulate glucose and amino acid uptake in renal cortical slices, and it has been suggested that this stimulation involves an increase in intracellular calcium activity as a regulatory signal (40). Also, the uptake of L-glutamine, which is the primary amino acid involved in aminogenesis, has been found to be increased in proximal tubular cells as well as brush border *and basolateral* membrane vesicles obtained from animals with chronic acidosis (36, 153). It seems likely that such adaptive changes are constantly occurring in response to diet, the level of metabolic activity, and disease. For example, might one expect the diabetic with increased and variable filtered loads of glucose to exhibit an increased T_m for glucose per nephron and perhaps a shift toward more high-capacity, low-affinity transport systems in the late proximal nephron? Questions such as these are intriguing areas for future research that would combine techniques at both the individual membrane and integrative levels.

Literature Cited

1. Angelides, K. J. 1980. Transport of catecholamines by native and reconstituted rat heart synaptic vesicles. *J. Neurochem.* 35:949–62
2. Aronson, P. S. 1978. Energy-dependence of phlorizin binding to isolated renal microvillus membranes. Evidence concerning the mechanism of coupling between the electrochemical Na^+ gradient and sugar transport. *J. Membrane Biol.* 42:81–98
3. Aronson, P. S., Sactor, B. 1975. The Na^+ gradient-dependent transport of D-glucose in renal brush border membranes. *J. Biol. Chem.* 250:6032–39
4. Arruda, J. A., Westenfelder, C., Lockwood, R., Kurtzman, N. A. 1976. Glucose and bicarboante reabsorption in edematous dogs. *Am. J. Physiol.* 231:749–53
5. Barfuss, D. W., Schafer, J. A. 1979. Active amino acid absorption by proximal convoluted and proximal straight tubules. *Am. J. Physiol.* 236:F149–62
6. Barfuss, D. W., Schafer, J. A. 1979. Flow dependence of nonelectrolyte absorption in the nephron. *Am. J. Physiol.* 236:F163–74
7. Barfuss, D. W., Schafer, J. A. 1981. Differences in active and passive glucose transport along the proximal nephron. *Am. J. Physiol.* 240:F322–32
8. Barfuss, D. W., Schafer, J. A. 1984. Rate of formation and composition of absorbate from proximal nephron segments. *Am. J. Physiol.* 247:F117–29
9. Barfuss, D. W., Schafer, J. A. 1984. Hyperosmolality of absorbate from isolated rabbit proximal tubules. *Am. J. Physiol.* 247:F130–39
10. Barfuss, D. W., Mays, J. M., Schafer, J. A. 1980. Peritubular uptake and transepithelial transport of glycine in isolated proximal tubules. *Am. J. Physiol.* 238: F324–33
11. Bashford, C. L., Smith, J. C. 1979. The use of optical probes to monitor membrane potential. In *Methods in Enzymology,* ed. S. Fleischer, L. Packer, 55:569–86. New York: Academic
12. Beck, J. C., Sacktor, B. 1975. Energetics of the Na^+-dependent transport of D-glucose in renal brush border membrane vesicles. *J. Biol. Chem.* 250:8674–80
13. Beck, J. C., Sacktor, B. 1978. The sodium electrochemical potential–mediated uphill transport of D-glucose in renal

brush border membrane vesicles. *J. Biol. Chem.* 253:5531–35

14. Beck, J. C., Sacktor, B. 1978. Membrane potential-sensitive fluorescence changes during Na+-dependent D-glucose transport in renal brush border membrane vesicles. *J. Biol. Chem.* 253:7158–62

15. Berner, W., Kinne, R. 1976. Transport of p-aminohippuric acid by plasma membrane vesicles isolated from rat kidney cortex. *Pflueger's Arch.* 361:269–77

16. Biber, J., Stange, G., Stieger, B., Murer, H. 1983. Transport of L-cystine by rat renal brush border membrane vesicles. *Pflueger's Arch.* 396:335–41

17. Brown, J. L., Samiy, A. H., Pitts, R. F. 1961. Localization of aminonitrogen reabsorption in the nephron of the dog. *Am. J. Physiol.* 200:370–72

18. Burckhardt, G., Kinne, R., Stange, G., Murer, H. 1980. The effects of potassium and membrane potential on sodium-dependent glutamic acid uptake. *Biochim. Biophys. Acta* 599:191–201

19. Burg, M. B., Patlak, C. S., Green, N., Villey, D. 1976. Organic solutes in fluid absorption by renal proximal convoluted tubles. *Am. J. Physiol.* 231:627–37

20. Busse, D. 1978. Transport L-arginine in brush border vesicles derived from rabbit kidney cortex. *Arch. Biochem. Biophys.* 191:551–60

21. Busse, D., John, A., Steinmaier, G. 1975. Carrier-mediated transfer of D-glucose in brush border vesicles derived from rabbit tubules. Na+-dependent versus Na+-independent transfer. *Biochim. Biophys. Acta* 401:231–43

22. Chan, A. W., Burch, H. B., Alvey, T. R., Lowry, O. H. 1975. A quantitative histochemical approach to renal transport. I. Aspartate and glutamate. *Am. J. Physiol.* 229:1034–44

23. Cheng, L., Sacktor, B. 1981. Sodium gradient-dependent phosphate transport in renal brush border membrane vesicles. *J. Biol. Chem.* 256:1556–64

24. Crane, R. K. 1962. Hypothesis for mechanism of intestinal active transport of sugars. *Fed. Proc.* 21:891–95

25. Crane, R. K., Malathi, P., Preiser, H. 1976. Reconstitution of specific Na+-dependent D-glucose transport in liposomes by Triton X-100 extracted proteins from purified brush border membranes of hamster small intestine. *Biochem. Biophys. Res. Comm.* 71:1010–16

26. Dantzler, W. H. 1982. Studies on non-mammalian nephrons. *Kidney Int.* 22:560–70

27. Dantzler, W. H., Bentley, S. K. 1980. Bath and lumen effects of SITS on PAH transport by isolated perfused renal tubules. *Am. J. Physiol.* 238:F16–25

28. Deetjen, P., Boylan, J. W. 1968. Glucose reabsorption in the rat kidney. *Pflueger's Arch.* 299:19–29

29. Ducis, I., Koepsell, H. 1983. A simple liposomal system to reconstitute and assay highly efficient Na+/D-glucose cotransport from kidney brush-border membranes. *Biochim. Biophys. Acta* 730:119–29

30. Edelman, A., Teulon, J., Anagnostopoulos, T. 1983. Pecularities of the Na+/D-glucose cotransport system in Necturus renal tubules. *Biochim. Biophys. Acta* 731:211–16

31. Eisenbach, G. M., Weise, M., Stolte, H. 1975. Amino acid reabsorption in the rat nephron. Free flow micropuncture study. *Pflueger's Arch.* 357:63–76

32. Eveloff, J. 1983. pH gradient stimulated-transport of p-aminohippurate into basal-lateral membrane vesicles from rabbit renal cortex. *Fed. Proc.* 42:1354

33. Evers, J., Murer, H., Kinne, R. 1976. Phenylalanine uptake in isolated renal brush border vesicles. *Biochim. Biophys. Acta* 426:598–615

34. Fairclough, P., Malathi, P., Preiser, H., Crane, R. K. 1979. Reconstitution into liposomes of glucose active transport from the rabbit renal proximal tubule. *Biochim. Biophys. Acta* 553:295–306

35. Fass, S. J., Hammerman, M. R., Sacktor, B. 1977. Transport of amino acids in renal brush border membrane vesicles. Uptake of the neutral amino acid L-alanine. *J. Biol. Chem.* 252:583–90

36. Foreman, J. W., Reynolds, R. A., Ginkinger, K., Segal, S. 1983. Effect of acidosis on glutamine transport by isolated rat renal brush-border and basolateral-membrane vesicles. *Biochem. J.* 212:713–20

37. Fox, M., Thier, S., Rosenberg, L., Segal, S. 1964. Ionic requirements for amino acid transport in the rat kidney cortex slice. I. Influence of extracellular ions. *Biochim. Biophys. Acta* 79:167–76

38. Frömter, E. 1982. Electrophysiologic analysis of rat renal sugar and amino acid transport. I. Basic phenomena. *Pflueger's Arch.* 393:179–89

39. Ganapathy, V., Leibach, F. H. 1982. Peptide transport in intestinal and renal brush border membrane vesicles. *Life Sci.* 30:2137–46

40. Goldstone, A. D., Koenig, H., Chung, Y. L. 1983. Androgenic stimulation of endocytosis, amino acid, and hexose transport in mouse kidney cortex involves increased calcium fluxes. *Biochim. Biophys. Acta* 762:366–71

41. Grantham, J. J. 1982. Studies of organic anion and cation transport in isolated segments of proximal tubules. *Kidney Int.* 22:519–25

42. Grasset, E., Gunter-Smith, P., Schultz, S. G. 1983. Effect of Na-coupled alanine transport on intracellular K activities and the K conductance of the basolateral membranes of Necturus small intestine. *J. Memb. Biol.* 71:89–94

43. Guggino, S. E., Martin, G. J., Aronson, P. S. 1983. Specificity and modes of the anion exchanger in dog renal microvillus membranes. *Am. J. Physiol.* 244:F612–21

44. Gunter-Smith, P. J., Grasset, E., Schultz, S. G. 1982. Sodium-coupled amino acid and sugar transport by Necturus small intestine. *J. Memb. Biol.* 66:25–39

45. Hammerman, M. R. 1982. Na^+-independent L-arginine transport in rabbit renal brush border membrane vesicles. *Biochim. Biophys. Acta* 685:71–77

46. Hammerman, M. R., Sacktor, B. 1977. Transport of amino acids in renal brush border membrane vesicles. Uptake of L-proline. *J. Biol. Chem.* 252:591–95

47. Hammerman, M. R., Sacktor, B. 1982. Na^+-dependent transport of glycine in renal brush border membrane vesicles. Evidence for a single specific transport system. *Biochim. Biophys. Acta* 686:189–96

48. Hare, D., Stolte, H. 1972. Rat proximal tubule D-glucose transport as a function of concentration, flow and radius. *Pflueger's Arch.* 334:207–21

49. Higgins, J. T., Meinders, A. E. 1975. Quantitative relationship of renal glucose and sodium reabsorption during ECF expansion. *Am. J. Physiol.* 229:66–71

50. Hilden, S. A., Sacktor, B. 1979. D-glucose–dependent sodium transport in renal brush border membrane vesicles. *J. Biol. Chem.* 254:7090–96

51. Hilden, S. A., Sacktor, B. 1981. L-arginine uptake into renal brush border membrane vesicles. *Arch. Biochem. Biophys.* 210:289–97

52. Hilden, S., Sacktor, B. 1982. Potential-dependent D-glucose uptake by renal brush border membrane vesicles in the absence of sodium. *Am. J. Physiol.* 242:F340–45

53. Holohan, P. D., Ross, C. R. 1980. Mechanisms of organic cation transport in kidney plasma membrane vesicles: 1. Countertransport studies. *J. Pharmacol. Exp. Ther.* 215:191–97

54. Holohan, P. D., Ross, C. R. 1981. Mechanisms of organic cation transport in kidney plasma membrane vesicles: 2.

Delta pH studies. *J. Pharmacol. Exp. Ther.* 216:294–98

55. Hopfer, U., Groseclose, R. 1980. The mechanism of Na^+-dependent D-glucose transport. *J. Biol. Chem.* 255:4453–62

56. Hori, R., Takano, M., Okano, T., Kitazawa, S., Inui, K-I. 1982. Mechanisms of p-aminohippurate transport by brush-border and basolateral membrane vesicles isolated from rat kidney cortex. *Biochim. Biophys. Acta* 692:97–100

57. Hosang, M., Vasella, A., Semenza, G. 1981. Specific photoaffinity inactivation of the D-glucose transporter in small intestinal brush border membrane using new phlorizin analogues. *Biochemistry* 20:5844–54

58. Hoshi, T., Sudo, K., Suzuki, Y. 1976. Characteristics of changes in the intracellular potential associated with transport of neutral, dibasic, and acidic amino acids in *Triturus* proximal tubule. *Biochim. Biophys. Acta* 448:492–504

59. Hwang, S. M., Foreman, J., Segal, S. 1982. Developmental pattern of cystine transport in isolated rat renal tubules. *Biochim. Biophys. Acta* 690:145–53

60. Imai, M., Seldin, D. W., Kokko, J. P. 1977. Effect of perfusion rate on the fluxes of water, sodium chloride, and urea across the proximal convoluted tubule. *Kidney Int.* 11:18–27

61. Jean, T., Ripoche, P., Poujeol, P. 1983. A sodium-independent mechanism for L-arginine uptake by rat renal brush border membrane vesicles. *Memb. Biochem.* 5:1–18

62. Kahn, A. M., Branham, S., Weinman, E. J. 1983. Mechanism of urate and p-aminohippurate transport in rat renal microvillus membrane vesicles. *Am. J. Physiol.* 245:F151–58

63. Kasher, J. S., Holohan, P. D., Ross, C. R. 1983. Na^+ gradient–dependent p-aminohippurate (PAH) transport in rat basolateral membrane vesicles. *J. Pharmacol. Exp. Ther.* 227:122–29

64. Kaunitz, J. D., Wright, E. M. 1984. Kinetics of sodium D-glucose cotransport in bovine intestinal brush border vesicles. *J. Memb. Biol.* 79:41–51

65. Kawamura, J., Mazumdar, D. C., Lubowitz, H. 1977. Effect of albumin infusion on renal glucose reabsorption in the rat. *Am. J. Physiol.* 232:F286–90

66. Kessler, M., Semenza, G. 1983. The small-intestinal Na^+, D-glucose cotransporter: An asymmetric gated channel (or pore) responsive to $\Delta\phi$. *J. Memb. Biol.* 76:27–56

67. Kinne, R., Baumann, K. 1974. Molecular basis of transepithelial transport in the proximal tubule of the rat kidney: Prop-

erties of the luminal and contraluminal cell membrane. *Fortschr. Zool.* 23:261–78

68. Kinne, R., Faust, R. G. 1977. Incorporation of D-glucose-, L-alanine- and phosphate-transport systems from rat renal brush-border membranes into liposomes. *Biochem. J.* 168:311–14

69. Kinne, R., Schwartz, I. L. 1978. Isolated membrane vesicles in the evaluation of the nature, localization and regulation of renal transport processes. *Kidney Int.* 14:547–56

70. Kinne, R., Murer, H., Kinne-Saffran, E., Thees, M., Sachs G. 1975. Sugar transport by renal plasma membrane vesicles. Characterization of the systems in the brush-border microvillae and basal-lateral plasma membranes. *J. Memb. Biol.* 21:375–95

71. Kinne, R., DaCruz, M. E. M., Lin, J. T. 1984. Sodium-D-glucose cotransport system: Biochemical analysis of active sites. In *Current Topics in Membranes and Transport,* ed. J. B. Wade, S. A. Lewis, 20:245–58. New York: Academic

72. Kinsella, J. L., Holohan, P. D., Pessah, N. I., Ross, C. R. 1979. Transport of organic ions in renal cortical luminal and antiluminal membrane vesicles. *J. Pharmacol. Exp. Ther.* 209:443–50

73. Kleinzeller, A. 1970. The specificity of the active sugar transport in kidney cortex cells. *Biochim. Biophys. Acta* 211:264–76

74. Kleinzeller, A., Kotyk, A. 1961. Cations and the transport of galactose in kidney cortex slices. *Biochim. Biophys. Acta* 54:367–69

75. Knight, T. F., Senekjian, H. O., Sansom, S. C., Weinman, E. J. 1980. Proximal tubule glucose efflux in the rat as a function of delivered load. *Am. J. Physiol.* 238:F499–503

76. Koepsell, H., Menuhr, H., Wissmüller, T. F., Ducis, I., Haase, W. 1980. Reconstitution of D-glucose transport and high-affinity phlorizin binding after solubilization of kidney brush border proteins. *Ann. N. Y. Acad. Sci.* 358:267–81

77. Koepsell, H., Menuhr, H., Ducis, I., Wissmüller, T. F. 1983. Partial purification and reconstitution of the Na$^+$-D-glucose cotransport protein from pig renal proximal tubules. *J. Biol Chem.* 258:1888–94

78. Koschier, F. J., Stokols, M. F., Goldinger, J. M., Acara, M., Hong, S. K. 1980. Effect of DIDS on renal tubular transport. *Am. J. Physiol.* 238:F99–106

79. Kragh-Hansen, U., Jorgensen, K. E., Sheihk, M. I. 1982. The use of a potential-sensitive cyanine dye for studying

ion-dependent electrogenic renal transport of organic solutes. Uptake of L-malate and D-malate by luminal-membrane vesicles. *Biochem. J.* 208:369–76

80. Kramp, R. A., Lorentz, W. B. 1982. Glucose transport in chronically altered rat nephrons. *Am. J. Physiol.* 243:F393–403

81. Kurtzman, N. A., White, M. G., Rogers, P. W., Flynn, J. J. III. 1972. Relationship of sodium reabsorption and glomerular filtration rate to renal glucose reabsorption. *J. Clin. Invest.* 51:127–33

82. Lappe, R. W., Henry, D. P., Willis, L. R. 1980. Mechanism of renal tubular secretion of norepinephrine in the rabbit. *J. Pharmacol. Exp. Ther.* 215:443–49

83. Leopolder, A., Burckhardt, G., Murer, H. 1980. Transport of L-ornithine across isolated brush border membrane vesicles from proximal tubule. *Renal Physiol.* 2:135–66

84. Linn, J. T., Cruz, M. E. M., Riedel, S., Kinne, R. 1981. Partial purification of hog kidney sodium-D-glucose cotransport system by affinity chromatography on a phlorizin polymer. *Biochim. Biophys. Acta* 640:43–54

85. Löw, I., Friedrich, T., Burckhardt, G. 1984. Properties of an anion exchanger in rat renal basolateral membrane vesicles. *Am. J. Physiol.* 246:F334–42

86. Malathi, P., Preiser, H., Crane, R. K. 1980. Protease-resistant integral brush border membrane proteins and their relationship to sodium-dependent transport of D-glucose and L-alanine. *Ann. N. Y. Acad. Sci.* 358:253–66

87. Maruyama, T., Hoshi, T. 1972. The effect of D-glucose on the electrical potential profile across the proximal tubule of newt kidney. *Biochim. Biophys. Acta* 282:214–25

88. McKinney, T. D. 1984. Further studies of organic base secretion by rabbit proximal tubules. *Am. J. Physiol.* 246:F282–89

89. McNamara, P. D., Ozegovic, B., Pepe, L. M., Segal, S. 1976. Proline and glycine uptake by renal brush border membrane vesicles. *Proc. Natl. Acad. Sci. USA* 73:4521–25

90. Medow, M. S., Foreman, J. W., Bovee, K. C., Segal, S. 1982. Developmental changes of glycine transport in the dog. *Biochim. Biophys. Acta* 693:85–92

91. Mircheff, A. K., van Os, C. H., Wright, E. M. 1980. Pathways for alanine transport in intestinal basal-lateral membrane vesicles. *J. Memb. Biol.* 52:83–92

92. Moran, A., Handler, J. S., Turner, R. J. 1982. Na$^+$-dependent hexose transport in

vesicles from cultured renal epithelial cell line. *Am. J. Physiol.* 243:C293–98

93. Mudge, G. H., Berndt, W. O., Valtin, H. 1973. Tubular transport of urea, glucose, phosphate, uric acid, sulfate, and thiosulfate. In *Handbook of Physiology,* ed. J. Orloff, R. W. Berliner, pp. 587–652. Washington DC: Am. Physiol. Soc.

94. Mullin, J. M., Kleinzeller, A. 1984. Sugar transport in the renal epithelial cell culture. In *Tissue Cultures in the Study of Epithelial Transport,* ed. M. Taub, in press. New York: Plenum

95. Murer, H., Hopfer, U. 1974. Demonstration of electrogenic Na$^+$-dependent D-glucose transport in intestinal brush border membranes. *Proc. Natl. Acad. Sci. USA* 71:484–88

96. Murer, H., Leopolder, A., Kinne, R., Burckhardt, G. 1980. Recent observations on the proximal tubular transport of acidic and basic amino acids by rat renal proximal tubular brush border vesicles. *Int. J. Biochem.* 12:222–28

97. Nelson, P. J., Dean, G. E., Aronson, P. S., Rudnick, G. 1983. Hydrogen ion cotransport by the renal brush border glutamate transporter. *Biochemistry* 22:5459–63

98. Oken, D. E., Weise, M. 1978. Micropuncture studies of the transport of individual amino acids by the Necturus proximal tubule. *Kidney Int.* 13:445–51

99. Peerce, B. E., Wright, E. M. 1984. Conformational changes in the intestinal brush border sodium-glucose cotransporter labeled with fluorescein isothiocyanate. *Proc. Natl. Acad. Sci. USA* 81:2223–26

100. Poiree, J. C., Mengual, R., Sudaka, P. 1979. Identification of a protein component of horse kidney brush border D-glucose transport system. *Biochem. Biophys. Res. Comm.* 90:1387–92

101. Rabito, C. A., Karish, M. V. 1983. Polarized amino acid transport by an epithelial cell line of renal origin (LLC-PK$_1$). The apical systems. *J. Biol. Chem.* 258:2543–47

102. Rennick, B. R. 1981. Renal tubule transport of organic cations. *Am. J. Physiol.* 240:F83–89

103. Reynolds, R. A., Wald, H., Segal, S. 1982. Glutamine uptake by rat renal basolateral membrane vesicles. *Biosci. Rep.* 2:883–90

104. Riggs, T. R., Walker, L. M., Christensen, H. N. 1958. Potassium migration and amino acid transport. *J. Biol. Chem.* 233:1479–84

105. Robson, A. M., Srivastava, P. L., Bricker, N. S. 1968. The influence of saline loading on renal glucose reabsorption in the rat. *J. Clin. Invest.* 47:329–35

106. Rosenberg, L. E., Blair, A., Segal, S. 1961. The transport of amino acids by rat kidney cortex slices. *Biochim. Biophys. Acta* 54:479–88

107. Ross, C. R., Holohan, P. D. 1983. Transport of organic anions and cations in isolated renal plasma membranes. *Ann. Rev. Pharmacol. Toxicol.* 23:65–85

108. Sabolic, I., Burckhardt, G. 1983. Proton pathways in rat renal brush-border and basolateral membranes. *Biochim. Biophys. Acta* 734:210–20

109. Sacktor, B. 1981. L-glutamate transport in renal plasma membrane vesicles. *Mol. Cell. Biochem.* 39:239–51

110. Sacktor, B. 1982. Na$^+$-gradient-dependent transport systems in renal proximal tubule brush border membrane vesicles. In *Membranes and Transport,* ed. A. Martinosi, 2:197–206. New York: Plenum

111. Sacktor, B., Rosenbloom, I. L., Liang, C. T., Cheng, L. 1981. Sodium gradient-and sodium plus potassium gradient-dependent L-glutamate uptake in renal basolateral membrane vesicles. *J. Memb. Biol.* 60:63–71

112. Samarzija, I., Frömter, E. 1982. Electrophysiologic analysis of rat renal sugar and amino acid transport. III. Neutral amino acids. *Pflueger's Arch.* 393:199–209

113. Samarzija, I., Frömter, E. 1982. Electrophysiologic analysis of rat renal sugar and amino acid transport. IV. Basic amino acids. *Pflueger's Arch.* 393:210–14

114. Samarzija, I., Frömter, E. 1982. Electrophysiologic analysis of rat renal sugar and amino acid transport. V. Acidic amino acids. *Pflueger's Arch.* 393:215–24

115. Samarzija, I., Hinton, B. T., Frömter, E. 1982. Electrophysiologic analysis of rat renal sugar and amino acid transport. II. Dependence on various transport parameters and inhibitors. *Pflueger's Arch.* 393:190–97

116. Schafer, J. A. 1972. An examination of the energetic adequacy of the ion gradient hypothesis for nonelectrolyte transport. In *Na-linked Transport of Organic Solutes,* ed. E. Heinz, pp. 68–63. Berlin: Springer

117. Schafer, J. A., Barfuss, D. W. 1980. Membrane mechanisms for transepithelial amino acid absorption and secretion. *Am. J. Physiol.* 238:F335–46

118. Schafer, J. A., Watkins, M. L. 1984. Transport of L-cystine in isolated perfused proximal straight tubules. *Pflueger's Arch.* 401:143–51

119. Schafer, J. A., Patlack, C. S., Andreoli,

T. E. 1975. A component of fluid absorption linked to passive ion flows in the superficial pars recta. *J. Gen. Physiol.* 66:445–71

120. Schafer, J. A., Troutman, S. L., Watkins, M. L., Andreoli, T. E. 1981. Flow dependence of fluid transport in the isolated superficial pars recta: Evidence that osmotic disequilibrium between external solutions drives isotonic fluid absorption. *Kidney Int.* 20:588–97

121. Schäli, C., Roch-Ramel, F. 1981. Uptake of ^{3}H PAH and ^{14}C urate into isolated proximal tubular segments of the pig kidney. *Am. J. Physiol.* 241:F591–96

122. Schell, R. E., Stevens, B. R., Wright, E. M. 1983. Kinetics of sodium-dependent solute transport by rabbit renal and jejunal brush-border vesicles using fluorescent dye. *J. Physiol.* 335:307–18

123. Schmidt, U. M., Eddy, B., Fraser, C. M., Venter, J. C., Semenza, G. 1983. Isolation of (a subunit of) the Na$^+$/D-glucose cotransporter(s) of rabbit intestinal brush border membranes using monoclonal antibodies. *FEBS Lett.* 161:279–83

124. Schneider, E. G., Sacktor, B. 1980. Sodium gradient-dependent L-glutamate transport in renal brush border membrane vesicles. Effect of an intravesicular > extravesicular potassium gradient. *J. Biol. Chem.* 255:7645–49

125. Schneider, E. G., Hammerman, M. R., Sacktor, B. 1980. Sodium gradient–dependent L-glutamate transport in renal brush border membrane vesicles. Evidence for an electroneutral mechanism. *J. Biol. Chem.* 255:7650–56

126. Schultz, S. G. 1981. Homocellular regulatory mechanisms in sodium-transport epithelia: avoidance of extinction by "flush-through." *Am. J. Physiol.* 241:F579–90

127. Schwartzman, L., Blair, A., Segal, S. 1967. Exchange diffusion of dibasic amino acids in rat kidney cortex slices. *Biochim. Biophys. Acta* 135:120–26

128. Segal, S., Thier, S. O. 1973. Renal handling of amino acids. In *Handbook of Physiology, Section 8, Renal Physiology,* ed. J. Orloff, R. W. Berliner, pp. 653–76. Washington DC: Am. Physiol. Soc.

129. Silbernagl, S., Foulkes, E. C., Deetjen, P. 1975. Renal transport of amino acids. *Rev. Physiol. Biochem. Pharmacol.* 74:105–67

130. Silverman, M. 1981. Glucose reabsorption in the kidney. *Can. J. Physiol. Pharmacol.* 59:209–24

131. Silverman, M., Turner, R. J. 1982. Deoxy-D-glucose transport in dog kidney. *Am. J. Physiol.* 242:F711–20

132. Slack, E. N., Liang, C.-C. T., Sacktor, B. 1977. Transport of L-proline and D-glucose in luminal (brush border) and contraluminal (basal-lateral) membrane vesicles from the renal cortex. *Biochem. Biophys. Res. Comm.* 77:891–97

133. Stieger, B., Stange, G., Biber, J., Murer, H. 1983. Transport of L-lysine by rat renal brush border membrane vesicles. *Pflueger's Arch.* 397:106–13

134. Toggenburger, G., Kessler, M., Semenza, G. 1982. Phlorizin as a probe of the small-intestinal Na$^+$, D-glucose cotransporter. A model. *Biochim. Biophys. Acta* 688:557–71

135. Tune, B. M., Burg, M. B. 1971. Glucose transport by proximal renal tubules. *Am. J. Physiol.* 221:580–85

136. Tune, B. M., Burg, M., Patlak, C. S. 1969. Characteristics of p-aminohippurate transport in proximal renal tubules. *Am. J. Physiol.* 217:1057–63

137. Turner, R. J. 1981. Kinetic analysis of a family of cotransport models. *Biochim. Biophys. Acta* 649:269–80

138. Turner, R. J. 1983. Quantitative studies of cotransport systems: models and vesicles. *J. Memb. Biol.* 76:1–15

139. Turner, R. J., Moran, A. 1982. Heterogeneity of sodium-dependent D-glucose transport sites along the proximal tubule: evidence from vesicle studies. *Am. J. Physiol.* 242:F406–14

140. Turner, R. J., Moran, A. 1982. Stoichiometric studies of renal outer cortical brush border membrane D-glucose transporter. *J. Memb. Biol.* 67:73–80

141. Turner, R. J., Moran, A. 1982. Further studies of proximal tubular brush border membrane D-glucose transport heterogeneity. *J. Memb. Biol.* 70:37–45

142. Turner, R. J., Silverman, M. 1978. Sugar uptake into brush border vesicles from dog kidney. II. Kinetics. *Biochim. Biophys. Acta* 511:470–86

143. Turner, R. J., Silverman, M. 1981. Interaction of phlorizin and sodium with the renal brush-border membrane D-glucose transporter: Stoichiometry and order of binding. *J. Memb. Biol.* 58:43–55

144. Ullrich, K. J. 1976. Renal tubular mechanisms of organic solute transport. *Kidney Int.* 9:134–148

145. Ullrich, K. J. 1979. Sugar, amino acid, and Na$^+$ cotransport in the proximal tubule. *Ann. Rev. Physiol.* 41:181–95

146. Ullrich, K. J., Rumrich, G., Klöss, S. 1974. Specificity and sodium dependence of the active sugar transport in the proximal convolution of the rat kidney. *Pflueger's Arch.* 351:35–48

147. Ullrich, K. J., Rumrich, G., Klöss, S. 1974. Sodium dependence of the amino

acid transport in the proximal convolution of the rat kidney. *Pflueger's Arch.* 351:49–60

148. Völkl, H., Silbernagl, S. 1982. Mutual inhibition of L-cystine/L-cysteine and other neutral amino acids during tubular reabsorption. A microperfusion study in rat kidney. *Pflueger's Arch.* 395:190–95

149. Völkl, H., Silbernagl, S. 1982. Reexamination of the interplay between dibasic amino acids and L-cystine/L-cysteine during tubular reabsorption. *Pflueger's Arch.* 395:196–200

150. Weiner, I. M. 1979. Urate transport in the nephron. *Am. J. Physiol.* 237:F85–92

151. Weinman, E. J., Suki, W. N., Eknoyan, G. 1976. D-glucose enhancement of water reabsorption in proximal tubule of the rat kidney. *Am. J. Physiol.* 231:777–80

152. Wen, S.-F. 1976. Micropuncture studies of glucose transport in the dog: mechanism of renal glycosuria. *Am. J. Physiol.* 231:468–75

153. Winders, D., Cohn, D., Klahr, S., Hammerman, M. R. 1984. Glutamine transport in renal basolateral vesicles from dogs with metabolic acidosis. *Am. J. Physiol.* 246:F78–86

154. Wright, E. M. 1984. Electrophysiology of plasma membrane vesicles. *Am. J. Physiol.* 246:F363–72

155. Wright, E. M. 1985. Transport of carboxylic acids by renal plasma membrane vesicles. *Ann. Rev. Physiol.* 47:127–41

Ann. Rev. Physiol. 1985. 47:127–41

TRANSPORT OF CARBOXYLIC ACIDS BY RENAL MEMBRANE VESICLES

Ernest M. Wright

Department of Physiology, School of Medicine, University of California, Los Angeles, California 90024

INTRODUCTION

The kidney avidly metabolizes Krebs-cycle intermediates, short-chain fatty acids, and ketone bodies (12, 41). These intermediates in plasma are filtered by the glomerulus and conserved in the proximal tubule. Unlike sugars and amino acids, relatively little was known about the renal handling of carboxylic acids until recently. One reason was the high rates of metabolism of these substrates and the lack of nonmetabolized analogs. With the advent of membrane vesicle preparations from the renal cortex (see 31), it became possible to examine membrane transport of the carboxylic acids in the absence of metabolism. In this review I will summarize work on the transport of carboxylic acids using vesicle preparations. In brush borders, two distinct Na-cotransport systems have been uncovered: one for monocarboxylic acids, and another for Krebs-cycle intermediates. A Na-cotransport system for the di- and tri-carboxylic acids is also found in renal basolateral membranes. On the other hand, the basolateral monocarboxylic-acid transport occurs simply by facilitated diffusion.

The plasma levels of Krebs-cycle intermediates, short-chain carboxylic acids, and ketone bodies range from 0.01 mM to 1.5 mM (17). However, the levels can vary widely with acid-base status, diet, diabetes, and starvation. For example, β-hydroxybutyrate levels increase from 1 mM to 6 mM on starvation, and citrate varies between 0.09 mM and 0.15 mM with changes in acid-base status. All are freely filtered, but urinary excretion is only 3–35% of the filtered load. Reabsorption occurs in the proximal tubule (see 40, 45). Marked excre-

127

0066-4278/85/0315-0127$02.00

tion of carboxylic acids occurs under physiological, pathological, and therapeutic conditions. Citrate excretion increases with metabolic alkalosis and vitamin D–resistant rickets (41). Perhaps the most dramatic case is the rapid net excretion of Krebs-cycle intermediates (7) upon placing patients on Li therapy.

MEMBRANE VESICLES

Since brush-border vesicles were introduced to epithelial physiology more than a decade ago, there has been rapid growth in their application to renal transport problems (see 31). The starting material for vesicle preparations is usually the minced renal cortex. A popular brush-border isolation is a divalent differential centrifugation procedure (see 52), whereas a Percoll density-gradient procedure is the current method of choice for basolateral membranes (see 11, 20, 27). These vesicles exist as closed structures with diameters in the range of 200–400 nm and volumes of 1–4 ul/mg membrane protein. Purity of preparations is judged by enrichments of enzyme markers (maltase, trehalase, γ-glutamyl transpeptidase for brush borders, and (Na^+,K^+)-ATPase for basolaterals).

Transport is assayed by measuring the uptake of radioactive tracers using a rapid mixing and filtration system. Earlier experiments focused on the ability of vesicles to support the uphill accumulation of substrates, e.g. D-glucose uptake by brush borders under Na-gradient conditions, but this is gradually being replaced by initial rate measurements under well-defined driving forces. Vesicles are preloaded with solutions of known composition, and the initial rates of tracer uptake are measured after rapid mixing of the vesicles with buffer of determined composition. Uptakes are measured as a function of extravesicular (cis) substrate and cofactor concentrations, intravesicular (trans) substrate and cofactor concentrations, and defined membrane potentials. Membrane potentials are clamped at predetermined values through the use of ion gradients and ionophores, e.g. K gradients + valinomycin, where the potentials are given by the Nernst equation. In view of the large surface to volume ratio, and the permeability of the membrane, it is necessary to measure the initial rates of uptake before there are significant changes in the imposed driving forces. Uptakes as low as 0.5 seconds can be obtained manually, and commercial equipment is available to measure uptakes at 0.1 second. Practical limitations are the specific activity of isotopes, the stop procedure, the separation of vesicles from the uptake medium, and theoretical limitations arising from low turnover numbers (~ 5–$10 \ sec^{-1}$) of the transporters. With carboxylic acids we find that 1-sec uptakes, rapid cooling of the uptake buffer, and Millipore filtration give fair estimates of initial rates under maximal driving forces. Efflux from vesicles can be measured using similar procedures (19), but here it is more difficult to obtain quantitative estimates of rates under well-defined conditions.

Membrane potentials are readily monitored in vesicles using voltage-sensitive dyes (47).

KREBS-CYCLE INTERMEDIATES

About seven years ago it became apparent that di- and tri-carboxylic acids of the Krebs cycle are transported across renal brush-border membranes by a common Na-cotransport system (21, 28). Our group has explored the specificity, kinetics, and mechanisms of this transport system (19, 37, 38, 47–54). Many of our observations have been confirmed in vesicles (2, 14, 16, 20, 23, 24) and in the rat tubule (40). There is some indication that these carboxylates are also transported across hamster, but not rabbit, small-intestine brush borders (10, 42).

Major features of this transport system are an overshoot in solute uptake in the presence of an inward Na gradient and a depolarization of the membrane potential. The requirement for Na is very specific. At low succinate concentrations (~ 100 uM) the relative rates of uptake in the presence of 100 mM–salt gradients are 40 Na > 2 Li > 1 Rb, 1 Cs, 1 NH_4, 1 choline > 0.1 sorbitol. The nature of the Na salt also influences the rate: the permeability of the anion influences the membrane potential, which in turn influences the rate of transport; and secondly, permeable anions behave as weak competitive inhibitors (26).

Specificity

Specificity of the transporter was elucidated by competitive effects of analogs on succinate, citrate, and α-ketoglutarate uptake (21, 51). The maximum velocities of these three substrates are identical, and succinate and citrate interactions are strictly competitive. These experiments also clearly established that the polycarboxylic acids are handled by a carrier that is not shared by sugars, amino acids, and monocarboxylic acids. The preferred substrates for the polycarboxylic-acid carrier are four carbon, terminal dicarboxylic acids with the carboxyl groups in the *trans* configuration (see Figure 1). Citrate is handled by this system, and pH and Ca^{++} experiments indicate that the third carboxylic-acid group (pK_a 6.4) needs to be protonated for transport to occur (2, 52). Nevertheless, trivalent citrate acts as a competitive inhibitor at an alkaline pH (2), and this suggests that the extra negative charge precludes transport. If in fact citrate^{--} is the only transported species, then the affinity (K_m) is much lower than estimated from the total citrate concentration (0.005 mM vs 0.95 mM at pH 7.5).

The aromatic dicarboxylates are less effective inhibitors than the aliphatic acids. Nevertheless, dicarboxylic acids of benzene, pyridine, pyrazine, pyrazol, and napthalene are well recognized (40, 51; E. M. Wright, unpublished observations). In this case the 1,4 dicarboxylates have the greatest inhibitory

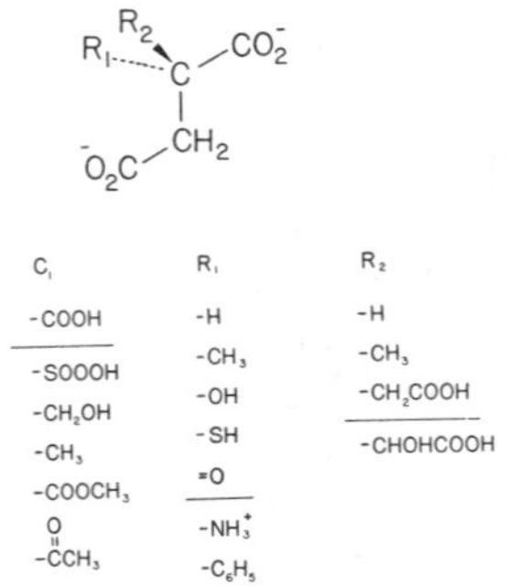

Figure 1   The structural specificity for dicarboxylate binding to the renal brush-border transporter. The optimal structure is shown and at each position C_1 (carboxyl residue), R_1, and R_2, the acceptable and unacceptable analogs are indicated. Those above the *horizontal line* are accepted and those below are not. Modified from (51).

action, and inspection of molecular models suggests that the optimal distance between the carboxylic-acid groups is 6–7Å. Steric factors are also important because large bulky hydrocarbon residues lower interaction with the carrier, e.g. 1,4 dicarboxy napthalene vs 1,4 dicarboxybenzene (terephthalic acid) and phenyl succinate vs succinate. This indicates that the dicarboxylate binding sites are located in a narrow cleft on the transport protein. Experiments with group-specific reagents reveal that a histidyl residue is at, or adjacent to, the succinate-binding site (5). Diethyl pyrocarbonate (DEP) inhibits succinate uptake, and this is blocked by the presence of succinate (or malate) and Na during the carbethoxylation reaction. The inhibition by DEP is reversed by hydroxylamine. The pH dependence of succinate transport is consistent with the presence of histidyl residues. Unlike the case of the intestinal glucose carrier (34, 35), there is no information available about the nature of the Na binding sites.

Kinetics

SUCCINATE   The kinetics of succinate uptake has been examined as a function of external *(cis)* and internal *(trans)* Na and succinate and as a function of membrane potential (50, 53). Under zero-*trans* conditions (*trans* Na and succinate = 0) succinate uptake at high-*cis* Na (100–150 mM) occurs by a single saturable system with a J_{max}^s of ~ 75 nmol mg^{-1} min^{-1} and a K_m of 0.7 mM (see also 2, 14). The contribution of diffusion to uptake is low, but the apparent permeability coefficient (1 ul mg^{-1} min^{-1}) is comparable to that for sugars and amino acids.

The kinetics obtained for succinate fluxes are summarized in Table 1. Influx experiments under zero-*trans* conditions (experiments 1–3) show that variations in *cis* Na produce changes in the succinate K_m^s, i.e. Na behaves as a competitive activator of succinate uptake. In contrast, increasing the *trans* Na concentration (experiments 4–5) reduced J_{max}^s such that in the absence of a Na gradient, the J_{max}^s was less than 1% of that under zero-*trans* conditions. Under equilibrium exchange conditions (experiment 6) ($Na_i = Na_o$; $Succ_i = Succ_o$), *trans* succinate partially relieves the *trans* Na inhibition, but note that the J_{max}^s is only 20% of that under zero-*trans* conditions. Finally, the succinate efflux J_{max}^s under zero-*trans* conditions (not shown) is only 25% of the influx J_{max}^s, and this points to a functional asymmetry of the carrier (19). Uptake is a function of the membrane potential: voltage clamping the vesicle negative relative to the external buffer increases uptake, whereas the reverse polarity decreases uptake. The potential alters only the K_m^s of the carrier for succinate and not the J_{max}^s. The K_m^s was 1.3 mM at +60 mV, 0.8 at 0, and 0.4 mM at −60 mV. One explanation of this affinity-type effect is that the fully loaded carrier is charged (+1) while the unloaded carrier is neutral, but this conclusion is very model-dependent (50).

SODIUM   Indirect information about the interaction of Na with the succinate carrier has been obtained from Na-activation curves at fixed succinate concentrations (14, 53). The activation curves are sigmoid, with Hill coefficients of 2, suggesting a minimum of two Na binding sites on the carrier.

More direct information has been obtained from [22]Na uptakes (48, 53). Initial experiments indicated that the succinate/Na coupling coefficient was 2–2.5, with 1–5-second estimates of rates. Likewise, Fukuhara & Turner (14) obtained a coupling of 2 using a static-head method. However, in recent experiments (48) where we have carefully analyzed the initial rates of Na and

Table 1   Kinetics of brush-border Na-dependent succinate transport[a]

Experiment	$[Na]_o$ mM	$[Na]_i$ mM	$[Succ]_i$	J_{max}^s $\dfrac{\text{nmoles}}{\text{mg} \times \text{min}}$	K_m^s mM
			Influx		
1	100	0	−	85 ± 4	0.68 ± 0.05
2	50	0	−	85 ± 4	1.37 ± 0.09
3	30	0	−	79 ± 5	2.56 ± 0.19
4	100	30	−	17 ± 1	0.61 ± 0.06
5	100	100	−	0.40 ± 0.04	0.14 ± 0.03
6	100	100	+	14 ± 0.80	2.80 ± 0.40

[a] The kinetics of succinate fluxes across renal brush-border vesicles were obtained from initial rates of influx when the membrane potential was short-circuited ($E_m = 0$). The kinetic parameters were measured as a function of the external (o) and internal (i) substrate concentrations. Data from (19, 50) and author's observations.

succinate uptake using a Li-quench and a curve-fitting procedure, a coupling coefficient of 3 was observed. This was independent of the *cis* Na (25–150 mM) and succinate (0.5–5 mM) concentrations. The close agreement between the Hill coefficients and direct coupling coefficients indicates that there is poor cooperativity between the three Na binding sites.

Experiments with voltage-sensitive dyes have demonstrated that dicarboxylic-acid transport is electrogenic (20, 23, 24, 37–39, 47, 54). These also confirmed the Na and substrate specificity of the system. Furthermore, using bi-ionic diffusion potentials, we showed that succinate transport was associated with an increase in Na permeability of the membrane. This increase accounted for an inward Na current of the same magnitude as the succinate influx. Together with the Na/succinate coupling coefficient of 3, this suggests that only one third of the Na flux carries the current that depolarizes the membrane potential.

At least under zero-*trans* conditions, the kinetics of succinate uptake can be explained by a rapid equilibrium, ordered system in which Na binds to the transporter before succinate (50). J^s is given by

$$J^s = J^s_{max} \frac{\dfrac{[S]\,[Na]^n}{K_s\,K_a^n}}{(1 + Na/K_a)^n + S[Na]^n/K_sK_a^n} \qquad\qquad 1.$$

where K_a is the apparent equilibrium constant for each Na binding site, K_s the apparent equilibrium constant for succinate, and n the number of Na binding sites. Coupling experiments suggest that there are three Na sites for each succinate site. At fixed Na concentrations, the equation reduces to

$$J^s = \frac{J^s_{max}[S]}{K^s_m + [S]}, \qquad\qquad 2.$$

where

$$K^s_m = \left(\frac{K_a^3}{[Na]^3} + \frac{3K_a^2}{[Na]^2} + \frac{3K_a}{[Na]} + 1 \right) K_s. \qquad\qquad 3.$$

Finally, at a fixed succinate concentration, Equation 1 predicts a sigmoid relationship between succinate uptake and *cis* Na concentration. It should be noted that fitting the Hill equation to the uptake predicted by Equation 1 yields a Hill coefficient of 2, as is observed experimentally.

The fixed coupling coefficient of 3 over a wide range of Na and succinate concentrations indicates that only the fully loaded and the empty carrier are able to cross the membrane, i.e. the partially loaded forms are unable to translocate. *Trans*-Na inhibition supports this view in that *trans*-Na ties up an immobile Na carrier complex at the *trans* face of the membrane to reduce the J^s_{max}. So far, there are no definite conclusions about the sequence of the dissociation reactions at the *trans* side. One experiment suggests glide symmetry. In this, *trans* Na produces mixed-type inhibition of succinate uptake, i.e. J^s_{max} is reduced 200-fold while K^s_m is only reduced 7-fold, and this suggests that Na is released first at the *trans* side (50). Other experiments indicate that succinate is released before Na at the *trans* face, i.e. Na activation of succinate influx under equilibrium exchange conditions is not inhibited at high (1 M) Na concentrations. Inhibition is expected if either Na binds after succinate at the *cis* face or is released before succinate at the *trans* face. One explanation of these diverse findings is that whereas the binding reactions at the *cis* side are ordered, the dissociation reactions at the *trans* side may be random (Figure 2).

Finally, comparison of succinate kinetics under zero-*trans* and equilibrium conditions suggest that the fully loaded carrier is less mobile than the unloaded carrier. This follows from the observation that the J^s_{max} at equilibrium exchange is only 20% of that under zero-*trans* conditions. This conclusion is in direct contrast to that reported for the intestinal glucose carriers. The Cleland reaction scheme summarizing the characteristics of succinate transport is shown in Figure 2.

Basolateral Membranes

Transport of citrate and methyl succinate have been studied in rabbit (20) and rat basolateral membrane vesicles (11). Overshoots were observed with Na-gradients but not with other cations. The J^s_{max} was about 6 nmol mg^{-1} min^{-1}, which is more than an order of magnitude lower than for brush borders. Both substrates appear to share the same carrier, and the specificity is similar to that

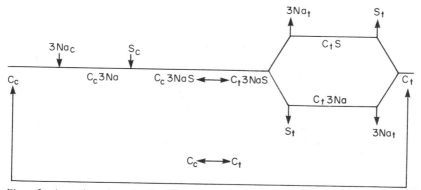

Figure 2   A reaction scheme for the kinetics of succinate uptake by renal brush borders. Carrier on the *cis* side *(C_c)* combines with *cis* Na and succinate in an ordered fashion, whereas the dissociation of substrates at the *trans* side of the membrane *(C_t)* is random.

in brush borders. Citrate uptake was neither electrogenetic nor sensitive to pH (5.5–8.5). This is in direct contrast to brush-border transport. However, methyl succinate and malate transport in basolaterals is electrogenic (11, 39) but, unlike brush borders, is insensitive to common inorganic anions (11, 26). The characteristics of methyl succinate transport across the basolateral membrane has been studied extensively in the intact renal tubule (44), where the results are virtually identical to those in vesicle preparations.

Effect of Lithium

One of the most striking disturbances of dicarboxylate transport in the kidney is observed with therapeutic doses of Li. In man and experimental animals, Li produces a rapid, specific loss of Krebs-cycle intermediates in the urine (1, 6, 7, 8, 25). For example, the fractional excretion of citrate increases from 4% to 140% within 20 min. This effect is at least in part due to inhibition of the cotransporter in the brush-border membrane (49). Although Li is a poor substitute for Na in promoting succinate/Na-cotransport, in the presence of Na, *cis* Li acts as a potent, competitive inhibitor and *trans* Li acts as a potent, noncompetitive inhibitor of transport. The relationship between the K_m^s and the *cis* Li concentration can be fitted by a noncooperative, three-site, competitive inhibitor model, where the affinity of Li is about six-fold greater than the affinity for Na (37). We postulate that when the transporter is occupied by Li, it cannot assume the conformation necessary for succinate binding. Li also inhibits dicarboxylate transport across rat basolateral membrane vesicles (11), and across the brush-border and basolateral membranes in the intact tubule (40, 44).

MONOCARBOXYLIC ACIDS

Lactate

Clear evidence has emerged for Na/lactate cotransport across renal brush borders. L-lactate is transiently accumulated within rat and rabbit brush-border vesicles in the presence of an inwardly directed Na gradient (3, 21, 32, 33). No overshoot is observed in the absence of Na gradients. It is clear from pH experiments that neither H/lactate cotransport nor nonionic diffusion account for a significant fraction of lactate uptake (3). The initial rate of lactate uptake is stimulated as much as 25-fold by Na and, at least under voltage-clamped conditions (26), is insensitive to inorganic anions. Uptake is a saturable function of the lactate concentration (Table 2) with a J_{max}^1 of 70–120 nmol mg^{-1} min^{-1} and a K_m^1 of 0.2–4.3 mM. Some of the variations are due to the different species, the uptake times, and variations in membrane potential.

Lactate cotransport is directly proportional to the membrane potential (29) and is electrogenic (23, 38). Frömter and his colleagues (36) also find that

Table 2   Kinetics of brush-border Na-dependent monocarboxylic-acid transport

Acid	J_{max}^1 (nmol mg^{-1} min^{-1})	K_m^1 (mM)	Species	Refs.	Notes
Renal					
L-lactate	120	4.3	rat	3	a
	50	0.5	rabbit	32	a, f
	—	0.2	rabbit	38	e
	70	1.1	horse	29	a, f
3-hydroxybutyrate	3.2	10	rat	15	c
acetoacetate	3.2	4	rat	15	c
nicotinic acid	0.8	0.3	rabbit	9	c
pyruvate	11	0.1	rabbit	32	b, f
	139	10	rabbit	32	b, f
	—	0.25	rabbit	38	e
Intestinal					
L-lactate	1.6	1	rat	18	d

Notes: (*a*) 5-sec uptakes; (*b*) 1-sec uptakes; (*c*) 15-sec uptakes; (*d*) 30-sec uptakes; (*e*) p. d. measurements; and (*f*) voltage-clamped at 0 mV.

L-lactate depolarizes the membrane in the renal tubule. As in the case of other Na-cotransport systems (37, 47), this depolarization is probably due to an increase in the Na conductance of the brush-border membrane. Although there is no direct evidence about the kinetic effects of membrane potential on lactate transport, our data (Table 2) suggests a K_m effect similar to that reported for succinate (50).

Some information about the kinetics of Na/lactate transport is available under zero-*trans* conditions, i.e. lactate uptake as a function of extravesicular (*cis*) na and lactate in the absence of intravesicular (*trans*) substrates. Mengual & Sudaka (29) find that *cis* Na changes the K_m^1 without changing the J_{max}^1, i.e. Na behaves as a competitive activator. As in the case of succinate (50), this is interpreted as an ordered reaction mechanism whereby Na binds first to increase the affinity of the transporter for lactate. In further experiments under equilibrium exchange conditions (30), lactate transport occurs by an iso-ordered Bi Bi process with glide symmetry. Namely, lactate uptake is activated by low Na and inhibited by high Na concentrations, and Na uptake was activated by low lactate and inhibited by high lactate concentrations. Taking the zero-*trans* and the equilibrium exchange experiments together, Mengual and associates concluded that Na binds first to the transporter at the *cis* side of the membrane and is the one to be released first at the *trans* side, i.e. first-in–first-out kinetics or glide symmetry.

There is conflicting evidence regarding the Na/lactate coupling coefficient. First, the Na activation curves, i.e. lactate uptake at a fixed lactate concentration vs *cis* Na, are hyperbolic (3, 29, E. P. Nord, unpublished observations). Second, reciprocal plots of uptake vs the square of the *cis* Na concentration are linear, and Hill plots have a slope of 2, under both zero-*trans* and equilibrium exchange conditions (29). Third, the lactate-dependent Na uptake is a hyperbolic function of *cis* Na at a fixed *cis* lactate (Nord, unpublished observations). Fourth, the J_{max} for lactate-dependent Na uptake was close to the J_{max} for Na-dependent lactate uptake (Nord, unpublished observations). And fifth, direct estimates of the lactate/Na coupling coefficients under equilibrium exchange ranged from 1.4 to 1.7 (30). Although the reason for these divergent results is unclear, it is generally thought that the coupling coefficient has to be at least 2 in order to explain the electrogenic nature of the monovalent organic-anion transporter.

Specificity

As indicated in Table 2, other monovalent acids are transported into renal brush-border vesicles by Na-cotransport. These include hydroxy acids, ketone bodies, and aromatic acids. The specificity has been extensively explored both in vesicles (33) and intact tubules (45, 46) using competition experiments. Despite differences in animals and experimental protocols, there is remarkable agreement between the conclusions reached. A wide range of monocarboxylic acids inhibit lactate transport (see Figure 3).

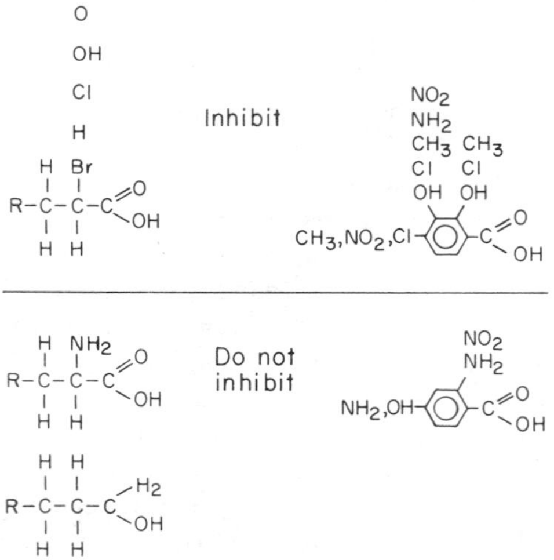

Figure 3   The structural specificity for monocarboxylate transport by renal brush borders. Those analogs above the *horizontal line* inhibit Na-dependent lactate transport, while those below do not. Replacement of $-COOH$ with $-SOOOH$, $-OH$, $-CONH_2$, or NH_2 leads to loss of interaction with the transporter.

The general findings are that:

1. A single carboxyl group is an absolute requirement, and preference is given to 3–6 carbon-chain aliphatic molecules and to single benzene or heterocyclic rings, i.e. monocarboxylic acids with a hydrophobic residue of optimal dimensions.

2. An amino group decreases the inhibitor constant 1–2 orders of magnitude.

3. Likewise, addition of ketone or hydroxyl groups decreases the inhibitor constant, and the effect increases the further away from the carboxyl group.

4. Intramolecular forces, notably inductive effects, may also play a role in substrate-carrier interactions. Although we found no correlation between pK_as and K_is for aliphatic acids, Ullrich's group found that meta- and para-substituted analogs of benzoic acid inhibit D-lactate transport, as predicted from Hammett's rules. One explanation for the difference is that the inductive effects may be overruled in the aliphatic acids by other effects (steric, hydrophobic bonding).

A discrepancy exists between these results and those of Barac-Nieto et al (3), who reported that acetate, pyruvate, and proprionate failed to inhibit lactate uptake into rat vesicles. The origin of this discrepancy is still not clear. The specificity of this Na-dependent L-lactate transport system is very reminiscent of that obtained for monocarboxylate transport in erythrocytes (13). Deuticke (13) suggested some structural elements of the red cell substrate binding site based on the substrate affinity, and these are summarized in Figure 4. Although the red cell carrier is presumably a H-lactate cotransporter, the site of H binding is undefined. The major conclusion from these experiments is that the lactate carrier has a very wide specificity for both aromatic and aliphatic monocarboxylic acids. A reservation about this attractive hypothesis is that the inhibitors of lactate transport may not all be in fact transported themselves. As indicated in Table 2, 3 hydroxybutyrate, acetoacetate, pyruvate, and nicotonic acid are transported by renal brush-border vesicles, but the J^s_{max} are more than an order of magnitude lower than that for lactate. This may be due to technical limitations of the experiments, but it suggests that lactate and these acids are not handled by the same carrier system. Other differences occur, such as the fact that 3 hydroxybutyrate, acetoacetate, and nicotinate transport are electroneutral (9, 15). This needs to be confirmed by more direct measurement of membrane potentials.

The transport of pyruvate appears to be more complex in that there are two pathways for Na-dependent uptake with rabbit vesicles: a high-affinity, low-capacity system, and a low-affinity, high-capacity system (32). The high-affinity system is more sensitive to inhibition by monocarboxylic acids than dicarboxylic acids, whereas the converse holds for the low-affinity system. We concluded that pyruvate shares both the mono- and the di-carboxylate carriers.

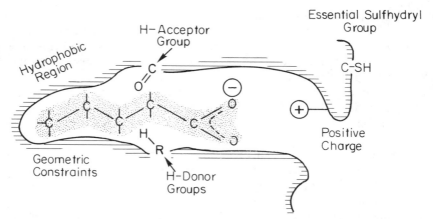

Figure 4   A schematic view of the carboxylate binding site of the renal Na/lactate cotransporter. This is based on the inhibitor constants of the aliphatic acids (33) and the position of the essential –SH group is based on the action of group-specific reagents (5). No information is available about the Na binding site.

Intestinal Lactate Transport

Hildman et al (18) reported that a Na-dependent uptake of lactate also occurred in rat intestinal brush borders. An overshoot is observed under Na-gradient conditions, and this was not seen with other salts. Although the system was saturable (Table 2), the J_{max}^l was substantially lower than that in the kidney. In rabbit vesicles, we (38, 42) were unable to detect any significant Na-dependent lactate transport. In rat, lactate uptake was inhibited by pyruvate and propionate as in the kidney. Pyruvate was transported across the brush-border surface of the hamster intestine by a Na-dependent, saturable system that was insensitive to the presence of Krebs-cycle intermediates (10).

Basolateral Membranes

In contrast to the brush border, lactate transport across both the rat intestinal and renal basolateral membranes occurs chiefly by facilitated diffusion (4, 43). It is possible that lactate transport occurs, in part, by an anion exchanger (27), in view of the common *trans*-stimulation and inhibitor effects.

CONCLUSIONS

Vesicle studies over the previous eight years have made a considerable impact in our understanding of renal carboxylate transport. Transport systems for both mono- and dicarboxylic acids have been identified and characterized, using kinetic approaches in both brush-border and basolateral preparations from the renal cortex. These studies now provide a firm conceptual basis for the understanding of the handling of carboxylates by the renal proximal tubule. Future studies will be directed towards the identification, purification, and reconstitution of these transporters with the goal of deducing both the mechanisms and regulation of these transport processes. So far, partial purification and reconstitution of brush-border glucose, amino acid, and carboxylic-acid transporters have been achieved (22), and histidyl residues have been located at, or near, the active site of the dicarboxylate carrier (5). Recently, a 50,000-dalton dicarboxylate binding protein has been isolated from rabbit renal brush border membranes (19a). The dissociation constants for succinate and malate binding were found to be comparable to those for transport in the brush borders. Even more progress has been obtained for the intestinal brush-border glucose transporter. The transport peptide, or a 75,000-dalton subunit, has been identified using photo-affinity labels, monoclonal antibodies, and covalent fluorescent probes, and it has been reconstituted into liposomes (see 34, 35). The fluorescent probe has also revealed that Na induces a conformational change in the transport protein and that a tyrosyl residue is at or near the Na binding site. So the immediate future holds considerable promise for elucidation of the molecular mechanisms involved in the transport of metabolites across renal and intestinal epithelial membranes.

Acknowledgments

I am grateful to my colleagues Niels Bindslev, Bruce Hirayama, Ian Kippen, Eddy Nord, Rick Schell, and Stee Wright for their many contributions to these studies. This work was supported by USPHS (AM 19567 and NS 90666).

Literature Cited

1. Angielski, S., Pempkowiak, L., Gmaj, P., Hoppe, A., Nowicka, C. 1976. The effect of maleate and lithium on renal function and metabolism. In *Renal Metabolism in Relation to Renal Function*, ed. U. Schmidt, U. C. Duboch, pp. 142–52. Bern, Switz: Huber
2. Barac-Nieto, M. 1984. Effects of pH, calcium, and succinate on Na-citrate cotransport in renal microvilli. *Am. J. Physiol.* In press
3. Barac-Nieto, M., Murer, H., Kinne, R. 1980. Lactate-sodium cotransport in rat renal brush border membranes. *Am. J. Physiol.* 239:F496–F506
4. Barac-Nieto, M., Murer, H., Kinne, R. 1982. Asymmetry in the transport of lactate by basolateral and brush border membranes of rat kidney cortex. *Pfluegers Arch.* 392:366–71
5. Bindslev, N., Wright, E. M. 1984. Histidyl residues at the active site of the Na/succinate cotransport in rabbit renal brush border. *J. Membr. Biol.* 81:159–70
6. Bond, P. A., Jenner, F. A. 1974. The effects of lithium and related metal ions on the urinary excretion of 2-oxoglutarate and citrate in the rat. *Br. J. Pharmacol.* 50:283–89
7. Bond, P. A., Jenner, F. A. 1975. The effects of lithium on organic acid excretion. In *Lithium Research and Therapy*, ed. F. N. Johnson, pp. 499–506. London: Academic
8. Bond, P. A., Jenner, F. A., Lee, C. R., Lenton, E., Pollitt, R. J., Sampson, G. A. 1972. Effects of lithium salts on urinary-excretion of α-oxoglutarate in man. *Br. J. Pharmacol.* 46:116–23
9. Boumendil-Podevin, E. F., Podevin, R. A. 1981. Nicotinic acid transport by brush border membrane vesicles from rabbit kidney. *Am. J. Physiol.* 240:F185–F191
10. Browne, J. L., Sanford, P. A., Smyth, D. H. 1978. Transfer and metabolism of

citrate, succinate, α-ketoglutarate, and pyruvate by hamster small intestine. *Proc. R. Soc. London Ser. B* 200:117–35

11. Burckhardt, G. 1984. Sodium-dependent dicarboxylate transport in rat renal basolateral membrane vesicles. *Pfluegers Arch.* 401:254–61

12. Cohen, J. J., Barac-Nieto, M. 1973. Renal metabolism of substrates in relation to renal function. In *Handbook of Physiology*, ed. S. R. Geiger, pp. 909–1001. Washington DC: Am. J. Physiol.

13. Deuticke, B. 1982. Monocarboxylate transport in erythrocytes. *J. Membr. Biol.* 70:89–103

14. Fukuhara, Y., Turner, R. J. 1983. Sodium-dependent succinate transport in renal outer cortical brush border membrane vesicles. *Am. J. Physiol.* 245: F374–F381

15. Garcia, M. L., Benavides, J., Valdivieso, F. 1980. Ketone body transport in renal brush border membrane vesicles. *Biochim. Biophys. Acta* 600:922–30

16. Grassl, S. M., Heinz, E., Kinne, R. 1983. Effect of K⁺ and H⁺ on sodium/citrate cotransport in renal brush border vesicles. *Biochim. Biophys. Acta* 736: 178–88

17. Guder, W. G., Wirthensohn, G. 1981. Renal turnover of substrates. In *Renal Transport of Organic Substances*, ed. R. Greger, F. Lang, S. Silbernagl, pp. 66–77. Berlin: Springer-Verlag

18. Hildmann, B., Storelli, C., Haase, W., Barac-Nieto, M., Murer, H. 1980. Sodium ion/L-lactate co-transport in rabbit small intestinal brush border membrane vesicles. *Biochem. J.* 186:169–76

19. Hirayama, B., Wright, E. M. 1984. Asymmetry of the Na-succinate cotransporter in rabbit renal brush border membranes. *Biochim. Biophys. Acta.* 775:17–21

19a. Jacobsen, C., Røigaard-Petersen, H., Jørgensen, K. E., Sheikh, M. I. 1984. Isolation and partial purification of dicarboxylic acid binding protein from luminal-membrane vesicles or rabbit kidney cortex. *Biochim. Biophys. Acta* 773:173–79

20. Jorgensen, K. E., Kragh-Hansen, U., Roigaard-Petersen, H., Sheikh, I. M. 1983. Citrate uptake by basolateral and luminal membrane vesicles from rabbit kidney cortex. *Am. J. Physiol.* 244: F686–F695

21. Kippen, I., Hirayama, B., Klinenberg, J. R., Wright, E. M. 1979. Transport of tricarboxylic acid cycle intermediates by membrane vesicles from renal brush bor-

der. *Proc. Natl. Acad. Sci USA* 76:3397–400

22. Koepsell, H., Korn, K., Ferguson, D., Menuhr, H., Ollig, D., Haase, W. 1984. Reconstitution and partial purification of several Na⁺ cotransport systems from renal brush border membranes: Properties of the L-glutamate transporter in proteoliposomes. *J. Biol. Chem.* 259:6548–58

23. Kragh-Hansen, U., Jorgensen, K. E., Sheikh, M. I. 1982. The use of potential-sensitive cyanine dye for studying ion-dependent electrogenic renal transport of organic solutes. Spectrophotometric measurements. *Biochem. J.* 208:359–68

24. Kragh-Hansen, U., Jorgensen, K. E., Sheikh, M. I. 1982. The use of potential-sensitive cyanine dye for studying ion-dependent electrogenic renal transport of organic solutes. Uptake of L-malate and D-malate by luminal membrane vesicles. *Biochem. J.* 208:359–68

25. Lee, C. R., Pollitt, R. J. 1973. The effect of lithium salts on the urinary excretion of some dicarboxylic acids. *Biochem. Soc. Trans.* 1:108–9

26. Levine, R., Hirayama, B., Wright, E. M. 1984. Sensitivity of renal brush border Na⁺-cotransport systems to anions. *Biochim. Biophys. Acta* 769:508–10

27. Löw, I., Friedrich, T., Burckhardt, G. 1984. Properties of an anion exchanger in rat renal basolateral membrane vesicles. *Am. J. Physiol.* 246:F334–F342

28. Medow, M. S., Baruch, S. B., Gutierrez, O., King, V. F., Leal-Pinto, E. 1978. Transport of citric acid by luminal and contra luminal membrane vesicles of dog renal cortex. *Fed. Proc.* 37:466

29. Mengual, R., Sudaka, P. 1983. The mechanism of Na⁺-L-lactate cotransport by brush border membrane vesicles from horse kidney: analysis of rapid equilibrium kinetics in absence of membrane potential. *J. Membr. Biol.* 71:163–71

30. Mengual, R., Leblanc, G., Sudaka, P. 1983. The mechanism of Na⁺-L-lactate cotransport by brush border membrane vesicles from horse kidney. *J. Biol. Chem.* 258:15071–78

31. Murer, H., Kinne, R. 1980. The use of isolated membrane vesicles to study epithelial transport processes. *J. Membr. Biol.* 55:81–95

32. Nord, E., Wright, S. H., Kippen, I., Wright, E. M. 1982. Pathways for carboxylic acid transport by rabbit renal brush border membrane vesicles. *Am. J. Physiol.* 243:F456–F462

33. Nord, E. P., Wright, S. H., Kippen, I., Wright, E. M. 1983. Specificity of the

Na$^+$-dependent monocarboxylic acid transport pathway in rabbit renal brush border membranes. *J. Membr. Biol.* 72:213–21

34. Peerce, B. E., Wright, E. M. 1984. Conformational changes in the intestinal brush border sodium-glucose cotransporter labeled with fluorescein isothiocyanate. *Proc. Natl. Acad. Sci. USA* 81:2223–26

35. Peerce, B. E., Wright, E. M. 1984. Sodium induced conformational changes in the glucose transporter of intestinal brush borders. *J. Biol. Chem.* In press

36. Samarzija, I., Molnar, V., Frömter, E. 1981. The stoichiometry of Na$^+$-coupled anion absorption across the brush border membrane of rat renal proximal tubule. In *Kidney and Body Fluids,* ed. L. Takacs, pp. 419–23. Budapest: Akademiai Kaido. Vol. 11

37. Schell, R. E., Wright, E. M. 1984. Electrophysiology of succinate transport across rabbit renal brush border membranes. *J. Physiol.* In press

38. Schell, R. E., Stevens, B. R., Wright, E. M. 1983. Kinetics of sodium-dependent solute transport by rabbit renal and jejunal brush border vesicles using a fluorescent dye. *J. Physiol.* 335:307–18

39. Sheikh, M. I., Kragh-Hansen, U., Jorgensen, K. E., Roigaard-Petersen, H. 1982. An efficient method for the isolation and separation of basolateral-membrane and luminal-membrane vesicles from rabbit kidney cortex. *Biochem. J.* 208:377–82

40. Sheridan, E., Rumrich, G., Ullrich, K. J. 1983. Reabsorption of dicarboxylic acids from the proximal convolution of rat kidney. *Pfluegers Arch.* 399:18–28

41. Simpson, D. P. 1983. Citrate excretion: a window on renal metabolism. *Amer. J. Physiol.* 244:F223–F234

42. Stevens, B. R., Wright, S. H., Hirayama, B. S., Gunther, R. D., Ross, V., et al. 1982. Organic and inorganic solute transport in renal and intestinal membrane vesicles preserved in liquid nitrogen. *Membr. Biochem.* 4:271–82

43. Storelli, C., Corcelli, A., Cassano, G., Hildmann, B., Murer, H., Lippe, C. 1980. Polar distribution of sodium-dependent and sodium-independent transport system for L-lactate in the plasma membrane of rat enterocytes. *Pfluegers Arch.* 388:11–16

44. Ullrich, K. J., Fasold, H., Rumrich, G., Klöss, S. 1984. Secretion and contraluminal uptake of dicarboxylic acids in the proximal convolution of rat kidney. *Pfluegers Arch.* 400:241–49

45. Ullrich, K. J., Rumrich, G., Klöss, S. 1982. Reabsorption of monocarboxylic acids in the proximal tubule of the rat kidney. II. Specificity for aliphatic compounds. *Pfluegers Arch.* 395:220–26

46. Ullrich, K. J., Rumrich, G., Klöss, S., Fasold, H. 1982. Reabsorption of monocarboxylic acids in the proximal tubule of the rat kidney. III. Specificity for aromatic compounds. *Pfluegers Arch.* 395:227–31

47. Wright, E. M. 1984. Electrophysiology of plasma membrane vesicles. *Am. J. Physiol.* 246:F363–F372

48. Wright, E. M., Hirayama, B., Levine, R. 1984. Na uptake via Na-succinate cotransport in renal brush borders. *Kidney Int.* 25:322

49. Wright, E. M., Wright, S. H., Hirayama, B., Kippen, I. 1982. Interactions between lithium and renal transport of Krebs cycle intermediates. *Proc. Natl. Acad. Sci. USA* 79:7514–17

50. Wright, S. H., Hirayama, B., Kaunitz, J. D., Kippen, I., Wright, E. M. 1983. Kinetics of sodium succinate cotransport across renal brush border membranes. *J. Biol. Chem.* 258:5456–62

51. Wright, S. H., Kippen, I., Klinenberg, J. R., Wright, E. M. 1980. Specificity of the transport system for tricaboxylic acid cycle intermediates in renal brush borders. *J. Membr. Biol.* 57:73–82

52. Wright, S. H., Kippen, I., Wright, E. M. 1982. Effect of pH on the transport of Krebs cycle intermediates in renal brush border membranes. *Biochim. Biophys. Acta* 684:287–90

53. Wright, S. H., Kippen, I., Wright, E. M. 1982. Stoichiometry of Na$^+$-succinate cotransport in renal brush border membranes. *J. Biol. Chem.* 257:1773–78

54. Wright, S. H., Krasne, S., Kippen, I., Wright, E. M. 1981. Na$^+$-dependent transport of tricarboxylic acid cycle intermediates by renal brush border membranes. *Biochim. Biophys. Acta* 640:767–78

Ann. Rev. Physiol. 1985. 47:143–71

TRANSPORT OF METABOLIC SUBSTRATES IN RENAL MITOCHONDRIA

Anton C. Schoolwerth and Kathryn F. LaNoue

Departments of Medicine and Physiology, The Milton S. Hershey Medical Center, The Pennsylvania State University, Hershey, Pennsylvania 17033

INTRODUCTION

Mitochondria are the organelles, found in cells, that contain enzymes of the citric acid cycle and the electron transport chain involved in the function of oxidative phosphorylation. As part of this function, a steady flow of metabolites, into and out of the mitochondrial matrix space, is necessary. O_2, ADP, phosphate, and electron-rich substrates such as pyruvate, fatty acids, and ketone bodies must enter the mitochondria, and the products, H_2O, CO_2, and ATP must leave. Although O_2, H_2O, and CO_2 are permeable to the inner mitochondrial membrane (59, 88), most metabolites are not, because of their highly hydrophillic nature. Specialized transporters are required for the transport of these substances in order for respiration and ATP formation to proceed efficiently.

This article reviews the role of mitochondrial transport systems in cell metabolism. The chemical characteristics and physiological significance of the mitochondrial transporters are considered. The discussion will be extended to a consideration of the specific role of the mitochondrial transporters in renal metabolism. Several comprehensive reviews of metabolite transport have been published in the last few years (59, 80, 92, 93, 108, 145). The emphasis of this review will be on general and specific characteristics of the transporters relevant to renal metabolism.

0066-4278/85/0315-0143$02.00

143

THE MITOCHONDRIAL TRANSPORT SYSTEMS

The Mitchell Hypothesis and $\Delta\mu H^+$

Mitochondria contain the enzymatic machinery for respiration. In most tissues, mitochondria are responsible for the synthesis of the majority of the cells' requirements for ATP. They are vesicles bounded by a double-membrane system (104), and the intact vesicular structure is required for ATP synthesis (119, 165). The explanation for this observation is found in the Mitchell hypothesis (95–97), which in its most general form proposes that the energy available due to the transfer of electrons from energy-rich substrates to oxygen is conserved in the form of an electrochemical gradient of protons across the mitochondrial membrane system. Thus, the energy of respiration is consumed to pump protons electrogenically. The electrochemical gradient of protons thus formed (usually referred to as $\Delta\mu H^+$) is then used directly by the mitochondrial ATP synthase as its source of energy. The symbol $\Delta\mu H^+$ is defined as:

$$\Delta\mu H^+ = \Delta\Psi - 2.3 \frac{RT}{F} \Delta pH$$

where ΔpH is the pH gradient across the mitochondrial inner membrane and $\Delta\Psi$ is the electrical gradient, R is the gas constant, T is absolute temperature, and F is the Faraday.

In order for the $\Delta\mu H^+$ to work efficiently as the intermediate storage form of energy from substrate oxidation, the vesicular membrane must remain intact and should not be "leaky." Dissipation of $\Delta\mu H^+$ via passive leaks of protons or other ions in the direction of their electrochemical gradients would compromise the cells' ability to synthesize ATP.

Extensive experimental testing over the past 15 years has convinced most biochemists that the Mitchell hypothesis is correct in its most general form, although the details of the precise molecular mechanism by which $\Delta\mu H^+$ is formed and used by the enzymes of oxidation and phosphorylation are not yet well understood (9, 43, 46, 121, 169). Additionally, some workers believe that the bulk phase $\Delta\mu H^+$ is not in the direct path of redox conversion to ATP but that localized electrical interactions of redox enzymes with the synthase may occur (103, 130).

The lipid-to-protein ratio of the outer mitochondrial membrane is higher than the inner membrane. The outer membrane is permeable to most small and medium-size molecules (molecular weights below 5,000) and thus does not present a significant permeability barrier to ions. It contains the membrane protein, porin, which forms channels in natural lipid bilayers (35). The function of the outer membrane is not well understood. The inner mitochondrial membrane is 70% protein, and these proteins include the enzymes of the electron transport chain and of ATP synthesis. The inner membrane is also relatively impermeable to H^+, Na^+, and K^+ and to most ions and hydrophillic compounds. It has been shown that isolated actively respiring mitochondria as well as mitochondria in situ maintain a bulk phase $\Delta\mu H^+$ of about 200 mvolts (53, 100, 157). The majority of this energy is stored in the form of the electrical potential, $\Delta\Psi$, which maintains the mitochondrial matrix space negative with respect to the outside.

Chemical Characteristics of the Mitochondrial Transporters

The substrates of mitochondrial enzymes must be transported into the mitochondria, and products must be transported out. Most mitochondrial metabolites are hydrophillic, polyvalent anions. As such, they would be excluded from the mitochondrial matrix space by the large negative $\Delta\Psi$. Transport of metabolites other than H_2O, CO_2, acetate, and NH_3 require specific proteins in the mitochondrial inner membrane (80, 81). Experimental proof that transport is catalyzed by specific proteins is as follows: (a) Transport of radiolabeled metabolites into the mitochondria exhibits saturation kinetics (80–82); (b) Exchange of specific metabolites across the membrane is faster than net transport, and there is great specificity for exchange of one metabolite with another (50, 82); (c) In most cases, only the natural stereoisomers are transported (81); and (d) Specific inhibitors of certain transporters have been identified (93, 166). Some of these inhibitors are natural products, toxins elaborated by plants and bacteria. Additionally, it is interesting to note that sulfhydryl reagents can be found that will inhibit almost all of the mitochondrial transporters (28, 30, 80). Sensitivity varies so that different sulfhydryl reagents are variously effective in inhibiting the different transporters. Evidently, the reactive SH group(s) in the different transporters exist in rather different chemical environments.

Twelve different transporters have been identified in the inner membranes of mammalian mitochondria. However, mitochondria from any given tissue source may not have the complete set of twelve. We have listed these transporters in Table I, along with their substrates and specific inhibitors. The carriers have been classified according to the manner in which they interact with $\Delta\mu H^+$. Mitchell, in 1961 (94), suggested on theoretical grounds that the anionic substrates of mitochondrial dehydrogenases are transported electroneutrally into the mitochondrial matrix space as free acids, i.e. in cotransport with H^+ to neutralize their negative charges. This would imply that the gradient of the substrate anions, at equilibrium, is inversely proportional to ΔpH.

$$\log \frac{(A^{n-})_i}{(A^{n-})_o} = n\Delta pH \qquad\qquad 1.$$

Table 1 Mitochondrial metabolite transporters

Category	Name	Physiological substrates	Inhibitors — Specific	Inhibitors — Sulfhydryl reagent
Electroneutral proton compensated	phosphate	phosphate, arsenate		organic mercurials, N-ethylmaleimide
	glutamate	glutamate	avenaciolide	N-ethylmaleimide
	pyruvate	monocarboxylic acids, ketone bodies, branched-chain ketoacids	α-cyano-3-hydroxycinnamate	organic mercurials, N-ethylmaleimide
	ornithine	ornithine, citrulline, lysine		
Electroneutral anion exchange	dicarboxylate	phosphate, malate, succinate, oxalacetate	butylmalonate, bathophenanthroline, iodobenzylmalonate phenylsuccinate, phthaonate	organic mercurials
	α-ketoglutarate	malate, α-ketoglutarate, succinate, oxalacetate	phthalonate, bathophenanthroline, phenylsuccinate, butylmalonate	
	tricarboxylate	citrate, isocitrate, phosphoenolpyruvate, malate, succinate	1,2,3-benzene-tricarboxylate, α-cetylcitrate, bathophenanthroline	
Neutral	carnitine	carnitine, acylcarnitine	sulfobetaines	organic mercurials, N-ethylmaleimide
	neutral amino acids	neutral amino acids		organic mercurials
	glutamine	glutamine		organic mercurials
Electrophoretic	glutamate-aspartate	glutamate/aspartate		
	adenine nucleotide	ADP, ATP	glisoxepide (nonspecific) atractyloside, carboxyatractyloside, bongkrekate, long-chain acyl CoA, α-cetylcitrate	

where $(A^{n-})_i$ is the concentration of permeant anion in the matrix space, and $(A^{n-})_o$ is the concentration outside the membrane. The relationship can be derived in two ways, assuming either that the free acid is transported on the carrier, or that (H^+) and (A^{n-}) are separate substrates of the carrier.

Thus at equilibrium the inward and outward transport rates must be equal such that: $k\ (H^+)_i^n\ (A^{n-})_i = k\ (H)_o^n\ (A^{n-})_o$

and $\dfrac{(A^{n-})_i}{(A^{n-})_o} = \dfrac{(H^+)_i^n}{(H^+)_o^n} = n\Delta pH$ and $\log \dfrac{(A^{n-})_i}{(A^{n-})_o} = -n\ \Delta pH$

where k is equal to the rate constant for the transporter, $(H^+)_i$ and $(A^{n-})_i$ are the inside concentrations of (H^+) and (A^{n-}), and $(H^+)_o$ and $(A^{n-})_o$ are the external concentrations. As discussed previously (80, 82), Equation 1 holds only for relatively low concentrations of substrates, where the carrier does not become saturated with substrate on either side of the membrane.

On the other hand, if H_nA is the permeant species, at equilibrium (H_nA) will be the same on both sides of the membrane. Therefore:

$$\frac{(H^+)_o^n\ (A^{n-})_o}{(H_nA)_o} = \frac{(H_i^+)^n\ (A_i^{n-})}{(H_nA)_i}$$

since:

$$(H_nA)_o = (H_nA)_i$$

then:

$$(H^+)_o\ (A^{n-})_o = (H^+)_i\ (A^{n-})_i$$

and $\dfrac{(A^{-n})_o}{(A^{-n})_i} = \dfrac{(H^+)_i^n}{(H^+)_o^n}$

It became possible to test the theoretical prediction when K^+ ionophores, such as valinomycin and nigericin, became available (118). Valinomycin catalyzes the electrophoretic movement of K^+ across the mitochondrial membrane. At high levels of K^+, it collapses $\Delta\Psi$ and can be used to manipulate $\Delta\Psi$ independently of ΔpH, using different levels of K^+. Likewise, nigericin catalyzes the electroneutral exchange of K^+ for H^+ and, therefore, can be used to manipulate ΔpH, independently of $\Delta\Psi$. In 1964, Palmieri et al (107) tested Equation 1 using the ionophores and external (H^+) changes to vary ΔpH independently of the mitochondrial energy state. It was found that $(A^{n-})_i/(A^{n-})_o$ varied as predicted with ΔpH.

The anion gradients were measured by rapidly separating mitochondria from their media using centrifugal filtration through silicone oil. Subsequent work, aimed at measuring the kinetic parameters of individual transporters, has made use of this technique or the so-called "inhibitor-stop method," which depends on the availability of suitable specific inhibitors to quench transport (26, 106, 110, 153).

Prior to the development of quantitative methods of measuring transport, most of the transporters were identified and characterized in terms of substrate specificity by swelling techniques (16). Mitochondria swell massively in the presence of high (isoosmolar) external concentrations of permeant substances as long as inward transport does not bring about a charge or pH imbalance (80). Swelling is visualized by means of the attendant changes in light scattering, which can be evaluated spectrophotometrically. The method cannot be used to determine the effect of substrate concentration on transport rates and, in general, is thought of as a qualitative method. However, quantitative data have been reported using light scattering as a tool (38, 57). Recent studies of K^+/H^+ exchange have, in fact, made extensive use of light scattering as a quantitative tool (38).

The early swelling studies demonstrated that only a few of the anionic substrates that cause swelling require concomitant proton transport. These are listed in Table I under the category "electroneutral proton compensated transporters" and include the phosphate (91), glutamate (54), and pyruvate (116) transporters. The ornithine transporter is also listed in this category. Although it is a cation at physiological pH, it is transported electroneutrally in exchange for a proton (90). At one time it was thought that the ornithine transporter catalyzed an electrophoretic exchange of positively charged ornithine for its neutral product, citrulline (37). The demonstration that ornithine transport is electroneutral (90), although it exchanges with citrulline, emphasizes (8, 13) the importance of the specificity of the protein carriers as opposed to the ionic state of the substrates in determining whether transport is electroneutral or electrophoretic in nature. It is likely that the cationic amino acids (58) are also transported electroneutrally in exchange for protons, possibly on the same transporter as ornithine (8).

Di- and tricarboxylic acid anionic metabolites such as malate, succinate, α-ketoglutarate, and citrate also accumulate in the mitochondrial matrix space as a function of the ΔpH across the matrix. As shown in Table I, these are transported electroneutrally by exchange carriers (109). One of these, the dicarboxylate carrier, catalyzes a 1:1 exchange of dicarboxylic acids such as malate with phosphate (115). Thus, the phosphate gradient supported by the ΔpH in turn supports the malate gradient. Other exchange carriers such as the α-ketoglutarate (110) and tricarboxylate carrier (114) catalyze exchange with malate. Because of this "cascade" effect stemming from the phosphate gradient, there are very significant gradients of the dicarboxylic and tricarboxylic acids across the mitochondrial membrane even in actively metabolizing mitochondria. It is important to emphasize that even when anions of apparently different charge exchange with each other on the di- and tricarboxylic acid carriers, the process is, nevertheless, neutral, because the charge is found experimentally to be balanced by protons. Thus, when citrate with three negative charges exchanges with malate, with two, a proton is transported with citrate (114).

Some of the transporters facilitate the transport of neutral molecules such as the neutral amino acids and carnitine. The glutamine transporter is one of these (19, 42). Metabolites transported by these neutral carriers are not accumulated in the mitochondrial matrix space, but at high external concentrations can cause massive mitochondrial swelling (71).

The final category of transporters include those that involve movement of charges across the membrane. These are termed electrophoretic because under physiological conditions they catalyze metabolite transport down the electrical gradient. Only two metabolite transporters fall in this category. The glutamate-aspartate translocase catalyzes an exchange of glutamate for aspartate and is electrophoretic because the carrier also transports a proton with glutamate, but not aspartate.

The electrophoretic nature of this transporter can be easily demonstrated in a variety of ways. The stoichiometry of proton transport to glutamate transport has been measured (78, 84, 111). The metabolism of glutamate via the transaminase pathway involves the glutamate-aspartate translocase. Glutamate enters the mitochondria in exchange for aspartate, the glutamate transaminates with oxalacetate, and the oxalacetate is transformed to aspartate, which then exchanges with the next molecule of glutamate entering the mitochondria. When $\Delta\Psi$ is collapsed by uncouplers or valinomycin and K^+, the rate of glutamate transamination decreases by an order of magnitude, and matrix aspartate levels increase (77, 98). Also, it has recently been shown (20) that when the mitochondria are allowed to establish an equilibrium in the presence of ATP and ADP, acetoacetate, and β-OH-butyrate, the ratio of glutamate and aspartate on either side of the membrane establishes an equilibrium with the membrane potential, $\Delta\Psi$, such that:

$$RT_{log} \frac{(glut/asp)_{in}}{(glut/asp)_{out}} = F\Delta\Psi$$

where R, T, and F have their conventional meanings.

Additional data show that the reverse exchange, aspartate into the mitochondria and glutamate out, is negligible under physiological conditions (163).

The other carrier that may operate electrophoretically is the adenine nucleotide carrier (61). The substrates of the adenine nucleotide carrier are ADP and ATP. AMP is not transported, nor are any natural nucleotides other than the adenine derivatives. The transporter does not transport protons (79), and the exchange of ATP, which has approximately four negative charges at pH 7, and ADP, which has three, results in the movement of one charge for each nucleotide pair exchanged. Klingenberg and coworkers initially suggested that the carrier was electrophoretic because the ratio of ATP/ADP inside the mitochondria is lower than the ratio outside when the $\Delta\Psi$ is physiologically high (52). The difference disappears in the presence of uncoupling agents. Later, more quantitative studies (65) demonstrated that:

$$RT \log \frac{(ATP/ADP)_{in}}{(ATP/ADP)_{out}} = F \Delta\Psi \qquad\qquad 2.$$

where R, T, and F have their conventional meanings.

The early discovery of two specific inhibitors of this translocase, which bind to the carrier from opposite sides of the membrane, have significantly aided in its study (166). Carboxyatractyloside, a toxin isolated from the thistle, binds to the carrier from the cytosolic side of the membrane, while bongkrekic acid, a mold toxin, binds from the matrix side. The availability of these specific inhibitors has aided in the isolation of the carrier (122), in studies of its kinetics (26, 101), and even in studies of the translocase biosynthesis (175). Far more is known about the structure and function of this transporter than any of the others. Several excellent reviews of the literature concerning the adenine nucleotide carrier are available, and the reader is referred to these for more information (60, 61, 166).

Physiological Significance of the Mitochondrial Transport Systems

Most mitochondria do not have the full set of 12 transporters. Among mammalian mitochondria, the presence or absence of a particular transport activity seems to depend on the nature of the organ from which the mitochondria were isolated rather than on the mammalian species. Thus, all liver mitochondria appear to be rather similar, but different from heart mitochondria. The activities of the transporters reflect the metabolic needs and requirements of the particular tissue. Thus, almost all mitochondria have transporters for adenine nucleotides (60), phosphate (117), pyruvate (50), and acyl carnitine (112, 113, 120), because these are all important for the synthesis of ATP. In heart mitochondria, additional activities are required for the transport of reducing equivalents from the cytosol to the mitochondria (131), because NADH generated during glycolysis is not permeable to the mitochondrial membrane. In heart, as well as liver (170) and kidney (127) (possibly the thick ascending limb of Henle's loop), this is accomplished by the so-called malate aspartate cycle (Figure 1A). Cytosolic NADH is converted to NAD by cytosolic malate dehydrogenase with generation of cytosolic malate. Malate enters the mitochondria in exchange for α-ketoglutarate. The cytosolic α-ketoglutarate generated reacts with cytosolic aspartate to form glutamate and oxalacetate. The glutamate enters the mitochondria in exchange for aspartate. The matrix malate is converted to oxalacetate by malate dehydrogenase. Efflux of oxalacetate is not rapid because of the very low physiological concentration and its rather high K_m for transport. The oxalacetate instead reacts with glutamate, converting its carbons to aspartate, which then completes the cycle by exchanging with glutamate. The transporters required for the cyclic activity are the α-ketoglutarate and the glutamate-aspartate carriers. The electrophoretic nature of the glutamate aspartate carrier allows the mitochondrial $\Delta\Psi$ to be used as an energy source to "pump" cytosolic NADH into the mitochondria and, in tissues where the cycle is active, the redox couple in the mitochondria is maintained 40–60 mvolts more negative inside than out (171). The tricarboxylate carriers and the dicarboxylate carriers are not needed in the heart, and their activities are consequently low (124, 152).

The cells of the proximal tubule in the kidney synthesize glucose from amino acids, pyruvate, and lactate (71a). Because part of the gluconeogenic pathway is inside and part outside the mitochondria, more types of transport carriers are needed than in the heart. The glutamine transporter has high activity (42), and the dicarboxylate carrier is also active (17) in kidney as opposed to heart. In order for malate formed metabolically in the kidney from glutamine to leave the mitochondria for conversion to glucose, the malate must exchange with phosphate rather than another carboxylic acid (Figure 1C). Otherwise, there would be a continuous drain of citric acid-cycle intermediates from the cytosol. The dicarboxylate carrier has high activity only in mitochondria from gluconeogenic tissue. It would be interesting to find out whether the carrier is absent from the more highly glycolytic tissues of the ascending limb of Henle's loop in the kidney. Thus far, kidney cortex mitochondrial preparations are undoubtedly a heterogeneous mixture of different types of mitochondria and cellular types; it is likely that the carrier activities are different from different cells.

It is apparent from the foregoing discussion that the carriers in the mitochondria play at least a permissive role in metabolism. They are present to provide the conduits for metabolic flow as determined by the metabolic pathways and the compartmentation of these pathways in different tissues. Their specificity for certain ionic states of their substrates and for protons allows interactions with the mitochondrial $\Delta\mu H^+$, providing a source of energy for acceleration of flow in a particular direction.

Whether the carriers that participate in metabolic pathways can also modulate fluxes in those pathways according to the needs of tissue is a matter of current conjecture. There is growing evidence that the metabolite carriers in mitochondria of the proximal tubules participate importantly in the regulation

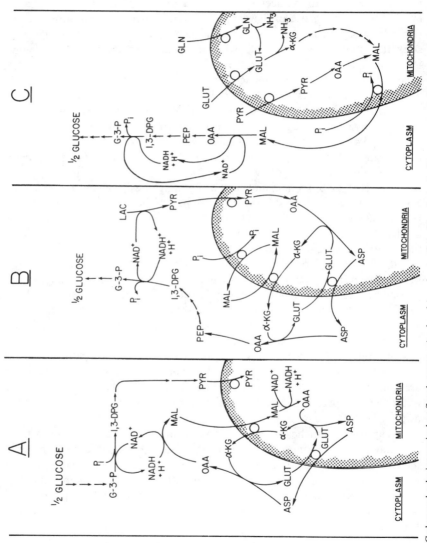

Figure 1   Carbon and reducing equivalent flow between *mitochondria* and *cytosol*. *A*: Glycolysis. *B*: Gluconeogenesis from lactate. *C*: Gluconeogenesis from pyruvate, glutamine, or glutamate.

of ammoniagenesis according to the needs of the organism for acid-base balance (133, 136, 143, 147). This will be discussed in a later section.

A variety of approaches have been used over the years in identifying rate-controlling steps in metabolic pathways. A discussion of the various approaches used can be found in a review by Newsholme & Start (99). A method frequently used in the past has been the so-called "cross-over" method, first introduced by Chance in studying respiratory control (14). According to this method, after perturbing the system in some way to alter flux, one measures all the metabolites in the pathway to discover at which step(s) the change in substrates and products cannot account for the measured change in flux. To use this method to assess control by the carriers, it is necessary to measure gradients across the mitochondrial membranes in intact cells. Methods for doing this have become available in recent years (2, 27, 174) and have been extensively applied in hepatocytes and to a lesser extent in the heart (154, 155). Recent reports of application of one of these methods to kidney tubules are encouraging (47). Even more recently, another approach has become popular in studying metabolic control and has been used extensively to assess the "control strength" of the metabolite carriers (74, 126). The newer approach takes into account the possibility that several steps in any given pathway may share the rate-controlling role (56). In order to assess and quantitate the "control strength" of a given step, a noncompetitive inhibitor of the enzyme or carrier is added to the system in increasing amounts. Control strength is defined as the initial fractional change in flux through the pathway divided by the fractional change in total enzyme activity. Operationally, one plots the flux through the pathway as a function of the inhibitor concentration, and the initial slope of the curve provides a measure of "control strength." It is assumed in this analysis that the sum of the control strengths of the individual steps in the pathway is equal to one. The greater the sigmoidicity of the control strength curve, the lower the control strength.

This method has been used to assess the "control strength" of the pyruvate transporter for pyruvate-supported respiration in isolated mitochondria (49, 87), for gluconeogenesis from lactate and pyruvate in isolated rat hepatocytes (141, 162), and for lipogenesis in adipocytes from pyruvate (162). The inhibitor used in these studies was α-hydroxycyanocinnamate.

The results suggest that mitochondrial pyruvate transport is an important rate-limiting step for respiration from pyruvate and for gluconeogenesis in the presence and absence of glucagon. It has been speculated that the pyruvate transporter is a target of gluconeogenic hormone action in the liver, but recent data throw some doubt on these speculations (35, 83, 157).

Inhibitor titrations have also been used to assess the control strength of the adenine nucleotide carrier for control of respiration in isolated mitochondria and in isolated hepatocytes. The mechanism of control of mitochondrial respiration remains an important question of mitochondrial bioenergetics. Chance & Williams (15) originally proposed that respiration is kinetically controlled by ADP availability, an hypothesis which has received renewed support recently (55). However, a major controversy has centered on whether or not the adenine nucleotide translocator is completely or even partially rate-controlling for respiration. As a consequence of this controversy, several hypotheses have emerged over the past several years. Wilson & Ericinska (28) have proposed a "near-equilibrium hypothesis" whereas others have advocated variations of a translocase hypothesis in which the adenine nucleotide carrier is fully or partially rate-controlling. Wilson and collaborators, in a series of papers (31, 32, 172, 173), have argued that respiration coupled to ATP synthesis is proportional to the inorganic phosphate (P_i) concentration as well as the ADP/ATP ratio. According to the near-equilibrium theory of control, respiration should respond to changes in the extramitochondrial phosphorylation potential as a whole and not to alterations in the concentrations of individual reactants, such as ATP/ADP ratios. Furthermore, at a constant NAD/NADH ratio, respiration should respond to the phosphorylation potential, and, if this latter term remains constant, respiration should also remain constant. These workers, therefore, argued against an important role for the adenine nucleotide translocator in the control of respiration, suggesting that it was too rapid to be significantly off equilibrium.

Alternative views have been expressed from several laboratories, indicating an important role for the adenine nucleotide carrier in the control of respiration (7, 21, 22, 24, 39, 40, 44, 45, 61–64, 73, 76, 85, 100, 101, 158, 159, 167). Two groups have utilized inhibitor titrations with carboxyatractyloside to quantitate the degree of control exerted by the carrier on respiration (7, 24, 39, 40, 44, 45, 73, 76, 85, 158, 159, 167). They have determined that the "control strength" is variable and depends upon the metabolic state, substrate availability, and so on, such that control may be considerable or minimal. Such a view also implies that the control strength may vary from tissue to tissue and from cell to cell within the tissue.

Recent papers by Radda and coworkers have a bearing on this controversy. If the adenine nucleotide carrier and the phosphate carrier were in thermodynamic equilibrium with the mitochondrial ATPase, one would expect the isotopic exchange rate between ATP and P_i to be an order of magnitude faster than the net rate of ATP synthesis under physiological conditions. The rate of ATP synthesis in highly oxidative tissues is likely to be approximately 2.5–3.0-fold the rate of oxygen utilization, because P/O ratios are generally assumed to be three. The isotopic exchange of ATP and P_i cannot be measured in intact tissues such as the kidney because the turnover time of ATP is so rapid. However, the turnover time of ATP can be measured by the saturation transfer technique of nuclear magnetic resonance (NMR) (36). A "label" is placed on the γ-phosphate of ATP by magnetizing the unpaired spin in the ^{31}P nucleus, and the magnetization can be followed as it is transferred chemically to the inorganic phosphate. Using NMR, it is possible to measure much shorter turnover times than one can with radioisotopes. Rates of ATP turnover have recently been measured in this way for the intact heart (89), brain (140), and kidney (34). The results suggest that the exchange rate between ATP and P_i is the same as the net rate of ATP synthesis as judged by O_2 consumption. This, in turn, implies that cytosolic ATP synthesis is not a rapidly reversible process. The most plausible explanation for this is that the adenine nucleotide carrier is far from equilibrium under physiological conditions and, therefore, may be rate-limiting for respiration.

There are still many uncertainties in these flux determinations using saturation-transfer NMR measurements, because, for example, the size of the metabolically active pool of inorganic phosphate is not known. Especially in the kidney, tissue heterogeneity is also a problem. However, the measurements are unlikely to be in error by an order of magnitude, and their stoichiometric consistency with O_2 consumption is striking. At the present time, it is not possible to resolve the controversies that exist with regard to factors controlling the rate of respiration. It is the view of these reviewers that the adenine nucleotide translocator is important, but not the sole controlling or rate-limiting step for respiration. It will be of great interest if specific studies are directed towards examination of the adenine nucleotide translocator in the control of respiration by the kidney.

ROLE OF MITOCHONDRIAL TRANSPORTERS IN RENAL METABOLISM

Gluconeogenesis

Rognstad & Katz (127) first demonstrated the presence of the "malate-aspartate" shuttle activity in kidney cortex. They demonstrated that with lactate as substrate, pyruvate formed from lactate dehydrogenase enters the mitochondria, is converted to oxaloacetate by pyruvate carboxylate, and then is transported out of the mitochondria on the glutamate-aspartate carrier. In the cytosol, aspartate is transaminated to oxaloacetate, which passes up to glucose. No mitochondrially produced reducing equivalents are required for glucose formation from lactate (cf Figure 1B). However, with pyruvate, glutamine, or glutamate as substrates, mitochondrially generated NADH must be transported into the cytosol for glucose formation to occur (cf Figure 1C). Rognstad & Katz demonstrated that under these circumstances, malate is transported out of the mitochondria and provides the reducing equivalents necessary for glucose formation upon its conversion to oxaloacetate in the cytosol. This implies a role for the malate/phosphate (dicarboxylate) transporter, and present data (17) strongly suggest malate efflux to be important, as suggested by these workers.

More recently, Ross and associates (129) have evaluated the importance of the glutamate transaminase pathway in the relationship between renal gluconeogenesis and sodium transport in the kidney. Utilizing the isolated perfused rat kidney preparation in which metabolic and transport functions can be assessed simultaneously, they evaluated the role of various metabolic and transport inhibitors on gluconeogenesis and sodium reabsorption. With lactate as substrate, they observed a significant inhibition of glucose formation by aminooxyacetate (a transaminase inhibitor) and inhibitors of gluconeogenesis at the phosphoenolpyruvate carboxykinase (mercaptopicolinate and quinolinate) step, consistent with the formulation by Rognstad & Katz mentioned above. Aminooxyacetate, but not mercaptopicolinate, also resulted in a significant inhibition of sodium reabsorption in the isolated kidney perfused with lactate. Ouabain inhibited both gluconeogenesis and sodium reabsorption to a comparable degree. D-Malate, an inhibitor of malate dehydrogenase, did not result in a significant effect on gluconeogenesis or sodium transport with lactate as substrate. However, a significant inhibition of glucose formation from pyruvate was noted. Similarly, with pyruvate as substrate, D-malate resulted in a significant decrease in sodium reabsorption. Mercaptopicolinate inhibited glucose formation from pyruvate as it had from lactate, but was without a significant effect on sodium transport. Although these studies indicated no consistent effect, they do suggest that the transaminase pathway has an important role not only in gluconeogenesis, but also, under appropriate circumstances, in sodium transport by the mammalian kidney. These studies extend the proposals made originally Schurek et al (139) and others (128, 164) that in the isolated perfused kidney optimum sodium transport is achieved only in the presence of certain oxidizable substrates.

The precise interrelationships between mitochondrial (metabolite) transport, metabolism, and epithelial transport remain to be elucidated. More recent studies by Silva et al have attempted to explore further this relationship (142). Again, using the isolated perfused rat kidney, these workers evaluated the relationship between gluconeogenesis, oxygen consumption, and sodium transport. They were able to demonstrate that when sodium transport was increased markedly, a reciprocal decline in gluconeogenesis was observed without a change in oxygen consumption. Conversely, inhibition of gluconeogenesis by mercaptopcolinate led to an increase in sodium reabsorption and in oxygen consumption.

Acid-Base Balance

The kidney responds to acute and chronic acidosis by increasing the renal utlization of glutamine, with formation and excretion of ammonia from glutamine metabolism. The mechanism of the increase in glutamine catabolism has been puzzling for some time because the initial enzyme in the pathway, phosphate-dependent glutaminase, has a distinctly alkaline pH optimum. Because it is generally accepted that the enzymes of renal ammoniagenesis are intramitochondrial (however, see 5, 6), answers have been sought in studies of the mitochondrial transport systems.

THE GLUTAMINE TRANSPORTER   Kovacevic et al first proposed a neutral uniport mechanism for the uptake of glutamine into kidney mitochondria (71). The suggestion was subsequently made that the entry of glutamine was stoichiometrically linked to the efflux of glutamate anion by an electrophoretic carrier (18), but this suggestion has been disproved (10). Also, it has been suggested that glutamine enters the mitochondrial matrix space by passive diffusion (168), but it is now generally accepted that glutamine uptake occurs by a neutral uniport carrier that is inhibited by organic mercurials (41, 70). However, considerable controversy still exists with respect to the role of mitochondrial glutamine transport in the augmented rate of ammonia synthesis in metabolic acidosis.

Adam & Simpson (1, 146) first suggested that the transport of glutamine into mitochondria might be a factor limiting its metabolism and that the activity of the transporter was increased in acute and chronic metabolic acidosis. They and others (10, 41, 42, 160) noted that the accumulation of carbon 14 in the matrix space of rat and dog kidney mitochondria incubated with U-^{14}C-glutamine was increased in both acute and chronic metabolic acidosis. The experiments were performed with rotenone to prevent glutamate metabolism but could not distinguish between the uptake and deamidation of glutamine, because ^{14}C-glutamate as well as ^{14}C-glutamine accumulation was measured under these conditions. Although glutamine itself could not be detected in the matrix space under any condition, activation of glutamine transport was postulated to be the regulatory step.

Subsequently, Curthoys & Shapiro (19) suggested that glutaminase activity, and not glutamine transport, was the rate-limiting step in rat renal mitochondrial metabolism. They demonstrated that if mitochondria were purified of contaminating phosphate-independent glutaminase and if phosphate, a potent activator of glutaminase, was removed from the incubation medium, glutamine could be detected in the matrix space. Because in chronic metabolic acidosis, Curthoys & Shipiro found no significant change in matrix glutamine levels, they interpreted the results to support a major role for glutaminase rather than for the glutamine transporter. This controversy has not been settled. Despite careful studies designed to remove contaminating phosphate-independent glutaminase activity, Simpson & Hecker (150, 151) were unable to detect glutamine within the matrix space. Because of this, they have even suggested the possibility that the transporter and glutaminase are physically linked (151).

More recent data (68, 69) have indicated that it is possible to detect high levels of glutamine in the matrix if the loading is performed under circumstances in which the glutaminase activity is reduced substantially (0°C and no phosphate present), suggesting that the transporter and enzyme are not one and the same molecule. Discrepancies between different laboratories with regard to the presence of glutamine in the matrix space may, in part, relate to the rapidity with which the mitochondria are separated from the incubation medium by silicone oil centrifugation. It does appear that the levels of glutamine within the matrix space may normally be quite low, because there is no obvious mechanism for its accumulation. Thus, if the mitochondria are not rapidly separated from the medium, these low levels of glutamine may be metabolized during the separation procedure.

Determination of the potential role for the glutamine transporter in glutamine metabolism has been hampered by the lack of an available specific inhibitor of glutaminase. Although Goldstein & Boylan (42) have reported kinetic characteristics of the transporter (K_m 2.7 mM and V_{max} 150–300 nmol min^{-1} mg^{-1} at 23°C), reliable kinetics await the availability of such an inhibitor. Nevertheless, the data of Goldstein & Boylan as well as those of Kovacevic and Bajin (69) suggest that the rate of transport may be an order of magnitude greater than the activity of glutaminase, implying that the capacity of the transporter does not limit metabolism, at least in normal kidney mitochondria. Because of the difficulties in separating the transport step from glutaminase in studies performed with kidney mitochondria incubated with glutamine and rotenone, physiological regulators of the transporter have not been definitely identified. Difficulties are illustrated by the situation with respect to α-ketoglutarate. Goldstein & Boylan (42) demonstrated that α-ketoglutarate at 0.3 mM was a competitive inhibitor of the glutamine transporter. However, these studies were subsequently explained by glutamate formation in the matrix space from the enhanced reductive amination of α-ketoglutarate under the conditions of these experiments (156). Further studies are required to elucidate the role of the mitochondrial glutamine transport in metabolic acidosis in vivo. It has been shown that the activity of glutaminase is increased dramatically during adaptation to chronic metabolic acidosis. Thus an increase in enzyme activity may partially explain the augmented ammoniagenesis under chronic conditions, but it is clear that the enzyme is inhibited in acute acidosis when ammoniagenesis is also increased, and thus other explanations must be sought.

THE TWO GLUTAMATE CARRIERS   Glutamate plays an important role in renal metabolism, particularly with respect to ammoniagenesis. Glutamate is present in high concentrations in renal tubular cells, is an end product inhibitor of glutaminase, and can yield ammonia when deaminated by glutamate dehydrogenase in the mitochondrial matrix space. As discussed earlier, two transporters for glutamate have been described in studies carried out mainly in rat liver and rat brain mitochondria (4, 23). One carrier is an electrophoretic glutamate-aspartate exchange carrier (78, 84). The activity of this carrier, which is essentially unidirectional (glutamate in, aspartate out), is inhibited at low pH and increased by high-pH values (163). When external glutamate exchanges with aspartate in order to cross the mitochondrial membrane, it is committed to the transaminase pathway of metabolism that does not produce ammonia. A reason for this commitment is that deamination of glutamate entering in exchange for aspartate would deplete the matrix of aspartate, and further entry of glutamate would cease. Another reason is that the glutamate-aspartate carrier in both kidney (133) and liver (25) appears to channel the external glutamate carbon directly to the transaminase without mixing isotopically with the majority of the matrix glutamate pool.

The second glutamate carrier is the electroneutral, proton-compensated glutamate carrier that has low activity in the kidney (135), but is, nevertheless, important in acid-base regulation. In the liver, glutamate can readily enter the mitochondria from the cytosol on this carrier and be metabolized by glutamate dehydrogenase. In kidney, the source of matrix glutamate used as the substrate of glutamate dehydrogenase for ammonia formation is phosphate-dependent glutaminase (72, 132, 133). An exception is in rabbit kidney, where the electroneutral glutamate carrier activity is high (12). The rabbit, however, does not have a mechanism to respond to metabolic acidosis and shows no augmented rate of ammoniagenesis in acidosis (123).

Kovacevic (67) was the first to suggest that the predominant pathway of external glutamate oxidation by rat kidney mitochondria was transamination. He suggested that glutamate deamination by glutamate dehydrogenase was limited by the transport of glutamate across the inner mitochondrial membrane on the electroneutral glutamate carrier. Additional support for this notion was provided by Schoolwerth et al (133, 137) and Kunin & Tannen (72), who clearly demonstrated that external glutamate was metabolized primarily by transamination in rat kidney mitochondria. This is in contrast to glutamate formed within the mitochondrial matrix from the deamidation of glutamine, which was deaminated to a greater extent, particularly in mitochondria obtained from acidotic rats (72, 133, 137).

Normal rat kidney mitochondria metabolize glutamine by a pathway that leads first to glutamate and then branches, with some glutamate leaving the mitochondria (on the electroneutral glutamate carrier) to return to the matrix on the glutamate-aspartate carrier, where it is metabolized via the transaminase pathway (133). The remainder of the glutamate stays in the mitochondria and is metabolized via glutamate dehydrogenase with attendant formation of ammonia. There is a striking stimulation of flux through glutamate transamination when external glutamate is added to kidney mitochondria-metabolizing glutamine (137), which is understandable in view of the requirement of the transaminase for external glutamate. Surprisingly, however, external glutamate also inhibits flux through glutamate dehydrogenase (132). Further studies demonstrated that there are two pools of glutamate in the matrix that do not mix well with each other (133). One interacts directly with external glutamate via the glutamate-aspartate carrier and is the substrate of the transaminase, not the dehydrogenase. However, α-ketoglutarate, the common product of the two glutamate-utilizing enzymes, does mix in the matrix, and the α-ketoglutarate formed by the transaminase reaction is a potent inhibitor of glutamate dehydrogenase (132). It has since become apparent that anything that inhibits transamination or the production of matrix α-ketoglutarate (134) will stimulate glutamate-dehydrogenase flux. This provides a partial explanation for the stimulation of ammonia formation by the kidney in acute acidosis. At acid pH, the K_m of α-ketoglutarate dehydrogenase is lowered and α-ketoglutarate levels in the mitochondrial matrix are decreased, due to increased α-ketoglutarate oxidation (86, 134, 138, 161). The effects of pH on ammoniagenesis in intact kidney can be mimicked with isolated mitochondria in the presence, but not in the absence, of physiological levels of α-ketoglutarate (134). However, a more complete explanation for augmented ammoniagenesis in acute acidosis is possible from a consideration of the kinetic characteristics of the weakly active, electroneutral renal glutamate carrier. The kinetic characteristics of the carrier have recently been measured and compared with those of liver.

Kidney mitochondrial glutamate uptake kinetics indicated that the K_m for external glutamate was 1.4 mM and the V_{max} was 3.2 nmol mg^{-1} min^{-1} at 28°C (135). In contrast to data obtained with liver (82), these kinetic values for uptake were not changed at pH values from 6.6 to 7.4 or in mitochondria obtained from kidneys of chronically acidotic rats (135). However, the results indicated that the glutamate transporter was quite slow, an order of magnitude slower than the carrier in liver, and was rate-limiting for the oxidative deamination of external glutamate. However, glutamate efflux was observed to be first order with respect to matrix glutamate (135, 136) and could reach significant values at high matrix glutamate levels. The efflux was markedly influenced by the external pH, such that efflux was reduced as pH in the medium was decreased (136). In contrast, alterations in matrix pH had no obvious effect on the rate of efflux.

Thus, the kinetic properties of the carrier explained in part the accelerated rate of glutamate deamination observed in acute acidosis (134–136). Although medium pH has no effect on glutamate uptake in kidney (135), as opposed to liver mitochondria (82), the decrease in glutamate efflux observed at acid medium pH leads to an increased concentration of matrix glutamate. The increase in matrix glutamate, as well as the accelerated rate of α-ketoglutarate oxidation stimulated by hydrogen ions (86, 134, 138, 161) leads to an increased matrix glutamate/α-ketoglutarate ratio that provides the driving force for augmented glutamate dehydrogenase flux (134). The increase in glutamate deamination results in the increased ammonia formation noted initially at acid-medium pH with no change in glutaminase flux.

Although it is clear that in acidosis with a constant supply of nitrogenous waste, ammoniagenesis in the kidney must increase while ureagenesis in the liver decreases equally (102), it also appears that regulation of ureagenesis in the liver should be mainly geared toward converting the supply of nitrogenous waste, which in actual fact must be quite variable, to urea. It does not seem likely, as recently proposed (3), that acid-base balance is importantly modulated by urea synthesis (51). It is intriguing to note that the mechanisms of control of ammonia formation from glutamate in liver are very similar to those in kidney (82). Therefore, the observation that the production of nitrogenous end products (NH_3 in the case of kidney and urea in the case of liver) is affected in opposite directions by pH changes is also intriguing and deserves further study.

THE α-KETOGLUTARATE/MALATE TRANSPORTER   It had been suggested previously that malate efflux from the mitochondrial matrix space may be an important regulatory mechanism in the enhanced rate of ammoniagenesis in chronic metabolic acidosis in the rat (66). Cheema-Dhadli & Halperin (17) reported on the kinetic characteristics of the dicarboxylate (malate/phosphate) transporter in kidney mitochondria from control rats and animals with chronic metabolic acidosis. They determined that the K_m for malate was 1.0 mM with a V_{max} of 2.7 nmol mg^{-1} min^{-1} at 0°C. However, no alterations in these kinetics were observed in mitochondria obtained from chronically acidotic rats. Brosnan et al (11) demonstrated, however, that the malate/α-ketoglutarate carrier was activated in chronic acidosis. They determined that the V_{max} for the carrier increased 70% in mitochondria from acidotic compared to control rats. Additional studies are required to characterize this effect fully and to determine its role in the overall process of augmented ammonia formation in metabolic acidosis. However, it is interesting to speculate that an increased activity of the malate/α-ketoglutarate carrier in chronic acidosis could lead to lower levels of matrix α-ketoglutarate, because α-ketoglutarate is generated inside the mitochondria. This would suggest that control of ammoniagenesis in chronic as well as in acute acidosis (134) could be a result of regulation of matrix α-ketoglutarate levels. A direct effect of α-ketoglutarate is to increase the K_m of matrix glutamate for glutamate dehydrogenase (132). This hypothesis is intriguing, and it may be significant that detailed studies of fluxes and substrate concentrations during metabolism of glutamine in isolated mitochondria show that there was a dramatic decrease in the apparent K_m of matrix glutamate for glutamate dehydrogenase in chronically acidotic rats as compared to control mitochondria (133).

METABOLITE COMPARTMENTATION AND pH CHANGES   Simpson and coworkers have proposed that an increase in the pH gradient (ΔpH) across the inner mitochondrial membrane may contribute to the metabolic alterations occurring in acute metabolic acidosis (see 15). In studies performed with rotenone-inhibited mitochondria from rat and rabbit (48, 145, 149), they observed that, particularly with a bicarbonate system, acidification of the medium resulted in an increase in the ΔpH. Because many metabolites distribute across this membrane in response to the ΔpH, they proposed that in acute acidosis a generalized increase in the transport of metabolites from the cytosol to mitochondria occurs with a resultant decrease in the cytosolic and an increase in the mitochondrial metabolite pools. The increased mitochondrial metabolite contents resulted in enhanced mitochondrial metabolism, returning the mitochondrial pool to its previous steady-state levels. The net result would be a decrease in total tissue metabolite levels, occurring almost exclusively within the cytosolic space. This hypothesis would account for the decrease in total tissue contents of many metabolites that have been observed in renal cortical tissue in vivo. It appears to these reviewers that although this hypothesis may, in part, explain some of the alterations noted, it is clearly too generalized to apply to all metabolites, even those transported in symport with protons. Other factors, such as intramitochondrial metabolism and the balance between uptake and efflux of various metabolites, will, of course, determine the net effect of acidification on metabolite gradients across the mitochondrial membrane.

Part of the difficulty in obtaining experimental support for the role of mitochondrial metabolite carriers in the regulation of intermediary metabolism has been the lack of techniques for measuring metabolite concentrations in the cytoplasm and in the mitochondrial compartment separately. Recently, several methods have been developed to measure the contents of various metabolites in these compartments separately (2, 27, 174). Of the described techniques, the digitonin fractionation method has been utilized most extensively. This method involves the use of digitonin to lyse the plasma membrane, after which the two cell compartments are separated by silicone oil filtration (174). This method has been used extensively in studies of liver metabolism, but has thus far been used only sparingly with respect to kidney. Guder & Purschel (47) have evaluated the method in isolated rat kidney cortex tubule suspensions. Using the digitonin method, these workers evaluated the intracellular α-ketoglutarate distribution in tubules incubated at pH 7.8 and 7.0. At the more acid pH level, a marked reduction in medium and cytosolic α-ketoglutarate levels was observed with relatively little change in the mitochondrial compartment. These results are compatible with the hypothesis of Simpson and coworkers. Under the conditions of these experiments, cytosolic α-ketoglutarate was found to represent 60–80% of the total cell content. A similar distribution was noted for glutamate. Additional studies are required to evaluate intracellular compartmentation within kidney tubule cells. The heterogeneity of renal tissue complicates this method even further.

BICARBONATE   Studies reported by Kurokawa & Rasmussen (75) and Simpson & Angielski (148) indicated that bicarbonate, independent of pH, may have a substantial effect on renal metabolism. Effects at the level of various enzymes have been reported. In addition, bicarbonate has been demonstrated to have an effect on mitochondrial metabolite transport. Robinson et al (125) demonstrated that bicarbonate stimulated the efflux of citrate from rat kidney mitochondria. The K_m for bicarbonate was 13.5 mM and the V_{max} was 0.59 nmol mg^{-1} min^{-1} of protein at 10°C. This bicarbonate-stimulated citrate efflux was prevented by inhibitors of the tricarboxylate, dicarboxylate, and the phosphate transporters. Because inhibition of these transporters all inhibited the bicarbonate-induced increase in citrate efflux, it was suggested that bicarbonate first stimulates phosphate efflux from the mitochondria via bicarbonate/phosphate exchange on the phosphate carrier. Phosphate exchanges with malate on the dicarboxylate carrier, and the malate then exchanges for citrate on the tricarboxylate carrier. Thus, a net exchange of bicarbonate for citrate results. By this scheme, three separate carriers work in an integrated fashion to carry out the net exchange with a velocity approaching that of direct malate/citrate or citrate/citrate exchanges. In these studies, bicarbonate was also shown to increase the activity of pyruvate dehydrogenase. However, this effect was not observed in broken mitochondria or whole tissue preparations and was prevented by inhibitors of citrate transport, suggesting that this effect was secondary to the effect on the transporters.

As mentioned above, Hager & Simpson (48) provided evidence for the influence of the bicarbonate buffer system on the ΔpH in rabbit renal cortex mitochondria. These workers observed that in mitochondria incubated with rotenone and an energy source (TMPD plus ascorbate), the pH gradient was less than in nonbicarbonate-buffered medium at pH 7.4. As the bicarbonate concentration of the medium was reduced with a constant gas mixture such that pH also decreased, the ΔpH increased from a value of 0.3 at 40 mM bicarbonate to 0.66 at 5 mM bicarbonate concentration. The effect was also observed, although to a lesser extent, when bicarbonate was varied at constant external pH. Under those circumstances, ΔpH rose from 0.4 to 0.6 when medium bicarbonate concentrations decreased from 40 to 5 mM.

As a weak anion, bicarbonate may effect the ΔpH in a fashion similar to that shown by Palmieri et al (105) for other permeable weak acids such as phosphate or malate. Whether a transporter for bicarbonate as such exists, as has been recently suggested by Simpson (144), or whether CO_2 crosses and bicarbonate is formed according to the pH and the bicarbonate-carbonic acid equilibrium within the mitochondrial matrix space, remains to be determined.

CONCLUSION

Numerous studies over the past several years have identified 12 metabolite transporters of the inner mitochondrial membrane. More recently, assessments of the molecular mechanisms and physiological significance of the transporters in the control of metabolism have been attempted. In comparison to other tissues, relatively few studies have been performed to characterize mitochondrial metabolite transporters in kidney and to determine their role in the modulation of metabolic fluxes. Nevertheless, accumulating evidence suggests an important regulatory function for the transporters in the kidney. The role of the glutamate transporter in the acute control of ammonia formation seems clear at this time, and it is anticipated that further studies will reveal important roles for other transporters in renal metabolism.

ACKNOWLEDGMENT

This work was supported in part by grants AM19714, AM26309, and AM29740 from the National Institutes of Health.

Literature Cited

1. Adam, W., Simpson, D. P. 1974. Glutamine transport in rat kidney mitochondria in metabolic acidosis. *J. Clin. Invest.* 54:165–74
2. Akerboom, T. P. M., van der Meer, R., Tager, J. M. 1979. Techniques for the investigation of intracellular compartmentation. In *Techniques in Metabolic Research,* B205:1–33. Amsterdam: Elsevier/North Holland
3. Atkinson, D. E., Camien, M. N. 1982. The role of urea synthesis in the removal of metabolic bicarbonate and the regulation of blood pH. *Curr. Top. Cell. Reg.* 21:261–302
4. Azzi, A., Chappell, J. B., Robinson, B. H. 1967. Penetration of the mitochondrial membrane by glutamate and aspartate. *Biochem. Biophys. Res. Commun.* 29:148–57
5. Bogusky, R. T., Lowenstein, L. M., Aoki, T. T. 1983. The relationship between glutamate deamination and gluconeogenesis in kidney. *Biochem. J.* 210:695–98
6. Bogusky, R. T., Lowenstein, L. M., Lowenstein, J. M. 1976. The purine nucleotide cycle. A pathway for ammonia production in the rat kidney. *J. Clin. Invest.* 58:326–35
7. Bohnensack, R., Küster, U., Letko, G. 1982. Rate-controlling steps of oxidative phosphorylation in rat liver mitochondria. A synaptic approach of model and experiment. *Biochim. Biophys. Acta* 680:271–280
8. Bradford, N. M., McGivan, J. D. 1980. Evidence for the existence of an ornithine/citrulline antiporter in rat liver mitochondria. *FEBS Lett.* 113:294–98
9. Brand, M. D., Chen, C. H., Lehninger, A. L. 1976. Stoichiometric relationship between energy-dependent proton ejection and electron transport in mitochondria. *Proc. Natl. Acad. Sci. USA* 73:437–41
10. Brosnan, J. T., Hall, B. 1977. The transport and metabolism of glutamine by kidney-cortex mitochondria from normal and acidotic rats. *Biochem. J.* 164:331–37
11. Brosnan, J. T., Redmond, W., Morgan, D., Whalen, P. 1980. The malate/2-oxoglutarate transporter in mitochondria

from rat kidney cortex: increased activity in metabolic acidosis. *Int. J. Biochem.* 12:131–33

12. Bryla, J., Dzik, J. M. 1978. Glutamate metabolism in relation to glutamate transport in kidney cortex mitochondria of rabbit. *Biochim. Biophys. Acta* 504:15–25

13. Bryla, J., Harris, E. J. 1976. Accumulation of ornithine and citrulline in rat liver mitochondria in relation to citrulline formation. *FEBS Lett.* 72:331–36

14. Chance, B., Holmes, W., Higgins, J., Connelly, C. M. 1958. Localization of interaction sites in multicomponent transfer systems: Theorems derived from analogues. *Nature* 182:1190–93

15. Chance, B., Williams, G. R. 1956. The respiratory chain and oxidative phosphorylation. *Adv. Enzymol.* 17:65–134

16. Chappell, J. B., Haarhoff, K. M. 1966. The penetration of the mitochondrial membrane by anion and cation. In *Biochemistry of Mitochondria,* ed. E. C. Slater, Z. Kaniriga, L. Wojtczak, pp. 75–92. New York: Academic

17. Cheema-Dhadli, S., Halperin, M. L. 1978. Ammoniagenesis in kidney cortex mitochondria of the rat: Role of the mitochondrial dicarboxylate anion transporter. *Can. J. Biochem.* 56:23–28

18. Crompton, M., Chappel, J. B. 1973. Transport of glutamine and glutamate in kidney mitochondria in relation to glutamine deamidation. *Biochem. J.* 132:35–46

19. Curthoys, N. P., Shapiro, R. A. 1978. Effect of metabolic acidosis and of phosphate on the presence of glutamine within the matrix space of rat renal mitochondria during glutamine transport. *J. Biol. Chem.* 253:63–68

20. Davis, E. J., Bremer, J., Akerman, K. E. 1980. Thermodynamic aspects of translocation of reducing equivalent by mitochondria. *J. Biol. Chem.* 255:2277–83

21. Davis, E. J., Davis-van Thienen, W. I. A. 1978. Control of mitochondrial metabolism by the ATP/ADP ratio. *Biochem. Biophys. Res. Commun.* 83:1260–66

22. Davis, E. J., Lumeng, L. 1975. Relationships between the phosphorylation potentials generated by liver mitochondria and respiratory state under conditions of adenosine diphosphate control. *J. Biol. Chem.* 250:2275–82

23. Dennis, S. C., Land, J. M., Clark, J. B. 1976. Glutamate metabolism and transport in rat brain mitochondria. *Biochem. J.* 156:323–31

24. Duszynski, J., Groen, A. K., Wanders, R. J. A., Vervoorn, R. C., Tager, J. M.

1982. Quantification of the role of the adenine nucleotide translocator in the control of mitochondrial respiration in isolated rat liver cells. *FEBS Lett.* 146:262–66

25. Duszynski, J., Mueller, G., LaNoue, K. F. 1978. Microcompartmentation of aspartate in rat liver mitochondria. *J. Biol. Chem.* 253:6149–51

26. Duychaerts, C., Sluse-Goffart, C. M., Fux, J. P., Sluse, F. E., Liebecq, C. 1980. Kinetic mechanism of exchanges catalyzed by the adenine nucleotide carrier. *Eur. J. Biochem.* 106:1–6

27. Elbers, R., Heldt, H. W., Schmucker, P., Soboll, S., Wiese, H. 1974. Measurement of the ATP/ADP ratio in mitochondria and in the extramitochondrial compartment by fractionation of freeze stopped liver tissue in nonaqueous media. *Hoppe-Seyler's Z. Physiol. Chem.* 355:378–93

28. Ericinska, H., Wilson, D. F. 1982. Regulation of cellular energy metabolism. *J. Membr. Biol.* 70:1–14

29. Fonyo, A., Ligetti, E., Palmieri, F. Quagliariello, E. 1975. Carrier-mediated transport of phosphate in mitochondria. In *Biomembranes, Structure and Function,* ed. G. Gardos, L. Szasz, pp. 287–306. Hungary: Akad. Kiado/Amsterdam: North Holland

30. Fonyo, A., Palmieri, F., Quagliariello, E. 1976. Carrier-mediated transport of metabolites in mitochondria. In *Horizons in Biochemistry and Biophysics,* ed. E. Quagliariello, F. Palmieri, T. P. Singer, 2:60–105. Reading, MA: Addison-Wesley

31. Forman, N. G., Wilson, D. F. 1982. Energetics and stoichiometry of oxidative phosphorylation from NADH to cytochrome *c* in isolated rat liver mitochondria. *J. Biol. Chem.* 257:12908–15

32. Forman, N., Wilson, D. F. 1983. Dependence of mitochondrial oxidative phosphorylation on activity of the adenine nucleotide translocase. *J. Biol. Chem.* 258:8649–55

33. Forsen, S., Hoffman, R. A. 1963. Study of moderately rapid chemical exchange reactions by means of nuclear magnetic double resonance. *J. Chem. Phys.* 39:2892–901

34. Freeman, D., Bartlett, S., Radda, G., Ross, B. 1983. Energetics of sodium transport in the kidney. Saturation transport ^{31}P-NMR. *Biochim. Biophys. Acta* 762:325–36

35. Freitag, H., Neupert, W., Benz, R. 1982. Purification and characterization of a pore protein of the intramitochon-

drial membrane from *neurospora crassa*. *Eur. J. Biochem.* 123:629–36

36. Gadian, D. G., Radda, G. K. 1981. NMR studies of tissue metabolism. *Ann. Rev. Biochem.* 50:69–83

37. Gamble, J. G., Lehninger, A. L. 1973. Transport of ornithine and citrulline across the mitochondrial membrane. *J. Biol. Chem.* 248:610–18

38. Garlid, K. D., Nakashima, R. A. 1983. Studies on the mechanism of uncoupling by amine local anesthetics: Evidence for mitochondrial proton transport mediated by lipophillic ion pairs. *J. Biol. Chem.* 258:7974–80

39. Gellerich, F. N., Bohensack, R., Kunz, W. 1983. Control of mitochondrial respiration. The contribution of the adenine nucleotide translocator depends on the ATP- and ADP-consuming enzymes. *Biochim. Biophys. Acta* 722:381–91

40. Gellerich, F., Saks, V. A. 1982. Control of heart mitochondrial oxygen consumption by creatine kinase. The importance of enzyme localization. *Biochim. Biophys. Res. Commun.* 105:1473–81

41. Goldstein, L. 1975. Glutamine transport by mitochondria isolated from normal and acidotic rats. *Am. J. Physiol.* 229:1027–33

42. Goldstein, L., Boylan, J. M. 1978. Renal mitochondrial glutamine transport and metabolism: Studies with a rapid-mixing rapid filtration technique. *Am. J. Physiol.* 234:F514–21

43. Gresser, M. J., Myers, J. A., Boyer, P. D. 1982. Catalytic site cooperativity of beef heart mitochondrial F_1 adenosine triphosphatase. *J. Biol. Chem.* 257:12030–38

44. Groen, A. K., van der Meer, R., Westerhoff, H. V., Wanders, R. J. A., Akerboom, T. P. N., Tager, J. H. 1982. Control of metabolic fluxes. In *Metabolic Compartmentation*, ed. H. Sies, pp. 9–37. London: Academic

45. Groen, A. K., Wanders, R. J. A., Westerhoff, H. V., van der Meer, R., Tager, J. M. 1982. Quantification of the contribution of various steps to the control of mitochondrial respiration. *J. Biol. Chem.* 257:2754–57

46. Grubmeyer, C., Cross, R. L., Penefsky, H. S. 1982. Mechanism of ATP hydrolysis by beef heart mitochondrial ATPase. *J. Biol. Chem.* 257:12092–100

47. Guder, W. G., Purschel, S. 1982. pH-Dependent compartmentation of metabolites involved in renal ammoniagenesis. *Contr. Nephrol.* 31:134

48. Hager, S. R., Simpson, D. P. 1982. Influence of bicarbonate buffer system on pH gradient in rabbit renal cortex

mitochondria. *Molec. Physiol.* 2:203–11

49. Halestrap, A. P. 1978. Stimulation of pyruvate transport in metabolizing mitochondria through changes in this transmembrane pH gradient induced by glucagon treatment. *Biochem. J.* 172:389–98

50. Halestrap, A. P., Scott, R. D., Thomas, A. P. 1980. Mitochondrial pyruvate transport and its hormonal regulation. *Int. J. Biochem.* 11:97–105

51. Halperin, M. L., Jungas, R. L. 1983. Metabolic production and renal disposal of hydrogen ions. *Kidney Int.* 24:709

52. Heldt, H. W., Klingenberg, M., Milovancev, M. 1972. Differences between the ATP/ADP ratios in the mitochondrial matrix and in the extramitochondrial space. *Eur. J. Biochem.* 30:434–40

53. Hoek, J. B., Nicholls, D. G., Williamson, J. R. 1980. Determination of the mitochondrial protonmotive force in isolated hepatocytes. *J. Biol. Chem.* 255:1458–64

54. Hoek, J. B., Njagu, R. M. 1976. Glutamate transport and the transmembrane pH gradient in isolated rat liver mitochondria. *FEBS Lett.* 71:341–46

55. Jacobus, W. E., Moreadith, R. W., Vandegaer, K. M. 1982. Mitochondrial respiratory control. Evidence against the regulation of respiration by extramitochondrial phosphorylation potentials or by [ATP]/[ADP] ratios. *J. Biol. Chem.* 257:2397–402

56. Kacser, H., Burns, J. A. 1979. Molecular democracy: Who shares the control? *Biochem. Soc. Trans.* 7:1149–61

57. Kadenbach, B., Freitag, H., Kolbe, H. 1978. On the mechanisms of phosphate and dicarboxylate transport in mitochondria. *FEBS Lett.* 89:161–64

58. King, M. J., Diwan, J. J. 1973. Permeability of rat liver mitochondria to leucine, tyrosine, α-aminoisobutyric acid, and lysine. *Arch. Biochem. Biophys.* 159:166–73

59. Klingenberg, M. 1970. Metabolite transport in mitochondria: An example for intracellular membrane function. *Essays in Biochem.* 6:119–59

60. Klingenberg, M. 1976. The ADP-ATP carrier in mitochondrial membranes. In *The Enzymes of Biological Membranes: Membrane Transport*, ed. A. N. Martonosi, 3:383–438. New York: Plenum

61. Klingenberg, M. 1980. The ADP-ATP translocation in mitochondria, a membrane potential controlled transport. *J. Membr. Biol.* 56:97–105

62. Klingenberg, M. 1981. The ADP, ATP translocation system of mitochondria. In

Mitochondria and Microsomes, ed. C. P. Lee, G. Schatz, G. Dallner, pp. 293–316. New York: Addison Wesley

63. Klingenberg, M. 1981. Substrate-carrier interaction and the catalytic translocation cycle of the ADP, ATP carrier. In *Structure and Functional Aspects of Enzyme Catalysis*, ed. H. Eggerer, R. Huber, pp. 202–12. Berlin: Springer-Verlag

64. Klingenberg, M., Heldt, H. W. 1982. The ADP/ATP translocation in mitochondria and its role in intracellular compartmentation. In *Metabolic Compartmentation*, ed. H. Sies. London: Academic

65. Klingenberg, M., Rottenberg, H. 1977. Relation between the gradient of the ATP/ADP ratio and the membrane potential across the mitochondrial membrane. *Eur. J. Biochem.* 73:125–30

66. Kopyt, N., Narins, R., Whereat, A., Relman, A. 1974. Regulation of mitochondrial transport of malate by pH: A possible control of ammoniagenesis. *Clin. Res.* 22:535A

67. Kovacevic, Z. 1971. The pathway of glutamine and glutamate oxidation in isolated mitochondria from mammalian cells. *Biochem. J.* 125:757–63

68. Kovacevic, Z., Bajin, K. 1982. Loading of mitochondria with ^{14}C-glutamine and study of the kinetics of its efflux from the organelles. *Contr. Nephrol.* 31:111–14

69. Kovacevic, Z., Bajin, K. 1982. Kinetics of glutamine efflux from liver mitochondria loaded with ^{14}C-labeled substrate. *Biochim. Biophys. Acta* 687:291–95

70. Kovacevic, Z., Bajin, K., Pavlovic, M. 1980. Volume changes of rat kidney mitochondria, transport of glutamine and its inhibition by mersalyl. *Int. J. Biochem.* 12:139–43

71. Kovacevic, Z., McGivan, J. D., Chappell, J. B. 1970. Conditions of activity of glutaminase in kidney mitochondria. *Biochem. J.* 118:265–74

71a. Krebs, H. A., Bennett, D. A. H., de-Gasquet, P., Gascoyne, T., Yoshida, T. 1963. Renal gluconeogenesis. The effect of diet on the gluconeogenic capacity of rat-kidney-cortex slices. *Biochem. J.* 86:22–27

72. Kunin, A. S., Tannen, R. L. 1979. Regulation of glutamate metabolism by renal cortical mitochondria. *Am. J. Physiol.* 237:F55–62

73. Kunz, W., Bohnensack, R., Bohme, G., Küster, U., Letko, G., Schönfeld, P. 1981. Relations between extramitochondrial and intramitochondrial adenine nucleotide systems. *Arch. Biochem. Biophys.* 209:219–29

74. Kunz, W., Bohnensack, R., Küster, V.,

75. Kurokawa, K., Rasmussen, H. 1973. Ionic control of renal gluconeogenesis. III. The effects of changes in pH, pCO_2, and bicarbonate concentration. *Biochim. Biophys. Acta* 313:42–58

76. Küster, U., Bohnensack, R., Kunz, W. 1976. Control of oxidative phosphorylation by the extramitochondrial ATP/ADP ratio. *Biochim. Biophys. Acta* 440:391–402

77. LaNoue, K. F., Bryla, J., Bassett, D. J. P. 1974. Energy-driven aspartate efflux from heart and liver mitochondria. *J. Biol. Chem.* 249:7514–21

78. LaNoue, K. F., Meijer, A. J., Brouwer, A. 1974. Evidence for electrogenic aspartate transport in rat liver mitochondria. *Arch. Biochem. Biophys.* 161:544–50

79. LaNoue, K. F., Mizani, S. M., Klingenberg, M. 1978. Electrical imbalance of adenine nucleotide transport across the mitochondrial membrane. *J. Biol. Chem.* 253:191–98

80. LaNoue, K. F., Schoolwerth, A. C. 1979. Metabolite transport in mitochondria. *Ann. Rev. Biochem.* 48:871–922

81. LaNoue, K. F., Schoolwerth, A. C. 1984. Metabolite transport in mitochondria. In *New Comprehensive Biochemistry*, ed. L. Ernster, III. Amsterdam: Elsevier Biomedical. In press

82. LaNoue, K. F., Schoolwerth, A. C., Pease, A. J. 1983. Ammonia formation in isolated rat liver mitochondria. *J. Biol. Chem.* 258:1726–34

83. LaNoue, K. F., Strzelecki, T., Finch, F. 1984. The effect of glucagon on hepatic respiratory capacity. *J. Biol. Chem.* 259:4116–21

84. LaNoue, K. F., Tischler, M. E. 1974. Electrogenic characteristics of the mitochondrial glutamate aspartate antiporter. *J. Biol. Chem.* 249:7522–28

85. Letko, G., Küster, U. 1979. Competition between extramitochondrial and intramitochondrial ATP-consuming processes. *Acta Biol. Med. Germ.* 38:1379–85

86. Lowry, M., Ross, B. D. 1980. Activation of oxoglutarate dehydrogenase in kidney in response to acute acidosis. *Biochem. J.* 190:771–80

87. Martin, A. D., Titherage, M. A. 1983. Hormonal stimulation of gluconeogenesis through increased mitochondrial metabolic flux. *Biochem. Soc. Trans.* 11:78–81

88. Massari, S., Frigeri, L., Azzone, G. F. 1972. Permeability to water, dimension of surface, and structural changes during

swelling in rat liver mitochondria. *J. Membr. Biol.* 9:57–70

89. Matthews, P. M., Bland, J. L., Gadian, D. G., Radda, G. K. 1981. The steady-state rate of ATP synthesis in the perfused rat heart measured by ^{31}P NMR saturation transfer. *Biochem. Biophys. Res. Commun.* 103:1052–59

90. McGivan, J. D., Bradford, N. M., Beavis, A. D. 1977. Factors influencing the activity of ornithine aminotransferase in isolated rat liver mitochondria. *Biochem. J.* 162:147–56

91. McGivan, J. D., Klingenberg, M. 1971. Correlation between H$^+$ and anion movement in mitochondria and the key role of the phosphate carrier. *Eur. J. Biochem.* 20:392–99

92. Meijer, A. J., Van Dam, K. 1974. The metabolic significance of anion transport in mitochondria. *Biochim. Biophys. Acta* 346:213–244

93. Meijer, A. J., Van Dam, K. 1981. Mitochondrial ion transport. In *Membrane Transport*, ed. A. C. Bonting, R. D. duPont, pp. 235–54. Amsterdam: Elsevier Biomedical

94. Mitchell, P. 1961. Coupling of phosphorylation to electron and hydrogen transfer by a chemiosmotic type of mechanism. *Nature* 191:144–48

95. Mitchell, P. 1966. Chemiosmotic coupling in oxidative and photosynthetic phosphorylation. *Glyn Res. Rep. 66/1.* Bodmin, Cornwall, England: Glyn Res. Ltd.

96. Mitchell, P. 1968. Chemiosmotic coupling and energy transduction. *Glyn Res. Rep. 68/1.* Bodmin, Cornwell, England: Glyn Res. Ltd.

97. Mitchell, P. 1979. *Les Priz Nobel 1978,* pp. 135–72. Stockholm: Nobel Found.

98. Murphy, E., Coll, K. E., Viale, R. O., Tischler, M. E., Williamson, J. R. 1979. Kinetics and regulation of the glutamate aspartate translocator in rat liver mitochondria. *J. Biol. Chem.* 254:8369–76

99. Newsholme, E. A., Start, C. 1973. Introduction to regulation in metabolic pathways. In *Regulation in Metabolism*, pp. 1–33. London: Wiley

100. Nicholls, D. G. 1974. The influence of respiration and ATP hydrolysis on the proton electrochemical gradient across the inner membrane of rat liver mitochondria as determined by ion distribution. *Eur. J. Biochem.* 50:305–15

101. Nohl, H., Klingenberg, M. 1978. Kinetics of ADP, ATP transport in mitochondria as studied by the quench-flow method. *Biochim. Biophys. Acta* 503:155–69

102. Oliver, J., Bourke, E. 1975. Adaptations in urea ammonium excretion in metabolic acidosis in the rat: A reinterpretation. *Clin. Sci. Mol. Med.* 48:515–20

103. Padan, E., Rottenberg, H. 1973. Respiratory control and the proton electrochemical gradient in mitochondria. *Eur. J. Biochem.* 40:431–37

104. Palade, G. E. 1953. An electron microscope study of the mitochondrial structure. *J. Histochem. Cytochem.* 1:188–211

105. Palmieri, F., Quagliariello, E., Klingenberg, M. 1970. Quantitative correlation between the distribution of anions and the pH difference across the mitochondrial membrane. *Eur. J. Biochem.* 17:230–38

106. Palmieri, F., Prezioso, G., Quagliariello, E., Klingenberg, M. 1971. Kinetic study of the dicarboxylate carrier in rat liver mitochondria. *Eur. J. Biochem.* 22:66–74

107. Palmieri, F., Quagliariello, E. 1969. Correlation between anion uptake and the movement of K$^+$ and H$^+$ across the mitochondrial membrane. *Eur. J. Biochem.* 8:473–81

108. Palmieri, F., Quagliariello, E. 1978. The mitochondrial transport systems for inorganic phosphate and Krebs cycle intermediates. In *Bioenergetics at Mitochondrial and Cellular Levels,* ed. L. Wojtczak, E. Lenartowicz, J. Zborowski, pp. 5–38. Warsaw: Nencki Inst. Exper. Biol.

109. Palmieri, F., Quagliariello, E., Klingenberg, M. 1970. Quantitative correlation between the distribution of anions and the pH difference across the mitochondrial membrane. *Eur. J. Biochem.* 17:230–38

110. Palmieri, F., Quagliariello, E., Klingenberg, M. 1972. Kinetics and specificity of the oxoglutarate carrier in rat liver mitochondria. *Eur. J. Bichem.* 29:408–16

111. Palmieri, F., Stepani, I., Jacobazzi, V. 1979. The transport of L-cysteinesulfinate in rat liver mitochondria. *Biochim. Biophys. Acta* 555:531–46

112. Pande, S. V. 1975. A mitochondrial carnitine acylcarnitine translocase system. *Proc. Natl. Acad. Sci. USA* 72:883:87

113. Pande, S. V., Parvin, R. 1980. Carnitine-acylcarnitine translocase catalyzes an equilibrating unidirectional transport as well. *J. Biol. Chem.* 255:2994–3001

114. Papa, S., Lofrumento, N. E., Kanduc, D., Paradies, G., Quagliariello, E. 1971. The transport of citric acid cycle intermediates in rat liver mitochondria. *Eur. J. Biochem.* 22:134–43

115. Papa, S., Lofrumento, N. E., Quagliariello, E., Meijer, A. J., Tager, J. M.

1971. Coupling mechanisms in anionic substrate transport across the inner membrane of rat liver mitochondria. *J. Bioenerg.* 1:287–307

116. Papa, S., Francavilla, A., Paradies, G., Meduri, B. 1971. The transport of pyruvate in rat liver mitochondria. *FEBS Lett.* 12:285–88

117. Pedersen, P. L., Wehrle, J. P. 1982. Phosphate transport processes of animal cells. In *Membranes and Transport*, ed. A. N. Martonosi, pp. 645–63. New York: Plenum

118. Pressman, B. C. 1968. Ionophorous antibiotics as models for biological transport. *Fed. Proc.* 27:1283–88

119. Racker, E. 1976. A new look at mechanisms on bioenergetics. New York: Academic

120. Ramsay, R. R., Tubbs, P. K. 1976. The effects of temperature and some inhibitors on the carnitine exchange system of heart mitochondria. *Eur. J. Biochem.* 69:299–303

121. Reynafarje, B., Brand, M. D., Lehninger, A. L. 1976. Evaluation of the $H^+/$ site ratio of mitochondrial electron transport from rat measurements. *J. Biol. Chem.* 251:7442–51

122. Riccio, P., Aquila, H., Klingenberg, M. 1975. Solubilization of the carboxyatractylate binding protein from mitochondria. *FEBS Lett.* 56:129–32

123. Richterich, R. W., Goldstein, L. 1958. Distribution of glutamine metabolizing enzymes and production of urinary ammonia in the mammalian kidney. *Am. J. Physiol.* 195:316–20

124. Robinson, B. H., Oei, J. 1975. Citrate transport in guinea pig heart mitochondria. *Can. J. Biochem.* 53:643–47

125. Robinson, B. H., Oei, J., Cheema-Dhadli, S., Halperin, H. L. 1977. Regulation of citrate transport and pyruvate dehydrogenase in rat kidney cortex mitochondria by bicarbonate. *J. Biol. Chem.* 252:5661–65

126. Rognstad, R. 1983. The role of mitochondrial pyruvate transport in the control of lactate gluconeogenesis. *Int. J. Biochem.* 15:1417–21

127. Rognstad, R., Katz, J. 1970. Gluconeogenesis in the kidney cortex. *Biochem. J.* 116:483–89

128. Ross, B. D., Epstein, F. H., Leaf, A. 1973. Sodium reabsorption in the perfused rat kidney. *Am. J. Physiol.* 225:1165–71

129. Ross, B., Silva, P., Bullock, S. 1981. Role of the malate-aspartate shuttle in renal sodium transport in the rat. *Clin. Sci.* 60:419–26

130. Rottenberg, H. 1983. Uncoupling of oxidative phosphorylation in rat liver mitochondria by general anaesthetics. *Proc. Natl. Acad. Sci. USA* 80:3313–17

131. Safer, B., Smith, C. M., Williamson, J. R. 1971. Control of the transport of reducing equivalents across the mitochondrial membrane in perfused rat heart. *J. Mol. Cell. Cardiol.* 2:111–24

132. Schoolwerth, A. C., Hoover, W. J., Daniel, C. H., LaNoue, K. F. 1980. Effect of aminooxyacetate and α-ketoglutarate on glutamate deamination by rat kidney mitochondria. *Int. J. Biochem.* 12:145–49

133. Schoolwerth, A. C., LaNoue, K. F. 1980. The role of microcompartmentation in the regulation of glutamate metabolism by rat kidney mitochondria. *J. Biol. Chem.* 255:3403–11

134. Schoolwerth, A. C., LaNoue, K. F. 1983. Control of ammoniagenesis by α-ketoglutarate in rat kidney mitochondria. *Am. J. Physiol.* 244:F399–408

135. Schoolwerth, A. C., LaNoue, K. F., Hoover, W. J. 1983. Glutamate transport in rat kidney mitochondria. *J. Biol. Chem.* 258:1735–39

136. Schoolwerth, A. C., LaNoue, K. F., Hoover, W. J. 1984. Effect of pH on glutamate efflux from rat kidney mitochondria. *Am. J. Physiol.* 246:F266–71

137. Schoolwerth, A. C., Nazar, B. L., LaNoue, K. F. 1978. Glutamate dehydrogenase activation and ammonia formation by rat kidney mitochondria. *J. Biol. Chem.* 253:6177–83

138. Schoolwerth, A. C., Strzelecki, T., LaNoue, K. F., Hoover, W. J. 1982. Effect of pH and α-ketoglutarate on mitochondrial ammonia production. *Contr. Nephrol.* 31:127–33

139. Schurek, H. J., Brecht, J. P., Lohfert, H., Hierholzer, K. 1975. The basic requirements for the function of the isolated cell-free perfused rat kidney. *Pfluegers Arch.* 354:349–65

140. Shoubridge, E. A., Briggs, R. N., Radda, G. K. 1982. ^{31}NMR saturation transfer measurement of the steady-state rates of creatine kinase and ATP synthetase in the rat brain. *FEBS Lett.* 140:288–92

141. Siess, E. A., Fahini, F. M., Wieland, O. H. 1981. Evidence that glucagon stabilizes rather than activates mitochondrial functions in rat liver. *Hoppe-Seyler's Z. Physiol. Chem.* 362:1643–51

142. Silva, P., Hallac, R., Spokes, K., Epstein, F. H. 1982. Relationship among gluconeogenesis, QO_2, and Na^+ transport in the perfused rat kidney. *Am. J. Physiol.* 242:F508–13

143. Simpson, D. P. 1980. Modulation of glu-

tamine transport and metabolism in mitochondria from dog renal cortex. *J. Biol. Chem.* 255:7123–28

144. Simpson, D. P. 1983. Mitochondrial bicarbonate carrier: A site of regulation of renal substrate metabolism by acid-base changes. *Clin. Res.* 31:551A

145. Simpson, D. P. 1983. Mitochondrial transport functions and renal metabolism. *Kidney Int.* 23:785–93

146. Simpson, D. P., Adam, W. 1975. Glutamine transport and metabolism by mitochondria from dog renal cortex. *J. Biol. Chem.* 250:8148–58

147. Simpson, D. P., Adam, D. P. 1975. Glutamine transport in dog kidney mitochondria. *Med. Clin. North Am.* 59:555–67

148. Simpson, D. P., Angielski, S. 1973. Regulation by bicarbonate ion of intramitochondrial citrate concentration in kidney mitochondria. *Biochim. Biophys. Acta* 298:115–23

149. Simpson, D. P., Hager, S. R. 1979. pH and bicarbonate effects on mitochondrial anion accumulation. Proposed mechanism for changes in renal metabolite levels in acute acid-base disturbances. *J. Clin. Invest.* 63:704–12

150. Simpson, D. P., Hecker, J. 1982. Glutamine distribution in mitochondria from normal and acidotic rat kidneys. *Kidney Int.* 21:774–79

151. Simpson, D. P., Hecker, J. 1982. Distribution of glutamine in rat kidney mitochondria. *Contr. Nephrol.* 31:105–10

152. Sluse, F. E., Meijer, A. J., Tager, J. M. 1971. Anion translocators in rat heart mitochondria. *FEBS Lett.* 18:149–53

153. Sluse-Goffart, C. M., Sluse, F. E., Duyckaerts, C., Richard, M., Hengisch, P., Liebecq, C. 1983. Conformational changes and possible structure of the oxoglutarate translocation of rat heart mitochondria revealed by the kinetic study of malate and oxoglutarate uptake. *Eur. J. Biochem.* 134:397–406

154. Soboll, S., Bunger, R. 1981. Compartmentation of adenine nucleotides in the isolated working guinea pig heart stimulated by noradrenaline. *Hoppe-Seyler's Z. Physiol. Chem.* 362:125–32

155. Soboll, S., Werdam, K., Bozsik, M., Müller, M., Erdmann, E., Heldt, H. W. 1979. Distribution of metabolites between mitochondria and cytosol of cultured fibroblastoid rat heart cells. *FEBS Lett.* 100:125–28

156. Strzelecki, T., Schoolwerth, A. C. 1981. α-Ketoglutarate modulation of glutamine metabolism by rat renal mitochondria. *Biochem. Biophys. Res. Commun.* 102:588–93

157. Strzelecki, T., Thomas, J. A., Koch, C. D., LaNoue, K. F. 1984. The effect of hormones on proton compartmentation in hepatocytes. *J. Biol. Chem.* 259:4122–29

158. Tager, J. M., Groen, A. K., Wanders, R. J. A., Duszynski, J., Westerhoff, H. V., Vervoorn, R. C. 1983. Control or mitochondrial respiration. *Biochem. Soc. Trans.* 11:40–43

159. Tager, J. M., Wanders, R. J. A., Groen, A. K., van der Meer, R., Akerboom, T. P. M., Meijer, A. J. 1981. Control mechanisms of energy-dependent metabolic pathways in hepatocytes. *Acta Biol. Med. Germ.* 40:895–906

160. Tannen, R. L., Kunin, A. S. 1976. Effect of pH on ammonia production by renal mitochondria. *Am. J. Physiol.* 231:1631–37

161. Tannen, R. L., Kunin, A. S. 1981. Effect of pH on metabolism of α-ketoglutarate by renal cortical mitochondria. *Am. J. Physiol.* 240:F120–26

162. Thomas, A. P., Halestrap, H. P. 1981. Identification of the protein responsible for pyruvate transport into rat liver and heart mitochondria by specific labeling with tritium-labeled N-phenylmaleimide. *Biochem. J.* 198:551–64

163. Tischler, M. E., Pachence, J., Williamson, J. R., LaNoue, K. F. 1976. Mechanism of glutamate aspartate translocation across the mitochondrial inner membranes. *Arch. Biochem. Biophys.* 173:448–62

164. Trimble, M. E., Bowman, R. H. 1973. Renal Na^+ and K^+ transport. Effect of glucose, palmitate and α-bromopalmitate. *Am. J. Physiol.* 225:1054–62

165. Tzagoloff, A. 1982. In *Mitochondria*, pp. 145–56. New York: Plenum. 342 pp.

166. Vignais, P. V. 1976. Molecular and physiological aspects of adenine nucleotide transport in mitochondria. *Biochim. Biophys. Acta* 456:1–38

167. Wanders, R. J. A., Green, A. K., Meijer, A. J., Tager, J. M. 1981. Determination of the free energy difference of the adenine nucleotide translocator reaction in rat liver mitochondria using intra- and extramitochondrial ATP-utilizing reactions. *FEBS Lett.* 132:201–6

168. Welbourne, T. C. 1974. Evidence for passive glutamine uptake coupled to glutaminase I. *Am. J. Physiol.* 226:549–54

169. Wikstrom, M., Krab, K., Saraste, M. 1981. Proton translocating cytochrome complexes. *Ann. Rev. Biochem.* 50:623–55

170. Williamson, J. R., Jakob, A., Refino, C.

1971. Control of the removal of reducing equivalents from the cytosol in perfused rat liver. *J. Biol. Chem.* 246:7632–41

171. Williamson, D. H., Lund, P., Krebs, H. A. 1967. The redox state of free nicotina-mide-adenine dinucleotide in the cyto-plasm and mitochondria of rat liver. *Biochem. J.* 103:514–27

172. Wilson, D. F., Ericinska, M., Schramm, V. L. 1983. Evaluation of the rela-tionship between the intra- and extrami-tochondrial [ATP]/[ADP] ratios using phosphoenolpyruvate carboxykinase. *J. Biol. Chem.* 258:10464–73

173. Wilson, D. F., Nelson, D., Erecinska, M. 1982. Binding of the intramitochon-drial ADP and its relationship to adenine nucleotide translocation. *FEBS Lett.* 143:228–32

174. Zuurendonk, P. F., Tager, J. M. 1974. Rapid separation of particulate compo-nent and soluble cytoplasm of isolated rat liver cells. *Biochim. Biophys. Acta* 333: 393–99

175. Zwizinski, C., Schleyer, M., Neupert, W. 1983. Transfer of proteins into mitochondria: Precursor of the ADP/ATP carrier binds to receptor sites on isolated mitochondria. *J. Biol. Chem.* 258:4071–74

GASTROINTESTINAL PHYSIOLOGY

Introduction, John G. Forte, *Section Editor*

Cell proliferation and differentiation are prominent activities of the gastrointestinal epithelium throughout life. It has been estimated that about 300 g of cells are lost, and replaced, every 24 hr from the human gastrointestinal tract (1). These high rates of cell turnover represent the normal physiological response to the "trauma" of alimentation. Moreover, there are profound and specific responses to endogenous trophic factors, as well as conditions of disease, that serve to alter gastrointestinal epithelial cell proliferation and differentiation. This section on Gastrointestinal Physiology reviews aspects of cellular development, differentiation, and epithelialization in the GI tract.

Dr. Lipkin's article discusses questions of growth and development of cells in the GI tract. He reviews new approaches to study the molecular basis of cell proliferation in response to normal and noxious stimuli. Emphasis is given to various stages of abnormal development and alteration associated with adverse physiological conditions.

The patterns of cellular differentiation and secretory responsiveness of the stomach just prior to birth and in the several days to weeks of postnatal life are reviewed by Dr. Johnson. The accelerating influences of hormones, such as corticosterone, and the dietary changes associated with weaning are emphasized, but it is concluded that the events of functional development are ultimately regulated by intrinsic or genetically programmed changes within the cells involved.

An important aspect of gastric epithelial physiology concerns the ability of the tissue to withstand harsh digestive conditions and dietary insults. Drs. Silen & Ito have used an in vitro stomach model to demonstrate the rapid process of re-epithelialization after surface cell desquamation. Cellular extensions and reformation of tight junctions form the basis for restitution of epithelial integrity, which occurs even in the absence of cell division but is dependent on processes of cell motility and morphological rearrangement on the lamina propria.

Dr. Henning addresses the question of how development in the small intestine is coordinated with other parts of the GI tract and with the process of weaning. Postnatal development is associated with changes in intestinal enzymes related to protein and carbohydrate digestion. Evidence relating to the regulatory role of diet, hormones, and other factors is reviewed.

The problem of the continued differentiation, migration, and maturation of the intestinal epithelium is the subject of Dr. Smith's article. As the enterocyte migrates from the intestinal crypt to the tip of the villus, specific changes in morphological and functional development can be mapped. Smith reviews recent techniques for the analysis of enterocyte maturation that suggest a phase separation for the development of enterocyte digestive function and microvillar development from that of absorption. He concludes that such approaches should provide the opportunity to evaluate the role of various local and systemic factors on development at the level of the individual enterocyte.

Literature Cited

1. Croft, D. N., Cotton, P. B. 1973. Gastro-intestinal cell loss in man. Its measurement and significance. *Digestion* 8:144–60

Ann. Rev. Physiol. 1985. 47:175–97

GROWTH AND DEVELOPMENT OF GASTROINTESTINAL CELLS

Martin Lipkin

Memorial Sloan-Kettering Cancer Center, 1275 York Avenue, New York, NY 10021, and Cornell University Medical College and Graduate School of Medical Sciences, 1300 York Avenue, New York, NY 10021

INTRODUCTION

Recent advances in our understanding of the growth and development of gastrointestinal cells have come from an expansion of conventional cell kinetic and biochemical measurements and from new developments in methodology. New approaches have been developed to analyze the molecular basis of cell proliferation in normal cells and the physiological responses of the cells to normal and noxious stimuli. Studies in these areas also have continued to increase our understanding of the properties of gastrointestinal cells in various stages of abnormal development, under physiological and adverse conditions.

Thus, results of recent studies have increased our knowledge of how gastrointestinal cells respond to a wide variety of stimuli that alter their growth and development. In this article we will summarize background information and recent advances on the proliferation and differentiation of normal and abnormal cells of the esophagus, stomach, and small and large intestine. We also describe newer biochemical and analytical methods important to this area, their contribution to a significant expansion of measurements of molecular properties of gastrointestinal cells, and their kinetic and physiologic correlates.

175

0066-4278/85/0315-0175$02.00

ESOPHAGUS

Normal Esophagus

In the esophagus, the epithelium is squamous, unlike the lining in the lower regions of the gastrointestinal tract. Proliferating cells are situated in the basal layer beneath the surface of the esophageal mucosa and are covered with stratified migrating and nondividing cells; they move toward the lumen and eventually are extruded from the mucosal surface. All basal cells can be labeled with tritiated thymidine ([3H]dThd) and are presumed to proliferate. Like normal stomach and small intestinal cells (71), esophageal cells that synthesize DNA are seen randomly among the basal layer of esophageal cells (14).

The renewal of epithelial cells in the basal layer of rodents occurs approximately every 4–5 days, and the entire rodent epithelium renews every 7–8 days. Renewal in humans is slower (8). As in other regions of the gastrointestinal tract, cells in the esophagus alter their structure after proliferating, as they become differentiated and migrate to the lumenal surface. After cell division, two daughter cells may stay basal and redivide, or one may remain in the basal layer while the other differentiates, or both may leave to differentiate.

Esophageal Disease

In diseases of the esophagus, proliferation rates of the epithelial cells are modified, as occurs in other regions of the gastrointestinal tract. For example, in patients with reflux esophagitis, organ-cultured biopsies have shown more cells incorporating [3H]dThd than in normal esophageal mucosa (76), confirming earlier findings of a high frequency of mitotic figures in the basal zone esophageal biopsies of patients, thus contributing to a thickened basal layer in diseased specimens (58, 59).

In esophageal biopsies of patients with Barrett's epithelium (i.e. columnar-lined esophagus), cell turnover also appeared to be increased (53). In three of four patients, labeled cells were observed in the characteristic villus-like epithelium. As noted above, [3H]dThd normally is incorporated in basal layer esophageal epithelial cells, similar to normal gastric and small bowel epithelium. However, in noncancerous areas of esophageal Barrett's epithelium, villous cells were labeled in a patient who had multiple foci of carcinoma in situ. The latter finding is similar to the ectopic migration of proliferative cells near the crypt surface, in colonic mucosa adjacent to polyps (11, 24, 33), and in atrophic intestinalized gastric mucosa (120). The finding in Barrett's epithelium appears to confirm the disease as a premalignant lesion (86).

STOMACH

Normal Stomach

Mucus-secreting cells cover the surface of the body and fundus of the stomach and extend down into the gastric pits; beneath these are long glands deep in the gastric mucosa. These glands are lined by acid and intrinsic factor–secreting parietal cells and pepsinogen-secreting chief cells, which empty into the gastric pits within the mucosa. Below the body of the stomach, the mucosa is pyloric in type; mucous-secreting cells also line the gastric pits, while glandular cells underneath have an alkaline secretion that contains pepsinogen. Endocrine cells that synthesize, store, and secrete the various hormones (45, 60, 81) are located in both types of mucosae, and mucous neck cells are believed to function as stem cells for these endocrine cells (20, 80). The latter are intermingled with other mucous cells and are mainly in the midzone of the gastric glands. The endocrine cells are believed to have originated from the neural crest and to respond to autonomic, mechanical, and intraluminal stimuli by discharging their granules into the circulation. Although there appear to be at least 11 different endocrine cell types in the gastrointestinal mucosa, the primary cells in the gastric fundus are the A cell or (enteroglucagon-secreting cell), the G cell (or gastrin cell), and the argentaffin cell, which secretes serotonin and histamine.

The mucosa of the pyloric antrum has gastric pits deeper than in the fundus, lined mainly with an epithelial cell similar to the mucous neck cell. The parietal acid secretory cells and the G cells (113), which secrete gastrin, are also present in this region; the most concentrated G cell population is in the middle third of the antral mucosa. Gastric mucous and specialized glandular cells renew at rates that differ markedly. In rodents and in humans, mucous epithelial cells in the stomach have proliferative parameters similar to epithelial cells of the colon; cell renewal in small intestine is slightly more rapid (69, 77, 104).

Renewal rates of mucosal epithelial cells of gastric mucosa in man using labeling and mitotic data have previously been described (32). In man the proliferative cell cycle time for gastric mucous epithelial cells is 2–3 days, and mucosal replacement takes 4–6 days (75, 77).

Few studies have been carried out on cell proliferation during early normal mammalian development. Recent findings on gastric cell proliferation during development in rodents have analyzed cell proliferation and loss during the first 4 weeks of life (78). The rate of DNA synthesis in cells of the mucosa remained elevated up to the age of 15 days and then decreased, most rapidly during the next 5–6 days. Actual rates of DNA synthesis in 5- to 15-day-old rats were 10–15-fold higher than in 20–30-day-old rats. Thymidine kinase activity in the mucosa was also higher in 10-day-old suckling than in 20–28-day-old rats.

DNA synthesis and thymidine kinase activity were significantly increased, and cell loss decreased by multiple injections of pentagastrin in 28-day-old rats compared with controls.

New studies on the effects of gastrin on cell proliferation in stomach have continued at a rapid pace. Thus, the proliferation of gastrin cells in antrum following vagotomy in rats was studied as a function of the total number of antral gastrin cells, the antral surface area, and the serum gastrin concentration (26). Three weeks after vagotomy and pyloroplasty, or pyloroplasty alone, the number of gastrin cells in the stomach was significantly elevated in vagotomized animals, and both the mucosal surface of the antrum and the concentration of gastrin cells were significantly higher. Serum gastrin values also were elevated after vagotomy. The hypergastrinemia observed after vagotomy could be explained in part by vagotomy inducing an antral gastrin-cell hyperplasia. When the antrum was excluded, however, elevated antral pH was not sufficient to produce proliferation of gastrin cells (3), suggesting that stimulation of high antral pH and passage of food contribute to gastrin cell proliferation.

The effect of fasting and refeeding on proliferation of antral gastrin cells also was studied in rats, by measuring the number of gastrin cells with injections of [^{3}H]dThd and microautoradiography, thus quantitating newly formed gastrin cells (9). The total number of gastrin cells decreased 68% after a 4-day period of fasting, whereas refeeding of rats for 6 days after a 4-day fasting period resulted in a significant 79% increase in gastrin cell mass. Thus, after refeeding, the labeling index of gastrin cells after injections of [^{3}H]dThd was significantly increased compared to controls, and the degree of proliferation during refeeding was comparable to the increase in number of gastrin cells during refeeding.

Current findings therefore indicate that a new population of gastrin cells is formed in the antral glands of the stomach when rats are refed after fasting. When bombesin tetradecapeptide was administered chronically, the antral gastrin content of rats also significantly increased with stimulation of antral gastrin cell proliferation, following which the antral gastrin cell population increased significantly (65). However, infusion of somatostatin transiently reduced [^{3}H]dThd incorporation and cell division both in fundic and in antral progenitor cells (66). In stomach stimulated by gastrin plus somatostatin, DNA synthesis was lower than in the gastrin-stimulated stomach. Thus, somatostatin appears to inhibit, perhaps indirectly, cell proliferation and to antagonize the trophic activity of gastrin in fundic and antral mucosae. Both endogenous gastrin and exogenous pentagastrin protected against aspirin-induced damage, and the protective effect of gastrin was directly related to the balance between cell production and cell loss (112).

Diseases of the Stomach

The overall rate of development of precancerous diseases in the stomach varies markedly according to nutritional intake. It has been postulated that conversion of precursor nitrogenous compounds of some foods to nitrosamines, mutagens, and carcinogens contributes to the development of precancerous diseases in the stomach (83). In normal stomach, microautoradiographic studies have shown that DNA, RNA, and protein synthesis are most active in the proliferative zones at the base of the gastric pits. However, with the development of gastritis, atrophic gastritis, and intestinalization of the gastric mucosa, increased synthetic activities are present in gastric surface cells (34), supporting the possibility that these changes are precancerous.

Recent microautoradiographic analyses were carried out to study cell proliferation in gastric epithelium; biopsy material was obtained from patients with various degrees of gastritis, from superficial to severe atrophy, peptic ulcer disease, and adenomatous polyposis (105). Levels of cell proliferation in patients with peptic ulcer disease and polyps was similar to nonatrophic gastritis and mild atrophy of the mucosa. However, cell proliferation increased in advancing atrophy and reached a peak in severe atrophic gastritis. Thus, chronic gastritis with marked atrophy of the mucosa appeared to be a major risk factor for cancer, with a hyperproliferative state developing in the gastric mucosa.

Further analysis of the rate of gastric epithelial cell proliferation in healthy humans and in patients with different degrees of gastritis revealed no significant difference between duration of the S-phase of the proliferative cell cycle in normal mucosa, superficial gastritis, mild atrophic gastritis, and severe atrophic gastritis (50). This important observation confirmed the likelihood that the labeling index can be used as a function of the rate of cell proliferation in human gastric mucosa. A significant correlation between the labeling indices and the degree of gastritis also was found in both antral and fundic mucosa in a separate experiments. In atrophic gastritis, more mitotic activity occurs in intestinal metaplastic glands than in normal gastric pits (67). The mitotic index doubles (1% to 2.3%) and the labeling index increases (48), together with the appearance of small intestinal cells in the stomach.

Recent studies have also analyzed the distribution of DNA content as a potential marker of precancerous or early malignant changes in digestive cells (16). Samples were derived from stomach, duodenum, and colon of normal donors via endoscopy, and patients affected with ulcer disease, atrophic gastritis, chronic gastritis, and polyps were studied. Normal samples exhibited the usual DNA distribution in G1/0,S and G2/M compartments, when stained for flow cytometric analysis using ethidium bromide and mithramycin. A subpopulation of aneuploid cells was found, similar to that of gastric adenocarcinoma, with DNA index ranging from 1.1 to 1.4 in comparison to 1.0. The percent aneuploid cells in most of the tumors, however, was generally higher than in gastritis. Polyps also exhibited an aneuploid peak, whereas ulcers were characterized by a normal, diploid DNA content. These findings supported the possibility that aneuploidy in these lesions indicates a precancerous condition or the presence of an early, small fraction of neoplastic cells.

In gastric mucosa, earlier work had shown a general association between the degree of metaplasia and histology of the cancer, with greater metaplasia occurring in more differentiated carcinoma; poorly differentiated adenocarcinoma occurs with less metaplasia (84). Metaplasia accompanies or precedes adenocarcinoma in 90% of gastric specimens studied. A higher degree of intestinal metaplasia is present in the gastric mucosa of patients with cancer than with gastric ulcer, implying again that the metaplasia is a precancerous disease (84, 88, 107).

Recently, using the stathmokinetic approach to analyze metaplastic mucosa, over 90% of mitotic cells were located in the lower half (i.e. proliferative region) of the mucosa (110). Following vincristine, the average mitotic index was slightly higher in metaplastic mucosa than in malignant lesions. The average cell production rate was slightly higher in metaplastic cells than in malignant cells.

Malignant lesions also had modifications of mitotic index, with increases paralleling changes in the gastric mucosa including increases in diameter, staging, and degree of invasion (110). The average mitotic index of early cancers was lower than in advanced cancers, while poorly differentiated adenocarcinoma had a higher mitotic index than well-differentiated adenocarcinoma. Metastatic lesions also showed a higher mitotic index than primary lesions. There was, however, no correlation between the mitotic index and the location, the degree of the stromal reaction, and the type of infiltration or the age and sex of the patients.

SMALL INTESTINE

Normal Intestine

In the normal small intestine, the epithelial layer is a single cell wide, which lines the crypts and covers the villi (18, 54). The types of epithelial cells in the small intestine have previously been described as columnar, mucous, Paneth, and enteroendocrine (18, 19, 21, 22). Columnar cells begin as immature proliferative cells. Starting at the base of the crypts, columnar cells migrate up to the villi, differentiating as they move toward the bowel lumen (13, 18, 19, 21, 22); the time duration of this proliferation and migration is approximately 5–6 days (69, 72, 74, 75, 77, 104) in most of the human small intestine, and 3 days in the ileum (75). In rodents the process takes 2–3 days (38, 39, 64, 82). A normal proximal-distal decrease in villous height (2) likely accounts for these variations, rather than differences in the rate of cell migration. Earlier findings also have indicated that basal columnar cells in the first four cell positions give rise to the other three types of epithelial cells (22).

The effects of epidermal growth factor (EGF) on cell production in adult rats and mice have recently been studied (1). Stathmokinetic measurements using vincristine arrest technique combined with the microdissection of the crypts were carried out to estimate the rate of cell production in the crypts. EGF had trophic effects in duodenum, jejunum, ileum, and colon, but no effect on the cell production rate in gastric glands.

Further study of inhibitory factors also was carried out, with an endogenous inhibitor of DNA synthesis in rabbit small intestine reported to be effective on the proliferation of adult mouse intestinal cells (101). It was suggested that one or more substances were present in rabbit small intestine that appeared to be active in the G_1-S transition of the cell cycle in the mouse intestine; however, only one of the factors appeared to be tissue-specific, and this was of low molecular weight.

Diseases of the Small Intestine

Further measurements of intracellular DNA loss in gluten-sensitive celiac disease in humans have indicated that rapid epithelial cell renewal exceeded that of control patients. The proliferative cycle of the epithelial cells was estimated to be one half of the normal duration (25, 114, 121). In this disease the epithelial cells, crypts, and villi often become markedly altered, and gluten enteropathy is associated with an increased incidence of carcinomas and lymphomas. The rate of cell proliferation can triple throughout the entire crypt, with a loss of villi, enlarged crypts, and an immature mucosal cell lining (4, 114), while the cell cycle time can decrease to less than 1 day.

LARGE INTESTINE

Normal Colon

The proliferative region of the large intestine normally occupies the basal three quarters of the crypts. Cells migrate toward the gut lumen and are extruded from the mucosal surface between crypts. These large intestinal crypts are more closely spaced than either in stomach or small intestine, and the surface of the large intestine is flat.

The colonic epithelial cells, columnar, mucous, and enteroendocrine, most likely originate in the crypt base (17). Migration of cells to the crypt surface takes 3–8 days in man (23, 32, 72, 75, 77, 104) and 2–3 days in rodents (17, 82). Argentaffin (enteroendocrine) cells of the human rectal mucosa undergo slow renewal in 35–100 days (30).

Several recent studies have analyzed cell proliferation in the colonic crypts, at several sites along the length of the large intestine, or along the length of the crypt in rodents. In rat (109) at different sites within the large intestine, major differences were found in the size and shape of the crypts. The distribution of the proliferating cells within the crypts also varied. The average cell cycle duration ranged from 58 hr in the descending colon to 25 hr in the cecum; this variation appeared to be brought about largely by changes in the duration of the G_1 phase of the proliferative cell cycle, the durations of the other phases remaining relatively constant. There also was variability in the cell cycle duration and growth fraction at different levels within the crypts; throughout, the bowel cells appeared to cycle more slowly at the very bottom of the crypt. Therefore, because the organization of cell proliferation in normal rat colon is complex, whether in normal or in diseased animals, studies of cell proliferation require a definition of anatomic location.

Somewhat different results were obtained by studying proliferative parameters at different sites within the crypt using flow technique; this indicated for the whole crypt a cell cycle time of 15.5 hr and a growth fraction for the whole crypt of 29% (28). The mean cell cycle duration of about 15–16 hr demonstrated little variation at different sites within the crypt, whereas the duration of DNA synthesis again fell with increasing cell position in the crypt. Growth fraction also decreased with rising cell position within the crypt.

When the mucosal crypts of the descending colon of the mouse were studied (28), quantitative estimates indicated the mean crypt length to be 31.1 cells, and the mean crypt circumference 22.5 cells, giving a total crypt population of about 700 cells. The mitotic index for the whole crypt column was 1.33%, and the labeling index 11.7% with peak values of about 27% occurring at the bottom of the crypt. Metaphase accumulation following vincristine showed the birth rate in the whole crypt to be 26.5 cells/1000 cells/hr, with a mitotic duration of 0.39 hr.

In the descending normal colon of the rat, epithelial cell loss in response to temporary ischemia also was recently investigated (96). Shortly after the temporary ischemia the number of cells per crypt decreased, with cell loss occurring mainly from the nonproliferating upper half of the crypt. The number of cells per crypt reached control values again after 24–48 hr. There was a marked increase in proliferative activity, as reflected by the labeling index after [3H]dThd and by the mitotic index, with peak values at 16 and 24 hr after ischemia. After 48 hr the proliferative indices were normal again.

A parallel decrease in epithelial cell kinetics also was found with experimental bypass in the rat descending colon (97). Results showed the number of cells per crypt markedly reduced at 6 weeks after bypass, and the percentage of labeled crypt cells, 1 hr after [3H]dThd, and the distribution of labeled cells in the crypt was normal. Also the life span of the epithelial cells was the same in control and bypassed colon.

Further findings after transverse colostomy were compared to those of a sham operation, and to transsection of the colon with reanastomosis; in rats microautoradiographic measurements after labeling with [^{3}H]dThd revealed a significant decrease in proliferative activity 5 days and 3 weeks later in the colonic segment distal to the colostomy (27). Atrophy of the mucosa and a significant decrease in DNA synthesis occurred in that segment, indicating that the intraluminal presence of fecal bulk is important in maintaining cell renewal in the colon. Other factors also are involved, because a delayed but significant decrease in cell proliferation was observed proximal to the colostomy; however, mucosal atrophy did not occur in that region.

Modifications of cell proliferation also have been demonstrated with hormonal and nutritional treatment (56). Thus, estrogen decreased the incorporation of [^{3}H]dThd into colonic epithelial cell DNA most markedly 4 hr after injection in the colonic mucosa. With refeeding of male mice after 48 hr of fasting, however, the colonic mucosa was not affected when mice were treated with estrogen implants for up to 4 days. Estrogen treatments caused no significant change in the DNA, RNA, or protein content of the colonic mucosa.

Further studies indicated that dibutryl cyclic adenosine monophosphate (dibutryl cAMP) also inhibited cell proliferation in colonic crypts and in colonic adenocarcinomas in rodents (116). In jejunum, dibutryl cAMP at high doses inhibited crypt cell proliferation, but lower doses were reported to accelerate jejunal crypt cell proliferation. Neither bilateral adrenalectomy nor chemical sympathectomy abolished the ability of dibutryl cAMP to stimulate jejunal crypt cell proliferation.

Testosterone treatment similarly accelerated cell proliferation in the small intestine and in colonic tumors; however, following castration, cell proliferation was retarded in colonic tumors but not in the small intestine (118). In colonic tumors cell proliferation also was inhibited by the antiandrogenic drug, Flutamide. In contrast, testosterone and castration each failed to influence cell proliferation in the colonic crypt epithelium of both normal and carcinogen-treated animals.

Comparative measurements of oophorectomy and treatment with ovarian hormones on cell proliferation have recently been made (117). The proliferation of colonic tumours decreased following oophorectomy, and the decrease was reversed by the administration of estradiol but not by the administration of progesterone. Oophorectomy did not retard cell proliferation in the colonic crypts. Because age-dependent variations are large, and sex differences also are found that increase the incidence of human bowel cancer, hormonal factors such as these could influence the cancer rates. Current findings in this area have thus suggested that both in colonic and jejunal crypts, cell proliferation is under both endocrine and autonomic neural control, whereas in colonic tumors it is subject to endocrine regulation alone (115).

During early development, DNA synthesis was measured at intervals after birth in four colonic segments, by the incorporation of [^{3}H]dThd (12). Findings indicated that growth of the colon may be under the control of glucocorticoid secretion at the weaning period. In studying the influence of nutrition on cell proliferation, epithelial cell proliferative rates were found to be significantly decreased in the colon of rats fed a liquid elemental diet (Vivonex) (108).

The possible role of pericryptal fibroblasts in regulating intestinal cell proliferation has been studied for many years. Recent measurements analyzed relationships in rat colonic mucosa after in vivo incorporation of [^{3}H]dThd (79). One hour after injection, the labeling index of pericryptal fibroblasts was only 2.4%, and labeled fibroblasts were slightly predominant along the lower two thirds of the crypts; within 24 hr most underwent at least one cell division. Cell migration was not observed and a significant fraction of the labeled fibroblasts was still present after three weeks, indicating that the fibroblasts constituted a slowly renewing cell population. Thus, current data failed to confirm the hypothesis of an "en bloc" migration of fibroblasts in synchrony with the epithelial cells.

The effects of damaging the colonic mucosa were further studied by measuring repopulation after repeated X-ray injury (46). Exposing the descending colon of 4-month and 2-year-old mice to 1250 rads was lethal to most of the epithelial cells, and surviving cells formed new crypts and surface epithelium in animals of both ages. These new crypts were larger in young mice, and the labeling index higher, than in unirradiated animals during the first week after irradiation. In older mice, the overshoot in labeling index and in crypt size began later and continued for a longer time than in the young animals, suggesting that control of cell proliferation is less precise in older than in young mice.

Further measurements of cell proliferation in the descending colon of 3–30-month old unirradiated mice were compared with others irradiated repeatedly from the age of 6 or 24 months (47). In the unirradiated mice, the number of crypts decreased significantly at 30 months, but no significant age-related changes were seen in crypt size or labeling index. Cell proliferation returned to control levels within 6 weeks of each X-ray dose and remained at this level for 20 weeks after the final dose. Later, cell proliferation in the irradiated colon fell significantly below control.

Diseased Colon

Relationships of cell damage to proliferative activity and neoplasia have recently been further studied. In ulcerative colitis in remission, findings showed a spatial pattern of proliferating cells in colonic mucosa similar to that seen in both regenerating and in precancerous mucosa (102). Patients with a short history of colitis had an abnormal proliferative pattern as frequently as others with a long history, indicating that proliferative activity itself does not signify impending malignant change. With ulcerative colitis in remission, the colonic mucosa also had an increased proportion of cells in DNA synthesis, similar to that seen in active colitis, suggesting the abnormal pattern observed in remission is the pattern of an actively regenerating mucosa. The high rate of mucosal turnover, observed not only during clinically active disease but throughout remission, may contribute to the increased incidence of carcinoma in this disease. In other organs, increasing the turnover of damaged cells is known to increase the rate of development of neoplasms.

In further studies of experimental damage to nuclear DNA, cell proliferation was studied in colonic adenocarcinomas of the rat after 1,2-dimethylhydrazine (DMH), and findings were compared to normal colon (92). Microautoradiographic observations revealed that the distinct zone of crypt-cell proliferation was not present in the tumors, and cells replicated in nearly all segments of the neoplasms. Tumor cells had a longer proliferative cell cycle, again due to an extension of the G_1 duration. They also had more heterogeneity in the durations of S phase and G_2. Adenocarcinoma cells resembled basal crypt cells of control animals, and the latter had subpopulations with varying durations of the proliferative cell cycle. When colonic epithelial cells became premalignant and malignant, impaired differentiation also led to decreased cell shedding into the intestinal lumen as benign and malignant tumors arose.

This was seen further in a sequential study of the perturbations developing in epithelial cell proliferation in the ileum and in the descending colon during tumor induction after DMH treatment (93). At an early stage, an expansion of the zone of epithelial cell proliferation in the crypts and migration of dividing cells as far as the crypt mouth were noted, as a manifestation of impaired enterocyte differentiation. The crypt cells mainly proliferated through a cell cycle, the mean duration of which was slightly greater than in normal intestinal cells. A reduced epithelial cell loss and resulting disturbance in steady state led to the accumulation of great numbers of atypical cells in the superficial layers of the crypts and formation of carcinomas in situ in the descending colon.

Bile acids are believed to function as tumor-promoting agents in the colon. The effects of varying bile-acids concentrations on epithelial cell proliferation contributed to a further understanding of this effect. In the rat, bile-acid concentrations were altered by intrarectally injecting either deoxycholic or lithocholic acid for 4 weeks or by increasing the dietary fat or fiber intake (43). When DMH was administered, findings indicated that the bile acids and dietary agar and wheat bran contributed to a slight hyperplasia in the colon.

Further study of intrarectal instillation of bile acids or the tumor-promoting agent (TPA) resulted in early, transient induction of ornithine decarboxylase (ODC) and an increase in [^{3}H]dThd uptake (111). In explant cultures of rat colon, bile acids or TPA stimulated ODC activity and DNA synthesis. This stimulation of ODC activity and DNA synthesis was greater with secondary bile acids than primary ones, further suggesting that TPA acts as a promoter of colon cancer, and secondary bile acids exert a promoting effect in colon carcinogenesis in a manner analogous to that of TPA in skin carcinogenesis.

Other proliferative modifiers, i.e. nutritional factors and total parenteral nutrition, also influence both cell proliferation and carcinogenesis. The oral administration of solid and liquid diets, regardless of chemical constituents, contributed to a DMH-induced increase in colonic epithelial cell proliferation; however, a DMH-induced increase in epithelial cell proliferation was not observed in rats maintained on total parenteral nutrition (52). Thus, the route of administration has a significant influence on epithelial cell proliferation in colonic epithelium of DMH-treated rats. The preneoplastic state is a committed state that appears not to be dependent upon the continued presence of a carcinogen; in the DMH models all crypt epithelium is preneoplastic, although not all cells progress to the overtly transformed state. It is important that total parenteral nutrition prevented the expression of a DMH-induced preneoplastic state together with decreased epithelial cell proliferation.

As these tumors grow there is a small decrease in cell loss, rather than an increased rate of cell proliferation (15). [^{3}H]dThd microautoradiography again demonstrated that carcinoma cells have a longer generation time than normal cells (51). The cell generation time was about 3–7 days for cancer cells compared to 1 day for normal cells. There is an increase in the life of cancer cells rather than extreme variations in the growth fraction. Volume-doubling time for human cancers in general is about 1–3 months, and about 1 year to several years for cancers of the large intestine.

In a unique in vivo analysis of human premalignant adenomas, characteristics of both normal cells and of malignant cells were observed in the benign neoplasms. The in vivo measurements of proliferation kinetics of the epithelial cells were made following intravenous pulse injection of [^{3}H]dThd, into a patient with familial polyposis and Gardner syndrome (68). Results demonstrated both in the adenomas and in adjacent flat mucosa that cells completed only a single proliferative cycle during 4 days of observation. Durations of G_2 and S phases of the cell cycle were approximately 5 hr and 15 hr, respectively, both in adenomas and in flat mucosa. After pulse injection, the locations of [^{3}H]dThd-labeled epithelial cells within the adenomatous crypts showed a distribution with maximum proliferation near the lumenal surface; however, in flat mucosa, maximum proliferation of labeled epithelial cells occurred in the lower portion of the colonic crypts. Migration rates were similar to earlier studies at 0.4 cell position hr^{-1} in crypts of adenomas, and 0.3 cell position hr^{-1} in crypts of adjacent flat mucosa. It was of particular interest that the direction of migration differed in adenoma and flat mucosal cells: in marked contrast to the migration of epithelial cells toward the lumenal surface of the crypts in flat mucosa, in adenomas a markedly abnormal retrograde average migration away from the surface of the mucosa appeared to occur, as occurs with malignant cells. However, the adenoma cells had not developed the additional property of malignant cells that enables them to invade through the submucosa.

In understanding mechanisms of carcinogenesis, biochemical studies have shown that carcinogens, such as aflatoxin B1, were activated to carcinogen-DNA adducts by cultured human tissues, including bronchus, esophagus, colon, and bladder; however, epidemiological studies have not implicated aflatoxin B1 as a cause of cancer at these tissues (49). Differences in carcinogen metabolism among people may be qualitative and/or quantitative. The magnitude of differences found ranged from 50- to 150-fold, similar to that found in pharmacogenetic studies of drug metabolism. The rate-limiting enzymatic reactions could differ among humans and tissue types.

RECENT DEVELOPMENTS IN EXPERIMENTAL AND ANALYTICAL METHODS TO FACILITATE STUDIES OF CELL PROLIFERATION AND DIFFERENTIATION

Most studies of proliferation and differentiation of gastrointestinal cells have been carried out by using the classic techniques of injecting [^{3}H]dThd into rodents or human subjects, or by using very short-term cultures of mucosal biopsies and isotopic precursors. The proliferation kinetic analyses used have been extensively described in earlier studies by many authors [e.g. in the text by Baserga (69)]. In recent years, newer techniques of study also have become available that increase the ability of investigators to study parameters related to cell proliferation and differentiation in response to physiological agents. These methods improve the stability of gastrointestinal epithelial cells in vitro and make it possible to analyze the effects of physiological agents, tumor promotors, and carcinogens on the cells. Because these new techniques will be particularly important to investigators in the future, recent advances in this area will be summarized below.

Improved Organ Culture of Gastrointestinal Biopsies

Previous studies of cell proliferation have encountered difficulty in maintaining explants of colonic mucosa in a normal viable state for more than short durations in the order of hours. This has markedly limited studies in which specimens of human mucosa are cultured and studied in vitro. Despite this limitation, however, the short-term culture of human gastrointestinal mucosal specimens has been valuable in defining the spatial distributions of proliferating and differentiating cells within the mucosa and abnormalities that develop in gastrointestinal diseases, as noted above.

It is particularly important to improve these methods because clinical endoscopic procedures for removing gastrointestinal biopsies from humans have improved in recent years and now can make available a wide variety of human mucosal biopsy specimens for explant culture and experimental evaluation. Advances in explant culture technology have recently begun to be reported, with concomitant improvement in the analysis of the morphologic and metabolic characteristics of gastrointestinal epithelial cells (6, 49, 95, 119).

In one study using newer methods (119), biopsy specimens of normal human colonic mucosa were maintained in explant culture for 4 days. Active cell replication was observed during a 24-hour period, and the number of cells synthesizing DNA increased when deoxycholic acid was added to the culture medium. However, with careful monitoring and despite morphological evidence of tissue viability at later times, DNA, RNA, and protein syntheses decreased in the colonic epithelial cells, and the total number of cells in the crypt columns declined. Thus, in short-term explant culture certain metabolic activities in colonic epithelial cells were maintained while others declined.

In earlier organ-culture studies of human colonic biopsies, it had been shown that an expansion of the proliferative compartment occurred during progressive stages of abnormal development, as epithelial cells gained an increased ability to proliferate and to accumulate in the mucosa during progressive stages of abnormal development (29, 31, 33, 35, 70). To increase the utility of the organ-culture approach, new analytical methods were recently developed to measure the patterns of the distribution of [3H]dThd-labeled epithelial cells in colonic crypts of human populations having increased susceptibility to colon cancer (73). For this purpose, labeled cells were segregated with respect to crypt height into a greater number of multiple compartments within the crypts. Significant differences were found in patients with familial polyposis or familial colon cancer and subjects at low risk when labeled cell distributions were compared over all the crypt-height compartments. In the upper 40% of the crypt, distributions of the fractions of labeled cells (denoted by the term ϕ_h) revealed a discriminant level that separated over 90% of low-risk subjects from a major fraction of those affected with familial colon cancer or polyposis, and from almost 50% of the at-risk progeny as expected for an autosomal dominant trait. Thus, the ϕ_h labeling distribution appeared to be a more precise measure of risk than previously used.

Tissue Culture

Tissue culture of gastrointestinal epithelial cells also has now been successfully applied to the in vitro study of colonic adenomas and normal colonic cells. In a recent study (37), human premalignant colonic epithelial cells from benign tumors for the first time were reproducibly grown in tissue culture. The cells grew as tightly packed colonies from small explants free of fibroblasts and remained viable for up to 8 weeks. Cells were identified as epithelial with electron microscopy, and the living cells transported water and salt.

Adenoma cells were cultured with approximately equal frequency from each premalignant class: tubular (low malignant potential), villotubular (intermediate malignant potential), and villous (high malignant potential).

This model has permitted the beginning of a series of measurements to determine the effects of physiological agents, tumor promotors, and other substances on colonic cells. For example, the effect of exogenous epidermal growth factor (EGF) on the cultured cells was measured by assaying the fraction of cells incorporating ^{3}H-thymidine with a continuous labeling. EGF increased the fraction of replicating cells cultured from tubular adenomas, whereas it had no effect on cells cultured from six villous adenomas or the one villotubular adenoma tested (37). EGF has a strong structural homology to human urogastrone, a tropic hormone in the intestine, suggesting that the in vitro results may mirror the in vivo growth modulation of benign tumors.

In a further study, the new methods of tissue culture made it possible to classify the colonic cells into a series based on stages of premalignancy determined by tumor-associated antigen expression. An antisera raised against human second-trimester fetal tissue and absorbed with pooled adult tissues was found to react with cultured adenoma cells (55). Thus, when cells were cultured from adenomas of different histopathologic classes and from colon carcinomas, fetal-associated antigen was found most frequently in carcinoma cells, and the frequency decreased in parallel with a decrease in malignant potential of the adenomas; antigen expression appeared in 71% of carcinomas, 43% of villotubular adenomas, and 18% of tubular adenomas. Many tumors synthesize proteins whose expression is otherwise limited to a particular period in fetal development, and benign adenoma cells were found to express this property with increasing frequency as they progressed toward malignancy.

Further measurements using tissue culture were carried out using two agents, TPA and DOC, that act as tumor promoters in the gastrointestinal tract of experimental animals; their effects were compared in primary cultures of the human premalignant colonic adenoma cells (36). DOC affected only early-stage premalignant cells, and among DOC, TPA, and EGF, DOC had the greatest stimulatory effect on DNA replication. The findings thus suggested that its major role in tumor progression in vivo could be to enlarge the proliferative cell population of normal colonic cells and early-stage premalignant cells, but not late premalignant or tumor cells.

TPA, on the other hand, differed from DOC with less stimulation of cell growth than DOC. The most pronounced effect of TPA was on intermediate and late-stage premalignant cell cultures, where it induced cell clustering, multilayering, and concomitant release of a protease with many properties similar to a plasminogen activator. Thus, with the development of new tissue-culture technique, the concept of a differential action of tumor-promoting agents on colonic cells during different stages of abnormal growth was developed.

Transplantation Technique

An additional technique has now been developed to facilitate measurements of physiological characteristics of gastrointestinal epithelial cells. Previous studies have indicated that nude mice accept transplants of human malignant tumors, e.g. tumors of colon, rectum, kidney, breast, melanoma, pancreas, pharynx, sarcomas, Burkitt's lymphoma, hepatoma, and epidermoid carcinoma (40–42, 61, 90, 91, 99, 100, 106).

Recently (10), benign adenomatous polyps of the human colon also were successfully transplanted under the kidney capsule of athymic or "nude" mice, in addition to colonic adenocarcinomas and normal colonic mucosa. The benign human adenomatous cells survived for periods of up to 28 days, normal rodent colonic epithelial cells for 45 days, and colonic carcinoma cells for 43 days, revealed by morphologic criteria and by the incorporation of tritiated thymidine into DNA of the epithelial cells. Thus, the technique of transplantation can now supplement in vitro methods for the maintenance of adenomatous tissue derived from human colonic mucosa, in order to facilitate studies of growth characteristics and transformation of the cells.

Related Genetic Markers Used to Define Abnormal Stages of Colonic Cell Maturation

ABNORMAL ANTIGENS   Much effort also has been devoted to identifying specific immunological and biochemical markers of transformation. The use of syngeneic animal systems has made it possible to identify several serologically demonstrable classes of antigens on murine tumors. In man, autologous typing (87) has provided evidence for the existence of cell surface antigens restricted to autologous tumor cells, present on autologous and some allogeneic tumor cells, or widely distributed on normal and malignant cells.

Certain antigens associated with human tumors have been observed as having a relatively restricted distribution among normal tissues, which are either organ- or tissue-specific. In gastrointestinal cancers, antigens have been described that have a more or less restricted site specificity. Some antigens (reviewed in 44) such as the intestinal mucosal specific glycoprotein (IMG), colonic mucoprotein antigen (CMA), colon specific antigen(s) (CSA), sulfated glycopeptidic antigen (SGA), goblet cell antigen (GOA), and colon-specific antigen-p (CSAp) appear to be cell-specific; none of these antigens, however, is cancer-specific. Characteristically, as detection methods become more sensitive, previous putative "tumor-specific" antigens have been reclassified as "tumor-associated" due to quantitative differences in the level of their expression in normal and transformed tissues. Nevertheless, the use of such antigens, particularly those that can be monitored in blood (such as alpha-fetoprotein, carcinoembryonic antigen, galactosyltransferase-isoenzyme, pancreatic oncofetal antigen, basic fetoprotein, TennaGen, and CSAp) (44), can be clinically relevant as adjunct parameters of prognostic evaluations and for assessments of tumor burden during the course of disease and in response to therapy.

Recently, the inappropriate or ectopic expression of particular gastrointestinal antigens (at anatomic sites in the adult GI tract at which they are not usually expressed) has provided an additional measurement for tumor classification (7, 55). The mucus-associated second trimester fetal antigen and antigens M1, M2, and M3 occur in the gastrointestinal tract and can be used for analysis of the effects on colonic cell development of the types of compounds referred to above.

NUCLEIC ACID SEQUENCES   It is now also possible to identify and clone nucleic acid sequences whose pattern of expression can uniquely identify premalignant and malignant colon tissue and which may be useful in following the progression of cells to malignancy.

More than ten years ago it was proposed (57) that normal cells harbor unexpressed genes (oncogenes or onc genes) whose activation leads to malignant transformation. Recent developments in cellular and molecular biology have led to an experimental analysis of the "oncogene hypothesis," and its essential validity has been confirmed. Thus, several groups have now demonstrated that DNA from some human tumor cells grown in culture are able to transform 3T3 cells by transfection (62, 63, 85, 89). Among the human tumor cell types that yielded transforming activity have been colon carcinoma (85, 89), bladder carcinoma (62, 89, 103), and lung carcinoma (85, 89). Among the colon carcinoma lines, SW-480 and SK-CO-1 have been shown to be positive (85, 89), whereas HT-29 cells are negative (89). Of further importance is the fact that two primary colon carcinomas, a lung carcinoma, a carcinoma of the pancreas, and an embryonal rhabdomyosarcoma each contained an activated transforming gene (94). In addition to demonstrating the existence of activated transforming genes, or oncogenes in human tumor cells, the incorporation of foreign sequences into host cells has been demonstrated. Several laboratories also were able to show that the transformed 3T3 cells had indeed incorporated some of the human tumor DNA to which they had been exposed (85, 89, 94).

Thus, recent work has demonstrated that human tumor cells in some cases contained activated oncogenes capable of transforming mouse cells, but the identity and function of such genes has been a matter of speculation. An important possibility has been that these human oncogenes are related to the transforming sequences of avian and rodent transforming retroviruses. The extent to which such activated oncogenes are present in human tumors has not been determined, nor have answers to the questions, in the tumors containing them, whether activation is an early or late event and what the role of oncogene products are in transformation. However, the discovery of activated human oncogenes homologous to those of the transforming retroviruses provides an important insight into the molecular mechanisms leading to tumor formation.

Important recent studies on oncogene expression in colonic epithelial cells have been carried out after carcinogen administration in a transplantable, DMH-induced mouse colon tumor (5). Approximately 400 sequences cloned from the messenger population of the tumor were screened for level of expression in the tumor and normal mouse colon, liver, and kidney. It was found that individual sequences were present whose level of expression differed, sometimes markedly, in the normal colon as compared to the tumor. The sequences also could be organized into groups based on their level of expression in each of the tissues, and patterns of expression emerged that characterized each tissue and defined a specific phenotype. Further, a sequence of particular interest was found (98). The sequence pMCT-1, a cloned cDNA that contained an IAP LTR, was highly elevated in expression in a mouse colon tumor as compared to the normal mouse colon. In situ hybridization of biotin-substituted pMCT-1 to fixed frozen sections showed that expression of pMCT-1 was seen throughout the tumor and was highly heterogeneous on a cellular basis, whereas expression was undetectable in any cell in the normal colonic mucosa (98).

This area of investigation is now being extended to measure the expression of these sequences by in situ hybridization, in order to identify the specific cells in the colon in which these sequences are expressed, and to evaluate how early during carcinogenesis this genetic reprogramming of individual cells takes place. This work is also being extended to analyze gene expression in human colon cancer.

ACKNOWLEDGMENT

Ms. Rosemary Petras provided valuable assistance in compiling bibliographic material in the preparation of this article.

Literature Cited

1. Al-Nafussi, A. I., Wright, N. A. 1982. The effect of epidermal growth factor (EGF) on cell proliferation of the gastrointestinal mucosa in rodents. *Virchows Arch. Cell. Pathol.* 40:(1)63–69

2. Altmann, G. G., Leblond, C. P. 1970. Factors influencing villus size in the small intestine of adult rats as revealed by transportation of intestinal segments. *Am. J. Anat.* 127:15–36

3. Alumets, J., El Munshid, H. A., Hakanson, R., Hedenbro, J., Liedberg, G., et al. 1980. Gastrin cell proliferation after chronic stimulation: effect of vagal denervation or gastric surgery in the rat. *J. Physiol.* 298:557–69

4. Anderson, K. E., Finlayson, N. D. C., Deschner, E. E. 1974. Intractable malabsorption with a flat jejunal mucosa and selective IgA deficiency: a case report with immunological and autoradiographic studies. *Gastroenterology* 67:709–16

5. Augenlicht, L. H., Kobrin, D. E. 1982. Cloning and screening of sequences expressed in a mouse colon tumor. *Cancer Res.* 42:1088–92

6. Autrup, H., Barrett, L. A., Jackson, F. E., Jesudason, M. L., Stoner, G., et al. 1978. Explant culture of human colon. *Gastroenterology* 74:1248–57

7. Bara, J., Hamelin, L., Martin, E., Bur-

tin, P. 1981. Intestinal M3 antigen, a marker for the intestinal-type differentiation of gastric carcinomas. *Int. J. Cancer* 28:711–19

8. Bell, B., Almy, T. P., Lipkin, M. 1967. Cell proliferation kinetics in the gastrointestinal tract of man. III. Cell renewal in esophagus, stomach, and jejunum of a patient with treated pernicious anemia. *J. Natl. Cancer. Inst.* 38:615–23

9. Bertrand, P., Willems, G. 1980. Induction of antral gastrin cell proliferation by refeeding of rats after fasting. *Gastroenterology* 78:918–24

10. Bhargava, D. K., Lipkin, M. 1981. Transplantation of adenomatous polyps, normal colonic mucosa and adenocarcinoma of colon into athymic mice. *Digestion* 21:225–31

11. Bleiberg, H., Mainguet, P., Galand, P. 1972. Cell renewal in familial polyposis. Comparison between polyps and adjacent healthy mucosa. *Gastroenterology* 63: 240–45

12. Buts, J. P., DeMeyer, R., Kolanowski, J. 1983. Ontogeny of cell proliferation and DNA synthesis in rat colon: role of glucocorticoids. *Am. J. Physiol.* 244(7): G469–74

13. Cameron, I. L. 1972. Cell proliferation and renewal in aging mice. *J. Gerontol.* 27:162–72

14. Cameron, I. L., Gosslee, D. G., Pilgrim, C. 1965. The spatial distribution of dividing and DNA-synthesizing cells in mouse epithelium. *J. Cell. Comp. Physiol.* 66: 431–35

15. Camplejohn, R. S. 1982. Colorectal cancer: cell kinetics. *Recent Results Cancer Res.* 83:21–30

16. Capurso, L., Teodori, L., DeVita, R., Galloni L., Tarquini, M., et al. 1982. DNA content as a marker of precancerous lesions of the digestive tract. *Gastroenterology* 82(5):1029 (Abstr.)

17. Chang, W. W. L., Leblond, C. P. 1971. Renewal of the epithelium in the descending colon of the mouse. I. Presence of three cell populations: vacuolated-columnar, mucous and argentaffin. *Am. J. Anat.* 131:73–100

18. Cheng, H. 1974. Origin, differentiation and renewal of the four main epithelial cell types in the mouse small intestine. II. Mucous Cells. *Am. J. Anat.* 141:481–502

19. Cheng, H. 1974. Origin, differentiation and renewal of the four main epithelial cell types in the mouse small intestine. IV. Paneth cells. *Am. J. Anat.* 141:521–36

20. Cheng, H., Leblond, C. P. 1974. Origin, differentiation and renewal of the four main epithelial cell types in the mouse small intestine. I. Columnar cells. *Am. J. Anat.* 141:461–80

21. Cheng, H., Leblond, C. P. 1974. Origin, differentiation and renewal of the four main epithelial cell types in the mouse small intestine. III. Enteroendocrine cells. *Am. J. Anat.* 141:503–20

22. Cheng, H., Leblond, C. P. 1974. Origin, differentiation and renewal of the four main epithelial cell types in the mouse small intestine. V. Unitarian theory of the origin of the four epithelial cell types. *Am. J. Anat.* 141:537–62

23. Cole, J. W., McKalen, A. 1961. Observations of cell renewal in human rectal mucosa in vivo with thymidine-H^3. *Gastroenterology* 41:122–25

24. Cole, J. W., McKalen, A. 1963. Studies on the morphogenesis of adenomatous polyps in the human colon. *Cancer* 16:998–1002

25. Croft, D. N., Loehry, C. A., Creamer, B. 1968. Small-bowel cell loss and weight loss in coeliac syndrome. *Lancet* 2:68–70

26. Delince, P., Willems, G., deGraef, J. 1978. Antral gastrin cell proliferation after vagotomy in rats. *Digestion* 18:27–34

27. Delvaux, G., Caes, F., Willems, G. 1983. Influence of a diverting colostomy on epithelial cell proliferation in the colon of rats. *Eur. Surg. Res.* 15:223–29

28. deRodriguez, M. S. B., Sunter, J. P., Watson, A. J., Wright, N. A., Appleton, D. R. 1979. Cell population kinetics in the mucosal crypts of the descending colon of the mouse. *Virchows Arch. Cell Pathol.* 29(6):351–61

29. Deschner, E. E., Lewis, C. M., Lipkin, M. 1963. *In vitro* study of human rectal epithelial cells. 1. Atypical zone of H^{3}thymidine incorporation in mucosa of multiple polyposis. *J. Clin. Invest.* 42: 1922–28

30. Deschner, E. E., Lipkin, M. 1966. An autoradiographic study of the renewal of argentaffin cells in human rectal mucosa. *Exp. Cell Res.* 43:661–65

31. Deschner, E. E., Lipkin, M. 1970. Study of human rectal epithelial cells *in vitro*. III. RNA, protein and DNA synthesis in polyps and adjacent mucosa. *J. Natl. Cancer Inst.* 44:175–85

32. Deschner, E. E., Lipkin, M. 1978. Proliferation and differentiation of gastrointestinal cells. In *Gastrointestinal Tract Cancer,* ed. M. Lipkin, R. A. Good, pp. 3–24. New York: Plenum

33. Deschner, E. E., Lipkin, M., Solomon, C. 1966. *In vitro* study of human epithelial cells. II. H^3 thymidine incorporation

into polyps and adjacent mucosa. *J. Natl. Cancer Inst.* 36:849–57

34. Deschner, E. E., Winawer, S. J., Lipkin, M. 1972. Patterns of nucleic acid and protein synthesis in normal human gastric mucosa and atrophic gastritis. *J. Natl. Cancer Inst.* 48:1567–74

35. Eastwood, G. L., Trier, J. S. 1974. Epithelial cell proliferation during organogenesis of rat colon. *Anat. Rec.* 179:303–10

36. Friedman, E. 1981. Differential response of premalignant epithelial cell classes to phorbial ester tumor promoters and to deoxycholic acid. *Cancer Res.* 41:4588–99

37. Friedman, E. A., Higgins, P. J., Lipkin, M., Shinya, H., Gelb, A. M. 1981. Tissue culture of human epithelial cells from benign colonic tumors. *In Vitro* 17:632–44

38. Fry, R. J. M., Lesher, S., Kisieleski, W. E., Sacher, G. 1963. Cell proliferation in the small intestine. In *Cell Proliferation*, ed. L. F. Lamerton, R. J. M. Fry, pp. 213–33. Philadelphia: F. A. Davis

39. Fry, R. J. M., Lesher, S., Kohn, H. I. 1961. Age effect on cell-transit time in mouse jejunal epithelium. *Am. J. Physiol.* 201:213–16

40. Giovanella, B., Morgan, A., Stehlin, J. 1973. Development of invasive tumors in the nude mouse injected with human cells cultured from Burkitt's lymphoma. *Proc. Am. Assoc. Cancer Res.* 14:20

41. Giovanella, B. C., Stehlin, J., Williams, L. J. 1974. Heterotransplantation of human malignant tumors in nude thymusless mice. *J. Natl. Cancer Inst.* 52:921–30

42. Giovanella, B. C., Yim, S. D., Stehlin, J. S., Williams, L. J. 1972. Development of invasive tumors in the nude mouse after injection of cultured human melanoma cells. *J. Natl. Cancer Inst.* 48:1531–33

43. Glauert, H. P., Bennink, M. R. 1983. Influence of diet or intrarectal bile acid injections on colon epithelial cell proliferation in rats previously injected with 1,2-dimethylhydrazine. *J. Nutr.* 113:475–82

44. Goldenberg, D. M. 1981. Immunobiology and biochemical markers of gastrointestinal cancer. In *Gastrointestinal Cancer*, ed. J. R. Stroehlein, M. M. Romsdale, pp. 65–81. New York: Raven

45. Greider, M. H., Steinberg, V., McGuigan, J. E. 1972. Electron microscopic identification of the gastrin cell of the human antral mucosa by means of immunocytochemistry. *Gastroenterology* 63:572–83

46. Hamilton, E. 1978. Cell proliferation and ageing in mouse colon. I. Repopulation after repeated x-ray injury in young and old mice. *Cell Tissue Kinet.* 11:423–31

47. Hamilton, E., Franks, L. M. 1980. Cell proliferation and ageing in mouse colon. II. Late effects of repeated x-irradiation in young and old mice. *Eur. J. Cancer* 16(5):663–69

48. Hansen, P. H., Peterson, T., Larsen, J. K. 1975. A method to study cell proliferation kinetics in human gastric mucosa. *Gut* 16:23–27

49. Harris, C. C., Trump, B. F., Grafstrom, R., Autrup, H. 1982. Differences in metabolism of chemical carcinogens in cultured human epithelial tissues and cells. *J. Cell Biochem.* 18(3):285–94

50. Hart-Hansen, O., Johansen, Aa., Larsen, J. K., Svendsen, L. B. 1979. Cell proliferation in normal and diseased gastric mucosa. Autoradiography after *in vitro* continuous labelling with tritiated thymidine. *Acta Pathol. Microbiol. Scand. Sect. A* 87:217–22

51. Hattori, T. 1981. Movement of large intestinal mucosa and rotation of large intestinal cancer cells. *Nippon Rinsho* 39(5):36–41

52. Heitman, D. W., Grubbs, B. G., Heitman, T. O., Cameron, I. L. 1983. Effects of 1,2-dimethylhydrazine treatment and feeding regimen on rat colonic epithelial cell proliferation. *Cancer Res.* 43:1153–62

53. Herbst, J. J., Berenson, M. M., Wiser, W. C., Freston, J. W. 1976. Cell proliferation in Barrett's esophageal epithelium. *Clin. Res.* 24:168A (Abstr.)

54. Hermos, J. A., Mathan, M., Trier, J. S. 1971. DNA synthesis and proliferation by villous epithelial cells in fetal rats. *J. Cell Biol.* 50:255–58

55. Higgins, P. J., Friedman, E., Lipkin, M., Hertz, R., Attiyeh, F., Stonehill, E. H. 1983. Expression of gastric-associated antigens by human premalignant and malignant colonic epithelial cells. *Oncology* 40:26–30

56. Hoff, M. B., Chang, W. W. L., Mak, K. M. 1981. Effect of estrogen on cell proliferation in colonic mucosa of mouse. *Virchows Arch. Cell Pathol.* 35(3)

57. Huebner, R. J., Todaro, G. J. 1964. Oncogenes of RNA tumor viruses as determinants of cancer. *Proc. Natl. Acad, Sci. USA* 64:1087–94

58. Ismail-Beigi, F., Horton, P. F., Pope, C. E. II. 1970. Histological consequences of gastroesophageal reflux in man. *Gastroenterology* 58:163–74

59. Ismail-Beigi, F., Pope, C. E. II. 1974.

Distribution of histologic changes of reflux. *Gastroenterology* 66:1109–13

60. Johnson, L. R., Guthrie, P. D. 1974. Secretin inhibition of gastrin-stimulated deoxyribonucleic acid synthesis. *Gastroenterology* 67:601–6

61. Klein, J., Gaiser, J., Hasper, J., 1972. Growth capacity of human tumors *in vitro* and in nude mice. *Rep. Ann. Rep. 1972*, pp. 54–56. Rijswijk, the Netherlands: Organ. Health TNO

62. Krontiris, T. G., Cooper, G. M. 1981. Transforming activity of human tumor DNAs. *Proc. Natl. Acad. Sci. USA* 78: 1181–84

63. Lane, M-A., Sainten, A., Cooper, G. M. 1981. *Proc. Natl. Acad. Sci. USA* 78: 5185–89

64. Leblond, C. P., Walker, B. E. 1956. Renewal of cell populations. *Physiol. Rev.* 36:255–76

65. Lehy, T., Accary, J. P., Labeille, D., Dubrasquet, M. 1983. Chronic administration of bombesin stimulates antral gastrin cell proliferation in the rat. *Gastroenterology* 84:914–19

66. Lehy, T., Dubrasquet, M., Bonfils, S. 1979. Effect of somatostatin on normal and gastric-stimulated cell proliferation in the gastric and intestinal mucosae of the rat. *Digestion* 19:99–109

67. Liavig, I. 1968. Mitotic activity of gastric mucosa. *Acta Pathol. Microbiol. Scand.* 72:43–63

68. Lightdale, C., Lipkin, M., Deschner, E. 1982. *In vivo* measurements in familial polyposis: kinetics and location of proliferating cells in colonic adenomas. *Cancer Res.* 42:4280–83

69. Lipkin, M. 1971. The proliferative cycle of mammalian cells. In *The Cell Cycle and Cancer*, ed. R. Baserga, pp. 6–26. New York: Marcel Dekker

70. Lipkin, M. 1974. Phase I and Phase II proliferative lesions of colonic epithelial cells in diseases leading to colon cancer. *Cancer* 34:878–88

71. Lipkin, M., Bell, B. 1968. Cell proliferation. In *Handbook of Physiology*, ed. C. F. Code, 5(Sect. 6):2861–79. Washington DC: Am. Physiol. Soc.

72. Lipkin, M., Bell, B., Sherlock, P. 1963. Cell proliferation kinetics in the gastrointestinal tract of man. I. Cell renewal in colon and rectum. *J. Clin. Invest.* 42:767–76

73. Lipkin, M., Blattner, W. E., Fraumeni, J. F. Jr., Lynch, H. T., Deschner, E., Winawer, S. 1983. Tritiated thymidine (ϕ_p, ϕ_h) labeling distribution as a marker for hereditary predisposition to colon cancer. *Cancer Res.* 43:1899–904

74. Lipkin, M., Sherlock, P., Bell, B. M. 1962. Generation time of epithelial cells in the human colon. *Nature* 195:175–77

75. Lipkin, M., Sherlock, P., Bell, B. 1963. Cell proliferation kinetics in the gastrointestinal tract of man. II. Cell renewal in stomach, ileum, colon and rectum. *Gastroenterology* 45:721–29

76. Livstone, E., Sheahan, D. G., Behar, J. 1976. *In vitro* tritiated ^{3}H thymidine uptake by esophageal squamous mucosa from patients with reflux esophagitis. *Gastroenterology* 70:909 (Abstr.)

77. MacDonald, W. C., Trier, J. S., Everett, N. B. 1964. Cell proliferation and migration in the stomach, duodenum, and rectum of man: radioautographic studies. *Gastroenterology* 46:405–17

78. Majumdar, A., Johnson, L. 1982. Gastric mucosal cell proliferation during development in rats and effects of pentagastrin. *Am. J. Physiol.* 242(5):G135–G139

79. Maskens, A. P., Rahier, J. R., Meersseman, F. P., Dujardin-Loits, R., Haot, J. G. 1979. Cell proliferation of pericryptal fibroblasts in the rat colon mucosa. *Gut* 20:775–79

80. Matsuyama, M., Suzuki, H. 1970. Differentiation of immature mucous cells into parietal, argyrophil and chief cells in stomach grafts. *Science* 169:385–87

81. McGuigan, J. E., Greider, M. H. 1971. Correlative immunochemical and light microscopic studies of the gastrin cell of the antral mucosa. *Gastroenterology* 60:223–36

82. Messier, B., Leblond, C. P. 1960. Cell proliferation and migration as revealed by radioautography after injection of thymidine-H^3 into rats and mice. *Am. J. Anat.* 106:247–94

83. Mirvish, S. S. 1981. Ascorbic acid inhibition of N-nitroso compound formation in chemical, food, and biological systems. In *Inhibition of Tumor Induction and Development*, ed. M. S. Zedeck, M. Lipkin, pp. 101–26. New York/London: Plenum. 233 pp.

84. Morson, B. 1955. Carcinoma arising from areas of intestinal metaplasia in the gastric mucosa. *Br. J. Cancer* 9:377–85

85. Murray, M. J., Shilo, B-Z., Shih, C., Cowing, D., Hsu, H. W., Weinberg, R. A. 1981. Three different human tumor cell lines contain different oncogenes. *Cell* 25:355–61

86. Naef, A. P., Savary, M., Ozzello, L. 1975. Columnar-lined lower esophagus: an acquired lesion with malignant predisposition. Report on 140 cases of Barrett's esophagus with 12 adenocarcinomas. *J. Thorac. Cardiovasc. Surg.* 70:826–35

87. Old, L. J. 1981. Cancer immunology: the

search for specificity. *Cancer Res.* 41: 361–75

88. Oota, K. 1967. Pathohistology. In *Carcinoma of the Stomach in Early Phase,* ed. T. Kurokawa, T. Kajetani, K. Oota, pp. 251–61. Tokyo: Nakayama-Shoten. 266 pp.

89. Perucho, M., Goldfarb, M., Shimizu, K., Lama, C., Fogh, J., Wigler, M. 1981. Human-tumor-derived cell lines contain common and different transforming genes. *Cell* 27:467–76

90. Povlsen, C. O., Fialkow, P. J., Klein, E., Klein, G., Rygaard, J., Wiener, F. 1973. Growth and antigenic properties of a biopsy derived Burkitt's lymphoma in thymus-less nude mice. *Int. J. Cancer* 11:30–39

91. Povlsen, C., Jacobsen, G., Rygaard, J. 1972. The mouse mutant nude as a model for the testing of anticancer agents. *5th Symp. Int. Comm. Lab. Animals, Hanover,* W. Germany, pp. 63–72. Stuttgart: Fischer

92. Pozharisski, K. M., Klimashevski, V. F., Gushchin, V. A. 1980. Study of kinetics of epithelial cell populations in normal tissues of the rat's intestines and in carcinogenesis. II. Peculiarities of kinetics of enterocyte populations in experimental tumours of the colon. *Exp. Pathol.* 18(7/8):407–13

93. Pozharisski, K. M., Klimashevski, V. F., Gushchin, V. A. 1982. Study of kinetics of epithelial cell populations in normal tissues of the rat's intestines and in carcinogenesis. III. Changes in kinetics of enterocyte populations in the course of experimental intestinal tumour induction in rats. *Exp. Pathol.* 21(3):165–79

94. Pulciani, S., Santos, E., Lauver, A. V., Long, L. K., Aaronson, S. A., Barbacid, M. 1982. Oncogenes in solid human tumors. *Nature* 30:539–42

95. Reiss, B., Williams, G. M. 1979. Conditions affecting prolonged maintenance of mouse and rat control in organ culture. *In Vitro* 15:877–90

96. Rijke, R. P. C., Gart, R. 1979. Epithelial cell kinetics in the descending colon of the rat. I. The effect of ischemia-induced epithelial cell loss. *Virchows Arch. Cell Pathol.* 31(1):15–22

97. Rijke, R. P. C., Gart, R., Langendoen, N. J. 1979. Epithelial cell kinetics in the descending colon of the rat. II. The effect of experimental bypass. *Virchows Arch. Cell Pathol.* 31(1):23–30

98. Royston, M. E., Augenlicht, L. H. 1983. Biotinated probe containing a long-terminal repeat hybridized to a mouse colon tumor and normal tissue. *Science* 222:1339–40

99. Ryggard, J., Povlsen, C. O. 1969. Heterotransplantation of a human malignant tumor to nude mice. *Acta Pathol. Microbiol. Scand. Sect. A* 77:758–60

100. Ryggard, J., Povlsen, C. O. 1971. Heterotransplantation of human adenocarcinoma of the colon and rectum to the mouse mutant nude. A study of nine consecutive transplantations. *Acta Pathol. Microbiol. Scand. Sect. A* 79:159–69

101. Sassier, P., Bergeron, M. 1980. Existence of an endogenous inhibitor of DNA synthesis in rabbit small intestine specifically effective on cell proliferation in adult mouse intestine. *Cell Tissue Kinet.* 13:251–61

102. Serafini, E. P., Kirk, A. P., Chambers, T. J. 1981. Rate and pattern of epithelial cell proliferation in ulcerative colitis. *Gut* 22(8):648–52

103. Shih, G., Padhy, L. C., Murray, M., Weinberg, R. A. 1981. Transforming genes of carcinomas and neuroblastomas introduced into mouse fibroblasts. *Nature* 290:261–64

104. Shorter, R. G., Moertel, C. G., Titus, J. L., Reitemeier, R. J. 1964. Cell kinetics in the jejunum and rectum of man. *Am. J. Dig. Dis.* 9:760–63

105. Sizikov, A. I., Azykbekov, R. 1981. Histoautoradiographic study of gastric epithelial DNA synthesis in precancerous lesions of the stomach. *Vopr. Onkol.* 27(10):19–22

106. Sordet, B., Fritsche, R., Mach, J. P., et al. 1974. Morphologic and function evaluation of human solid tumors serially transplanted in nude mouse. *1st Int. Workshop on Nude Mice, Copenhagen, 1973,* p. 15. Stuttgart: Fischer (Abstr.)

107. Stemmermann, G. N., Hayashi, T. 1968. Intestinal metaplasia of the gastric mucosa: a gross and microscopic study of its distribution in various disease states. *J. Natl. Cancer Inst.* 4:627–34

108. Storme, G., Willems, G. 1981. The effect of a liquid elemental diet on cell proliferation in the colon of rats. *Cell Tissue Res.* 216(1):221–25

109. Sunter, J. P., Watson, A. J., Wright, N. A., Appleton, D. R. 1979. Cell proliferation at different sites along the length of the rat colon. *Virchows Arch. Cell Pathol.* 32(1):75–87

110. Tabuchi, Y., Inoue, K., Takiguchi, Y., Kawaguchi, K., Mitsuno, T. 1980. Mitotic activity of human gastric cancer cells under stathmokinetic effect of vincristine sulfate. *Gann* 71:84–93

111. Takano, S., Akagi, M., Misumi, A., Matsuda, M., Inamori, Y., et al. 1982. *In vivo* and *in vitro* induction of rat colonic ornithine decarboxylase (ODC) and

DNA synthesis by TPA or bile acid. *Proc. Jpn. Cancer Assoc., 41st Ann. Meet., Osaka*. 425 pp.

112. Takeuchi, K., Johnson, L. 1982. Effect of cell proliferation and loss on aspirin-induced gastric damage in the rat. *Am. J. Physiol*. 243(6):G463–68

113. Tominaga, K. 1975. Distribution of parietal cells in the antral mucosa of human stomachs. *Gastroenterology* 69: 1201–07

114. Trier, J. S., Browning, T. H. 1970. Epithelial-cell renewal in cultured duodenal biopsies in celiac sprue. *N. Engl. J. Med*. 283:1245–50

115. Tutton, P. J. M., Barkla, D. H. 1980. Neural control of colonic cell proliferation. *Cancer* 45:1172–77

116. Tutton, P. J. M., Barkla, D. H. 1980. The influence of dibutyryl adenosine cyclic monophosphate on cell proliferation in the epithelium of the jejunal crypts, the colonic crypts and in colonic carcinomata of rat. *Clin. Exp. Pharmacol. Physiol*. 7(3):275–80

117. Tutton, P. J. M., Barkla, D. H. 1982. Differential effects of oestrogenic hormones on cell proliferation in the colonic crypt epithelium and in colonic carcinomata of rats. *Anticancer Res*. 2:199–202

118. Tutton, P. J. M., Barkla, D. H. 1982. The influence of androgens, anti-androgens and castration on cell proliferation in the jejunal and colonic crypt epithelia, and in dimethylhydrazine-induced adenocarcinoma of rat colon. *Virchows Arch. Cell Pathol*. 38(3): 351–55

119. Usugane, M., Fujita, M., Lipkin, M., Palmer, R., Friedman, E., Augenlicht, L. 1982. Cell replication in explant cultures of human colon. *Digestion* 24:225–33

120. Winawer, S. J., Lipkin, M. 1969. Cell proliferation kinetics in the gastrointestinal tract of man. IV. Cell renewal in the intestinalized gastric mucosa. *J. Natl. Cancer Inst*. 42:9–17

121. Wright, N., Watson, A., Morley, A., Appleton, D., Marks, J., Douglas, A. 1973. The cell cycle in the flat (avillous) mucosa of the human small intestine. *Gut* 14:603–6

Ann. Rev. Physiol. 1985. 47:199–215

FUNCTIONAL DEVELOPMENT OF THE STOMACH

Leonard R. Johnson

Department of Physiology and Cell Biology, University of Texas Medical School, Houston, Texas 77025

INTRODUCTION

This review summarizes most of the existing literature dealing with the functional development of the stomach. Numerous investigators have described the occurrence and pattern of the various morphological events in gastric development, but there have been relatively few studies (compared to the small intestine, for example) of the development of gastric function and even fewer that have attempted to understand that development and its regulation. Existing studies in man are almost totally descriptive and are discussed in two relatively recent review articles (6, 7). Almost all studies dealing with the development of the regulation of gastric function and the mechanisms controlling that development have been done in rats. Out of necessity, therefore, this article concentrates on the results of experiments done in the rat and a few other species.

The stomach has three basic functions, the most studied and best known of which is its secretory activity. The cells of the gastric mucosa secrete hydrochloric acid, pepsinogen, intrinsic factor, mucus, water, and a few other electrolytes. Acid is produced by parietal cells in concentrations approximating 160 mEq liter^{-1} in most species (53). Acid digests some protein, kills bacteria, and converts inactive pepsinogen into the active enzyme, pepsin. Pepsin digests protein by cleaving interior peptide linkages. Intrinsic factor is secreted by the parietal cells in man and is necessary for the adequate absorption of vitamin B_{12} (8). Mucus serves to lubricate the walls of the stomach and prevent physical damage by the ingesta.

The stomach also has an endocrine function. The mucosa of the antral region produces the hormone, gastrin, that with the vagal mediator, acetylcholine, regulates the stimulation of gastric acid secretion (71). These two substances

199

0066-4278/85/0315-0199$02.00

interact with the third major stimulator of the parietal cells, histamine, to produce large increases in acid secretion in response to a meal. Gastrin also stimulates the growth of the mucosa of the oxyntic gland portion of the stomach (32). The gastric mucosa and its nerves contain somatostatin and bombesin, respectively, two substances that may have physiological functions in regulating gastrin release (71).

A third group of activities carried out by the stomach falls under the heading of motility (40). These include its function as a reservoir, the ability to mix food and fluid, thereby reducing the size of the particles, and the ability to propel contents into the duodenum at a regulated rate.

ACID

Following an ultrastructural study of the developing rat gastric mucosa, Helander (24) concluded that the gastric epithelial cells do not begin to differentiate until the 19th day of embryological life. On the 17th and 18th days of gestation only one cell type could be distinguished, and this cell was poorly differentiated. According to Helander, its primary function was to divide. The same type of cells were found in the rabbit gastric mucosa in 19- to 23-day embryos (22). By day 19 Helander (24) found glands present in the rat mucosa and primitive parietal cells that had intracellular canaliculi and microvilli. At this time carbonic anhydrase was also detected (24, 70). There was a rapid increase from 18% to 35% in the volume of parietal-cell cytoplasm occupied by mitochondria during the first 5 days after birth. The conclusion from most ultrastructural studies is that the gastric mucosa of most species is capable of secreting acid shortly before birth (7).

Basal Secretion

Accurate measurement of acid secretion in fetal and newborn rats is difficult because of the small volumes of fluid involved. In general, investigators have taken four different approaches to this problem. Measurement of the pH of the gastric contents has been used to detect acid secretory activity, but this tells nothing about the quantity of acid produced (17, 18). Fetal stomachs mounted in Ussing-type chambers are capable of basal secretion and of responding to stimuli, but the results are difficult to relate to the intact animal (9, 19). Gastric juice can easily be collected from newborn rats following pylorus ligation (30, 57, 66), but this procedure does not yield true basal secretion because pylorus ligation itself is a weak stimulant. Ackerman (1) has used continuous saline perfusion of the gastric lumen of anesthetized rats to determine acid output. Although this technique is certainly the most accurate in terms of measuring the acid secreted, it introduces anesthesia as another variable. Despite shortcomings in these techniques, however, a relatively clear pattern of the onset of acid secretion has emerged.

Garzon et al (18) found the pH of the gastric contents of 19-day rat fetuses to be nearly neutral. The pH remained about 6 throughout day 20 and then fell to below 4 shortly before birth on day 21. On the other hand, we found the gastric pH of rats 5 and 10 days after birth to be around 6 and not to fall to 4 until day 15 (30, 66). On day 15 we were able to measure significant basal acid secretion. This apparent discrepancy was addressed by Garzon et al (19) using a modified Ussing-type in vitro chamber in which they measured net transepithelial H^+ flux. They found significant H^+ secretion on days 20 and 21 of gestation, but no basal secretion of acid 5 days after birth. Thus, there appears to be a biphasic development of the ability of the rat stomach to secrete acid basally (19).

Significant development of basal acid secretion occurs during the third week of life. In the rat, weaning also takes place at this time. During this time gastric pH decreases from 4 to around 2.5. Although basal acid secretion can be measured on day 14, it is quite small compared to that present after weaning (66). Ackerman (1) found values ranging from 5.1 to 7.6 μEq H^+ hr^{-1} in 2-week-old pups. We have reported similar values in 15-day-old animals that increase to 15–20 mEq hr^{-1} in 20-day-old rats (30, 66).

From the above studies, it is obvious that the rat is capable of secreting acid shortly before birth. The amount of basal acid secretion, however, remains of little or no consequence until the third week of life, during which the animal begins to eat solid food. Between days 15 and 21, gastric pH decreases almost two log units and basal acid output increases from 4% or 5% of adult levels to about 25%. By day 25, basal secretion approaches 40% of the adult level, which is reached on approximately day 40 (6). The rat is a basal secretor of gastric acid, and basal secretion occupies as much as 40–60% of the response to maximal stimulation (30, 38, 61).

Response to Stimuli

As one would expect, there is a parallelism between the development of basal gastric acid secretion and the development of the response to stimuli. In general, all stimulants have been shown to decrease the pH of gastric contents in 20-day-old rat fetuses. The quantity of acid produced, however, is small and in comparison to adult levels is negligible until the third week of life.

In the fetal rat stomach, Garzon et al (17) demonstrated that pentagastrin, histamine, carbamylcholine, gastrin-17, and 2-deoxyglucose decreased the pH of the gastric contents from control levels of 6.2 to 4.9, 5.5, 5.3, 5.2, and 4.2, respectively. Cimetidine blocked the response to histamine but not pentagastrin or carbamylcholine, and atropine blocked the response to carbamylcholine and 2-deoxyglucose but not to pentagastrin or histamine. The authors concluded that the fetal gastric mucosa is sensitive to the three primary stimulants of acid secretion at the time when differentiated parietal cells start secreting acid. Using in vitro chambers to determine transepithelial H^+ fluxes, this same group demonstrated that pentagastrin stimulated secretion in 20- and 21-day-old fetuses but failed to do so in the 5-day-old newborn rat (19). Other groups have shown that newborn human (11), pig (13), and rat (66) stomachs were insensitive to gastrin.

We have found slight but statistically insignificant increases in acid secretion in response to pentagastrin in 15- and 18-day-old rats (30, 66). A significant increase in acid secretion did not occur until day 20. In order to explain these findings and the fact that newborn rats don't secrete acid in response to endogenously elevated serum gastrin, Takeuchi et al (66) measured the binding of ^{125}I-5-Leu-gastrin 17 to rat gastric mucosal membranes. Specific binding of gastrin to its receptor was not detected until day 20. Thus, it appears that the reason for gastrin insensitivity in newborn rats is the lack of receptors for the hormone (66). Peitsch et al (57) injected 7-day-old rats with corticosterone and found that gastrin receptors developed precociously 3 days later. By day 12 there was a significant premature acid secretory response to gastrin coincident with a highly significant increase in specific gastrin binding (57). These data support the hypothesis that the development of sensitivity to secretagogues may be determined by the presence or absence of receptors (66).

Sensitivity to cholinergic stimulation appears to develop earlier than to gastrin. We found a significant acid secretory response to carbachol in 15-day-old rats (30). In the same study, animals of identical age failed to respond significantly to histamine or gastrin. We used [^{3}H]QNB (quinuclidinyl benzilate) to measure the appearance of cholinergic receptors in rat gastric mucosa and to correlate it with the acid response to 160 μ kg^{-1} carbachol (61). In contrast to the gastrin receptor, cholinergic receptors were found to be present at birth in concentrations comparable to those in adult rats. The affinity of the receptor for QNB actually decreased about 5-fold from birth to 40 days of age. This dose of carbachol, which was 4-fold higher than that used in our earlier study (30), caused a significant increase in acid secretion in rats aged 0.5, 5, and 10 days as well as in the older animals. It appears, therefore, that the response to cholinergic stimuli is present from birth along with the necessary receptors. Beginning on day 18, however, there was a dramatic increase in the secretory response to cholinergic stimulation. The response on day 18 was 3-fold that on day 15 and by day 25 was 12-fold the level at day 15 (61).

The development of the secretory response to histamine in the rat is, in general, similar to that of gastrin and cholinergic stimuli, with the major increase in sensitivity appearing during the third week of life (1, 30). Ackerman (1) was unable to measure a statistically significant response to histamine in the 14-day-old rat. The same-aged animals responded well to pentagastrin and carbachol. Based on these data he concluded that histamine cannot act as a final mediator of acid secretion in the newborn rat. This conclusion was supported by the failure of cimetidine to block pentagastrin-stimulated acid secretion in 14-day-old rats (1).

On the other hand, in one study we found significant responses to both histamine and pentagastrin on day 20 and to carbachol on day 15 (30). In a different study the response to pentagastrin again appeared on day 20, but the response to histamine appeared on day 15 (66). The amounts of acid secretion involved and the differences between statistically significant and insignificant responses, however, are small. In summary, in the rat it appears that sensitivity to carbachol is present the earliest and with high doses can be demonstrated from birth, and responsiveness to gastrin and histamine follow between days 14 and 20. Biologically significant acid secretion in response to all stimuli is established at the end of the third week.

The newborn human infant has hypergastrinemia and hyposecretion of acid (10, 11). Basal hyposecretion appears to last for at least 8 hr (10). During the first 48 hr there is no difference between basal- and pentagastrin-stimulated acid secretion. Therefore, the newborn human is insensitive to exogenous as well as endogenous gastrin. In newborn dogs there is little or no acid secretion until day 9, in spite of high serum gastrin levels, and exogenous gastrin has no effect on acid secretion or motility until day 9 (55). These data are similar to those in the rat and may be explained by the absence of gastrin receptors in these species as well (66). There are few data in human infants involving histamine. One study, however, demonstrated a response to histamine beginning on day 1 (2). In that study the basal concentration of H^+ was increased from 3.3 mEq liter^{-1} to 8.1 mEq liter^{-1} after histamine. Acid output in response to histamine, however, was only 0.03 mEq hr^{-1}. One other study involving sensitivity to different secretagogues has been done in newborn pigs (13). Forte et al (13) found that in vitro mucosa from piglets aged 1–5 days responded to histamine, but to neither pentagastrin nor acetylcholine.

There is excellent evidence that histamine acting as a paracrine potentiates the effects of both cholinergic stimulants and gastrin (64). The role of histidine decarboxylase in this process is uncertain. It is only in the rat that this enzyme responds to feeding and secretagogues. Studies of whole mucosae from a variety of mammals including the cat and dog have not been able to demonstrate the presence of the enzyme (3). It remains to be seen whether the enzyme can be induced in isolated histamine-containing cells from species in which the enzyme is undetectable in whole mucosa.

In a recent study, histidine decarboxylase was undetectable in rat gastric mucosa until day 10 (30). Significant amounts of enzyme activity were present on days 10 and 15, but none of the three major secretagogues increased activity. By day 18, pentagastrin significantly increased enzyme activity. Neither histamine nor carbachol increased histidine decarboxylase activity in rats of any age. In fact, in 25- and 40-day-old animals these two agents decreased enzyme activity (30). The appearance of histidine decarboxylase activity described above is similar to that found previously by Hakanson et al (21) for mucosal histamine content.

The parallels between the development of acid secretion and histidine decarboxylase are striking. Enzyme activity is high in fetal rat gastric mucosa until the 19th day after mating and then disappears at birth on the 22nd day after mating (3). This pattern is nearly identical to that described by Garzon et al (19) for acid secretion using the in vitro chamber preparation.

In the human, the parietal cell also secretes intrinsic factor. We know little about the development of its secretion, and to my knowledge all available data come from human studies. Intrinsic factor is detectable in gastric mucosa during the 14th week of gestation and increases 7-fold by week 25 (6). Intrinsic factor secretion rises progressively over the first 10 days of life to adult levels (2). During this time secretion of intrinsic factor parallels acid output in response to betazole.

PEPSINOGEN

Helander (25) found peptic activity in homogenates of rat gastric mucosa beginning on the 19th day of gestation. He recognized primitive surface epithelial and mucous neck cells from the 20th day of gestation, and peptic cells first appeared 1 day later. Under the electron microscope, zymogen cells contained a large number of secretory granules at birth. These, however, were sparse during the first 10 days of life. Twenty days after birth, rat peptic cells attained a normal adult appearance (25).

Tissue Content

Furihata et al (15) measured the activity of mucosal pepsinogen in rats of various ages from birth to adulthood. Activity remained constant for the first 17 days at levels approximately 20% of those found in adults. Mucosal pepsin activity began to increase on day 18 and reached adult levels by day 30. The differences in the molecular species of pepsinogen found in newborns and adults suggested that the mucous neck cell was the source of pepsin in the newborns, whereas the chief cell contained most of the pepsinogen in the adult (15). The appearance of mature chief cells (25) coincided with the elevation in peptic activity and change in molecular species observed by Furihata et al (15). In a subsequent study the same group determined that the peptic activity and molecular species of pepsinogen in the rat pyloric mucosa were constant from birth (14). The changes observed in the previous study were due entirely to maturation of mucosal glands in the fundus. Kumegawa et al (43) measured mucosal pepsinogen activity in mice aged 10, 20, and 28 days. The activity on day 20 was 4-fold that present on day 10 and then doubled between days 20 and 28.

In general, the few studies examining mucosal pepsinogen levels indicate a developmental pattern similar to that for acid secretion. Low levels of mucosal pepsinogen are present at birth, and these rapidly increase during the third week of life.

Response to Stimuli

To my knowledge, only two reports have included data on the development of pepsin secretion as opposed to tissue content of the enzyme. Basal pepsinogen secretion occurs from birth, but it is probably biologically insignificant until approximately day 15 (61). By day 15, basal secretion was equal to about 1% of adult levels. By day 20 it had increased to 5% and by day 25 to 20% of adult amounts.

A significant biological response to secretagogues also appeared during the third week of life (30). Carbachol effectively increased pepsin output on day 15, whereas histamine and pentagastrin were not effective until day 20. Using higher doses of carbachol, Seidel & Johnson (61) found a statistically significant response on the first day after birth, but in this study, as well, the amount of pepsin secreted was biologically insignificant until the third week of life.

The presence of physiological amounts of H^+ in the dog stomach stimulates pepsin secretion (34, 35). The mechanism involves a mucosal receptor sensitive to H^+ that can be blocked with topical xylocaine. Receptor activation triggers a cholinergic reflex that can be blocked by atropine (35). The finding that topical 0.1N HCl stimulated pepsin secretion in 15-day-old rats is further evidence that the cholinergic receptor system on chief cells is developed by this time (30).

Thus it is apparent that, as was the case for acid secretion, pepsin secretion is first capable of being stimulated by cholinergic agents. Because pepsin activity is dependent on acid secretion, this is not surprising. The autonomic nervous system of the gut also develops early. In the longitudinal smooth muscle of the fetal rabbit and mouse, functional cholinergic innervation and responsiveness to acetylcholine appeared at the 16th to 17th day of gestation (20). A recent report demonstrates that choline acetyltransferase and acetylcholinesterase activity of the rat gastric pylorus are as great 1 day after birth as 50 days after birth (23). Finally, histological studies suggest the enteric plexus is well developed in the neonate. Although having fewer total nerve cells than the adult, the neonate rat plexus had a density of 64 K nerve cells cm^2 of the gastrointestinal surface area compared to 9 K nerve cells for the same area in the adult (16).

GASTRIN

Development of the gastrin radioimmunoassay in 1970 (56, 73) made it possible to study tissue and serum gastrin levels. Numerous investigators have reported that human infants at birth have elevated serum gastrin compared to adults (10, 11, 51, 58). Most investigators agree that the hypergastrinemia is of short duration—lasting only for a few days (10, 11, 51). One report of human fetal antral gastrin indicates amounts equal to about 10% of adult levels (69).

Most studies involving the ontogeny of gastrin have been performed on the rat. Studies of developmental changes in serum gastrin have involved larger mammals—primarily the sheep. In general, the animal data are similar to the human results, demonstrating hypergastrinemia and low tissue levels of the hormone in newborns.

Tissue Levels

Immunoreactive gastrin first appears on the 18th day of gestation in the rat (5, 46). It gradually increases until the 18th day after birth and then increases dramatically to adult levels by day 21 (49).

Lichtenberger & Johnson (49) found that rat antral gastrin levels were approximately 2 μg g^{-1} tissue from birth through day 18. By day 21 there was a 10-fold increase. Takeuchi et al (66) recently reported similar values. This abrupt change coincides with the weaning period and the major changes in gastric secretion already discussed. In the sheep, gastrin first appears in significant amounts in the 107-day-old fetus. The abomasal gastrin is almost totally G-17, with a small peak eluting with G-34 (48, 62). This same pattern persists through birth and at least until 6 days after birth (48). Thus, in the sheep, anyway, there are no changes in the molecular species of gastrin during development.

Serum Levels

In addition to humans, neonatal hypergastrinemia occurs in dogs (55), sheep (48, 62), and rats (31, 66). Malloy et al (55) found that serum gastrin in puppies rises above adult levels shortly after birth and continues to increase through the ninth day of life. In the sheep, Shulkes & Hardy (62) detected gastrin in the serum of 101-day-old fetuses. Serum levels then rose steadily to adult levels by the 124th day of gestation and to 5-fold adult levels on the fifth day after birth. By day 15 serum gastrin had returned to adult levels. Similar results were reported in another study except that hypergastrinemia remained through day 60 after birth (48). We found markedly elevated serum gastrin levels in newborn rats that decreased abruptly (3–4-fold) on day 18 and reached adult levels by day 40 (66).

A number of explanations for hypergastrinemia in newborn animals exist. Lichtenberger (47) has suggested that the high protein and calcium content of the neonate's diet plays a role, because both of these are releasers of gastrin. This, however, seems unlikely because hypergastrinemia in the human disappears long before there is a change in the diet (10, 11). Furthermore, if the newborn rat is prevented from weaning, serum gastrin levels decrease at the same time as those of weaned littermates eating only solid food (66).

Gastrin release is inhibited when the pH of the antral contents drops to approximately 3.0 (72). As described in the previous sections of this article, there is little gastric acid secretion and the pH of the contents remains above 4.0 until 18 days after birth. This is not low enough to significantly inhibit gastrin release. If 150 mN of HCl is introduced into the stomachs of 10- and 15-day-old rats, there is a prompt and significant decrease in circulating gastrin (31). This experiment clearly demonstrates that a significant portion of postnatal hyper-gastrinemia is of antral origin and is due to insufficient acid to trigger the inhibitory mechanism.

It is important to note that when the gastric contents were acidified in the above experiment, serum gastrin did not decrease to adult values (31). This might be expected if some of the gastrin were derived from extra-antral sources. However, on a per gram basis the duodenal mucosa of the unweaned rat contains only one fiftieth as much gastrin as the antrum (49). Incomplete development of the inhibitory mechanism itself could also account for this finding. A number of observations indicate that somatostatin may mediate the acid inhibition of gastrin release (44, 45, 60) and that somatostatin exerts a tonic inhibition on gastrin release (59). Somatostatin injection had no effect on serum gastrin levels in 10- and 15-day-old rats (31). Beginning on day 18, somatostatin significantly lowered serum gastrin. The antral mucosa of new-born rats, therefore, appears to lack receptors and/or the mechanism to respond to somatostatin until weaning. Furthermore, Koshimiza (42) has shown that gastric somatostatin content gradually increases in the rat until the time of weaning, when there is an abrupt, large increase. Therefore, there is evidence that the decrease in serum gastrin levels at the time of weaning is due to two independent mechanisms: an acid-sensitive one, triggered by the onset of significant acid secretion, that is intact before weaning, and a separate mecha-nism, dependent on somatostatin, that is not present until after weaning.

Growth

Changes in growth of the gastric mucosa can be expected to affect its functional development. Unfortunately only two studies have addressed this topic. The rate of DNA synthesis per unit of DNA in the gastric mucosa of the 5- and 10-day-old rat is about 5-fold higher than in the adult (66). Between days 15 and 20, the rate decreases to adult levels. During this time, however, the mucosa undergoes a rapid increase in DNA content and weight, and as gastrin receptors appear, it becomes sensitive to the trophic action of gastrin (32, 33).

In adults, normal populations of gastric mucosal cells are maintained by sustained proliferation of progenitor cells, their maturation, and exfoliation (see article by M. Lipkin in this volume). We demonstrated that the high rate of

DNA synthesis in unweaned rats is matched by a high rate of cell loss (52). While there was a decrease in the rate of DNA synthesis per cell at the time of weaning, there was a significant increase in DNA content and DNA synthesis of the entire oxyntic gland mucosa. These data indicate that as the mucosa develops, a larger proportion of cells are removed from the proliferative pool. One would expect that these cells mature into functioning mucosal cells, but this has not been examined.

REGULATION

The inescapable conclusion from the material presented in this review is that all the gastric mucosal functions in the rat undergo important developmental changes at approximately the same time. These occur during the third week of life coincident with the beginning of weaning. The coordination of these events suggests the presence of an overriding factor or factors that regulate that development. The most obvious candidates for this role are hormones, the change to a solid diet or the weaning process itself, and intrinsic or genetically programmed changes. Most of these have been examined in great detail in relation to small intestinal development (see article by S. J. Henning in this volume), however, only a few comparable studies have been carried out on gastric function.

Diet or Weaning

Throughout this review I have mentioned that changes have taken place coincident with weaning. This was in no way meant to imply that these developmental changes were triggered or regulated by the act of weaning or the dietary change that occurs at that time. Actually, the evidence from other gastrointestinal tissues is that weaning plays only a minor role, if any, in modulating these changes (4, 26). Ontogenic changes in the small intestine, liver, and pancreas begin at the normal time in rats prevented from weaning.

Similar results have been obtained from our laboratory regarding antral and serum gastrin (49, 57, 66). Antral gastrin levels begin to increase in unweaned rats at the same time as in normally weaned animals. The rate of increase, however, is less, and the final level of hormone reached in the tissue is significantly lower (66). Serum gastrin also falls at the same time, as it does in weaned rats. In fact the decrease in serum gastrin is more rapid in unweaned animals. The important finding in this experiment is that the changes still took place at the same time. The differences in final levels of tissue and serum gastrin in unweaned animals are not related to development but are dependent on the stimulation of gastrin release, which is significantly less in rats ingesting their calories in liquid form (36, 63). In rats separated from their mothers and weaned prematurely on day 13, there were no significant differences in antral or serum gastrin when they were killed on day 18 and compared with normally developing animals of the same age. A positive result in the above study, however, would be suspect, because premature weaning causes stress, elevating corticosterone, which is the true mediator of such changes.

There are no reports of the effect of weaning on development of acid and pepsin secretion or other gastric functional changes.

Hormones

Glucocorticoids and thyroid hormones are known to affect the development of many small intestinal and liver enzymes and functions (see 26, for review). There have been a few similar studies indicating a role for the glucocorticoids in gastric development, but to my knowledge only one study involving thyroid hormones has been reported. Studies implementing glucocorticoids in development fall into two general categories. First, exogenous hormone is injected to produce a premature or precocious change in development. Second, adrenalectomy has been shown to delay developmental changes. In the rat plasma, concentrations of free corticosterone begin to rise on day 13 and reach peak levels between days 15 and 19 (27). This period of high plasma corticosterone coincides with the start of the normal weaning period on day 15 or 16. Thus, the increase in corticosterone precedes the maturational changes and could trigger them.

During the first or second postnatal week, injection of hydrocortisone (32, 34, 68), ACTH (34), or corticosterone (30) has been shown to prematurely increase the amount of gastric mucosal pepsinogen. In one of these studies thyroxine also caused a premature increase in pepsinogen activity (43). The effect of thyroxine was less than that of hydrocortisone, and combinations of the two hormones were additive. Because thyroxine has been shown to increase glucocorticoid levels (54), it is impossible to know from the above study whether the effect was mediated by thyroxine or corticosterone. In order to prove an effect of thyroxine, this type of study should be performed in adrenalectomized rats (39). Neither hydrocortisone nor thyroxine had any effect on pepsinogen levels if administered on day 23 (43). Henning and coworkers (28, 29) have shown that intestinal enzyme development loses sensitivity to glucocorticoids at roughly the same age. Thus, it is likely that gastric mucosal development is sensitive to corticosterone only to the same point in time.

Injection of 250 mg per kg corticosterone on postnatal day 7 caused a premature appearance of gastrin receptors on day 10 (57). By day 12 gastrin binding was well developed and the stomach secreted significant amounts of acid in response to pentagastrin. In the same rats, antral levels of gastrin also developed prematurely and by day 15 had reached 80% of adult levels. Adrenalectomy delayed the normal development of both gastrin receptors and tissue levels of the hormone by approximately 5–7 days. After this period, however, development proceeded to normal levels. The delay in the onset of development was prevented if adrenalectomized animals were treated with corticosterone (57). In order to see full development of receptors and tissue gastrin, the rats had to be maintained on normal solid laboratory pellets as opposed to liquid diets. This dietary dependence reflects the necessity for gastrin release to maintain both tissue levels of the hormone and receptor levels (67). Corticosterone has also been shown to precociously induce sensitivity of the acid secretory mechanism to both carbachol and histamine as well as well as pentagastrin (30). In these same animals, corticosterone increased the secretion of pepsin in response to cholinergic stimulation.

To this point I have made no distinction between male and female rats. Male rats secrete more gastric acid (37, 65) and have higher concentrations of serum gastrin (37, 50) and gastrin receptors (37) than females. Development of receptors and serum gastrin in the two sexes is identical until day 40, which is the approximate time of puberty in the rat (37). At that time, levels plateau in the female but keep increasing in the male. Both gastrin levels and receptors reach final adult values by day 60 in the male (37). If female rats are ovariectomized, development proceeds to male levels. Castration of males has no effect on development of final levels of either serum gastrin or receptors. Injection of castrated males with estrogen, however, lowers these values. Serum gastrin values and, hence, gastrin receptor concentration are dependent on food intake (67). Because male rats begin to eat more than females after puberty, this explains part of the differences. However, we found that if ovariectomized females were pair fed to normal females, they still developed significantly higher serum gastrins and mucosal gastrin–binding capacities. If ovariectomized females were adrenalectomized as well and pair fed to females, gastrin levels and receptors were not significantly different from that of males (37).

In summary, gastric functional development is dependent on glucocorticoids up until the normal initiation of change during the third week of life. This dependence, however, is for timing only, because development, although delayed, reaches normal levels in adrenalectomized rats. Normal intake of solid food is necessary for total development of gastrin levels and receptor-binding capacities. Estrogen influences development in female rats, resulting in reduced food intake, reduced acid secretion, reduced serum gastrin, and gastrin receptors. These effects are in part due to direct hormonal action and in part to indirect effects of reduced food intake.

Intrinsic Mechanisms

Although the dietary and hormonal changes associated with the weaning period modulate, and in the case of corticosterone may trigger events in gastric functional development, it is obvious that development can proceed in the absence of those changes. This suggests that the time course as well as the events themselves are ultimately regulated intrinsically by the genetic material of the cells involved. This hypothesis is strengthened by the observations that small intestinal mucosa taken from a near-term fetal rat and implanted under the kidney capsule of a syngeneic adult host shows normal patterns of sucrase, lactase (12, 41), and β-galactosidase (41) development. It is also interesting to note that the jejuno-ileal gradient of enzyme activity developed fully in the isografts without exposure to luminal contents (41). Similar studies using gastric tissue have not been reported.

SUMMARY

Large increases in gastric acid and pepsin secretion, antral gastrin concentration, and decreases in serum gastrin occur during the third week of life in the neonatal rat. At the same time gastrin receptors appear and gastrin release becomes sensitive to somatostatin, indicating that absence and then appearance of specific hormone receptors may be responsible for some of the ontogenic pattern. At this time the mucosa also begins to grow rapidly, with a greater proportion of cells leaving the proliferative pool and differentiating. For the first 2.5–3 weeks these ontogenic changes can be triggered by corticosterone. Their full expression depends on dietary changes associated with weaning. Neither hormones, dietary changes, nor the weaning process itself is essential for development, because in the absence of these, all of the changes still occur—although they may be delayed or be smaller in magnitude. Figure 1 provides a generalized summary of the normal functional development of the stomach and how it is altered by changes in corticosterone levels and the absence of weaning. These findings indicate that ontogeny is genetically programmed and that the full expression of this program depends on hormones, luminal contents, and other environmental factors.

In comparison with the small intestine, for example, gastric ontogeny has not received adequate attention. There are essentially no studies directed toward understanding changes in motility during this period. There is really only one study examining the growth pattern of the mucosa during development, and this study is aimed at changes in DNA synthesis and cell loss. Experiments involving the cell cycle are needed to understand whether existing cells mature and differentiate or whether newly created cells suddenly leave the proliferative pool to differentiate. There have been no experiments in which the effects of thyroid hormone on gastric development have been adequately examined. In addition, little or nothing is known about EGF in the ontogenic process. Studies implanting fetal tissue into adult hosts are needed to determine which gastric functions can develop in the absence of luminal stimulation and hormone changes.

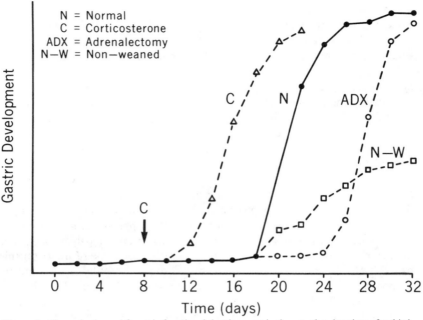

N = Normal
C = Corticosterone
ADX = Adrenalectomy
N—W = Non—weaned

Figure 1   General scheme of gastric functional development in the rat related to time after birth. Effects of prevention of weaning and alteration of glucocorticoid levels are shown.

The cell biology of the gastric mucosa is difficult to examine—especially that involving the cells concerned with growth and differentiation. The stem cells are dispersed throughout the tissue and are a small portion of the cell population. These have never been isolated for study. In vitro culture of mucosal cells, however, is a technique that can possibly be used to examine development at the cellular and molecular level.

ACKNOWLEDGMENTS

Studies referred to from the author's laboratory were supported by NIH Grants AM-18164 and AM-16505.

Literature Cited

1. Ackerman, S. H. 1982. Ontogeny of gastric acid secretion in the rat: Evidence for multiple response systems. *Science* 217: 75–77
2. Agunod, M., Yamaguchi, N., Lopez, R., Luhby, A. L., Glass, G. B. J. 1964. Correlative study of hydrochloric acid, pepsin, and intrinsic factor secretion in newborns and infants. *Am. J. Dig. Dis.* 14:400–14
3. Aures, D., Davidson, W. D., Hakanson, R. 1969. Histidine decarboxylase in gastric mucosa of various animals. *Eur. J. Pharmacol.* 8:100–17
4. Boyle, J. T., Koldovsky, O. 1980. Critical role of adrenal glands in precocious increase in jejunal sucrase activity following premature weaning in rats: negligible effect of food intake. *J. Nutr.* 101:169–77

5. Braaten, J. T., Greider, M. H., McGuigan, J. E., Mintz, D. H. 1976. Gastrin in the perinatal rat pancreas and gastric antrum: Immunofluorescence localization of pancreatic gastrin cells and gastrin secretion in monolayer cell cultures. *Endocrinology* 99:684–91
6. Christie, D. L. 1981. Development of gastric function during the first month of life. In *Textbook of Gastroenterology and Nutrition in Infancy*, ed. E. Lebenthal, 1:109–20. New York: Raven. 670 pp.
7. Deren, J. S. 1971. Development of structure and function in the fetal and newborn stomach. *Am. J. Clin. Nutr.* 24:144–59
8. Donaldson, R. M. Jr. 1981. Intrinsic factor and the transport of cobalamin. See Ref. 32, 1:641–58
9. Ducroc, R., Desjeux, J.-F., Garzon, B., Onoflo, J.-P., Geloso, J.-P. 1981. Acid secretion in fetal rat stomach *in vitro*. *Am. J. Physiol.* 240:G206–10
10. Euler, A. R., Byrne, W. J., Cousins, L. M., Ament, M. E., Leaks, R. D., Walsh, J. H. 1977. Increased serum gastrin concentration and gastric acid hyposecretion in the immediate newborn period. *Gastroenterology* 72:1271–3
11. Euler, A. R., Byrne, W. J., Meis, P. J., Leake, R. D., Ament, M. E. 1979. Basal and pentagastrin stimulated acid secretion in newborn human infants. *Pediatr. Res.* 13:36–37
12. Ferguson, A., Gershowitch, V. P., Russell, R. I. 1973. Pre- and post-weaning disaccharidase patterns in isografts of fetal mouse intestine. *Gastroenterology* 64:292–97
13. Forte, J. G., Forte, T. M., Machen, T. E. 1975. Histamine stimulated hydrogen ion secretion by *in vitro* piglet gastric mucosa. *J. Physiol.* 244:15–31
14. Furihata, C., Iwasaki, Y., Sagimura, T., Tatematsu, M., Takahashi, M. 1973. Differentiation of pepsinogen-producing cells in the fundic and pyloric mucosa of developing rats. *Cell Different.* 2:179–89
15. Furihata, C., Kawachi, T., Sugimura, T. 1972. Premature induction of pepsinogen in developing rat gastric mucosa by hormones. *Biochem. Biophys. Res. Commun.* 47:705–11
16. Gabella, G. 1971. Neuron size and number in the myenteric plexus of the newborn and adult rat. *J. Anat.* 109:81–95
17. Garzon, B., Ducroc, R., Geloso, J.-P. 1982. Ontogenesis of gastric response to agonists and antagonists of acid secretion in fetal rat. *J. Devel. Physiol.* 4:195–205
18. Garzon, B., Ducroc, R., Geloso, J.-P. 1981. Ontogenesis of gastric acid secretion in fetal rat. *Pediatr. Res.* 15:921–25
19. Garzon, B., Ducroc, R., Onoflo, J.-P.,

Desjeux, J.-F., Geloso, J.-P. 1982. Biphasic development of pentagastrin sensitivity in rat stomach. *Am. J. Physiol.* 242:G111–15
20. Gershon, M. D., Thompson, E. B. 1973. The maturation of neuromuscular function in a multiple innervated structure: Development of the longitudinal smooth muscle of the fetal mammalian gut and its cholinergic excitatory, adrenergic inhibitory, and nonadrenergic inhibitory innervation. *J. Physiol.* 234:257–77
21. Hakanson, R., Owman, C., Sjöberg, N. P. 1967. Cellular stores of gastric histamine in the developing rat. *Life Sci.* 6:2535–43
22. Hayward, A. F. 1967. The fine structure of gastric epithelial cells in the suckling rabbit with particular reference to the parietal cell. *Z. Zellforsch.* 78:474–83
23. Heitkemper, M. M., Marotta, F. 1983. Development of neurotransmitter enzyme activity in the rat gastrointestinal tract. *Am. J. Physiol.* 244:G58–64
24. Helander, H. F. 1969. Ultrastructure and function of gastric parietal cells in the rat during development. *Gastroenterology* 56:35–52
25. Helander, H. F. 1969. Ultrastructure and function of gastric mucoid and zymogen cells in the rat during development. *Gastroenterology* 56:53–70
26. Henning, S. J. 1981. Postnatal development: Coordination of feeding, digestion, and metabolism. *Am. J. Physiol.* 241:G199–214
27. Henning, S. J. 1978. Plasma concentrations of total and free corticosterone during development in the rat. *Am. J. Physiol.* 235:E451–56
28. Henning, S. J., Leeper, L. L. 1982. Coordinate loss of glucocorticoid responsiveness by intestinal enzymes during postnatal development. *Am. J. Physiol.* 242:G89–94
29. Henning, S. J., Sims, J. M. 1979. Delineation of the glucocorticoid-sensitive period of intestinal development in the rat. *Endocrinology* 104:1158–63
30. Ikezaki, M., Johnson, L. R. 1983. Development of sensitivity to different secretagogues in the rat stomach. *Am. J. Physiol.* 244:G165–70
31. Johnson, L. R. 1984. Effects of somatostatin and acid on inhibition of gastrin release in newborn rats. *Endocrinology* 114:743–46
32. Johnson, L. R. 1981. Regulation of gastrointestinal growth. In *Physiology of the Gastrointestinal Tract*, ed. L. R. Johnson, 1:169–96. New York: Raven. 1492 pp.
33. Johnson, L. R. 1976. The trophic action

of gastrointestinal hormones. *Gastroenterology* 70:278–88

34. Johnson, L. R. 1971. Pepsin secretion stimulated by topical hydrochloric and acetic acids. *Gastroenterology* 62:33–38

35. Johnson, L. R. 1972. Regulation of pepsin secretion by topical acid in the stomach. *Am. J. Physiol.* 223:847–50

36. Johnson, L. R., Guthrie, P. D. 1983. Regulation of antral gastrin content. *Am. J. Physiol.* 245:G725–29

37. Johnson, L. R., Peitsch, W., Takeuchi, K. 1982. Mucosal gastrin receptor. VIII. Sex-related differences in binding. *Am. J. Physiol.* 243:G469–74

38. Johnson, L. R., Tumpson, D. B. 1970. Effect of secretin on histamine-stimulated secretion in gastric fistula rats. *Proc. Soc. Exp. Biol. Med.* 133:125–27

39. Jumawan, J., Koldovsky, O. 1978. Comparison of the effect of various doses of thyroxine on jejunal disaccharidases in intact and adrenalectomized rats during the first 3 weeks of life. *Enzyme* 23: 206–9

40. Kelly, K. A. 1981. Motility of the stomach and gastroduodenal junction. See Ref. 32, 1:393–410

41. Kendall, K., Jumawan, J., Koldovsky, O. 1979. Development of jejuno-ileal differences of activity of lactase, sucrase, and acid β-galactosidase in isografts of fetal rat intestine. *Biol. Neonate* 36:206–14

42. Koshimizu, T. 1983. The development of pancreatic and gastrointestinal somatostatin-like immunoactivity and its relationship to feeding in neonatal rats. *Endocrinology* 112:911–16

43. Kumegawa, M., Takuma, T., Hosoda, S., Kunii, S., Kanda, Y. 1978. Precocious induction of pepsinogen in the stomach of suckling mice by hormones. *Biochem. Biophys. Acta* 543:243–50

44. Larsson, L. I. 1980. Peptide secretory pathways in GI tract: cytochemical contributions to regulatory physiology of the gut. *Am. J. Physiol.* 239:G237–46

45. Larsson, L.-I., Goltermann, N., De-Magistris, L., Rehfeld, J. F., Schwartz, T. W. 1979. Somatostatin cell processes as pathways for paracrine secretion. *Science* 205:1393–95

46. Larsson, L. I., Hakanson, R., Rehfeld, J. F., Stadil, F., Sandler, F. 1974. Occurrence of neonatal development of gastrin immunoreactivity in the digestive tract of the rat. *Cell Tissue Res.* 149:275–81

47. Lichtenberger, L. M. 1984. A search for the origin of neonatal hypergastrinemia. *J. Pediatr. Gastroent. Nutr.* 3:161–66

48. Lichtenberger, L. M., Crandell, S. S., Plama, P. A., Morriss, F. H. Jr. 1981.

Ontogeny of tissue and serum gastrin concentrations in fetal and neonatal sheep. *Am. J. Physiol.* 241:G234–41

49. Lichtenberger, L., Johnson, L. R. 1974. Gastrin in the ontogenic development of the small intestine. *Am. J. Physiol.* 227:390–95

50. Lichtenberger, L. M., Nance, D. M., Gorski, R. A. 1976. Sex-related differences in antral and serum gastrin levels in the rat. *Proc. Soc. Exp. Biol. Med.* 151:785–88

51. Lucas, A., Adrian, T. E., Christofides, N., Bloom, S. R., Aynsley-Green, A. 1980. Plasma motilin, gastrin, and enteroglucagon and feeding in the human newborn. *Arch. Dis. Child.* 55:673–77

52. Majumdar, A. P. N., Johnson, L. R. 1982. Gastric mucosal cell proliferation during development in rats and effects of pentagastrin. *Am. J. Physiol.* 242:G135–39

53. Makhlouf, G. M. 1981. Electrolyte composition of gastric secretion. See Ref. 32, 1:551–56

54. Malinowska, K. W., Chan, W. S., Nathanelz, P. W., Hardy, R. N. 1974. Plasma adrenocorticosteroid changes during thyroxine-induced accelerated maturation of the neonatal rat intestine. *Experientia* 30:61

55. Mallow, M. H., Morriss, F. H., Denson, S. E., Weisbrodt, N. W., Lichtenberger, L. M., Adcock, E. W. III. 1979. Neonatal gastric motility in dogs: Maturation and response to pentagastrin. *Am. J. Physiol.* 236:E562–66

56. McGuigan, J. E., Trudeau, W. L. 1970. Studies with antibodies to gastrin: Radioimmunoassay in human serum and physiological studies. *Gastroenterology* 58:139–50

57. Peitsch, W., Takeuchi, K., Johnson, L. R. 1981. Mucosal gastrin receptor. VI. Induction by corticosterone in newborn rats. *Am. J. Physiol.* 240:G442–49

58. Rogers, I. M., Davidson, D. C., Lawrence, J., Ardill, J., Buchanan, K. D. 1974. Neonatal secretion of gastrin and glucagon. *Arch. Dis. Child.* 49:796–801

59. Saffouri, B., Weir, G. C., Bitar, K. N., Makhlouf, G. M. 1979. Stimulation of gastrin secretion from the vascularly perfused rat stomach by somatostatin antiserum. *Life Sci.* 20:1749–54

60. Schusdziarra, V., Harris, V., Conlon, J. M., Arimura, A., Unger, R. 1978. Pancreatic and gastric somatostatin release in response to intragastric and intraduodenal nutrients and HCl in the dog. *J. Clin. Invest.* 62:509–18

61. Seidel, E. R., Johnson, L. R. 1984.

Ontogeny of the gastric mucosal muscarinic receptor and sensitivity to carbachol. *Am. J. Physiol.* 246:G550–55

62. Shulkes, A., Hardy, K. J. 1982. Ontogeny of circulating gastrin and pancreatic polypeptide in the foetal sheep. *Acta Endocrinologica* 100:565–72

63. Sircar, B., Johnson, L. R., Lichtenberger, L. M. 1980. Effect of chemically defined diets on antral and serum gastrin levels in rats. *Am. J. Physiol.* 238:G376–83

64. Soll, A. H. 1978. The interaction of histamine with gastrin and carbamylcholine on oxygen uptake by isolated mammalian parietal cells. *J. Clin. Invest.* 61:381–9

65. Takeuchi, K., Okabe, S., Tagaki, K. 1974. Influence of pregnancy and lactation on the healing process of gastric and duodenal ulcers in rats. *Experientia* 30:366–68

66. Takeuchi, K., Peitsch, W., Johnson, L. R. 1981. Mucosal gastrin receptor. V. Development in newborn rats. *Am. J. Physiol.* 240:G163–69

67. Takeuchi, K., Speir, G. R., Johnson, L. R. 1980. Mucosal gastrin receptor. III.

Regulation by gastrin. *Am. J. Physiol.* 238:G135–40

68. Tatematsu, M., Takahashi, M., Tsada, H., Hirose, M., Furihata, C., Sugimura, T., 1975. Precocious differentiation of immature chief cells in fundic mucosa of infant rats induced by hydrocortisone. *Cell Differ.* 4:285–94

69. Track, N. S., Creatzfeldt, C., Litzenberger, J., Neuhoff, C., Arnold, R., Creutzfeldt, W. 1979. Appearance of gastrin and somatostatin in the human fetal stomach, duodenum, and pancreas. *Digestion* 19:292–306

70. Vollrath, L. 1959. Über Entwicklung und Funktion der Belegzellen der Magendrusen. *Z. Zellforsch.* 50:36–60

71. Walsh, J. H. 1981. Gastrointestinal hormones and peptides. See Ref. 32, 1:59–145

72. Woodward, E. R., Lyon, E. S., Landor, J., Dragstedt, L. R. 1954. The physiology of the gastric antrum; experimental studies on isolated antrum pouches in dogs. *Gastroenterology* 27:766–85

73. Yalow, R. S., Berson, S. A. 1970. Radioimmunoassay of gastrin. *Gastroenterology* 58:1–14

Ann. Rev. Physiol. 1985. 47:217–29

MECHANISMS FOR RAPID RE-EPITHELIALIZATION OF THE GASTRIC MUCOSAL SURFACE

William Silen and Susumu Ito

The Departments of Surgery and Anatomy, Harvard Medical School and the Department of Surgery and the Charles A. Dana Research Institute, Beth Israel Hospital, Boston, Massachusetts

INTRODUCTION

Defects in the mucosal surface of the stomach are generally thought to be re-epithelialized by cells generated from proliferating stem cells in the neck region of the gastric glands. Regeneration by mitotic proliferation, however, would require at least 1–2 days for the migration and differentiation of the surface mucous cells (13, 21). It seems reasonable that there be a more rapid process of re-epithelialization to repair superficial defects incurred in daily living, especially because the gastric mucosal surface can be and is damaged by many common foods and drugs. The early recognition that the stomach could repair itself rapidly was by Grant (6), who in 1945 reported that the damage of the superficial third of the mucosa of cat stomachs exposed to 60% ethanol was repaired within 4 hr. In this early study the process was interpreted to be regeneration, but the cellular mechanism was not otherwise clarified. Morris & Wallace (15) recently proposed that the reestablishment of rat gastric mucosal epithelial continuity after ethanol injury occurred by migration of underlying epithelial cells from the gastric pits. In 1982, we described the cellular process of "reconstitution" in in vitro amphibian gastric mucosa mounted in an Ussing chamber, a process in which reestablishment of epithelial continuity occurred following destruction of the surface layer with hypertonic NaCl (22). More recently, gastric mucosal restitution has been identified in the in vitro guinea

0066-4278/85/0315-0217$02.00

pig (18) and in intact rats (11). The major purpose of this review is to describe the process of restitution and to review what is known about the factors that influence this process.

WHAT IS RESTITUTION?

We define gastric restitution as the process by which epithelial integrity and continuity are rapidly reestablished following injury, before cell proliferation or extensive inflammatory response occurs. We have avoided the term healing when referring to restitution because the process of healing is so intimately associated with inflammation and by definition *requires* inflammation. Whereas inflammation of varying degree may be encountered after gastric mucosal injury in vivo, restitution in its purest form is accomplished in vitro in the absence of inflammation. Restitution occurs by migration of still viable remaining epithelial cells from areas adjacent to or just beneath the injured surface cells to cover the denuded area (11, 18, 22). A mandatory requisite for restitution is that the mucosal damage is limited to the surface and part of the gastric pit and does not destroy the entire mucosal thickness. It is likely but not yet proved that the process requires an intact basal lamina, a proposal suggested by Vracko (25). Because restitution can occur in vitro (18, 22) in the absence of blood flow and because cell proliferation is not required, it is a process dependent upon inherent properties of the epithelial cells themselves. The process of restitution is extraordinarily rapid, occurring within minutes in mammalian stomach in vivo, thus clearly not dependent upon cell differentiation or replication. It is to be distinguished from the much slower evolution of wound healing. In our early communications, we used the terms reconstitution and restitution interchangeably. We now prefer to use the term restitution, because it more accurately describes the process without implications of molecular or biochemical processes.

Restitution In Vitro

The study of restitution in vitro has served to facilitate the identification, description, and understanding of the process, because factors affecting restitution could be much more readily examined and controlled in vitro. In the frog gastric mucosa in vitro, exposure of the luminal surface to 1 M NaCl for 10 min results in uniform and extensive damage to the superficial cell layers (Figures 1 and 2), and no normal surface mucosa remains. However, some deeper gastric pit, mucous neck, and oxynticopeptic cells, although shrunken, were still viable. The gland lumens were markedly distended. Thirty minutes after removal of the 1 M NaCl, the disrupted superficial layer of lysed nonviable cells remained attached as a thick mucoid layer that contained dead cells and cellular debris to the underlying, still viable, pit and gland cells. At the transition zone between the dead lysed cells and those that were still intact, there was a layer of vacuolated and disorganized cells that appeared to be less injured and possibly recovering from the injury. Damage to the epithelial cells did not appear to be selective for cell types but rather reflected the degree of exposure to the injurious hypertonic NaCl. Because oxynticopeptic cells are more deeply placed, they were the predominant remaining cell type after destruction of the superficial cells, although surface and mucous neck cells were always present.

The next step was the exfoliation of the damaged cells as a fluffy mucoid mass and the exposure of the bare lamina. Disruption of the basal lamina was rare following injury to in vitro frog mucosa with 1M NaCl. By 1–1.5 hr after injury, denuded areas were being covered by migrating flattened mucous cells that extended thin lamellapodia over the wavy or pleated bare basal lamina (Figure 3). As soon as epithelial cells migrated and contacted other cells covering the denuded area, they formed typical functional complexes, including tight junctions. After 2–4 hr of restitution, areas of incomplete coverage were rare because the continuity of the epithelial surface had been restored with flattened mucous cells that progressively became more cuboidal with time (Figure 4). When epithelial continuity had been reestablished, the gastric pits were greatly shortened, and mucous neck cells and occasional oxynticopeptic cells were found very near the gastric luminal surface. The cuboidal surface cells contained mucous granules similar to those in the typical frog surface epithelial cells, but in reduced amounts (Figure 4). The course of restitution was so uniform that a blinded observer could predict the approximate time that had elapsed following injury. The process in vivo in the rat is similar except that it occurs much more rapidly (Figures 5–10).

During the exposure to 1M NaCl, the transmucosal potential difference, short circuit current, and resistance of in vitro frog mucosae mounted in an Ussing chamber decrease to almost zero. After washout of the hypertonic NaCl, the electrical values slowly recover to almost pre-injury or control values after 6 hr (Figure 11). A net luminal alkalinization occurred during the first 4 hr, changing to a net acid secretion comparable to that of control tissues by 6 hr (Figure 12). At 6 hr the addition of histamine to the nutrient solution resulted in consistent stimulation of H^+ secretion.

That the process of restitution was not unique to the amphibian gastric mucosa in vitro was shown by the restitution of in vitro guinea pig gastric mucosa in Ussing chambers within 30 min after injury by exposure to 1.25 M NaCl for 5 min (18). Some denuded areas were covered within 5 min of the injury, and PD, R, and I_{sc} returned to control levels by 2 hr. A remarkable finding was that after the initial restitution had occurred, the process could be repeated a second and even a third time in the same tissue. Histologically, the process of restitution in the guinea-pig mucosa was similar to that noted in the frog. However, the injury produced in the guinea-pig mucosa by 1.25 M NaCl for 5 min was less severe, more superficial, and more focal than that produced

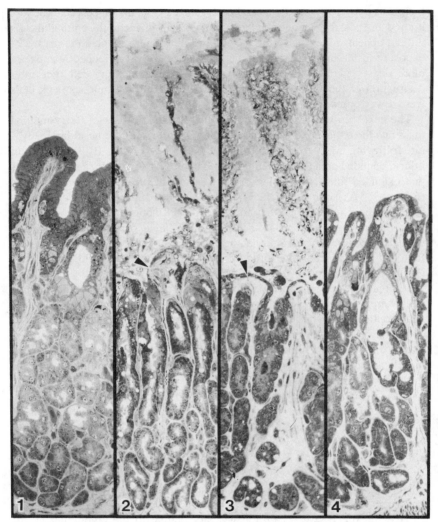

Figures 1–4 Photomicrographs of frog gastric mucosa in Ussing chambers. x 190. *1*. Control mucosa 6 hr in vitro. *2*. Damaged mucosa 1 hr after 1 M NaCl exposure, necrotic cells still attached. *3*. Restituted mucosa *(arrow)* 4 hr after hypertonic salt. *4*. Restituted mucosa 6 hr after 1 M NaCl.

by 1 M NaCl for 10 min in the frog. Furthermore, increasing the time of exposure of the guinea-pig mucosa to 1.25 M NaCl to as long as 15 min did not increase the damage or the time necessary for restitution. It is possible that the thinner guinea-pig mucosa might allow a more rapid flow of isotonic serosal fluid across the tissue to decrease the damaging effect of the hyperosmolar NaCl and hence reduce the extent of the injury.

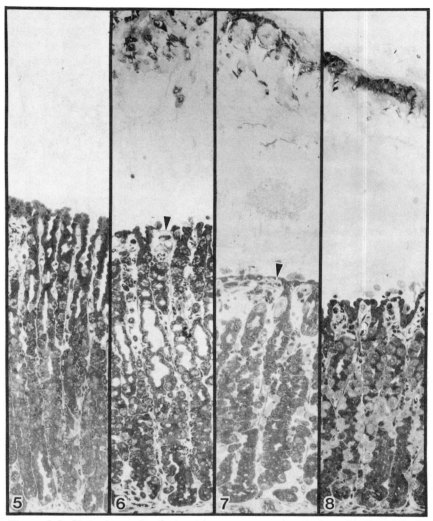

Figures 5–8 Photomicrographs of rat gastric mucosa exposed to absolute ethanol. × 161. *5.* Control mucosa. *6.* Damaged mucosa 15 min after ethanol exposure. Discontinuous epithelium *(arrow)* and partial restitution. *7.* Restitution of mucosa *(arrow)* after 30 min. *8.* Restitution after 1 hr.

It is of interest to note that the process of epithelial restitution is not confined to the mammalian or amphibian stomach. Hudspeth has reported that the epithelium of the Necturus gall bladder reestablishes both morphologic and electrical integrity within minutes following physical removal of single cells by a glass microelectrode (10). Furthermore, Vraco (25) has suggested that

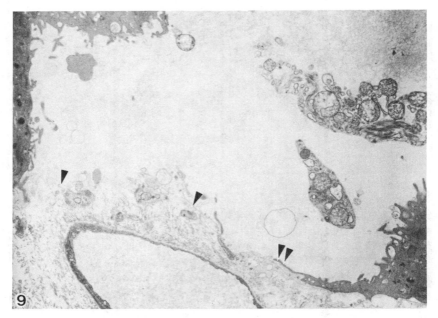

Figure 9   Electron micrograph of rat gastric mucosa undergoing restitution after ethanol damage. Lamellipodia *(double arrows)* extended over bare basal lamina *(arrows).* × 4,042.

restitution occurs in a variety of epithelial tissues such as renal tubules, liver, pancreas, and skin so long as the basal lamina is not irreversibly injured. Thus it seems reasonable to speculate that restitution is a general phenomenon whereby an epithelium rapidly repairs defects in its continuity caused by injury or other factors.

Hypertonic injury is not the only injury that has been shown to be followed regularly by restitution in vitro. Our ongoing studies indicate that exposure of the frog stomach to luminal aspirin in vitro is also followed by restitution.

Restitution In Vivo

It is likely that the great rapidity of gastric restitution in vivo is the reason that the actual process had previously escaped detection. As early as 1971, Hingson & Ito noted in mice that the marked injury seen in the surface epithelium after exposure to 20 mM aspirin was scarcely detectable at 30 min (9). Yeomans and coworkers (28, 29) suggested on the basis of experiments in rats exposed to aspirin on the luminal surface of the stomach that "the initial restoration of epithelium in many areas of complete surface desquamation must be due to rearrangement or migration of existing cells." In chambered rat gastric mucosa Morris & Wallace (15) recognized that epithelial continuity by migration of

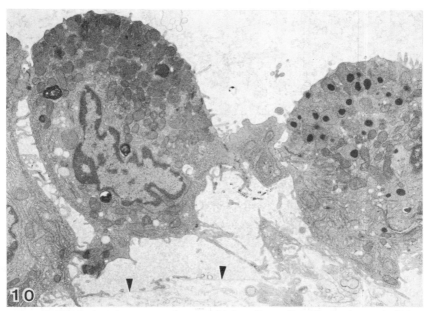

Figure 10   Restitution of rat mucosa after ethanol injury. Some of basal lamina *(arrows)* still free of cells. × 3,100.

cells from gastric pits was remarkably complete by 60 min after exposure to 40% ethanol. They also identified a network of fibrin in the overlying mucus protecting the injured tissue from further damage by luminal acid. On the basis of some earlier studies, Becker (1) interpreted the fibrinoid necrotic zone in gastric ulcers to be an important structural basis for the development and healing of gastric ulcers. The changes in transmural PD closely follow the damage and restitution process (15, 26). The PD commences to return only after there is significant evidence of restitution after dropping to almost zero immediately after 40% ethanol exposure. Lacy & Ito (11) recently demonstrated the cellular process of restitution by light, as well as transmission and scanning electron microscopy of rat stomachs exposed to luminal ethanol. The early phases of restitution were detectable within 5 min. After 30 min more than half, and by 1 hr greater than 90% of the mucosa was re-epitheliazed (Figures 5–10).

FACTORS THAT INFLUENCE RESTITUTION

1. Luminal Acid

Of prime interest in the stomach is the effect of luminal acid on an injury. Morris & Wallace (15) have shown in their ex vivo rat stomach preparations

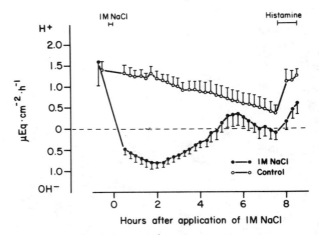

Figure 11   Net secretion of H^+ or OH^- by frog fundic mucosa after exposure to 1 M NaCl luminal solution for 10 min. Paired tissues not treated with 1 M NaCl served as controls. Mean values ± SE are plotted for seven observations.

that hemorrhagic erosions following 40% luminal ethanol occurred only when 50 mM luminal acid was present but not when saline bathed the luminal surface. They demonstrated that the luminal acid destroyed the basal lamina and thus probably removed "the substratum necessary for orderly epithelial re-establishment." Because the hemorrhagic erosions occurred only in hyperemic regions, it was speculated that ischemic cells were irreversibly damaged by the acid, and in addition, acid seemed to destroy the fibrin network in the adherent mucus coat and the platelet thrombi in that area (7).

Luminal pH of 3.0 or less in the in vitro amphibian mucosa completely inhibits the process of restitution and the recovery of the PD, I_{sc}, and R to control levels following injury with 1 M NaCl, and in many areas the exposed basal lamina has been destroyed (23). Interestingly, increasing the $[HCO_3^-]$ of the nutrient solution to 48 mM rather than the standard 18 mM allows restitution to proceed in the usual manner even though luminal pH is kept at 3.0. It is likely that this 48 mM HCO_3^- provides a sufficiently high $[HCO_3^-]$ at the level of the injured epithelium to neutralize the effects of the luminal acid. Neither stimulation with histamine nor treatment with H_2-blocking agents affects restitution in the in vitro amphibian mucosa, but these factors have not been studied systematically in vivo.

Luminal acid has a somewhat different effect on recovery from the hypertonic saline injury in the guinea-pig gastric mucosa in vitro (19). If the luminal pH is reduced to 2.0 immediately or within 5 min after the injury, restitution is inhibited and the mucosa is destroyed. However, if there is a 10–15 min period of wash with 0.15 M NaCl after injury and before acidification to a luminal pH

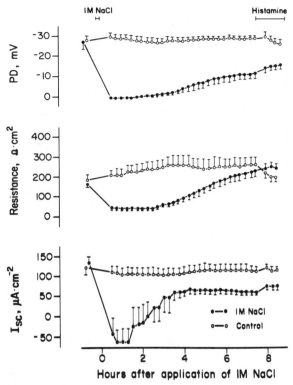

Figure 12   Changes in electrical measurements caused by exposure of frog fundic mucosa to 1 M NaCl luminal solution for 10 min. Mean values ± SE are plotted for seven observations. Same experiment as *Figure 11*.

of 2.0, accelerated restitution occurs and there is sudden and rapid return of PD, R, and I_{sc} to control values. The explanation for this surprising observation is not clear.

2. Calcium, Microfilaments, and Microtubules

Aside from the effects of luminal acid on restitution in vivo reported by Morris & Wallace (15), studies of other factors that might affect the process in vivo are limited. The in vitro system is ideally suited to examine these factors and has been used almost exclusively to assess the effects of alterations in cellular calcium, microfilaments, and microtubules on restitution after gastric injury.

Dissolution of junctional complexes between cells of the *normal uninjured* frog gastric mucosa was previously observed by Sedar & Forte, (20) who depleted calcium with EDTA. Our own observations have confirmed these findings, and in addition have clearly shown that removing calcium from the in vitro frog gastric mucosa has a profound effect on restitution (4). Simple washing of the tissues with calcium-free media after the 1 M NaCl injury lowers the tissue calcium content and inhibits the formation of junctional complexes by the migrating cells but does not prevent most of the restitution process (14). However, more stringent depletion of calcium by EDTA and washing with Ca^{++}-free solutions completely prevents any migration of epithelial cells over the bare basal lamina following injury with hypertonic NaCl (4). Whether this inhibition is due to failure of cells to attach to the basal lamina or to altered cell motility is not known.

That the microfilaments of the epithelial cells play a role in restitution is strongly suggested by our finding that cytochalasin B completely inhibits the migration of cells over the exposed basal lamina (3). This finding is in sharp contrast to the lack of effect of either colchicine or cyclohexamide in doses known to depolymerize microtubules or inhibit protein synthesis. The absence of an effect of colchicine is further emphasized by the lack of increased incorporation of tritiated thymidine following injury of the frog gastric mucosa with 1 M NaCl.

3. Prostaglandins

In their ex vivo rat stomach preparations, Wallace et al (26) have found that luminal PGE_2 did not prevent damage to the luminal epithelium by 40% ethanol, but rather reduced the areas of necrotic lesions by minimizing deep mucosal vasocongestion. The nature of these studies does not permit the conclusion that PGE_2 has little or no influence on the process of restitution in vivo, but this suggestion was proposed. A striking and consistent effect of prostaglandin treatment is the reduction or elimination of formation of necrotic lesions after exposure to damaging agents. In this sense prostaglandins could be interpreted as facilitating restitution. The necrotic lesion areas, however, are repaired much more slowly than the nonlesion areas, and the repair process, which involves inflammation and true mucosal regeneration, requires many hours or days.

In vitro, however, the effects of prostaglandins are very clear. Neither luminal nor nutrient prostaglandins affect either favorably or adversely the process of restitution in frog mucosa following injury with 1 M NaCl (24). This lack of effect was not influenced by the dose of prostaglandin or by whether the prostaglandin had an inhibitory effect on gastric acid secretion. Consonant with these observations is our finding that indomethacin, which inhibits endogenous prostaglandin synthesis, does not affect restitution. Furthermore, pretreatment of the mucosa with prostaglandins for 1 hr prior to injury with 1 M NaCl did not alter the extent of the initial injury or the process of restitution. We have also recently demonstrated that pretreatment with prostaglandins fails to protect the frog mucosa in vitro against the injury induced by luminal aspirin (W. Silen &

S. Ito, unpublished observations). These findings were surprising in view of the remarkable "cytoprotective" properties ascribed by others (2, 16, 17) to prostaglandins. The morphological study of Lacy & Ito (12) clearly showed that prostaglandin treatment did not reduce the area of the rat gastric mucosa damaged by 100% ethanol. Prostaglandin did reduce the depth of the mucosal damage as well as the hemorrhage and hyperemia. Taken together with the in vivo studies of Wallace & Morris, who showed that pretreatment with topical PGE$_2$ did not result in qualitative change in mucosal structure after exposure to 40% ethanol, it seems likely that the effect of prostaglandins is mainly one that reduces mucosal hemorrhage and hyperemia rather than one of producing an increase in inherent resistance of the mucosa to damage.

IMPLICATIONS OF RESTITUTION

The first clear elucidation of the process of restitution of the gastric epithelium following injury in vitro in the frog was probably made possible by the fact that it occurred rather slowly in this model. There were previous indications that epithelial integrity could be rapidly restored in vivo, but the process was so rapid that the morphological techniques that were employed were inadequate to reveal the structural correlates of restitution. That this process has important implications in gastric injury and reestablishment of normal function is now clearly evident. Restitution is very involved in the repair of the injuries sustained after intake of various foodstuffs and after thermal, mechanical, or hyperosmolar damage. It provides a first-line defense mechanism for the rapid repair of injuries that do not extensively injure the basal lamina. Thus, epithelial defects are covered long before this could be accomplished by regeneration of epithelium from progenitor cells and without the need to mount an inflammatory response (because restitution occurs in vitro). In addition, because gastric surface cells are short-lived and die after a few days, restitution may be a continual and ongoing process for the repair of defects at the site of cell exfoliation.

Second, we believe that the demonstration of restitution demands a reevaluation of previous studies designed to assess the so-called "cytoprotective" effects of a variety of agents (e.g. prostaglandins, antisecretory substances) against injury of the gastric epithelium by many different modalities including heat, 100% ethanol, aspirin, strong acids and alkali, and bile salts (2, 16, 17). Virtually all of these studies except those specifically cited above have evaluated the in vivo gastric mucosa subjected to such injury (with or without protection) about 1 hr after the damaging agent has been applied, a time interval during which restitution clearly occurs. Furthermore, many of the studies to evaluate "cytoprotection" have utilized gross observation of the gastric mucosa only and have indicated "cytoprotection" when gross hemorrhagic streaks are prevented, but without histologic proof that epithelial cells were in fact intact or destroyed. Thus, caution is to be exercised in the interpretation of such investigations.

Mammalian and amphibian gastric mucosae, when initially mounted in Ussing chambers in vitro, usually have a low PD and R, which slowly rise to characteristic steady-state levels over variable periods of time, depending on the species and the conditions. This property, shared with other epithelia, has generally been attributed to edge damage (5, 8, 27). Careful studies have recently shown, however, that the freshly mounted guinea-pig gastric mucosa, when examined morphologically, has diffuse superficial damage of the epithelial cells, albeit not to the extent induced by 1M NaCl (18). Because the time course of the rise of the PD and R in the uninjured freshly mounted guinea-pig gastric mucosa is similar to that during restitution after injury with 1M NaCl, it is tempting to speculate that what has been attributed to edge damage may be in part due to epithelial injury during preparation of the mucosal sheet. Further morphological and physiological studies are needed to substantiate this possibility.

Previous studies of the "gastric mucosal barrier" have suggested that disruption of the barrier by aspirin, ethanol, bile salts, and a host of other agents represents a physiological phenomenon, because recovery of the PD and R following luminal exposure to such agents is rapid and complete. More recent investigations indicate that disruption of the mucosal barrier by these luminal agents is invariably associated with severe injury to the surface epithelial cells of the stomach. We have recently demonstrated restitution in vitro in amphibian gastric mucosa following exposure to luminal aspirin and believe that recovery after "barrier disruption" by other agents is very likely attributable to the process of restitution.

Finally, because restitution has already been convincingly demonstrated in gastric and gall bladder epithelium (10), it is likely that restitution is a basic feature of all epithelia and that the mechanisms underlying the process are similar in a variety of tissues.

Literature Cited

1. Becker, V. 1973. The significance of the fibrinoid necrotic zone for the development and healing of gastric ulcer. *Acta Hepatogastroenterol.* 20:185–87
2. Chaudhury, T. K., Robert, A. 1980. Prevention by mild irritants of gastric necrosis produced in rats by sodium taurocholate. *Dig. Dis. Sci.* 25:830–36
3. Critchlow, J., Magee, D., Ito, S., Silen, W. 1982. Effects of inhibition of protein synthesis, microtubules, and microfilaments on the repair of gastric surface cell injury. *Am. Coll. Surgeons Surgical Forum* 33:147–49
4. Critchlow, J., Takeuchi, K., Ito, S., Magee, D., Silen, W. 1982. Effect of calcium depletion on the restitution of gastric mucosal injury. *Gastroenterology* 82:1038
5. Dobson, J. G., Kidder, G. W. III. 1968. Edge damage effect in in vitro frog skin preparation. *Am. J. Physiol.* 214:719–24
6. Grant, R. 1945. Rate of replacement of

the surface epithelial cells of the gastric mucosa. *Anat. Rec.* 91:175–85

7. Green, F. W., Kaplan, M. M., Curtis, L. E., Levine, P. H. 1978. Effect of acid and pepsin on blood coagulation and platelet aggregation: a possible contributor to prolonged gastroduodenal mucosal hemorrhage. *Gastroenterology* 74:38–43

8. Helman, S. I., Miller, D. A. 1971. In vitro techniques for avoiding edge damage in studies of frog skin. *Science* 173:146–48

9. Hingson, D. J., Ito, S. 1971. Effect of aspirin and related compounds on the fine structure of mouse gastric mucosa. *Gastroenterology* 61:156–77

10. Hudspeth, A. J. 1975. Establishment of tight junctions between epithelial cells. *Proc. Natl. Acad. Sci. USA* 72:2711–13

11. Lacy, E. R., Ito, S. 1984. Ethanol-induced insult to the superficial rat gastric epithelium: a study of damage and rapid repair. In *Mechanisms of Mucosal Protection in the Upper Gastrointestinal Tract*, ed. A. Allen, et al, pp. 49–56. New York: Raven

12. Lacy, E. R., Ito, S. 1982. Microscopic analysis of ethanol damage to rat gastric mucosa after treatment with a prostaglandin. *Gastroenterology* 83:619–25

13. Lipkin, M., Sherlock, P., Bell, B. 1963. Cell proliferation kinetics in the gastrointestinal tract of man. II. Cell renewal in stomach, ileum, colon and rectum. *Gastroenterology* 45:721–29

14. Logsdon, C. D., Machen, T. E. 1981. Involvement of extracellular calcium in gastric stimulation. *Am. J. Physiol.* 241:6365–75

15. Morris, G. P., Wallace, J. L. 1981. The roles of ethanol and of acid in the production of gastric erosions in rats. *Virchow's Arch. B.* 38:23–28

16. Robert, A. 1979. Cytoprotection by prostaglandins. *Gastroenterology* 77:761–67

17. Robert, A., Lancaster, C., Hanchar, A. J., Nezamins, J. E. 1978. Mild irritants prevent gastric necrosis through prostaglandin formation: Histological study. *Gastroenterology* 74:1086

18. Rutten, M. J., Ito, S. 1983. Morphology and electrophysiology of guinea pig gastric mucosal repair in vitro. *Am. J. Physiol. Gastrointest. Liver Physiol.* 244(7):G171–82

19. Rutten, M. J., Ito, S. 1984. Luminal acid effects on reconstitution of damaged guinea pig gastric mucosa in vitro. See Ref. 11, pp. 41–47

20. Sedar, A. W., Forte, J. G. 1964. Effects of calcium depletion on the junctional complex between oxyntic cells of gastric glands. *J. Cell Biol.* 22:123–88

21. Stevens, C. E., Leblond, C. P. 1953. Renewal of the mucous cells in the gastric mucosa of the rat. *Anat. Rec.* 115:231–43

22. Svanes, K., Ito, S., Takeuchi, K., Silen, W. 1982. Restitution of the surface epithelium of the in vitro frog gastric mucosa after damage with hyperosmolar NaCl. *Gastroenterology* 82:1409–27

23. Svanes, K., Takeuchi, K., Ito, S., Silen, W. 1983. Effect of luminal pH and nutrient bicarbonate concentration on restitution after gastric surface cell injury. *Surgery* 94:494–500

24. Svanes, K., Critchlow, J., Takeuchi, K., Magee, D., Ito, S., Silen, W. 1984. Factors influencing reconstitution of frog gastric mucosa: role of prostaglandins. See Ref. 11, pp. 33–39

25. Vracko, R. 1974. Basal lamina scaffold: anatomy and significance for maintenance of orderly tissue structure: a review. *Am. J. Pathol.* 77:314–38

26. Wallace, J. L., Morris, G. P., Krousse, E. J., Greaves, S. E. 1982. Reduction by cytoprotective agents of ethanol-induced damage to the rat gastric mucosa: a correlated morphological and physiological study. *Can. J. Physiol. Pharmacol.* 60:1686–99

27. Walser, M. 1970. Role of edge damage in sodium permeability of toad bladder and a means of avoiding it. *Am. J. Physiol.* 219:252–55

28. Yeomans, N. D. 1976. Electron microscopic study of the repair of aspirin-induced gastric erosions. *Am. J. Dig. Dis.* 21(7):533–41

29. Yeomans, N. D., St. John, D. J., de Boer, W. G. 1973. Regeneration of gastric mucosa after aspirin-induced injury in the rat. *Am. J. Dig. Dis.* 18:773–80

Ann. Rev. Physiol. 1985. 47:231–45

ONTOGENY OF ENZYMES IN THE SMALL INTESTINE

Susan J. Henning

Department of Biology, University of Houston, Houston, Texas 77004

INTRODUCTION

In this review, the rat is used as a model system for a discussion of the postnatal development of intestinal enzymes. Emphasis is placed on the regulation and mechanisms of the enzymic changes. Because of space limitations, the review focuses on the major advances of recent years, not attempting to be comprehensive.

The postnatal development of the rat small intestine is characterized by an array of enzymic changes during the third week. To understand the functional significance of these changes, it is important to realize that they are temporally coordinated with the process of spontaneous weaning in this species. Moreover, the changes in the enzymology of the small intestine are paralleled by maturation of digestive functions in other parts of the gastrointestinal tract, namely the mouth, the stomach, and the pancreas. The details of the coordination between weaning and the changes occurring throughout the gastrointestinal tract are discussed elsewhere (26). Not surprisingly, there are substantial similarities in the regulation of the digestive changes in various parts of the tract. This point will become apparent by reading the paper of L. R. Johnson (this volume) in conjunction with the present review.

EMBRYOLOGY AND MORPHOLOGY OF THE SMALL INTESTINE

One of the most elegant studies of intestinal development in recent years is that by Kedinger et al (38), investigating the role of epithelial-mesenchyme interactions in the embryology of the small intestine. These authors made

231

0066-4278/85/0315-0231$02.00

xenoplastic recombinations of chick mesoderm with rat endoderm and vice versa. By examining the pattern of enzymes after 11 days of intracoelomic graft in chick embryos, they were able to conclude that "the endodermal tissue carries the specific characteristics of its future biochemical differentiation."

By the time of birth, the intestinal mucosa of the rat displays a high level of structural development characterized by villi lined with a single layer of columnar epithelial cells that have well-defined microvilli at their absorptive surface (16, 37, 61). After birth, continuous proliferation of epithelial cells occurs only in the lower regions of the crypts (3, 6), and cells migrate from there onto and along the villi, eventually being extruded from the tips into the lumen of the intestine. In adult rats and mice the generation time for the crypt cells is 10–14 hr (5), and the transit time along the length of the villus is approximately 48 hr (46). The details of proliferation and migration of enterocytes in adult animals are dealt with in the review by M. Lipkin (this volume). In neonatal rats, generation and migration of the cells is much slower than in adults (33, 46). During the third postnatal week there are significant changes in cell kinetics, leading to the more rapid proliferation that is characteristic of the adult animal (33). Enhanced polyamine production in the intestinal mucosa appears to play a critical role in this increase in epithelial proliferation (52). As will be explained later, these changes of cell kinetics may at least partly account for some of the changes in mucosal enzymology in the third postnatal week.

In both neonatal and adult animals, the crypt-villus unit is a classical example of a system wherein proliferation precedes differentiation. The epithelial cells of the villus have many specialized enzymatic functions concerned with the processes of digestion and absorption (19, 69). In contrast, the progenitor cells of the crypt are relatively nondifferentiated but, as would be expected of proliferating tissue, contain high activities of various enzymes involved in synthesis of DNA (31, 34). Many of the specialized functions of the villus cells are associated with the luminal surface, i.e. with the microvilli.

The continuous renewal of the intestinal epithelium adds a degree of complexity to ontogenic studies with this organ. When dealing with the postnatal development of most other organs, one considers the change with time in the enzymatic properties of a stable population of cells. Contrastingly, in the intestine, there are two ways in which enzyme patterns can be changed: by changes in a given population of enterocytes within their brief life-span; and by simple replacement of one type of cell by another type from the proliferating pool. In a later section, evidence will be presented that it is the latter mechanism that is operative in the ontogenic changes that occur during the third week of life.

ENZYMES THAT DECLINE IN ACTIVITY DURING POSTNATAL DEVELOPMENT

In terms of digestive capacity, the neonatal rat intestine has hydrolytic activities that are specific for, and largely restricted to, the components of maternal milk. This is demonstrated very nicely by a consideration of carbohydrate digestion. Milk is relatively low in total carbohydrates, and the carbohydrates present are those not generally found in adult diets. The major carbohydrate in the milk of most placental mammals is lactose (35), and high activities of its disaccharidase, lactase, are found in the intestinal mucosa of suckling animals (11, 47). In the rat, lactase is detectable on day 18 of gestation, has maximal activity during the first week after birth, and then begins to decline, reaching adult values by the end of the fourth week (13). Many other species, including the human, have lower lactase activity in the adult than the newborn (11) and, accordingly, show an inability to utilize ingested lactose in the postweaning period (47).

Although lactose is the major carbohydrate received by the suckling mammal, the milks of various species are also known to contain sialic acid. Interestingly, the digestive enzyme for this component, namely neuraminidase, has been found to have an ontogenic profile very similar to that of lactase (12). The physiological importance of neuraminidase as a digestive enzyme during the neonatal period is indicated by the finding that the neuraminidase activity in the intestine of various mammals is proportional to the amount of sialic acid in their respective milks (12).

Neuraminidase is one member of a whole family of lysosomal hydrolases that, in the rat, display high activities during the first and second postnatal weeks then declining activities during the third postnatal week (41, 45). The functional significance of the high neonatal activities of many of the lysosomal enzymes (e.g. β-galactosidase, β-glucuronidase, and arylsulphatase) is not apparent. For the cathepsins (10a, 80), it is likely that the high activity during the first two postnatal weeks is important in: (a) the rapid turnover of brushborder proteins that occurs in the neonatal intestine (80); and (b) allowing intracellular digestion of protein at a time when extracellular digestion by pancreatic proteases has not yet matured (77). In regard to the latter, it is relevant to note that the neonatal rat intestine has substantial capacity for the absorption of macromolecules, including proteins, by the process of pinocytosis (26).

ENZYMES THAT INCREASE IN ACTIVITY DURING POSTNATAL DEVELOPMENT

Intestinal hydrolases that are involved in digestion of carbohydrate components of solid food are absent or low at birth, then appear and/or increase in activity.

Maltase has low activity during the first two postnatal weeks, then undergoes a 5–10-fold increase during the next two weeks (75, 78). For sucrase, isomaltase, and trehalase, the transition is even more sudden. These enzymes cannot be detected in the intestine during the first and second postnatal week, but their activities appear on approximately day 16 and rise rapidly, reaching adult levels by the end of the fourth week (14, 75, 78). The activity changes of the disaccharidases are paralleled by quantitative changes in the protein bands of microvillus membrane preparations studied by electrophoresis (20, 21, 81, 83).

These developmental changes in the disaccharidase activities of the intestine clearly have physiological significance in allowing the young animal to make the dietary change from lactose as the major carbohydrate during suckling to maltose, isomaltose, and sucrose as the major disaccharides after weaning (26). The temporal relationship between the developmental rise of sucrase activity and the process of weaning has been noted previously (26). The possibility of a causal relationship between these two phenomena is discussed below.

In addition to the disaccharidases, many workers have measured the marked increase in duodenal alkaline phosphatase activity that occurs during the third week of life in rats and mice (11). Much of the pioneer work by Moog on the development of intestinal function was accomplished with this enzyme (65, 66). The function of alkaline phosphatase in the intestine is not understood, although its distribution along the crypt-villus unit (69) and its localization in the microvilli of enterocytes (7, 18) are suggestive of some role in digestion or absorption.

REGULATION OF ENZYMIC CHANGES

Role of Diet

The possibility of dietary influence over the regulation of intestinal development is an obvious one considering the temporal correlation between the major enzymic changes in the intestine and the onset of weaning. It is clear, however, that this dietary change cannot be considered the primary cause of the various enzymic changes that occur in the intestine during the third postnatal week. We have shown (30) that when weaning is prevented, the appearance of sucrase activity in the jejunum is not delayed. Similarly, prolonged suckling delays, but does not prevent, the usual decline of lactase activity (49). Conversely, oral administration of sucrose to 12-day-old rats has no effect on the developmental pattern for sucrase (48). If sucrose is administered by gastrostomy to suckling rats, precocious increase of sucrase is observed; however, because this does not occur if the animals have been previously adrenalectomized, it is probably a stress response rather than a dietary response (48). The same comment applies to the precocious appearance of sucrase, maltase, isomaltase, and alkaline phosphatase following early weaning (22, 74). These conclusions are supported by the observations that sucrase develops normally in bypassed intestinal segments (86) and that when intestinal explants from 6-day-old rats are cultured in the presence of various sugars, there is no stimulatory effect on sucrase or maltase activity (73).

Given, then, that the intestinal changes of the third week are initiated by some factor other than the dietary change of weaning, there still remains the question of whether the dietary change modulates the extent or the timing of the ontogenic events. The case of sucrase development is particularly interesting. Although the timing of the appearance of jejunal sucrase is not affected by prevention of weaning, the plateau of enzyme activity (days 25–27) is approximately half that seen in control (weaned) animals (30). The critical difference between milk and chow concerns the relative proportions of carbohydrate and fat (27). Regardless of the nature of the carbohydrate, a diet such as chow, which is high in carbohydrates and low in fat, will elicit a high plateau activity of sucrase, whereas a diet such as milk, which is low in carbohydrates and high in fat, will elicit a low plateau (27). Correspondingly, in intestinal explants from suckling rats that have been treated with dexamethasone to elicit sucrase and maltase, addition of sugars to the culture medium increases the activities of these enzymes (73).

Role of Glucocorticoid Hormones

The glucocorticoids are attractive candidates for the regulation of intestinal development because circulating concentrations of corticosterone (the principal glucocorticoid in the rat) increase at the beginning of the third postnatal week (25, 76). Figure 1 shows that plasma concentrations of free corticosterone are low through day 12 and then increase markedly. Analysis of jejunal sucrase and lactase activities in the same animals (Figure 1) reveals that the rise of free corticosterone begins about 48 hr before the enzymic changes are initiated. This delay is consistent with the fact that glucocorticoid action on the intestinal epithelium is mediated by the crypt cells (see below).

Administration of glucocorticoids to suckling rats during the first two postnatal weeks causes precocious increases in the activities of sucrase (14, 21, 28), maltase (21, 29, 67), trehalase (21), amino peptidase (21, 66), and alkaline phosphatase (65), as well as precocious decreases of lactase (29) and various lysosomal hydrolases (29, 45). Correspondingly, addition of glucocorticoids to intestinal explants from rats aged 4–13 days elicits a precocious appearance of sucrase and a stimulation of maltase activity (14, 39, 84, 85).

Conversely, it has been shown that if rats are subject to neonatal adrenalectomy or hypophysectomy, the usual decrease of lactase (29) and lysosomal hydrolases (29, 44), and the usual increase of alkaline phosphatase (65, 91), sucrase (42, 44, 57, 91), and maltase (44, 57, 91) are delayed, although not

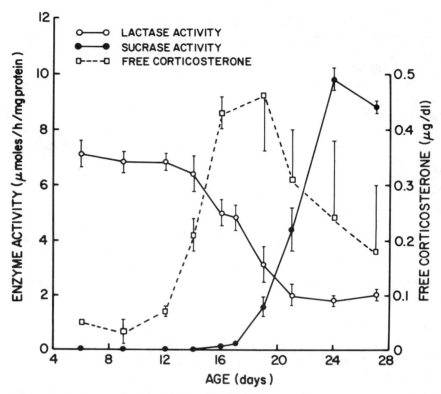

Figure 1 Developmental patterns for the activities of the enzymes lactase and sucrase in jejunal mucosa as compared with free corticosterone in plasma: (o——o) lactase activity; (●——●) sucrase activity; (□----□) free corticosterone. Values are given as mean ± SEM (n = 5). Absence of error bars indicates that the SEM was smaller than the symbol. Reproduced with permission (from 25).

prevented. In hypophysectomized infant rats, cortisone administration restores sucrase development to normal (92), indicating that, at least for this enzyme, the critical effect of ablation of the anterior pituitary is the removal of ACTH and thus of corticosterone.

In an earlier section it was pointed out that there are two possible mechanisms by which enzymic changes of the intestinal epithelium could occur: by alteration of the enzyme levels in the differentiated cells that are present on the villi; or by replacement of one population of villus cells by another that has altered enzymology. There is now considerable evidence to indicate that the latter method is operative in the various postnatal changes that are observed in the rat intestine. When the distribution of sucrase along the length of the crypt-villus unit after glucocorticoid administration to 9-day-old rats was studied by cryostat sectioning of the intestine (28, 32), it was found that 24 hr after administration of the steroid, no sucrase activity was detectable on the villi but very small amounts were present at the mouths of the crypts. By day 11 this activity had increased and extended along the lower halves of the villi. The process continued and by day 13 sucrase activity had reached the tips of the villi, and the pattern through the whole depth of the mucosa was very similar to that for adult animals (69).

These results indicate that the ability of hydrocortisone to cause precocious appearance of sucrase is mediated via the cells of the crypt. The cells that are on the villi at the time of administration are apparently unaffected by the hormone. The rate at which the enzyme activity appeared at the base of the villi and then spread along the lengths of the villi correlated with reported migratory rates for the epithelial cells (32, 46).

Similar results for the pattern of precocious appearance of sucrase have been obtained by immunological techniques (15, 23). The same series of events apparently occurs when endogenous glucocorticoids participate in the normal appearance of sucrase (23) and loss of pinocytosis (88) during the third postnatal week. Thus, the whole array of enzymic changes that usually occur at this time reflect a change in the cellularity of the intestinal epithelium. Such a mechanism would account for the report that inhibition of the rate of proliferation causes the developmental increase of maltase activity to be delayed (52).

As detailed above, the involvement of glucocorticoids in intestinal development has been extensively studied. However, the question of whether intestinal maturation is absolutely dependent on glucocorticoids has not been addressed in the literature. As indicated earlier, several studies have shown that enzymic development is delayed but not abolished in adrenalectomized rat pups (10, 42, 44, 65). The problem with these studies was that none of them included either mineralocorticoid replacement or measurement of serum corticosterone following the adrenalectomy. We have recently found that without mineralocorticoid administration following neonatal adrenalectomy, the only pups that survive long enough to study have substantial amounts of corticosterone in the serum. Even with mineralocorticoid replacement, it is essential to measure serum corticosterone in all adrenalectomized pups so as to eliminate those with detectable levels of corticosterone (57). Data from a recent study incorporating these precautions are shown in Figure 2. It can be seen that although adrenalectomy markedly suppressed the rate of the sucrase rise, the time of appearance of the enzyme (day 17) was not delayed, and by day 26 the activity of the enzyme in the pups having no detectable serum corticosterone (i.e. the adX + vehicle group) was the same as in the sham-operated controls. Corticosterone replacement therapy in adrenalectomized pups caused a slightly precocious rise of sucrase activity, illustrating the difficulty of achieving physiological concentrations of corticosterone by exogenous administration. In the

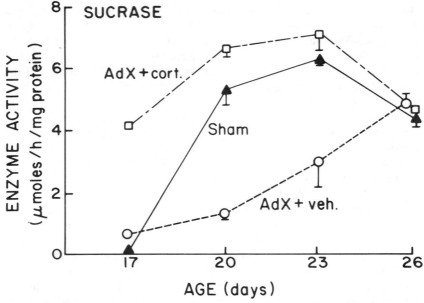

Figure 2   Effect of adrenalectomy on the development of jejunal sucrase. Enzyme activities are shown for the sham-operated animals (▲——▲), for adrenalectomized animals receiving vehicle injections (○——○), and for adrenalectomized animals receiving corticosterone injections (□---□). For the adX + veh. group, only pups having undetectable concentrations of serum corticosterone were included for sucrase assay. Results are given as means ± SEM. The number of animals represented for each group at each age ranged from four to seven. Absence of error bars indicates the SEM was smaller than the symbol. Reproduced with permission (from 58).

same study, the rate of maturation of maltase, lactase, and acid β-galactosidase was reduced but not abolished by adrenalectomy (58).

The results of this study have led us to conclude that developmental changes in intestinal enzymes are not absolutely dependent on corticosterone. It seems that the timing for the initiation of enzyme development is intrinsically programmed in the intestinal tissue and that the developmental surge of serum corticosterone at the beginning of the third postnatal week controls only the rate of expression of the intestinal program. Such a mechanism is consistent with the observation that sucrase, maltase, lactase and acid β-galactosidase develop normally in fetal intestinal tissue that is transplanted into the stable hormonal environment of an adult host (40, 64).

In view of the above conclusions, we believe that the significance of glucocorticoids in intestinal development is that they provide a mechanism for precocious maturation if pups are subjected to precocious loss of their dam, i.e. that the stress of forced weaning would cause a sufficient elevation of plasma corticosterone to induce precocious maturation of intestinal enzymes. This suggestion is consistent with the finding that jejunal sucrase activity is elevated following early weaning (2, 50, 93), but only if the adrenal glands are present (2). Precocious decreases of lactase activity (50, 93) and increases of maltase activity (50) have also been reported in early-weaned rats. Moreover, serum corticosterone is elevated by more than three-fold as a result of early weaning (50).

Role of Thyroxine

Thyroxine (T_4) has received considerable attention as a candidate for regulation of intestinal development in the rat because its circulating concentration rises significantly during the second postnatal week (8, 17, 79, 89). Administration of T_4 or triiodothyronine has been shown to cause precocious decline of jejunal lactase activity (71) and ileal lysosomal hydrolases (43) and precocious increases of jejunal sucrase and maltase (36). Conversely, hypothyroidism delays but does not prevent the usual decline of lysosomal hydrolases (44) and the usual increases of sucrase (24, 44, 91) and maltase (44, 91) activities. The significance of findings such as these must be questioned in view of the fact that administration of T_4 causes a precocious increase in plasma corticosterone (9, 54, 72) and that hypothyroidism virtually abolishes the developmental rise of corticosterone (9, 91). At least for sucrase and maltase development, the effects of thyroid manipulations seem to be secondary to the accompanying changes of serum corticosterone (57, 91). Specifically, the suppressive effect of hypothyroidism on the developmental rises of sucrase and maltase can be reversed just as effectively by glucocorticoid administration as by T_4 treatment (57, 91). Conversely, when T_4 is administered during the first two postnatal weeks, there is no stimulation of sucrase and maltase unless serum corticosterone is also allowed to increase (57). The conclusion that T_4 plays no role in the normal development of jejunal sucrase and maltase is supported by the finding that T_4 (in contrast to glucocorticoid) is unable to elicit increases in the activity of these enzymes in jejunal explants from suckling rats (84).

Thyroxine may play a role in the regulation of enzymes that normally decline during development. For neuraminidase and acid β-galactosidase, administration of T_4 together with a saturating dose of cortisone acetate causes a greater precocious decline of activity than when cortisone acetate is given alone (51). For lactase, the developmental effects of hypophysectomy are fully restored by administration of T_4, but only partially restored by administration of cortisone (90). The involvement of T_4 in the ontogenic decline of these enzymes may reflect the fact that this hormone, perhaps acting in conjunction with insulin (56), is a potent stimulator of mitotic activity in the intestinal epithelium (91).

There is evidence that, at least for lactase, the declining activity during the third postnatal week is largely due to the decreased life span of enterocytes, which accompanies the increased rates of proliferation and migration of these cells at this time (71, 87). Thus, if the latter increases are caused by T_4, then this hormone could indirectly contribute to the developmental decline of enzyme activities during the third postnatal week. The finding that T_4 does not cause a decline of lactase activity in intestinal explants (84) could be explained if other factors, such as nutrients, limit the rate of proliferation of enterocytes in culture.

Other Factors

Other factors that have been recently studied as potential regulators of postnatal development of the small intestine in rats and mice are glucagon, prostaglandins, epidermal growth factor (EGF), and insulin. Administration of pancreatic glucagon to suckling rats does not elevate sucrase activity, and it has been concluded that this hormone has little or no effect on the maturation of intestinal enzymes (4). Treatment of suckling rats with prostacyclin (PGI_2) thrice daily for four days results in precocious increases in the specific activities of sucrase and maltase (68). However, as the authors themselves recognized, these effects of PGI_2 could have been secondary to elevations in serum corticosterone. This would be consistent with their finding that PGI_2 is without effect on sucrase and maltase activities in 23-day-old animals (68), which are beyond the period of glucocorticoid sensitivity (30).

Administration of EGF to mice during the second postnatal week results in the precocious appearance of intestinal sucrase activity and precocious increases in several other brush-border hydrolases (55). Although clearly detectable, these effects are very modest compared with those of glucocorticoids. Using data from the same laboratory, for instance, the sucrase activity elicited in 11-day-old mice after the highest dose of EGF (55) is less than 10% that elicited by cortisone (56). Moreover, it has been pointed out that a physiological role of endogenous EGF in intestinal maturation is unlikely because the developmental increase in EGF production occurs after the enzymic changes in the small intestine (55).

Exogenous insulin causes precocious maturation of the small intestine in mice (56, 63). These effects cannot be secondary to insulin-induced elevation of endogenous corticosterone because: (*a*) the effect of insulin has a shorter lag time than that of glucocorticoids (63); (*b*) when insulin is administered to suckling mice together with saturating doses of cortisone acetate, resulting activities of sucrase and maltase are higher that when cortisone acetate is administered alone (56); and (*c*) insulin induces the appearance of sucrase activity in intestinal explants from suckling mice (62). The question of the extent to which endogenous insulin is responsible for the normal development of intestinal enzymes has not been addressed. A role for endogenous insulin is plausible in view of the fact that circulating concentrations increase steadily from 10 to 25 days of age (1). Experiments of the future could profitably examine intestinal development in animals in which the developmental increase of insulin is abolished.

MOLECULAR MECHANISMS

A major challenge of this field is to elucidate the molecular mechanisms underlying the ontogenic changes in enzymes of the small intestine. In this regard, it is important to note that the enzymic changes discussed in this review represent only a portion of the total changes in the biochemistry of the rat intestine during postnatal development. For instance, microvillus membranes (MVM) from suckling animals display markedly different patterns of glycosylation than do those of adults (53). In terms of overall structure, the MVM is more disordered in the newborn rat than in the adult (70). The biochemical nature of mucus secreted by the small intestinal epithelium also changes during postnatal development (82). Furthermore, the mucosal content of the receptor for vitamin D increases markedly during the third week of life (59). For the latter there is evidence that, just as for the digestive enzymes discussed earlier, the pattern of maturation represents the operation of an intrinsic ontogenic program whose rate is under glucocorticoid control (59, 60).

Unfortunately, studies of the molecular events of intestinal development are complicated by the fact that the enzymic changes are not due to altered synthesis within the differentiated cells of the villi, but rather to replacement of those cells by a new population emerging from the proliferative pool in the crypts (see earlier). Thus, the expression of the ontogenic program is inextricably linked with cell cycling. A consequence is that changes of gene expression occurring during the third postnatal week are passed on to the daughter cells (in the crypts) in an apparently irreversible fashion. In most other tissues, such a pattern of development is limited to the embryonic period. When molecular techniques are applied to the postnatally developing intestine, it will be very interesting to compare the mechanisms with those operating in other organ systems during early tissue differentiation.

ACKNOWLEDGMENTS

This work was supported by grant number R01-HD-14094 from the National Institutes of Health. The author wishes to thank Dr. M. V. Rao for his helpful comments on the manuscript.

Literature Cited

1. Blazquez, E., Montoya, E., Quijada, C. L. 1970. Relationship between insulin concentrations in plasma and pancreas of foetal and weanling rats. *J. Endocrinol.* 48:553–61

2. Boyle, J. T., Koldovsky, O. 1980. Critical role of adrenal glands in precocious increase in jejunal sucrase activity following premature weaning in rats: Negligible effect of food intake. *J. Nutr.* 110:169–77

3. Burholt, D. R., Schultze, B., Maurer, W. 1976. Mode of growth of the jejunal crypt cells of the rat: an autoradiographic study using double labelling with ^{3}H- and ^{14}C-thymidine in lower and upper parts of crypts. *Cell Tiss. Kinet.* 9:107–17

4. Buts, J-P., DeMeyer, R., Van Craynest, M-P., Maldague, P. 1983. Pancreatic glucagon does not alter mucosal growth and maturation of sucrase and thymidine kinase activity in rat small intestine. *Biol. Neonate* 43:253–62

5. Cairnie, A. B., Lamerton, L. F., Steel, G. G. 1965. Cell proliferation studies of the intestinal epithelium of the rat. I. Determination of kinetic parameters. *Exptl. Cell Res.* 39:528–38

6. Cheng, H., Leblond, C. P. 1974. Origin, differentiation, and renewal of the four main epithelial cell types in the mouse small intestine. I. Columnar cell. *Am. J. Anat.* 141:461–80

7. Clark, S. L. 1961. The localization of alkaline phosphatase in tissues of mice using the electron microscope. *Am. J. Anat.* 109:57–83

8. Clos, J., Crepel, J., Legrand, C., Legrand, J., Rabie, A., Vigoroux, E. 1974. Thyroid physiology during the postnatal period in the rat: a study of the development of thyroid function and of the morphogenetic effects of thyroxine with special reference to cellular maturation. *Gen. Comp. Endocrinol.* 23:178–92

9. D'Agostino, J. B., Henning, S. J. 1982. Role of thyroxine in coordinate control of corticosterone and CBG in postnatal development. *Am. J. Physiol.* 242:E33–39

10. Daniels, V. G., Hardy, R. N., Malinowska, K. W. 1973. The effect of adrenalectomy or pharmacological inhibition of adrenocortical function on macromolecule uptake by the newborn rat intestine. *J. Physiol.* 229:697–707

10a. Davies, P. H., Messer, M. 1984. Intestinal cathepsin B and D activities of suckling rats. *Biol. Neonate* 45:197–202

11. Deren, J. J. 1968. Development of intestinal structure and function. In *Handbook of Physiology, Section 6, Alimentary Canal, Intestinal Absorption,* ed. C. F. Code, 3:1099–123. Washington, DC: Am. Physiol. Soc.

12. Dickson, J. J., Messer, M. 1978. Intestinal neuraminidase activity of suckling rats and other mammals: relationship to the sialic acid content of milk. *Biochem. J.* 170:407–13

13. Doell, R. G., Kretchmer, N. 1962. Studies of the small intestine during development. I. Distribution and activity of β-galactosidase. *Biochim. Biophys. Acta* 62:353–62

14. Doell, R. G., Kretchmer, N. 1964. Intestinal invertase: precocious development of activity after injection of hydrocortisone. *Science* 143:42–44

15. Doell, R. G., Rosen, G., Kretchmer, N. 1965. Immunological studies of intestinal disaccharidases during normal and precocious development. *Proc. Natl. Acad. Sci. USA* 54:1268–73

16. Dunn, J. S. 1967. The fine structure of the absorptive epithelial cells of the developing small intestine of the rat. *J. Anat.* 101:57–68

17. Dussault, J. H., Labrie, F. 1975. Development of the hypothalamic-pituitary-thyroid axis in the neonatal rat. *Endocrinology* 97:1321–24

18. Etzler, M. E., Birkenmeier, E. H., Moog, F. 1969. Localization of alkaline phosphatase isozymes in mouse duodenum by immunofluorescence microscopy. *Histochemie* 20:99–104

19. Fortin-Magana, R., Hurwitz, R., Herbst, J. J., Kretchmer, N. 1970. Intestinal enzymes: indicators of proliferation and differentiation in the jejunum. *Science* 167:1627–28

20. Galand, G., Forstner, G. G. 1974. Soluble neutral and acid maltases in the suckling-rat intestine. *Biochem. J.* 144:281–92

21. Galand, G., Forstner, G. G. 1974. Isolation of microvillus plasma membranes from suckling rat intestine. The influence of premature induction of digestive enzymes by injection of cortisol acetate. *Biochem. J.* 144:293–302

22. Goldstein, R., Klein, T., Freier, S., Menczel, J. 1971. Alkaline phosphatase and disaccharidase activities in the rat intestine from birth to weaning. 1. Effect of diet on enzyme development. *Am. J. Clin. Nutr.* 24:1224–31

23. Hauri, H.-P., Quaroni, A., Isselbacher, K. J. 1980. Monoclonal antibodies to sucrase/isomaltase: Probes for the study

of postnatal development and biogenesis of the intestinal microvillus membrane. *Proc. Natl. Acad. Sci. USA* 77:6629–33

24. Henning, S. J. 1978. Permissive role of thyroxine in the ontogeny of jejunal sucrase. *Endocrinology* 102:9–15

25. Henning, S. J. 1978. Plasma concentrations of total and free corticosterone during development in the rat. *Am. J. Physiol.* 235:E451–56

26. Henning, S. J. 1981. Postnatal development: coordination of feeding, digestion, and metabolism. *Am. J. Physiol.* 241: G199–214

27. Henning, S. J., Guerin, D. M. 1981. Role of diet in the determination of jejunal sucrase activity in the weanling rat. *Pediatr. Res.* 15:1068–72

28. Henning, S. J., Helman, T. A., Kretchmer, N. 1975. Studies on normal and precocious appearance of jejunal sucrase in suckling rats. *Biol. Neonate* 26:249–62

29. Henning, S. J., Leeper, L. L. 1982. Coordinate loss of glucocorticoid responsiveness by intestinal enzymes during postnatal development. *Am. J. Physiol.* 242:G89–94

30. Henning, S. J., Sims, J. M. 1979. Delineation of the glucocorticoid-sensitive period of intestinal development in the rat. *Endocrinology* 104:1158–63

31. Herbst, J. J., Fortin-Magana, R., Sunshine, P. 1970. Relationship of pyrimidine biosynthetic enzymes to cellular proliferation in rat intestine during development. *Gastroenterology* 59:240–46

32. Herbst, J. J., Koldovsky, O. 1972. Cell migration and cortisone induction of sucrase activity in jejunum and ileum. *Biochem. J.* 126:471–76

33. Herbst, J. J., Sunshine, P. 1969. Postnatal development of the small intestine of the rat. *Pediat. Res.* 3:27–33

34. Imondi, A. R., Balis, M. E., Lipkin, M. 1969. Changes in enzyme levels accompanying differentiation of intestinal epithelial cells. *Exp. Cell Res.* 58:323–30

35. Jenness, R., Regehr, E. A., Sloan, R. E. 1964. Comparative biochemical study of milks. II. Dialysable carbohydrates. *Comp. Biochem. Physiol.* 13:339–52

36. Jumawan, J., Koldovsky, O. 1978. Comparison of the effect of various doses of thyroxine on jejunal disaccharidases in intact and adrenalectomized rats during the first three weeks of life. *Enzyme* 23:206–9

37. Kammeraad, A. 1942. The development of the gastrointestinal tract of the rat. I. Histogenesis of the epithelium of the stomach, small intestine, and pancreas. *J. Morphol.* 20:323–49

38. Kedinger, M., Simon, P. M., Grenier, J. F., Haffen, K. 1981. Role of epithelial-mesenchymal interactions in the ontogenesis of intestinal brush-border enzymes. *Dev. Biol.* 86:339–47

39. Kedinger, M., Simon, P. M., Raul, F., Grenier, J. F., Haffen, K. 1980. The effect of dexamethasone on the development of rat intestinal brush-border enzymes in organ culture. *Develop. Biol.* 74:9–21

40. Kendall, K., Jumawan, J., Koldovsky, O., Krulich, L. 1977. Effect of the host hormonal status on development of sucrase and acid β-galactosidase in isografts of rat small intestine. *J. Endocr.* 74:145–46

41. Koldovsky, O., Herbst, J. J. 1971. N-acetyl-β-glucosaminidase in small intestine and its changes during postnatal development of the rat. *Biol. Neonate* 17: 1–9

42. Koldovsky, O., Jirsova, V., Heringova, A. 1965. Effect of aldosterone and corticosterone on β-galactosidase and invertase activity in the small intestine of rats. *Nature* 206:300–1

43. Koldovsky, O., Jumawan, J., Palmieri, M. 1974. Thyroxine-evoked precocious decrease of acid hydrolases in the ileum of suckling rats. *Proc. Soc. Exp. Biol. Med.* 146:661–64

44. Koldovsky, O., Jumawan, J., Palmieri, M. 1975. Effect of thyroidectomy on the activity of α-glucosidases and acid hydrolases in the small intestine of rats during weaning. *J. Endocr.* 66:31–36

45. Koldovsky, O., Palmieri, M. 1971. Cortisone-evoked decrease in acid β-galactosidase, β-glucuronidase, N-acetyl-β-glucosamidase and arylsulphatase in the ileum of suckling rats. *Biochem. J.* 125:697–701

46. Koldovsky, O., Sunshine, P., Kretchmer, N. 1966. Cellular migration of intestinal epithelia in suckling and weaned rats. *Nature* 212:1389–90

47. Kretchmer, N. 1971. Lactose and lactase—a historical perspective. *Gastroenterology* 61:805–13

48. Lebenthal, E., Sunshine, P., Kretchmer, N. 1972. Effect of carbohydrate and corticosteroids on activity of α-glucosidases in intestine of infant rat. *J. Clin. Invest.* 51:1244–50

49. Lebenthal, E., Sunshine, P., Kretchmer, N. 1973. Effect of prolonged nursing on the activity of intestinal lactase in rats. *Gastroenterology* 64:1136–41

50. Lee, P. C., Lebenthal, E. 1983. Early weaning and precocious development of

small intestine in rats: genetic, dietary, or hormonal control. *Pediatr. Res.* 17:645–50

51. Leeper, L. L., Henning, S. J. 1983. Hormonal control of postnatal development of ileal neuraminidase and acid β-galactosidase. *Biol. Neonate* 44:28–35

52. Luk, G. D., Marton, L. J., Baylin, S. B. 1980. Ornithine decarboxylase is important in intestinal mucosal maturation and recovery from injury in rats. *Science* 210:195–98

53. Mahmood, A., Torres-Pinedo, R. 1983. Postnatal changes in lectin binding to microvillus membranes from rat intestine. *Biochem. Biophys. Res. Comm.* 113:400–6

54. Malinowska, K. W., Chan, W. S., Nathanielsz, P. W., Hardy, R. N. 1974. Plasma adrenocorticosteroid changes during thyroxine-induced accelerated maturation of the neonatal rat intestine. *Experientia* 30:61

55. Malo, C., Menard, D. 1982. Influence of epidermal growth factor on the development of suckling mouse intestinal mucosa. *Gastroenterology* 83:28–35

56. Malo, C., Menard, D. 1983. Synergistic effects of insulin and thyroxine on the differentiation and proliferation of epithelial cells of suckling mouse small intestine. *Biol. Neonate* 44:177–84

57. Martin, G. R., Henning, S. J. 1982. Relative importance of corticosterone and thyroxine in the postnatal development of sucrase and maltase in rat small intestine. *Endocrinology* 111:912–18

58. Martin, G. R., Henning, S. J. 1984. Enzymic development of the small intestine: are glucocorticoids necessary? *Am. J. Physiol.* 246:G695–99

59. Massaro, E. R., Simpson, R. U., DeLuca, H. F. 1983. Glucocorticoids and appearance of 1,25-dihydroxyvitamin D₃ receptor in rat intestine. *Am. J. Physiol.* 244:E230–35

60. Massaro, E. R., Simpson, R. U., DeLuca, H. F. 1982. Stimulation of specific 1,25-dihydroxyvitamin D₃ binding protein in cultured postnatal rat intestine by hydrocortisone. *J. Biol. Chem.* 257:13736–39

61. Mathan, M., Moxey, P. C., Trier, J. S. 1976. Morphogenesis of fetal rat duodenal villi. *Am. J. Anat.* 146:73–92

62. Menard, D., Malo, C. 1981. Establishment of an *in vitro* model for studying hormonal influences on developing intestinal mucosa. *J. Cell Biol.* 91:35

63. Menard, D., Malo, C., Calvert, R. 1981. Insulin accelerates the development of intestinal brush-border hydrolytic activities of suckling mice. *Dev. Biol.* 85:150–55

64. Montgomery, R. K., Sybicki, M. A., Grand, R. J. 1981. Autonomous biochemical and morphological differentiation in fetal rat intestine transplanted at 17 and 20 days of gestation. *Develop. Biol.* 87:76–84

65. Moog, F. 1953. The functional differentiation of the small intestine. III. Influence of the pituitary-adrenal system on the differentiation of phosphatases in the duodenum of the suckling mouse. *J. Exptl. Zool.* 124:329–46

66. Moog, F. 1971. Corticoids and the enzymic maturation of the intestinal surface: alkaline phosphatase, leucyl naphthylamidase, and sucrase. In *Hormones in Development*, ed. M. Hamburgh, E. J. W. Barrington, pp. 143–60. New York: Meridith

67. Moog, F., Denes, A. E., Powell, P. M. 1973. Disaccharidases in the small intestine of the mouse: normal development and influence of cortisone, actinomycin D, and cycloheximide. *Develop. Biol.* 35:143–59

68. Neu, J., Hoffmann, R. G., Crim, W. N. 1983. Prostaglandin-mediated effects on growth and markers of biochemical development in the rat. *Pediatr. Res.* 17:537–40

69. Nordstrom, C., Dahlqvist, A., Josefsson, L. 1968. Quantitative determination of enzymes in different parts of the villi and crypts of rat small intestine. Comparison of alkaline phosphatase, disaccharidases, and dipeptidases. *J. Histochem. Cytochem.* 15:713–21

70. Pang, K. Y., Bresson, J. L., Walker, W. A. 1983. Development of the gastrointestinal mucosal barrier. V. Comparative effect of calcium binding on microvillus membrane structure in newborn and adult rats. *Pediatr. Res.* 17:856–61

71. Paul, T., Flatz, G. 1983. Temporary depression of lactase activity by thyroxine in suckling rats. *Enzyme* 30:54–58

72. Poland, R. E., Weichsel, M. E. Jr., Rubin, R. T. 1979. Postnatal maturation patterns of serum corticosterone and growth hormone in rats: effect of chronic thyroxine administration. *Horm. Metab. Res.* 11:222–27

73. Raul, F., Kedinger, M., Simon, P. M., Grenier, J. F., Haffen, K. 1981. Comparative in vivo and in vitro effect of mono- and disaccharides on intestinal brush-border enzyme activities in suckling rats. *Biol. Neonate* 39:200–7

74. Raul, F., Simon, P. M., Kedinger, M., Grenier, J. F., Haffen, K. 1978. Sucrase

and lactase synthesis in suckling rat intestine in response to substrate administration. *Biol. Neonate* 33:100–5

75. Reddy, B. S., Wostmann, B. S. 1966. Intestinal disaccharidase activities in the growing germfree and conventional rat. *Arch. Biochem. Biophys.* 113:609–16

76. Redman, R. S., Sreebny, L. M. 1976. Changes in patterns of feeding activity, parotid secretory enzymes, and plasma corticosterone in developing rats. *J. Nutr.* 106:1295–306

77. Robberecht, P., Deschodt-Lanckman, M., Camus, J., Bruylands, J., Christophe, J. 1971. Rat pancreatic hydrolases from birth to weaning. *Am. J. Physiol.* 221:376–81

78. Rubino, A., Zimbalatti, F., Auricchio, S. 1964. Intestinal disaccharidase activities in adult and suckling rats. *Biochim. Biophys. Acta* 92:305–11

79. Samel, M. 1968. Thyroid function during postnatal development in the rat. *Gen. Comp. Endocrinol.* 10:229–34

80. Seetharam, B., Yeh, K-Y., Alpers, D. H. 1980. Turnover of intestinal brush-border proteins during postnatal development in the rat. *Am. J. Physiol.* 239: G524–31

81. Seetharam, B., Yeh, K-Y., Moog, F., Alpers, D. H. 1977. Development of intestinal brush-border membrane proteins in the rat. *Biochim. Biophys. Acta* 470: 424–36

82. Shub, M. D., Pang, K-Y., Swann, D. A., Walker, W. A. 1983. Age-related changes in chemical composition and physical properties of mucus glycoproteins from rat small intestine. *Biochem. J.* 215:405–11

83. Simon, P. M., Kedinger, M., Raul, F., Grenier, J. F., Haffen, K. 1979. Developmental pattern of rat intestinal brush-border enzymic proteins along the villus-crypt axis. *Biochem. J.* 178:407–13

84. Simon, P. M., Kedinger, M., Raul, F., Grenier, J. F., Haffen, K. 1982. Organ

culture of suckling rat intestine: Comparative study of various hormones on brush-border enzymes. *In Vitro* 18:339–46

85. Simon-Assmann, P. M., Kedinger, M., Grenier, J. F., Haffen, K. 1982. Control of brush-border enzymes by dexamethasone in the fetal rat intestine cultured *in vitro*. *J. Pediatr. Gastro. Nutr.* 1:257–65

86. Tsuboi, K. K., Kwong, L. K., Ford, W. D. A., Colby, T., Sunshine, P. 1981. Delayed ontogenic development in the bypassed ileum of the infant rat. *Gastroenterology* 80:1550–56

87. Tsuboi, K. K., Kwong, L. K., Neu, J., Sunshine, P. 1981. A proposed mechanism of normal intestinal lactase decline in the postweaned mammal. *Biochem. Biophys. Res. Comm.* 101:645–52

88. Williams, R. M., Beck, F. 1969. A histochemical study of gut maturation. *J. Anat.* 105:487–501

89. Wysocki, S. J., Segal, W. 1972. Influence of thyroid hormones on enzyme activities of myelinating rat central-nervous tissue. *Eur. J. Biochem.* 28:183–89

90. Yeh, K-Y., Moog, F. 1974. Intestinal lactase activity in the suckling rat: Influence of hypophysectomy and thyroidectomy. *Science* 182:77–79

91. Yeh, K-Y., Moog, F. 1977. Influence of the thyroid and adrenal glands on the growth of the intestine of the suckling rat, and on the development of intestinal alkaline phosphatase and disaccharidase activities. *J. Exp. Zool.* 200:337–48

92. Yeh, K-Y., Moog, F. 1978. Hormonal influences on the growth and enzymic differentiation of the small intestine of the hypophysectomized rat. *Growth* 42:495–504

93. Yeh, K-Y. 1983. Small intestine of artificially reared rat pups: weight gain and changes in alkaline phosphatase, lactase, and sucrase activities during development. *J. Nutr.* 113:1489–95

Ann. Rev. Physiol. 1985. 47:247–60

EXPRESSION OF DIGESTIVE AND ABSORPTIVE FUNCTION IN DIFFERENTIATING ENTEROCYTES

M. W. Smith

Department of Cell Biology, AFRC Institute of Animal Physiology, Babraham, Cambridge CB2 4AT, United Kingdom

INTRODUCTION

The intestinal epithelium is a labile tissue capable of changing its properties rapidly in response to alterations in its immediate environment. These changes have been classified recently according to whether they take place in a continuous or discontinuous manner. Discontinuous events occur at birth and at weaning; continuous events occur throughout the life of the animal (34). I would like to begin this review by suggesting that this type of division is to some extent artificial. The main problem that is always faced by an intestine is how to make nonfunctional cells differentiate within a strictly limited and often variable period of time. The mesenchyme plays an essential role in enabling the enterocyte to achieve this end. This basic drive to differentiate is further influenced by hormones, and much has already been written about this aspect of development. This review concentrates instead upon more recent work that shows the prime importance of mesenchyme in laying down basic rules for enterocyte development. Comparisons are also made between different aspects of normal enterocyte development measured at the cellular level.

DIFFERENT ASPECTS OF ENTEROCYTE DEVELOPMENT

Stem cells located towards the base of crypts give rise to Paneth, goblet, enteroendocrine, and columnar epithelial cells by a process of primary dif-

247

0066-4278/85/0315-0247$02.00

ferentiation, although it is still debatable as to whether all types of cells derive from a common precursor (40). Differences in the relative abundance of these separate cell types occur normally along the intestinal tract (4). At least part of this local specialization is established during early postnatal development (49). The proportion of goblet to columnar epithelial cells also changes following adoptive transfer immunization (32) and when stem cells differentiate in close proximity to lymphoid tissue (8). The control of such specialization remains completely unknown.

Cells programmed to become columnar enterocytes change both their function and structure during migration to the tips of villi. Structural maturation of the brush-border membrane bears only limited correspondence to maturation of its digestive capacity, however, and the capacity of the membrane to transport nutrients only begins when structural differentiation has finished (18–20).

Enterocytes also synthesize increasing amounts of Ia antigen (29) and apoproteins (2) while migrating towards the tips of villi. The amount of Ia antigen produced increases markedly in graft-vs-host disease (27), while that for apoproteins is rapidly stimulated by the presence of lipid (45). Corresponding switch-off mechanisms must exist for enzymes concerned with cell replication in the crypt (23), but further consideration of this type of change is outside the scope of this review.

Mesenchyme Induction of Enterocyte Development

Inductive interactions leading to the differentiation of epithelial cells overlying mesenchymal tissue are already known to be particularly important in the general development of epithelia (1). Indirect evidence that similar interactions control the proliferation and subsequent differentiation of enterocytes has also become apparent recently. Some of this evidence comes from work with fetal tissue, villus formation due to invagination of the mesenchyme being associated with structural differentiation of villus enterocytes and restriction of mitosis to the base of villi (54). Epithelial cytoplasmic processes contact mesenchymal cells during postnatal development (28), and fibroblasts in the adult form a continuous sheath around each crypt, mitosis, and migration of these cells corresponding to that seen in the overlying epithelium (25, 26). Epithelioid cells from rat intestine cultured in the absence of mesenchyme fail to differentiate (41), and epithelial cells migrating over lymphoid tissue fail to synthesize Ia antigen (29). The ability of these enterocytes to transport amino acids is also severely restricted (52). All these results suggest that mesenchymal tissue is needed to initiate enterocyte differentiation.

More direct evidence that mesenchymal tissue controls the morphological differentiation of enterocytes comes from work with cultured quail epithelioid cells prepared by mucosal trypsinization. Subsequent combination of these cells with chick embryonic intestinal mesenchyme, followed by in vivo culture in the coelomic cavity of chick embryos, leads to the formation of previllus ridges covering well-vascularized intestinal segments. Epithelial cells covering these ridges are made up entirely of quail cells, identified by their characteristic nucleolar condensations (13). It has also been shown that rat duodenal fibro-blasts can induce disaccharidase expression by fetal chick endoderm; none of these effects can be produced by fibroblasts obtained from different sources (14).

All of the above results have been obtained by placing isolated cells (epithe-lioid or fibroblastic) against corresponding fetal tissue. Recently it has been possible to see similar organotypic differentiation taking place from a complete mixture of these two cell types. Trypsinized cells from fetal rat intestine, cultured initially in vitro in Gelfoam, form typical villi following long-term implantation into syngeneic hosts. This differentiated tissue also synthesizes brush-border membrane hydrolases (33). Xenoplastic recombination of com-ponents from fetal chick and rat intestines shows this pattern of enzyme development to be determined by endodermal rather than mesenchymal tissue (16). This whole subject is now itself in an exciting state of development.

Structural Differentiation of Enterocytes

Part of the process of structural differentiation of enterocytes involves the physical elongation of individual microvilli in the brush-border membrane. This process changes during neonatal development (31, 37) and in response to disease (53).

Recently it was decided to make a quantitative assessment of microvillus growth using intestines taken from a number of species maintained under a variety of conditions. The results obtained, summarized in Figure 1, show initial microvillus elongation to proceed slowly. There is then a period of rapid elongation followed by a final period when growth is negligible. Curves fitting these data have been constructed according to the equation $y = a + c/[1 + \exp(-b(x-m))]$, where a is the lower asymptote, $a + c$ is the upper asymptote, m is the point of inflexion, and b is an exponential coefficient describing the change in microvillus length y in going from a to $a + c$. None of these parameters are related to the physical size of the villus or to the time taken for enterocytes to migrate to villus tips. Significant correlations are, however, found between a and m and the size of the crypt.

Transposing these results to a time base reveals a further highly significant correlation between crypt depth and $bc/4$, the maximum rate at which microvil-lus formation takes place during enterocyte maturation. Both the potential of enterocytes to produce newly formed microvilli (a) and the subsequent rate at which microvilli grow ($bc/4$) are directly related to the physical size of the crypt

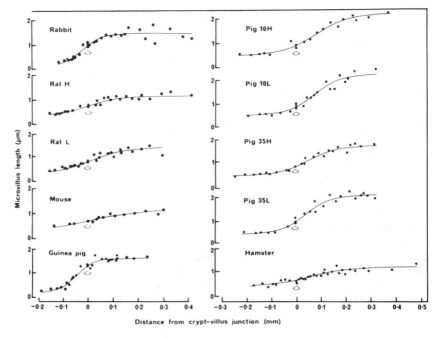

Figure 1   Microvillus elongation in migrating enterocytes. *Arrows* show the positions of the crypt-villus junction. H-Pigs had been adapted to twice the food intake of L-pigs. H- and L-rats had been fed isoenergetic diets containing 20% or 5% protein respectively. *35* and *10:* environmental temperatures at which pigs were kept, in °C [from 50].

from which they originate. These correlations do not depend on the rate of cell proliferation taking place within the crypt. This is shown by working with pigs adapted to a cold environment, a procedure that decreases cell turnover without affecting the size of the crypt (7).

Digestive Function of Enterocytes

Knowledge of how enterocytes develop the capacity to hydrolyze peptides and disaccharides derives originally from the introduction of a serial sectioning technique, allowing different areas of villus and crypt to be collected separately for subsequent analysis (36). This method has been widely used since to determine the developmental pattern of disaccharidase and peptidase activities in the adult intestine and during early development. The results obtained, showing hydrolase activities to increase as enterocytes migrate along the crypt-villus axis, have since been confirmed by microanalysis of enterocyte fractions prepared sequentially using the "cell washing" technique of Weiser (57).

The main disadvantage associated with the serial section technique lies in not knowing accurately the point at which crypts become villi. The extent of this problem was illustrated recently by calculating the percentage distribution of villi, crypts, and connective tissue in serial sections of human jejunum (46). Using this method one can still detect gradients of enzyme activity extending along the crypt-villus axis, but these gradients are far too crude to warrant further critical analysis. The sequential collection of cells is a better technique in that only epithelial cells are collected and estimates of enzyme activity can be made on separated brush-border membranes. Anyone who has carried out this technique, however, knows the difficulty of obtaining reproducible fractions for assay, presumably because mixing takes place between cells of different ages as some villi shed enterocytes ahead of others. One way to overcome these disadvantages is to adopt quantitative cytochemistry as a preferred means of analysis.

The basic principles of cytochemistry are already well established. The usefulness of the technique depends on the maintenance of cellular integrity, the specificity of enzyme hydrolysis, and the speed at which reaction products are deposited at the site of hydrolysis. Modern improvements in all these aspects of cytochemistry have been reviewed recently by Gossrau (10). The most recent advance in this subject has been to establish cytochemistry as a quantitative form of biochemistry. This has been achieved partly through the use of tissue homogenates to establish optimal conditions necessary for the specific hydrolysis of substrates. This information has then been applied to tissue sections, and kinetic constants for enzyme activities compared to check the validity of the procedures adopted (11, 12). Initial rates of hydrolysis measured at saturating concentrations of substrate are now used routinely for these kinds of estimate. Aminopeptidase A and N and dipeptidylpeptidase IV activities can all now be measured quantitatively within the brush-border membrane of the enterocyte (12, 56). There also exists a specific method for the estimation of lactase (24), but measurement of α-glucosidase activities is still subject to error. Part of the reason for this stems from the overlapping specificity of sucrase, isomaltase, and glucoamylase for both natural and artificial substrates. There are at least two ways of dealing with this complexity. The first is to regard all three enzymes as if they were one for the purposes of calculating kinetic constants (12). The second is to increase the specificity of the method by including sucrose in medium containing artificial substrate (18). A major portion of the enzyme reaction product formed under these conditions will be due to the action of isomaltase.

Recently it was decided to measure the profiles for isomaltase and aminopeptidase N development along the crypt-villus axis of rat jejunum to see what effect change of diet had upon these parameters. The results obtained from these experiments are summarized in Figure 2. The rates at which isomaltase and aminopeptidase N activities appear within the brush-border

membrane change during enterocyte migration in a way similar to that seen for
microvillus elongation. Maximal rates of expression take place shortly after
enterocytes leave the crypt. Net increases in enzyme activities then decline to
zero as enterocytes continue to migrate towards the villus tip. This again is
similar to what happens to microvillus elongation. Feeding 20% instead of 5%
protein leads to subsequent increase in crypt depth, villus height, and the speed
of enterocyte migration. Adaptive responses to diet include alterations in the
timing, magnitude, and profile of the growth curves used to describe enterocyte
differentiation. The net effect of these changes is to complete differentiation by
the time enterocytes reach the lower regions of the villus. It has been generally
assumed that increases in mitotic rate lead to the appearance of immature

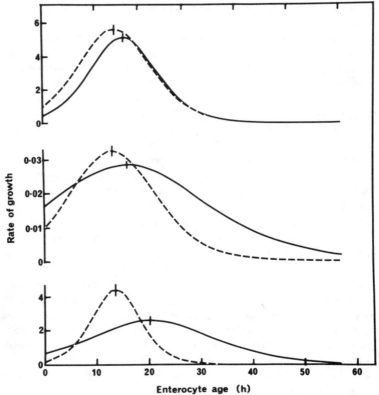

Figure 2 Differential curves for aminopeptidase N *(upper panel)*, microvillus membrane *(middle panel)*, and isomaltase development *(lower panel)* in jejunal enterocytes. Rats were fed isoenergetic diets containing 20% or 5% protein *(broken* and *continuous lines* respectively). *Vertical lines:* calculated times for maximal rates of expression of development function *(bc/4)*. Rates of change are given in absorbance units h^{-1} for isomaltase and aminopeptidase N activities and as μ h^{-1} for increases in microvillus length (from 18).

enterocytes upon the villus. Present results show that this is only likely to occur when the normal capacity of an enterocyte to adapt becomes inadequate.

Controlled changes in diet exert more or less specific effects on digestive enzyme appearance in the brush-border membrane. Feeding a diet rich in sucrose to food-deprived rats, for instance, leads to a significant increase in sucrase and maltase activities and to decreases in the aminopeptidase activity of the whole mucosa (42). Other work shows sucrose to be the best inducer of sucrase in rats maintained on low-starch diets (22). There is some disagreement as to whether sucrose exerts this effect on mature as well as immature enterocytes (22, 42). Work with quantitative cytochemistry suggests that both cell types are involved in the final response. Feeding a diet rich in starch (the 5% protein diet shown in Figure 2) reduces the maximal rate at which isomaltase appears within the brush-border membrane of so-called immature enterocytes. The ability to induce synthesis of isomaltase earlier and to maintain synthesis longer in mature enterocytes is, nevertheless, sufficient to switch the ratio of aminopeptidase N to isomaltase activity from 2.4 to 1.6 calculated for the whole villus (18).

Present work shows a close similarity to exist between the way enterocytes undergo microvillus membrane and enzyme development. Basic programs governing this type of change are probably all laid down before birth (9, 21). Minor modifications to these programs can, however, still cause marked and relatively specific effects on the final capacity of enterocytes to digest nutrients. Steroids undoubtedly play a role in initiating changes in digestive enzyme expression. Recent work with rat intestine in organ culture shows that nutrients also exert direct effects on enzyme development provided steroid is present (17).

Absorptive Function of Enterocytes

The ability of the intestine to absorb sodium actively and to transport both sugars and amino acids from lumen to blood was originally established from experiments carried out in intact animals and on isolated pieces of tissue. Many of these early results have since been confirmed and extended in experiments carried out with brush-border membrane vesicles (35). In spite of this wealth of information there has, until recently, been little or not attempt to relate these findings to the developmental state of the individual enterocyte. The work that has been published comes from applying autoradiography to frozen sections of hamster intestine (20) or from measuring the size of intercellular spaces along the folds of rabbit gall bladder (3). Work with gall bladder, which in many ways behaves as an intestine (43), shows older "crest" cells to transport fluid (and therefore sodium) more readily than "crypt" cells (3). Experiments with autoradiography show it to be only the enterocytes in the top third of the villus that can transport sugars and amino acids (20). In further work it was shown that villus tip enterocytes contained over twice the number of sodium pumps found in the crypt (44). Changes in membrane potential encountered when impaling enterocytes along the crypt-villus axis of intestines taken from neonatal and adult animals probably reflect an increase in sodium-pump activity (6, 55).

Recently it was decided to re-examine the possibility of using autoradiography to determine the cellular distribution of radiolabeled amino acids in neonatal intestine. Glutaraldehyde was used to cross-link tritiated amino acids to cellular protein to facilitate subsequent processing of sectioned material. Using this technique it was possible to demonstrate alanine transport in enterocytes located along the whole length of the newborn pig villus and to show that cells in the crest region of newborn pig proximal colon also transported phenylalanine (15, 47). It has since been possible to accelerate the process of autoradiographic development and convert readings of Ag grain density into direct measurements of intracellular amino acid concentration (19, 38, 52). Experimental results are now also fitted by logistic growth curves to provide a quantitative description of development (18, 48).

The conditions used to determine enterocyte absorptive function, involving short-term exposure of the luminal surface of isolated pieces of tissue to stirred solutions of radioactive medium prior to washing and fixation in glutaraldehyde, might give rise to diffusion artifacts affecting the final pattern of amino acid uptake. This possibility has been eliminated by the finding that neither the rate of stirring nor the time of contact with isotope could affect the pattern of uptake (19, 39). These results, which are of prime importance in establishing the method as a valid means of quantitative analysis, are in agreement with earlier work showing rapid distribution of inulin to take place within the intervillus space of hamster intestine (20). Using autoradiography it has subsequently been possible to demonstrate pronounced changes in developmental profiles occurring naturally during neonatal development (47, 48) and artificially as a result of adopting procedures designed to change enterocyte proliferation and turnover (7, 18, 30).

The developmental profiles for amino acid transport into pig enterocytes depend on the age of the animal. All enterocytes transport alanine at birth, but this pattern changes during the first two weeks of postnatal life. Intestines taken from 15-day-old pigs show a sigmoid pattern of development that is further modified at the time of weaning (48). It is possible, in a superficial way, to relate these changes to the rate of cell turnover in the tissue. Cell replacement is slow at birth, giving individual enterocytes more time to develop. Weaning is associated with an increase in mitotic activity that is maintained in the adult. Evidence that the intestine exerts an independent adaptive control over the expression of absorptive function, however, comes from work with rats carried out before and after proximal resection of the small intestine (30). Some of the results obtained from this work are summarized in Figure 3.

Rat enterocytes are normally about 30 hr old when they first begin to transport alanine and lysine. Similar results have been reported previously

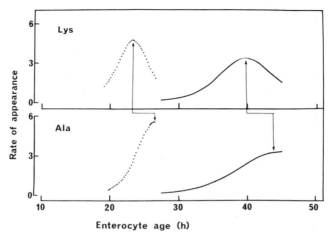

Figure 3   Differential curves showing the rate of change for lysine *(Lys)* and alanine *(Ala)* transport into enterocytes. Tissue came from rats before *(solid lines)* or after *(broken lines)* intestinal resection. *Arrows* show the calculated times for maximal rates of expression of transport function *(bc/4)*. Rates of change of transport functions are given in arbitrary absorbance units h^{-1} *(modified from 30)*.

when measuring valine uptake by rat enterocytes (18). Resection reduces this time period by about 10 hr. Additional effects of resection include a sharpening of the developmental profiles and an increase in the maximal rates at which absorptive functions are expressed. All these changes bear a qualitative similarity to those reported previously when measuring the effect of diet upon microvillus elongation and digestive enzyme appearance in the brush-border membrane (18). In that case, however, change in diet had no effect upon the developmental profile for valine transport. The level of stimulus needed to initiate changes in absorptive function appears, from this, to be greater than that needed to change microvillus structure and digestive enzyme development.

The characteristics of a number of transport systems having overlapping specificities for a variety of amino acids have been determined recently using a new form of interactive kinetic analysis (see 51 for a summary of five years of work). The simplest description of how amino acids cross the brush-border membrane now involves postulating the presence of two separate carriers for neutral amino acids (one of which only operates in the presence of sodium) and two separate carriers for the transport of basic amino acids (one of which is able to transport small amounts of neutral amino acids). Conditions favoring one or other of these transport systems have been used to perform separate autoradiographic analyses of absorptive function. The results obtained show the low-affinity transport system for basic amino acids to develop more slowly than the rest (19). Results illustrated in Figure 3 show the maximal rate for expression of a high-affinity carrier for basic amino acids (lysine used at 1 mM concentration) to take place 3–4 hr earlier than the high-affinity carrier for neutral amino acids (alanine at 1 mM in the presence of Na). This is true using intestines taken both before and after intestinal resection. There seems, from these results, to be a sequential development of transport functions in older enterocytes analagous to that seen earlier for the appearance of digestive enzymes in the brush-border membranes of younger enterocytes.

INTEGRATIVE ASPECTS OF ENTEROCYTE DEVELOPMENT

The formation of villus-like structures from trypsin-dissociated cells prepared from the fetal rat intestine seems to be a finding of some importance (33). Cell sorting under these conditions can be defined as an initial problem of cell recognition and response. The fact that such sorting then leads to the synthesis of brush-border enzymes shows further communication between different cell types to directly initiate enterocyte differentiation. Fibroblast production of an extracellular matrix could provide the signal to differentiate; so could the secretion of soluble messenger or physical contact between the two cell types. Recombination work of the kind described by Haffen et al (14), but with tissues separated by membranes containing pores of known size, might be one way to distinguish between some of these different possibilities.

A cell triggered to differentiate undergoes a series of events leading first to the appearance of a microvillus membrane containing digestive enzymes and then to the appearance of absorptive function. These two developmental stages can be divided further, different membrane hydrolases and transport functions appearing sequentially during early and late development (18, 19, 30). Events appear to be "planned" because they take place in a definite order, but this may be to overestimate the complexity of the process. The idea that enterocyte development is governed by a program that is tightly controlled is supported by work showing embryonic endoderm to carry the specific characteristics of future biochemical development (16). This does not mean, however, that the subsequent readout of the program cannot be influenced by further conversations with the underlying tissue. Chemically induced inhibition of mitosis, to see if this would allow premature development of transport function in "immature" enterocytes, would be one way to test for such a positional control of development.

A related question is why there should be two apparently distinct stages of development during enterocyte migration along the crypt-villus axis. Present results suggest that digestive enzymes are regarded as structural components of the brush-border membrane. Structural differentiation has to finish before the membrane can be "told" to absorb nutrients. Recently we found both membrane potential and intracellular K^+ concentration to increase during this initial phase of enterocyte development. Microvillus elongation might reduce K^+ conductance, and this could cause intracellular K^+ to rise. Increase in intracellular K^+ could then act as a second signal enabling enterocytes to initiate a further stage of development (5). Selective inhibition of microvillus assembly, possibly by activation of villin, might provide one way to test such a hypothesis.

Various local and systemic factors are able to stimulate cell proliferation in the intestinal crypt. The general response of the enterocyte to this situation is to increase the speed and intensity at which it differentiates (18, 30). This type of effect, which has not been studied previously, allows the intestine to adapt to wide fluctuations in the rates at which cells are produced in the crypt. Homeostatic control over intestinal function has been thought previously to be exerted upon the rate at which cells proliferate, much work being devoted to the discovery of numerous growth factors and attempts to justify a negative feedback control between the functional and proliferative compartments of the intestinal epithelium. Recent research shifts the emphasis for homeostatic control onto the enterocyte itself, while leaving unanswered the question of how important a separate control over cell proliferation might be.

The ability of hormones to influence the capacity of enterocytes to express specific functions during development is well known. This ability can be seen as a way to introduce fine control over cruder forms of homeostasis. It is now possible to use modern techniques to study hormone action at the level of individual enterocytes. Work on this aspect of differentiation is likely to prove of increasing importance in the near future.

CONCLUSION

The level at which a scientist chooses to study a problem will inevitably affect his perception of how systems operate. The reductionist point of view is that the whole can be understood completely by understanding its parts and the nature of their sum. To put this belief into practice, however, requires defining what you consider to be a suitably sized part and how you intend to study their sum. Present work in the intestine suggests that enterocytes can be defined as parts in this context, firstly because their behavior can be studied separately and secondly because it is now possible to detect higher levels of organization occurring as a result of interactions taking place between whole populations of cells. We are particularly fortunate at the present time in finding methods that allow us to study both those levels of organization in a tissue as interesting as the intestine.

Literature Cited

1. Alberts, B., Bray, D., Lewis, J., Raff, M., Roberts, K., Watson, J. D. 1983. Cellular mechanisms of development. In *Molecular Biology of the Cell,* ed. B. Alberts, et al, pp. 813–90. New York: Garland

2. Bisgaier, C. L., Glickman, R. M. 1983. Intestinal synthesis, secretion, and transport of lipoproteins. *Ann. Rev. Physiol.* 45:625–36

3. Blom, H., Helander, H. F. 1977. Quantitative electron microscopical studies on in vitro incubated rabbit gallbladder epithelium. *J. Membr. Biol.* 37:45–61

4. Cheng, H., Leblond, C. P. 1974. Origin, differentiation and renewal of the four main epithelial cell types in the mouse small intestine. I. Columnar cell. *Am. J. Anat.* 141:461–80

5. Cremaschi, D., James, P. S., Meyer, G., Rossetti, G., Smith, M. W. 1984. Developmental changes in intra-enterocyte cation activities in hamster terminal ileum. *J. Physiol.* 354:363–73

6. Cremaschi, D., James, P. S., Meyer, G., Smith, M. W. 1984. Positional dependence of enterocyte membrane potential in hamster and rabbit enterocytes. *Comp. Biochem. Physiol.* 78A:661–66

7. Dauncey, M. J., Ingram, D. L., James, P. S., Smith, M. W. 1983. Modification by diet and environmental temperature of enterocyte function in piglet intestine. *J. Physiol.* 341:441–52

8. Faulk, W. P., McCormick, J. N., Goodman, J. R., Yoffey, J. M., Fudenberg, H. H. 1970. Peyer's patches: morphologic studies. *Cell Immunol.* 1:500–20

9. Ferguson, A., Gerskowitch, V. P., Russell, R. I. 1973. Pre- and postweaning disaccharidase patterns in isografts of fetal mouse intestine. *Gastroenterology* 64:292–97

10. Gossrau, R. 1980. Conventional techniques for membrane-bound enzymes. *Ciba Found. Symp.* 73:67–80

11. Gutschmidt, S., Gossrau, R. 1981. A quantitative histochemical study of dipeptidylpeptidase IV (DPP IV). *Histochemistry* 73:285–304

12. Gutschmidt, S., Kaul, W., Riecken, E.-O. 1979. A quantitative histochemical technique for the characterization of α-glucosidases in the brush border membrane of rat jejunum. *Histochemistry* 63:81–101

13. Haffen, K., Kedinger, M., Simon, P. M., Raul, F. 1981. Organotypic potentialities of rat intestinal epithelioid cell cultures. *Differentiation* 18:97–103

14. Haffen, K., Lacroix, B., Kedinger, M., Simon-Assmann, P. M. 1983. Inductive properties of fibroblastic cell cultures derived from rat intestinal mucosa on epithelial differentiation. *Differentiation* 23:226–33

15. Jarvis, L. G., Morgan, G., Smith, M. W., Wooding, F. B. P. 1977. Cell replacement and changing transport function in the neonatal pig colon. *J. Physiol.* 273:717–29

16. Kedinger, M., Simon, P. M., Grenier, J. F., Haffen, K. 1981. Role of epithelial-mesenchymal interactions in the ontogenesis of intestinal brush-border enzymes. *Devl. Biol.* 86:339–47

17. Kedinger, M., Simon, P. M., Raul, F., Grenier, J. F., Haffen, K. 1982. Effect of various hormones and dietary sugars on the stimulation of intestinal brush-border enzymes in organ culture in *Mechanisms of Intestinal Adaptation,* ed. J. W. L. Robinson, R. H. Dowling, E.-O. Riecken, pp. 285–96. Lancaster: MTP Press

18. King, I. S., Paterson, J. Y. F., Peacock, M. A., Smith, M. W., Syme, G. 1983. Effect of diet upon enterocyte differentiation in the rat jejunum. *J. Physiol.* 344:465–81

19. King, I. S., Sepúlveda, F. V., Smith, M. W. 1981. Cellular distribution of neutral and basic amino acid transport systems in rabbit ileal mucosa. *J. Physiol.* 319:355–68

20. Kinter, W. B., Wilson, T. H. 1965. Autoradiographic study of sugar and amino acid absorption by everted sacs of hamster intestine. *J. Cell. Biol.* 25:19–39

21. Koldovský, O. 1979. Development of sucrase activity: effect of maternal hormonal status and fetal programming of jejuno-ileal differences. *Ciba Found. Symp.* 70:147–68

22. Koldovský, O., Bustamante, S., Yamada, V. 1982. Adaptability of lactase and sucrase activity in jejuno-ileum of adult rats to changes in intake of starch, sucrose, lactose, glucose, fructose and galactose. In *Mechanisms of Intestinal Adaptation,* ed. J. W. L. Robinson, R. H. Dowling, E.-O. Riecken, pp. 153–68. Lancaster: MTP Press

23. Lipkin, M. 1981. Proliferation and differentiation of gastrointestinal cells in normal and disease states. In *Physiology of the Gastrointestinal Tract,* ed. L. R. Johnson, 1:145–68. New York: Raven

24. Lojda, Z., Slabý, J., Kraml, J., Kolinská, J. 1973. Synthetic substrates in the

histochemical demonstration of intestinal disaccharidases. *Histochemie* 34:361–69

25. Marsh, M. N., Trier, J. S. 1974. Morphology and cell proliferation of subepithelial fibroblasts in adult mouse jejunum. I. Structural features. *Gastroenterology* 67:622–35

26. Marsh, M. N., Trier, J. S. 1974. Morphology and cell proliferation of subepithelial fibroblasts in adult mouse jejunum. II. Radioautographic studies. *Gastroenterology* 67:636–45

27. Mason, D. W., Dallman, M., Barclay, A. N. 1981. Graft-versus-host disease induces expression of Ia antigen in rat epidermal cells and gut epithelium. *Nature* 293:150–51

28. Mathan, M., Hermos, J. A., Trier, J. S. 1972. Structural features of the epitheliomesenchymal interface of rat duodenal mucosa during development. *J. Clin. Biol.* 52:577–88

29. Mayrhofer, G., Pugh, C. W., Barclay, A. N. 1983. The distribution, ontogeny and origin in the rat of Ia-positive cells with dendritic morphology and of Ia antigen in epithelia, with special reference to the intestine. *Eur. J. Immunol.* 13:112–22

30. Menge, H., Sepúlveda, F. V., Smith, M. W. 1983. Cellular adaptation of amino acid transport following intestinal resection in the rat. *J. Physiol.* 334:213–23

31. Merrill, T. G., Sprinz, H., Tousimis, A. J. 1967. Changes of intestinal absorptive cells during maturation: an electron microscopic study of prenatal, postnatal and adult guinea pig ileum. *J. Ultrastruct. Res.* 19:304–26

32. Miller, H. R. P., Nawa, Y. 1979. *Nippostrongylus brasiliensis;* intestinal goblet cell response in adoptively immunized rats. *Exp. Parasitol.* 47:81–90

33. Montgomery, R. K., Zinman, H. M., Smith, B. T. 1983. Organotypic differentiation of trypsin-dissociated fetal rat intestine. *Devl. Biol.* 100:181–89

34. Moog, F. 1979. The differentiation and redifferentiation of the intestinal epithelium and its brush-border membrane. *Ciba Found. Symp.* 70:31–44

35. Murer, H., Kinne, R. 1980. The use of isolated membrane vesicles to study epithelial transport processes. *J. Membrane Biol.* 55:81–95

36. Nordström, C., Dahlqvist, A., Josefsson, L. 1968. Quantitative determination of enzymes in different parts of the villi and crypts of rat small intestine. Comparisons of alkaline phosphatase, disaccharidases and dipeptidases. *J. Histochem. Cytochem.* 15:713–21

37. Overton, J. 1965. Fine structure of the free cell surface in developing mouse intestinal mucosa. *J. Exp. Zool.* 159:195–202

38. Paterson, J. Y. F., Sepúlveda, F. V., Smith, M. W. 1982. Distribution of transported amino acid within rabbit ileal mucosa. *J. Physiol.* 331:523–35

39. Paterson, J. Y. F., Smith, M. W. 1982. Testing the hypothesis that substrate availability determines the cellular distribution of amino acid uptake by rabbit ileal mucosa. *J. Physiol.* 327:96–97P

40. Potten, C. S., Hendry, J. H. 1983. Stem cells in murine small intestine. In *Stem Cells: Their Identification and Characterisation,* ed. C. S. Potten, pp. 155–99. Edinburgh: Churchill Livingstone

41. Quaroni, A., Wands, J., Trelstad, R. L., Isselbacher, K. J. 1979. Epithelioid cell cultures from rat small intestine. *J. Cell. Biol.* 80:248–65

42. Raul, F., Simon, P. M., Kedinger, M., Grenier, J. F., Haffen, K. 1980. Effect of sucrose refeeding on disaccharidase and aminopeptidase activities of intestinal villus and crypt cells in adult rats. Evidence for a sucrose-dependent induction of sucrase in the crypt cells. *Biochim. Biophys. Acta* 630:1–9

43. Rose, R. C. 1981. Absorptive functions of the gallbladder. In *Physiology of the Gastrointestinal Tract,* ed. L. R. Johnson, 2:1021–33. New York: Raven

44. Rowling, P. J. E., Sepúlveda, F. V. 1984. The distribution of Na^+K^+-ATPase along the villus-crypt axis in the rabbit small intestine. *Biochim. Biophys. Acta.* 771:35–41

45. Schonfeld, G., Bell, E., Alpers, D. H. 1978. Intestinal apoproteins during fat absorption. *J. Clin. Invest.* 61:1539–50

46. Skovbjerg, H. 1981. Immunoelectrophoretic studies on human small-intestinal brush border proteins. Relation between enzyme activity and immunoreactive enzyme along the villus-crypt axis. *Biochem. J.* 193:887–90

47. Smith, M. W. 1981. Autoradiographic analysis of alanine uptake by newborn pig intestine. *Experientia* 37:868–69

48. Smith, M. W. 1984. Effect of postnatal development and weaning upon the capacity of pig intestinal villi to transport alanine. *J. Agric. Sci.* 102:625–33

49. Smith, M. W., Jarvis, L. G. 1978. Growth and cell replacement in the newborn pig intestine. *Proc. R. Soc. London Ser. B* 203:69–89

50. Smith, M. W., Paterson, J. Y. F., Peacock, M. A. 1984. A comprehensive description of brush border membrane development applying to enterocytes taken from a wide variety of mammalian

species. *Comp. Biochem. Physiol.* 77A: 655–62

51. Smith, M. W., Sepúlveda, F. V., Paterson, J. Y. F. 1983. Cellular aspects of amino acid transport. In *Intestinal Transport. Fundamental and Comparative aspects,* ed. M. Gilles-Baillien, R. Gilles, pp. 46–63. Heidelberg/Berlin: Springer-Verlag

52. Smith, M. W., Syme, G. 1982. Functional differentiation of enterocytes in the follicle-associated epithelium of rat Peyer's patch. *J. Cell. Sci.* 55:147–56

53. Trier, J. S. 1967. Structure of the mucosa of the small intestine as it relates to intestinal function. *Fed. Proc.* 26:1391–404

54. Trier, J. S., Moxey, P. C. 1979. Morphogenesis of the small intestine during fetal development. *Ciba Found. Symp.* 70:3–29

55. Tsuchiya, W., Okada, Y. 1982. Membrane potential changes associated with differentiation of enterocytes in the rat intestinal villi in culture. *Devl. Biol.* 94:284–90

56. Wachsmuth, E. D., Donner, P. 1976. Conclusions about aminopeptidases in tissue sections from studies of amino acid naphthylamide hydrolysis. *Histochemistry* 47:271–83

57. Weiser, M. M. 1973. Intestinal epithelial cell surface membrane glycoprotein synthesis. I. An indicator of cellular differentiation. *J. Biol. Chem,.* 248:2536–41

SPECIAL TOPIC: GAP JUNCTIONS

Introduction, David C. Spray, *Special Topic Editor*

It has been recognized for more than 20 years that electrical current injected into one cell could spread to neighbors (a process termed electrotonic coupling) and that membrane specializations (now termed gap junctions) might be responsible (1, 4, 5). As the association between electrotonic coupling and its structural correlate have been strengthened, research on gap junctions has gathered momentum. Now with a history and the current efforts of many workers, it can be considered a field of its own. The purpose of this special section is to update several of the most rapidly advancing aspects of this field.

The structural characteristics of gap junctions were treated extensively in an earlier *Annual Review of Physiology* paper by Page & Shibata (3). Recent application of image analysis techniques to x-ray diffraction and electron microscopy of isolated gap junction membranes have allowed reconstruction of its structure at high resolution; a diagram of the gap junction that incorporates many of these findings is shown in Figure 1.

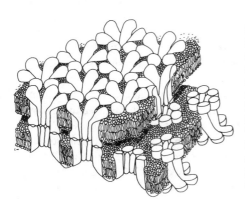

Figure 1 Diagram of a portion of a gap junction from mouse liver. Gap junction channels are comprised of hemichannels or connexons contributed by each cell and drawn here surrounded by the lipid bilayers of the plasma membrane; each hemichannel is a hexamer of identical subunits that are tilted slightly away from the axis of the channel that they surround. This drawing is reproduced from a paper by Dr. Makowski and coworkers (2) and includes essential features seen by Drs. Unwin & Zampighi (6) obtained by analysis of electron microscope images.

In freeze-fracture views, gap junctions are generally discoid arrays of intramembrane particles (corresponding to the structures shown spanning the lipid bilayers in Figure 1) that cleave with the P fracture face in most nonarthropod phyla and with the E face in arthropods; complementary pits are commonly observed on the other fracture surface. Immunological properties of the proteins of which these particles are made, particularly the cytoplasmic aspects (the petals of the structures in Figure 1), are considered in the paper by Dr. Hertzberg. A depression is often observed in the center of each membrane particle that is believed to represent the gap junction channel. Each channel

262

extends from the cytoplasm of one cell to the cytoplasm of a coupled neighbor without access to extracellular space; the walls of each channel are thought to be formed by six identical subunits contributed by each cell that are aligned end to end. The paper by Dr. Revel and his colleagues deals with the biochemical properties of the subunits isolated from lens, liver, and heart, presenting a preliminary reconstruction of the lens polypeptide based on its amino acid sequence, including how and where the subunits may be joined together. Given that these channels are responsible for allowing flow of substances from one cell to another, several questions arise. First, what is their function? In excitable tissues, the answer is apparently straightforward, because direct current flow allows rapid transmission and synchronization of activity (see review by Drs. Spray & Bennett). In inexcitable tissues the role is less clear, but function with respect to embryogenesis has been the subject of considerable speculation and is reviewed here by Dr. Caveney. A second category of questions asks how the channels are regulated and whether this regulation might be physiologically relevant. Over the short term, opening and closing channels is termed gating; factors that gate conductance of the junctional membrane and their physiological relevance are considered by Drs. Spray & Bennett, who also discuss longer term control mechanisms. Regulation of gap junctions over the long term is apparently exerted by changes in the number of intercellular channels; Drs. Sheridan & Atkinson review examples of such changes and consider the extent to which changes in electrotonic coupling and gap junction size can be induced by various physiological stimuli.

Although the field of gap junction research is still relatively young, the virtual ubiquity of these channels in vertebrate and invertebrate tissues and their regulation suggest that they are probably important in both maintaining tissue homeostasis and in allowing the plasticity that accompanies tissue growth and differentiation. We hope that these reviews adequately summarize the history of the gap junction field and that they define the frontiers as the authors see them. Although much has been learned about these channels using diverse methodological approaches, we are most excited about the next step, which will be the understanding of the channel that will ultimately come from integration of its structural, immunological, biochemical, functional, and regulatory properties.

Literature Cited

1. Furshpan, E. J., Potter, D. D. 1959. Transmission at the giant motor synapses of the crayfish. *J. Physiol.* 145:289–325
2. Makowski, L., Caspar, D. L. D., Phillips, W. C., Baker, T. S. 1984. Gap junction structure. VI. Variation and conservation in connexon conformation and packing. *Biophys. J.* 45:208–18
3. Page, E., Shibata, Y. 1981. Permeable junctions between cardiac cells. *Ann. Rev. Physiol.* 43:431–41
4. Revel, J. P., Karnovsky, M. 1967. Hexagonal array of subunits in intercellular junctions of the mouse heart and liver. *J. Cell Biol.* 33:C7–12
5. Robertson, J. D. 1963. The occurence of a subunit pattern in the unit membranes of club endings in Mauthner cell synapse in goldfish brains. *J. Cell Biol.* 19:201–21
6. Unwin, P. N. T., Zampighi, G. 1980. Structure of the gap junction between communicating cells. *Nature* 283:545–49

Ann. Rev. Physiol. 1985. 47:263-79

CHEMISTRY OF GAP JUNCTIONS

J.-P. Revel,[1] *B. J. Nicholson,*[2] *and S. B. Yancey*

Division of Biology and Division of Chemistry,[2] California Institute of Technology, Pasadena, California 91125

INTRODUCTION

Gap junctions [also called nexus (15) or maculae communicantes (102)] represent transcellular channels that permit the exchange of small molecules and ions between neighboring cells (28, 33, 74, 75, 82, 86, 89, 103). They differ from other membrane channels in a number of respects: they provide a pathway between cells rather than across one cell membrane; they are nonspecific; and they allow for passive diffusion. Gap junctions link cells to their neighbors in almost every organ of the body (31) and are essentially ubiquitous in the animal kingdom; they can be recognized in many systems by their very characteristic morphology. In thin sections they are seen as paired parallel plasma membranes of unusually smooth outline, separated from each other by a narrow space of constant width (94, 97), the "gap." In freeze-cleaved (39, 55)[or negatively stained (35)] specimens, patches of closely packed membrane particles (the connexons) (41) in one membrane are in register with similar structures in the membrane of the apposed cell (10). Each connexon presumably consists of protein subunits arranged so as to form a channel (9, 101, 112). From a physiological standpoint they allow for electrical coupling or exchange of molecules up to 800–1200 daltons (28–30, 86, 103). Permeability of the junction can usually be modulated by changes in pH (105, 111), pCO_2 (110), pCa (83, 98, 99), or membrane potential (46, 104). It is the purpose of this paper to review what is known about the chemistry of these proteins and to analyze our understanding of the relationship between their structure and the overall organization and physiology of gap junctions [recent reviews are found

[1]To whom correspondence should be sent.

0066-4278/85/0315-0263$02.00

263

in (3, 12, 53, 56, 67, 70, 71, 83, 93)]. We will begin with a consideration of isolation procedures, because they affect the properties of the final purified material.

ISOLATION PROCEDURES

Early approaches to the isolation of gap junctions consisted of preparing plasma membrane fractions followed by detergent treatment, which left the junctions relatively intact while dispersing much of the rest of the membrane (2, 36). More recent procedures for junction isolation often prepare plasma membranes by simplified techniques (69, 77), some even skipping membrane isolation altogether (25). Sucrose gradients are then used for purification of the fractions. In the case of cells containing large numbers of cytoplasmic filaments (cardiac muscle), it is usually necessary to remove the contractile proteins by using high concentrations of KI before proceeding (44, 61, 73).

It is beyond our scope to review all of the techniques that are available or the specific problems that arise when trying to isolate proteins from different organs. Rather, we will emphasize those features that affect the nature of the proteins found in gap-junction fractions (77). Unless specified otherwise, the techniques discussed apply to hepatic junctions.

Procedures Utilizing Detergents

The first successful approach to the isolation of gap junctions had as a first step the preparation of hepatic "bile fronts," i.e. the bile canaliculus and attached tight junctions and desmosomal components as well as associated plasma membrane. It is the latter that contains most of the gap junction. Application of deoxycholate (DOC) (2, 17, 18) disperses much of this material (2), leaving behind the gap junctions. Another detergent, Sarkosyl (sodium sarcosinate) (2, 24, 36, 49, 50), is commonly used today. Gap junctions are generally less sensitive to detergents than other regions of the plasma membrane (see 72). This is not to say that the junctions themselves are impervious to detergents. Zamphigi & Robertson (118) published images illustrating the sensitivity of junctional plaques to various detergents, and Finbow has recently studied the effect of various concentrations of SDS on the structure of gap junctions (25). There are gradual changes in morphology, as the concentration increases. It must be emphasized that junctions derived from different tissues exhibit large differences in sensitivity to various detergents; heart junctions are destroyed under conditions whereby liver junctions are not visibly affected (72). It also seems that previous steps will influence the sensitivity of the gap junction protein to subsequent detergent treatment.

The preparations obtained by Sarkosyl treatment of membrane fractions can contain a large number of polypeptides, some of which represent contaminants while others represent proteolytic fragments as well as aggregation products of the junction proteins (47, 50, 78). Addition of proteases (14, 35) was found to give morphologically cleaner preparations of junctions but gave junction proteins of low molecular weight (M_r 10,000 or less). Avoiding such treatments and exercising appropriate care (including use of protease inhibitors) raises the apparent molecular weight of junctions proteins seen on gels (16, 50). Equally bothersome are numerous peptides of high M_r that plagued researchers until Henderson et al (47) showed that the junctional protein was poorly soluble in hot SDS and aggregated under the very conditions that most investigators were using to try to dissolve their recalcitrant protein. With the precautions outlined, most investigators now isolate a material that contains a single band of $M_r \sim$ 27,000–29,000 (16, 24, 44, 47, 50, 51, 78, 79, 109).

A new procedure that permits isolation of junctional plaques from a large variety of tissue rather than being specific for a particular system has recently been developed by Finbow et al (25) but yields a protein of significantly lower M_r (16,000 daltons) than those commonly obtained. We will return to this protein in our discussion of the molecular weight of the gap junction protein.

Isolation of Gap Junctions Without the Use of Detergents

In some instances it is possible to isolate gap junctions without detergent treatment. Thus urea treatment can be used in preparing lens fiber junctions (1, 8) (there is some question as to whether or not these are actually the same as gap junctions encountered in other tissues, a problem that will be discussed later). Junctions can be isolated from liver by replacing the treatment with detergent with one employing NaOH (54). Although not yet widely used, the procedure looks promising because of the excellent yields it provides. It must be recognized, however, that alkali treatment could release fatty acids, with formation of soaps and of lysophosphatides. One must therefore be cautious in interpreting the results as being obtained under completely detergent-free conditions.

Use of Proteases

Proteases were originally introduced into the junction preparation protocols in order to eliminate contaminating collagen (18, 35) and other interfering proteins. The morphology of junctions is strikingly resistant to protease treatments, although exogenously added enzymes, like endogenous ones, significantly lower the M_r of the junction protein. In the last few years, the increase in purity and yield of junction protein resulting from improvements in other parameters in the isolation procedure makes the use of proteases during isolation unnecessary. As a result, proteases are now added intentionally only to study the accessibility of cleavage sites of the junction protein in whole membranes (44, 52, 79) or, sometimes, to isolate junction protein from smaller amounts of material (1 g of fresh tissue) than is possible otherwise (117). If it is not essential to recover an intact junctional polypeptide, the use of exogenous proteases at an early stage of the preparation can still be a useful adjunct to the isolation procedure.

JUNCTION CONSTITUENTS

Criteria of Purity

Progress in the purification of junction proteins has been slowed down considerably by the absence of assays other than electron microscopy of isolated junctional fractions (77). The major drawback is that it isn't really the protein itself that is being visualized under these conditions, but the whole junctional plaque. A priori the junctional plaque could contain several different proteins or have adventitious material associated with it. Besides, as we have mentioned already, even excellent preservation of electron microscopic appearance does not guarantee integrity of the junction protein. Another problem is the presence of morphologically minor components that represent highly concentrated protein, such as uricase (M_r=33,000–34,000), derived from microbody cores (50). Attempts have been made to run two-dimensional gels of the proteins from junction fractions in order to have a more sensitive test of the number of polypeptides involved. Unfortunately, it has not yet been possible to focus the intact undegraded (native) protein. Because of these problems, Finbow et al (25) have defined criteria that can be used to identify the junction protein based on its behavior under different experimental conditions. These guidelines have proved useful in the identification of the liver protein. They unfortunately are tissue-specific.

Other approaches to the identification of junction proteins that have proved successful are one-dimensional (52) and especially two-dimensional peptide maps (21, 77, 79), which have been used to differentiate junctional from other proteins in fractions from several cell types. Peptide maps, however, are time-consuming to prepare and tend to emphasize differences rather than similarities (79). In spite of this, two-dimensional maps have been used to unravel the complex SDS gel patterns (44, 79) found in junction fractions under unfavorable conditions. In comparative studies, identical peptide maps are obtained from proteins isolated from the same tissue in different mammalian species (79). However, the proteins isolated from different tissues have given different maps (44, 79). Peptide mapping therefore is useful in identifying previously characterized junctional proteins, but is of limited help in previously unstudied cases.

Now that partial sequences of some junction proteins are known (44, 78, 79), another, more direct way to identify a particular gap-junction protein would be to sequence it. With the development of a microsequencing apparatus of great sensitivity (58) and the availability of larger and larger amounts of protein, this may eventually be a method of choice for the identification of the junctional protein. At present, however, it is prohibitive both in terms of amounts of junction necessary and overall amount of effort expended in order to obtain results. From a practical standpoint it would seem that a combination of electron microscopic examination and SDS gel electrophoresis still is a primary standard when examining unknown junctions. Adequate preparations should be electron microscopically pure and should yield a simple, interpretable pattern by SDS polyacrylamide gel electrophoresis. If possible this should then be followed by peptide mapping or sequencing to confirm the junctional nature of the protein bands.

Nonprotein Components of Gap Junctions

At present, besides protein, only lipid is known to be present in gap junctions (9, 50, 92, 93). Hertzberg & Gilula (50) have stated that the lipid composition of liver gap junctions was similar to that of the plasma membrane fraction from which they were derived, except for the lack of sphingomyelin. Analysis of isolated junctions may not give reliable information as to the composition of the junctions in vivo because of the detergent treatments used (93). Although the presence of cholesterol has been reported, it has not been detected cytochemically by the use of filipin (95, 96). No evidence has been found for the presence of carbohydrates (45, 50, 114), and nothing is known about possible nucleic acid components.

How Many Proteins in the Gap Junction?

The evidence provided by SDS polyacrylamide gels suggests that there is one major protein in hepatic gap junctions (47, 77, 78). Estimates of the amount of protein that could be overlooked on a gel indicate that other proteins could at most represent 15–20% of the total, although there could be junction-associated proteins that are lost during purification of the junctions. There have been suggestions in fact that cytoskeletal proteins could be associated with junctions (68), and factors affecting cytoskeleton integrity have an effect on junctional morphology and assembly (84). However, this does not mean that cytoskeletal proteins are necessarily part of junctions.

PROPERTIES OF THE GAP-JUNCTIONAL PROTEIN

Molecular Weight

As indicated previously, a number of molecular weights have been proposed for the gap-junction protein. For the sake of simplicity we consider the gap-junction protein of liver fractions before comparing it to the proteins isolated from other tissues.

MOLECULAR WEIGHT OF LIVER JUNCTION PROTEIN   At present, most authors accept an M_r of about 27,000 as determined by polyacrylamide gel electrophoresis in the presence of SDS. Different laboratories obtain slightly different values (16, 24, 47, 50, 51, 109), and this probably reflects more the vagaries of the technique as applied in different places than real differences between the proteins. Multiple bands seen on SDS gels of morphologically homogeneous junction preparations can be shown to represent either aggregation products or breakdown products (or a combination of the two) of one polypeptide rather than separate proteins (47, 78).

Other polypeptides have been reported, particularly of M_r of 16,000 (25), 33,000 (19), and 45,000 (48). The evidence suggests that the 33,000-dalton entity is likely a contaminant (18, 24, 50). Because the 45,000-dalton protein has not been extensively characterized, it seems most appropriate at the present to assume that the problem will eventually be resolved either by showing that the higher-M_r entity is the real gap-junction protein, in which case the 27,000-dalton peptide would be a breakdown product, or that it is an impurity or represents an artifact caused by aggregation or other mechanisms.

Extensive efforts have been made to establish that the 16,000-dalton protein described recently by Finbow and his collaborators (25) behaves as one would expect of a junctional polypeptide. In particular, the experimenters have shown that the amount of the protein decreases upon hepatectomy and after administration of phorbol esters, two treatments that are known to reduce the number of gap junctions present on cell surfaces (115, 116). Electron microscope examination of the junction preparations suggests that appropriate fractions have been isolated. The procedure that leads to the recovery of this 16,000-dalton polypeptide differs from the usual procedure in that plasma membrane fractions are not isolated. Instead, a detergent (Triton X-100) is used to disperse whole-tissue homogenates. The low M_r of the junction protein isolated by Finbow could result from the action of peptidases released by the detergent treatment from structures that normally are separated from junctions during membrane isolation. One must also postulate that the protease inhibitors tried cannot halt the action of these proteases. Only further work, including a comparison of the primary sequences of both the 16,000- and 27,000-dalton proteins will permit the reconciliation of the data. Up to now (Finbow, personal communication) there seems to be no correlation between the 16,000-dalton and other known junction proteins. Antibodies prepared against mouse 27,000-dalton protein does not seem to react with the 16,000-dalton species (Finbow, personal communication). Other antibodies will have to be tried, because this result may only indicate that the determinant recognized by the antibody in the 27,000-dalton species has been lost in the 16,000-dalton one.

JUNCTION PROTEINS IN OTHER TISSUES   As just described for the liver, there has been some debate about the size of the protein component of gap junctions isolated from other organs. In the case of the heart, Kensler & Goodenough (61) and Manjunath & Page (73) have described a number of bands, some as high as 65,000 daltons. Colaco & Evans (13) also suggest multiple polypeptides. Gros et al (44) find a major band of 28,000 daltons that may be derived from an entity of about 30,000 daltons. Isolation of lens-fiber junctions yields a polypeptide (MIP26) of 26,000 daltons (1, 5, 8, 42, 62, 79, 107). The same polypeptide can be isolated directly from lens membrane fractions (8, 113). Gorin, Yancey, et al (43) have recently cloned a sequenced the lens-fiber protein. On the basis of the deduced amino acid sequence, MIP26 actually has a molecular weight of 28,000. The discrepancy may reflect the hydrophobicity of the protein. Intramolecular interactions could be strong enough to prevent SDS binding and complete extension of the polypeptide, which would then run faster than expected for a protein of its size.

Gap junctions have also been isolated from invertebrate tissues (25). In the junctions from the hepatopancreas of Homarus (25) and of crayfish (4), a polypeptide of 18,000 daltons has been isolated. In some but not all instances (see 91), there are morphological and physiological differences between junctions of invertebrates, particularly arthropods (22, 65), and those of other organisms. A much more thorough analysis of these observations is needed to study the possible correlation of specific differences in appearance or behavior with particular junction proteins.

Effects of Proteases on the Junction Protein

An isolated gap junction consists of portions of two cell membranes held together by the interaction of the extracellular portions of their connexons. It is believed that it is the presence of these extracellular portions that keep the apposed membranes separated by the narrow 2-nm gap found in sectioned material. After lanthanum staining of whole organs (94) or negative staining of isolated fractions (2, 35, 36, 66, see 112) it is possible to delineate the structures that cross the gap. As one probes the organization of gap junctions by treatment with proteolytic enzymes, the fragments produced will depend not only on the specificity of the enzyme and the sequence and tertiary structure of the junction protein, but also on the configuration of the proteins in the membrane. Obviously those portions of the junctional polypeptide that are exposed at the cytoplasmic face of the isolated junctions will be much more readily attacked than those that are buried in the hydrophobic portions of the membranes or those that are present in the intercellular gap. Trypsin has a hydrated diameter of 5 nm (106), i.e. distinctly larger than the space between membranes ($\sim$ 2 nm), also not penetrated by peroxidase (38), and the width of the channel within the connexon ($\sim$ 1.5 nm). SDS-solubilized protein treated with trypsin or other proteases is reduced to numerous small fragments rather than to the rather sizeable polypeptides observed after protease treatment of whole junctions, thus supporting the notion that large parts of the junctional polypeptide are not accessible unless junctional structure is disrupted.

Treatment with proteolytic enzymes such as trypsin or chymotrypsin does not affect the appearance of the junctions [except for forming large vesicles from flat sheets (35)], but it causes a marked reduction in the M_r of the junctional proteins, indicating that some groups are accessible to the action of the enzyme. In the lens-junction fractions the protein is reduced to 21,000 daltons, in the heart to $\sim$ 12,000 daltons, and in liver to $\sim$ 10,000 daltons. However, estimates of the amount of protein recovered from liver and heart junctions after trypsinization suggests that, as in the lens, two thirds of the protein are protected within the bilayer or by the close apposition of the external faces of the membranes characteristic of the gap junction. Peptide mapping indicates that the most hydrophobic portions of the molecule are preserved and that the hydrophilic components are lost after trypsinization of whole junctions. Because the size of the polypeptides recovered in the case of liver and heart are approximately a third of the size of the original protein, one must presume that there are at least two polypeptides to account for the recovery, of two thirds of the protein (77, 78). Sequencing of the liver protein after trypsinization supports the idea of at least two polypeptides and shows that one of these peptides forms the amino-terminal portion of the intact protein (77). Proteolysis appears restricted to the carboxy terminus and to a segment between the two 10,000-dalton polypeptides that is presumably part of a cytoplasmic loop. The 21,000-dalton peptide generated by treatment of the lens MIP with protease has lost the carboxy terminus of the 26,000-dalton protein and a pentapeptide containing the amino terminus (44, 79). If proteolysis only takes place at the cytoplasmic face as postulated, then the polypeptide must make an even number of passes through the membrane to account for the cleavage pattern.

STRUCTURE OF JUNCTION PROTEINS

Primary Sequence

Obviously it would be most instructive to look at the primary sequences of all the gap-junction proteins. The task of obtaining these sequences has only begun. Even with the availability of microsequencing approaches (58), a protein molecule of 250 or so amino acids (corresponding to a molecular weight of $\sim$ 27,000) cannot be sequenced directly but must first be broken down into a number of peptides, the relative position of which must be determined and which must all be very carefully characterized. As yet amino acid sequence data is available only for small portions of liver (78), heart (44), and lens (79).

The very surprising finding is that the known sequences for liver and lens appear to be essentially unrelated to each other (79). Preliminary results, however, obtained by sequencing heart junction protein show that 40% of the residues at the amino-terminus of the molecule are identical to those found at the same positions in liver (Nicholson, Gros, Kent & Revel, unpublished observations). The differences are uniformly distributed along the sequence. If the 28-residue segment available for comparison is typical of the rest of the molecule, there should be sufficient similarity to explain cross-reaction by antibodies between junctional proteins of different origins yet enough differences to account for the distinct peptide maps obtained, because fragments of different charge and/or size would be generated by proteolysis.

In the liver sequence, residues 23–45 form a segment that could traverse the hydrophobic core of the membrane. This region is largely constituted of hydrophobic amino acid residues, with the major exception of arginine at position 32. A very similar pattern, unfortunately incomplete, seems to emerge from the heart sequence, where all residues identified after position 23 are hydrophobic, except for arg 32. The data on heart and liver indicate sufficient homology to suggest that their junction proteins are part of a family, but it is not clear why these two proteins, found in different tissues of the same organism, should be so distant from each other. This may have to do with germ layer of origin or with differing mechanisms for permeability control. The lens protein appears essentially unrelated to the other two. Here a complete sequence has recently become available by translation of the nucleotide sequence of cDNA corresponding to the lens protein (43). Both the amino acid sequence determined by Edman sequencing (79) and that deduced from the DNA sequence (43) suggest an almost total lack of primary sequence homology with liver, a finding supported by a near-complete lack of immunological cross-reactivity (6, 81, 109, 120). Yet even here there is some suggestion of similarities: In the lens the first putative transcore helix (beginning at residue 17) contains a charged group, an arginine at residue 33, rather close to the state of affairs in liver and heart. Obviously this could be a coincidence, but the rest of the primary sequence of lens MIP so strongly suggests that MIP may be part of a transmembrane channel that this may in fact be significant.

Model of the Lens Fiber Major Intrinsic Protein (MIP)

PRESENT STATUS OF THE LENS FIBER JUNCTIONS   The isolation and characterization of two cDNA clones that cover the coding region of the mRNA for MIP26 has provided the first opportunity to look, in some detail, at a membrane protein that might represent a junction protein by morphological (63) and other criteria (40, 42). MIP26 is a major intrinsic membrane protein from lens fibers (8). It has long been equated with the junction protein in that tissue (42). There have been a number of problems with this idea, however, because of the nearly total lack of sequence homology with liver indicated by Edman degradation (79) and because the lens junction differs from other junctions in significant ways (5, 45, 100, 119). The most damaging data for those who see MIP as a junction protein has been the finding of an antibody against MIP that reacted only with "single" membranes, or structures called "thin junctions" (81). These are believed not to be true junctions but an apposition of membranes occurring as a result of the isolation procedure. The antibody in question does not bind to junctions of standard morphology (81). Other antibodies to MIP (27, 60, 120), however, have been shown to react with both junctional and nonjunctional MIP. The root cause of the discrepancy has not yet been resolved. One possibility is that MIP in single membranes has a different configuration from MIP in a junctional array. As shown below, the configuration of MIP derived from its amino acid sequence could provide an explanation if the Paul & Goodenough antibody (81) were to bind to portions of the polypeptide that are exposed at the external surface of the membrane. Other clues about the putative junctional nature of MIP can be derived from examination of the deduced amino acid sequence.

DEDUCED SEQUENCE OF MIP   As shown by Gorin, Yancey, and collaborators (43), the deduced amino acid sequence comprises 263 amino acids. The calculated molecular weight would be 28,200, somewhat larger, but not unreasonably so, than the 26,000 quoted by many investigators on the basis of SDS gel electrophoresis (1, 5, 42, 79, 107). The deduced sequence reveals both the amino terminal region and a cyanogen bromide–generated peptide (108) that had been previously sequenced by Edman degradation. Fifty-three percent of the amino acids are hydrophobic, and there is a large preponderance of positively charged residues compared to negatively charged ones. One potential N-linked glycosylation site is found. Its location in a putative transcore region of the molecule suggests that this signal might not be used.

PREDICTED OVERALL STRUCTURE OF THE PROTEIN   Using a combined approach based on the ideas of Chou & Fassman (11) and of Garnier (32), to detect the likelihood of turns and a determination of the distribution of hydrophobic regions of the molecule (20, 57, 64) along with a few reasonable assumptions about the length of transcore segments and the preferential occurrence of charged groups in hydrophilic rather than hydrophobic portions of the membrane, it is possible to build a model of the molecule that satisfies a number of independently made observations. In this model (Figure 1)(not necessarily the only one that could be built) there would be six transmembrane segments with both amino and carboxyl termini at the cytoplasmic side of the membrane as expected from the results of experiments on the effect of proteolytic enzymes on intact junctions.

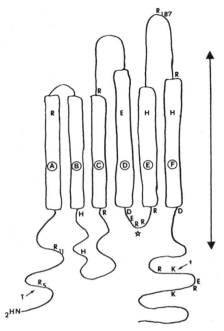

Figure 1. The diagram depicts a conceptualization of the MIP protein deduced from its amino acid sequence as described in the text. The diagram is more or less to scale, assuming a random coil configuration for all portions of the polypeptide except the segments that might be traversing the hydrophobic core of the membrane and are therefore represented by α-helices labeled A–F. A known site of tryptic attack is at arginine (*R*) residue 5 (*T*), and an inferred site is at the arginine or lysine (*K*) 226 or 228 (*t*); it is known that arg11 is not accessible to trypsin, so that the first group available on the cytoplasmic side of the model would be arg226 or lys228(*t*). Arg187 is in the extracellular space. It is presumably not split by trypsin because it is in a protected location, such as the site of interaction between connexons. There is a very curious, highly charged loop between transcore segments *D* and *E* (*star*). Segment *F* is amphiphilic and may be part of the aqueous pore of a putative junctional channel. It contains a histidine residue (*H*) that might be relevant in terms of modulation of permeability. To form a channel, several MIP would be associated with each other. The model suggests a number of experiments that can be used to test the true junctional nature of the protein. Not all charged groups are shown, particularly at the carboxy terminal end of the molecule. The *double-headed arrow* represents the total thickness of the membrane, with its cytoplasmic face at the *bottom* of the illustration. The one letter convention used for amino acids is: *D*: Asp; *E*: Glu; *H*: His; *K*: Lys; *R*: Arg.

The model was chosen because it can explain the results of treatment of lens junctions with trypsin as well as with chymotrypsin and V_8 protease (43, 60). It also suggests the presence of peptide loops extending at the extracellular and cytoplasmic faces of the membrane. The portion of the polypeptide exposed at the extracellular face could be involved in the cell-cell (actually connexon-connexon) interactions needed to form a junction. If they were to represent binding sites for the "Paul & Goodenough antibody," they could explain why this antibody binds only to nonjunctional MIP (81). It is worth noting that the sequences postulated to take part in end-to-end interactions of the connexons are likely to support hydrophobic interactions or hydrogen bonding rather than covalent or electrostatic bonds. This would be quite in line with observations such as those of Goodenough & Gilula (37) and Manjunath et al (72) on the splitting of gap junctions. Whether these observations and those of Hirokawa & Heuser (55) are germane to interactions in the lens is, of course, not established at present. It is also interesting to point out that heterologous junctions form easily (22, 76, 85), a phenomenon that would be readily explained on the basis of the model presented.

There are other interesting features of the putative structure of the lens function suggested by the deduced sequence. Among these is the presence at the cytoplasmic face of the membrane of a cluster of highly charged residues: could a cluster of this type be involved in the charge selectivity detected by Brink & Dewey (7) when testing earthworm septate axon junctions with molecules near the permeability threshold?

Also interesting is the transcore region F, representing residues 190–210. By the use of several methods this portion of the molecule is identified as an amphiphilic helix (20, 26), which could be an important element in providing the hydrophilic wall of a transmembrane channel. A similar structure is believed to be part of the channel in the ACh receptor (26). Histidine residues found in transcore F could then be exposed in the channel. These may represent sites for channel modulation as previously suggested in other gap junctions by Spray and his collaborators (105).

CONCLUSIONS

There are very many problems to be solved before a real understanding of the relationship of structure and function in gap junctions becomes evident. In spite of our limited knowledge, however, or perhaps because of it, we seem at present poised at the edge of a new era, where it will be possible to do direct experiments to test some of the ideas that have tantalized us for so long. Understanding the primary structure of the junction protein will give us a handle in our attempts at deciphering how the channel is formed and what groups participate in its control; it may permit us to understand why there are such drastic differences between the proteins in different tissues and, along with other approaches such as development of antibodies or other reagents specific for different regions of the molecule, will allow experiments to test where and how the protein is made (23, 80, 117), how it is inserted (34, 59, 80, 84, 87, 88) in the membrane, how two cells come together to form junctions (71, 90), and what roles gap junctions play in the economy of the organism.

[For new, further evidence for the possible existence of junctional polypeptides larger than 28Kd, see (121, 122).]

ACKNOWLEDGMENTS

The personal work reported here was largely supported by grants from the National Institutes of Health, Institute of General Medical Sciences, GM 06965, and the A. B. Ruddock Fund. We would also like to express our appreciation to Renee Thorf for her expert and patient typing of the manuscript.

Literature Cited

1. Alcala, J., Lieska, N., Maisel, H. 1975. Protein composition of bovine lens cortical fiber cell membranes. *Exp. Eye Res.* 21:581–95
2. Benedetti, E. L., Emmelot, P. 1968. Hexagonal array of subunits in tight junctions separated from rat liver plasma membranes. *J. Cell Biol.* 38:15–24
3. Bennett, M. V. L., Spray, D. C., Harris, A. L. 1981. Gap junctions and development. *Trends Neurosci.* 4:159–63
4. Berdan, R. C., Gilula, N. B. 1983. Isolation and preliminary biochemical analysis of an invertebrate gap junction. *J. Cell Biol.* 95:94a
5. Bloemendal, H. 1977. The vertebrate eye lens. A useful system for the study of fundamental biological processes on a molecular level. *Science* 197:127–38
6. Bok, D., Dockstader, J., Horwitz, J. 1982. Immunocytochemical localization of the lens main intrinsic polypeptide (MIP26) in communicating junctions. *J. Cell Biol.* 92:213–20
7. Brink, P. R., Dewey, M. M. 1980. Evidence for fixed charge in the nexus. *Nature* 285:101–2
8. Broekhuyse, R. M., Kuhlmann, E. D., Stols, A. L. H. 1976. Lens membranes. II. Isolation and characterization of the main intrinsic polypeptide (MIP) of bovine lens fiber membranes. *Exp. Eye Res.* 23:365–71
9. Caspar, D. L. D., Goodenough, D. A., Makowski, L., Phillips, W. C. 1977. Gap junction structures. I. Correlated electron microscopy and X-ray diffraction. *J. Cell. Biol.* 74:605–28
10. Chalcroft, J. P., Bullivant, S. 1970. An interpretation of liver cell membrane and junction structure based on observation of freeze-fracture replicas of both sides of the fracture. *J. Cell Biol.* 47:49–60
11. Chou, P. Y., Fasman, G. D. 1978. Empirical predictions of protein conformation. *Ann. Rev. Biochem.* 47:251–76
12. Colaco, C. A., Evans, W. H. 1983. Plasma membrane intercellular junctions. In *EM Electron Microscopy of Proteins*, ed.

J. R. Harris, 4:331–63. London: Academic
13. Colaco, C. A., Evans, W. H. 1982. Partial purification of an intercalated disc-containing cardiac plasma membrane fraction. *Biochim. Biophys. Acta* 684: 40–46
14. Culvenor, J. G., Evans, W. H. 1977. Preparation of hepatic gap (communicating) junctions. *Biochem. J.* 168:475–81
15. Dewey, M. M., Barr, L. 1962. Intercellular connection between smooth muscle cells: the nexus. *Science* 137:670–72
16. Duguid, J., Revel, J.-P. 1976. The protein components of the gap junction. *Cold Spring Harbor Symp. Quant. Biol.* 40:45–47
17. Dunia, I., Sen, K., Benedetti, E. L., Zweers, A., Bloemendal, H. 1974. Isolation and protein pattern of eye lens fiber junction. *FEBS Lett.* 45:139
18. Ehrhart, J. C. 1981. Further purification of mouse liver gap junctions with deoxycholate and protein composition. *Cell Biol. Int. Rep.* 5:1055–61
19. Ehrhart, J. C., Chauveau, J. 1977. The protein component of mouse hepatocyte gap junctions. *FEBS Lett.* 78:295–99
20. Eisenberg, D., Weiss, R. M., Terwilliger, T. C. 1982. The helical hydrophobic moment: a measure of the amphiphilicity of a helix. *Nature* 299:371–74
21. Elder, J. H., Pickett, R. A., Hampton, J., Lerner, R. A. 1977. Radioiodination of proteins in single polyacrylamide gel slices. *J. Biol. Chem.* 252:6510–15
22. Epstein, M. L., Gilula, N. B. 1977. A study of communication specificity between cells in culture. *J. Cell Biol.* 75:769–87
23. Fallon, R. F., Goodenough, D. A. 1981. Five hour half-life of mouse liver gap junction protein. *J. Cell Biol.* 90:521–26
24. Finbow, M., Yancey, S. B., Johnson, R., Revel, J.-P. 1980. Independent lines of evidence suggesting a major gap junctional protein with a molecular weight of 26,000. *Proc. Natl. Acad. Sci. USA* 77:970–74
25. Finbow, M. E., Shuttleworth, J., Hamil-

ton, A. E., Pitts, J. D. 1983. Analysis of vertebrate gap junction protein. *EMBO J.* 2:1479–86

26. Finer-Moore, J., Stroud, R. M. 1984. Amphipathic analysis and possible formation of the ion channel in an ACh receptor. *Proc. Natl. Acad. Sci. USA* 81:155–59

27. Fitzgerald, P. G., Bok, D., Horwitz, J. 1984. Immunocytochemical localization of the main intrinsic polypeptide (MIP) in ultrathin frozen sections of rat lens. *J. Cell Biol.* 1491–99

28. Flagg-Newton, J. 1980. The permeability of the cell-to-cell membrane channel and its regulation in mammalian cell junction. *In Vitro* 16:1043–48

29. Flagg-Newton, J., Loewenstein, W. R. 1979. Experimental depression of junctional membrane permeability in mammalian cell culture. A study with tracer molecules in the 300 to 800 dalton range. *J. Membr. Biol.* 50:65–100

30. Flagg-Newton, J., Simpson, I., Loewenstein, W. R. 1979. Permeability of the cell-cell membrane channels in mammalian cell junction. *Science* 205:404–9

31. Friend, D. S., Gilula, N. B. 1972. Variations in tight and gap junctions in mammalian tissues. *J. Cell Biol.* 53:758–76

32. Garnier, J., Osguthorpe, D. J., Robson, B. 1978. Analysis of the accuracy and implications of simple methods for predicting the secondary structure of globular proteins. *J. Mol. Biol.* 120:97–120

33. Gilula, N. B., Reeves, R. O., Steinbach, A. 1972. Metabolic coupling, ionic coupling and cell contacts. *Nature* 235:262–65

34. Goodenough, D. A. 1974. Bulk isolation of hepatocyte gap junctions. *J. Cell Biol.* 61:557–63

35. Goodenough, D. A. 1976. In vitro formation of gap junction vesicles. *J. Cell Biol.* 68:220–31

36. Goodenough, D. A., Stoeckenius, W. 1972. The isolation of mouse hepatocyte gap junctions. Preliminary chemical characterization and X-ray diffraction. *J. Cell Biol.* 54:646–56

37. Goodenough, D. A., Gilula, N. B. 1974. The splitting of hepatocyte gap junctions and zonula occludentes with hypertonic disaccharides. *J. Cell Biol.* 61:571–90

38. Goodenough, D. A., Revel, J.-P. 1971. The permeability of isolated and in situ mouse hepatic gap junctions studied with enzymatic tracers. *J. Cell Biol.* 50:81–91

39. Goodenough, D. A., Revel, J.-P. 1970. A fine structural analysis of intercellular junctions in the mouse liver. *J. Cell Biol.* 45:272–90

40. Goodenough, D. A., Dick, J. S. II, Lyons, J. E. 1980. Lens metabolic cooperation: a study of mouse lens transport and permeability visualized with freeze-substitution autoradiography and electron microscopy. *J. Cell Biol.* 86:576–89

41. Goodenough, D. A. 1975. Methods for the isolation and structural characterization of hepatocyte gap junctions. In *Methods in Membrane Biology, Plasma Membranes,* ed. E. D. Korn, pp. 51–80. New York: Plenum

42. Goodenough, D. A. 1979. Lens gap junctions: A structural hypothesis for nonregulated low-resistance intercellular pathways. *Invest. Ophthalmol.* 18:1104–22

43. Gorin, M., Yancey, S. B., Cline, J., Revel, J.-P., Horwitz, J. 1984. *Cell:* In press

44. Gros, D. B., Nicholson, B. J., Revel, J.-P. 1983. Comparative analysis of the gap junction protein from rat heart and liver: Is there a tissue specificity of gap junctions? *Cell* 35:539–49

45. Gros, D., Bruce, B., Challice, C.E., Schrevel, J. 1982. Ultrastructural localization of ConA and WGA binding sites in adult and embryonic mouse myocardium. Problems of controls in cytochemical methods using peroxidase. *J. Histochem. Cytochem.* 30:193–200

46. Harris, A. L., Spray, D. C., Bennett, M. V. L. 1983. Control of intercellular communication by voltage dependent gap junction conductance. *J. Neurosci.* 3:79–100

47. Henderson, D., Eibl, H., Weber, K. 1979. Structure and biochemistry of mouse hepatic gap junctions. *J. Mol. Biol.* 132:193–218

48. Henderson, D., Weber, K. 1982. Immunological analysis of gap junction proteins from liver, lens and heart muscle. *Biology of the Cell,* 45:229a

49. Hertzberg, E. 1983. Isolation and characterization of liver gap junctions. *Methods Enzymol.* 98:501–10

50. Hertzberg, E. L., Gilula, N. B. 1979. Isolation and characterization of gap junctions from rat liver. *J. Biol. Chem.* 254:2138–47

51. Hertzberg, E. L., Anderson, D. J., Friedlander, M., Gilula, N. B. 1982. Comparative analysis of the major polypeptides from liver gap junctions and lens fiber junctions. *J. Cell Biol.* 92:53–59

52. Hertzberg, E. L. 1980. Biochemical and immunological approaches to the study of gap junctional communication. *In Vitro* 16:1057–67

53. Hertzberg, E. L., Lawrence, T. S., Gilula, N. B. 1981. Gap junctional com-

munication. *Ann. Rev. Physiol.* 43:479–91

54. Hertzberg, E. L. 1984. A detergent independent procedure for the isolation of gap junctions from rat liver. *J. Biol. Chem.* In press

55. Hirokawa, N., Heuser, J. 1982. The inside and outside of gap junction membranes visualized by deep etching. *Cell* 30:395–406

56. Hooper, M. L., Subak-Sharpe, J. H. 1981. Metabolic cooperation between cells. *Int. Rev. Cytol.* 69:45–104

57. Hopp, T. P., Woods, K. R. 1981. Prediction of protein antigenic determinants from amino acid sequences. *Proc. Natl. Acad. Sci. USA* 78:3824–28

58. Hunkapiller, M. W., Hood, L. E. 1980. New protein sequenator with increased sensitivity. *Science* 207:523–25

59. Johnson, R. G., Hammer, J. D., Sheridan, J. J. D., Revel, J.-P. 1974. Gap junction formation between reaggregated Novikoff hepatoma cells. *Proc. Natl. Acad. Sci. USA* 71:4536–40

60. Keeling, P., Johnson, K., Sas, D., Klukas, K., Donahue, P., Johnson, R. 1983. Arrangement of MP26 in lens junctional membranes: Analysis with proteases and antibodies. *J. Membr. Biol.* 74:217–28

61. Kensler, R. W., Goodenough, D. A. 1980. Isolation of mouse myocardial gap junctions. *J. Cell Biol.* 86:755–64

62. Kuszak, J. R., Alcala, J., Maisel, H. 1981. Biochemical and structural features of chick lens gap junction. *Exp. Eye Res.* 33:157–66

63. Kuszak, J. R., Rae, J. L., Pauli, B. U., Weinstein, R. S. 1982. Rotary replication of lens gap junctions. *J. Ultrastruct. Res.* 81:249–56

64. Kyte, J., Doolittle, R. F. 1982. A simple method for displaying the hydropathic character of a protein. *J. Mol. Biol.* 157:105–21

65. Lane, N., Skaer, H., Le, B. 1980. Intercellular junctions in insect tissues. *Adv. Insect Physiol.* 15:35–213

66. Larsen, W. J., Heidger, P. M., Herr, J. C., Goodenough, D. A. 1976. Channels traversing two junctional membranes and intervening "gap." *J. Cell Biol.* 71:333–35

67. Larsen, W. J. 1983. Biological implications of gap junction structure, distribution and composition: a review. *Tissue Cell* 15:645–71

68. Larsen, W. J., Tung, H. N., Murray, S. A., Swenson, C. A. 1979. Evidence for the participation of actin microfilaments and bristle coats in the internalization of gap junction membrane. *J. Cell Biol.* 83:576–87

69. Lesko, L., Donlin, M., Marinetti, G. W., Hare, J. D. 1973. A rapid method for the isolation of rat liver plasma membrane using an aqueous two phase polymer system. *Biochim. Biophys. Acta* 311:173–79

70. Loewenstein, W. R. 1981. Junctional intercellular communication. The cell to cell membrane channel. *Physiol. Rev.* 61:829–913

71. Makowski, L., Caspar, D. L. D., Phillips, W. C., Goodenough, D. A. 1977. Gap junction structures. II. Analysis of the X-ray diffraction data. *J. Cell Biol.* 74:629–45

72. Manjunath, C. K., Goings, G. E., Page, E. 1984. Detergent sensitivity and splitting of isolated liver gap junctions. *J. Membr. Biol.* 78:147–55

73. Manjunath, C. K., Goings, G. E., Page, E. 1982. Isolation and protein composition of gap junctions from rabbit hearts. *Biochem. J.* 205:189–94

74. McNutt, N. S., Weinstein, R. S. 1970. The ultrastructure of the nexus. A correlated thin section and freeze-cleave study. *J. Cell Biol.* 47:666–88

75. Meyer, D., Yancey, B., Revel, J. P., Peskoff, A. 1981. Intercellular communication in normal and regenerating rat liver. *J. Cell Biol.* 91:505–23

76. Michalke, W., Loewenstein, W. R. 1971. Communication between cells of different types. *Nature* 232:121–22

77. Nicholson, B. J., Revel, J.-P. 1983. Gap junctions in liver: Isolation, morphological analysis and quantitation. *Methods Enzymol.* 98:519–37

78. Nicholson, B. J., Hunkapiller, M. W., Grim, L. B., Hood, L. E., Revel, J.-P. 1981. The rat liver gap junction protein: Properties and partial sequence. *Proc. Natl. Acad. Sci. USA* 78:7594–98

79. Nicholson, B. J., Takemoto, L. J., Hunkapiller, M. W., Hood, L. E., Revel, J.-P. 1983. Differences between the liver gap junction protein and lens MIP26 from rat: Implications for tissue specificity of gap junctions. *Cell* 32:967–78

80. Paul, D. L., Goodenough, D. A. In vitro synthesis and membrane insertion of bovine MP26 an integral membrane protein from the lens fiber plasma membrane. *J. Cell Biol.* 96:636–38

81. Paul, D. L., Goodenough, D. A. 1983. Preparation, characterization and localization of antisera against bovine MP26, an integral membrane protein of the lens fiber. *J. Cell Biol.* 96:625–32

82. Payton, B. W., Bennett, M. V. L., Pappas, G. D. 1969. Permeability and structure of junctional membranes at an electronic synapse. *Science* 166:1642–43

83. Peracchia, C. 1980. Structural correlates of gap junction permeation. *Int. Rev. Cytol.* 66:81–146

84. Pinto da Silva, P., Tadvalkar, G. 1983. In vitro rapid assembly of gap junctions is induced by cytoskeletal disruptors. *J. Cell Biol.* 96:1279–87

85. Pitts, J. D., Burk, R. R. 1976. Specificty of junctional communication between animal cells. *Nature* 264:762–64

86. Potter, D. D., Furshpan, E. J., Lennox, E. S. 1966. Connections between cells of the developing squid as revealed by electrophysiological methods. *Proc. Natl. Acad. Sci. USA* 55:328–35

87. Preus, D., Johnson, R., Sheridan, J. 1981. Gap junctions between Novikoff hepatoma cells following dissociation and recovery in the absence of cell contact. *J. Ultrastruct. Res.* 77:248–62

88. Preus, D., Johnson, R., Sheridan, J., Meyer, R. 1981. Analysis of gap junctions and formation plaques between reaggregating Novikoff hepatoma cells. *J. Ultrastruct. Res.* 77:263–76

89. Revel, J.-P., Yee, A. G., Hudspeth, A. J. 1971. Gap junctions between electrotonically-coupled cells in tissue culture and in brown fat. *Proc. Natl. Acad. Sci. USA* 68:2924–27

90. Revel, J.-P., Griepp, E. B., Finbow, M., Johnson, R. 1978. Possible steps in gap junction formation. *Zoon.* 6:139–44

91. Revel, J.-P., 1984. Gap junctions in development. *Am. Zool.* In press

92. Revel, J. P. 1983. Molecular organization of gap junctions. In *Falk Symp. 34, Structural Carbohydrates in the Liver,* ed. H. Popper, W. Reutter, E. Kottgen, F. Gudat, pp. 209–19. Lancaster, U.K: MTP

93. Revel, J.-P., Nicholson, B. J., Yancey, S. B. 1984. Molecular organization of gap junctions. *Fed. Proc.* 43:2672–77

94. Revel, J.-P., Karnovsky, M. J. 1967. Hexagonal array of subunits in intercellular junctions of the mouse heart and liver. *J. Cell Biol.* 33:C7–C12

95. Risinger, M. A., Larsen, W. J. 1983. Interactions of filipin with junctional membranes at different stages of the junction's life history. *Tissue Cell* 15:1–15

96. Robenek, H., Jung, W., Gebhardt, R. 1982. The topography of filipin-cholesterol complexes in the plasma membrane of cultered hepatocytes and their relation to cell junction formation. *J. Ultrastruct. Res.* 79:95–106

97. Robertson, J. D. 1963. The occurrence of a subunit pattern in the unit membranes of club endings in Mauthner cell synapse in goldfish brains. *J. Cell Biol.* 19:201–21

98. Rose, B., Simpson, I., Loewenstein, W. R. 1977. Calcium ion produces graded changes in permeability of membrane channels in cell junction. *Nature* 267:625–27

99. Rose, B., Loewenstein, W. R. 1975. Calcium ion distribution in cytoplasm visualized by Aequorin: diffusion in cytoplasm restricted by energized sequestering. *Science* 190:1204

100. Schuetze, S. M., Goodenough, D. A. 1982. Dye transfer between cells of embryonic chick lens becomes less sensitive to CO_2 treatment with development. *J. Cell Biol.* 92:694–705

101. Sikerwar, S. S., Tewari, J. P., Malhotra, S. K. 1981. Subunit structure of the connexons in hepatocyte gap junctions. *Eur. J. Cell Biol.* 24:211–15

102. Simionescu, M., Simionescu, N., Palade, G. 1975. Segmental variations of cell junctions in the vascular endothelium: the microvasculature. *J. Cell Biol.* 67:863–85

103. Simpson, I., Rose, B., Loewenstein, W. R. 1977. Size limit of molecules permeating the junctional membrane channels. *Science* 195:294–96

104. Spray, D. C., Harris, A. L., Bennett, M. V. L. 1979. Voltage dependence of junctional conductance in early amphibian embryos. *Science* 204:432–34

105. Spray, D. C., Harris, A. L., Bennett, M. V. L. 1981. Gap junctional conductance is a simple and sensitive function of intracellular pH. *Science* 211:712–15

106. Stroud, R. M., Kay, L. M., Dickerson, R. E. 1974. The structure of bovine Trypsin electron density maps of the inhibited enzyme at 5A and 2.7 A resolution. *J. Mol. Biol.* 83:185–208

107. Takemoto, L. J., Hansen, J. S. 1981. Gap junctions from the lens: purification and characterization by chemical cross-linking reagent. *Biochem. Biophys. Res. Commun.* 99:324–31

108. Takemoto, L. J., Hansen, J. S., Nicholson, B. J., Hunkapiller, M., Revel, J.-P., Horwitz, J. 1983. Major intrinsic polypeptide of the lens membrane. Biochemical and immunological characterization of the major cyanogen bromide fragment. *Biochim. Biophys. Acta* 731: 267–74

109. Traub, O., Janssen-Timmen, U., Druge, P. M., Dermietzel, R., Willecke, K. 1982. Immunological properties of gap junction protein from mouse liver. *J. Cell Biochem.* 19:27–44

110. Turin, L., Warner, A. 1977. Carbon dioxide reversibly abolishes ionic communication between cells of early amphibian embryo. *Nature* 270:56–57

111. Turin, L., Warner, A. E. 1980. Intracellular pH in early Xenopus embryos:

CHEMISTRY OF GAP JUNCTIONS 279

its effect on current flow between blastomeres. *J. Physiol.* 300:489–504
112. Unwin, P. N. T., Zampighi, G. 1980.
Structure of the junctions between communicating cells. *Nature* 283:545–49
113. Vermorken, A. J. M., Hilderink, J. M.
H., Dunia, I., Benedetti, E. L.,
Bloemendal, H. 1977. Changes in membrane protein pattern in relation to lens
cell differentation. *FEBS Lett.* 83:301–6
114. Williams, E. H., Kumar, N. M., Gilula,
N. B. 1983. Techniques for studying the
cell free synthesis of the major lens fiber
polypeptide. *Methods Enzymol.* 98:510–
19
115. Yancey, S. B., Edens, J. E., Trosko, J.
E., Change, C.-C., Revel, J.-P. 1982.
Decreased incidence of gap junctions between Chinese hamster V-79 cells upon
exposure to the tumor promoter 12-o-
tetradecanoyl phorbol-12-acetate. *Exp.
Cell Res.* 139:329–40
116. Yancey, S. B., Easter, D., Revel, J.-P.
1979. Cytological changes in gap junctions during liver regeneration. *J. Ultrastruct. Res.* 67:229–42
117. Yancey, S. B., Nicholson, B. J., Revel,
J.-P. 1981. The dynamic state of liver
gap junctions. *J. Supramol. Struct. Cell.
Biochem.* 16:221–32
118. Zampighi, G., Robertson, J. D. 1973.
Fine structure of the synaptic discs separated from the goldfish medulla oblonga-
ta. *J. Cell Biol.* 56:92–105
119. Zampighi, G., Simon, S., Robertson, J.,
McIntosh, T., Costello, M. 1982. On the
structural organization of isolated bovine
lens fiber junctions. *J. Cell Biol.* 93:175–
89
120. Zigler, J. S., Horwitz, J. 1981. Immunochemical studies on the major intrinsic polypeptides from human lens
membrane. *Invest. Ophthalmol. Vis. Sci.*
21:46–51
121. Manjunath, C. K., Goings, G. E., Page,
E. 1984. Cytoplasmic surface and intramembrane components of rat heart gap
junctional proteins. *Am. J. Physiol.*
246:H865–75
122. Warner, A. E., Guthrie, S. C., Gilula, N.
B. 1984. Antibodies to gap junctional
protein selectively disrupt junctional
communication in the early amphibian
embryo. *Nature* 311:127–31

Ann. Rev. Physiol. 1985. 47:281–303

PHYSIOLOGY AND PHARMACOLOGY OF GAP JUNCTIONS

D. C. Spray and M. V. L. Bennett

Department of Neuroscience, Albert Einstein College of Medicine, 1300 Morris Park Avenue, Bronx, New York 10461

INTRODUCTION TO PHYSIOLOGICAL STUDIES OF COUPLING

In embryonic and adult organisms, most tissues contain intercellular channels that connect each cell with all the neighbors that it contacts (as in liver) or divide the tissue into coupled subsets (as in various regions of the nervous system). These channels provide cytoplasmic continuity with regard to ions and small molecules, and their aggregates belong to a single ultrastructurally recognizable class: gap junctions (cf. 98). Recently a number of specific treatments have been found that operate to open and close, i.e. gate, the channels; some of these treatments, and others, operate over a longer time course to affect the formation or disappearance of the channels. The intent of this review is to summarize the static and dynamic characteristics of gap junctions obtained using electrophysiological techniques. Although we highlight diversity among electrophysiological properties of junctions from different tissues, our message is that there are general regulatory mechanisms that act on this class of membrane channels.

One role that gap junctions presumably play is linked to their permeability to relatively large molecules. Nonarthropod gap junctions are permeable to spheroid molecules at least as large as 1000 daltons, whereas arthropod junctions apparently allow flux of molecules $\sim$ 50% larger in diameter (cf. 104). (A problem with measurements of channel size has been the absence of a sufficiently large range of spherical probes with higher molecular weights and the absence of quantitative permeability data for determining selectivity for the

281

0066-4278/85/0315-0281$02.00

probes that are available.) Whatever the upper size limit for permeability [and whether or not there is charge selectivity (cf. 15, 16)], the apparently large channel diameter allows the diffusion of many molecules that could convey signals intercellularly, including mono- and divalent cations, small peptides, and cyclic nucleotides. Included in this size range are putative morphogens in *Hydra* (cf. 25). Large polypeptides, RNA, DNA, and cellular organelles are excluded (cf. 90). The large channel diameter probably results in a high single-channel conductance, which is relevant to efficient electrotonic spread. Mediation of electrotonic transmission is an obvious function of the gap junction in excitable tissues and can be important in rapid impulse propagation and synchronization of coupled elements.

Electrical communication via gap junctions is controlled by factors that operate directly on the gap junctional membrane (to be considered below) and by agents that change other properties of coupled cells. Strength of coupling between cells depends upon conductances of nonjunctional membranes, as well as of the junctions, and impulse transmission is affected by changes in excitability. In a few known cases, changes in nonjunctional properties produce physiologically significant plasticity in coupling while the junctional membrane is unaffected.

In the buccal ganglia of the mollusc *Navanax,* coupled motoneurons apparently can be activated synchronously to provide pharyngeal expansion or asynchronously to mediate peristalsis (cf. 110). When activity is asynchronous, electrotonic coupling is profoundly reduced. The dramatic change in strength of coupling associated with these two patterns of firing is attributable to shunting of intercellular current by activation of inhibitory chemical synapses (110). Although a change in resistance of the junctional membrane has not been totally ruled out, the morphological localization of chemical synapses near the site of coupling and the changes in input and transfer resistances recorded in the two states are consistent with uncoupling due solely to changes in nonjunctional resistances (54, 110). This sort of uncoupling may also occur in the inferior olive in the mammalian CNS (109). Reduced electrotonic coupling produced by ACh application to pancreatic acinar cells (66) and mammalian cardiac tissue (34) are certainly at least partially due to increases in nonjunctional conductance caused by the drug. Decreased conductance synapses in *Aplysia* abdominal ganglia increase coupling by a similar mechanism operating in reverse (19). Increased transmission at electrotonic synapses resulting from increase in the presynaptic action potential and from afterdepolarizations are also known (6, 11, 96).

Analogous phenomena may occur in diffusion of ions or molecules across gap junctions. A concentration coupling coefficient can be defined as the ratio of concentrations in donor and recipient cells (or pre- and post-cells), where the donor cell generates or is injected with the substance of interest. For molecules to which nonjunctional membranes are impermeant and which are not altered by the cells, the concentration coupling coefficient is unity, provided there is even minimal junctional permeability. However, with large cells and permeabilities of commonly used fluorescent dyes, the time constants of equilibration may be many minutes to hours (13, 119). Simple relations are easily derived from the electrical relations where concentration, volume, and junctional permeability correspond to voltage, capacity, and g_j respectively, and nonjunctional leak and cell metabolism correspond to nonjunctional conductances.

In order to determine gating properties of gap junction channels, g_j must be measured unambiguously. Several techniques have been used, all of which measure spread of current between two cells where the region of coupling is isopotential on each side, often with two electrodes in each cell for separate current delivery and potential measurement. Junctional current and g_j are measured by passing current pulses in each cell in turn, measuring input and transfer resistances and solving the pi-tee transform (6). Alternatively, the junctional membrane can be voltage-clamped by clamping each cell to a common holding potential with independent voltage-clamp circuits (117). A command pulse to one cell then causes transjunctional currents that are just equalled by the clamp on the second cell to keep its voltage constant. Thus the current in the second cell divided by the voltage in the first cell gives junctional conductance directly. Originally, this dual voltage-clamp technique employed two separate two-electrode voltage-clamp circuits to control the potential of each cell; more recently, the whole cell voltage clamp using patch-clamp circuits has allowed application of the technique to smaller cells, because only a single patch electrode is required for voltage control of each cell (135).

Another technique involved a patch pipette and perfusion of the internal aspect of the junctional membrane of one cell with solutions of known composition. The relative conductance of the remaining patch of membrane including junctions was measured by passing current in the bath and measuring voltage with a microelectrode in the intact cell and in the patch pipette (122). (Current passage in the intact cell would allow direct measurement of the patch conductance.)

An often simpler technique for determining if coupling is present is observation of dye coupling. Nonleaking and nondegradable probes such as Lucifer Yellow (124) diffuse between many kinds of coupled cells in situ and in vitro. With opaque tissue, flux can be evaluated after fixation and sectioning. There is little doubt that dye spread usually occurs via gap junctions (7, 8, 115), but there are several possible sources of error. Short-term measurements where equilibration times are long may give false negatives (13), the shish-kabob artifact (skewering of multiple cells along an electrode track) (39, 72) or fixation may artifactually couple cells (7), and, because large molecules such as horseradish peroxidase are sometimes transmitted between cells by a non–gap junction pathway (125a), smaller molecules may also be. Cytoplasmic bridges are known but have different permeability and presumably gating properties from gap junctions. Studies of metabolic cooperation and transmission of radiolabeled substances has been very useful although necessarily on a much slower time scale (90).

Using electrophysiological techniques we have assessed the responses of the gap junction membrane to intracellular H and Ca, various pharmacological treatments, and transjunctional and inside-outside potential. The remainder of this chapter summarizes our data and those of others with regard to gating properties of gap junction channels and modification of these properties by certain pharmacological agents.

GATING OF GAP JUNCTION CHANNELS

Gating by pH

Turin & Warner (127) reported that exposure to CO_2, a treatment reducing intracellular pH (pH_i), dramatically decreased coupling between cells in the early amphibian embryo. Correlating pH_i and coupling changes during CO_2 application, they reported that acidification below pH 7 was required to reduce coupling substantially (128). Using cell pairs to unambiguously measure g_j and nonjunctional conductances and using recessed-tip glass microelectrodes to measure pH_i in one cell, we demonstrated that the pH_i-g_j relation in fish and amphibian blastomeres is steep and occurs over a pH_i range that may be physiologically relevant (118). The response is not due to extracellular acidification; strong acids and impermeant buffers do not decrease g_j, and decreasing pH_i at constant extracellular pH is effective. Conductance of the nonjunctional membrane is also reduced by acidifying treatments, explaining the lower apparent pK obtained for coupling coefficient in the whole embryo as compared to the pK for g_j itself.

pH sensitivity of gap junctions has now been quantified in a variety of preparations (Table 1). In early embryonic cells from fish and amphibia (normal pH_i 7.6–7.8), the pK is ~ 7.3 and the Hill coefficient, n, is ~ 4.5. In earthworm and crayfish septate axons (normal pH_i ~ 7.1), cells uncouple as the cytoplasm is acidified, but the pK is lower than in vertebrate embryos (~ 6.7) and the curve is less steep (n: 2–3). In mammalian cardiac ventricular myocytes and Purkinje fibers (normal pH_i = 7.1–7.3), the pH_i-g_j relation is even less steep (n near unity) and the pK is < 7.0. The pH_i-g_j curve is steepest near normal pH_i, and g_j of cardiac cells is apparently significantly changed by even a slight shift in either the acid or base direction. Although buffering power of cytoplasm is considerable near normal pH_i and fluctuations in g_j during normal

Table 1   Gating properties of gap junctions in various preparations

Preparation (reference)	pH_i	(pK)	Voltage dependence Transjunctional $(V_0)^a$	Inside-outside
Amphibian blastomeres (115, 117, 118)	yes	(7.3)	yes (14 mV)	no
Fish blastomeres (118, 134)	yes	(7.3)	yes (28 mV)	no
Squid blastomeres (12, 123)	yes	(lower)	yes	weaker
Chironomus salivary gland (83, 102)	yes	(lower?)	weaker	stronger
Mammalian heart (36, 97, 135)	yes	($\sim$ 6.8)	no	no
Mammalian liver (113)	yes	($\sim$ 6.3)	no	no
Mammalian lens (103)	maybe not		?	?
Fish horizontal cells[b]	?		no	no
Mammalian SCG neurons[c]	yes	(?)	no	no
Molluscan neurons(14a)	yes	($\sim$ 6.8)	no	no
Limulus retinular cells (108)	?		yes	?
Crayfish septate axon (22, 50, 51, 68, 69)	yes	(6.75)	no	no
Earthworm septate axon (16, 130)	yes	($\sim$ 6.5)	no	no
Crayfish rectifying synapse (48, 75)	yes[d]	(?)	yes (20 mV)	no
Hatchetfish rectifying synapse (2)	?		yes	?
Leech synapse (5, 80, 139)	?		maybe	?

[a] V_0 is the voltage at which the changeable fraction of g_j is reduced by 50%.
[b] R. L. White, D. C. Spray, E. Lasater, J. E. Dowling & M. V. L. Bennett, unpublished observations.
[c] D. C. Spray, J. C. Saez & J. A. Kessler, unpublished observations.
[d] C. Giaume & H. Korn, unpublished observations.

physiological operation are likely to be small, cytoplasmic acidification large enough to affect g_j is known to accompany ischemic episodes of even brief duration (67). In pairs of hepatocytes freshly dissociated from rat liver, pH_i is $\sim$ 7.4. Reduction in g_j does not begin until pH_i is decreased by $\sim$ 1 unit, but around pH 6.3 the curve is very steep (113). This low pK, combined with the very high degree of coupling between hepatocytes, may account for the relative insensitivity of coupling in liver to CO_2 exposure (77).

Although not yet quantified, g_j is reduced at decreased pH_i in a number of other tissues (Table 1). pH sensitivity is apparently weak or absent for coupling among differentiated lens fibers in chicken (103) and also between rods in toad retina (Griff & Pinto, personal communication). In these last two instances pH_i has not been measured, and the possibility of buffering and/or a steep dependence at low pH_i, as in liver, has not been ruled out.

Weak acids cross membranes in the undissociated form and then dissociate to yield H ions; the effect on pH_i depends upon concentration and pK of the weak acid used, extracellular pH, membrane permeability to the undissociated acid, capability of cells to extrude liberated protons, and intracellular buffering capacity (cf. 120). Cytoplasmic acidification can also be achieved by extracellular application of a number of membrane permeant esters that are hydrolyzed by intrinsic esterases to release acid and alcohol (121). Appropriate esters require much lower concentration than weak acids to achieve the same decrease in pH_i and have fewer side effects. Among the effective esters are derivatives of o-nitrobenzoic acid. 6-Carboxyfluorescein diacetate, which is used to load cells with 6-carboxyfluorescein as an optical indicator of pH_i, also decreases pH_i, and one should not forget that any ester used to load cells with indicator or other active moiety will produce some decrease in pH_i. Acidification can be reversed, however, by prolonged washing. Tumor-promoting phorbol esters and dibutyryl derivatives of cyclic nucleotides are other compounds that can acidify the cytoplasm and decrease g_j.

Sensitivity to Ca

Reduction in intercellular coupling has been shown to result from bathing in solutions very low in Ca and from elevation of intracellular Ca (Ca_i) to relatively high levels (cf. 100; 101). Although it is difficult to be sure to what degree the observed uncoupling is due to action on the junctions, because most studies have not controlled for effects of nonjunctional shunting, these data do suggest that Ca has opposite effects on two sites, one extracellular (perhaps involved in intercellular adhesion) with high affinity and one intracellular (presumably involved in gating) with low affinity. The effects of low extracellular Ca have also been ascribed to increased Ca_i, but direct measurements have not been made, nor have other possibilities such as decrease in pH_i been considered.

The possibility that cytoplasmic acidification might reduce coupling as a secondary effect of elevated Ca_i through H:Ca exchange has been rejected in several systems. In fish and amphibian embryos, exposure to CO_2 can produce uncoupling with little change in Ca_i measured with aequorin (9) or ion-sensitive microelectrodes (99). In Purkinje fibers, acidification actually reduces Ca_i (64). In *Fundulus* blastomeres, perfusion experiments indicate that reduction in g_j requires free Ca_i in excess of 0.1 mM, pH_i being buffered to 7.6 (122). The apparent pK of the g_j-Ca_i relation corresponds to a free Ca_i concentration of $\sim$ 0.5 mM and the Hill coefficient is $\sim$ 2 (Figure 1a). This stoichiometry is similar to that obtained for the low-affinity Ca binding site in isolated cardiac ventricular membranes (82). Coupling between *Chironomus* salivary gland and mammalian heart cells is also quite insensitive to cytoplasmic Ca activity; a Ca level between 40 and 80 μM was required to decrease coupling in *Chironomus* (84), and at least this level is required for healing over in cardiac tissue (81). A number of studies using the Ca ionophore A23187 have reported greater sensitivity of coupling in arthropods compared to other phyla (4, 21, 45, 52). Because Ca shifts the voltage dependence of g_j in *Chironomus*, (83, 100), depolarization caused by increased Ca_i could account for greater apparent sensitivity of the gap junction channel in arthropods as compared to vertebrates. In conclusion, the Ca_i levels required to reduce g_j in any tissue are high, probably higher than occur under physiological conditions. However, these levels may be exceeded in pathological conditions that violate the integrity of the cell membrane, exposing the interior aspect of the junction to extracellular levels of Ca. Action of pH and Ca are presumably upon the same gating structure, H ions binding with much higher affinity, although the only direct evidence is from the similar action of these ions on the V_{i-o} gate in *Chironomus* (83). Competition experiments or those with agents that prevent the blocking action of decreased pH_i should resolve this issue.

Johnston & Ramon (69) inferred from internal perfusion experiments on crayfish septate axon that gating by H_i and Ca_i might be mediated by a diffusible cytoplasmic molecule: bathing of intact axons with weak acids or the Ca ionophore A23187 reduced g_j, but internal perfusion with solutions high in Ca or H ions had no effect. We suspect that the perfusion procedure may have formed cytoplasmic bridges between cells, a proposition that could be tested with large probes such as fluoresceinated dextran or albumin.

The reduction in coupling caused by bathing in solutions very low in Ca or containing Ca chelators has not been quantified, but some cells uncouple in solutions containing 0.1 mM free Ca, while others do not. Although the intercellular action of Ca is presumably on a gating portion of the molecule, extracellular Ca may be required for connecting the extracellular aspect of the hemichannels in each cell. Extracellular Ca may also simply be necessary for cell adherence, and some cell adhesion molecules are Ca-dependent (40). It follows from this summary of Ca dependence that high resolution structural studies comparing isolated junctions dialyzed either against moderate (50 μM) or very low (0.1 μM) concentrations of Ca may be comparing effects on junctional association mediated extracellularly rather than on gating mediated intracellularly (cf. 129).

Voltage Dependence

The rectifying synapse of the crayfish was one of the first gap junctions examined electrophysiologically, and a strong asymmetric voltage dependence was observed (48; see Figure 1b and below). Since then voltage dependence has been discovered in gap junctions connecting cells in a few other tissues. The most thoroughly characterized voltage-dependent gap junction is that between early embryonic cells of amphibia (115, 117). In this case the phenomenon is easily demonstrated by injecting current pulses into one cell of a pair. During pulses of sufficient amplitude and duration, the input resistance of the injected cell increases and the transfer resistance measured in the other cell decreases. The uncoupling is more rapid with larger pulses of either polarity.

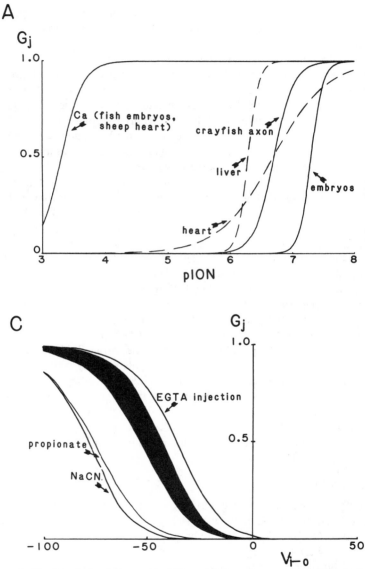

Figure 1   Physiological and pharmacological controls operating on gap junctions. *A*: Effects of Ca$_i$ *(leftmost curve)* and H$_i$ on normalized junction conductance (G$_j$). *Solid curves* are Hill equations fit by eye (22, 118, 120); *dashed curves* are from preliminary data. pH$_i$ was measured with ion-selective microelectrodes. For fish blastomeres, Ca concentration at the junctional region was maintained at fixed levels by an internal perfusion technique (122). Ca curve for sheep heart represents low-affinity binding to isolated membranes (82). *B*: Effects of transjunctional potential (V$_j$) on g$_j$. *Curves* for vertebrates were obtained under voltage-clamp conditions (117, 134, 135)

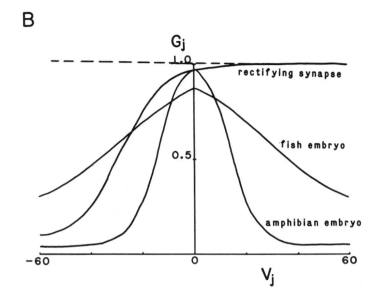

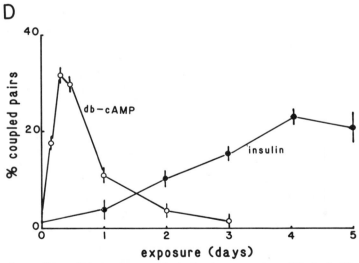

and that for crayfish rectifying synapse was obtained under current-clamp (75). *Dashed line* at top represents junctions without V_j dependence. *C*: Effect of inside-outside potential on G_j. *Filled area* represents span of control curves matching each treatment, and *solid curves* represent effects of agents that reduced (EGTA) and presumably increased intracellular Ca and H (83). *D*: Time course of effects of insulin *(filled circles)* and of db-cAMP *(open symbols)* on electrotonic coupling between pairs of neonatal rat superior cervical ganglion cells in culture (71); *bars* indicate standard errors.

Voltage-clamp studies reveal that g_j is decreased symmetrically by V_j of either sign. The relation between steady state g_j and V_j is quite steep (e-fold for 4 mV, as steep as Na activation in axonal membrane), but changes are quite slow (time constants maximally $\sim$ 200 msec). Both increases and decreases obey first-order kinetics (57). Channel closure presumably involves a dipole moment change, and transjunctional voltage acts by shifting the distribution of channels between open and closed states. The data are well fit by a Boltzmann distribution, where the energy difference between the two states is a linear function of transjunctional potential (117). g_j Is independent of the potential between cytoplasm and bath, and evidently there is no significant dipole moment shift between inside and outside of the channel (but see below for a different case). Each channel apparently possesses two gates in series, and when only one gate is closed, all the transjunctional potential occurs across it; the closed gate must open before the gate in series with it can be acted upon by the transjunctional potential (57). This conclusion is derived from experiments where V_j is suddenly reversed. The presence of two gates in series allows four states: both gates open, either gate closed, and both gates closed. Series gating in principle allows cycling through the four states because the gate on one side sees less of V_j when the gate on the other side is closed [(12); see also discussion in (123)]. Cycling probably could be detected in single-channel recordings, but it has no obvious functional significance.

In amphibian blastomeres the pH and voltage-gating mechanisms appear to be independent, because as g_j is decreased by acidification, its voltage sensitivity remains unchanged (123). Also, certain pharmacological agents selectively reduce pH sensitivity without affecting voltage sensitivity (see below).

Under current clamp conditions, the voltage dependence of amphibian embryonic junctions is sufficiently steep to give rise to a bistability in coupling (58). Thus, depending on history, cells can be either coupled or uncoupled over a range of applied or endogenous currents. Such behavior could operate physiologically, allowing one population of embryonic cells to uncouple from adjacent populations. This mechanism could thus give rise to boundaries between embryonic cells with distinct developmental fates (14, 25, 119). Action potentials in Rohon Beard cells of Xenopus can cause uncoupling (111). Although the dependence of g_j on V_j is independent of pH_i over the range of pH 7.6–7.0, the two gating mechanisms can enhance the effects of one another (123).

Transjunctional voltage operates to affect g_j in several other tissues (Table I, Figure 1b). In the rectifying synapse of the crayfish, the first well-characterized case of electrical coupling, g_j is normally low (48, 75). It is increased by V_j of one sign, presynaptic depolarization or postsynaptic hyperpolarization, and slightly decreased by V_j of opposite sign. Although the steady state V_j-g_j relation is not as steep as in amphibian embryos (Figure 1b), the kinetics are faster by a factor of at least 1000. The kinetics are also very fast at the hatchetfish rectifying synapse (2). The voltage dependence is comparable to the crayfish synapse, but the conductance is about half maximal at $V_j = 0$. In Fundulus blastomeres, dependence of g_j on V_j is symmetrical and about half as steep as in amphibian blastomeres (Figure 1b; 134); slow voltage dependence like that in amphibian blastomeres is present in *Limulus* retinular cells (108) but has not been quantified. Leech ganglia have a number of sites of electrotonic coupling, some of which are functionally rectifying (80). Unusual forms of rectification have also been reported but apparently arise from nonjunctional membrane properties (139). Voltage dependence is weak or absent in pairs of cells from mammalian liver, heart, and superior cervical ganglion and in septate axons from crayfish and earthworm.

In *Chironomus* salivary glands, g_j is strongly affected by the voltage between cytoplasm and bath (inside-outside voltage, V_{i-o}). Equal hyperpolarization of both cells of a coupled pair increases g_j, and depolarization of both cells decreases it (Figure 1c; 83). The data are consistent with two gates in series as in amphibia. The data are explained quantitatively in terms of a dipole moment shift, but between the cytoplasm and intercellular gap rather than transjunctionally. However, the model does not predict g_j when V_j is not zero, and there is a component of V_j sensitivity as well that has not yet been quantitatively considered. The voltage dependence is shifted in the depolarizing direction without change in slope by increases in H_i or Ca_i (Figure 1c). Evidently H, Ca, and V_{i-o} all act on the same mechanism, unlike the case in amphibia. The role of this gating mechanism cannot yet be assigned. It may function as an H gate in normal situations or as a Ca gate in pathological ones, and voltage dependence may be an epiphenomenon. Alternatively, the high voltage sensitivity is suggestive of a functional role, and the cells may "use" membrane potential to alter the degree of coupling.

In squid blastomeres, g_j is also affected by both V_j and V_{i-o} (cf. 123). At normal pH_i, g_j is very large and voltage sensitivity is absent or at least difficult to demonstrate. When g_j is lowered by acidification, voltage sensitivity becomes apparent and action of H_i and voltage on the same gating mechanism is probably like that in *Chironomus*. The sensitivity to V_{i-o} is of the same sign as in *Chironomus*, but weaker. There is also a more pronounced sensitivity to V_j that, when pH_i is decreased by bathing in weak acids, may be either symmetrical or asymmetrical. If acid is injected into one cell, g_j is increased by making that cell positive or the other cell negative. Because the nearer gate should be more strongly affected by the acid, we can identify this gate as the one opened by V_j positive on the side of injection. This conclusion contrasts to the situation in amphibia, where symmetry obscures the polarity of sensitivity of the series gates. When bath-applied agents are used to change pH_i, the symmetrical voltage dependence presumably arises because of equal pH_i changes in the two cells. In this situation V_j increases g_j rather than decreasing it. Presumably channels singly closed on one side are opened more rapidly than doubly open channels are closed. (g_j never approaches its maximum value, so there should be enough channels to make this mechanism possible.) As pH_i is decreased further, the junctions become insensitive to V_j, perhaps because all the channels are closed on both sides and V_j can't open them. The degree of voltage sensitivity in squid blastomeres is low enough that it seems unlikely to have a functional role, and pH sensitivity is more likely to be operative in normal cell function.

Sensitivity to both V_j and V_{i-o} can be explained in terms of a conformational change, with a dipole moment shift having components in both transjunctional and inside-outside directions. This kind of dual sensitivity has not been seen in vertebrate junctions where there is dependence on V_j.

Temperature Dependence

In crayfish septate axon, g_j decreases smoothly as a function of temperature, with a Q_{10} of ~ 3 if cooling is relatively rapid [1 min for 20°/C, (85)]. Slow cooling, on the other hand, decreases g_j very little, as would be expected for a simple aqueous channel (95). The effect of fast cooling seems likely to involve a gating process; the lesser effect of slow cooling may represent an accommodative reaction of the axon. (Prolonged holding at low temperature also decreases g_j, apparently as a secondary change and involving separation of junctional membranes.) g_j Between amphibian neurons is insensitive to cooling, but voltage-dependent changes are slowed (56). Coupling of leech neurons is little affected by low temperature in contrast to marked depression of chemical synapses (80).

In earthworm septate axon, g_j is gradually reduced as temperature is lowered, but permeability to several dye molecules can show abrupt block (16). This affect is more pronounced in D_2O solutions and is ascribed to increased stability of the hydration shells at lower temperature, which increases molecular size.

PHARMACOLOGY OF GAP JUNCTION CHANNELS

A large number of agents have been shown to affect intercellular coupling. These treatments variously modify g_j, change nonjunctional conductance, membrane or transjunctional potential, act through a change in pH_i or Ca_i, or affect the sensitivity of g_j to agents that directly affect gating.

Cations

Extracellular application or intracellular injection of Li^+, Na^+, La^{+++}, Ba^{++}, Mn^{++}, Sr^{++}, Co^{++}, and Mg^{++} have each been shown to decrease coupling in at least one system; in heart and arthropod salivary gland, potencies of partial series of cations have been tested (33, 84). A general problem with experiments of this kind is knowing intracellular concentrations of the tested ion and the effects on other ions such as H and Ca to which g_j has some sensitivity. Although g_j is insensitive to Ca_i, there is enough bound Ca intracellularly to raise Ca_i into the effective range. Li and Na effects (cf. 100) may well involve increase in H_i or Ca_i as a result of effects on coupled Na:H or Ca extrusion; divalent cation and La effects have been interpreted as direct actions on a Ca-sensitive site, but quantitative data on g_j reductions by known cytoplasmic concentrations of these ions are not yet available. Because H:Ca exchange is a common form of intracellular buffering, cytoplasmic acidification might also result from treatment with other divalent cations; likewise, cytoplasmic free Ca would be expected to rise as the result of decrease in pH_i. Gap junctions are permeable to at least some of these putative blocking cations, as would be expected from their size. Intracellularly injected Co^{++} passes from one segment of crayfish septate axon to the next if cytoplasmic concentration is low but decreases g_j and fails to cross if Co^{++} concentration is high (93). It has thus been used at low concentration to trace polysynaptic electrotonic pathways (53). Colloidal La^{3+} added extracellularly during fixation appears in the central portion of *en face* views of sectioned gap junctions, implying entry into the channel (cf. 10), but whether this permeation can occur prior to fixation is not demonstrated. Junctions are presumably permeable to protons, calcium, and other ions with or without blocking action, because permeability to the much larger tetraethylammonium ion has been demonstrated (38, 131).

Group-Specific Protein Reagents

Several authors have applied various protein reagents to coupled cells. Among the sulfhydryl reagents tested, n-ethylmaleimide (NEM) is the most potent. NEM decreases coupling in *Chironomus* salivary gland (91) and in crayfish septate axon (20, 21). In the latter case, uncoupling is due to a profound decrease in g_j without change in pH_i. In fish blastomeres, NEM at high concentration (2 mM) reduces g_j, but this effect is attributable to an accompanying cytoplasmic acidification. In crayfish, diamide and—to a lesser extent—5-5' dithiobis-2-nitrobenzoic acid (DTNB) uncouple (21, 51). Diamide reduces g_j in vertebrate embryonic cells; effects on pH_i have not been excluded.

Most amino and carboxyl group reagents are without effect on g_j in crayfish and, although the list of reagents used is less extensive, in vertebrate blastomeres. Exceptions to the lack of effect include aldehydes, discussed below, and bis-ethoxy-N-ethoxy-dihydroquinoline (EEDQ), a bifunctional carboxyl-group cross-linking reagent. In crayfish septate axon (21) and frog blastomeres (23, 112), EEDQ does not affect normal g_j but selectively blocks the reduction in g_j caused by cytoplasmic acidification; it does not affect voltage dependence in amphibian embryonic cells.

Indirect Agents

Several compounds have been used to reduce g_j that are known or suspected to act primarily by increasing H_i or Ca_i, including ouabain (e.g. 30, 132), dinitrophenol (DNP), weak acids [e.g. acetic, lactic, and propionic (e.g. 1, 118), all of which have a pKa within 3 pH units of normal pH_i, and ionophores (primarily the divalent ionophore A23187 and the H^+/K^+ exchanger nigericin). DNP and the calcium ionophore have been presumed to act exclusively in changing free Ca_i (cf. 102); however, DNP is a weak acid (pKa $\sim$ 4) and cytoplasmic acidification would be expected to accompany its application. Furthermore, Ca uptake might elevate H ions through intracellular Ca:H exchange. Because g_j is so much more responsive to H^+ than to Ca^{++} but both ions are strongly buffered, interpretation of the mechanism of action of these agents is ambiguous. Moreover, the strongly interactive dependence of g_j in *Chironomus* on pH, Ca, and V_{i-o} (83) renders underlying mechanisms uncertain in that tissue.

Calmodulin

The insensitivity of perfused crayfish septate axon to H_i and Ca_i (see above) suggested the possibility that a diffusible intermediate might control the gating. Such a molecule might be calmodulin (CaM), a membrane-associated protein that exhibits conformational change when exposed to various Ca and H levels (cf. 28). Isolated gap junction proteins from lens and liver exhibit high-affinity CaM binding (61, 62). The nonspecific CaM antagonists chlorpromazine (CPZ) and trifluoperazine (TFP) have been reported to uncouple insect epidermal cells (74) and to increase coupling in heart (136). Although exposure to TFP and calmidazolium have been reported to reduce pH sensitivity of coupling in intact early amphibian embryos (88), this effect may involve the pH dependence of the nonjunctional membrane. Our efforts to reproduce this finding in pairs of cells, where g_j and pH_i are measurable, have been unsuccessful. If H and Ca act at the same sites, the pH gate is also by definition a Ca-binding protein. At first glance CaM itself would appear to be an unlikely candidate for mediator of gap-junction regulation; its H and Ca sensitivities are conferred by carboxyl residues with affinities far above that shown for Ca action on g_j and far below that expected for H sensitivity. On the other hand, a phosphodiesterase isolated from molluscan tissue possesses pH sensitivity approximating that of vertebrate gap junctions and is inhibited by anticalmodulin drugs (18). Combined with emerging evidence for cAMP involvement in gap junctions (see below), more work on intermediate molecules is merited.

Alcohols and Aldehydes

Longer-chain alcohols, especially heptanol and octanol, reduce g_j in crayfish septate axon (70), vertebrate blastomeres (123), and adult heart (32, 135). In amphibian blastomeres exposed to 0.1 mM octanol, voltage dependence is reduced and the time constant is prolonged; pH dependence is not blocked. The aldehydes formaldehyde, valeraldehyde, and glutaraldehyde all decrease g_j irreversibly in fish and amphibian blastomeres (116); glutaraldehyde apparently acts similarly on Purkinje strands (32, 47). The rate of blockade is dose-dependent, with concentrations of about 10, 1, and 0.01 mM of formaldehyde, valeraldehyde, and glutaraldehyde respectively reducing g_j by 50% in 1 min. These doses are far lower than fixative concentrations, which are usually in excess of 100 mM. Aldehyde effects on gating are determinable from the response of residual conductance to V_j and pH_i. The formaldehyde effect in amphibian blastomeres is accompanied by a slowing of voltage dependence without effect on pH dependence. Valeraldehyde (a five-carbon straight-chain monoaldehyde) reduces g_j but does not noticeably affect either gating function. Glutaraldehyde (the dialdehyde analog of valeraldehyde) reduces g_j without affecting voltage dependence of the residual g_j; pH dependence, however, is abolished (112). This specificity of action of glutaraldehyde on the pH gate provides evidence for its distinctness from the voltage gate. Glutaraldehyde is a cross-linking agent, and it may act to cross-link amino acid residues in the gap-junction hexamer. Whatever their modes of action, these aldehydes close gap-junction channels, and morphological studies on aldehyde-fixed material may not reveal the open conformational state of the channel (cf. 55, 87). [During the fixation process, in crayfish axon and Purkinje fibers, g_j rises dramatically and then falls after some time. The later decrease is ascribable to intercellular bridge formation rather than opening gap junction channels (7)].

Tumor Promoters

Phorbol esters in nanomolar to micromolar concentrations decrease metabolic cooperativity in cultured cells (79, 138). Subsequent reports have shown similar effects of the structurally unrelated promoters saccharin and benzoyl peroxide (107, 126). These observations have been extended to show that tumor promoters block electrotonic coupling (43, 44).

We have recently found that saccharin (10 mM) and tumor-promoting phorbol esters decrease junctional conductance in amphibian embryos (D. C. Spray, unpublished observations); the tumor-promoting phorbols also decrease intracellular pH. Nonpromoting phorbol esters have no effect on pH_i or g_j; possibly nonpromoting esters are less membrane-permeant or are poorer substrates for enzymatic hydrolysis. Although these experiments suggest that the phorbol ester effect on g_j may be a secondary consequence of their hydrolysis, we cannot exclude uncoupling by activation of protein kinase c. This latter possibility is especially intriguing because of the apparent involvement of a cAMP-dependent kinase in gap-junction formation (see below).

Hormones, Vitamins, Neurotransmitters, and Intracellular Messengers

Vitamin A produces a profound elaboration of gap junctions in epithelial tissues (41, 42), although the effect is slow and conductance changes have not been assessed. Retinoic acid acts quickly in amphibian embryonic cells to reduce the dependence of g_j on pH_i (112), and it reduces metabolic cooperation in various cultured cell lines (M. Finbow, personal communication). Angiotensin II (60) and norepinephrine (D. C. Spray & R. L. White, unpublished observations) increase g_j in rat heart; the latter effect at least may be partially explicable in terms of an increase in pH_i. Insulin increases intracellular pH in skeletal muscle (78); although not yet reported, effects on g_j in systems where pH_i is near the gap junction's pK would be expected. In turtle retina, GABA antagonists increase both electrical and dye coupling among horizontal cells (89). Apparently the effect is mediated by disinhibition of presynaptic dopaminergic neurons whose postsynaptic action is due to increase in cAMP. The sign of the effect, decrease in g_j with rise in cAMP, is the opposite to that seen in several other tissues (see below).

Evidence from several sources is converging on cyclic nucleotide involvement in regulation of gap junctions. Chronic exposure of cultured cells to various hormones and alteration of hormonal balance in vivo can alter the incidence of gap junctions and the extent of coupling (cf. 31; 73; 76, 105). In some cases, such as the increase in coupling during parturition and the decrease in gap junctions accompanying ovulation, the hormonal effects on gap junctions appear to play a physiological role (cf. 17, 49, 106), i.e. differentiation of the oocyte and increased synchronization of contraction of uterine muscle.

In many cases, the hormonal effect on coupling is explicable in terms of elevated cyclic nucleotide levels. In cultured cell lines known to respond to adrenergic drugs and prostaglandins with a rise in cAMP, gap-junction incidence and intercellular dye spread are dramatically increased by application of these agents (94). Coupling is also increased in *Drosophila* salivary glands (59) and *Tenebrio* epithelial cells (24, 26, 27) exposed to the molting hormone β-ecdysone, but the involvement of cAMP is made questionable by its opposite effects on coupling in the two preparations. An instance in which a hormone produces a change in coupling without a change in cAMP level is found in cultured superior cervical ganglion neurons (71). When these cells are dissociated and cultured in the presence of serum, electrotonic coupling is rare (65, 71). However, coupling is common when cells are cultured in an insulin-containing defined medium lacking serum, or when insulin is added to serum-containing medium (71). This effect develops over the course of several days (Figure 1d) and is independent of a promoting effect on coupling of cAMP, as shown by lack of elevation of cAMP level after insulin exposure and summation of the stimulatory effects of the two agents.

Other direct and indirect evidence for cAMP dependence of gap junctions comes from recent work on horizontal cells of vertebrate retina. Dopamine application increases the response of fish and turtle horizontal cells to a spot of light and decreases sizes of their fields; moreover, intercellular spread of Lucifer Yellow is reduced (89, 125). This effect is mimicked by forskolin, db-cAMP, and IBMX, suggesting involvement of cAMP.

Direct effects of cAMP on coupling have been reported in several other systems, including heart (cf. 35, 37). The earliest report was that current spread increased in *Drosophila* salivary glands (59), although in this case interaction with voltage sensitivity of g_j could have caused an indirect effect. In various cell lines, db-cAMP or phosphodiesterase inhibitors increase electrical and dye coupling and also increase the incidence of gap junctions (3, 46). In superior cervical ganglion, db-cAMP exposure leads to rapid development of electrotonic coupling that peaks within 12 hours (Figure 1d). The lack of coupling in serum-containing medium may be due to the reduced cAMP levels under these conditions (71).

Although changes in pH_i and Ca_i or other indirect consequences of cAMP elevation might be responsible for some of the reported changes in coupling, direct action through protein phosphorylation is suggested in certain cultured cells where coupling is increased by cAMP-dependent protein kinase (133).

Antibodies

An antibody has recently been prepared against liver gap junctions (see 61) that, when injected into pairs of cells dissociated from adult rat heart, liver, and cultured superior cervical ganglion neurons, produces a rapid irreversible block of g_j and dye transfer (61, 63). Affinity-purified antibody prepared against other membrane fractions and preimmune serum have no effect on g_j. This antijunction antibody is ineffective when applied extracellularly and presumably provides a more selective blockade of gap junctions than the pharmacological agents surveyed above. With this antibody or agents like it, the question of the role that gap junctions play in various tissues should be answerable.

CONCLUSIONS

Conductance of gap junctions is controlled in the short term by altering the proportion of channels that are open by one or more gating mechanisms. Pharmacological agents, some of which may have a physiological role as indicated above, operate through these mechanisms and probably through other less specific effects as well. Over a longer time course, g_j is determined by the number of channels in the membrane that are available to these mechanisms, but what governs appearance and turnover of gap junctions is now only poorly understood. Because formation in vitro and in vivo can be enhanced by certain manipulations [touched upon above and treated more fully in an accompanying paper (105], the fundamental questions of how expression of this abundant intercellular channel is regulated are becoming accessible.

ACKNOWLEDGMENTS

Work reported here from our laboratory was supported in part by NIH grants NS 16524 and NS 19830 (D. C. S.) and HD 04248 and NS 07512 (M. V. L. B.), a Grant-In-Aid from the American Heart Association, and a McKnight Development Award (D. C. S.). The contributions of our past and present colleagues (R. Bodmer, A. C. Campos de Carvalho, R. D. Ginzberg, D. H. Hall, A. L. Harris, J. A. Kessler, J. Saez, M. E. Spira, V. Verselis, and R. L. White) to this work is gratefully acknowledged.

Literature Cited

1. Asada, Y., Bennett, M. V. L. 1971. Experimental alteration of coupling resistance at an electrotonic synapse. *J. Cell Biol.* 49:159–72
2. Auerbach, A. A., Bennett, M. V. L. 1969. A rectifying synapse in the central nervous system of a vertebrate. *J. Gen. Physiol.* 53:211–37
3. Azarnia, R., Dahl, G., Loewenstein, W. R. 1981. Cell junction and cyclic AMP: III. Promotion of junctional membrane permeability and junctional membrane particles in a junction-deficient cell type. *J. Membr. Biol.* 63:133–46
4. Baux, G., Simmoneau, M., Tauc, L., Segundo, J. P. 1978. Uncoupling of electrotonic synapses by calcium. *Proc. Natl. Acad. Sci. USA* 75:4577–81
5. Baylor, D. A., Nicholls, J. G. 1969. Chemical and electrical synaptic connexions between cutaneous mechanoreceptor neurones in the central nervous system of the leech. *J. Physiol.* 203:591–609
6. Bennett, M. V. L. 1966. Physiology of electrotonic junctions. *Ann. NY Acad. Sci.* 137:509–39
7. Bennett, M. V. L. 1973. Permeability and structure of electrotonic junctions and intercellular movement of tracers. In *Intracellular Staining Techniques in Neurobiology*, ed. S. Kater, C. Nicholson, pp. 115–33. New York: Springer-Verlag
8. Bennett, M. V. L. 1977. Electrical transmission: a functional analysis and comparison to chemical transmission. In *Cellular Biology of Neurons, Handbook of Physiology of the Nervous System.* ed.

E. Kandel, I:357–416. Baltimore: Williams & Wilkins
9. Bennett, M. V. L., Brown, J. E., Harris, A. L., Spray, D. C. 1978. Electrotonic junctions between *Fundulus* blastomeres: reversible block by low intracellular pH. *Biol. Bull.* 155:442
10. Bennett, M. V. L., Goodenough, D. M. 1978. Gap junctions, electrotonic coupling and intercellular communication. *Neurosci. Res. Program Bull.* 16:373–486
11. Bennett, M. V. L., Pappas, G. D. 1983. The electromotor system of the stargazer: a model for integrative actions at electrotonic synapses. *J. Neurosci.* 3:748–61
12. Bennett, M. V. L., Spray, D. C. 1984. Gap junctions: Two voltage dependent gates in series allow voltage induced steady state cycling around a circular reaction scheme. *Biophys. J.* 45:60a
13. Bennett, M. V. L., Spira, M. E., Spray, D. C. 1978. Permeability of gap junctions between embryonic cells of *Fundulus*: a reevaluation. *Dev. Biol.* 65:114–25
14. Bennett, M. V. L., Spray, D. C., Harris, A. L. 1981. Electrical coupling in development. *Amer. Zool.* 21:413–27
14a. Bodmer, R., Spray, D. C. 1985. Permeability and electrophysiological properties of *Aplysia* neurons in situ and in culture. *Biophys. J.* In press
15. Brink, P. R., Dewey, M. M. 1980. Evidence for fixed charge in the nexus. *Nature* 285:101–2
16. Brink, P. R., Verselis, V., Barr, L. 1984. Solvent-solute interactions within the nexal membrane. *Biophys. J.* 45:121–24

17. Burghardt, R. C., Anderson, E. 1979. Hormonal modulation of ovarion interstitial cells with particular reference to gap junctions. *J. Cell Biol.* 81:104–14

18. Calhoon, R. D., Gillette, R. 1983. Ca^{2+} activated and pH sensitive cyclic AMP phosphodiesterase in the nervous system of the mollusc *Pleurobranchaea*. *Brain Res.* 271:371–74

19. Carew, T. J., Kandel, E. R. 1976. Two functional effects of decreased conductance EPSPs: Synaptic augmentation and increased electrotonic coupling. *Science* 192:150–53

20. Carvalho, A., Ramon, F. 1982. The effect of protein reagents on the gap junctions of crayfish septate axons. *Biophys. J.* 37:287a

21. Campos de Carvalho, A. C., Ramon, F., Spray, D. C. 1985. Effects of group specific protein reagents on electrotonic coupling in crayfish septate axon. *J. Physiol.* Submitted for publication

22. Campos de Carvalho, A. C., Spray, D. C., Bennett, M. V. L. 1984. pH dependence of transmission at electrotonic synapses of the crayfish septate axon. *Brain Res.* In press

23. Carvalho, A. C., Spray, D. C., White, R. L., Bennett, M. V. L. 1982. Pharmacological alteration of gating properties of the gap junction channel. *Soc. Neurosci. Abstr.* 8:944

24. Caveney, S. 1978. Intercellular communication in insect development is hormonally controlled. *Science* 199:192–95

25. Caveney, S. 1985. The role of gap junctions in development. *Ann. Rev. Physiol.* 47:319–35

26. Caveney, S., Blennerhassett, M. G. 1979. Elevation of ionic conductance between insect epidermal cells by β-ecdysone in vitro. *J. Insect Physiol.* 26:13–25

27. Caveney, S., Berdan, R. C., McLean, S. 1980. Cell-to-cell ionic communication stimulated by 20-hydroxyecdysone occurs in the absence of protein synthesis and gap junction growth. *J. Insect Physiol.* 26:557–67

28. Cheung, W. Y. 1980. *Calcium and Cell Function*. New York: Academic 397 pp.

29. Connors, B. W., Benardo, L. S., Prince, D. A. 1984. Carbon dioxide sensitivity of dye coupling among glia and neurons of the neocortex. *J. Neurosci.* 4:1324–30

30. Dahl, G., Isenberg, G. 1980. Decoupling of heart muscle cells: correlation with increased cytoplasmic calcium activity and with changes of nexus ultrastructure. *J. Membr. Biol.* 53:63–75

31. Decker, R. S. 1976. Hormonal regulation of gap junction differentiation. *J. Cell Biol.* 69:669–85

32. Deleze, J., Herve, J. C. 1983. Effect of several uncouplers of cell-to-cell communication on gap junction morphology in mammalian heart. *J. Membr. Biol.* 74:203–15

33. DeMello, W. C. 1975. Effect of intracellular injection of calcium and strontium on cell communication in heart. *J. Physiol.* 250:231–45

34. DeMello, W. C. 1982. Cell-to cell communication in heart and other tissues. *Prog. Biophys. Molec. Biol.* 39:147–82

35. DeMello, W. C. 1982. Intercellular communication in cardiac muscle. *Circ. Res.* 51:1–9

36. DeMello, W. C. 1983. The influence of pH on the healing-over of mammalian cardiac muscle. *J. Physiol.* 339:299–307

37. DeMello, W. 1984. Effect of intracellular injection of cAMP on the electrical coupling of mammalian cardiac cells. *Biochem. Biophys. Res. Commun.* 119:1001–7

38. Deschenes, M., Bennett, M. V. L. 1974. Qualification to the use of TEA as a tracer for monosynaptic pathways. *Brain Res.* 77:169–72

39. Dudek, F. E., Andrew, R. D., MacVicar, B. A., Hatton, G. I. 1982. Intracellular electrophysiology of mammalian peptidergic neurons in rat hypothalamic slices. *Fed. Proc.* 41:2953–58

40. Edelman, G. M. 1983. Cell adhesion molecules. *Science* 219:450–57

41. Elias, P. M., Friend, D. S. 1976. Vitamin A induced mucous metaplasia. An in vitro system for modulating tight and gap junction differentiation. *J. Cell Biol.* 68:173–88

42. Elias, P. M., Grayson, S., Caldwell, T. M., McNutt, N. S. 1980. Gap junction proliferation in retinoic acid-treated human basal cell carcinoma. *Lab. Invest.* 42:469–74

43. Enomoto, T., Sasaki, Y., Shiba, Y., Kanno, Y., Yamasaki, H. 1981. Tumor promoters cause a rapid and reversible inhibition of the formation and maintenance of electrical cell coupling in culture. *Proc. Natl. Acad. Sci. USA* 78:5628–32

44. Enomoto, T., Sasaki, Y., Shiba, Y., Kanno, Y., Yamasaki, H. 1981. Inhibition of the formation of electrical cell coupling of FL cells by tumor promoters. *Gann* 72:631–34

45. Flagg-Newton, J., Simpson, I., Loewenstein, W. R., 1979. Permeability of the cell-to-cell membrane channels in mammalian cell junction. *Science* 205:404–7

46. Flagg-Newton, J. L., Dahl, G., Loewenstein, W. R. 1981. Cell junction and cyclic AMP: I. Upregulation of junctional membrane permeability and junctional membrane particles by administration of cyclic nucleotide or phosphodiesterase inhibitor. *J. Membr. Biol.* 63:105–21

47. Fozzard, H. A., Dominguez, G., 1969. Effect of formaldehyde and glutaraldehyde on electrical properties of cardiac Purkinje fibers. *J. Gen. Physiol.* 53:530–40

48. Furshpan, E. J., Potter, D. D. 1959. Transmission at the giant motor synapses of the crayfish. *J. Physiol.* 145:289–325

49. Garfield, R. E., Kannan, M. S., Daniel, E. E. 1980. Gap junction formation in myometrium: control by estrogens, progesterone, and prostaglandins. *Am. J. Physiol.* 238:C81–89

50. Giaume, C., Korn, H. 1982. Ammonium sulfate induced uncouplings of crayfish septate axons with and without increased junctional resistance. *Neuroscience* 7: 1723–30

51. Giaume, C., Spira, M. E., Korn, H. 1980. Uncoupling of invertebrate electrotonic synapses by carbon dioxide. *Neurosci. Lett.* 17:197–99

52. Gilula, N. B., Epstein, M. 1976. Cell-to-cell communication, gap junctions, and calcium. *Symp. Soc. Exp. Biol.* 30:251–272

53. Gilette, R., Pomeranze, B. 1975. Ultrastructural correlates of interneuronal function in the abdominal ganglion of *Aplysia californica*. *J. Neurobiol.* 6:463–74

54. Hall, D. H., Spray, D. C., Bennett, M. V. L. 1983. Gap junctions and septate-like junctions between neurons of the opisthobranch mollusssc, *Navanax inermis*. *J. Neurocytol.* 12:831–46

55. Hanna, R. B., Reese, T. S., Ornberg, R. L., Spray, D. C., Bennett, M. V. L. 1981. Fresh frozen gap junctions: Structural detail in the coupled and uncoupled states. *J. Cell Biol.* 91:125a

56. Harris, A. L., Spray, D. C., Bennett, M. V. L. 1980. Temperature dependence of voltage dependent junctional conductance. *Soc. Neurosci. Abstr.* 6:96

57. Harris, A. L., Spray, D. C., Bennett, M. V. L. 1981. Kinetic properties of a voltage dependent junctional conductance. *J. Gen. Physiol.* 77:95–117

58. Harris, A. L., Spray, D. C., Bennett, M. V. L. 1983. Control of intercellular communication by a voltage dependent junctional conductance. *J. Neurosci.* 3:79–100

59. Hax, W. M. A., van Venrooji, G. E. M. P., Vossenberg, J. B. 1974. Cell communication: A cyclic-AMP mediated phenomenon. *J. Membr. Biol.* 19:253–66

60. Heimsmeyer, K. 1980. Angiotensin II increases electrical coupling in mammalian ventricular myocardium. *Circ. Res.* 47:524–29

61. Hertzberg, E. 1985. Antibody probes in the study of gap junctional communication. *Ann. Rev. Physiol.* 47:305–18

62. Hertzberg, E., Gilula, N. B. 1981. Liver gap junctions and lens fiber junctions: Comparative analysis and calmodulin interactions. *Cold Spring Harbor Symp. Quant. Biol.* 46:639–45

63. Hertzberg, E., Spray, D. C., Bennett, M. V. L. 1984. An antibody to gap junctions blocks gap junctional conductance. *J. Cell Biol.* 99:343a

64. Hess, P., Weingart, R. 1980. Intracellular free calcium modified by pH$_i$ in sheep cardiac Purkinje fibers. *J. Physiol.* 307:60–61P

65. Higgins, D., Burton, H. 1982. Electrotonic synapses are formed by fetal rat sympathetic neurons maintained in a chemically defined culture medium. *J. Neurosci.* 7:2241–53

66. Iwatsuki, N., Petersen, O. H. 1979. Pancreatic acinar cells: the effect of carbon dioxide, ammonium chloride, and acetylcholine on intercellular communication. *J. Physiol.* 291:317–26

67. Jacobus, W. E., Pores, I. H., Lucas, S. K., Kallman, C. H., Weisfeldt, M. L., Flaherty, J. T. 1982. The role of intracellular pH in the control of normal and ischemic myocardial contractility. In *Intracellular pH*, ed. R. Nuccitelli, D. Deamer, pp. 537–65. New York: Liss

68. Johnston, M. F., Ramon, F. 1982. Voltage independence of an electrotonic synapse. *Biophys. J.* 39:115–17

69. Johnston, M. F., Ramon, F. 1982. Electrotonic coupling in internally perfused crayfish segmented axons. *J. Physiol.* 317:509–18

70. Johnston, M. F., Simon, S. A., Ramon, F. 1980. Interaction of anesthetics with electrical synapses. *Nature* 286:498–500

71. Kessler, J. A., Spray, D. C., Saez, J. C., Bennett, M. V. L. 1984. Determination of synaptic phenotype: Insulin and cAMP independently initiate development of electrotonic coupling between cultured sympathetic neurons. *Proc. Natl. Acad. Sci. USA* 81:6235–39

72. Knowles, W. D., Funch, P. G., Schwartzkroin, P. A. 1982. Electrotonic and dye coupling in hippocampal CA1 pyramidal cells in vitro. *Neuroscience* 7:1713–22

73. Larsen, W. J. 1977. Gap junctions

and hormone action. In *Transport of Ions and Water in Epithelia*, ed. B. J. Wall, J. L. Oschman, B. Moreton, B. Gupta, pp. 333–61. London: Academic

74. Lees-Miller, J. P., Caveney, S. 1982. Drugs that block calmodulin activity inhibit cell-to-cell coupling in the epidermis of *Tenebrio molitor*. *J. Membr. Biol.* 69:233–45

75. Margiotta, J. F., Walcott, B. 1983. Conductance and dye permeability of a rectifying electrical synapse. *Nature* 305: 52–55

76. Meda, P., Perrelet, A., Orci, L. 1979. Increase of gap junctions between pancreatic B-cells during stimulation of insulin secretion. *J. Cell Biol.* 82:441–48

77. Meyer, D. J., Revel, J. P. 1981. CO_2 does not uncouple hepatocytes in rat liver. *Biophys. J.* 33:105a

78. Moore, R. D., Fidelman, M. L., Hasen, J. C., Otis, J. N. 1982. The role of intracellular pH in insulin action. In *Intracellular pH*, ed. D. Deamer, R. Nuccitelli, pp. 385–416. New York: Liss

79. Murray, W. W., Fitzgerald, D. J. 1979. Tumor promoters inhibit metabolic cooperation in cocultures of epidermal and 3T3 cells. *Biochem. Biophys. Res. Commun.* 91:395–401

80. Nicholls, J. G., Purves, D. 1972. A comparison of chemical and electrical synaptic transmission between single sensory cells and a motoneurone in the central nervous system of the leech. *J. Physiol.* 225:637–56

81. Nishiye, H. 1977. The mechanism of Ca^{2+} action on the healing-over process in mammalian cardiac muscles: A kinetic analysis. *Jpn. J. Physiol.* 27:451–66

82. Nishiye, H., Ishida, A., Machima, H. 1980. Ca binding of isolated nexus membranes related to intercellular coupling. *Jpn. J. Physiol.* 30:131–36

83. Obaid, A. L., Socolar, S. J., Rose, B. 1983. Cell-to-cell channels with two independent regulated gates in series: analysis of junctional channel modulation by membrane potential, calcium and pH. *J. Membr. Biol.* 73:69–89

84. Oliviera-Castro, G. M., Loewenstein, W. R. 1971. Junctional membrane permeability: Effects of divalent cations. *J. Membr. Biol.* 5:51–77

85. Payton, B. W., Bennett, M. V. L., Pappas, G. D. 1969. Temperature-dependence of resistance at an electrotonic junction. *Science* 165:594–97

86. Payton, B. W., Loewenstein, W. R. 1967. Stability of electrical coupling in leech giant nerve cells: Divalent cations, propionate ions, tonicity and pH. *Biochim. Biophys. Acta* 150:156–58

87. Peracchia, C. 1980. Structural correlates of gap junction permeation. *Int. Rev. Cytol.* 66:81–104

88. Peracchia, C., Bernardini, G., Peracchia, L. L. 1983. Is calmodulin involved in the regulation of gap junction permeability? *Pfluegers Arch.* 399:152–54

89. Piccolino, M., Neyton, J., Witkovsky, P., Gerschenfeld, H. M. 1982. GABA antagonists decrease functional communication between L-horizontal cells of the retina. *Proc. Natl. Acad. Sci. USA* 79:3671–75

90. Pitts, J. D., Sims, J. W. 1977. Permeability of junctions between animal cells. Intercellular transfer of nucleotides but not of macromolecules. *Exp. Cell. Res.* 104:153–63

91. Politoff, A. L., Socolar, S. J., Loewenstein, W. R. Permeability of a cell membrane junction. Dependence on energy metabolism. *J. Gen. Physiol.* 53:498–515

92. Politoff, A. L., Pappas, G. D. 1972. Mechanisms of increase in coupling resistance at electrotonic synapses of the crayfish septate axon. *Anat. Rec.* 172: 384–85

93. Politoff, A., Pappas, G. D., Bennett, M. V. L. 1974. Cobalt ions cross an electrotonic synapse if cytoplasmic concentration is low. *Brain Res.* 76:343–46

94. Radu, A., Dahl, G., Loewenstein, W. R. 1982. Hormonal regulation of cell junction permeability. Upregulation by catecholamine and prostaglandin E1. *J. Membr. Biol.* 70:239–51

95. Ramon, F., Zampighi, G. 1980. On the electrotonic coupling mechanism of crayfish segmented axons: temperature dependence of junctional conductance. *J. Membr. Biol.* 54:165–71

96. Rayport, S. G. 1982. A possible role for electrical synapses in epilepsy: mechanisms underlying enhancement of electrical transmission by epiloptogenic agents. In *Physiology and Pharmacology of Epileptogenic Phenomena*, ed. M. R. Klee, pp. 213–25. New York: Raven

97. Reber, W. R., Weingart, R. 1982. Ungulate cardiac Purkinje fibres: the influence of intracellular pH on the electrical cell-to-cell coupling. *J. Physiol.* 328:87–104

98. Revel, J.-P., Nicholson, B. J., Yancey, S. B. 1985. Chemistry of gap junctions. *Ann. Rev. Physiol.* 47:263–79

99. Rink, T. J., Tsien, R. Y., Warner, A. E. 1980. Free calcium in *Xenopus* embryos measured with ion-selective microelectrodes. *Nature* 283:658–60

100. Rose, B., Loewenstein, R. 1970. Junc-

tional membrane permeability. Depression by substitution of Li for extracellular Na and by long-term lack of Ca and Mg; restoration by cell repolarization. *J. Membr. Biol.* 5:20–50

101. Rose, B., Loewenstein, W. R. 1975. Permeability of cell junctions depends on local cytoplasmic calcium activity. *Nature* 254:250–52

102. Rose, B., Rick, R. 1978. Intracellular pH, intracellular free Ca, and junctional cell-cell coupling. *J. Membr. Biol.* 44:377–415

103. Scheutze, S. M., Goodenough, D. A. 1982. Dye transfer between cells of the embryonic chick lens becomes less sensitive to CO_2 treatment during development. *J. Cell Biol.* 92:694–705

104. Schwartzmann, G., Wiegandt, H., Rose, B., Zimmerman, A., Ben-Haim, D., Loewenstein, W. R. 1981. Diameter of the cell-to-cell junctional membrane channels as probed with neutral molecules. *Science* 213:551–53

105. Sheridan, J. D., Atkinson, M. 1985. Physiological roles of permeable junctions: some possibilities. *Ann. Rev. Physiol.* 47:337–53

106. Sims, S. M., Daniel, E. E., Garfield, R. E. 1982. Improved electrical coupling in uterine smooth muscle is associated with increased numbers of gap junctions at parturition. *J. Gen. Physiol.* 80:353–75

107. Slaga, T. J., Klein-Szanto, A. J. P., Tripleh, L. L., Yotti, L. P., Trosko, J. E. 1981. Skin tumor–promoting activity of benzoyl peroxide, a widely used free radical-generating compound. *Science* 213:1023–25

108. Smith, T. G., Baumann, F. 1969. The functional organization within the ommatidium of the lateral eye of the *Limulus*. *Prog. Brain Res.* 31:313–49

109. Sotelo, C., Llinas, R., Baker, R. 1972. Structural study of inferior olivary nucleus of the cat: morphological correlates of electrotonic coupling between neurons. *Brain Res.* 37:294–300

110. Spira, M. E., Spray, D. C., Bennett, M. V. L. 1980. Synaptic organization of expansion motoneurons of *Navanax inermis*. *Brain Res.* 195:241–69

111. Spitzer, N. 1982. Voltage- and stage-dependent uncoupling of Rohon-Beard neurones during embryonic development of *Xenopus* tadpoles. *J. Physiol.* 330:145–62

112. Spray, D. C., White, R. L., Campos de Carvalho, A. C., Bennett, M. V. L. 1983. Internal pH and transjunctional voltage control gap junctional conductance by separable mechanisms. *Int. Congr. Physiol. Sci. Abstr.* 15:502

113. Spray, D. C., Ginzberg, R. D., Morales, E. A., Bennett, M. V. L., Babayatsky, M., et al. 1984. Physiological and pharmacological properties of gap junctions between dissociated pairs of rat hepatocytes. *J. Cell. Biol.* 99:344a

114. Deleted in proof

115. Spray, D. C., Harris, A. L., Bennett, M. V. L. 1979. Voltage dependence of junctional conductance in early amphibian embryos. *Science* 204:432–34

116. Spray, D. C., Harris, A. L., Bennett, M. V. L. 1980. Glutaraldehyde differentially affects gap junctional conductance and its pH and voltage dependence. *Biophys. J.* 33:108a

117. Spray, D. C., Harris, A. L., Bennett, M. V. L. 1981. Equilibrium properties of a voltage dependent junctional conductance. *J. Gen. Physiol.* 77:75–94

118. Spray, D. C., Harris, A. L., Bennett, M. V. L. 1981. Gap junctional conductance is a simple and sensitive function of intracellular pH. *Science* 211:712–15

119. Spray, D. C., Harris, A. L., Bennett, M. V. L. 1982. Control of communication via gap junctions. In *Cellular Communication During Development*, ed. R. Hilfer, J. Sheffield, pp. 57–84. New York: Springer-Verlag

120. Spray, D. C., Harris, A. L., Bennett, M. V. L. 1982. Comparison of pH and Ca dependence of gap junctional conductance. In: *Intracellular pH* ed. D. Deamer, R. Nuccitelli, pp. 445–61. New York: Liss

121. Spray, D. C., Nerbonne, J. M., Connor, J. A., Harris, A. L., Carvalho, A. C., Bennett, M. V. L. 1982. Nitrobenzyl esters reversibly decrease gap junctional conductance. *J. Cell Biol.* 95:109a

122. Spray, D. C., Stern, J. H., Harris, A. L., Bennett, M. V. L. 1982. Comparison of sensitivities of gap junctional conductance to H and Ca ions. *Proc. Natl. Acad. Sci. USA* 79:441–45

123. Spray, D. C., White, R. L., Campos de Carvalho, A. C., Harris, A. L., Bennett, M. V. L. 1984. Gating of gap junction channels. *Biophys. J.* 45:219–30

124. Stewart, W. W. 1978. Functional connections between cells as revealed by dye-coupling with a highly fluorescent naphthalimide tracer. *Cell* 14:741–59

125. Teranishi, T., Negishi, K., Kato, S. 1982. Dopamine modulates S-potential amplitude and dye-coupling between external horizontal cells in carp retina. *Nature* 301:243–46

125a. Triller, A., Korn, H. 1981. Interneuronal transfer of horseradish peroxidase associated with exo/endocytotic activity on adjacent membranes. *Exp. Brain Res.* 43:233–36

126. Trosko, J. E., Dawson, B., Yotti, L. P., Chang, C. C. 1981. Saccharin may act as a tumor promoter by inhibiting metabolic cooperativity between cells. *Nature* 285:109–110

127. Turin, L., Warner, A. E. 1978. Carbon dioxide reversibly abolishes ionic communication between cells of early amphibian embryo. *Nature* 270:56–57

128. Turin, L., Warner, A. E. 1980. Intracellular pH in early *Xenopus* embryos: its effects on current flow between blastomeres. *J. Physiol.* 300:489–504

129. Unwin, N. T., Zampighi, G. 1980. Structure of the junction between communicating cells. *Nature* 283:545–49

130. Verselis, V., Brink, P. R. 1984. Voltage-clamp of the earthworm septum. *Biophys. J.* 45:147–50

131. Verselis, V., Spray, D. C., White, R. L., Bennett, M. V. L. 1984. Relative permeabilities of gap junctions to symmetrical tetra-alkylammonium ions. *Soc. Neurosci. Abstr.* 10:243

132. Weingart, R. 1977. The actions of ouabain on intercellular coupling and conduction velocity in mammalian ventricular muscle. *J. Physiol.* 264:341–65

133. Weiner, E. C., Loewenstein, W. R. 1983. Correction of cell-to-cell communication defect by introduction of a protein kinase into mutant cells. *Nature* 305:433–435

134. White, R. L., Spray, D. C., Carvalho, A. C., Bennett, M. V. L. 1982. Voltage dependent gap junctional conductance between fish embryonic cells. *Soc. Neurosci. Abstr.* 8:944

135. White, R. L., Spray, D. C., Campos de Carvalho, A. C., Wittenberg, B. A., Bennett, M. V. L. 1985. Some physiological and pharmacological properties of cardiac myocytes dissociated from adult rat. *Am. J. Physiol.* Submitted for publication

136. Wojtczak, J. A. 1984. Effects of general and local anesthetics on intracellular coupling in heart muscle. *Biophys. J.* 45:22a

137. Yancey, S. B., Easter, D., Revel, J. P. 1979. Cytological changes in gap junctions during liver regeneration. *J. Ultrastruct. Res.* 67:229–42

138. Yotti, L. P., Chag, C. C., Trosko, J. E. 1979. Elimination of metabolic cooperation in Chinese hamster cells by a tumor promoter. *Science* 306:1089–91

139. Zipser, B. 1979. Voltage-modulated membrane resistance in coupled leech neurons. *J. Neurophysiol.* 42:465–75

Ann. Rev. Physiol. 1985. 47:305–18

ANTIBODY PROBES IN THE STUDY OF GAP JUNCTIONAL COMMUNICATION

Elliot L. Hertzberg

Verna and Marrs McLean Department of Biochemistry, Baylor College of Medicine, Houston, Texas 77030

INTRODUCTION

Gap junctions are thought to contain intercellular channels, insulated from the extracellular space, that permit direct cell-cell communication via the passage of small molecules. Until recently, the study of gap junctional communication has been based on the detection of gap junctions by electron microscopic analysis of thin section and freeze-fracture samples and on the physiological measurement of radiolabeled metabolite transfer (metabolic coupling), fluorescent dye transfer (dye coupling), and ion movement (electrical coupling) between adjacent cells. Although several effectors that regulate gap junctional conductance have been identified with this approach (3, 12, 47, 51, 55, 57, 63), it is not known whether they influence the gap junction polypeptide(s). In the absence of specific probes for these polypeptides, it has proven difficult to examine these mechanisms, gap junction biogenesis, and the various roles that have been suggested for gap junctional communication in normal and pathological tissues (for reviews see 6, 31, 37, 38, 48).

The focus of this review is to describe the recent progress made in using immunological probes to analyze gap junction–mediated cell-cell communication in vivo and in vitro.

ISOLATION AND CHARACTERIZATION OF GAP JUNCTIONS

The major sources from which gap junctions have been isolated are mouse and rat liver. The earliest protocol for their purification from liver plasma mem-

0066-4278/85/0315-0305$02.00

branes utilized the principle that gap junctions are relatively insoluble in N-lauroylsarcosinate (Sarkosyl) (16). Using detergent resistance as a general approach, gap junctions have since been isolated by extraction of plasma membranes with deoxycholate (15), Triton X-100 and urea (25), N-lauroylsarcosinate (Sarkosyl) (11, 19, 23, 26, 29), as well as combinations of detergents (54). The earlier approaches also employed proteases, such as trypsin and/or collagenase (11, 23), to aid in tissue dissociation, a practice that led to much confusion concerning the molecular weight of the major gap junction polypeptide (25, 26, 29). Subsequently, protease-free protocols have been developed that give a more consistent polypeptide profile.

Recently, an alternative procedure has been introduced for the isolation of gap junctions from liver based on their resistance to extraction in alkali (27), a property that is exhibited by integral membrane proteins (58). Following alkali extraction of plasma membranes, the gap junctions are purified from the residue using differential and sucrose density-gradient centrifugation. The major advantage of this new approach is its improved yield of gap junction protein: 2–3 mg from 30 rat livers, as compared to about 300 μg obtained earlier (26). It has since been observed that isolated gap junctions are slowly solubilized by Sarkosyl, as well as by deoxycholate and Triton X-100, perhaps accounting for the reduced recoveries of the protocols employing these detergents (E. Hertzberg, unpublished observations).

The major constituent of the liver gap junctions is a 27,000-dalton polypeptide (25, 26, 29), termed "connexin" by Goodenough (22). Structural studies (4, 25, 39, 64, 65) suggest that six connexin molecules comprise each gap junction hemichannel (termed a "connexon" and presumably the equivalent of a particle as observed in freeze-fracture analysis).

One of the characteristic properties of the liver gap junction polypeptide is its tendency to undergo heat-induced aggregation in SDS (25, 26). Aggregation under these conditions is increased by the presence of other membrane proteins, whether gap junctional or not (25). Aggregation, in the case of the rat liver gap junction polypeptide, which has a greater tendency to aggregate than that from mouse liver, yields a major band with an apparent M_r of 47,000 on SDS-polyacrylamide gels. Peptide maps have demonstrated that the 27,000- and 47,000-dalton polypeptides are identical (25, 26). This aggregation property has been used in the analysis of junction proteins in other tissues and species (below).

Amino acid analysis of detergent-treated gap junctions (25), which has been essentially confirmed with alkali-extracted gap junctions (Hertzberg & Bradley, unpublished observations), has demonstrated an amino acid composition similar to that of other integral membrane proteins. Trypsin digestion of isolated gap junctions yields a residue with a substantially higher content of hydrophobic amino acids than the starting material. This observation is consistent with removal of hydrophilic residues from the cytoplasmic surface of the gap junction, leaving a hydrophobic domain that presumably surrounds the aqueous channel within the phospholipid bilayer (25).

No carbohydrate appears to be associated with gap junction protein. Efforts to detect glycosylation of the gap junction polypeptide have included binding of radioiodinated lectins (Concanavalin A and wheat germ agglutinin) (29), incorporation of tritium label from NaB_3H_4 subsequent to treatment with galactose oxidase (with or without pretreatment with neuraminidase) (29), and analysis of amino acid composition (25). Although the latter suffers from poor sensitivity and the others from restricted specificity, it does appear from these studies that the gap junction polypeptide, at least in its mature, assembled form, is one of the few plasma membrane proteins not glycosylated.

Analysis of the lipid content of gap junctions isolated by detergent-dependent protocols has demonstrated reduced levels of sphingomyelin relative to plasma membranes (29) and an enrichment for cholesterol (25); lipid analysis of gap junctions isolated by alkali-resistance procedures has not, as yet, been carried out. The observations concerning sphingomyelin may only reflect its selective solubilization during detergent treatment (29). The high cholesterol content of isolated gap junctions probably reflects the in vivo state, based upon the fact that detergent-extraction conditions were nonselective towards cholesterol (25), although the significance of this enrichment is not clear.

ANTIBODIES TO THE 27,000-DALTON LIVER GAP JUNCTION POLYPEPTIDE AND THEIR APPLICATIONS

Recently, antibodies to the liver gap junction polypeptide have been generated in rabbits by Willecke and his coworkers (34, 60) as well as in a sheep by this reviewer's laboratory (27). The antibodies developed by these two groups appear to have generally similar properties. They are directed against multiple determinants on the junction polypeptide, based upon double diffusion analysis in which precipitin arcs were observed (27, 60). That they are specific for the 27,000-dalton gap junction polypeptide has been demonstrated by immunoreplica analysis of liver plasma membranes and isolated gap junctions (27, 60). By indirect immunofluorescence staining (27, 34), the antibodies appear to bind to punctuate regions of the hepatocyte plasma membrane in a manner consistent with the distribution of gap junctions determined by electron microscopy (42, 43, 50).

In addition, Willecke and his coworkers have shown by immunoelectron microscopy that their antibodies bind to isolated gap junctions. On the basis of their data, they estimate that nonjunctional plasma membrane does not contain any appreciable quantity of unassembled 27,000-dalton gap junction polypeptide (34). However, given the decreased antibody-binding capacity of the gap junctions in their plasma membrane preparation relative to that of isolated gap junctions and given the high background binding of preimmune immunoglobulin, the validity of this interpretation is subject to question.

Generation of these probes has constituted an elusive goal for many years. The rabbit antibodies were raised against gap junctions prepared by a detergent-dependent protocol. In the case of the sheep antibody, milligram quantities of rat liver gap junction protein, made available by the new isolation procedure using alkali, were injected. It is not yet clear, however, what factors are critical in obtaining an antibody response to gap junctions.

Characterization of Liver Gap Junction Polypeptides

Although there is general agreement concerning the identification of the 27,000-dalton polypeptide as the major constituent of liver gap junctions, the polypeptide profiles of isolated gap junctions reveal a variable number of other components representing aggregation products (see above) as well as proteolytic fragments or possible contaminants, as discussed below. These have been tested for homology to the 27,000-dalton polypeptide by immunoreplica analysis (Western blots). For this procedure, samples are resolved on SDS-polyacrylamide gels and electrophoretically transferred to nitrocellulose whereupon they are incubated with antibodies to the 27,000-dalton rat liver gap junction polypeptide (see below). Cross-reaction is then evaluated by subsequent visualization of antibody binding, using a variety of techniques. By this procedure it was shown that antibodies to the 27,000-dalton gap junction polypeptide recognize the heat-aggregated 47,000-dalton polypeptide as well as higher aggregates (27).

The polypeptide profile of rat liver gap junctions reveals a 22,000-dalton polypeptide as a minor component ($\sim$ 5% of total protein) (26). It is observed in isolated junctions prepared by either the detergent- or the alkali-resistance approaches. Antibodies to the 27,000-dalton polypeptide did not cross-react with the 22,000-dalton polypeptide, although they did recognize other, lower-molecular-weight fragments generated by proteolysis of the major gap junction polypeptide (27). Hence, it is not clear whether the 22,000-dalton polypeptide represents a different junction protein or a contaminant present in rat liver gap junctions.

Isolated mouse liver gap junctions are also characterized by a 21,000-dalton polypeptide, which was found to be related to the 27,000-dalton polypeptide by peptide mapping (25). Immunoreplica analyses, using antibodies to the 27,000-dalton rat liver polypeptide, have detected the 21,000-dalton polypeptide in isolated mouse liver gap junctions but not in whole liver homogenates (E. Hertzberg, unpublished observations), suggesting that it arises by proteolysis of the larger polypeptide during the preparative procedure. However, another study, reported by Willecke and his colleagues, did not find cross-reaction between these two polypeptides using antibodies specific for either of them (60). In their immunocytological localization of antibody binding (34), apparently only the anti–27,000-dalton antibodies were used, leaving unresolved the question of whether the 21,000-dalton polypeptide that they detected was a contaminant or a constituent of gap junctions.

Recent reports from one laboratory have described the isolation of a 16,000-dalton gap junction polypeptide from not only liver but also a number of other tissues and cultured cells, using a modified Triton X-100 extraction and a trypsin treatment step (18). This polypeptide has been found to bind antibodies to the 27,000-dalton rat liver gap junction polypeptide (E. Hertzberg & M. Finbow, unpublished observations). In the opinion of this reviewer, it is therefore likely that the 16,000-dalton polypeptide constitutes a fragment derived by proteolysis from the 27,000-dalton liver gap junction polypeptide.

Analysis of Tissue and Species Specificity of the Major Liver Gap Junction Polypeptide

A number of studies have examined the tissue and species specificity of gap junctional communication (14, 44). In these investigations, vertebrate cells from different tissues that were capable of forming gap junctions and communicating with each other in culture were found to communicate with other communication-competent cells in heterologous coculture. At a molecular level, this suggests that vertebrate gap junctions share homology at least in their extracellular domain such that complementary junction hemichannels are able to recognize and interact with each other. In a similar analysis of vertebrate and invertebrate cells, invertebrate cells were unable to communicate with vertebrate cells, and some specificity was observed among the various invertebrate species as well (14).

The question of homology has been further explored by comparative peptide map analyses and immunological studies of isolated gap junctions. In the case of the major liver gap junction polypeptides from rat, mouse, rabbit, and calf, a high degree of homology is indicated by peptide mapping (26, 46). Antibodies to the rat liver gap junction polypeptide have been used to extend these findings to liver gap junction polypeptides in chicken and goldfish as well as several mammalian species (rat, mouse, human, monkey, rabbit, and sheep). Antibody binding was localized in situ by indirect immunofluorescence staining, and the polypeptides responsible for binding were identified by immunoreplica analysis of liver extracts (32). In all cases, indirect immunofluorescence demonstrated binding in a punctate pattern to the cell periphery. Western blots confirmed the presence of a 27,000-dalton polypeptide, with a tendency to aggregate when heated in SDS prior to electrophoresis. These results are consistent with the peptide map analyses cited above, providing further evidence that a highly homologous polypeptide comprises liver gap junctions in a number of diverse vertebrate species.

In lens, an avascular organ, cell-cell communication takes place between lens fiber cells, enabling nutrient uptake and waste-product removal via an epithelial cell layer surrounding the lens that is in contact with the bathing aqueous humor. There is a growing body of evidence that the gap junction-like structure isolated from lens fiber cells represents a unique class of intercellular junctions. No homology was observed by comparative peptide mapping of the 26,000-dalton lens fiber junction polypeptide (MP26, MIP) (1, 8, 13) and the 27,000-dalton liver gap junction polypeptide (28, 46). Furthermore, antibodies generated against MP26 failed to cross-react with purified liver gap junctions (28, 30) or with proteins from any nonlens tissue (9). Studies of the structure (71) and regulatory properties (53) of lens fiber junctions have also indicated that they are not similar to those of liver gap junctions.

The only other tissue from which gap junctions have been isolated is heart (24, 36, 40, 41). Although studies of these junctions have been more limited than those of liver gap junctions, there is general agreement that heart gap junctions are characterized by a ~ 29,000-dalton polypeptide. Peptide map analysis did not indicate homology between liver and heart gap junctions, although sequence analysis revealed partial homology in their first 20 N-terminal residues (24).

Based upon the peptide map studies of junctions cited above, it has been suggested that gap junctions in different tissues might be comprised of distinct polypeptides (24, 28, 30, 46, 61), specific to each germ layer (24), perhaps representing a multigene family with a common ancestral DNA sequence (61). However, a different conclusion has been reached using the sheep antibodies against rat liver gap junctions to further examine the question of gap junction homology in a number of other rat tissues, as described below (32).

Indirect immunofluorescence was used to localize antibody binding on frozen sections of rat exocrine pancreas and heart ventricle (32). In the case of pancreas, fluorescence was found in punctate regions of the plasma membrane, whereas in heart the distribution was consistent with binding to intercalated discs. In both cases, the distribution of fluorescence was consistent with the disposition of gap junctions in these tissues as observed in electron microscopic analysis (20, 42, 43, 50). Immunocytological techniques at the level of resolution of the electron microscope will be required to more precisely localize antibody binding in these tissues.

Antibody binding to specific polypeptides in these and other tissues was evaluated by immunoreplica analysis of tissue extracts that were electophoretically separated on SDS-polyacrylamide gels (32). In addition, samples were heated in SDS prior to electrophoresis in order to determine if they shared the anomalous behavior of the liver gap junction polypeptide that undergoes aggregation under these conditions. Binding was detected to a 27,000-dalton polypeptide, which aggregated upon heating in SDS, in extracts prepared from pancreas, kidney, heart, adrenal gland, stomach, and brain. The strong cross-reaction obtained with these proteins of the same apparent M_r and aggregation tendency suggests that *a highly homologous, or identical polypeptide is found in nearly all rat tissues.*

The single exception to this rule was lens fiber tissue; no homology was detected by either immunofluorescence staining or immunoreplica analysis. Willecke and coworkers, using their affinity-purified antibodies to the liver gap junction polypeptide in an analysis limited to evaluating cross-reaction with lens liver junction polypeptide, have reported a slight interaction (about 1%) (61). Although objections might be raised to this study because their preimmune IgG interacted with MP26, and contamination with gap junctions derived from epithelial cells was possible, it is likely that some minor cross-reaction does occur. Its extent, however, suggests that the liver and lens polypeptides must represent different gene products.

Antibody-Induced Perturbation of Gap Junctional Conductance

The available antibodies against the rat liver gap junction have yet to be characterized in detail as to their binding site on the gap junction polypeptide. When the rabbit antibodies were applied extracellularly to communicating cultures of 3T6 mouse fibroblast cells, no effect on the ability of these cells to transfer radiolabeled metabolites (metabolic coupling) was detected (60). Similarly, extracellular application of the sheep antibodies was without effect on electrical coupling between primary cultures of hepatocytes, superior cervical ganglion neurons and myocardial cells (33).

However, upon microinjection into cultured cells, the sheep antibodies were found to inhibit both fluorescent dye transfer (dye coupling) and electrical coupling (33). These experiments were carried out in primary cultures of hepatocytes, myocardial cells, and superior cervical ganglion neurons. Each cell of a cell pair was impaled with two electrodes, one for passing current pulses and the other for measuring the resulting voltage deflection, with one cell also impaled with a micropipette for pressure-injection of antibody. Current pulses were applied in an alternating manner to each cell of the cell pair in order to continuously monitor both gap junctional conductance and nonjunctional membrane conductance (5). Using a dilute solution of antibody, each pulse of antibody was found to rapidly inhibit gap junctional conductance, with additional pulses eliciting further inhibition of conductance in a dose-dependent manner. Inhibition of fluorescent dye transfer was also observed. Addition of antibody using a more concentrated solution was observed to cause a rapid and complete inhibition of gap junctional communication. No inhibition of gap junctional conductance was observed when preimmune IgG or affinity-purified antibodies to other membrane proteins were used.

These experiments provide a direct demonstration that the 27,000-dalton gap junction polypeptide and, by extension, gap junctions are indeed involved in cell-cell communication. The studies also demonstrate that the sheep antibodies recognize determinants on the gap junction polypeptide located on the cytoplasmic domain and that these domains are homologous in neurons, hepatocytes, and myocardial cells. When taken together with data from coculture experiments and immunochemical analyses cited above, the results indicate that a highly homologous polypeptide is responsible for gap junctional communication in cells derived from all three germ layers: endoderm (hepatocytes), ectoderm (neurons), and mesoderm (myocardial cells). Further biochemical characterization of the gap junction polypeptide from these different cell types will be necessary to determine the extent of homology. Nonetheless, it is clear that a powerful probe is now available for selectively perturbing communication in vertebrate cells.

CONTRIBUTION OF ANTIBODY PROBES TO STUDY OF THE MECHANISMS OF REGULATION OF GAP JUNCTIONAL CONDUCTANCE

Studies of gap junctional conductance in vertebrate cells have demonstrated that it can be regulated by elevated intracellular Ca^{++} concentration (37, 38, 51, 57), reduced intracellular pH (51, 56, 57, 62, 63), and transjunctional potential (55). However, the mechanisms by which these different effectors influence gap junctional conductance is not clear. The possibilities range from direct effects on the gap junction polypeptide to action via other modulator proteins.

One particularly attractive hypotheses is that regulation occurs through the interaction of the gap junction polypeptide(s) with effector-sensitive regulatory proteins (30, 32, 35). In other words, junction-associated proteins may be "subunits" of communicating gap junctions, much as calmodulin is a subunit of phosphorylase kinase (10). Such a model might account for both the regulation diversity of cell-cell communication (pH, Ca^{++}, transjunctional potential) as well as the results of the immunochemical and biochemical studies described above indicating that gap junctions of most vertebrate tissues are composed of a single or, perhaps, a small family of homologous polypeptides. The regulation of gap junctional conductance by the association of effector-specific proteins with the major gap junction polypeptide also provides a plausible explanation for the phenomenon of rectification of junctional conductance, such as that observed in crayfish giant motor synapses (21) and a hatchetfish motor neuron (2), as well as for alterations in communication that occur in developmentally significant contacts such as compartment boundaries (7, 52, 66, 67).

The observations that calmodulin can interact with gap junction polypeptides in vitro (30) and that calmodulin antagonists can profoundly influence gap junctional communication (47) strengthen the case for this model. Because calmodulin structure and function are profoundly influenced by pH (49) in the range that influences gap junctional conductance (pH 6.5–7.5)(56, 57, 62, 63), it is possible that both Ca^{++} and pH effects are manifested by the interaction of calmodulin with the gap junction polypeptide.

In two attempts to test this model by internally perfusing cells to remove the cytoplasm and determine the effect on the regulation of junctional communication by pH and Ca^{++}, different results were obtained. In the case of perfused crayfish segmented axons, junctional conductance was rendered insensitive to variations of pH and Ca^{++} (35), whereas in perfused *Fundulus* blastomeres, gap junctional conductance retained sensitivity to both pH and Ca^{++} (57). The basis for this discrepancy is not clear, suggesting that alternative approaches will be required for its resolution.

The fact that native associations of gap junctions polypeptides with regulatory proteins have not been detected thus far is probably due to their disruption under the relatively harsh conditions employed for gap junction isolation. In this regard, immunoprecipitation of complexes, using antibodies to the gap junction polypeptide, may succeed in preserving such associations, eventually enabling purification of the associated proteins. Ideally then, the purified components might be combined to rigorously test this as well as other models of gap junction regulation by the in vitro reconstitution of gap junctional conductance in artificial lipid bilayers. Only in such a system will it be possible to control all the variables.

The use of antibody probes to assay the gap junction polypeptide in vivo is not, as yet, widespread, but is proving to be a powerful approach. The studies described below serve to illustrate this point, providing evidence that cell-cell communication may be regulated by de novo synthesis of gap junction protein as well as by the assembly of preexisting subunits into communicating junctions.

Regenerating Liver

The loss of gap junctions and reduction of cell-cell communication during liver regeneration following partial hepatectomy, most extensively studied by Revel and his colleagues (19, 45, 70), creates one of the systems most amenable to studying in vivo modulation of gap junctional conductance. Morphometric analysis demonstrated a 99% reduction of gap junction content 28–35 hr after partial hepatectomy, correlating with a decrease of cell-cell communication (45). The loss of morphologically-identifiable gap junctions appears to have coincided with a loss of gap junction polypeptides, as determined by analysis of Sarkosyl-resistant fractions of livers (19). However, this result is somewhat difficult to interpret because the basis for detergent-resistance of gap junctions is not clear. Indeed, as mentioned above, isolated gap junctions can be solubilized by Sarkosyl and other detergents. If strong lateral and intercellular interactions between subunits render gap junction plaques kinetically less soluble in detergents when compared with nonjunctional plasma membrane, then the solubilization of small or unassembled gap junctions by Sarkosyl might be mistaken for a loss of gap junction polypeptide.

An alternative immunochemical approach to this problem, using Western blots to analyze the gap junction polypeptide during regeneration subsequent to partial hepatectomy, was undertaken by Willecke and his coworkers (59). In these experiments, in which plasma membrane fractions were analyzed, the level of the 27,000-dalton liver gap junction polypeptide decreased with a half time of 3–6 hr, reaching a minimum equal to about 15% of control values at 28–35 hr after partial hepatectomy. It should be noted that the rate of loss correlates well with the reported half-life of the junction polypeptide in vivo (17, 69), suggesting inhibition of de novo synthesis in the regenerating liver. The residual level of gap junction polypeptide might well be adequate to account for the level and pattern of communication present in these livers (45) and is consistent with other studies in which cell-cell communication has been detected in the absence of assembled gap junctions (68).

Gap Junction Polypeptides in Communication-Defective Cell Lines

The transformation state and tumorigenicity of several cell lines often correlates with a loss or reduction in cell-cell communication (for review, see 37). It is not known in any of these cases whether the impairment is the result of alterations in cell surface properties preventing adjacent cells from getting close enough to form stable gap junctions or some defect in the pathway of synthesis and assembly of communicating channels. Among the more interesting cases is Cl-1D, an L cell-derived line that is inducible for cell-cell communication upon incubation with dibutyryl cAMP and caffeine (3).

Western blot analysis of extracts from both induced and noninduced cultures of Cl-1D indicates that the 27,000-dalton gap junction polypeptide is present in roughly equivalent amounts in both cases (E. Hertzberg, unpublished observations). Thus, the mere presence of the gap junction polypeptide is not sufficient for establishing communication. Studies are in progress to further characterize these cells in order to establish whether the lesion in uninduced cells lies in some terminal step in gap junction assembly as well as to elucidate the mechanism by which communication is induced. It appears likely that analysis of other communication-defective cell lines might reveal different lesions and that this approach may be a useful one in dissection of the pathway of biogenesis of communicating gap junctions.

In Cl-1D, communication induction required at least 1–2 hr and was sensitive to addition of protein synthesis inhibitors (3). In contrast, microinjection of heart Purkinje fibers with cAMP increased gap junctional conductance within 30 sec, reaching a maximum in 60–90 sec (12), consistent with a primary effect such as phosphorylation via a cAMP-dependent protein kinase. Thus, it seems as though the inductive effects of cAMP on cell-cell communication in these two systems may be manifested by different mechanisms.

PROSPECTS FOR THE FUTURE

It is already clear that the appliation of antibodies to the study of gap junctional communication and analysis of the gap junction polypeptide has proven productive. In principle, antibodies should also permit isolation of a cDNA clone, leading to analysis of the gap junction gene(s) and an ability to study gap junctions and their regulation from the time of transcription through the assembly and regulation of mature channels. As inhibitors of gap junctional conductance, antibodies will prove invaluable in the establishment of in vitro systems for analysis of the properties and regulation of purified channels and gap junction–associated proteins. In addition, antibodies, by electrically isolating cells into which they are microinjected, may enable study of other plasma membrane channel activities in individual cells within larger systems (e.g. epithelial cell layers).

Lastly, and perhaps most significantly, it is anticipated that the use of antibody reagents in well selected model systems will clarify the role of gap junctional communication in the regulation of cell growth and development. After many years of hypothesizing about the significance of gap junctional communication in these processes, a direct examination is now possible, and we can look forward to the change in direction of the field that the use of these probes will usher in.

ACKNOWLEDGMENTS

I would like to thank Kathe M. Hertzberg for her assistance in preparation of this manuscript and Lutz Birnbaumer and Karl Matlin for their helpful criticisms. Investigations in the author's laboratory were supported by grants from the National Institutes of Health (GM 30667) and The Robert A. Welch Foundation (Q 961).

Literature Cited

1. Alcala, J., Lieska, N., Maisel, H. 1975. Protein composition of bovine lens cortical fiber cell membranes. *Exp. Eye Res.* 21:581–95

2. Auerbach, A. A., Bennett, M. V. L. 1969. A rectifying synapse in the central nervous system of a vertebrate. *J. Gen. Physiol.* 53:211–37

3. Azarnia, R., Dahl, G., Loewenstein, W. R. 1981. Cell junction and cyclic AMP: III. Promotion of junctional membrane permeability and junctional membrane particles in a junction-deficient cell type. *J. Memb. Biol.* 63:133–46

4. Baker, T. S., Caspar, D. L. D., Hollingshead, C. J., Goodenough, D. A. 1983. Gap junction structures. IV. Asymmetric features revealed by low-irradiation microscopy. *J. Cell Biol.* 96:204–16

5. Bennett, M. V. L. 1966. Physiology of electrotonic junctions. *Ann. NY Acad. Sci.* 137:509–39

6. Bennett, M. V. L., Goodenough, D. A. 1978. Gap junctions, electrotonic coupling and intercellular communication. *Neuro, Res. Prog. Bull.* 16:373–486

7. Blennerhassett, M. G., Caveney, S. 1984. Separation of developmental compartments by a cell type with reduced junctional permeability. *Nature* 309: 361–64

8. Broekhuyse, R. M., Kuhlmann, E. D., Stols, A. L. H. 1976. Lens membranes. II. Isolation and characterization of the main intrinsic polypeptide (MIP) of bovine lens fiber membranes. *Exp. Eye Res.* 23:365–71

9. Broekhuyse, R. M., Kuhlmann, E. D., Winkens, H. J. 1979. Lens membranes, VII. MIP is an immunologically specific component of lens fiber membranes and is identical with 26K band protein. *Exp. Eye Res.* 29:303–13

10. Cohen, P., Burchell, A., Foulkes, J. G., Cohen, P. T. W., Vanaman, T. C., Nairn, A. C. 1978. Identification of the Ca^{++}-dependent modulator protein as the fourth subunit of rabbit skeletal muscle phorphorylase kinase. *FEBS Lett.* 92:287–93

11. Culvenor, J. G., Evans, W. H. 1977. Preparation of hepatic gap (communicating) junctions. Identification of the constituent polypeptide subunits. *Biochem. J.* 168:475–81

12. DeMello, W. C. 1984. Effect of intracellular injection of cAMP on the electrical coupling of mammalian cardiac cells. *Biochem. Biophys. Res. Commun.* 119:1001–7

13. Dunia, I., Sen Gosh, C., Benedetti, E. L., Zweers, A., Bloemendal, H. 1974. Isolation and protein pattern of eye lens fiber junctions. *FEBS Lett.* 45:139–44

14. Epstein, M. L., Gilula, N. B. 1977. A study of communication specificity between cells in culture. *J. Cell Biol.* 75:769–87

15. Erhart, J. C. 1981. Further purification of mouse liver gap junctions with deoxycholate and protein composition. *Cell Biol. Int. Rep.* 5:1055–61

16. Evans, W. H., Gurd, J. W. 1972. Preparation and properties of nexuses and lipid-enriched vesicles from mouse liver plasma membranes. *Biochem. J.* 128: 691–700

17. Fallon, R. F., Goodenough, D. A. 1981. Five-hour half-life of mouse liver-gap-junction protein. *J. Cell Biol.* 90:521–26

18. Finbow, M. E., Shuttleworth, J., Hamilton, A. E., Pitts, J. D. 1983. Analysis of vertebrate gap junction protein. *EMBO J.* 2:1479–86

19. Finbow, M. E., Yancey, S. B., Johnson, R., Revel, J.-P. 1980. Independent lines of evidence suggesting a major gap junctional protein with a molecular weight of 26,000. *Proc. Natl. Acad. Sci. USA* 77:970–74

20. Friend, D. S., Gilula, N. B. 1972. Variations in tight and gap junctions in mammalian tissues. *J. Cell Biol.* 53:758–76

21. Furshpan, E. J., Potter, D. D. 1959. Transmission at the giant motor synapses of the crayfish. *J. Physiol.* 145:289–325

22. Goodenough, D. A. 1974. Bulk isolation of mouse hepatocyte gap junctions. Characterization of the principle protein, Connexin. *J. Cell Biol.* 61:557–63

23. Goodenough, D. A., Stoeckenius, W. 1972. The isolation of mouse hepatocyte gap junctions. Preliminary characterization and X-ray diffraction. *J. Cell Biol.* 54:646–56

24. Gros, D. B., Nicholson, B. J., Revel, J.-P. 1983. Comparative analysis of the gap junction protein from rat heart and liver: Is there a tissue specificity of gap junctions? *Cell* 35:539–49

25. Henderson, D., Eibl, H., Weber, K. 1979. Structure and biochemistry of mouse hepatic gap junctions. *J. Mol. Biol.* 132:193–218

26. Hertzberg, E. L. 1980. Biochemical and immunological approaches to the study of gap junctional communication. *In Vitro* 16:1057–67

27. Hertzberg, E. L. 1984. A detergent-independent procedure for the isolation of gap junctions from rat liver. *J. Biol. Chem.* 259:9936–43

28. Hertzberg, E. L., Anderson, D. J., Friedlander, M., Gilula, N. B. 1982. Comparative analysis of the major polypeptides from liver gap junctions and lens fiber junctions. *J. Cell Biol.* 92:53–59

29. Hertzberg, E. L., Gilula, N. B. 1979. Isolation and characterization of gap junctions from rat liver. *J. Biol. Chem.* 254:2138–47

30. Hertzberg, E. L., Gilula, N. B. 1981. Liver gap junctions and lens fiber junctions: comparative analysis and calmodulin interaction. *Cold Spring Harbor Symp. Quant. Biol.* 46:639–45

31. Hertzberg, E. L., Lawrence, T. S., Gilula, N. B. 1981. Gap junctional communication. *Ann. Rev. Physiol.* 43:479–91

32. Hertzberg, E. L., Skibbens, R. V. 1984. A protein homologous to the 27,000-dalton liver gap junction protein is present in a wide variety of species and tissues. *Cell* 39:61–69

33. Hertzberg, E. L., Spray, D. C., Bennett, M. V. L. An antibody to gap junctions

blocks gap junctional conductance. 1985. *Proc. Natl. Acad. Sci. USA* In press

34. Janssen-Timmen, U., Dermietzel, R., Frixen, U., Leibstein, A., Traub, O., Willecke, K. 1983. Immunocytochemical localization of the gap junction 26 K protein in mouse liver plasma membranes. *EMBO J.* 2:295–302

35. Johnston, M. F., Ramon, F. 1981. Electrotonic coupling in internally perfused crayfish segmented axons. *J. Physiol.* 317:509–18

36. Kensler, R. W., Goodenough, D. A. 1980. Isolation of mouse myocardial gap junctions. *J. Cell Biol.* 86:755–64

37. Loewenstein, W. R. 1979. Junctional intercellular communication and the control of cell growth. *Biochim, Biophys. Acta* 560:1–65

38. Loewenstein, W. R. 1981. Junctional intercellular communication: the cell-to-cell membrane channel. *Physiol. Rev.* 61:829–913

39. Makowski, L., Caspar, D. L. D., Phillips, W. C., Goodenough, D. A. 1977. Gap junction structures. II. Analysis of the X-ray diffraction data. *J. Cell Biol.* 74:629–45

40. Manjunath, C. K., Goings, G. E., Page, E. 1982. Isolation and protein composition of gap junctions from rabbit hearts. *Biochem. J.* 205:189–94

41. Manjunath, C. K., Goings, G. E., Page, E. 1982. Protein composition of cardiac gap junctions: Comparison between mammalian species and between junctions from rat heart and liver. *J. Cell Biol.* 95:88a

42. McNutt, N. S., Weinstein, R. S. 1970. The unltrastructure of the nexus. A correlated thin section and freeze-cleave study. *J. Cell Biol.* 47:666–88

43. McNutt, N. S., Weinstein, R. S. 1973. Membrane ultrastructure at mammalian intercellular junctions. *Prog. Biophys. Mol. Biol.* 46:45–101

44. Michalke, W., Loewenstein, W. R. 1971. Communication between cells of different types. *Nature* 232:121–22

45. Myer, D. J., Yancey, S. B., Revel, J.-P. 1981. Intercellular communication in normal and regenerating rat liver: a quantitative analysis. *J. Cell Biol.* 91:505–23

46. Nicholson, B. J., Takemoto, L. J., Hunkapiller, M. W., Hood, L. E., Revel, J.-P. 1983. Differences between liver gap junction protein and lens MIP 26 from rat: Implications for tissue specificity of gap junctions. *Cell* 32:967–78

47. Peracchia, C., Bernardini, G., Peracchia, L. L. 1983. Is calmodulin involved in the regulation of gap junctional permeability? *Pfluegers Arch.* 399:152–54

48. Pitts, J. D. 1980. The role of junctional communication in animal tissues. *In Vitro* 16:1049–56

49. Pundak, K., Roche, R. S. 1984. Tyrosine and tyrosinate fluorescence of bovine testes calmodulin: Calcium and pH dependence. *Biochemistry* 23:1549–55

50. Revel, J.-P., Karnovsky, M. 1967. Hexagonal array of subunits in intercellular junctions of the mouse heart and liver. *J. Cell Biol.* 33:C7–12

51. Rose, B., Rick, R. 1978. Intracellular pH, intracellular free Ca, and junctional cell-cell coupling. *J. Membr. Biol.* 44:377–415

52. Ryerse, J. S. 1982. Gap junctions are nonrandomly distributed in *Drosophila* wing discs. *Wilhelm Roux' Arch. Entwicklungsmech. Org.* 191:335–39

53. Schuetze, S. N., Goodenough, D. A. 1982. Dye transfer between cells in embryonic chick lens becomes less sensitive to CO_2 treatment with development. *J. Cell Biol.* 92:694–705

54. Sikerwar, S. S., Malhotra, S. K. 1983. A structural characterization of gap junctions isolated from mouse liver. *Cell Biol. Int. Rep.* 7:897–903

55. Spray, D. C., Harris, A. L., Bennett, M. V. L. 1979. Voltage dependence of junctional conductance in early amphibian embryos. *Science* 204:432–34

56. Spray, D. C., Harris, A. L., Bennett, M. V. L. 1981. Gap junctional conductance is a simple and sensitive function of intracellular pH. *Science* 211:712–15

57. Spray, D. C., Harris, A. L., Bennett, M. V. L. 1982. Gap junctional conductance: comparison of sensitivities to H and Ca ions. *Proc. Natl. Acad. Sci. USA* 79:441–45

58. Steck, T. L. 1974. The organization of proteins in the human red blood cell membrane. *J. Cell Biol.* 62:1–19

59. Traub, O., Druge, P. M., Willecke, K. 1983. Degradation and resynthesis of gap junction protein in plasma membrancs of regenerating liver after partial hepatectomy or cholestasis. *Proc. Natl. Acad. Sci. USA* 80:755–59

60. Traub, O., Janssen-Timmen, U., Druge, P. M., Dermietzel, R., Willecke, K. 1982. Immunological properties of gap junction protein from mouse liver. *J. Cell. Biochem.* 19:27–44

61. Traub, O., Willecke, K. 1982. Cross reaction of antibodies against liver gap junction protein (26K) with lens fiber junction protein (MIP) suggests structural homology between these tissue-

specific gene products. *Biochem. Biophys. Res. Commum.* 109:895–901

62. Turin, L., Warner, A. 1977. Carbon dioxide reversibly abolishes ionic communication between cells of early amphibian embryo. *Nature* 270:56–57

63. Turin, L., Warner, A. E. 1980. Intracellular pH in early *Xenopus* embryos: its effect on current flow between blastomeres. *J. Physiol.* 300:489–504

64. Unwin, P. N. T., Ennis, P. D. 1983. Calcium-mediated changes in gap junction structure: Evidence from the low-angle X-ray pattern. *J. Cell Biol.* 97:1459–66

65. Unwin, P. N. T., Zampighi, G. 1980. Structure of the junction between communicating cells. *Nature* 283:545–49

66. Warner, A. E., Lawrence, P. A. 1982. Permeability of gap junctions at the segmental border in insect epidermis. *Cell* 28:243–52

67. Weir, M. P., Lo, C. W. 1984. Gap junctional communication in compartments in the *Drosophila* wing imaginal disk. *Dev. Biol* 102:130–46

68. Williams, E. H., DeHaan, R. L. 1981. Electrical coupling among heart cells in the absence of ultrastructurally defined gap junctions. *J. Membr. Biol.* 60:237–48

69. Yancey, S. B., Nicholson, B. J., Revel, J.-P. 1981. The dynamic state of liver gap junctions. *J. Supramol. Struct. Cell. Biochem.* 16:221–32

70. Yee, A. G., Revel, J.-P. 1978. Loss and reappearance of gap junctions in regenerating liver. *J. Cell Biol.* 78:554–64

71. Zampighi, G., Simon, S. A., Robertson, J. D., McIntosh, T. J., Costello, M. J. 1982. On the structural organization of isolated bovine lens fiber junctions. *J. Cell Biol.* 93:175–89

Ann. Rev. Physiol. 1985. 47:319–35

THE ROLE OF GAP JUNCTIONS IN DEVELOPMENT

S. Caveney

Department of Zoology, University of Western Ontario, London, Ontario, Canada N6A 5B7

INTRODUCTION

The gap junction, a membrane specialization found in most growing and mature metazoan tissues, is the site of dynamic cell-to-cell channels permeable to inorganic ions and small organic metabolites (up to about $M_r = 2000$). These channels allow the cytoplasmic interiors of adjacent cells to be directly coupled, in a functional sense, because in sharing their ion and metabolite pools, the cells engage in internal tissue homeostasis (66).

Gap junctions appear early during embryogenesis, and it is widely alleged that they allow the cell-to-cell transmission of as yet unidentified regulatory signals important in growth control, pattern formation, and differentiation in tissues (reviewed in 4, 43, 61, 62, 65, 66). The principal evidence that gap junctions are important in development is that they appear at embryonic stages when cell-cell interactions leading to cell determination occur (suggesting a role in signal transmission) and that they are absent or less permeable between regions of embryonic tissue destined to form different structures (suggesting that they restrict regulatory signals to the appropriate developmental compartments). The purpose of this short review is to consider critically the evidence suggesting that gap junctional communication contributes to tissue development. Because gap junctions constitute only one of a spectrum of routes through which cells interact, they are probably not responsible for all determinative events that occur during embryogenesis. Some of these events, in which gap junctions were previously implicated, will also be discussed.

The suggestion that the presence and physiological state of gap junctions are essential to the normal progress of development is supported by their abundance: Gap junctions are present between oocyte and surrounding follicular

0066-4278/85/0315-0319$02.00

319

cells in the ovary when oocyte growth is tightly regulated (76, 99) and when one or more of the primary axes of future embryonic symmetry are established (80), and although lost briefly when the oocyte is shed (44, 56), gap junctions reform in the early blastula stage (24, 25, 68) and persist throughout embryogenesis (4, 31, 108). Later, regional patterns in junctional communication in tissues lead to the formation of "communication compartments" (64), in which the cell members communicate normally but communication is severely restricted between compartments (7, 62, 103–5). Because gap junctional communication can be reversibly modulated in both embryonic and postembryonic cells (11, 13, 97), reduced communication at compartment borders may involve transient alterations in channel state, rather than a loss of gap junctions (7). Junctional communication may be lost permanently, however, between regions of an embryo destined to form very different structures (5, 53, 83).

The abundance of gap junctions throughout development offers an avenue of intercellular signaling: In addition to providing a direct route for the cell-to-cell propagation of diffusible cytoplasmic signals of transient nature, gap junctions may also allow chemical gradients to be set up during development (62, 108). That spatially graded distributions of molecules in embryonic tissues may influence cell behavior and lead to the spatial patterning of cell types ["regional specification" (92)] is a key morphogenetic concept with considerable heuristic value. Gradient contours could provide tissue cells with positional information (107); gradient slope could influence tissue growth (59) and polarity (107). Gradients with set upper and lower boundary values could determine the size of the developmental field (107). Furthermore, regional patterns of junctional communication in a developing embryo could determine in which cells the morphogenetic gradient is established (7, 62). While a simple morphogenetic gradient might be set up by the passive diffusion from its source in the tissue to the surrounding cells, thus establishing a concentration gradient used by the surrounding cells to determine their relative positions (17, 65), more complex mechanisms, involving morphogen sinks in the tissue (59), or involving the cell-to-cell transfer of two or more morphogens (reviewed in 74, 79) have been suggested. While the absence of any identified morphogen [with the notable exception of the hydra morphogens (87)] frustrates further speculation about molecular mechanisms, it would be worth knowing whether there are sufficient gap junctional channels in developing cells to allow for the rapid passage of morphogenetic signals required in early development.

Wolpert's (107) observation that embryonic fields are typically less than 100 cells wide (about 1 mm) when they are established and that the process is completed within at most a few hours prompted Crick (17) to speculate that diffusible morphogens are probably small organic molecules with effective diffusion coefficients in developing tissues of about 3×10^{-7} cm^2 sec^{-1}. Although the permeability limit of gap junctions (34, 91) suggests that they would allow molecules in the size range of the few identified morphogens [hydra morphogens range in M_r from 500–1100 (87, 88)] to pass, doubt has been expressed as to whether enough channels exist between developing cells to allow such a rapid rate of diffusion (108).

Recent reports of rapid rates of cell-to-cell movement of cytoplasmic molecules may dispel this doubt. In the mouse embryo, fluorescent dye injected into a blastomere at the 8-cell stage equilibrates throughout the embryo within 20 min (73); in the 16-cell stage the equilibration time is less then 5 min (72) and it is almost as rapid in the embryo after implantation (64). A similar rapid rate is seen among blastoderm cells of the intact fish embryo (53). In the post-embryonic insect epidermis, which is strongly coupled ionically (11, 13), tissue diffusion coefficients for two fluorescent tracers injected into cells are $1-4 \times 10^{-7}\,\text{cm}^2\,\text{sec}^{-1}$ less than an order of magnitude slower than in water and only a few-fold lower than their predicted rates in cytoplasm alone (86). The junctional channels remain, however, the major barrier to molecular diffusion in the epidermis. Furthermore, their permeability to molecules of similar size is selective (86) and may be based on molecular charge (34). This discrimination may be important in development. Several reaction-diffusion models of cell patterning in developing tissues (74, 79) involve pairs of morphogens diffusing (presumably via gap junctions) at rates ten-fold or greater in difference (79). The ratio of their diffusion rates determines the spacing of pattern elements (54, 79). Because the junctional channels are permeable only to small molecules, such differences in morphogen diffusion rate are unlikely unless the channels were able to discriminate in this way (in the absence of preferential binding or breakdown of one morphogen as it diffuses through the tissue).

OOCYTE GAP JUNCTIONS

Development does not begin at fertilization; many events affecting the spatial pattern of embryonic growth take place while the oocyte is still growing and maturing in the ovary. The maternal ovary exerts considerable influence on future embryonic symmetry. The primary embryonic axis, the anterior/posterior axis, is laid down in animal oocytes prior to ovulation and establishes embryonic polarity. In addition, the dorsoventral plane of bilateral symmetry is frequently set up in the oocyte before ovulation (80). Only rarely, as in the alga *Fucus,* is the primary embryonic axis specified after the egg is shed, when it appears to be determined by the geometry of a field of electrical current generated across the zygote membrane (47).

Gap junctions may well be involved in the specification of polarity and pattern in the oocyte in several groups of animals, notably the chordates and arthropods. In the ovary of these animals, the oocyte is enclosed within a shell of follicle cells, with which it makes membrane contact. Gap junctions are present at these interfaces in amphibians (9, 101), mammals (1, 37), and insects (44). Intercellular signals passing from follicle cells to the oocyte to determine oocyte symmetry might use the junctional route, but this remains speculation.

Gap junctions are, however, needed for normal oocyte growth (8, 42, 78) and maturation (30, 76). In the mammalian ovarian follicle, membrane contact between the oocyte and follicle cells is required for the transfer of many nutrients to the oocyte (15, 42, 78) and for the control of germinal vesicle breakdown and meiotic arrest (30). Patterns of gap junctional connectivity in the follicle make it a functional compartment. The growing oocyte is coupled to the follicle cells that immediately surround it (the corona radiata cells) by small and abundant gap junctions, which link the oolemma with fine membrane projections of the corona cells that traverse the zona pellucida (1, 37). The corona cells in turn are coupled by larger gap junctions to the other cells of the cumulus oophorus and to the peripheral cells of the follicle (the granulosa cells) (2). The formation of these gap junctions during follicle growth is stimulated by estrogen (10, 75). As the oocyte grows, it remains coupled metabolically (42, 78) and physiologically (37) to the follicle cells. The molecules that regulate oocyte maturation may well pass to the oocyte via gap junctions (21). Meiosis appears to be arrested by the intercellular transmission of a signal, possibly cAMP, from cumulus to oocyte (21). This cyclic nucleotide is suggested to have a second function, because elevated levels (induced by the gonadotropins LH and hCG binding to membrane receptors on the peripheral granulosa cells) can lead to the disruption of junctional communication between oocyte and corona cells shortly before ovulation (21). Whether communication is lost initially due to a direct effect of cAMP on the permeability of oolemmal gap junctions or due to the coronal cell processes retracting or snapping is unclear (78). Although it has been suggested that junctional uncoupling leads to a resumption of meiosis and oocyte maturation (20), it is more likely that quantitative or qualitative changes in intercellular signals passing to the oocyte are involved, because junctional communication persists after oocyte maturation is initiated in follicles in vivo (30, 100) and in vitro (21, 77). This participation of gap junctions in the control of follicular growth and maturation in the mammalian ovary implies that they pass regulatory signals between cells in other developing tissues.

Although the generally reported way in which gap junctions are lost from the follicle cell surfaces as the follicular shell around the oocyte disintegrates is by their internalization (references in 56), junctional communication between follicle cells can also be slowly and reversibly uncoupled by cytoplasmic acidification in CO_2-rich medium. This process is associated instead with the lateral dispersal of junctional particles in the follicle cell membranes (60). Whether the junctional permeability of preformed follicle junctions is modulated in this manner during normal oocyte development, and to what purpose, is not known.

In the amphibian ovarian follicle, where gap junctions connect the oocyte to its follicle cell layer (9, 101), a similar temporal pattern of junctional communication may also be hormonally regulated. Junctional coupling between oocyte and follicle cells is raised by gonadotropin (hCG), and these gap junctions may transfer a signal to the oocyte initiating vitellogenin uptake (9). They do not appear to be involved in the relief of meiotic arrest, however, because meiotic maturation in the frog follicle is triggered by progesterone binding directly to the oolemma (70, 71). This leads to a sharp reduction in oocyte cAMP (70), most likely through the specific inhibition of oocyte adenylate cyclase (49). Maturation is, however, temporally correlated with the loss of junctional coupling between the oocyte and its follicle cells (102). Although the trophic function of oocyte–follicle cell gap junctions in follicular growth has been convincingly demonstrated (42, 77), their involvement in the regulation of this process (through the transmission of inhibitory or inductive stimuli) has yet to be proved (76).

In insects, as in amphibia, the oocyte is tightly enclosed within a single layer of follicle cells and is connected to these cells by gap junctions and is ionically and dye-coupled to them (44, 106, 109). In many (106, 109) but not all insects (99), the oocyte is coupled via follicle cell junctions to the other oocytes in its ovariole. The oocyte-follicle cell junctions may permit the follicle cells to have a direct trophic function and several higher-level functions, such as transmitting signals that regulate the sequence of follicle growth in each ovariole (45). Gap junctions also provide a low-resistance pathway for the electrical fields that are generated in and around follicles (48), which may play a role in localizing morphogenetic factors that affect the symmetry of the future embryo (47). During the last step in oogenesis in the insect, chorion formation, the gap functions are lost from the oolemmal surface (44). The basic pattern of gap junctional communication thus appears to be similar to that seen in the vertebrate follicle.

GAP JUNCTIONS IN EARLY EMBRYONIC DEVELOPMENT

Gap junctions arise during early cleavage to become a general feature in all chordate embryos as well as in those of most invertebrates (4, 31, 61, 98, 108). The situation in echinoderm embryos, where coupling patterns seem to be limited and dependent on cytoplasmic bridges, may be different (19, 82, 93); in arthropods, where cleavage is initially acellular, gap junctions appear as the blastoderm becomes cellular (28).

Gap junctional plaques may be detected by freeze-fracture methods in as early as the 2-cell (24) to 4-cell (25) stage, although typically they appear later, from the 8-cell stage (27, 68) to the morula stage of early development. The acquisition of functional coupling between blastomeres via gap junctions, as distinct from coupling through cytoplasmic bridges prevalent during early cleavage, has been demonstrated unequivocally from the 8-cell stage onwards (38, 39, 63, 73).

An embryo that has been subject to considerable ultrastructural and physiological examination recently is that of the gastropod mollusc. In the embryo of the limpet *Patella,* gap junctions first appear during the 2-cell stage, whereas junctional communication between blastomeres appears to be delayed until the 32-cell stage (24, 26). At this time, blastomere gap junctions increase in both size and number (24), and the cell-to-cell passage of the fluorescent tracer Lucifer Yellow is first detected (26). The physiological trigger that either opens preexisting channels or stimulates the formation of new channels at this time is not known. During the 32-cell stage the symmetry of the embryo changes from radial to bilateral, and this process involves the spatial rearrangement of the vegetal blastomeres (26). Cell-deletion experiments have shown that this transition requires a contact-dependent interaction between the polar quartet of animal blastomeres (the central micromeres) and one vegetal blastomere (the 3D macromere) to set up dorsoventral polarity in the embryo. Because this interaction also commits this macromere to become the mesoderm stem cell (mesentoblast cell), the temporal correlation between the onset of junctional communication in the embryo and these determinative events hinted that membrane channels may be involved in the transmission of the inductive signal (22). The observation that dye injected into the 3D macromere passed directly and selectively into the central micromeres in the intact embryo (22) supported this contention, but further work failed to show gap junctions connecting this macromere with these micromeres at this stage, and serial sections of dye-injected embryos failed to show direct dye passage between the cells (26). Presumably junctional coupling between the polar micromeres and the 3D macromere is indirect and via the equatorial blastomeres. Direct junctional communication between the animal micromere quartet and the 3D macromere is not essential for its determination as the stem cell of the mesoderm. However, regional patterns of gap junctional distribution in the pond snail *Lymnaea* during cleavage (25), and patterns of dye spread in *Patella,* suggest that communication domains reflect the axis of bilateral symmetry and may aid transformation from radial to bilateral symmetry in the gastropod embryo (26).

Patterns of junctional communication also develop in eggs that undergo meroblastic cleavage, such as in the fish. In the teleost *Fundulus,* the cells at the margin of the embryonic blastoderm uncouple selectively from the giant yolk cell in the late blastula stage, just prior to gastrulation (53). A similar process occurs in the squid embryo (83). In the fish embryo, junctional uncoupling involves the closure of gap junctional channels (cytoplasmic bridges, which are present in the early blastula, are absent by this time) and creates two communication domains, the multicellular blastoderm and the syncytial yolk-cell cytoplasm (53). It is tempting to suggest that loss of junctional coupling is important to gastrulation and tissue determination (the periblast of the yolk cell might otherwise act as a nonspecific sink for developmental signals transmitted within the embryo, whose cells form a single communication compartment until at least the midgastrula stage). On the other hand, junctional uncoupling could be merely a mechanical necessity in meroblastic eggs to facilitate blastomere migration as the blastoderm spreads over the yolk cell during epiboly.

Gap junctions are also present in the early mouse embryo, from the 8-cell stage onwards (27, 68). Before this, coupling is limited to sister blastomeres via cytoplasmic bridges (63). The general appearance of junctional coupling between the 8-cell blastomeres coincides with (63, 73) or begins slightly earlier than (38, 39) blastomere compaction. This stage-specific acquisition of gap junctions does not appear to be causally related to compaction (38, 72), a process that increases the area of membrane contact between blastomeres. Gap junction formation before the 8-cell stage does not occur because the small pool of channel precursors that exist by the 4-cell stage are prevented from forming open channels prematurely (38, 39, 73), and synthesis of new channel components is only initiated in 8-cell blastomeres (72). Because a contact-dependent induction of cell polarity in the 8-cell embryo leads to the determination of the trophectoderm layer (111), is it possible that the gap junctions present at this time are involved? Recent findings make a causal role for gap junctions in establishing cell lineage highly improbable. Cell polarization can occur in the absence of junctional coupling (38, 39). The divergence of the two primary cell lineages, the trophectoderm and inner cell mass, appears to be more dependent on physical cues (111) than on diffusible signals. The junctions may play a role, however, in subsequent interactions leading to the further divergence of the lineages and to their commitment (39). The least exciting possibility is that gap junctions form at the 8-cell stage to maintain strong metabolic coupling between the blastomeres as cleavage continues and cytoplasmic bridges couple proportionally fewer cells in the embryo (39). Regional differences or patterns in dye coupling are not seen in the mouse morula, unlike in the fish and gastropod blastula, but are present in the postimplantation embryo (see below).

GAP JUNCTIONS AND DEVELOPMENTAL COMPARTMENTS

During development, an organism becomes divided into groups of cells, called developmental "fields" (92) or "compartments" (18), that function semiautonomously and give rise to different structures. Based on genetic studies of insect development, the "compartment hypothesis" (18, 36) states that cell fate in an embryo becomes progressively restricted due to the formation of a series of developmental compartments. These compartments are separated by distinct borders ("compartment boundaries") that are drawn across embryonic tissues without respect for cell ancestry. Once a compartment boundary is established, however, the cells and their progeny within a compartment are committed to a developmental fate different from that of cells in adjacent compartments. Although the mechanism of compartment formation is unknown, the sequence and position in which compartment boundaries appear in the wing imaginal disc of *Drosophila* have been accurately predicted by a biochemical model involving molecules undergoing reaction and diffusion in the growing disc (51, 52). Because the model assumes rapid cell-to-cell diffusion in the disc, it is worth noting that gap junctions are first present in the wing disc at the time of compartment formation (28), and they have been implicated in the compartmentation process (105). Furthermore, it is possible that regional differences in gap junction number or state in the wing disc may allow chemical gradients to be set up that could regulate its growth and differentiation (85). Recent physiological studies support the notion that junctional communication may be involved in the formation and maintenance of developmental compartments.

The borders of developmental compartments, as defined by the clonal analysis of genetically marked cells (18, 36), frequently coincide with the margins of "communication compartments," as mapped by the cell-to-cell spread of injected fluorescent tracer (7, 103–5). Although the cells within a communication compartment are strongly coupled with respect to the cell-to-cell spread of fluorescent tracer, its margin is marked by a local restriction to dye passage. Communication compartments are present in the postembryonic epidermis of several insects: the bug *Oncopeltus* (7, 103), and the flies *Drosophila* (104, 105) and *Calliphora* (103), as well as in the postimplantation mouse embryo (64).

In *Oncopeltus* the segment border separating the developing epidermal compartments of adjoining body segments is a compartment boundary (57). Each segment develops to a large extent independently of the others. It has its own morphogenetic gradient (57) that controls tissue polarity and pattern and may be set up by morphogens diffusing within the plane of the epidermis (17). This segmentally repeating gradient has a monotonic slope with its peak at one (the anterior or posterior) segment boundary and its low point at the other (57). If this gradient were based on a diffusible morphogen passing through junctional channels, how might its concentration limits be stabilized, and morphogen prevented from spreading into adjacent compartments? One obvious solution would be for the cells at the segment border to have a reduced junctional permeability and thus prevent morphogen in one segment from spilling over into adjacent segments. This appears to be the case, because the gap junctions at the border selectively block the cell-to-cell movement of several fluorescent tracers (7), whereas ionic coupling across the border is not affected (6). Junctional communication between segmental compartments is therefore less than that within a compartment.

In the *Drosophila* wing disc, in which several developmental compartments have been mapped genetically, the situation is more complex but the principle appears the same. It was first demonstrated that the boundary between the anterior and posterior wing compartments corresponds in position with a line at which the cell-to-cell passage of fluorescent tracer is considerably restricted (104); more recently this work has been extended to reveal the presence of at least nine lines at which junctional communication is restricted (105). In addition to the anterior/posterior communication-restriction line, several (in particular the wing/notum and dorsal/ventral restriction lines) coincide in space with known boundaries of developmental compartments (105).

The reduced transfer of dye across compartment borders in both the body segment and wing disc appears to result from the presence of a discrete population of "border cells" (7, 104, 105). These cells form a 1–3-cell-wide strip at the compartment margin, normally have low junctional permeability to organic tracers, and serve to block dye injected into one compartment from spreading to adjacent ones. This restriction is not permanent, however, and under certain in vitro conditions the border-cell junctions have near-normal permeability to organic tracers (7). These cells may modulate the size range and/or speed of molecular traffic passing from compartment to compartment at different times during development (7). Border cells in *Oncopeltus* are reported to have the normal complement of gap junctions (58) and normal levels of ionic coupling (M. G. Blennerhassett, unpublished observations). Gap junctions, although not uniformly distributed in the *Drosophila* wing disc (85), are numerous in the cells in the region of the anterior/posterior compartment boundary (85), and the cells are ionically coupled across it (105). It appears that the permeability of the border-cell junctions is normally depressed, compared to that of cells within compartments (7). Whether this results from a greater proportion of membrane channels being closed in these cells, or channel aperture being smaller, is an open question.

If the gradient morphogen were a small organic molecule, its cell-to-cell diffusion could be selectively blocked by the junctions of the border cells. By remaining neutral in their gradient properties, these cells would allow adjoining segments a certain degree of developmental autonomy (7); in the wing disc, by delineating the edges of communication compartments, they may be important in controlling the appropriate differentiation of the wing pattern (105).

Communication compartments are also present in the mouse embryo after implantation (64). At least two compartments have been detected in vitro: the inner cell mass, destined to form the embryo proper; and the trophoblast region, which forms part of the placenta. During implantation the trophoblast cells gradually become dye-uncoupled from each other and, as a consequence, from the inner cell mass. This loss of coupling is incomplete, however, because ionic coupling between the inner cell mass and trophoblast cells is still detectable.

Furthermore, the cells of the inner cell mass remain strongly dye-coupled. Because the junctional properties of the trophoblast cells in the mouse embryo are similar to those of the border cells in insect developmental compartments, it follows that the trophoblast cells have been assigned a similar functional role. In isolating the embryonic compartment from that of the maternal uterus, the reduced junctional permeability of the trophoblast cells may allow chemical gradients to be set up independently in the inner cell mass without a complete loss of functional coordination with other parts of the differentiating embryo (64).

The discovery in developing tissues of communication domains that correspond in space to known developmental compartments may be significant. Although it remains to be shown that the specification of developmental compartments involves the transmission of signals via gap junctions, restricted junctional communication between compartments may serve to maintain their stability, once established, and allow their further differentiation. In a few instances, communication compartments have been reported in mature tissues, suggesting that patterns of junctional communication that arise during development may be important for the normal metabolic activity of the differentiated tissue as well. Such functional compartments—groups of cells functionally isolated from surrounding cells by spatially limited patterns of junctional communication—are found in the mouse pancreas (32) and cockroach rectum in vivo (12) and between certain established cell lines (81) but not between primary cell cultures in vitro (46).

LOSS OF GAP JUNCTIONS DURING TISSUE DIFFERENTIATION

In a few tissues, gap junctions disappear entirely from the plasma membranes of all the cells during differentiation. This is seen in excitable tissues such as skeletal muscle and nervous tissue, and is a late embryonic event that occurs after the cells have assumed most of their histospecific morphology and molecular identity. Loss of functional coupling via gap junctions is associated with the final stages of cell differentiation leading to normal physiological function in the mature tissue. This process stands in sharp contrast to the regional loss of gap junctions in the embryo that creates "tight" compartments, or the reduction in the embryo that creates "leaky" compartments, discussed above. Although the loss of junctional communication in nerve and muscle does not appear to be obligatory to their differentiation (except possibly the last few steps), the time when it is present may provide significant clues as to its developmental role. This reasoning has lead to the suggestion that gap junctions are involved in the control of proliferation, cell patterning, and contact-mediated induction in these tissues.

In the embryonic nervous system, gap junctions are temporary or transient and are normally lost during neuronal differentiation. In the developing vertebrate eye, for example, gap junctions connect the proliferating neural retina cells (future photoreceptors and associated neurons) to each other and to the cells of the pigmented epithelium (23, 33, 35). These heterotypic junctions could also allow the pigmented epithelium to control the proliferation of the retinal cells (35) and the retinal cells to inhibit formation of ectopic neuroretina by pigmented epithelium (33). Although gap junctions disappear as the retinal cells become postmitotic and differentiate (35), the proposed involvement of gap junctions in pattern formation in the retina (23) has been contested (16). A similar temporal pattern of gap junctions is seen in the developing arthropod eye. Gap junctions between immature photoreceptor cells in *Schistocerca* are lost as they differentiate as small cell clusters to form the visual units (ommatidia) of the retina (29). The axon bundle from each of these visual units extends into the underlying optic lamina, and in *Daphnia* the leading axon makes contact with undifferentiated neuroblasts, leading to the formation of transient gap junctions (67). The differentiation of the laminar cartridge (where the photoreceptor cells of each ommatidium synapse with the laminar interneurons) depends on membrane contact between the photoreceptor fibers and the laminar neuroblasts (67). While these morphological observations hint that gap junctions provide a route for the passage of chemical messages at critical times in eye development, the evidence is circumstantial and the physiological state of these junctions has yet to be studied.

Gap junctions are also found between embryonic muscle cells during at least the early stages of differentiation in vertebrate skeletal muscle (3, 5, 14). In vitro studies on mammalian myoblasts suggested that gap junctions may be involved in myoblast fusion leading to myotube formation (50), but in vivo studies on frog myotome muscle cells indicate that gap junctions can be lost many hours before fusion (3). In *Xenopus*, electrotonic coupling between myotome muscle cells drops precipitously after the onset of neuromuscular transmission and electrical excitability in the muscle membrane (3). Because this is associated with the first swimming movements in the embryo, junctional coupling may allow functional coordination in prefusion myoblasts of the myotome before the full pattern of innervation is established (3, 5). The timing of gap junctional loss is species-specific, because rat skeletal muscle fibers remain coupled by gap junctions long after myotube formation and fiber differentiation, to disappear at birth (89). This variability in their persistence in embryonic muscle suggests that gap junctions are not needed to transmit signals that trigger myoblast fusion. Although the specific role of gap junctions in early muscle development has yet to be established, it is clear that junctional uncoupling occurs too late in the embryo to be of any significance to muscle patterning.

Neurons, too, display considerable morphological differentiation and may become electrically excitable before electrotonic coupling is lost. In the grasshopper embryo, neurons develop the ability to generate action potentials at about the time gap junctional coupling is lost, but there is not obligatory relationship between these two events (40). In the *Xenopus* tadpole, loss of junctional coupling between the Rohon-Beard neurons of the spinal cord is stage-specific, occurring before the free-swimming stage, but occurs after the cells have finished dividing, have extended neurites, and have become excitable (94). Nevertheless, for direct cell-to-cell signals to be important in the acquisition of electrical excitability, they have to be transmitted by the neural plate stage, as neurons isolated in vitro at this time subsequently develop excitability (95). While the loss of gap-junctional coupling in embryonic-nerve and striated-muscle cells could in principle trigger the final stages in tissue differentiation (94), there is at present no strong evidence for such a causal relationship. Indeed, development of these tissues in the late embryo appears rather indifferent to the state of junctional coupling.

CONCLUSIONS

Gap junctions provide a direct intercellular pathway for the contained diffusion of small cytoplasmic metabolites, including second messengers such as cAMP, necessary for the normal growth of the oocyte and the early embryo. It is premature to conclude that gap junctions also transmit regulatory or inductive signals involved in specifying morphogenetic fields and regional patterns of differentiation in embryonic tissues. As plausible as morphogen movement through junctional channels may be, the most direct evidence available at present is equivocal, for several reasons. First, cytoplasmic regulators of tissue growth and pattern formation have yet to be identified. Irrefutable proof that they form part of the cell-to-cell traffic through gap junctions requires that the molecular identity and mode of action of the signals be known. In the short term, the claim that gap junctions are involved in morphogenesis would be strengthened considerably by the discovery of agents that alter junctional permeability and cause errors in development with minimal effect on basic cell activity.

Second, these regulatory signals would presumably form a small fraction of the total molecular flux through gap junctions. Consequently, it may be unrealistic to expect junctional channels to form or disappear at critical stages of cell patterning in the embryo, when more basic demands on the channels have to be met. The regional loss of gap junctions in some tissues during morphogenesis may simply be a necessary prelude to cellular rearrangement, although separate communication compartments are formed in the process.

Although the temporary reappearance of gap junctions in some excitable tissues during differentiation may be required to pass determinative signals, their loss is frequently a late event in differentiation associated with the conversion from electrical to chemical means of coordination. The role of gap junctions in developing tissues is more likely to depend on subtle changes in channel number and quality and be influenced by changes in the nature of the effector molecules as well as the responsiveness of the target cells.

In this context, it is worth noting that the level of junctional coupling between embryonic cells may be physiologically controlled. Channel state in fish and frog blastomeres is reversibly affected by imposed changes in cytoplasmic pH (96) and transjunctional voltage (41). The developmental significance of these findings will depend on whether such changes are shown to occur naturally (41). The sensitivity of embryonic cell junctions to such treatments declines with age (90, 94). Individual channels in isolated pairs of vertebrate blastomeres appear to open and close in an all-or-none manner (97) as may those in cell pairs from an insect salivary epithelium (110). If this mode of channel closure is generally applicable to embryonic cells, it should strongly influence future concepts of how the channels control the passage of regulatory molecules. On the other hand, the situation is probably more complex. Gap junctions in different mature tissues vary in their structure and biochemistry (55), and physiological studies suggest the presence of more than one functional class of channel in embryonic (97) and differentiated cells (69). The presence of graded channel closure in some intact tissues (84) cannot be ruled out. It is also possible that junctional permeability in embryonic cells is modulated during normal growth in a manner too subtle or complex to be detected by present physiological methods. The rather recent discovery of limited junctional communication between developmental compartments is a case in point.

Finally, even if gap junctions are important in cell-cell interactions in the embryo, they are not always required. Gap junctions are absent between certain embryonic cells at a time when they interact to establish new spatial patterns (39). Such contact-mediated interactions between cells are more likely based on fixed properties of the cell surface and not on diffusible signals.

Acknowledgments

I have benefited greatly from discussions with my colleagues M. Blennerhassett, J. McLachlin, Y. Ouellette, R. Safranyos, and R. Schlamp, and from the use of their unpublished data. Rosemary Melchin showed considerable patience in typing the manuscript. I acknowledge generous support from the Natural Sciences and Engineering Research Council of Canada.

Literature Cited

1. Albertini, D. F., Anderson, E. 1974. The appearance and structure of intercellular connections during the ontogeny of the rabbit ovarian follicle with particular reference to gap junctions. *J. Cell Biol.* 63:234–50

2. Albertini, D. F., Fawcett, D. W., Olds, P. J. 1975. Morphological variations in gap junctions of ovarian granulosa cells. *Tissue Cell* 7:389–405

3. Armstrong, D. L., Turin, L., Warner, A. E. 1983. Muscle activity and the loss of electrical coupling between striated muscle cells in *Xenopus* embryos. *J. Neurosci.* 3:1414–21

4. Bennett, M. V. L., Spray, D. C., Harris, A. L. 1981. Electrical coupling in development. *Am. Zool.* 21:413–27

5. Blackshaw, S. E., Warner, A. E. 1976. Low resistance junctions between mesoderm cells during development of trunk muscles. *J. Physiol.* 255:209–30

6. Blennerhassett, M. G. 1984. *Selectivity in junctional communication.* PhD thesis. Univ. Western Ontario, Canada.

7. Blennerhassett, M. G., Caveney, S. 1984. Separation of developmental compartments by a cell type with reduced junctional permeability. *Nature* 309:361–64

8. Brower, P. T., Schultz, R. M. 1982. Intercellular communication between granulosa cells and mouse oocytes: existence and possible nutritional role during oocyte growth. *Dev. Biol.* 90:144–53

9. Brown, C. L., Wiley, S. H., Dumont, J. N. 1979. Oocyte-follicle cell gap junctions in *Xenopus laevis* and the effects of gonadotropin on their permeability. *Science* 203:182–83

10. Burghardt, R. C., Anderson, E. 1981. Hormonal modulation of gap junctions in rat ovarian follicles. *Cell Tissue Res.* 214:181–93

11. Caveney, S. 1978. Intercellular communication in insect development is hormonally controlled. *Science* 199:192–95

12. Caveney, S., Berdan, R. 1982. Selectivity in junctional coupling between cells of insect tissues. In *Insect Ultrastructure,* ed. R. C. King, H. Akai, 1:434–65. New York: Plenum. 485 pp.

13. Caveney, S., Blennerhassett, M. G. 1980. Elevation of ionic conductance between insect epidermal cells by B-ecdysone in vitro. *J. Insect Physiol.* 26:13–25

14. Chow, I., Poo, M. M. 1984. Formation of electrical coupling between embryonic *Xenopus* muscle cells in culture. *J. Physiol.* 346:181–94

15. Colonna, R., Mangia, F. 1983. Mechanisms of amino acid uptake in cumulus-enclosed mouse oocytes. *Biol. Reprod.* 28:797–803

16. Cooke, J. 1980. Specification in the developing eye for orientation and mapping to the brain. Cellular autonomy or intercellular communication? *Trends Neurosci.* 3:45–48

17. Crick, F. 1970. Diffusion in embryogenesis. *Nature* 225:420–22

18. Crick, F. H. C., Lawrence, P. A. 1975. Compartments and polyclones in insect development. *Science* 189:340–47

19. Dale, B., de Santis, A., Ortolani, G., Rasotto, M., Santella, L. 1982. Electrical coupling of blastomeres in early embryos of ascidians and sea urchins. *Exp. Cell Res.* 140:457–61

20. Dekel, N., Beers, W. H. 1980. Development of the rat oocyte in vitro: Inhibition and induction of maturation in the presence or absence of the cumulus oophorus. *Dev. Biol.* 75:247–54

21. Dekel, N., Lawrence, T. S., Gilula, N. B., Beers, W. H. 1981. Modulation of cell-to-cell communication in the cumulus-oocyte complex and the regulation of oocyte maturation by LH. *Dev. Biol.* 86:356–62

22. de Laat, S. W., Tertoolen, L. G. J., Dorresteijn, A. W. C., van den Biggelaar, J. A. M. 1980. Intercellular communication patterns are involved in cell determination in early molluscan development. *Nature* 287:546–48

23. Dixon, J. S., Cronly-Dillon, J. R. 1972. The fine structure of the developing retina in *Xenopus laevis. J. Embryol. Exp. Morph.* 28:659–66

24. Dorresteijn, A. W. C., Bilinski, S. M., van den Biggelaar, J. A. M., Bluemink, J. G. 1982. The presence of gap junctions during early *Patella* embryogenesis: An electron microscopical study. *Dev. Biol.* 91:397–401

25. Dorresteijn, A. W. C., van den Biggelaar, J. A. M., Bluemink, J. G., Hage, W. J. 1981. Electron microscopical investigation of the intercellular contacts during the early cleavage stages of *Lymnaea stagnalis* (Mollusca, Gastropoda). *Roux's Arch. Dev. Biol.* 190:215–20

26. Dorresteijn, A. W. C., Wagemaker, H. A., de Laat, S. W., van den Biggelaar, J. A. M. 1983. Dye-coupling between blastomeres in early embryos of *Patella vulgata* (Mollusca, Gastropoda): Its relevance for cell determination. *Roux's Arch. Dev. Biol.* 192:262–69

27. Ducibella, T., Albertini, D. F., Ander-

son, E., Biggers, J. D. 1975. The preimplantation mouse embryo; Characterization of intercellular junctions and their appearance during development. *Dev. Biol.* 45:221–50

28. Eichenberger-Glinz, S. 1979. Intercellular junction during development and in tissue cultures of *Drosophila melanogaster:* An electron microscopic study. *Roux's Arch. Dev. Biol.* 186:333–49

29. Eley, S., Shelton, P. M. J. 1976. Cell junctions in the developing compound eye of the desert locust *Schistocerca gregaria*. *J. Embryol. Exp. Morph.* 36:409–23

30. Eppig, J. J. 1982. The relationship between cumulus cell–oocyte coupling, oocyte meiotic maturation, and cumulus expansion. *Dev. Biol.* 89:268–72

31. Finbow, M. E. 1982. A review of junctional mediated intercellular communication. In *The Functional Integration of Cells in Animal Tissues,* ed. J. D. Pitts, M. Finbow, pp. 1–37. Cambridge, UK: Cambridge Univ. Press. 360 pp.

32. Findlay, I., Petersen, O. H. 1983. The extent of dye-coupling between exocrine acinar cells of the mouse pancreas. The dye-coupled acinar unit. *Cell Tissue Res.* 202:121–27

33. Fisher, S. K., Lindberg, K. A. 1975. Intercellular junctions in the early human embryonic retina. *J. Ultrastr. Res.* 51: 69–78

34. Flagg-Newton, J., Simpson, I., Loewenstein, W. R. 1979. Permeability of the cell-to-cell membrane channels in mammalian cell junction. *Science* 205:404–7

35. Fujisawa, H., Morioka, H., Watanabe, K., Nakamura, H. 1976. A decay of gap junctions in association with cell differentiation of neural retina in chick embryonic development. *J. Cell Sci.* 22:585–96

36. Garcia-Bellido, A., Ripoll, P., Morata, G. 1973. Developmental compartmentalization in the wing disc of *Drosophila*. *Nature New Biol.* 245:251–53

37. Gilula, N. B., Epstein, M. L., Beers, W. H. 1978. Cell-to-cell communication and ovulation. A study of the cumulus-oocyte complex. *J. Cell Biol.* 78:58–75

38. Goodall, H., Johnson, M. H. 1982. Use of carboxyfluorescein diacetate to study formation of permeable channels between mouse blastomeres. *Nature* 295:524–26

39. Goodall, H., Johnson, M. H. 1984. The nature of intercellular coupling within the preimplantation mouse embryo. *J. Embryol. Exp. Morph.* 79:53–76

40. Goodman, C. S., Spitzer, N. C. 1981.

The development of electrical properties of identified neurones in grasshopper embryos. *J. Physiol.* 313:385–403

41. Harris, A. L., Spray, D. C., Bennett, M. V. L. 1983. Control of intercellular communication by voltage dependence of gap junctional conductance. *J. Neurosci.* 3:79–100

42. Heller, D. T., Cahill, D. M., Schultz, R. M. 1981. Biochemical studies of mammalian oogenesis: Metabolic cooperativity between granulosa cells and growing mouse oocytes. *Dev. Biol.* 84:455–64

43. Hertzberg, E. L., Lawrence, T. S., Gilula, N. B. 1981. Gap junctional communication. *Ann. Rev. Physiol.* 43:479–91

44. Huebner, E. 1981. Oocyte-follicle cell interaction during normal oogenesis and atresia in an insect. *J. Ultrastruct. Res.* 74:95–104

45. Huebner, E. 1984. Developmental interactions in female insect reproductive organs. In *Advances in Invertebrate Reproduction,* ed. W. Engels, 3:97–105. Amsterdam: Elsevier. 665 pp.

46. Hunter, G. K., Pitts, J. D. 1981. Nonselective junctional communication between some different mammalian cell types in primary culture. *J. Cell Sci.* 49:163–75

47. Jaffe, L. 1979. Control of development by ionic currents. In *Membrane Transduction Mechanisms,* ed. R. A. Cone, J. E. Dowling, pp. 199–231. New York: Raven. 236 pp.

48. Jaffe, L. F., Woodruff, R. I. 1979. Large electrical currents traverse developing cecropia follicles. *Dev. Biol.* 76:1328–32

49. Jordana, X., Allende, C. C., Allende, J. E. 1982. Differential inhibition by progesterone of the adenylate cyclase of oocytes and follicle cells of *Xenopus laevis*. *FEBS Lett.* 143:124–28

50. Kalderon, N., Epstein, M. L., Gilula, N. B. 1977. Cell to cell communication and myogenesis. *J. Cell Biol.* 75:788–806

51. Kauffman, S. 1981. Pattern formation in the *Drosophila* embryo. *Philos. Trans. R. Soc. London Ser. B* 295:567–94

52. Kauffman, S. A., Shymko, R., Trabert, K. 1978. Control of sequential compartment formation in *Drosophila*. *Science* 199:259–70

53. Kimmel, C. B., Spray, D. C., Bennett, M. V. L. 1984. Developmental uncoupling between blastoderm and yolk cell in the embryo of the teleost *Fundulus*. *Dev. Biol.* 102:483–87

54. Lacalli, T. C., Harrison, L. G. 1979. Turing's conditions and the analysis of

morphogenetic models. *J. Theor. Biol.* 76:419–36

55. Larsen, W. J. 1983. Biological implications of gap junction structure, distribution, and composition: A review. *Tissue Cell* 15:645–71

56. Larsen, W. J., Tung, H. N., Polking, C. 1981. Response of granulosa cell gap junctions to human chorionic gonadotropin (hCG) at ovulation. *Biol. Reprod.* 25:1119–34

57. Lawrence, P. A. 1981. The cellular basis of segmentation in insects. *Cell* 26:3–10

58. Lawrence, P. A., Green, S. M. 1975. The anatomy of a compartment border. The intersegmental boundary in *Oncopeltus. J. Cell Biol.* 65:373–82

59. Lawrence, P. A., Crick, F., Munro, M. 1972. A gradient of positional information in an insect, *Rhodnius. J. Cell Sci.* 11:815–53

60. Lee, W. M., Cran, D. G., Lane, N. J. 1982. Carbon dioxide induced disassembly of gap-junctional plaques. *J. Cell Sci.* 57:215–28

61. Lo, C. W. 1980. Gap junctions in early development. In *Development in Mammals,* ed. M. H. Johnson, 4:39–80. Amsterdam: Elsevier. 327 pp.

62. Lo, C. W. 1982. Gap junctional communication compartments and development. See Ref. 31, pp. 167–79

63. Lo, C. W., Gilula, N. B. 1979. Gap junctional communication in the preimplantation mouse embryo. *Cell* 18:399–409

64. Lo, C. W., Gilula, N. B. 1979. Gap junctional communication in the postimplantation mouse embryo. *Cell* 18:411–22

65. Loewenstein, W. R. 1979. Junctional intercellular communication and the control of growth. *Biochem. Biophys. Acta* 560:1–65

66. Loewenstein, W. R. 1981. Junctional intercellular communication: The cell-to-cell membrane channel. *Physiol. Rev.* 61:829–913

67. Lopresti, V., Macagno, E. R., Levinthal, C. 1974. Structure and development of neuronal connections in isogenic organisms: transient gap junctions between growing optic neurons and lamina neuroblasts. *Proc. Natl. Acad. Sci. USA* 71:1098–1102

68. Magnuson, T., Demsey, A., Stackpole, C. W. 1977. Characterization of intercellular junctions in the preimplantation mouse embryo by freeze-fracture and thin-section electron microscopy. *Dev. Biol.* 61:252–61

69. Margiotta, J. F., Walcott, B. 1983. Conductance and dye permeability of a rec-

tifying electrical synapse. *Nature* 305:52–55

70. Maller, J. L., Krebs, E. G. 1980. Regulation of oocyte maturation. *Curr. Top. Cell. Regul.* 16:271–311

71. Masui, Y., Clarke, H. J. 1979. Oocyte maturation. *Int. Rev. Cytol.* 57:186–282

72. McLachlin, J. R. 1984. *Control of compaction and junctional communication in the preimplantation mouse embryo.* PhD thesis. Univ. Western Ontario, Canada. 211 pp.

73. McLachlin, J. R., Caveney, S., Kidder, G. M. 1983. Control of gap junction formation in early mouse embryos. *Dev. Biol.* 98:155–64

74. Meinhardt, H. 1982. *Models of Biological Pattern Formation.* London: Academic. 230 pp.

75. Merk, F. B., Botticelli, C. R., Albright, J. T. 1972. An intercellular response to estrogen by granulosa cells in the rat ovary; an electron microscopy study. *Endocrinology* 90:992–1007

76. Moor, R. M., Osborn, J. C. 1982. The functional integration of cells in ovarian follicles. See Ref. 31, pp. 133–48

77. Moor, R. M., Osborn, J. C., Cran, D. G., Walters, D. W. 1981. Selective effect of gonadotrophins on cell coupling, nuclear maturation, and protein synthesis in mammalian oocytes. *J. Embryol. Exp. Morph.* 61:347–65

78. Moor, R. M., Smith, M. W., Dawson, R. M. C. 1980. Measurement of intercellular coupling between oocytes and cumulus cells using intracellular markers. *Exp. Cell Res.* 126:15–29

79. Murray, J. D. 1982. Parameter space for Turing instability in reaction diffusion mechanisms: a comparison of models. *J. Theor. Biol.* 98:143–63

80. Nusslein-Volhard, C., Lohs-Schardin, M., Sander, K., Cremer, C. 1980. A dorso-ventral shift of embryonic primordia in a new maternal-effect mutant of *Drosophila. Nature* 283:474–76

81. Pitts, J. D., Burk, R. R. 1976. Specificity of junctional communication between animal cells. *Nature* 264:762–64

82. Pochapin, M. B., Sanger, J. M., Sanger, J. W. 1983. Microinjection of Lucifer yellow CH into sea urchin eggs and embryos. *Cell Tissue Res.* 234:309–18

83. Potter, D. D., Furshpan, E. J., Lennox, E. S. 1966. Connections between cells of the developing squid as revealed by electrophysiological methods. *Proc. Natl. Acad. Sci. USA* 55:328–35

84. Rose, B., Simpson, I., Loewenstein, W. R. 1977. Calcium ion produces graded changes in permeability of membrane

channels in cell junction. *Nature* 267: 625–27

85. Ryerse, J. 1982. Gap junctions are non-randomly distributed in *Drosophila* wing discs. *Roux's Arch. Dev. Biol.* 191:335–39

86. Safranyos, R. G. A., Caveney, S. 1984. Rates of diffusion of fluorescent molecules via cell-to-cell membrane channels in a developing tissue. *J. Cell Biol.* In press

87. Schaller, H. C. 1981. Morphogenetic substances in hydra. *Fortschr. Zool.* 26:153–62

88. Schaller, H. C., Bodenmuller, H. 1981. Isolation and amino acid sequence of a morphogenetic peptide from hydra. *Proc. Natl. Acad. Sci. USA* 78:7000–4

89. Schmalbruch, H. 1982. Skeletal muscle fibers of newborn rats are coupled by gap junctions. *Dev. Biol.* 91:485–90

90. Schuetze, S. M., Goodenough, D. A. 1982. Dye transfer between cells of the embryonic chick lens becomes less sensitive to CO_2 treatment during development. *J. Cell Biol.* 92:694–705

91. Schwarzmann, G., Wiegandt, H., Rose, B., Zimmerman, A., Ben-Haim, D., Loewenstein, W. R. 1981. Diameter of the cell-to-cell junctional channels as probed with neutral molecules. *Science* 213:551–53

92. Slack, J. M. W. 1983. *From Egg to Embryo, Determinative Events in Early Development*. Cambridge, UK: Cambridge Univ. Press. 241 pp.

93. Spiegel E., Howard, L. 1983. Development of cell junctions in sea-urchin embryos. *J. Cell Sci.* 62:27–48

94. Spitzer, N. C. 1982. Voltage- and stage-dependent uncoupling of Rohon-Beard neurons during embryonic development of *Xenopus* tadpoles. *J. Physiol.* 330:145–62

95. Spitzer, N. C., Lamborghini, J. E. 1976. The development of the action potential mechanism of amphibian neurons isolated in culture. *Proc. Natl. Acad. Sci. USA* 73:1641–45

96. Spray, D. C., Harris, A. L., Bennett, M. V. L. 1981. Gap junctional conductance is a simple and sensitive function of intracellular pH. *Science* 211:712–15

97. Spray, D. C., White, R. L., Carvalho, A. C., Harris, A. L., Bennett, M. V. L. 1984. Gating of gap junction channels. *Biophys. J.* 45:219–30

98. Takahashi, K., Yoshi, M. 1981. Development of sodium, calcium, and potassium channels in the cleavage-arrested embryo of an ascidian. *J. Physiol.* 315:515–29

99. Telfer, W. H., Huebner, E., Smith, D. S. 1982. The cell biology of vitellogenic follicles in *Hyalophora* and *Rhodnius*. See Ref. 12, pp. 118–49

100. Tesarik, J., Dvorak, M. 1982. Human cumulus oophorus preovulatory development. *J. Ultrastr. Res.* 78:60–72

101. Vandenhoef, M. H. F., Dictus, W. J. A. G., Hage, W. J., Bluemink, J. G. 1984. The ultrastructural organization of gap junctions between follicle cells and the oocyte in *Xenopus laevis*. *Eur. J. Cell Biol.* 33:242–47

102. Vilain, J. P., Moreau, M., Guerrier, P. 1980. Uncoupling of oocyte-follicle cells triggers reinitiation of meiosis in amphibian oocytes. *Dev. Growth Differ.* 22:687–91

103. Warner, A. E., Lawrence, P. A. 1982. Permeability of gap junctions at the segmental border in insect epidermis. *Cell* 28:243–52

104. Weir, M., Lo, C. W. 1982. Gap junctional communication compartments in the *Drosophila* wing disc. *Proc. Natl. Acad. Sci. USA* 79:3232–35

105. Weir, M. P., Lo, C. W. 1984. Gap-junctional communication compartments in the *Drosophila* wing imaginal disk. *Dev. Biol.* 103:102–46

106. Wollberg, Z., Cohen, E., Kalina, M. 1976. Electrical properties of developing oocytes of the migratory locust, *Locusta migratoria*. *J. Cell Physiol.* 88:145–58

107. Wolpert, L. 1969. Positional information and the spatial pattern of cellular differentiation. *J. Theor. Biol.* 25:1–47

108. Wolpert, L. 1978. Gap junctions: channels for communication in development. In *Intercellular Junctions and Synapses*, ed. J. Feldman, N. B. Gilula, J. D. Pitts, 5:83–94. London: Chapman & Hall. 246 pp.

109. Woodruff, R. I. 1979. Electrotonic junctions in Cecropia moth ovaries. *Dev. Biol.* 69:281–95

110. Zimmerman, A. L., Rose, B. 1983. Analysis of cell-to-cell diffusion kinetics: changes in junctional permeability without accompanying changes in selectivity. *Biophys. J.* 41:216 (Abstr.)

111. Ziomek, C. A., Johnson, M. H. 1980. Cell surface interaction induces polarization of mouse 8-cell blastomeres at compaction. *Cell* 21:935–42

Ann. Rev. Physiol. 1985. 47:337–53

PHYSIOLOGICAL ROLES OF PERMEABLE JUNCTIONS: SOME POSSIBILITIES

J. D. Sheridan and M. M. Atkinson

Department of Anatomy, University of Minnesota, Minneapolis, Minnesota 55455

INTRODUCTION

It has been nearly two decades since permeable intercellular junctions were first detected between electrically nonexcitable cells (27, 33). Considerable progress has been made in our understanding of the structure, permeability, distribution, and biochemistry of the junctions (see 9, 24, 54, 71 in this volume). Much less progress has been made, however, in our understanding of the biological roles played by the junctions, despite the common use of the term "junctional communication." In fact most of the original functional speculations, e.g. involvement in exchange of nutrients (27), maintenance of tissue homeostasis (73), regulation of cell growth and differentiation (25, 50), and transmission of intracellular molecular signals (61), are still frequently cited in the literature with rather little in the way of experimental support. A major problem in trying to design experiments to test these various ideas has been the lack of a specific and reversible method for interrupting junctional permeability. Consequently, it has been necessary to rely on more indirect approaches, for example correlating patterns of junctional distribution and changes in junctional permeability with specific physiological and pathological events.

In this review we discuss a few of the recently studied systems in which these indirect approaches have been quite useful. Rather than be exhaustive, we have selected cell systems that reflect general concepts regarding junctional communication, that illustrate the range of strategies currently available to study the physiology and pathology of the junctions, and that have particular promise for

337

0066-4278/85/0315-0337$02.00

aiding our understanding of specific biological processes. In view of space limitations, we have not discussed junctional transfer of electrical potentials but have focused on processes involving small molecules.

GENERAL CONCEPTS AND STRATEGIES

Before discussing specific systems, however, it is useful to review the general features to be expected in a physiological process that is dependent on junctional communication. These ideas, which follow directly from the evidence that the junctional channels act as sieves (32), allowing small molecules to diffuse passively from cell to cell, have been discussed in greater detail in earlier reviews (22, 30, 62, 63) and need only to be summarized. First, the process must be affected critically by one or more small molecules (< 1.5 nm in limiting diameter (69). Second, the process must occur in cells that tend to accumulate different amounts of the critical small molecule(s), at least in the absence of permeable junctions. This tendency could be due to intrinsic variations in the cells or different external inputs or environments or both. Third, the number of patent channels in the permeable junctions must be sufficient to allow appreciable transfer of the critical small molecules from cell to cell. Different numbers of channels may be needed for different cell systems, depending on such nonjunctional factors as cell volume, rates of generation, and/or degradation of putative signals, kinetics of the affected processes, and so on.

In principle, these features may occur in three possible configurations:

1. The concentration of the critical molecule(s) and the amount and permeability of the junctions may be relatively constant over an appreciable time period. This configuration might, for example, be well suited to long-term metabolic interactions or tissue homeostasis.

2. The molecule(s) concentrations may change while the junctions remain constant. This configuration might, for example, be associated with transmission of a hormonal or nerve-induced signal throughout the cell population.

3. The junctions may change, leading secondarily to changes in the concentrations of the critical molecules. This configuration might, for example, alter the composition or size of interacting cell groups, facilitating communication between some cells while restricting that between others.

In order to obtain evidence for the first two possibilities, it would be necessary to know ahead of time which molecule or class of molecules were likely to be transferred and what the expected physiological effects might be. Then the junctionally dependent transfer of the molecules would have to be demonstrated. Rather few systems have been found to meet all of these conditions either because there is too little information about the molecules involved or because their transfer is difficult or impossible to detect.

The third possibility has attracted renewed interest because of the mounting evidence that junctional channels are much more dynamic, both in terms of formation and degradation (51, 64) and in terms of opening and closing (71), than was previously appreciated. Evidence for this configuration could in principle be obtained, provided the methods for measuring the amount and permeability of the junctions were sufficiently sensitive when applied to the system in question. Changes in these junctional parameters in close association with physiological or pathological events would strongly suggest some biological function. Of course, identification of the molecules involved in the transfer and determination of their effects would ultimately be necessary for a complete understanding of the importance of the junctions in the process.

Recent experiments will be described that illustrate, at least in part, each of the three possibilities. In no case has a physiological role for the junctions yet been proved, but the results are encouraging and suggest that future studies of these types are promising.

SELECTED FUNCTIONAL EXAMPLES

Metabolic Interactions

It has long been recognized that a population of cells, coupled by a rather stable complement of permeable junctions, forms a continuous intracellular compartment for those molecules small enough to move through the junctions. Thus, at the most fundamental level, coupled cell populations can remain autonomous with respect to macromolecules, but interdependent with respect to small metabolites.

This general concept gained some early support from experiments utilizing cell mutants that lacked hypoxanthine phosphoribosyl transferase (HPRT), a so-called "salvage pathway" enzyme necessary for cells to incorporate exogenous hypoxanthine into the nucleotide pools and ultimately into nucleic acids. When these mutant cells were grown in contact (and formed permeable junctions) with wild-type cells, the mutants as well as the wild-type cells incorporated radiolabeled hypoxanthine into nucleic acids (73). Later experiments indicated that the incorporation by the mutant cells resulted from junctional transfer of labeled nucleotides from the wild-type cells (49). This coculture phenomenon was originally termed "metabolic cooperation," although there was little evidence for any metabolic consequences of the nucleotide transfer.

Recently, it has been shown that "metabolic cooperation" indeed occurs in cocultures of mutant (HPRT−) and wild-type (HPRT+) cells (66). The experiments were designed to distinguish two possibilities:

1. The amount of radiolabeled hypoxanthine converted into nucleotides (i.e. the HPRT activity) is simply a function of the number of wild-type cells and independent of the number of mutant cells. This result would amount to metabolite transfer without any metabolic effects.

2. The mutant cells "stimulate" the wild-type cells to produce more nucleotides so that the incorporation of label into the coculture depends on the number of mutant cells. This result would represent true "metabolic cooperation."

The results obtained from scintillation counts of cell extracts supported the second possibility, and in fact the effect of increasing the relative numbers of HPRT− cells was quite marked; e.g. at 9:1 ratios of HPRT−:HPRT+ cells there was a 150% increase of total incorporation above that calculated from the number of HPRT+ cells alone. Similar results were obtained from autoradiographic analysis, which in addition showed that there was a unimodal distribution of nucleotides throughout the population and that the wild-type and mutant cells had indistinguishable patterns of labeling.

Further demonstration of a true metabolic interaction was obtained with the same cell system using labeled formate as a marker for nucleotides synthesized de novo. Formate incorporation is substantially inhibited in HPRT+ cells exposed to high levels of hypoxanthine, which competes for the phosphoribosylpyrophosphate (PRPP) needed in de novo synthesis. Exogenous hypoxanthine has no effect, however, on formate incorporation by HPRT− cells. When the two cell types were grown in coculture, there was a greater inhibition of formate incorporation than could be accounted for by the number of HPRT+ cells. Thus, according to both the hypoxanthine and formate incorporation experiments, the nucleotide metabolism of a population of HPRT+ and HPRT− cells is different from that of either cell type alone or of a simple addition of the two.

Recently, it has been shown that the effects just described depend on the junctional transfer of PRPP from the HPRT− cells to the HPRT+ cells (77). Conditions that increase the PRPP levels in the HPRT− cells lead to greater stimulation of apparent HPRT activity in the cocultures, whereas conditions decreasing PRPP levels have the opposite effect. The explanation is that HPRT activity in the presence of moderate levels of exogenous hypoxanthine is limited by the availability of PRPP supplied by the HPRT− cells via the junctions. Thus, the metabolic cooperation is quite complex even in this simple system: the HPRT− cells first transfer PRPP to the HPRT+ cells; then the HPRT+ cells produce more labeled nucleotides and return them to the HPRT− cells.

We can only speculate about the physiological significance of this particular example of metabolic cooperation. At the very least it provides a possible mechanism by which cells can share the responsibilities for salvaging exogenous purines and for de novo nucleotide synthesis. As discussed in outline earlier (62), this sort of sharing could be of particular importance if the amounts of HPRT and PRPP synthetase happen to vary independently. Such independence could lead to cells that have a mismatch between the enzymic capability to utilize exogenous hypoxanthine (or guanine) and the necessary rate of PRPP synthesis. Junctional transfer of PRPP and nucleotides throughout a cell population could avoid deleterious consequences of such mismatches.

Transfer of Molecular Signals

One of the more intriguing functions suggested for permeable junctions is the transmission of molecular signals from cell to cell, which might serve, for example, as a means of distributing hormonal effects throughout a tissue (61). A well-known intracellular mediator of the effects of certain hormones, the so-called "second messenger," cyclic AMP, is similar in size and charge to molecules known to be transferred from cell to cell via permeable junctions. Consequently it was suggested some time ago that cAMP might be a junctionally transmitted signal (60, 61). Support for this suggestion came originally from studies of heart muscle strips that apparently allowed the longitudinal spread, from cell to cell, of radiolabeled cAMP and/or its metabolites (76). Subsequently, it was shown that ovarian granulosa cells and heart cells in coculture exchanged hormonal effects in a manner consistent with cAMP transfer (28), although there was no direct evidence that cAMP levels had increased in the recipient cells.

Recently, a new approach to this question has been devised using an elegant method for detecting and quantitating activation of cAMP-dependent protein kinase on an individual cell basis (21). The method involves the use of a fluorescein-tagged protein (F:PKI) that binds tightly to the free catalytic subunit of the protein kinase. Because the catalytic subunit is available only after cAMP binds to the regulatory subunit and causes dissociation, increased amount of bound F:PKI reflects the presence of increased cAMP levels.

This approach has been applied to cocultures of ovarian granulosa cells and Y-1 adrenocortical tumor cells (43). To distinguish the cells in the cocultures, Y-1 cells were labeled with latex beads derivatized with rhodamine isothiocyanate. The cultures were then exposed to one of the following test substances: 8BrcAMP, FSH (which causes an increase in cAMP in the granulosa cells), and ACTH (which causes an increase in cAMP in the Y-1 cells). Following preparation for F:PKI localization, the relative amount of bound F:PKI was measured microspectrophotometrically over numerous cells of each type, either in contact or not in contact with cells of the other type. The effect of the test substance was expressed as percent increase in intensity over that of unstimulated, noncontacting cells used as a reference. The results indicated that stimulated, noncontacting cells had increased fluorescence when treated with 8BrcAMP or with the appropriate specific hormone but not with the hormone specific for the other cell type. Cells in heterotypic contact, on the other hand, frequently responded to all three substances, including the hormone specific for the heterotpyic partner. Not only was there an increase in F:PKI binding, but in at least one of the combinations stimulating one cell with its hormone (granulosa cells with FSH) caused the other cell to carry out its cAMP-dependent function (Y-1 cells secreted steroids). In order to exclude the possibility that cell fusion led to intermixing of membrane receptors in heterokaryons, bead-labeled Y-1 cells were cocultured with ferritin-labeled granulosa cells. No cells were found having both beads and ferritin label. Moreover, ^{125}I-labeled FSH bound only to granulosa cells even in coculture. Thus, the results demonstrated contact-dependent transfer of hormonal signals between the two cell types.

The mechanism of transfer, however, and the molecule(s) transferred remain uncertain. Although gap junctions connect the two cell types, no direct correlation between some other form of well-documented junctional transfer (e.g. injected dyes, electrical coupling) and the reciprocal hormonal effects were provided. Therefore, some other sort of contact-dependent mechanism cannot be ruled out. Because the evidence clearly shows dissociation of cAMP-dependent protein kinase, it is likely that cAMP levels have gone up in both cells, and, therefore, the most likely substance to be transferred is cAMP itself. Nevertheless, the authors cautiously list some other possibilities that need to be explored.

Despite the uncertainties, these experiments, along with the earlier ones of Lawrence et al (28), bring us closer to understanding the possible role of permeable junctions in distributing hormonal signals. Yet we might ask if cells with such differences in hormonal specificity and responsiveness ever form permeable junctions in or between naturally occurring tissues. In fact, heterotypic gap junctions (the probable structural counterpart of permeable junctions) have been described in several cases, but only recently have any been studied with physiological methods.

One of these cases is particularly relevant to our earlier discussions because it involves granulosa cells of the cumulus oophorus and their close association with the oocyte. Permeable junctions between these two cell types have been well described by electron microscopy (1, 8) and by physiological measurements of dye (23) and metabolite (42) transfer. The transfer of metabolites may be of functional significance in the ovary by allowing the granulosa cells, as "support cells," to directly provide nutrients to the oocyte. In addition, the junctions may play another role of special significance prior to ovulation (11). Preovulatory oocytes are in a state of meiotic arrest that can be relieved either by luteinizing hormone (LH) or by removal of the cumulus cells from the oocyte in vitro. The resumption of meiosis in denuded oocytes can be inhibited by treatment with phosphodiesterase inhibitors or dibutyryl-cAMP. These observations have led to the hypothesis that cAMP from the cumulus cells enters the oocyte through permeable junctions and maintains the oocyte in meiotic arrest (11, 12). The LH surge preceding ovulation, it is suggested, interrupts the junctional flow of cAMP, permitting the oocyte to resume meiosis. Despite the attractiveness of this hypothesis, it has not yet been possible to demonstrate that cAMP in fact is transferred from the cumulus cells to the oocyte (57), although the PKI has not been applied. Moreover, there is no indication that the two cells are uncoupled at the time that meiosis resumes (15, 41), but a transient uncoupling preceding germinal vesicle breakdown has not been excluded.

A second case involves the interactions between endothelial and nonendothelial cells in small vessels. Rhodin previously noted the close apposition between capillary and venular endothelial cells and nearby pericytes (55). While the structures of the appositions were (and remain) poorly defined, he suggested that they might be the sites of bidirectional signal transfer. For example, bloodborne substances could act via the endothelium to influence pericyte activity, e.g. eliciting contraction, and vasoreactive substances in the tissue space could act via pericytes to affect the endothelium, e.g. influencing transport. Evidence from our lab (65, 68) indicates that pericytes are extensively coupled by dye-permeable junctions to each other and to more peripheral fibroblasts, as well as occasionally to underlying endothelial cells. Thus, these studies provide some additional support for possible pericyte-endothelial interaction of the sort hypothesized by Rhodin.

A third case involves the pancreatic islet of Langerhans. This microorgan secretes several hormones—insulin, glucagon, somatostatin, pancreatic polypeptide—critically involved in the regulation of blood glucose and various metabolic processes. The cells secreting each hormone are distinct but are intermixed in patterns characteristic of the species. In the rat islet, the parenchyma of the central region is composed exclusively of insulin-producing B cells, whereas the periphery contains glucagon-producing A cells, somatostatin-producing D cells, and pancreatic polypeptide-producing PP cells as well as B cells. Ultrastructural studies have indicated that small gap junctions connect cells of different secretion type (e.g. B cells to A cells) as well as cells of the same type (e.g. B cells to B cells) (46, 47). Recently, experiments from our lab have shown that these same combinations of cells are dye-coupled in small groups, confirming the implications of the EM studies (40). The procedure involved injecting the fluorescent dye, Lucifer yellow, into a peripheral islet cell and monitoring the dye spread (if any) into adjacent cells. The islet was subsequently sectioned and the types of cells containing dye were distinguished using immunocytochemistry to detect the different islet hormones.

In general, junctional coupling of the heterologous islet cells appears consistent with a need to coordinate secretion of the various hormones influencing blood glucose. However, the coupling of A and B cells initially seems paradoxical. The primary agent controlling insulin secretion is blood glucose which stimulates the B cell to secrete. On the other hand, glucose inhibits A-cell secretion of glucagon. The paradox might be resolved if any integrating effect of the junctions were overwhelmed by the independent and opposite effects of glucose on the two cells. A more interesting possibility is that the B cell is the primary target of glucose, which generates an internal signal that simply has two different effects, stimulatory in the B cell and, after junctional transfer, inhibitory to the A cell. There is evidence consistent with this second possibility. When B cells are lost, glucose no longer reduces glucagon secretion by A cells (53). Although administration of insulin lowers the basal glucagon secretion somewhat, the glucose sensitivity of the A cells is not restored. Quite aside from the details of these possibilities, the presence of permeable junctions between the different islet cell types provides an important alternative to paracrine interactions between the cells.

Modulation of Junctional Capacity

All of the foregoing discussion assumed the invariance of permeable junctions, but this is neither necessary nor, in light of our current understanding, even likely for many physiological situations. Not only are the distributions, quantities, and detailed structure of permeable junctions different from cell type to cell type and from tissue to tissue, but also, under various conditions, even from moment to moment within a homotypic cell population (71). Indeed, by altering the effective numbers of permeable channels, the junctional changes could themselves be primary signals leading to significant increases or decreases in intracellular concentration of functionally important molecules. Alternatively, independent changes in the junctions and the cellular molecules could act in concert. Some of the developmental examples discussed by Caveney fall into this category (9). Here we will consider a few other examples of systems in which junctional changes may be primary events in physiological and pathological processes.

In light of some of our earlier discussion it is appropriate to consider, as our first example, hormone effects on permeable junctions and in particular the possible role of cAMP in modulating junction formation and permeability. The first evidence that cyclic nucleotides might affect permeable junctions was obtained from studies of junction formation between Novikoff hepatoma cells (64, 67). Cyclic AMP was reported to stimulate and cGMP to inhibit initial events in formation, as determined with electrophysiological and ultrastructural methods.

Recently cAMP has been implicated in more dramatic increases in junction formation and, apparently, in junction permeability in cell culture (3, 19, 20,

52). These studies have correlated increases in cellular cAMP, generated by direct treatment with membrane-permeant cAMP derivatives, by changes in serum concentration or by treatment with norepinephrine or prostaglandin, with increases in dye coupling and sizes of gap junctions. One of the more striking effects is seen with a cell line (Cl-1D) derived from mouse L cells (3). This cell line has commonly been used as a control cell because of its lack of permeable junctions under typical culture conditions. However, when these cells are grown in the presence of low serum or dibutyryl-cAMP (or, in fact, at very low density), the cells develop appreciable dye and electrical coupling and form readily detectable gap junctions. The changes occur after a substantial time delay and depend on protein synthesis. Thus, it is unclear where cAMP is having its effect. There may, for example, be some direct and relatively selective effect on the expression of the gene for junctional protein or for some other protein necessary for formation to occur. Alternatively, a more complex differentiation process may be put into operation with the junctional changes being only one of a number of coordinated events. Whatever the mechanism, however, some involvement of cAMP seems well supported.

An increase of junctional permeability, presumably associated with elevated intracellular cAMP, has also been demonstrated in the more physiological situation involving hormone activation of adenylate cyclase (52). As for junctional responses produced by exogenously applied cAMP, the effect of the hormones is observed only after several hours, despite the fact that the induced increase in cAMP is rapid and transient. Clearly the time delay precludes acute, synergistic effects of the junctional increase and passage of cAMP through junctional channels. Nevertheless, the potential for reinforced, tissue-wide, hormonal responses exists.

Another example in this category involves B cells in the pancreatic islet. As considered above, these cells secrete insulin when stimulated by elevated blood glucose or other natural or pharmacological secretagogues. The earliest indications that B-cell coupling might be affected by agents causing insulin release came from dye-injection studies on cultured fetal islet cells (26) and from freeze-fracture studies on intact adult islets (36). The physiological studies showed that increased glucose in the medium caused an increase in the number of dye-coupled cells. The problem with these studies was that the culture condition might have altered the basal and stimulated coupling from the normal, in vivo state. Furthermore, the increases, although statistically significant, were quite small. The ultrastructural studies also indicated significant, although small, increases in the amount of gap junction (measured by a variety of parameters, e.g. frequency, individual size) after stimulation in vivo with glibenclamide, a potent B-cell secretagogue. Treatment of isolated islets with enough glucose to evoke maximum insulin secretion increased the frequency of the junctions but decreased the average size, causing a marginal effect on total junctional area. The relatively small magnitude of the junctional changes detected with freeze-fracture and the impossibility of determining from the structure alone which junctions have open channels raised the question of whether or not any of the changes significantly modified junctional transfer.

In order to address the problems and unanswered questions from the earlier studies, experiments were initiated to test the effects of B-cell secretagogues on B-cell dye coupling and also to determine if any effects were dependent on insulin release (35). Rats were treated in vivo for 24 hr with multiple injections of glibenclamide, glibenclamide plus diazoxide (an inhibitor of insulin release), and diazoxide alone. Isolated islets were then studied either with freeze-fracture (to ensure that structural changes paralleled those seen earlier and to test the effect of inhibiting insulin release) or with dye injection. With no pretreatment, B-cell coupling was restricted to only a few cells at each injection site. Moreover, extending the injection time did not produce larger coupled groups. Islets from animals injected with glibenclamide or glibenclamide plus diazoxide showed nearly a doubling of the sizes of the coupled B-cell groups. Freeze-fracture of similar islets revealed a comparable increase in amount of gap junctions. However, diazoxide alone produced a dramatic increase in dye coupling: coupled groups had nearly a ten-fold increase in average number of cells. Because the amount of junction seen with freeze-fracture was not different from that seen with the other treatments, it seemed possible that there had been an increase in junctional permeability, although selective formation of new junctions linking coupled groups could not be excluded.

The results, therefore, clearly demonstrated that release of insulin was not required for the increases in coupling and amount of junction. The most dramatic result, however, was the unexpected and initially unexplained increase in coupling with diazoxide. We now believe that hyperglycemia, induced by the diazoxide, was responsible for the coupling change. This belief is supported by the comparable increases in coupling produced in islets from animals infused with glucose for 24 hr and having similar maintained levels of blood glucose (> 250 mg dl^{-1}) (Meda & Sheridan, unpublished observations).

Prolonged hyperglycemia is quite unphysiological, however, and it is reasonable to ask whether or not there is any physiological state in which B-cell coupling is similarly extensive. Michaels, in our lab, has recently reported such a state, lactation, in which there is a ten-fold increase in coupling compared to that in islets from virgin animals (38, 39). These animals are either normo- or slightly hypo-glycemic, and therefore elevated blood glucose is not the cause of the junction change. The animals also secrete increased amounts of insulin that assists in managing the increased metabolic demands of lactation, but our previous experiments revealed no direct link between insulin per se and coupling change. A clue as to the possible effector of the increased coupling came from experiments on islets from animals bearing mammosomatotropic tumors. These animals also display enhanced coupling and share with the lactating animals a pronounced elevation of prolactin. The most direct evidence that prolactin causes increased coupling came from studies of islets treated in vitro with the hormone (39). After a 90-min exposure to a prolactin concentration between the serum concentrations seen during lactation and in the tumor-bearing animals, the extent of coupling had increased nearly seven-fold on average. Not only do these results implicate prolactin as the mediator of the coupling increase found in lactation, but they also represent one of the more conclusive examples of a direct effect of prolactin on the islet.

It is not yet clear whether the increased coupling is due to increased amounts of junction or increased junctional permeability. In fact it is even possible that prolactin causes the B-cell junctions to become more sensitive to the effects of glucose. These possibilities are under further investigation.

The functional consequences of the increased coupling can only be suggested. An interesting possibility has been raised by experiments on glucose-induced insulin secretion by perfused pancreata from mammasomatotropic tumor-bearing animals (70). There is a pronounced shift in glucose threshold to lower values as well as an increase in insulin secretion at suprathreshold glucose concentrations. Similar results were found with islets treated in vitro with prolactin and different levels of glucose; i.e. 50 mg dl^{-1} glucose, which is ineffective at eliciting insulin release by itself, became effective in islets pretreated with prolactin. Therefore, it is possible that the increase in B-cell coupling is somehow responsible for enhanced glucose-stimulated insulin secretion. We are currently investigating the following working hypothesis, which is based on the "pacemaker" concept suggested by Meissner (37): (a) Coupled groups of B cells secrete in synchrony once the glucose reaches the threshold of the most sensitive cell in the group. (b) Under basal conditions, e.g. 50 mg dl^{-1}, very few groups are secreting. (c) Prolactin causes the various groups to become coupled to each other so that the groups with the lowest threshold "recruit" those with higher threshold, shifting the entire glucose-response curve to the left. This hypothesis predicts that other conditions of high lactogenic activity should cause decreased glucose threshold and increased B-cell coupling. Sorenson et al (70) have shown that half of this prediction is true, i.e. that there is a decrease in glucose threshold in pancreata from pregnant rats, but have not yet tested lactating animals showing elevated prolactin. Assessing B-cell coupling during pregnancy and glucose-induced B-cell secretion during lactation should serve to confirm or reject the hypothesis.

The last topic of this review concerns one possible consequence of defective permeable junctions. The earliest reports of coupling loss in certain tumors (34) and transformed cell lines (7) spawned the hypothesis that permeable junctions are necessary for growth control and that their absence causes abnormal, unregulated cellular growth (30, 31). Not surprisingly, several laboratories pursued this line of investigation, and it soon became evident that tumors and transformed cultured cells frequently do possess gap junctions and are coupled, at least electrically (22, 59). Nevertheless, the possibility remained that these cells had a diminished junctional capacity that was not detectable with the probes being utilized.

It now appears that, for certain virally transformed cell lines at least, just such reductions in junctional permeability do occur. We have shown (2) with dye-injection techniques that NRK (normal rat kidney) cells containing a transformation-defective, temperature-sensitive mutant (LA 25) of Rous sarcoma virus (RSV) are coupled, but the coupling is substantially reduced when the cells are grown at transformation-permissive temperatures. Our approach was to provide a numerical index of the coupling efficiency for these cells; the indices were measurements of the time interval between the beginning of an injection of dye into one cell to the first detectable appearance of dye in any adjacent cell. We found that the "transfer time intervals" for cells grown at the permissive temperatures were generally 5–7-fold those for cells grown at nonpermissive temperatures. These transformed cells, then, do indeed contain permeable junctions, but the permeability of those junctions is considerably reduced.

Using a method we recently developed for quantitating junctional dye permeability between pairs of cultured cells (29), we have begun to examine NRK cells transformed by two other retroviruses. The new method, which utilizes a silicon-intensified target (SIT) camera and computer-assisted video analysis, provides a more precise and reliable way of assessing junctional capacity. Initial results with NRK cells transformed by a temperature-sensitive mutant [t.s. 110 (6)] of Moloney murine sarcoma virus, and by Kirsten murine sarcoma virus, show that a substantial reduction of junctional permeability is associated with the transformed phenotype. Thus, partial as well as complete restriction of junctional permeability can be associated with neoplastic transformation.

More powerful arguments for a close association of impaired junctional permeability with transformation come from studies in which the transformed state is induced or modified, and the permeable junctions are correspondingly altered. One group has shown that, in cultures of a human-mouse hybrid cell system, the traits of the human cell progenitors, i.e. junctional competency and regulated growth, were dominant over the characteristics of the transformed mouse-cell progenitors, i.e. junctional incompetency and unregulated growth (4). Most importantly, hybrid cells that eventually lost growth control were found to have also lost demonstrable permeable junctions.

Perhaps the most intriguing evidence of this kind is that obtained from studies on two model systems for transformation, one related to two-stage carcinogenesis and the other related to the viral oncogene theory. Studies of the effects of various tumor promoters, e.g. TPA, on metabolic cooperation have shown a positive correlation between the efficacy of the agent as a tumor promoter and the severity of the decrease in cooperation (79). In at least one of these systems, V79 cells treated with TPA, there is a decrease in gap junctions and in the amount of a putative junctional protein (18, 78); in another system there is a demonstrable decrease in electrical coupling (14). The time required for these junctional responses to develop is appreciable (1 or 2 days), so that the relationship between TPA treatment and the junctional response involves a number of unknown mechanisms (44).

The virally infected cell system, temperature-sensitive for transformation, studied in this laboratory provides a number of unique advantages, foremost of which is the ability to rapidly and reversibly induce transformation by simple temperature shifts. As already discussed, NRK cells infected with the RSV mutant, LA25, display a significant reduction in junctional permeability when the cells have been maintained at transformation-permissive temperatures (33°C–35°C). Remarkably, the change in junctional permeability is detectable 15 min after the cells are shifted to 35°C, and by 1 hr the junctional permeability is maximally reduced. The reestablishment of full junctional competency is equally rapid with shifts to nonpermissive temperatures (39°C–40.5°C).

These kinetics demonstrate a very close relationship between onset of the transformation process and closure of junctional channels. Also of great import mechanistically is the apparent temporal relationship between the activity of the transforming gene product, pp60^{src}, and junctional permeability. This transforming protein contains protein kinase activity that is thought to be responsible for initiating transformation (16, 58). The kinetics are consistent with the possibility that pp60^{src} exerts its effect on the junction by directly phosphorylating junctional protein (80).

Other possibilities include increases in intracellular free calcium (32, 45, 56, 71), calmodulin (which might be necessary for calcium to have its effect), and hydrogen ion (56, 71, 72). In this regard it is interesting that calmodulin reportedly increases in conjunction with the expression of the transformed phenotype in cells with active pp60^{src} (13).

Whatever the mechanism underlying the effect of pp60^{src}, the junctional response appears to involve modification of existing junctional channels rather than increased formation or removal of channels. We found that the size and number of gap junctions remained remarkably constant after LA25-NRK cells were shifted to transformation-permissive or nonpermissive temperatures for 1 hr, a time sufficient to allow full expression of the effect on junctional permeability. Interestingly, changes in the packing arrangement of junctional particles were seen, with more regular packing correlating with increased junctional permeability both in uninfected NRK cells and in LA25-NRK cells grown at the nonpermissive temperature. Although a full time course for the change in packing following temperature shifts has not been done, this morphological response appears to lag behind the permeability changes. As an aside, the particle arrangements correlated with increased coupling were opposite those frequently reported (48), reemphasizing the difficulty in predicting junctional permeability from junctional morphology.

In considering the implications and directions provided by these studies, it is useful also to consider the genetic elements that may be involved. Recent investigations show that certain oncogenes once thought to be the unique creation of retroviruses are now demonstrable in human tumor cells (e.g. 17) and chemically induced animal tumors (75). Thus, the oncogene theory (5, 10) provides a common theme for various models of cancerous cell growth. Modified junctional permeability is also demonstrable in some of these systems and, in one case at least, is closely associated with expression of the oncogene product. From this perspective, it is clear that the representative studies we have discussed, together with others not mentioned here, provide strong circumstantial evidence in support of the involvement of junctional deficiencies in neoplastic transformation.

CONCLUSION

In a brief review such as this, it has not been possible to do full justice to the complex problem of trying to elucidate the biological roles of permeable junctions. We have selected a few examples of cell systems in which a junctional role is strongly suggested if not well understood. We expect that these and other studies not discussed will continue to be productive and to improve our understanding of junctional physiology and pathology. Nevertheless, future efforts will have to include development of more direct approaches, for example the use of junction-specific antibodies to perturb junctional permeability.

Literature Cited

1. Anderson, E., Albertini, D. F. 1976. Gap junctions between the oocyte and companion follicle cells in the mammalian ovary. *J. Cell Biol.* 71:680–86
2. Atkinson, M. M., Menko, A. S., Johnson, R. G., Sheppard, J. R., Sheridan, J. D. 1981. Rapid and reversible reduction of junctional permeability in cells infected with a temperature-sensitive mutant of avian sarcoma virus. *J. Cell Biol.* 91:573–78
3. Azarnia, R., Dahl, G., Loewenstein, W. R. 1981. Cell junction and cyclic AMP. III. Promotion of junction membrane permeability and junctional membrane particles in a junction-deficient cell type. *J. Membr. Biol.* 63:133–46
4. Azarnia, R., Larsen, W. J., Loewenstein, W. R. 1974. The membrane junctions in communicating and noncommunicating cells, their hybrids, and segregants. *Proc. Natl. Acad. Sci. USA* 71:880–84
5. Bishop, J. M. 1983. Cellular oncogenes and retroviruses. *Ann. Rev. Biochem.* 52:301–54
6. Blair, D. G., Hull, M. A., Finch, E. A. 1979. The isolation and preliminary characterization of temperature-sensitive transformation mutants of Moloney sarcoma virus. *Virology* 95:303–16
7. Borek, C., Higashino, S., Loewenstein, W. R. 1969. Intercellular communication and tissue growth. IV. Conductance

of membrane junctions of normal and cancerous cells in culture. *J. Membr. Biol.* 222:78–86

8. Burghardt, R. C., Matheson, R. L. 1982. Gap junction amplification in rat ovarian granulosa cells. *Dev. Biol.* 94:206–15

9. Caveney, S. 1985. The role of gap junctions in development. *Ann. Rev. Physiol.* 47:DND–000

10. Cooper, G. M. 1982. Cellular transforming genes. *Science* 218:801–6

11. Dekel, N., Beers, W. H. 1980. Development of the rat oocyte in vitro: Inhibition and induction of maturation in the presence or absence of the cumulus oophorus. *Dev. Biol.* 75:247–57

12. Dekel, N., Lawrence, T. S., Gilula, N. B., Beers, W. H. 1981. Modulation of cell-to-cell communication in the cumulus-oocyte complex and the regulation of oocyte maturation by LH. *Dev. Biol.* 86:356–62

13. Durkin, J. P., Whitfield, J. F., MacManus, J. P. 1983. The role of calmodulin in the proliferation of transformed and phenotypically normal tsASV-infected rat cells. *J. Cell. Physiol.* 115:313–19

14. Enomoto, T., Sasaki, Y., Shiba, Y., Kanno, Y., Yamasaki, H. 1981. Tumor parameters cause a rapid and reversible inhibition of the formation and maintenance of electrical cell coupling in culture. *Proc. Natl. Acad. Sci. USA* 78:5628–32

15. Eppig, J. J. 1982. The relationship between cumulus cell-oocyte coupling, oocyte meiotic maturation and cumulus expansion. *Dev. Biol.* 89:268–72

16. Erikson, R. L., Purchio, A. F., Erikson, E., Collett, M. S., Brugge, J. S. 1980. Molecular events in cells transformed by Rous sarcoma virus. *J. Cell Biol.* 87:319–25

17. Feig, L. A., Bast, R. C. Jr., Knapp, R. C., Cooper, G. M. 1984. Somatic activation of ras^k gene in a human ovarian carcinoma. *Science* 223:698–700

18. Finbow, M. E., Shuttlewood, J., Hamilton, A. E., Pitts, J. D. 1983. Analysis of vertebrate gap junction protein. *EMBO J.* 2:1479–86

19. Flagg-Newton, J. L., Dahl, G., Loewenstein, W. R. 1981. Cell junction and cyclic AMP. I. Upregulation of junctional membrane permeability and junctional membrane particles by administration of cyclic nucleotide or phosphodiesterase inhibitor. *J. Membr. Biol.* 63:105–21

20. Flagg-Newton, J. L., Loewenstein, W. R. 1981. Cell junction and cyclic AMP. II. Modulations of junctional membrane permeability, dependent on serum and cell density. *J. Membr. Biol.* 63:123–31

21. Fletcher, W. H., Byus, C. V. 1982. Direct cytochemical localization of catalytic subunits dissociated from cAMP-dependent protein kinase in Reuber H-35 hepatoma cells. I. Development and validation of fluorescinated inhibitor. *J. Cell Biol.* 93:719–26

22. Furshpan, E. J., Potter, D. D. 1968. Low resistance junctions between cells in embryos and tissue culture. *Curr. Top. Dev. Biol.* 3:95–127

23. Gilula, N. B., Epstein, M. L., Beers, W. H. 1978. Cell-to-cell communication and ovulation: A study of the cumulus-oocyte complex. *J. Cell Biol.* 78:58–75

24. Hertzberg, E. L. 1985. Antibody probes in the study of gap junctional communication. *Ann. Rev. Physiol.* 47:DND–000

25. Kanno, Y., Loewenstein, W. R. 1966. Cell-to-cell passage of large molecules. *Nature* 212:629–30

26. Kohen, E., Kohen, C., Thorell, B., Mintz, D. H., Rabinovitch, A. 1979. Intercellular communication in pancreatic islet monolayer cultures: a microfluorometric study. *Science* 204:862–65

27. Kuffler, S. W., Potter, D. D. 1964. Glia in the leech central nervous system: physiological properties and neuron-glia relationships. *J. Neurophysiol.* 27:290–320

28. Lawrence, T. S., Beers, W. H., Gilula, N. B. 1978. Transmission of hormonal stimulation by cell-to-cell communication. *Nature* 272:501–6

29. Liu, T. F., Kam, E. Y., Sheridan, J. D. 1982. Dye transfer through permeable junctions between cultured mammalian cells: Quantitative video analysis. *J. Cell Biol.* 95:107a (Abstr.)

30. Loewenstein, W. R. 1968. Communication through cell junctions. Implications in growth control and differentiation. *Dev. Biol.* 190 Suppl. 2:151–83

31. Loewenstein, W. R. 1979. Junctional intercellular communication and the control of growth. *Biophys. Biochim. Acta* 560:1–65

32. Loewenstein, W. R. 1981. Junctional intercellular communication: the cell-to-cell membrane channel. *Physiol. Rev.* 61:829–913

33. Loewenstein, W. R., Kanno, Y. 1964. Studies on an epithelial (gland) cell junction. I. Modification of surface membrane permeability. *J. Cell Biol.* 22:565–86

34. Loewenstein, W. R., Kanno, Y. 1967. Intercellular communication and tissue growth. I. Cancerous growth. *J. Cell Biol.* 33:225–34

35. Meda, P., Michaels, R., Halban, P.,

Orci, L., Sheridan, J. 1983. *In vivo* modulation of gap junctions and dye coupling between B-cells of the intact pancreatic islet. *Diabetes* 32:858–68

36. Meda, P., Perrelet, A., Orci, L. 1979. Increase of gap junctions between pancreatic B-cells during stimulation of insulin secretion. *J. Cell Biol.* 82:441–48

37. Meissner, H. 1976. Electrophysiological evidence for coupling between B cells of pancreatic islets. *Nature* 262:502–4

38. Michaels, R. L. 1982. Increased dye coupling among cells in prolactin stimulated pancreatic islets. *J. Cell Biol.* 95:94a (Abstr.)

39. Michaels, R. L. 1983. *Dye coupling and junctional communication between cells of the rat pancreatic islet of Langerhans.* Ph.D. thesis. Univ. Minnesota, Minneapolis

40. Michaels, R. L., Sheridan, J. D. 1981. Islets of Langerhans: dye coupling among immunocytochemically distinct cell types. *Science* 214:801–3

41. Moor, R. M., Osborn, J. C., Cran, D. G., Walters, D. G. 1981. Selective effect of gonadotropins on cell coupling, nuclear maturation and protein synthesis in mammalian oocytes. *J. Embryol. Exp. Morph.* 61:347–65

42. Moor, R. M., Smith, M. W., Dawson, R. M. C. 1980. Measurement of intercellular coupling between oocytes and cumulus cells using intracellular markers. *Exp. Cell Res.* 126:15–29

43. Murray, S. A., Fletcher, W. H. 1984. Hormone-induced intercellular signal transfer dissociates cyclic AMP-dependent protein kinase. *J. Cell Biol.* 98:1710–19

44. Newbold, R. F. 1982. Metabolic cooperation in tumor promotion and carcinogenesis. In *Functional Integration of Cells in Animal Tissues,* ed. J. D. Pitts, M. E. Finbow, pp. 301–17. Cambridge: Cambridge Univ. Press

45. Oliviera-Castro, G. M., Loewenstein, W. R. 1971. Junctional membrane permeability: effects of divalent cations. *J. Membr. Biol.* 5:51–77

46. Orci, L., Malaisse-Lagae, F., Ravazzola, M., Rouiller, D., Renold, A., et al. 1975. A morphological basis for intercellular communication between A- and B-cells in the endocrine pancreas. *J. Clin. Invest.* 56:1066–70

47. Orci, L., Unger, R., Renold, A. 1973. Structural coupling between pancreatic islet cells. *Experientia* 29:1015–18

48. Peracchia, C. 1980. Structural correlates of gap junction permeation. *Int. Rev. Cytol.* 66:81–146

49. Pitts, J. D., Simms, J. W. 1977. Permeability of junctions between animal cells. Intercellular transfer of nucleotides, but not of macromolecules. *Exp. Cell Res.* 104:153–63

50. Potter, D. D., Furshpan, E. J., Lennox, E. S. 1966. Connections between cells of the developing squid as revealed by electrophysiological methods. *Proc. Natl. Acad. Sci. USA* 55:328–39

51. Preus, D., Johnson, R., Sheridan, J., Meyer, R. 1981. Analysis of gap junctions and formation plaques between reaggregating Novikoff hepatoma cells. *J. Ultrastruct. Res.* 77:263–76

52. Radu, A., Dahl, G., Loewenstein, W. R. 1982. Hormonal regulation of cell junction permeability: upregulation by catecholamine and prostaglandin E_1. *J. Membr. Biol.* 70:239–51

53. Raskin, P., Unger, R. 1978. The effect of insulin therapy on the profiles of plasma immunoreactive glucagon in juvenile-type and adult-type diabetics. *Diabetes* 27:411–19

54. Revel, J. P., Nicholson, B. J., Yancey, S. B. 1985. Chemistry of gap junctions. *Ann. Rev. Physiol.* 47:DND–000

55. Rhodin, J. A. G. 1968. Ultrastructure of mammalian venous capillaries, venules, and small collecting veins. *J. Ultrastruc. Res.* 25:242–500

56. Rose, B., Rick, R. 1978. Intracellular pH, intracellular free Ca, and junctional cell-cell coupling. *J. Membr. Biol.* 44:377–415

57. Schultz, R. M., Montgomery, R. R., Ward-Bailey, P. F., Eppig, J. J. 1983. Regulation of oocyte maturation in the mouse: possible roles of intercellular communication, cAMP, and testosterone. *Dev. Biol.* 95:294–304

58. Sefton, B. M., Hunter, T., Beemon, K., Eckhart, W. 1980. Evidence that the phosphorylation of tyrosine is essential for cellular transformation by Rous sarcoma virus. *Cell* 20:807–16

59. Sheridan, J. D. 1970. Low-resistance junctions between cancer cells in various solid tumors. *J. Cell Biol.* 45:91–99

60. Sheridan, J. D. 1971. Dye movement and low resistance junctions between reaggregated embryonic cells. *Dev. Biol.* 26:627–36

61. Sheridan, J. D. 1971. Electrical coupling between fat cells in newt fat body and mouse brown fat. *J. Cell Biol.* 50:795–803

62. Sheridan, J. D. 1974. Low resistance junctions: some functional considerations. In *The Cell Surface in Development,* ed. A. A. Moscone, pp. 187–206. New York: Wiley

63. Sheridan, J. D. 1976. Cell coupling and

cell communication during embryogenesis. In *The Cell Surface in Animal Embryogenesis and Development*, ed. G. Poste, G. L. Nicolson, pp. 409–47. Amsterdam: Elsevier/North Holland

64. Sheridan, J. D. 1978. Junction formation and experimental modification. In *Receptors and Recognition*, ed. J. Feldman, N. B. Gilula, J. D. Pitts, Series B, 2:39–59. New York: Halsted

65. Sheridan, J. D. 1980. Dye transfer in small vessels from the rat omentum: homologous and heterologous junctions. *J. Cell Biol.* 87:61a (Abstr.)

66. Sheridan, J. D., Finbow, M. E., Pitts, J. D. 1979. Metabolic interactions between animal cells through permeable intercellular junctions. *Exp. Cell Res.* 123:111–17

67. Sheridan, J. D., Hammer, M. G., Johnson, R. G. 1975. Cyclic nucleotide-induced changes in formation of low-resistance junctions. *J. Cell Biol.* 67: 395a (Abstr.)

68. Sheridan, J. D., Larson, D. M. 1982. Junctional communication in the peripheral vasculature. In *Functional Integration of Cells in Animal Tissues*. ed. J. D. Pitts, M. E. Finbow, pp. 264–83. Cambridge: Cambridge Univ. Press

69. Simpson, I., Rose, B., Loewenstein, W. R. 1977. Size limit of molecules permeating the junctional membrane channels. *Science* 195:294–96

70. Sorenson, R., Michaels, R., Parsons, J., Sheridan, J. 1983. Association of the glucose threshold of insulin release with gap junctional coupling of B-cells. *Diabetes* 32:9A

71. Spray, D. C., Bennett, M. V. L. 1985. Physiology and pharmacology of gap junctions. *Ann. Rev. Physiol.* 47:281–304

72. Spray, D. C., White, R. L., deCarvalho, A. C., Harris, A. L., Bennett, M. V. L. 1984. Gating of gap junction channels. *Biophys. J.* 45:219–30

73. Subak-Sharpe, H., Burk, R. R., Pitts, J. D. 1969. Metabolic cooperation between biochemically marked mammalian cells in culture. *J. Cell Sci.* 4:353–67

74. Deleted in proof

75. Sukumar, S., Notario, V., Martin-Zanca, D., Barbacid, M. 1983. Induction of mammary carcinomas in rats by nitroso-methylurea involves malignant activation of H-ras-1 locus by single point mutations. *Nature* 306:658–61

76. Tsien, R. W., Weingart, R. 1976. Inotropic effect of cyclic AMP in calf ventricular muscle studied by a cut end method. *J. Physiol.* 260:117–41

77. Vitkauskas, G., Kole, J., Canellakis, E. S. 1983. Biochemical assay of inhibitors of metabolic cooperation. *Exp. Cell Res.* 145:15–30

78. Yancey, S. B., Edens, J. E., Trosko, J. E., Chang, C. C., Revel, J. P. 1982. Decreased incidence of gap junctions between Chinese hamster V-79 cells upon exposure to the tumor promoter 12-O-tetra-decanoyl phorbol-13-acetate. *Exp. Cell Res.* 139:329–40

79. Yotti, L. P., Chang, C. C., Trosko, J. E. 1979. Elimination of metabolic cooperation in Chinese hamster cells by a tumor promoter. *Science* 206:1089–91

80. Ziemiecki, A., Friis, R. R. 1980. Phosphorylation of pp60src and the cyclohexamide insensitive activation of the pp60src-associated kinase activity of transformation-defective, temperature-sensitive mutants of Rous sarcoma virus. *Virology* 106:391–94

ENDOCRINOLOGY

Introduction, Jack L. Kostyo, *Section Editor*

Remarkable progress has been made in recent years in unraveling the mechanisms by which peptide hormones exert their physiological actions on target cells. Major advances in protein chemistry, and more recently in recombinant DNA technology, have provided the means to isolate native peptide hormones in highly purified form or to produce them synthetically. Thus current work on the mechanisms of action of the peptide hormones does not suffer from the many ambiguities that plagued earlier work with impure hormone preparations. Moreover, cellular systems have been developed that respond to peptide hormones in a physiologically relevant fashion, thereby permitting the investigator to focus on a specific action of the hormone on a particular target cell in isolation from other actions that the hormone may have on the organism. Additionally, many biochemical tools are now available with which to probe the interaction of the hormone with its target cell at the molecular level.

A group of metabolically related peptide hormones that have been investigated intensively during the past several years, and about which much has been learned, include insulin, the insulin-like growth factors, and pituitary growth hormone. Consequently, this year's section on Endocrinology has been devoted to a review of current work on the nature of the receptors for these substances and the cellular mediators of their actions. Individual chapters describe the substantial progress that has been made in defining the molecular character of the plasma membrane receptors for these substances and the mechanisms by which the receptors themselves are regulated and internalized by the cell. Coverage is also given to current knowledge of the intriguing, but somewhat elusive, intracellular mediator(s) of the action of insulin on target cells. Last, recent work on the cellular actions of the insulin-like growth factors and pituitary growth hormone are reviewed in detail, as well as current views of the physiological relationships that exist between these two groups of hormones.

Ann. Rev. Physiol. 1985. 47:357–81

THE NATURE AND REGULATION OF THE INSULIN RECEPTOR: STRUCTURE AND FUNCTION

Michael P. Czech

Department of Biochemistry, University of Massachusetts Medical Center, 55 Lake Avenue North, Worcester, Massachusetts 01605

INTRODUCTION

Insulin is a peptide hormone, secreted by the β cells of the pancreas, that elicits a remarkable array of biological responses. Although liver, muscle, and fat tissue are probably the major physiological targets of insulin in respect to overall metabolic homeostasis in vivo (6), many other cell types also exhibit regulatory effects of insulin. The biological actions of insulin include activations of transport systems such as those for hexoses, amino acids, and ions, acute activations of enzyme systems such as glycogen synthase and pyruvate dehydrogenase, acute inhibitions of enzyme systems such as the hormone-sensitive lipase of adipocytes, and modulation of transcription of specific mRNA species such as that for phosphoenolpyruvate carboxykinase [several reviews of these actions are (6, 12–14, 17, 28, 34, 50, 62, 76)]. These effects of insulin vary in their time of onset from very rapid responses of transport systems and enzymes (seconds to minutes) to quite slow modulations of cell proliferation that take many hours to be expressed (85, 91).

At the molecular level, many of the enzymes that are acutely modulated by insulin action undergo phosphorylation or dephosphorylation in response to insulin. Examples of insulin-mediated dephosphorylations include glycogen synthase (116) and pyruvate dehydrogenase (51), which are activated in response to hormone. These enzymes are similarly activated in vitro upon dephosphorylation. In contrast, insulin action mediates the apparent phosphorylation of acetyl-CoA carboxylase (5, 130), ATP-citrate lyase (1, 108),

0066-4278/85/0315-0357$02.00

357

and the S-6 ribosomal protein (93, 120), although phosphorylations of these proteins in vitro have not demonstrated functional changes in their biological activities. Thus, it is not clear what role protein phosphorylations play in mediating biological effects of insulin, nor is it understood why both phosphorylations and dephosphorylations occur in the cellular responses to insulin. Detailed reviews on the cellular processes under the control of insulin that involve alterations in phosphorylation can be found in a recent volume (17).

A large body of accumulated evidence suggests that the biological actions of insulin summarized above are initiated by interaction of the hormone with specific cell-surface receptors that mediate one or more cellular signaling mechanisms. An important approach toward unraveling the detailed molecular events involved in transducing the actions of insulin has been the analysis of structure-function relationships within the receptor complex itself. Although early studies were limited to assessing insulin receptors by their ability to bind radiolabeled insulin, several technical advances over the last decade, including affinity purification, affinity labeling, and immunological techniques have led to major new advances in our information about the insulin receptor structure. In addition, the discovery that the insulin receptor structure is associated with tyrosine kinase activity has led to detailed enzymological studies of this receptor. It is the purpose of this review to summarize our current knowledge about the structure-function relationships related to the insulin receptor structure and its associated kinase activity.

GENERAL PROPERTIES OF INSULIN RECEPTOR

Even before the availability of reliable methods to assess insulin binding to cell-surface receptors, indirect experiments suggested that insulin receptors of protein nature resided on cell membranes and initiated the biological actions of the hormone. Thus, trypsinization of isolated adipocytes was found to block insulin action under conditions where the cellular responses to other hormones were little effected (74, 75). With the development of sound methodologies for preparing radioiodinated-insulin preparations that specifically bind to insulin receptors with low-background nonspecific binding activity (10, 111), a large number of experiments were performed assessing the kinetics of ^{125}I-insulin association with and dissociation from insulin receptors. In addition, the effects of a variety of agents and treatments of cells on ^{125}I–insulin receptor interaction could be studied. Using this strategy, treatment of cells with phospholipases was found to increase ^{125}I-insulin binding (9), while trypsinization was shown to dramatically decrease ^{125}I-insulin binding to isolated adipocytes (77). In addition, the ability of ^{125}I-insulin to bind and thus label solubilized receptors led to the characterization of the hydrodynamic properties of the insulin receptor. The results of such studies are briefly described below.

Binding Kinetics

The binding of radioiodinated insulin to insulin receptors in intact cells, purified membrane preparations, and in detergent-solubilized form usually exhibits complex kinetics, as reflected in curvilinear Scatchard plots (63). The concave nature of insulin-binding curves analyzed by such plots has suggested that multiple insulin-receptor sites with different affinities reside on cell membranes or that the insulin receptor structure exhibits negative cooperativity, or both. That the insulin receptor structure participates in negative cooperative interactions was proposed by DeMeyts and colleagues (23–27), who showed that diluting cells or membranes containing bound ^{125}I-insulin with buffer containing excess unlabeled insulin leads to increased dissociation of the labeled hormone from its receptors. This interpretation has been challenged based on experimental findings (106) and more general considerations (107). However, recent work has shown that whereas most modifications of the insulin molecule simply lead to analogs that possess lower affinity for insulin receptors and exhibit similar curvilinear Scatchard plots, certain insulin analogs are devoid of apparent negative cooperative effects (24, 27). Thus, such insulin analogs are incapable of stimulating the dissociation of ^{125}I-insulin bound to receptors upon dilution. Furthermore, other complex kinetic phenomena have been reported, such as time-dependent increases in insulin receptor affinity during ligand-binding experiments (30, 98). In addition, recent data indicates that the insulin receptor exhibits positive cooperativity over a range of low insulin concentrations (83).

Taken together, this series of complexities in the analyses of ^{125}I-insulin–binding data suggest the possibility of multiple binding sites per insulin receptor unit. This conclusion is in fact suggested by the symmetrical nature of the proposed insulin receptor subunit configuration that is discussed later in this review (see Figure 1). Recent results with two distinct insulin probes suggest that each insulin receptor unit binds two insulin molecules but that the two binding sites have markedly different affinities for insulin (99). Such a model of multiple, kinetically distinct binding sites on a complex insulin receptor structure having the potential for cooperative interactions might explain the complicated binding isotherms observed in various laboratories. Future experiments will be needed to resolve this issue.

Physicochemical Properties

The hydrodynamic and sedimentation equilibrium properties of the insulin receptor from liver and fat cell membranes as well as cultured human lymphoblastoid cells have been determined (11, 105). The data indicate that the receptor complex in Triton X-100 exhibits a Stokes radius of between 70 Å (105) and 81 Å (11), as determined by gel filtration. The insulin-receptor complex exhibits a sedimentation coefficient of about 11S in Triton X-100 (11,

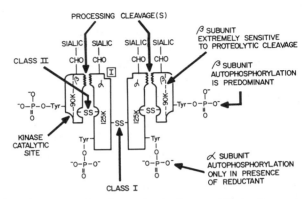

Figure 1   Schematic representation of several major features of the insulin receptor structure as currently understood. The major form of the mature insulin receptor structure appears to be a heterotetrameric, disulfide-linked configuration of α and β subunits (19, 54). The disulfide linkages are of two classes *(class I and class II)* that can be distinguished experimentally by their differential sensitivity to reduction by dithiothreitol and other reductants (86). Both α and β subunits contain oligosaccharide and sialic acid (48, 109, 125). The mature α and β subunits appear to be derived from a single precursor polypeptide chain by a proteolytic cleavage or cleavages (29, 47, 57, 109). The β subunit exhibits a site at about the center of its amino acid sequence that is exquisitely sensitive to elastase-like proteases (88). Tyrosine-kinase catalytic sites are associated with the β subunits that are autophosphorylated in vitro in the presence or absence of reductant (69). α Subunits, which appear to bind insulin, are also autophosphorylated on tyrosine residues in vitro, but only in the presence of millimolar concentrations of reductants. The insulin receptor tyrosine kinase activity is markedly activated upon binding insulin. See text for further details.

105). This value is not altered upon digestion of membranes with phospholipase or extraction of membranes with organic solvent prior to solubilizing receptors with detergent (11). A high frictional coefficient ratio (f/f$_O$) of about 1.6 was obtained in these studies. Taken together, the results from these hydrodynamic and sedimentation equilibrium measurements indicate that the receptor structure has a molecular weight of approximately 300,000 and that the receptor protein binds 0.5 g Triton X-100 per g protein (11, 105).

PROTEIN CHEMISTRY OF INSULIN RECEPTOR

The importance of understanding the detailed protein chemistry of the insulin receptor derives from the presumption that insulin receptor functions are determined by insulin-receptor structure. Structural information within the receptor must participate in such processes as biological signal transduction (12), ligand-induced receptor internalization (122), desensitization (46), and receptor recycling (84). Thus, the availability of biochemical approaches in assessing the molecular details of receptor structure has been particularly important. Rigorous identification of the true insulin receptor subunit types has not proved to be a trivial task, in spite of the availability of powerful affinity labeling, affinity purification, and specific immunoprecipitation techniques. Although these experimental methodologies are designed to be quite specific for insulin receptors, persistent problems with background contamination as well as sample proteolysis have been difficult to eliminate fully. Nevertheless, there is now solid agreement that a minimum of two insulin receptor subunit types reside in the mature cell-surface insulin-receptor complex.

Identification of Subunit Types

There is general concensus that one insulin receptor subunit, denoted as the α subunit (87), exhibits an apparent $M_r = 125,000-135,000$. This conclusion was first suggested by visualization of protein-stained electrophoretic gels containing a preparation of insulin receptor that had been affinity purified by adsorption and elution from insulin-agarose (60). A band of similar apparent mass was subsequently identified by photoaffinity labeling (129, 132, 134–136) and affinity cross-linking techniques (19, 87, 102, 103). Competitive inhibition of insulin receptor α-subunit affinity labeling by increasing concentrations of unlabeled insulin demonstrated that this species exhibits the high affinity for insulin expected for the insulin receptor (103, 134). The fact that this subunit is the predominant labeled species using affinity cross-linking techniques, which involve incubation of membranes with ^{125}I-insulin and chemical cross-linkers such as disuccinimidyl suberate, suggests but does not prove the concept that this subunit contains the hormone binding site or sites. This α subunit can now be readily identified by photoaffinity labeling (132), affinity cross-linking (19), affinity purification (54–56), immunoaffinity purification (45, 49), and specific immunoprecipitation of insulin receptors (68). Immunoprecipitation with specific anti–insulin receptor serum of affinity-labeled insulin receptors leads to visualization of the affinity–cross-linked α subunit, indicating the two reagents interact with identical insulin receptor species (68). The insulin receptor α subunit is a glycoprotein, as first evidenced by an altered electrophoretic mobility after treatment with neuroaminidase (55). Subsequent experiments have shown incorporation of labeled saccharides into the α subunit by specific insulin receptor immunoprecipitations using a variety of anti–insulin receptor antibody preparations (48, 66, 79, 113, 125). Although most of the above studies have been performed in rodent and human tissues, an insulin receptor α subunit of similar features has been identified in tissues of the hagfish, indicating substantial conservation of its properties over the last 500 million years of evolution (18).

A second authentic insulin-receptor subunit has a mass of about 90,000 daltons and has been more elusive in respect to its identification. The reason for this is that it is very poorly labeled by most (19), although not all, affinity-labeling procedures (132). Furthermore, this 90,000-dalton subunit stains poorly with Coomassie blue or silver staining compared to the α subunit (38), and it is relatively more sensitive to fragmentation by proteases (88, 114). It was first observed in affinity purification studies as a receptor band (55, 56) and was deduced to be part of the native insulin receptor structure by affinity cross-linking (19) and affinity purification (54) techniques and two-dimensional gel electrophoresis in the presence and absence of reductant. Subsequent results with large-scale affinity-purified receptor preparations (38) suggested that the 90,000-dalton subunit is present in the receptor complex in approximately the same stoichiometry as the α subunit. Interestingly, this subunit contains a site at about the center of its amino acid sequence that is particularly sensitive to one or more cleavages by elastase (88). This subunit is autophosphorylated by insulin receptor solubilized in detergent solution and reacted with [γ-^{32}P]ATP or in insulin-treated intact cells labeled with ^{32}P (69). Affinity labeling of insulin receptors with analogs of ATP also lead to the labeling of this subunit, indicating that it contains a catalytic site for the insulin receptor–associated tyrosine kinase (112, 118, 127). The 90,000-dalton subunit contains oligosaccharide, as evidenced by its biosynthetic labeling with labeled monosaccharides (48). This glycoprotein subunit is denoted as the β subunit of the insulin receptor (87).

Recent evidence suggests that the α and β subunits are synthesized in cells as a single polypeptide precursor that is ultimately processed to the mature cell-surface receptor subunits by proteolytic cleavages. Thus immunoprecipitation of biosynthetically labeled insulin receptor leads to the visualization of 190,000-dalton and 210,000-dalton labeled bands on electrophoretic gels that predominate at early pulses of [^{35}S]methionine label (29, 47, 57, 109). When a short pulse of added ^{35}S-methionine is followed by a chase with unlabeled methionine in intact cells, it is observed that the label is decreased sequentially in the 190,000- and 210,000-dalton species and increased in the α and β subunit bands.

Experiments by Ronnett et al (109) have provided further details about the processing steps in insulin-receptor biosynthesis. In these experiments, label in the 210K receptor precursor was chased into 125K and 83K precursors of the mature insulin receptor α and β subunits, respectively. The 190K and 210K precursors and the 125K and 83K proteolytically processed precursors were all sensitive to endoglycosidase H treatment, suggesting that these polypeptides contain an N-linked high mannose–type core oligosaccharide without terminal sialic acid moieties. In contrast, the mature 135K and 95K α and β subunits were resistant to endoglycosidase H digestion, indicating their oligosaccharide units are capped by terminal sialic acids. Interestingly, the time at which the receptor acquires sialic acids, as evidenced by sensitivity to neuroaminidase, appears to correspond to the time at which the receptor is inserted into the plasma membrane (109). Taken together, these data indicate that the insulin receptor subunits are synthesized on a high-M_r polypeptide precursor that is rapidly glycosylated and identified as an endoglycosidase H–sensitive 190K species. This is followed by further glycosylation yielding a 210K precursor. The endoglycosidase H–sensitive 210K species is a substrate for one or more proteolytic processing cleavages, which result in the formation of 125K and 83K subunit precursors. These two precursors contain oligosaccharide chains that are ultimately capped with sialic acid residues near the time of their appearance at the cell surface. A major impact of these studies is the verification that two major subunits of the insulin receptor are the α and β species previously identified by completely different methodologies.

Peptide-mapping experiments have demonstrated that a high-M_r (210K) polypeptide that is immunoprecipitated by specific anti-insulin receptor antibody exhibits a complex peptide-mapping profile containing peptides similar to those of both α and β subunits, consistent with the above interpretations (66). The overall peptide maps of the α and β subunits are quite distinct, using several proteases (66). These different peptide profiles imply distinct polypeptide structures for the α and β subunits. Furthermore, this presumed structural distinction between α and β subunits is consistent with the apparent different functional roles of the subunits, whereby the α subunit binds hormone while the β subunit carries tyrosine kinase activity and is the predominant subunit autophosphorylated in detergent solution.

Very recent results suggest, however, that regions of sequence homology may exist within the α and β subunit polypeptides (K. Yu & M. P. Czech, submitted for publication). These similarities seem to be localized within the receptor peptide regions that are phosphorylated. Thus, under conditions where both α and β subunits are phosphorylated when purified insulin receptor is incubated with [γ-^{32}P]ATP and high concentrations of reductant, an unexpected similarity of radiolabeled phosphopeptide profiles is observed for the α and β subunits upon tryptic hydrolysis and high-pressure liquid chromatography. Each of the corresponding ^{32}P-labeled peptides from the receptor α and β subunits eluted in the high-pressure liquid chromatograph exhibits identical electrophoretic mobility on thin-layer cellulose plates as well. Furthermore, a sequential digestion of the respective tryptic hydrolysates of the phosphorylated receptor α and β subunits with *Staphylococcus aureus* V8 protease leads to identical electrophoretic profiles of the resulting doubly digested phosphopeptides from the α and β subunits. These results suggest that the α and β insulin receptor subunit phosphopeptide regions may be homologous in amino acid sequence, even though the overall structures of the two subunits appear quite different. The possibility that small amounts of β subunit contaminate the α subunit on dodecyl sulfate gels cannot yet be eliminated, however.

Beside the α and β subunits, other peptide species derived from insulin receptor preparations have exhibited properties expected for insulin receptor subunits. For example, an affinity-purified and affinity-labeled receptor protein of 45–50K identified on electrophoretic gels was found to be derived from the insulin receptor complex (55, 56, 87). This species, however, was demonstrated to be a proteolytic fragment of the native 90K β subunit (88). Results from recent experiments have suggested that a 40K receptor species exhibits properties expected for a native insulin receptor subunit (132). Yip and colleagues (131–133) discovered that this 40K species is photolabeled when isolated adipocytes are incubated with B-29 monoazidobenzoyl insulin or B-1 monoazidobenzoyl insulin and irradiated. This reaction product was not observed in plasma membranes. The 40K receptor species differed in its sensitivity to trypsin when labeled with the B-1 monoazidobenzoyl insulin rather than B-29 monoazidobenzoyl insulin, leading to the suggestion that two distinct 40K subunits reside in the insulin receptor complex. That the 40K species is a proteolytic product of the α or β subunit or a contaminant in the receptor preparation has not yet been rigorously eliminated. Analysis of highly purified insulin receptors or of immunoprecipitated insulin-receptor subunits does not seem to reveal this 40K band, indicating that it may be derived from a higher-M_r subunit. Although further experimentation will be required to elucidate the nature of this 40K peptide, current data unequivocally documents the existence of only two insulin receptor subunit types, α and β.

Subunit Stoichiometry and Receptor Structure

A large body of evidence generated by a variety of approaches is consistent with the concept that the major form of the native insulin receptor complex is a heterotetrameric disulfide-linked structure composed of two α and two β subunits, as depicted in Figure 1. This general model for the insulin receptor subunit configuration was originally proposed independently by Jacobs and colleagues (54–56) using affinity-purification and photolabeling techniques and by Massague et al (15, 19, 87) using affinity cross-linking techniques developed for assessing hormone-receptor structures (20, 102). Several observations strongly suggest the $\alpha_2\beta_2$ stoichiometry and the disulfide-linked configuration. Affinity-purified or affinity–cross-linked insulin receptors were observed to migrate on dodecyl sulfate gels in the 350K–400K region when electrophoresed in the absence of reductant (55, 87, 103). Addition of reductants leads to the complete loss of this native insulin receptor species and the concomitant appearance of α and β subunits at 125K and 90K, respectively (55, 87). In most such experiments, the insulin-receptor structure is resolved into three distinct bands under nonreducing conditions, indicating receptor heterogeneity. This heterogeneity was discovered to be the result of sequential β subunit proteolysis, whereby an apparent 320K receptor species is formed when one β subunit is cleaved, and an apparent 290K receptor species is observed upon cleavage of both β subunits by elastase or elastase-like proteases

(Figure 1). Generation of these two nicked insulin receptor complexes can be achieved by incubation of native, intact insulin receptor with elastase (88). Elastase treatment of the insulin receptor complex under such conditions correlates with the sequential disappearance of the β subunit, as visualized under reducing conditions, and the appearance of an apparent 49K β subunit proteolytic product, denoted as β_1. It is still not known whether β subunit cleavage at this site is a part of the mechanism whereby the insulin receptor is degraded physiologically.

Studies involving incubation of native insulin receptor preparations with varying concentrations of exogeneous reductant led to the concept that at least two classes of receptor disulfides are present in the insulin receptor complex (19, 54, 55, 86, 87). At low concentrations of dithiothreitol, native $\alpha_2\beta_2$ insulin-receptor structures are partially reduced to yield a 210K fragment in addition to free subunits. This partially reduced receptor fragment is composed of α and β subunits and results from the reduction of one or more receptor disulfides denoted as class I (Figure 1). At higher concentrations of reductant, class II disulfides linking α and β subunits are cleaved, yielding free α and β subunits (86). An important result leading to the model presented in Figure 1 indicated that reduction of class I disulfides in the partially nicked 320K receptor structure led to the identification of two partially reduced receptor fragments (87). One fragment contained α and β subunits, while the other fragment contained α and the 49K proteolytic product of the β subunit. It is important to note that unequivocal evidence is not yet available to document that the class I disulfides, linking the two insulin receptor α-S-S-β halves, actually reside on the α subunits rather than β subunits.

Since the β-S-S-α-S-S-α-S-S-β insulin-receptor subunit configuration was proposed, considerable new results have been obtained that support the model. For example, Fujita-Yamaguchi (38, 39) published results confirming the $\alpha_2\beta_2$ insulin-receptor complex as the major receptor form that is affinity purified by methods that allow acquisition of receptors in good yield. This highly purified receptor preparation exhibits high-affinity ^{125}I-insulin binding (39), contains significant tyrosine kinase activity (69), and is visualized on dodecyl sulfate gels by silver staining as three major forms in the absence of reductant (38), as previously revealed by affinity cross-linking techniques (87). Analysis of the subunit configuration in this purified insulin receptor preparation by two-dimensional gel electrophoresis in the presence and absence of reductant confirms the basic findings of Jacobs et al (54–56) and Massague et al (19, 87). Two-dimensional gel electrophoresis of immunoprecipitated insulin receptors in the absence and presence of reductant also revealed a major insulin receptor structure of about 350K that contains approximately equal amounts of α and β subunits, as expected (66). In that study, a higher-M_r receptor complex was observed that additionally contained a 210K protein, presumably the receptor precursor polypeptide described in the previous section. Different oligomeric structures containing α and β subunits were also found after denaturation in dodecyl sulfate (66). It is not clear whether these forms represent native oligomeric states of the receptor in the native membrane or whether they reflect dodecyl sulfate-disrupted $\alpha_2\beta_2$ receptor forms that were partially reduced in the cells. There is evidence that the disulfide-linked $\alpha_2\beta_2$ structure remains associated upon reduction of the disulfide linkages unless dodecyl sulfate is added to dissociate them (86).

A fundamental tenet of hormone receptor theory is that ligand binding leads to one or more changes in receptor structure such that a variety of functions, including biological signaling, may proceed. Several lines of evidence are now available that directly demonstrate such ligand-sensitive structural changes in the insulin receptor. Alterations in the structural properties of the insulin receptor in response to binding insulin include increased susceptibility of the α subunit to hydrolysis by trypsin in intact cells and isolated membranes (104), altered chromatographic migration on molecular sieving columns (41, 89), altered migration properties on nondenaturing electrophoretic gels (80), and altered reactivity with labeled N-ethylmaleimide (89). The ability of insulin to dramatically activate intrinsic receptor tyrosine kinase activity (69) also emphatically demonstrates this point. Such effects of insulin on insulin receptor structure could involve altered association of the receptor with regulatory components or direct conformation changes within the insulin receptor protein structure. The latter concept is supported by the observation that a highly purified preparation of insulin receptor containing only minor amounts of proteins other than the major α and β subunits exhibits insulin-activated tyrosine kinase activity (69).

Immunological Properties

A growing number of specific anti–insulin receptor antibody preparations, including monoclonal, polyclonal, and anti-idiotypic immunoglobulins (33, 115), are now available for studies on the insulin receptor. The anti-idiotypic antibody preparations have not yet been used for immunoprecipitation assays. That the purified insulin receptor, at least from rat liver, is a viable immunogen in rabbits was demonstrated by Jacobs et al (53). The polyclonal rabbit antibody produced in these experiments has no effect on the binding of insulin to insulin receptors but is able to specifically immunoprecipitate insulin receptors biosynthetically labeled with [^{35}S]methionine or labeled with ^{125}I using lactoperoxidase (78). This laboratory group also succeeded in preparing specific anti–insulin receptor antibody by immunizing rabbits with isolated α insulin receptor subunit following its electrophoresis on dodecyl sulfate gels (55). This anti-receptor antiserum also is active in immunoprecipitation of solubilized insulin receptors bound to ^{125}I-insulin or denatured α insulin receptor subunits but is not active in modulating ^{125}I-insulin binding to the insulin receptor.

Potent anti–insulin receptor immunoglobulins have also been obtained from a rare group of patients exhibiting acanthosis nigricans and extreme insulin resistance (35, 37). Although the anti–insulin receptor antiserum preparations differ somewhat among patients, a hallmark of these antibodies is a dramatic inhibition of ^{125}I-insulin binding to insulin receptors (36). Furthermore, the binding of the human anti–insulin receptor immunoglobulin to insulin receptors can be inhibited by insulin itself (61), indicating that at least some of the anti–insulin receptor immunoglobulins present in the serum compete with insulin for binding to the receptor. These human anti–insulin receptor antibody preparations have been useful in characterizing the insulin receptor following immunoprecipitation from cellular extracts. Immunoblotting experiments have demonstrated that a human anti–insulin receptor serum as well as the rabbit anti–native insulin receptor antiserum react with both α and β subunits of the insulin receptor (82).

Three monoclonal anti–insulin receptor antibody preparations have been produced by Kull et al (78, 79) using purified insulin receptor from human placenta. Three viable hybridoma clones were grown in large amounts of ascites fluid. The antibodies produced by these clones react with both insulin and IGF-I receptors with different preferential activities. The reason for this cross-reactivity is that insulin-receptor preparations may be contaminated with IGF-I receptors, or that these two receptor types share homologous structural features, as suggested by their structural characterizations to date (16), or both. A preparation of monoclonal antibody with high specificity toward the insulin receptor failed to immunoprecipitate either the α or β subunit after denaturation with dithiothreitol and dodecyl sulfate (79). It is therefore not clear which subunit contains the immunoglobulin binding site. A monoclonal antibody preparation with specificity toward the IGF-I receptor appears to react with the α subunit (79). Another monoclonal anti–insulin receptor antibody has been prepared by Roth et al (113), who used intact IM-9 lymphocytes for immunization of Balb/c mice. This monoclonal antibody preparation is effective in immunoprecipitating [^{35}S]methionine-labeled insulin receptor and appears to recognize the α subunit of the insulin receptor (114).

Both the human and rabbit polyclonal anti–insulin receptor antibody preparations mimic insulin action on acute metabolic and transport processes (53, 64) as well as on stimulation of thymidine incorporation into DNA (91). Monovalent F_{ab} fragments of the human anti–insulin receptor immunoglobulins lack biological actions, indicating that multivalency is necessary for bioactivity (64). Cross-linking of insulin receptor–bound F_{ab} fragments restores insulinomimetic activity. The reason for this is not yet apparent. The monoclonal antibody preparation of Roth et al (113, 114) contrasts with the above properties in that it exhibits no insulin-like actions but rather antagonizes the effects of insulin. The antagonism is presumably due to its ability to inhibit insulin binding to insulin receptor. It is possible that the lack of agonist activity by this monoclonal antibody preparation is due to its inability to mediate receptor cross-linking into aggregates on the cell surface, which may occur in response to the polyclonal antibody preparations. In any case, the various available anti–insulin receptor antibody preparations continue to be very useful in probing insulin receptor structure and function.

ENZYMOLOGY OF INSULIN RECEPTOR TYROSINE KINASE

An important advance in the field of receptor biology has resulted from the discoveries that a number of hormone and growth factor receptors are enzymes that catalyze tyrosine phosphorylation. The pioneering work of Cohen and colleagues (8) demonstrated this property for the EGF receptor system. Subsequent experiments strongly suggest that the receptors for platelet-derived growth factor (32, 94), insulin (71), and insulin-like growth factor I (58) are also tyrosine kinases. This is particularly intriguing because of the extreme low abundance of tyrosine phosphorylations compared to serine and threonine phosphorylations in intact cells, and because several retroviral products that promote cellular transformation also exhibit tyrosine kinase activity. Indeed, one viral transforming glycoprotein product, derived from the avian erythroblastosis virus, has been shown to be homologous with a large portion of the EGF receptor structure (31), indicating that mechanisms of cellular growth modulation by some transforming viruses and growth factor receptors may be quite similar. Moreover, the insulin and growth factor receptor tyrosine kinases have provided a new focus for experimental strategies designed to elucidate the molecular details of receptor-signal transduction related to both the acute and long-term biological actions of these receptors.

Kasuga et al (67, 72) first demonstrated that insulin stimulates insulin receptor phosphorylation in ^{32}P-labeled cultured human lymphocytes and rat hepatoma cells. Similar results have also been obtained in normal cell types such as isolated adipocytes (44) and rat hepatocytes (126). Insulin receptor phosphorylation is temperature-dependent, as one would expect for an enzymatic reaction. In intact ^{32}P-labeled cell systems, insulin action is observed to direct the phosphorylation of serine, threonine, and tyrosine residues on the β insulin-receptor subunit (72, 124). This contrasts with experiments on solubilized insulin receptor in detergent solution where autophosphorylation of the β subunit is either solely or predominantly on tyrosine residues (71). The magnitude of the insulin effect in intact cells is usually 2–3-fold, although the real effect may be larger due to the technical difficulties in completely eliminating phosphatase activity during receptor preparation.

A large number of laboratories have demonstrated that insulin receptors undergo a rapid autophosphorylation reaction in the presence of $[\gamma\text{-}^{32}P]ATP$

when extracted from membranes with detergent (3, 4), when partially purified by affinity chromatography on immobilized wheat-germ agglutinin (101, 138) or other columns (81), or when purified to near homogeneity by adsorption to immobilized insulin (69, 70, 137). The autophosphorylation reaction on tyrosine residues of the insulin β subunit has been demonstrated with solubilized receptors from many cell types, including human placenta (3, 70, 101, 137), rat hepatocytes (126), 3T3-L1 adipocytes (101), cultured human lymphocytes (114), and human erythrocytes (42). In contrast to the EGF receptor autophosphorylation reaction, which is supported by Mg^{2+} and Co^{2+} as well as Mn^{2+}, the insulin receptor autophosphorylation requires the presence of Mn^{2+} (3, 138). The concentrations of Mn^{2+} needed to permit optimal receptor phosphorylation indicate that this requirement for Mn^{2+} is not only related to its ability to form a complex with ATP; Mn^{2+} appears to act as a receptor cofactor as well.

Insulin activates the insulin receptor autophosphorylation reaction many-fold by changing the apparent V_{max} rather than the K_m for ATP (128). On the other hand, Mn^{2+} appears to decrease the insulin receptor kinase K_m for ATP. The tyrosine phosphorylation sites on the insulin receptor β subunit can be resolved into several phosphopeptide fractions by high-pressure liquid chromatography (128, 137). The insulin receptor autophosphorylation reaction is very rapid under optimal conditions, can be readily observed at 0°C as is also the case for the EGF receptor, and leads to the incorporation of about 200 pmol of phosphate per mg of insulin receptor protein (128). At this level of phosphorylation, it can be calculated that approximately two molecules of phosphate are present per insulin binding site. Receptor autophosphorylation is markedly stimulated in the presence of reductants (117), which also leads to detectable levels of insulin-receptor α subunit phosphorylation (K.-T. Yu & M. P. Czech, submitted for publication). The insulin receptor–catalyzed phosphorylation of the receptor β subunit in vitro appears to be an intramolecular reaction because it is not inhibited by dilution of insulin receptor in a reaction mixture where other components are held constant (128).

In addition to catalyzing the autophosphorylation reaction, the solubilized insulin receptor readily catalyzes phosphorylation of a variety of exogenous substrates in vitro (70, 123). These include angiotensin II, a synthetic peptide related to the amino acid sequence surrounding the site of tyrosine phosphorylation in the transforming protein kinase of Rous sarcoma virus, tubulin, casein, and histone H2B. Interestingly, anti-src IgG is also a substrate for insulin-stimulated insulin receptor kinase, although the receptor kinase does not appear to catalyze phosphorylation of anti-insulin receptor Ig. Analysis of the substrate specificities of the insulin-activated receptor kinase indicated general similarity to that reported for the src and epidermal growth factor receptor protein kinases (123). These results have led to attempts to determine whether physiologically relevant endogenous substrates may exist for the insulin receptor tyrosine kinase. To date no substrates that are rapidly tyrosine-phosphorylated in response to insulin in intact cells have been found, although further studies on this point are in progress.

Although such endogenous substrates may be important for one or more functions of the insulin receptor, including signal transduction, it is also possible that the insulin receptor itself is the important substrate. Phosphorylation of the receptor itself could lead to changes in one or more receptor activities, ultimately resulting in initiation of cellular signaling. It is noteworthy that two studies have indicated a lack of activation of the insulin receptor kinase by anti–insulin receptor immunoglobulin preparations that mimic the biological actions of insulin (119, 139). These results have been used to suggest that the receptor kinase may not be involved in biological signaling, although antibody action may proceed by a different mechanism than that for insulin. This important issue will require future definitive resolution.

REGULATION OF INSULIN RECEPTOR FUNCTION

Although it is well appreciated that the insulin receptor plays a major physiological role by its ability to initiate biological signal transduction, recent experiments have also been directed toward the concept that it may also be an important target for regulation. That regulation of insulin receptor structure and functions may be mediated by distinct cellular signaling systems is consistent with general biochemical principles that dictate that initiating or branch points of pathways usually serve as major points of regulatory control. Furthermore, the number of receptor systems that have been found to be tightly regulated by the actions of other receptor systems is growing rapidly. The direction (activation or inhibition), magnitude, and mechanisms of such receptor-receptor regulatory pathways differ depending on the biological relationships between receptor systems involved.

Regulation of Insulin Binding

A large number of agents and altered physiological conditions are known to effect insulin binding to target cells. For example, addition of catecholamines or glucagon (100) or glucocorticoids (95) to cells, as well as the conditions of diabetes (96) and obesity (65, 97), modify insulin-receptor activity. Insulin itself when added to isolated cells in vitro leads to dramatic inhibition of steady-state cell-surface receptors by inducing insulin receptor internalization (40, 84, 122). That the insulin-induced decrease in insulin receptor binding in intact cells is due to internalization of receptors and loss of receptor numbers on the cell-surface membrane is strongly supported by morphological and biochemical techniques. However, alterations in insulin receptor affinity for the hormone, as assessed by Scatchard analysis of binding isotherms, are also prevalent (95, 100).

The detailed underlying molecular mechanisms whereby insulin receptor affinity or cellular localization is regulated are not currently known. However, it is interesting to note that the actions of three agents that modify ^{125}I-insulin binding activity in intact cells also appear to cause concomitant phosphorylations of the insulin receptor itself or other proteins that may effect the insulin receptor. These agents are catecholamines (100), phorbol diesters (43, 59, 124), and insulin itself (67). Recent results indicate that addition of isoproterenol to isolated fat cells leads to a 50% decrease in ^{125}I-insulin binding (100). This effect is abolished by simultaneous addition of propanolol and is mimicked by agents such as methylxanthines that elevate cyclic AMP (cAMP) levels. No effect of α-adrenergic agonists is observed. The effect of β-adrenergic agents to inhibit insulin binding to adipocytes occurs at physioloical catecholamine concentrations. Inhibition of ^{125}I-insulin binding occurs at low but not high insulin concentrations, indicating that an affinity change is responsible for the catecholamine effect (100). This conclusion is supported by recent data showing no change due to isoproterenol in the number of cell-surface insulin receptors as assessed by specific anti–insulin receptor antibody (J. E. Pessin & M. P. Czech, submitted for publication). Because this apparent decrease in insulin receptor affinity in isolated fat cells appears to occur through a cAMP-dependent mechanism, it seems likely that these effects result, at least in part, from the involvement of a phosphorylation pathway via the cAMP-dependent protein kinase.

Parallel observations on the response of insulin receptors to addition of phorbol esters have recently been reported (43). Thus, the tumor-promoting phorbol diesters decreased the apparent affinity of insulin receptors in IM-9 lymphocytes when ^{125}I-insulin binding was assessed by Scatchard analysis. Independent studies in other laboratories have demonstrated that phorbol esters stimulate the phosphorylation of insulin receptors when added to ^{32}P-labeled HL-60 cells or FAO hepatoma cells in culture (59, 124). Insulin receptors are phosphorylated on serine and threonine residues in response to these agents. This result that serine/threonine phosphorylations of the insulin receptor are directed by phorbol esters is not completely unexpected, because several studies have indicated that the calcium-phospholipid–dependent protein kinase, denoted as C-kinase, is directly activated by phorbol esters (2, 73, 92). As noted above, insulin binding to insulin receptors in intact ^{32}P-labeled cells also leads to inhibition of insulin receptor binding activity (40, 84, 122) and to incorporaton of ^{32}P into predominately serine and threonine residues of the insulin receptor (67, 124).

Taken together, the data appear to fit into a pattern whereby decreases of insulin receptor binding activity, as reflected in either decreased cell-surface receptor numbers or affinity for insulin, appear to correlate with increased cellular serine/threonine phosphorylations in general and of the insulin receptor in particular, at least with respect to phorbol ester and insulin actions. These considerations lead to the hypothesis, which must be considered unproven at present, that serine/threonine phosphorylations at one or more sites on the insulin receptor itself may lead to an inhibited insulin-receptor affinity for hormone (as schematically represented in Figure 2) or to internalization of insulin receptors (not shown in Figure 2). Although the data cited above must be considered incomplete at present, similar experiments using A431 cells show a remarkable correlation between phorbol ester-mediated phosphoryla-

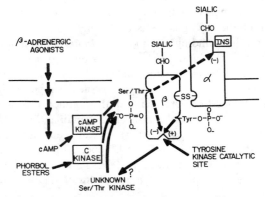

Figure 2 Hypothetical pathways whereby the insulin receptor kinase may be regulated by β-adrenergic agonists, phorbol esters, and insulin in intact cells. Recent data indicate that β-adrenergic agonists and other agents that elevate cAMP inhibit insulin binding (100) and insulin-receptor tyrosine kinase activation in isolated fat cells (J. E. Pessin & M. P. Czech, submitted for publication). Similarly, phorbol esters have been shown to inhibit insulin binding (43), activate phosphorylation of insulin receptor on serine/threonine residues (59), and block insulin receptor tyrosine autophosphorylation activity (124). These data suggest the working hypothesis that cAMP and phorbol esters, acting via the cAMP-dependent protein kinase or the calcium-phospholipid–dependent C-kinase, respectively, either directly *(as shown in the figure)* or indirectly *(not shown)* lead to phosphorylation of insulin receptor on serine and/or threonine residues. An indirect mode of action of the cAMP-dependent protein kinase is suggested by recent data, indicating this kinase phosphorylates purified insulin receptor very poorly in vitro (K.-T. Yu & M. P. Czech, unpublished observations). It is postulated that such phosphorylation can lead to inhibition of insulin receptor affinity and tyrosine-kinase activity. *Dashed arrows* indicate inhibitory activity. The evidence that serine/threonine phosphorylation of insulin receptors mediated by these agents inhibits receptor tyrosine kinase activity also suggests the hypothesis that serine/threonine phosphorylation of insulin receptor in response to insulin itself may be involved in desensitization of insulin receptor kinase activity. In contrast, tyrosine phosphorylation of insulin receptor in vitro catalyzed either by autophosphorylation (110, 137) or purified src kinase (K.-T. Yu et al, submitted for publication), is associated with activation of the insulin receptor kinase activity. Taken together, the data presently available suggest that a complex network of serine/threonine and tyrosine phosphorylations might modulate insulin-receptor activity in an antagonistic manner.

tion of EGF receptors and inhibition of EGF binding to these cells (7, 21, 52). In this system, the effects of the phorbol esters are mimicked by low concentrations of the cell-permeable diacylglycerol, sn-1,2,-dioctylglycerol (22), indicating that C-kinase is involved in these biochemical events. Of further interest is that the general hypothesis that receptor phosphorylation may be involved in receptor internalization has also been tested with the transferrin receptor system. Phorbol esters were reported to direct a concomitant loss of cell-surface transferrin receptors and an enhanced phosphorylation state of this receptor (90).

Regulation of Receptor-Associated Tyrosine Kinase

Direct evidence is now available suggesting that the insulin receptor tyrosine kinase is dramatically regulated by tyrosine phosphorylation on its β subunit. Thus, insulin receptor–catalyzed tyrosine phosphorylation is enhanced with time after addition of ATP as the receptor itself is phosphorylated (140). Rosen et al (110) showed directly that incubation of insulin receptor with unlabeled ATP prior to a second incubation with [γ-^{32}P]ATP plus substrate resulted in markedly enhanced substrate phosphorylation by insulin receptor. Rosen et al (110) also demonstrated that the phosphorylated, activated insulin-receptor kinase no longer exhibits sensitivity to modulation by insulin itself. Thus, the insulin receptor appears to be converted upon tyrosine phosphorylation of its β subunit to a form that is hormone-independent with respect to its tyrosine kinase activity.

Experiments by Yu & Czech (137) further characterized the apparent phosphorylation sites responsible for insulin receptor tyrosine kinase regulation. A purified insulin receptor preparation was phosphorylated with increasing concentrations of ATP while the receptor was immobilized on insulin-Sepharose. The phosphorylated β subunit was then analyzed by trypsin hydrolysis and high-pressure liquid chromatography of the resulting phosphopeptides. Three major phosphopeptide fractions exhibited increased labeling with increasing concentrations of [γ-^{32}P]ATP. One of the phosphopeptide fractions accounted for about 90% of the dephosphorylation of the receptor in response to added alkaline phosphatase. Such tyrosine dephosphorylation also led to a marked inhibition in tyrosine kinase activity. These results suggest that phosphorylation of one or more specific receptor phosphopeptides that elute in a single chromatography peak leads to activation of the receptor kinase, and dephosphorylation of these site(s) leads to kinase deactivation. Insulin-receptor kinase activation has also been recently demonstrated in response to phosphorylation of insulin receptor catalyzed by purified src kinase (K.-T. Yu et al, submitted for publication). Similar tyrosine-containing receptor phosphopeptides are phosphorylated by src kinase, compared to the autophosphorylation reaction.

While direct data are now available implicating a role for tyrosine phosphorylation in the regulation of insulin receptor kinase, indirect data recently obtained suggests the hypothesis that serine and threonine phosphorylations lead to decreased receptor kinase in the presence of insulin. Thus, under conditions where β-adrenergic agonists lead to decreased apparent insulin receptor affinity, a marked decrease in insulin-activated receptor autophosphorylation is observed in insulin receptors extracted from isoproterenol-treated adipocytes (J. E. Pessin & M. P. Czech, submitted for publication). The inhibition of insulin receptor autophosphorylation by isoproterenol occurs in the presence of very high insulin concentrations, which saturate the insulin receptors in spite of the decreased apparent affinity. Thus, elevations of cAMP in adipocytes appears to uncouple the insulin receptor kinase from activation by insulin. No change due to isoproterenol is observed in receptor autophosphorylation in the absence of insulin. Parallel findings have been made using phorbol esters as the receptor modifying reagent (124). Addition of phorbol esters to rat hepatoma cells leads to a stimulation of insulin receptor phosphorylation on serine/threonine residues and a decrease in the ability of insulin to enhance ^{32}P incorporation into tyrosine residues on the insulin receptor β subunit (124, K.-T. Yu & M. P. Czech, unpublished observations). Although the studies with both isoproterenol and phorbol esters have used insulin receptor autophosphorylation rather than actual substrate phosphorylation as an index of receptor tyrosine kinase activity, the data are consistent with the postulate that receptor tyrosine kinase activity is inhibited upon phosphorylation of serine and threonine residues on the receptor β subunit. Recent experiments on the EGF receptor system have also revealed a concomitant inhibition of EGF receptor autophosphorylation on tyrosine residues and a phorbol ester–directed serine/threonine phosphorylation of the EGF receptor itself (7, 21, 22, 52).

Taken together, these new results suggest that serine and/or threonine phosphorylation of the insulin receptor, mediated either directly by cAMP-dependent protein kinase or C-kinase (as shown in Figure 2) or indirectly by the actions of these kinases (not shown in Figure 2), modifies receptor tyrosine kinase. An indirect mode of receptor regulation by the cAMP-dependent pathway is suggested by recent data showing that cAMP-dependent protein kinase catalyzes the phosphorylation of insulin receptor in vitro very poorly (K.-T. Yu & M. P. Czech, unpublished observations). The hypothesis that insulin receptor phosphorylation mediated by insulin itself also leads to inhibition of tyrosine kinase activity, as suggested schematically in Figure 2, must be considered highly speculative at present. The receptor sites phosphorylated in response to insulin in intact cells appear to differ from those phosphorylated under the direction of phorbol esters (124), and there is currently no data directly demonstrating alterations in insulin receptor tyrosine kinase activity after serine/threonine phosphoryations directed by insulin.

It is interesting to note that ligand-induced receptor phosphorylation correlates with desensitization of receptor activity in other systems such as the β-adrenergic receptor (121). Desensitization of insulin receptor action on glycogen synthase is mediated by phorbol esters along with insulin receptor phosphorylation (124). Thus, it is tempting to speculate that one or more of the serine and threonine phosphorylations that occur on the insulin receptor in response to insulin binding plays some role in regulating receptor activity, such as in a feedback inhibition loop. Unfortunately, this postulate is complicated by the fact that phorbol esters actually potentiate the effects of both EGF (22) and insulin (R. J. Davis & M. P. Czech, unpublished observations) on cell proliferation. Thus, the complete physiological implications of the insulin receptor modulations discussed here are yet to be solved.

SUMMARY AND CONCLUSIONS

1. Native, cell-surface insulin receptor consists of two glycoprotein subunit types with apparent masses of about 125,000 daltons (α subunit) and 90,000 daltons (β subunit). The α and β subunits are derived from a single polypeptide precursor by one or more proteolytic cleavages. The predominant subunit configuration in the native insulin receptor is a disulfide-linked heterotetrameric structure containing two α and two β subunits.

2. The α and β insulin-receptor subunits seem to have distinct functions such that α appears to bind hormone whereas β appears to possess intrinsic tyrosine kinase activity. In detergent extracts, insulin activates receptor autophosphorylation of tyrosine residues on its β subunit, whereas in the presence of reductant, the α subunit is also phosphorylated. Other physiologically relevant substrates of the insulin receptor tyrosine kinase in target cells, if any, have not yet been identified. In intact cells, insulin activates serine/threonine phosphorylation of insulin receptor β subunit as well as tyrosine phosphorylation. The biological role of the receptor-associated tyrosine kinase is not known.

3. Tyrosine phosphorylation, catalyzed by either autophosphorylation or purified src kinase, of insulin receptor β subunit in vitro activates the receptor kinase activity, whereas dephosphorylation with alkaline phosphatase deactivates the receptor kinase.

4. The insulin receptor kinase is regulated by β-adrenergic agonists and other agents that elevate cAMP in adipocytes, presumably via the cAMP-dependent protein kinase. Such agents decrease receptor affinity for insulin and partially uncouple receptor tyrosine kinase activity from activation by insulin. These effects appear to contribute to the biological antagonism between insulin and β-agonists. The insulin receptor kinase is also inhibited in intact cells by phorbol esters that mediate serine/threonine

phosphorylation of the insulin receptor, presumably via the Ca^{++}-phospholipid–dependent protein kinase. These data suggest the hypothesis that a complex network of tyrosine and serine/threonine phosphorylations on the insulin receptor modulate its binding and kinase activities in an antagonistic manner.

Literature Cited

1. Alexander, M. C., Palmer, J. L., Pointer, R. H., Kowaloff, E. M., Koumijian, L., Avruch, J. 1982. Insulin-stimulated phosphorylation of ATP-citrate lyase in isolated hepatocytes. *J. Biol. Chem.* 257:2049–55

2. Ashendel, C. L., Staller, J. M., Boutwell, R. K. 1983. Protein kinase activity associated with a phorbol ester receptor purified from mouse brain. *Cancer Res.* 43:4333–37

3. Avruch, J., Nemenoff, R. A., Blackshear, P. J., Pierce, M. W., Osathanondh, R. 1982. Insulin-stimulated tyrosine phosphorylation of the insulin receptor in detergent extracts of human placental membranes. *J. Biol. Chem.* 257:15162–66

4. Blackshear, P. J., Nemenoff, R. A., Avruch, J. 1984. Characteristics of insulin and epidermal growth factor stimulation of receptor autophosphorylation in detergent extracts of rat liver and transplantable rat hepatomas. *Endocrinology* 114:141–52

5. Brownsey, R. M., Denton, R. M. 1982. Evidence that insulin activates fat-cell acetyl-CoA carboxylase by increased phosphorylation at a specific site. *Biochem. J.* 202:77–86

6. Cahill, G. F. Jr. 1971. Physiology of insulin in man. *Diabetes* 20:785–99

7. Cochet, C., Gill, G. N., Meisenhelder, J., Cooper, J. A., Hunter, T. 1984. C-kinase phosphorylates the epidermal growth factor receptor and reduces its epidermal growth factor–stimulated tyrosine protein kinase activity. *J. Biol. Chem.* 259:2553–58

8. Cohen, S., Carpenter, G., King, L. E. Jr. 1980. Epidermal growth factor–receptor-protein kinase interactions: co-purification of receptor and epidermal growth factor–enhanced phosphorylation activity. *J. Biol. Chem.* 255:4834–42

9. Cuatrecasas, P. 1971. Unmasking of insulin receptors in fat cells and fat membranes. *J. Biol. Chem.* 246:6532–42

10. Cuatrecasas, P. 1971. Insulin-receptor interactions in adipose tissue cells: direct measurement and properties. *Proc. Natl. Acad. Sci. USA* 68:1264–68

11. Cuatrecasas, P. 1972. Properties of the insulin receptor isolated from liver and fat cell membranes. *J. Biol. Chem.* 247:1980–91

12. Czech, M. P. 1977. Molecular basis of insulin action. *Ann. Rev. Biochem.* 46:359–84

13. Czech, M. P. 1980. Insulin action and the regulation of hexose transport. *Diabetes* 29:399–409

14. Czech, M. P. 1981. Second messengers. In *Handbook of Diabetes Mellitus*, ed. M. Brownlee. New York: Garland

15. Czech, M. P. 1981. Insulin action. *Am. J. Med.* 70:142–50

16. Czech, M. P. 1982. Structural and functional homologies in the receptors for insulin and the insulin-like growth factors. *Cell* 31:8–10

17. Czech, M. P., ed. 1985. *The Molecular Basis of Insulin Action.* New York: Plenum

18. Czech, M. P., Massague, J. 1982. Subunit structure and dynamics of the insulin receptor. *Fed. Proc.* 41:2730–35

19. Czech, M. P., Massague, J., Pilch, P. F. 1981. The insulin receptor: structural features. *Trends Biochem. Sci.* 6:222–25

20. Czech, M. P., Oppenheimer, C. L., Massague, J. 1983. Interrelationships among receptor structures for insulin and peptide growth factors. *Fed. Proc.* 42:2598–601

21. Davis, R. J., Czech, M. P. 1984. Tumor-promoting phorbol diesters mediate phosphorylation of the epidermal growth factor receptor. *J. Biol. Chem.* 259:8545–49

22. Davis, R. J., Ganong, B. R., Bell, R. M., Czech, M. P. 1984. sn-1,2-dioctanoylglycerol: a cell-permeable diacylglycerol that mimics phorbol diester action on the epidermal growth factor receptor and mitogenesis. *J. Biol. Chem.* 259, in press

23. DeMeyts, P. 1976. Cooperative properties of hormone receptors in cell membranes. *J. Supramol. Struct.* 4:241(201)–258(218)

24. DeMeyts, P. 1980. Insulin receptors: experimental validation of the negative cooperativity concept. In *Hormones and*

Cell Regulation, ed. J. Dumont, J. Nunez, 4:107–21. Amsterdam: Elsevier/ North-Holland Biomedical

25. DeMeyts, P., Bianco, A. R., Roth, J. 1976. Site-site interactions among insulin receptors. *J. Biol. Chem.* 251: 1877–88

26. DeMeyts, P., Roth, J. 1975. Cooperativity in ligand binding: a new graphic analysis. *Biochem. Biophys. Res. Commun.* 66:1118–26

27. DeMeyts, P., Van Obberghen, E., Roth, J., Wollmer, A., Brandenburg, D. 1978. Mapping of the residues responsible for the negative cooperativity of the receptor-binding region of insulin. *Nature* 273:504–9

28. Denton, R. M., Brownsey, R. W., Belsham, G. J. 1981. A partial view of the mechanisms of insulin action. *Diabetologia* 21:347–62

29. Deutsch, P. J., Wan, C. F., Rosen, O. M., Rubin, C. S. 1983. Latent insulin receptors and possible receptor precursors in 3T3-L1 adipocytes. *Proc. Natl. Acad. Sci. USA* 80:133–36

30. Donner, D. B., Corin, R. E. 1980. Formation of a receptor state from which dissociates slowly in hepatic cells and plasma membranes. *J. Biol. Chem.* 255:9005–8

31. Downward, J., Yarden, Y., Mayes, E. Scrace, G., Totty, N., Stockwell, P., Ullrich, A., Schlessinger, J., Waterfield, M. D. 1984. Close similarity of epidermal growth factor receptor and v-erb-B oncogene protein sequences. *Nature* 307:521–27

32. Ek, B., Heldin, C. H. 1982. Characterization of a tyrosine-specific kinase activity in human fibroblast membranes stimulated by platelet-derived growth factor. *J. Biol. Chem.* 257:10486–92

33. Elias, D., Maron, R., Cohen, I. R., Shechter, Y. 1984. Mouse antibodies to the insulin receptor developing spontaneously as anti-idiotypes. *J. Biol. Chem.* 259:6416–19

34. Fain, J. N. 1974. Mode of insulin action. In *Biological Membranes,* ed. H. V. Rickenberg, Baltimore: University Park.

35. Flier, J. S., Kahn, C. R., Jarrett, D. B., Roth, J. 1976. Characterization of antibodies to the insulin receptor. *J. Clin. Invest.* 58:1442–49

36. Flier, J. S., Kahn, C. R., Jarrett, D. B., Roth, J. 1977. Autoantibodies to the insulin receptor. *J. Clin. Invest.* 60:784–94

37. Flier, J. S., Kahn, C. R., Roth, J., Bar, R. W. 1975. Antibodies that impair insulin receptor binding in an unusual diabetic syndrome with severe insulin resistance. *Science* 190:63–65

38. Fujita-Yamaguchi, Y. 1984. Characterization of purified insulin receptor subunits. *J. Biol. Chem.* 259:1206–11

39. Fujita-Yamaguchi, Y., Choi, S., Sakamoto, Y., Itakura, K. 1983. Purification of insulin receptor with full binding activity. *J. Biol. Chem.* 258:5045–49

40. Gavin, J. R. III, Roth, J., Neville, D. M. Jr., DeMeyts, P., Buell, D. N. 1974. Insulin-dependent regulation of insulin receptor concentrations. A direct demonstration in cell culture. *Proc. Natl. Acad. Sci. USA* 71:84–88

41. Ginsberg, B. H., Kahn, C. R., DeMeyts, P. 1976. Insulin-induced dissociation of its receptor into subunits: possible molecular concomitant of negative cooperativity. *Biochem. Biophys. Res. Commun.* 73:1068–74

42. Grigorescu, F., White, M. F., Kahn, C. R. 1983. Insulin binding and insulin-dependent phosphorylation of the insulin receptor solubilized from human erythrocytes. *J. Biol. Chem.* 258:13708–16

43. Grunberger, G., Gordon, P. 1982. Affinity alteration of insulin receptor induced by a phorbol ester. *Am. J. Physiol.* 6:E319–24

44. Haring, H. U., Kasuga, M., Kahn, C. R. 1982. Insulin receptor phosphorylation in intact adipocytes and in a cell-free system. *Biochem. Biophys. Res. Commun.* 108:1538–45

45. Harrison, L. C., Itin, A. 1980. Purification of the insulin receptor from human placenta by chromatography on immobilized wheat germ lectin and receptor antibody. *J. Biol. Chem.* 255:12066–72

46. Heaton, J. H., Krett, N. L., Alvarez, J. M., Gelehrter, T. D., Romanus, J. A., Rechler, M. M. 1984. Insulin regulation of insulin-like growth factor action in rat hepatoma cells. *J. Biol. Chem.* 259: 2396–402

47. Hedo, J. A., Kahn, C. R., Hayashi, M., Yamada, K. M., Kasuga, M. 1983. Biosynthesis and glycosylation of the insulin receptor. *J. Biol. Chem.* 258: 10020–26

48. Hedo, J. A., Kasuga, M., Van Obberghen, E., Roth, J., Kahn, C. R. 1981. Direct demonstration of glycosylation of insulin receptor subunits by biosynthetic and external labeling: evidence for heterogeneity. *Proc. Natl. Acad. Sci. USA* 78:4791–95

49. Heinrich, J., Pilch, P. F., Czech, M. P. 1980. Purification of the adipocyte insulin receptor by immunoaffinity chromatography. *J. Biol. Chem.* 255:1732–37

50. Hepp, K. D. 1977. Studies on the mechanism of insulin action: Basic con-

cepts and clinical implications. *Diabetologia* 13:177–86

51. Hughes, W. A., Brownsey, R. W., Denton, R. M. 1980. Studies on the incorporation of [^{32}P]phosphate into pyruvate dehydrogenase in intact rat fat cells. *Biochem. J.* 192:469–81

52. Iwashita, S., Fox, C. F. 1984. Epidermal growth factor and potent phorbol tumor promoters induce epidermal growth factor receptor phosphorylation in a similar but distinctively different manner in human epidermoid carcinoma A431 cells. *J. Biol. Chem.* 259:2559–67

53. Jacobs, S., Chang, K.-J., Cuatrecasas, P. 1978. Antibodies to purified insulin receptor have insulin-like activity. *Science* 200:1283–84

54. Jacobs, S., Cuatrecasas, P. 1981. Insulin receptor: structure and function. *Endocr. Rev.* 2:251–63

55. Jacobs, S., Hazum, E., Cuatrecasas, P. 1980. The subunit structure of rat liver insulin receptor. *J. Biol. Chem.* 255: 6937–40

56. Jacobs, S., Hazum, E., Schecter, Y., Cuatrecasas, P. 1979. Insulin receptor: covalent labeling and identification of subunits. *Proc. Natl. Acad. Sci. USA* 76:4918–21

57. Jacobs, S., Kull, F. C. Jr., Cuatrecasas, P. 1983. Monensin blocks the maturation of receptors for insulin and somatomedin C: identification of receptor precursors. *Proc. Natl. Acad. Sci. USA* 80:1228–31

58. Jacobs, S., Kull, F. C. Jr., Earp, H. S., Svoboda, M. E., Van Wyk, J. J., Cuatrecasas, P. 1983. Somatomedin C stimulates the phosphorylation of the β-subunit of its own receptor. *J. Biol. Chem.* 258:9581–84

59. Jacobs, S., Sahyoun, N. E., Saltiel, A. R., Cuatrecasas, P. 1983. Phorbol esters stimulate the phosphorylation of receptors for insulin and somatomedin C. *Proc. Natl. Acad. Sci. USA* 80:6211–13

60. Jacobs, S., Shechter, Y., Bissell, K., Cuatrecasas, P. 1977. Purification and properties of insulin receptors from rat liver membranes. *Biochem. Biophys. Res. Commun.* 77:981–88

61. Jarrett, D. B., Roth, J., Kahn, C. R., Flier, J. S. 1976. Direct method for detection and characterization of cell surface receptors for insulin by means of ^{125}I-labeled autoantibodies against the insulin receptor. *Proc. Natl. Acad. Sci. USA* 73:4115–19

62. Jungas, R. L. 1975. Metabolic effects on adipose tissue in vitro. In *Handbook of Experimental Pharmacology,* ed. A. Hasselblatt, F. V. Bruchhausen. New York: Springer-Verlag

63. Kahn, C. R. 1976. Membrane receptors for hormones and neurotransmitters. *J. Cell Biol.* 70:161–86

64. Kahn, C. R., Baird, K. L., Jarrett, D. B., Flier, J. S. 1978. Direct demonstration that receptor cross-linking aggregation is important in insulin action. *Proc. Natl. Acad. Sci. USA* 75:4209–13

65. Kahn, C. R., Neville, D. M. Jr., Roth, J. 1973. Insulin-receptor interaction in the obese-hyperglycemic mouse. *J. Biol. Chem.* 248:244–50

66. Kasuga, M., Hedo, J. A., Yamada, K. M., Kahn, C. R. 1982. The structure of insulin receptor and its subunits. *J. Biol. Chem.* 257:10392–99

67. Kasuga, M., Karlsson, F. A., Kahn, C. R. 1982. Insulin stimulates the phosphorylation of the 95,000-dalton subunit of its own receptor. *Science* 215:185–87

68. Kasuga, M., Van Obberghen, E., Yamada, K. M., Harrison, L. C. 1981. Autoantibodies against the insulin receptor recognize the insulin binding subunits for an oligomeric receptor. *Diabetes* 30: 354–57

69. Kasuga, M., Fujita-Yamaguchi, Y., Blithe, D. L., Kahn, C. R. 1983. Tyrosine-specific protein kinase activity is associated with the purified insulin receptor. *Proc. Natl. Acad. Sci. USA* 80:2137–41

70. Kasuga, M., Fujita-Yamaguchi, Y., Blithe, D. L., White, M. F., Kahn, C. R. 1983. Characterization of the insulin receptor kinase purified from human placental membranes. *J. Biol. Chem.* 258:10973–80

71. Kasuga, M., Zick, Y., Blithe, D. L., Crettaz, M., Kahn, C. R. 1982. Insulin stimulates tyrosine phosphorylation of the insulin receptor in a cell-free system. *Nature* 298:667–69

72. Kasuga, M., Zick, Y., Blithe, D. L., Karlsson, F. A., Haring, H. U., Kahn, C. R. 1982. Insulin stimulation of phosphorylation of the β subunit of the insulin receptor. *J. Biol. Chem.* 257:9891–94

73. Kikkawa, U., Takai, Y., Tanaka, Y., Myake, R., Nishizuka, Y. 1983. Protein kinase C as a possible receptor protein of tumor-promoting phorbol esters. *J. Biol. Chem.* 258:11442–45

74. Kono, T. 1969. Destruction of insulin effector system of adipose tissue cells by proteolytic enzymes. *J. Biol. Chem.* 244:1772–78

75. Kono, T. 1969. Destruction and restoration of the insulin effector system of isolated fat cells. *J. Biol. Chem.* 244:5777–84

76. Kono, T. 1982. Translocation hypothesis of the insulin-dependent activation of

glucose transport in fat cells. In *Membranes and Transport*, ed. A. N. Martonosi, 2:551–54. New York: Plenum. 679 pp.

77. Kono, T., Barham, F. W. 1971. The relationship between the insulin binding capacity of fat cells and the cellular response to insulin. *J. Biol. Chem.* 246:6210–16

78. Kull, F. C. Jr., Jacobs, S., Su, Y-F., Cuatrecasas, P. 1982. A monoclonal antibody to human insulin receptor. *Biochem. Biophys. Res. Commun.* 106:1019–26

79. Kull, F. C. Jr., Jacobs, S., Su, Y-F., Svoboda, M. E., Van Wyk, J. J., Cuatrecasas, P. 1983. Monoclonal antibodies to receptors for insulin and somatomedin-C. *J. Biol. Chem.* 258:6561–66

80. Krupp, M. N., Livingston, J. N. 1978. Insulin binding to solubilized material from fat cell membranes: evidence for two binding species. *Proc. Natl. Acad. Sci. USA* 75:2593–97

81. Machicao, F., Urumow, T., Wieland, O. H. 1982. Phosphorylation-dephosphorylation of purified insulin receptor from human placenta. *FEBS Lett.* 149:96–100

82. Maron, R., Kahn, C. R., Jacobs, S., Fujita-Yamaguchi, Y. 1984. *Diabetes.* In press

83. Marsh, J. W., Westley, J., Steiner, D. F. 1984. Insulin-receptor interactions. *J. Biol. Chem.* 259:6641–49

84. Marshall, S., Green, A., Olefsky, J. M. 1981. Evidence for recycling of insulin receptors in isolated rat adipocytes. *J. Biol. Chem.* 256:11464–70

85. Massague, J., Blinderman, L. A., Czech, M. P. 1982. The high affinity insulin receptor mediates growth stimulation in rat hepatoma cells. *J. Biol. Chem.* 257:13958–63

86. Massague, J., Czech, M. P. 1982. Role of disulfides in the subunit structure of the insulin receptor. *J. Biol. Chem.* 257:6729–38

87. Massague, J., Pilch, P. F., Czech, M. P. 1980. Electrophoretic resolution of three major insulin receptor structures with unique subunit stoichiometries. *Proc. Natl. Acad. Sci. USA* 77:7137–41

88. Massague, J., Pilch, P. F., Czech, M. P. 1981. A unique proteolytic cleavage site on the β subunit of the insulin receptor. *J. Biol. Chem.* 256:3182–90

89. Maturo, J. M. III, Hollenberg, M. D., Aglio, L. S. 1983. Insulin receptor: insulin-modulated interconversion between distinct molecular forms involving disulfide-sulfhydryl exchange. *Biochemistry* 22:2579–86

90. May, W. S., Jacobs, S., Cuatrecasas, P. 1984. Association of phorbol ester–induced hyperphosphorylation and reversible regulation of transferrin membrane receptors in HL60 cells. *Proc. Natl. Acad. Sci. USA* 81:2016–20

91. Mottola, C., Czech, M. P. 1984. The type II insulin-like growth factor receptor does not mediate increased DNA synthesis in H-35 hepatoma cells. *J. Biol. Chem.* 259:12705–13

92. Niedel, J. E., Kuhn, L. J., Vandenbark, G. R. 1983. Phorbol diester receptor copurifies with protein kinase C. *Proc. Natl. Acad. Sci. USA* 80:36–40

93. Nilsen-Hamilton, M., Allen, W. R., Hamilton, R. T. 1981. Rapid and efficient method for analyzing phosphorylation of the S6 ribosomal protein in $^{32}P_i$-labeled tissue culture cells. *Anal. Biochem.* 115:438–49

94. Nishimura, J., Huang, J. S., Deul, T. F. 1982. Platelet-derived growth factor stimulates tyrosine-specific protein kinase activity in Swiss mouse 3T3 cell membranes. *Proc. Natl. Acad. Sci. USA* 79:4303–7

95. Olefsky, J. M. 1975. Effect of dexamethasone on insulin binding, glucose transport and glucose oxidation of isolated rat adipocytes. *J. Clin. Invest.* 56:1499–508

96. Olefsky, J. M. 1976. The insulin receptors: its role in insulin resistance of obesity and diabetes. *Diabetes* 25:1154–65

97. Olefsky, J. M. 1976. Decreased insulin binding to adipocytes and circulating monocytes from obese subjects. *J. Clin. Invest.* 57:1165–72

98. Olefsky, J. M., Kobayashi, M., Chang, H. 1979. Interactions between insulin and its receptors after the initial binding event. Functional heterogeneity and relationships to insulin degradation. *Diabetes* 28:460–71

99. Pang, D. T., Shafer, J. A. 1984. Evidence that insulin receptor from human placenta has a high affinity for only one molecule of insulin. *J. Biol. Chem.* 259:8589–96

100. Pessin, J. E., Gitomer, W., Oka, Y., Oppenheimer, C. L., Czech, M. P. 1983. β-Adrenergic regulation of insulin and epidermal growth factor receptors in rat adipocytes. *J. Biol. Chem.* 258:7386–94

101. Petruzzelli, L. M., Ganguly, S., Smith, C. J., Cobb, M. H., Rubin, C. S., Rosen, O. M. 1982. Insulin activates a tyrosine-specific protein kinase in extracts of 3T3-L1 adipocytes and human placenta. *Proc. Natl. Acad. Sci. USA* 79:6792–96

102. Pilch, P. F., Czech, M. P. 1979. Interaction of cross-linking agents with the in-

sulin effector system of isolated fat cells: covalent linkage of ^{125}I-insulin to a plasma membrane receptor protein of 140,000 daltons. *J. Biol. Chem.* 254: 3375–81

103. Pilch, P. F., Czech, M. P. 1980. The subunit structure of the high affinity insulin receptor. *J. Biol. Chem.* 255:1722–31

104. Pilch, P. F., Czech, M. P. 1980. Hormone binding alters the conformation of the insulin receptor. *Science* 210:1152–53

105. Pollet, R. J., Haase, B. A., Standaert, M. L. 1981. Characterization of detergent-solubilized membrane proteins. *J. Biol. Chem.* 256:12118–126

106. Pollet, R. J., Standaert, M. L., Haase, B. A. 1977. Insulin binding to the human lymphocyte receptor. *J. Biol. Chem.* 252:5828–34

107. Pollet, R. J., Standaert, M. L., Haase, B. A. 1980. Hormone-receptor interactions are noncooperative: application to the β-adrenergic receptor. *Proc. Natl. Acad. Sci. USA* 77:4340–44

108. Pucci, D. L., Ramakrishna, S., Benjamin, W. B. 1983. ATP-citrate lyase phosphorylation in rat adipose tissue. *J. Biol. Chem.* 258:12907–11

109. Ronnett, G. V., Knutson, V. P., Kohanski, R. A., Simpson, T. L., Lane, M. D. 1984. Role of glycosylation in the processing of newly translated insulin proreceptor in 3T3-L1 adipocytes. *J. Biol. Chem.* 259:4566–75

110. Rosen, O. M., Herrera, R., Olowe, Y., Petruzzelli, L. M., Cobb, M. 1983. Phosphorylation activates the insulin receptor tyrosine protein kinase. *Proc. Natl. Acad. Sci. USA* 80:3237–40

111. Roth, J. 1975. Methods for assessing immunologic and biologic properties of iodinated peptide hormones. *Methods Enzymol.* 37:223–33

112. Roth, R. A., Cassell, D. J. 1983. Insulin receptor: evidence that it is a protein kinase. *Science* 219:299–301

113. Roth, R. A., Cassell, D. J., Wong, K. Y., Maddux, B. A., Goldfine, I. D. 1982. Monoclonal antibodies to the human insulin receptor block insulin binding and inhibit insulin action. *Proc. Natl. Acad. Sci. USA* 79:7312–16

114. Roth, R. A., Mesirow, M. L., Cassell, D. J. 1983. Preferential degradation of the β subunit of purified insulin receptor. *J. Biol. Chem.* 258:14456–60

115. Shechter, Y., Elias, D., Maron, R., Cohen, I. R. 1984. Mouse antibodies to the insulin receptor developing spontaneously as anti-idiotypes. *J. Biol. Chem.* 259:6411–15

116. Sheorain, V. S., Khatra, B. S., Soderling, T. R. 1982. Hormonal regulation of skeletal muscle glycogen synthase through covalent phosphorylation. *Fed. Proc.* 41:2618–22

117. Shia, M. A., Rubin, J. B., Pilch, P. F. 1983. The insulin receptor protein kinase. *J. Biol. Chem.* 258:14450–55

118. Shia, M. A., Pilch, P. F. 1983. The β subunit of the insulin receptor is an insulin-activated protein kinase. *Biochemistry* 22:717–21

119. Simpson, I. A., Hedo, J. A. 1984. Insulin receptor phosphorylation may not be a prerequisite for acute insulin action. *Science* 223:1301–4

120. Smith, C. J., Wejksnora, P. J., Warner, J. R., Rubin, C. S., Rosen, O. M. 1979. Insulin-stimulated protein phosphorylation in 3T3-L1 preadipocytes. *Proc. Natl. Acad. Sci. USA* 76:2725–29

121. Stadel, J. M., Nambi, P., Shorr, G. L., Sawyer, D. F., Caron, M. G., Lefkowitz, R. J. 1983. Catecholamine-induced desensitization of turkey erythrocyte adenylate cyclase is associated with phosphorylation of the β-adrenergic receptor. *Proc. Natl. Acad. Sci. USA* 80:3173–77

122. Standaert, M. L., Pollet, R. J. 1984. Equilibrium model for insulin-induced receptor down regulation. *J. Biol. Chem.* 259:2346–54

123. Stadtmauer, L. A., Rosen, O. M. 1983. Phosphorylation of exogenous substrates by the insulin receptor-associated protein kinase. *J. Biol. Chem.* 258:6682–85

124. Takayama, S., White, M. F., Lauris, V., Kahn, C. R. 1984. Phorbol esters modulate insulin receptor phosphorylation and insulin action in cultured hepatoma cells. *Proc. Natl. Acad. Sci. USA* 81, in press

125. Van Obberghen E., Kasuga, M., LeCam, A., Hedo, J. A., Itin, A., Harrison, L. C. 1981. Biosynthetic labeling of insulin receptor: studies of subunits in cultured human IM-9 lymphocytes. *Proc. Natl. Acad. Sci. USA* 78:1052–56

126. Van Obberghen, E., Kowalski, A. 1982. Phosphorylation of the hepatic insulin receptor. *FEBS Lett.* 143:179–82

127. Van Obberghen, E., Rossi, B., Kowalski, A., Gazzano, H., Ponzio, G. 1983. Receptor-mediated phosphorylation of the hepatic insulin receptor: evidence that the M_r = 95,000 receptor subunit is its own kinase. *Proc. Natl. Acad. Sci. USA* 80:945–49

128. White, M. F., Haring, H. U., Kasuga, M., Kahn, C. R. 1984. Kinetic properties and sites of autophosphorylation of the partially purified insulin receptor from

hepatoma cells. *J. Biol. Chem.* 259:255–64

129. Wisher, M. H., Baron, M. D., Jones, R. H., Sonksen, P. H. 1980. Photoreactive insulin analogues used to characterize the insulin receptor. *Biochem. Biophys. Res. Commun.* 92:492–98

130. Witters, L. A. 1981. Insulin stimulates the phosphorylation of acetyl-CoA carboxylase. *Biochem. Biophys. Res. Commun.* 100:872–78

131. Yip, C. C., Moule, M. L., 1983. Structure of the insulin receptor of rat adipocytes. *Diabetes* 32:760–67

132. Yip, C. C., Moule, M. L. 1983. Insulin receptor: its subunit structure determined by photoaffinity labeling. *Fed. Proc.* 42:2842–45

133. Yip, C. C., Moule, M. L., Yeung, C. W. T. 1982. Subunit structure of insulin receptor of rat adipocytes as demonstrated by photoaffinity labeling. *Biochemistry* 21:2940–45

134. Yip, C. C., Yeung, C. W. T., Moule, M. L. 1978. Photoaffinity labeling of insulin receptor of rat adipocyte plasma membrane. *J. Biol. Chem.* 253:1743–45

135. Yip, C. C., Yeung, C. W. T., Moule, M. L. 1980. Photoaffinity labeling of receptor proteins of liver plasma membrane preparations. *Biochemistry* 19:70–76

136. Yip, C. C., Yeung, C. W. T., Moule, M. L. 1980. Photoaffinity labeling of insulin receptor with an insulin analogue selectively modified at the amino terminal of the B chain. *Biochemistry* 19:2196–203

137. Yu, K.-T., Czech, M. P. 1984. Tyrosine phosphorylation of the insulin receptor β subunit activates the receptor-associated tyrosine kinase activity. *J. Biol. Chem.* 259:5277–86

138. Zick, Y., Kasuga, M., Kahn, C. R., Roth, J. 1983. Characterization of insulin-mediated phosphorylation of the insulin receptor in a cell-free system. *J. Biol. Chem.* 258:75–80

139. Zick, Y., Rees-Jones, R. W., Taylor, S. I., Gorden, P., Roth, J. 1984. The role of antireceptor antibodies in stimulating phosphorylation of the insulin receptor. *J. Biol. Chem.* 259:4396–400

140. Zick, Y., Whittaker, J., Roth, J. 1983. Insulin-stimulated phosphorylation of its own receptor. *J. Biol. Chem.* 258:3431–34

Ann. Rev. Physiol. 1985. 47:383–403

UPTAKE OF INSULIN AND OTHER LIGANDS INTO RECEPTOR-RICH ENDOCYTIC COMPONENTS OF TARGET CELLS: THE ENDOSOMAL APPARATUS

J. J. M. Bergeron, J. Cruz, M. N. Khan, and B. I. Posner

Departments of Anatomy and Medicine, McGill University, Montréal, Québec, Canada H3A 2B2

INTRODUCTION

The paradigm of receptor-mediated endocytosis is often considered to be based on the low-density lipoprotein (LDL) pathway delineated by Goldstein, Brown, Anderson, and colleagues (5, 22, 23, 25, 59, 59a). These investigators, puzzled as to the mechanism of cholesterol entry into cells, postulated and verified experimentally the presence of receptors on target cells. This was followed by the discovery of the near exclusive location of LDL receptors in coated pits and entry of LDL into the secondary lysosome via membrane-bound structures. These findings have been the subject of recent reviews (5, 26, 59, 112) and will not be elaborated on here.

The general application of the LDL pathway to the endocytosis of insulin and several other peptide hormones as well as ligands for membrane-bound lectins, immune complexes, viruses, toxins, and so on has pointed to interesting differences in the handling of ligands by target cells. These differences are found on the cell surface as well as in the intracellular compartments accumulating and concentrating ligands prior to intracellular destruction.

383

0066-4278/85/0315-0383$02.00

CELL-SURFACE EVENTS

The initial interaction of all ligands with their corresponding receptors is accepted to be on the cell membrane. However, only the LDL receptor appears to be located in majority within coated pits (6, 113). In the case of insulin and other peptide hormones in particular, as well as in the case of a variety of other ligands, the initial location of the ligand-receptor complexes appears to be dispersed over the entire cell surface.

Shortly thereafter coated pits, especially in cultured cells, have been found to accumulate ligand prior to endocytosis (112, 113, 165). Attempts to document the participation of the coated pit in vivo for insulin, prolactin, and other peptide hormones have been disappointing (17–19), although subcellular fractionation has recently pointed to a small but significant accumulation of insulin in a coated vesicle fraction prepared from liver homogenates (117). Ligand-receptor events at the cell surface have been reviewed elsewhere (5, 113, 135, 144).

INTRACELLULAR EVENTS

The major advances in documenting the nature of the intracellular structures that accumulate ligands have been based on the techniques of subcellular fractionation, radioautography, and immunocytochemistry. Here, a significant extension of the LDL paradigm has been found in that the majority of intracellular ligand, especially for insulin and other peptide hormones, has been observed in nonlysosomal structures. Various investigators have coined a plethora of terms for these structures, as illustrated in Table 1. Of equal significance are the intracellular structures that have been shown conclusively to harbor specific receptors for several of these same ligands (Table 1). Can this bewildering array of apparently different components be grouped into distinct entities? A primary consideration is to what extent is the nonlysosomal compartment uniform or heterogenous?

HETEROGENEITY OF THE ENDOSOMAL APPARATUS

As first defined by Stockem (147, 148) and more recently by Helenius et al (71), "endosome" is a convenient term to cover all of the intracellular nonlysosomal components involved in the uptake of exogenous substances into cells. At least three endosomal components can be distinguished by subcellular fractionation (Table 2). The first is a small vesicular fraction that probably originates from a series of uncoated vesicles and tubules probably in close proximity to the cell surface (122, 124). A variety of ligands have been localized to the equivalent of this compartment (Table 1), which may also include coated vesicles.

A second major endocytic compartment consists of larger structures, often vesicular and often with associated tubules. The evidence that this compartment is receptor-enriched and contains intact ligand (especially insulin and prolactin) has been documented by subcellular fractionation (80, 88, 127). In our hands, this compartment does not seem to be sensitive to or to accumulate the lysosomotropic agent chloroquine and is therefore not considered to be a low-pH compartment (Table 2). In cultured cells, these structures are often electronluscent, with a diameter of ~ 150–500 nm and the presence of one or no intraluminal vesicles (Table 1).

The third class of endosomal structures is heterogenous and is lysosome-like in that small amounts of acid phosphatase may be present (53a, 88, 89, 104). Most investigators agree that at least one of the endosomal compartments may be of low pH, accumulate chloroquine, and contain an ATP-dependent proton pump (53a, 87, 103a, 154; Table 2). It has been suggested by several that this low-pH endosomal compartment serves as a locus for segregating ligand from receptor and for recycling the receptor back to the cell surface (14, 60, 154, 167). A key observation in favor of this hypothesis has been the visualization of a segregation of receptor to a restricted membrane domain of this endosomal component while ligand is diffusely found within the lumen (56–58). The acronym CURL (Compartment for Uncoupling of Receptor and Ligand) has been proposed by Strous, Schwartz, Lodish, and colleagues for this endosomal component.

PURIFICATION AND PROPERTIES OF THE ENDOSOMAL APPARATUS

Subcellular fractionation has led to the identification of several receptor-enriched compartments participating in the concentrative receptor-mediated endocytosis of insulin as well as prolactin and other ligands (Table 2). Our own studies arose out of a finding that hepatic Golgi fractions, considered to be highly purified, were markedly enriched in receptors for insulin and prolactin (13, 15).

Two criteria were used to identify the receptor-enriched components as Golgi. The first was a morphological marker, intraluminal lipoprotein particles. The second was the Golgi marker-enzyme galactosyltransferase. Nonetheless, a significant proportion of the ligand internalized into Golgi fractions, and a proportion of the receptor found in Golgi fractions may be attributed to endosomal contamination.[1] Further separation of a Golgi fraction on Percoll gradients has resolved two lipoprotein-filled components, both

---

[1] Recent application by the authors of the DAB shift protocol of Courtoy et al (33) has resolved in Percoll gradients the majority of internalized ^{125}I-insulin from galactosyl transferase–containing components (86).

Table 1 Localization of ligands and receptors to the endosomal apparatus[a]

Structure	Ligand	Receptor
I. Coated vesicle	α2 macroglobulin (162), glucagon (78), ASGP (42), IgG (107)[b]	
A. Near cell membrane	IgG (130), ASGP (55, 57), LDL (66)	IgG (1), ASGP (57)
B. 50–200 nm	IgG, transferrin (114), insulin (117), LDL (66), Semi-liki Forest virus (70, 98)	
1. Luminal aspect (60 nm)		LDL (103)
2. Near Golgi		mannose-6-phosphate (24)
II. Small (< 200 nm) uncoated vesicles	α melanotropin (106)[b]	
A. < 100 nm	EGF (47, 100)	
1. Near cell membrane	insulin (128), ASGP (156), EGF (146)	ASGP (56)
2. Near multivesicular body 65 nm	prolactin (157)	
3. Near Golgi apparatus	EGF (64)	EGF (64)
	α2 macroglobulin, VSV (44)	mannose-6-phosphate (24)
B. < 200 nm	prolactin (18), negatively charged liposomes (150)	
1. 120 nm	EGF (64)	EGF (64)
2. 150–160 nm	EGF (100)	EGF (47)
3. Near Golgi apparatus	ASGP (156)	mannose-6-phosphate (24)
III. Tubular vesicles		
A. Peripheral cytoplasm	transferrin (73)	transferrin (73, 74)
1. 40 nm		
2. Associated with other elements		
a. Connected to vacuoles CURL	transferrin (73), ASGP (168)	transferrin (73, 74) ASGP (57, 58), mannose-6-phosphate, IgA (58)

b. Vesicles (> 100 nm) — ASGP (156), EGF (47)

B. Deep cytoplasm — tetanus toxin (133)

  1. Associated with other elements

    a. Connected to vacuoles or vesicles

      1. CURL — ASGP (156); ASGP (55) — transferrin (73, 74); ASGP, mannose-6-phosphate, IgA (58)

      2. Containing 30 nm vesicles — transferrin (73)

    b. Near lysosomes — EGF (46)

    c. Near multivesicular bodies — prolactin (157)

  2. Juxtanuclear — transferrin (73, 74)

    a. Connecting or connected to multivesicular bodies — transferrin (73), ASGP (42)

  3. Transreticular Golgi; Golgi-lysosome area:

    a. Associated with other structures

      1. Coated pits — ASGP (65), EGF (11)

      2. Multivesicular body — transferrin (160), EGF (164)

      3. (300 nm Average; < 1 μm) vesicle — ASGP (42), EGF (47); ASGP, EGF (71)

      4. 60×500 nm, Associated with dumbbell-shaped structure — transferrin (160)

      5. 100–300 nm — cholera toxin (81)

IV. Structures with tubular extensions

  A. Thick membrane, straight frilled edge, empty-looking, one or no vesicles, near cell membrane and Golgi apparatus: RECEPTOSOME (150–400 nm) — α2 macroglobulin (44, 113, 155, 161, 163, 166), ASGP (42, 65), LDL (31, 155), hCG (3), VSV (44, 111), transferrin (160), EGF (164), β galactosidase (166), GRHA (45), ASGP (48) — transferrin (43), ASGP (56); mannose-6-phosphate (165a)

  B. Multivesicular bodies — prolactin (157)

  C. Lipoprotein-filled vesicles [including endosomes type III (71)] — ASGP (55, 65, 71, 149, 156), LDL (66, 75), EGF (71), insulin (15, 19) — transferrin (73, 74)

    1. Near Golgi — prolactin (18), insulin (19), ASGP (42)

    2. Near sinusoid (colchicine) — prolactin (18)

Table 1 *(Continued)*

Structure	Ligand	Receptor
V. Non-lysosomal large vesicles and vacuoles		
A. Partially coated (> 300 nm)	Semiliki Forest virus (70), LDL (4), EGF (61)	
B. Uncoated		
1. Polymorphic	tetanus toxin (133), α2 macroglobulin (161)	ASGP (56), mannose-6-phosphate (24)
2. Acid phosphatase negative, electronluscent, irregular	α2 macroglobulin (154)	
3. Near Golgi-lysosome area	ASGP (156, 168), insulin (19)	
4. Apical	IgG (1, 130)	
VI. Multivesicular bodies	NGF (133, insulin (27, 35) hCG (32)	mannose-6-phosphate (24)
1. Luminal aspect	LDL (28), EGF (61, 100, 146)[b]	
2. Acid phosphatase + or −	LDL (66), EGF (64)	
3. 400 nm	hGH (8)	
4. 50 nm Intraluminal vesicles	EGF (95)	EGF (64)
5. Golgi area		EGF (47)
	transferrin (74)	transferrin (74)
VII. Secretory and secretory-like components		
A. Secretory granules		
1. Premelanosomes	α melanotropin (106)	
2. Gonadotropin granules	GRHA (45), LHRH (145)	LHRH (145)
3. Zymogen granules	insulin (35)	IgA (58)
4. Exocytic vesicle of bile canaliculus	IgA (58)	
B. Golgi complex	GRHA (45), IgA (58)	

VIII. Nonlysosomal subcellular fractions

A. Sucrose gradients		
1. ρ 1.10 – 1.11 (Diacytosomes: 60–120 nm)		
a. Luminal aspect	AST type III (38, 39), insulin (38)	insulin (38)
b. Cytosolic aspect		ASGP (38)
2. ρ 1.11 – 1.13	ASGP (34, 93, 127, 152), IgA (34), AST (152)	
3. ρ 1.12 – 1.17	ASGP (12, 152, 153), IgA (109), insulin (76)	
B. Percoll gradients		
1. ρ 1.03 – 1.04	Fab fragment (102), ASGP (67)	
2. ρ 1.040 – 1.049	EGF (104), insulin (88), β hexoseaminidase, LDL (104)	insulin (88)
3. ρ 1.057	insulin (88)	insulin (88, 89) human GH (89)
C. Discontinuous sucrose gradients		
1. Golgi fractions	insulin (41, 79, 123, 124), prolactin (80, 125)	EGF (97), prolactin (120), ASGP (129), human GH (120), IGF (119), insulin (13, 15, 41, 121)
a. Luminal aspect		ASGP (38, 126), insulin (15, 38), lactogen (15)
b. Lipoprotein vesicles of low density	prolactin (9, 80), insulin (88)	insulin (88)
c. Lipoprotein filled vesicles of high density	insulin (88)	
D. Coated vesicles	EGF (53), transferrin (21)	insulin (88), prolactin (87), transferrin (21), insulin (117)

[a] Abbreviations: ASGP, asialoglycoprotein; AST, asialotransferrin; CURL, compartment of uncoupling of receptor and ligand; GRHA, analog of gonadotropin-releasing hormone; hGH, human growth hormone; LDL, low density lipoprotein; NGF, nerve growth factor; VSV, vesicular stomatitis virus.

[b] Details of structure and localization not provided.

Table 2 Properties of purified endosomes from rat liver homogenates [taken from (88) and M. N. Khan, S. Savoie, J. J. M. Bergeron & B. I. Posner, unpublished data]

Component	Isolation Parent fraction	Isolation Gradient used	Yield protein mg/g	Receptor insulin % S.B.[e]	Endocytosis of ^{125}I-insulin[a] 1 min cpm/g ×10^{-3}	1 min RSA[f]	5 min cpm/g ×10^{-3}	5 min RSA	10 min cpm/g ×10^{-3}	10 min RSA	Chloroquine[b] 5 min RSA	Enzymes GT[c] RSA	AP[d] RSA
Small vesicles	Microsomes	sucrose	1.2	4.5	132.8	14.2	142.8	13.7	59.5	10.6	1.3	10.7	1.3
Low density lpv[g]	Golgi intermediate	Percoll	0.14	9.7	33.3	46.8	75.3	94.6	63.0	65.5	0.3	120.0	2.0
High density lpv	Golgi intermediate	Percoll	0.046	10.5	0.75	5.3	8.8	67.5	10.5	182.3	3.6	< 6.0	3.5
High density lpv	L intermediate[h]	sucrose	0.109	5.5	ND[i]	ND	27.9	94.8	ND	ND	3.3	< 4.0	6.4

[a] Radioactive content of endosomes after purification from rats injected with 30–37.5 × 10^6 dpm of ^{125}I-insulin (~ 150 μCi/μg).

[b] Chloroquine content of endosomal components expressed as an enrichment over the homogenate.

[c] GT, galactosyl transferase.

[d] AP, acid phosphatase.

[e] % S.B., percent specific binding, proportion of near physiological concentrations of ^{125}I-insulin bound by 50 μg protein of endosomes at steady-state conditions.

[f] RSA, relative specific activity, i.e. enrichment over the homogenate.

[g] lpv, lipoprotein-filled vesicle.

[h] L intermediate, refers to endosomes floated from parent L fractions and recovered at 0.6–0.86 M sucrose interface.

[i] ND, not determined.

of which are enriched in receptors as well as internalized ligand (Table 2). Furthermore, flotation of endosomal components from crude lysosomal fractions has also yielded a highly purified lipoprotein-filled endosome with no apparent marker-enzyme activity (Table 2). The morphology of lipoprotein-filled endosomal components purified from Golgi fractions is illustrated in Figure 1. It has been conclusively established by EM radioautography that receptors for insulin and receptors for lactogenic hormones have been localized to the membrane of lipoprotein-containing components (15), which in situ can be observed in the Golgi region of the hepatocyte (18, 19). The same is true for internalized insulin and prolactin (80, 124). Other ligands have also been localized to similar intrahepatic structures (33, 42, 149). However, the recent demonstration from Steinberg, Havel, and colleagues that the hepatocyte is the major site of uptake of serum lipoprotein and that this internalized lipoprotein often accumulates in lipoprotein-filled vesicles near the stacked saccules of the hepatic Golgi apparatus (7, 31, 66, 75) indicates that some or all of the content of these lipoprotein-containing vesicles may be derived from extracellular sources.

CONTROL OF INTRACELLULAR TRANSPORT OF INSULIN AND OTHER LIGANDS

Work has recently accumulated on the perturbation of the endocytic process by a variety of pharmacological agents. It seems that agents perturbing the pH of endocytic structures and agents that affect microtubules profoundly alter the extent and fate of internalized ligand (10, 12, 18, 37, 68, 75, 104, 110, 123, 167). Temperature also plays an important role, with temperature-sensitive steps noted at the cell surface as well as within the endosomal apparatus. Internalization is markedly diminished by temperatures less that 5°C, and discharge from the endosomal compartment(s) into secondary lysosomes is inhibited by temperatures less than 20°C (48, 73, 98).

How are these agents working? In contrast to what was originally believed (40), lysosomotropic agents clearly affect internalization and ligand routing at an endosomal stage (75, 104, 123, 167). Indeed, the term lysosomotropic agent has been recently renamed acidotropic agent (39a). Microtubule polymerization is also directed at endosomal structures, as are temperatures less than 20°C (18, 48, 73, 110, 125, 167). The temperature effects may indicate a unique lipid composition of the phospholipid bilayer of "late" endosomes that must undergo an alteration of the membrane bilayer structure in order to enable membrane coalescence, presumably with secondary or primary lysosomes. The acidotropic weak bases, in addition to inhibiting dissociation of ligand from receptor within low-pH endosomes, may also prevent membrane fusion-fission events among components of the endosomal apparatus and lysosomes.

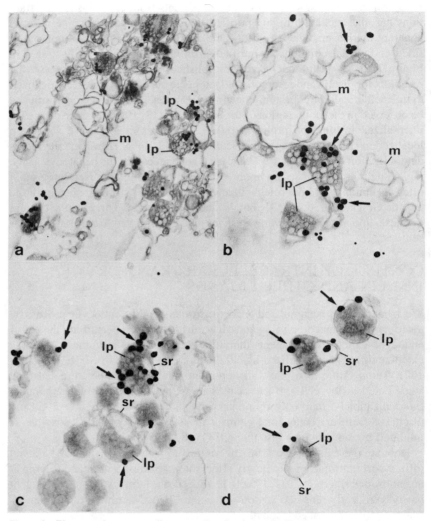

Figure 1   Electron microscope radioautography of endosomal components present in the hepatic fractions. At 5 min after the injection of ^{125}I-insulin, the Golgi intermediate fraction was isolated and subfractionated on Percoll gradients into low *(a, b)* and higher density *(c, d)* components. The highest-density component *(d, $\rho > 1.06$)* is $> 60\%$ pure as judged by the proportion of labeled structures, whereas the low-density component *(a, b, $\rho < 1.04$)* is heterogenous and only $\sim 15\%$ pure with free membranous structures *(m)* observed as contaminants. The lipoprotein content *(lp)* of the endosomal structures is apparent. Both the low- and high-density lipoprotein-filled endosomes are ~ 250–500 nm in diameter. The magnifications are: *a,* X 21,000; *b, c, d,* X 32,000. [Taken from (88)].

RECEPTOR INTERNALIZATION AND RECYCLING

The rapid uptake of ligands by receptor-mediated processes along with the presence of receptors in the same cell fractions into which internalized ligand is concentrated (118, 122) suggest that ligand-receptor complexes are internalized by target cells. Furthermore, ligands are metabolized by cells far more rapidly than are their receptors (140, 143, 151), thereby suggesting receptor recycling. Thus, whereas insulin is metabolized by target cells quite rapidly ($t_{1/2} < 30$ min), the insulin receptor has a $t_{1/2}$ around 10 hr (92).

The demonstration that photoaffinity-labeled EGF receptors were internalized by 3T3 cells constituted direct evidence for receptor internalization (36). This technique has been recently used by several investigators to demonstrate ligand-receptor internalization and recycling. Thus photoaffinity-labeled insulin receptors of cultured hepatocytes become trypsin-insensitive on incubation at 37°C (50). More extended incubation (up to 6 hr) resulted in a partial return of trypsin sensitivity, indicating a return to enzyme accessibility at the cell surface (51). Comparable studies on rat adipocytes also indicated that photolabeled receptors were internalized (20).

Although these studies can be criticized on the basis that they generate an unnatural linkage between receptor and ligand, they are supported by a variety of other observations. The demonstration that exposing cultured chick liver cells to insulin resulted in a loss (down regulation) of cell-surface receptors, with no change in total receptor content, strongly implied that there had been ligand-induced receptor internalization (92). The demonstration that the systemic injection of insulin resulted in a loss of insulin receptors from liver-cell plasma membranes (116), along with the correlative increase in receptors in hepatic Golgi fractions, provided strong evidence for ligand-induced receptor internalization (41). It has also been shown that insulin treatment of incubating adipocytes reduced cell-surface receptors while increasing intracellular receptors (62) and that EGF induced intracellular accumulation of its receptors in perfused liver (47) as well as in fibroblasts in the presence of the acidotropic agent methylamine (90).

The preparation of antibodies to various receptors has contributed greatly to the development of a more precise picture of the receptor's fate. Basu et al, using an antibody to the LDL receptor, showed that LDL receptors accumulated in perinuclear vacuoles of cultured fibroblasts when these cells were exposed to both LDL and monensin (10). Enns et al used antibodies to both transferrin and the transferrin receptor to show aggregation of ligand and receptor intracellularly in K562 human erythroid cells (49). Mellman et al showed that Fc receptors are rapidly internalized and degraded by macrophages during phagocytosis of IgG-coated erythrocytes (101), and Geuze, Schwartz, and colleagues have used double-label immunoelectron microscopy to colocalize several ligands with their corresponding receptors (56–58 vide supra).

Such studies have shown that there are different routes for the handling of ligands, depending, presumably at least in part, on the ease with which they are dissociated from their receptor. Thus Hopkins, using tranferrin-peroxidase to mark ligand and a transferrin-specific antibody, has shown the existence of both a peripheral endosomal system and a juxtanuclear area involved in the handling of ligand-receptor complexes (73). He suggests that each compartment plays a specific role in directing internalized receptors to particular cellular domains. In a study comparing the uptake of the asialoglycoprotein receptor with that for polymeric IgA (membrane secretory component), Geuze, Schwartz, and colleagues showed that the intracellular routes for these two receptors corresponded at an early stage but subsequently diverged, with each entering distinctive endosomal regions (58). Selection and segregation of ligands into distinct endosomes was previously suggested by the studies of Abrahamson & Rodewald, who showed segregation of transcytosed IgG linked to receptor from a fluid phase endocytic tracer (1). The extraordinarily high concentration of several different receptors in Golgi saccules (58, Table 1), as defined by quantitative immunocytochemistry, has indicated a role for this organelle not only in receptor biogenesis but also in receptor recycling to the cell surface (58).

SIGNIFICANCE OF INTERNALIZATION INTO THE ENDOSOMAL APPARATUS

There are three main reasons one might immediately think of for the internalization of peptide hormones and their receptors. The first is that of ligand targeting for destruction. There is no question that in most target cells, internalized hormone is degraded—albeit at very different rates for different ligands—even within the same target cell (105, 112). This could conceivably be a mechanism for ensuring that hormone once bound to the receptor on the cell surface cannot dissociate and interact with another receptor. In addition, hormone internalization could conceivably be a homeostatic mechanism for removing ligand from the circulation. Receptor-mediated endocytosis is not, however, the sole mechanism for clearing hormone from the circulation. The proximal convoluted tubule of the kidney is the major site of nonspecific uptake of insulin as well as probably most other peptide hormones (16, 18, 158) and is probably an important physiological site for hormone clearance from the circulation.

A second possible reason for internalization concerns the phenomenon of "down-regulation." The ligand-induced loss of receptors and ligand-induced desensitization of target cells has been described by Roth and others (29, 30, 47, 54, 72, 82, 91, 96, 108, 134, 137, 138, 139, 141, 142). A postreceptor defect has been invoked in some cases in order to explain the lack of bioresponse induced by chronic exposure to ligand (2, 69). Nevertheless, the initial redistribution of receptors to intracellular structures (endosomes) followed by an increased rate of degradation of the intracellular receptors leads to marked alterations in receptor content and receptor distribution in "down-regulated" cells. As peptide hormones have been shown to undergo wide variations in their output from parent endocrine cells (52, 159), then temporary "down-regulation" of receptors could ensure that, following a bolus of high hormone concentration, target cells remain desensitized until circulating levels of the hormone drop to negligible levels.

An opposite but not exclusive point of view is that one role for the internalization of some peptide hormones may be bioresponse.[2] It is noteworthy that the anabolic hormones insulin and epidermal growth factor contain as an integral part of their structure a cytosolically exposed protein kinase domain (32a, 32b, 63, 77, 84, 85, 85a–c, 99, 115, 131, 132, 136, 154a, 154b, 169, 170, 171). The potential for trans membrane signaling and amplification of a hormone signal by such a structure is obvious. From our own studies with insulin in liver parenchymal cells and EGF in placental cells, a tight association of ligand with the bounding membrane of endocytic components (endosomes) has been observed. These structures have volumes of approximately 10^{-14} ml (14, 95). At neutral pH, ligand-receptor disocciation would be markedly inhibited in such small volumes even if only a single ligand receptor complex were found within an endosome [K_d for insulin and EGF is $\sim 10^{-8}$–10^{-9} M (94, 121)]. Therefore, internalization of ligand into receptor-rich endosomes of neutral pH could be a mechanism for ensuring a tight ligand-receptor association and extended amplification of a cytosolic signal via the protein-kinase domain well after blood ligand levels have decreased. Given this scenario, then an acidic endosomal compartment for dissociating ligand from receptor to enable degradation of the former in receptor-poor lysosomes and recycling of the latter to the cell surface becomes understandable.

Clarification of the functional significance of the heterogenous endosomal components will almost certainly await biochemical dissection of endosomes after purification to near homogeneity. In this regard our own subcellular fractionation attempts (Tables 1, 2) have indicated the heterogeneity of the endosomal apparatus as well as regulated steps in the transport of insulin and other ligands through these compartments (18, 88, 89, 123). The recent innovation of Courtoy et al (33) should help in the eventual purification of all endosomal components from any target cell. These investigators have defined conditions for altering the buoyant density of endosomes by linking the enzyme

---

[2]This is almost certainly not the case for hormones that stimulate adenylate cyclase. Indeed, crude and purified endosomal components reveal undetectable basal or hormone-stimulated adenylate cyclase activity (J. J. M. Bergeron, D. Goltzman & B. I. Posner, unpublished data; and 43).

horseradish peroxidase to a ligand. After crude purification, endosomes are then reacted with diaminobenzidine. This compound is polymerized within the lumina of endosomes by the action of horseradish peroxidase, thereby rendering endosomes more dense. Subsequent density gradient centrifugation leads to highly purified endosomes (33, 127). This technique is potentially applicable to any organ or cell line for which biologially active ligand-horseradish peroxidase complexes can be constructed.

In conclusion, most cells possess an extensive endosomal system for concentrating and accumulating a variety of exogenous substances by endocytosis. The biological importance of the ligands (e.g. insulin and other peptide hormones) and their receptors, which subsequently accumulate in the endosomal apparatus of target cells, point to important physiological actions of this intracellular complex that remain to be discovered.

ACKNOWLEDGMENTS

This work was supported by grants from the Medical Research Council of Canada, the US Public Health Service, the National Cancer Institute of Canada, and the Fonds de la Recherche en Santé du Québec.

Literature Cited

1. Abrahamson, D. R., Rodewald, R. 1981. Evidence for the sorting of endocytic vesicle contents during the receptor-mediated transport of IgG across the newborn rat intestine. *J. Cell Biol.* 91:270–80
2. Amatruda, J. M., Newmeyer, H. W., Chang, C. L. 1982. Insulin-induced alterations in insulin binding and insulin action in primary cultures of rat hepatocytes. *Diabetes* 31:145–48
3. Amsterdam, A., Nimrod, L., Lamprecht, S. A., Burstein, Y., Lindner, H. R. 1979. Internalization and degradation of receptor-bound HCG in granulosa cell cultures. *Am. J. Physiol.* 236:E129–38
4. Anderson, R. G. W., Brown, M. S., Goldstein, J. L. 1977. Role of the coated endocytic vesicle in the uptake of receptor-bound low density lipoprotein in human fibroblasts. *Cell* 10:351–61
5. Anderson, R. G. W., Kaplan, J. 1983. Receptor-mediated endocytosis. *Modern Cell Biol.* 1:1–52
6. Anderson, R. G. W., Vasile, E., Mello, R. J., Brown, M. S., Goldstein, J. L. 1978. Immunocytochemical visualization of coated pits and vesicles in human fibroblasts: relation to low density lipoprotein receptor distribution. *Cell* 15:919–33
7. Attie, A. D., Pittman, R. C., Steinberg, D. 1982. Hepatic catabolism of low den-

sity lipoprotein: mechanisms and metabolic consequences. *Hepatology* 2:269–81
8. Barazzone, P., Lesniak, M. A., Gorden, P., Van Obberghen, E., Carpentier, J.-L., et al. 1980. Binding, internalization, and lysosomal association of ^{125}I-Human Growth Hormone in cultured lymphocytes: A quantitative morphological and biochemical study. *J. Cell Biol.* 87:360–69
9. Basset, M., Smith, G. D., Pease, R., Peters, T. J. 1984. Uptake and processing of prolactin by alternative pathways in rat liver. *Biochim. Biophys. Acta* 769:79–84
10. Basu, S. K., Goldstein, J. L., Anderson, R. G. W., Brown, M. S. 1981. Monensin interrupts the recycling of low density lipoprotein receptors in human fibroblasts. *Cell* 24:493–502
11. Beguinot, L., Lyall, R. M., Willingham, M. C., Pastan, I. 1984. Down-regulation of the epidermal growth factor receptor in KB cells is due to receptor internalization and subsequent degradation in lysosomes. *Proc. Natl. Acad. Sci. USA* 81: 2384–88
12. Berg, T., Tolleshaug, H. 1980. The effects of ammonium ions and chloroquine on uptake and degradation of ^{125}I-labeled asialo-fetuin in isolated rat

hepatocytes. *Biochem. Pharmacol.* 29:917–25

13. Bergeron, J. J. M., Evans, W. M., Geschwind, I. I. 1973. Insulin binding to rat liver Golgi fractions. *J. Cell Biol.* 59:771–76

14. Bergeron, J. J. M., Posner, B. I. 1981. Intracellular polypeptide hormone receptors: Location and significance. *Receptor-Mediated Binding and Internalization of Toxins and Hormones.* ed. J. M. Middlebrook, L. D. Kohn, pp. 197–218. New York: Academic

15. Bergeron, J. J. M., Posner, B. I., Josefsberg, Z., Sikstrom, R. 1978. Intracellular polypeptide hormone receptors: The demonstration of specific binding sites for insulin and human growth hormone in Golgi fractions isolated from the liver of female rats. *J. Biol. Chem.* 253:4058–66

16. Bergeron, J. J. M., Rachubinski, R., Searle, N., Borts, D., Sikstrom, R., et al. 1980. Polypeptide hormone receptors in vivo: demonstration of insulin binding to adrenal gland and gastrointestinal epithelium by quantitative radioautography. *J. Histochem. Cytochem.* 28:824–35

17. Bergeron, J. J. M., Rachubinski, R., Searle, N., Sikstrom, R., Borts, D., et al 1980. Radioautographic visualization of in vivo insulin binding to the exocrine pancreas. *Endocrinology* 107:1069–80

18. Bergeron, J. J. M., Resch, L., Rachubinski, R., Patel, B. A., Posner, B. I. 1983. Effect of colchicine on internalization of prolactin in female rat liver: an in vivo radioautographic study. *J. Cell Biol.* 96:875–86

19. Bergeron, J. J. M., Sikstrom, R., Hand, A. R., Posner, B. I. 1979. Binding and uptake of ^{125}I-insulin into rat liver hepatocytes and endothelium *J. Cell Biol.* 80:427–43

20. Bernahu, P., Olefsky, J. M., Tsai, P., Thamm, P., Saunders, D., et al. 1982. Internalization and molecular processing of insulin receptors in isolated rat hepatocytes. *Proc. Natl. Acad. Sci. USA* 79:4069–73

21. Booth, A. G., Wilson, M. J. 1981. Human placental coated vesicles contain receptor-bound transferrin. *Biochem. J.* 196:355–62

22. Brown, M. S., Anderson, R. G. W., Basu, S. K., Goldstein, J. L. 1982. Recycling of cell surface receptors: observations from the LDL receptor system. *Cold Spring Harb. Symp.* 46:713–21

23. Brown, M. S., Anderson, R. G. W., Goldstein, J. L. 1983. Recycling receptors: the round trip itinerary of migrant membrane proteins. *Cell* 32:663–67

24. Brown, W. J., Farquhar, M. G. 1984.

The mannose-6-phosphate receptor for lysosomal enzymes is concentrated in cis Golgi cisternae. *Cell* 36:295–307

25. Brown, M. S., Goldstein, J. L. 1979. Receptor-mediated endocytosis. Insights from the lipoprotein receptor system. *Proc. Natl. Acad. Sci. USA* 76:3330–37

26. Brown, M. S., Goldstein, J. L. 1983. Lipoprotein metabolism in the macrophage: implications for cholesterol deposition in atheroschlerosis. *Ann. Rev. Biochem.* 52:223–61

27. Carpentier, J.-L., Gorden, P., Barazzone, P., Freychet, P., LeCam, A., et al. 1979. Intracellular localization of ^{125}I-labeled insulin in hepatocytes from intact rat liver. *Proc. Natl. Acad. Sci. USA* 76:2803–7

28. Carpentier, J.-L., Gorden, P., Goldstein, J. L., Anderson, R. G. W., Brown, M. S., et al. 1979. Binding and internalization of ^{125}I-LDL in normal and mutant human fibroblasts. *Exp. Cell Res.* 121:135–42

29. Catt, K. J., Dufau, M. L. 1977. Peptide hormone receptors. *Ann. Rev. Physiol.* 39:529–54

30. Catt, K. J., Harwood, J. P., Aquilera, G., Dufau, M. L. 1979. Hormonal regulation of peptide receptors and target cell responses. *Nature* 280:109–16

31. Chao, Y.-S., Jones, A. L., Hradek, G. T., Windler, E. E. T., Havel, R. J. 1981. Autoradiographic localization of the sites of uptake, cellular transport, and catabolism of low density lipoproteins in the liver of normal and estrogen-treated rats. *Proc. Natl. Acad. Sci. USA* 78:597–601

32. Chen, T. T., Abel, J. H., McClellan, M. C., Sawyer, H. R., Dickman, M. A. et al. 1977. Localization of gonadotropic hormones in lysosomes of ovine luteal cells. *Cytobiologie* 14:412–20

32a. Cohen, S., Carpenter, G., King, L. Jr. 1980. Epidermal growth factor–receptor–protein kinase interactions: Co-purification of receptor and epidermal growth factor–enhanced phosphorylation activity. *J. Biol. Chem.* 255:4834–42

32b. Cohen, S., Ushiro, H., Stoscheck, C., Chinkers, M. 1982. A native 170,000 epidermal growth factor–receptor–kinase complex from shed plasma membrane vesicles. *J. Biol. Chem.* 257:1523–31

33. Courtoy, P. J., Quintart, J., Baudhuin, P. 1984. Shift of equilibrium density induced by 3,3'-diaminobenzidine cytochemistry: a new procedure for the analysis and purification of peroxidase-containing organelles. *J. Cell Biol.* 98:870–76

34. Courtoy, P. J., Quintart, J., Limet, J. N., DeRoe, C., Baudhuin, P. Intracellular

sorting of galactosylated proteins and polymeric IgA in rat hepatocytes. *J. Cell Biol.* 95:425a

35. Cruz, J., Posner, B. I., Bergeron, J. J. M. 1984. Receptor-mediated endocytosis of ^{125}I-insulin into pancreatic acinar cells in vivo. *Endocrinology* 115:1996–2008

36. Das, M., Fox, C. F. 1978. Molecular mechanism of mitogen action: processing of receptor induced by epidermal growth factor. *Proc. Natl. Acad. Sci. USA* 75:2644–48

37. Dean, R. T., Jessup, W., Roberts, C. R. 1984. Effects of exogenous amines on mammalian cells, with particular reference to membrane flow. *Biochem. J.* 217:27–40

38. Debanne, M. T., Evans, W. H., Flint, N., Regoeczi, E. 1982. Receptor-rich intracellular membrane vesicles transporting asialotransferrin and insulin in liver. *Nature* 298:398–400

39. Debanne, M. T., Regoeczi, E. 1981. Subcellular distribution of human asialotransferrin type 3 in the rat liver. *J. Biol. Chem.* 256:11266–72

39a. de Duve, C. 1983. Lysosomes revisited. *Eur. J. Biochem.* 137:391–97

40. de Duve, C., de Bousy, T., Poole, B., Trouet, A., Tuikens, P., et al. 1974. Lysomotropic agents. *Biochem. Pharmacol.* 23:2495–2531

41. Desbuquois, B., Lopez, S., Burlet, H. 1982. Ligand-induced translocation of insulin receptors in intact rat liver. *J. Biol. Chem.* 257:10852–60

42. Deschuyteneer, M., Prieels, J.-P., Mosselmans, R. 1983. Galactose-specific adsorptive endocytosis: an ultrastructural qualitative and quantitative study in cultured rat hepatocytes. *Biol. Cell.* 50:17–29

43. Dickson, R. B., Bequinot, L., Hanover, J. A., Richert, N. D., Willingham, M. C., et al. 1983. Isolation and characterization of a highly enriched preparation of receptosomes (endosomes) from a human cell line. *Proc. Natl. Acad. Sci. USA* 80:5335–39

44. Dickson, R. B., Willingham, M. C., Pastan, I. 1981. α2-macroglobulin adsorbed to colloidal gold: a new probe in the study of receptor-mediated endocytosis. *J. Cell Biol.* 89:29–34

45. Duello, T. M., Nett, T. M., Farquhar, M. G. 1983. Fate of a gonadotropin-releasing hormone agonist internalized by rat pituitary gonadotrophs. *Endocrinology* 112:1–10

46. Dunn, W. A., Hubbard, A. L. 1982. Receptor-mediated endocytosis of epidermal growth factor (EGF) by liver. *J. Cell Biol.* 95:425a

47. Dunn, W. A., Hubbard, A. L. 1984. Receptor mediated endocytosis of epidermal growth factor by hepatocytes in the perfused rat liver: ligand and receptor dynamics. *J. Cell Biol.* 98:2148–59

48. Dunn, W. A., Hubbard, A. L., Aronson, N. N. Jr. 1980. Low temperature selectively inhibits fusion between pinocytic vesicles and lysosomes during heterophagy of ^{125}I-asialofetuin by the perfused rat liver. *J. Biol. Chem.* 255:5971–78

49. Enns, C. A., Larrick, J. W., Suomalainen, H., Schroder, J., Sussman, H. H. 1983. Co-migration and internalization of transferrin and its receptor on K562 cells. *J. Cell Biol.* 97:579–85

50. Fehlmann, M., Carpentier, J.-L., LeCam, A., Thamm, P., Saunders, D., et al. 1982. Biochemical and morphological evidence that the insulin receptor is internalized with insulin in hepatocytes. *J. Cell Biol.* 93:82–87

51. Fehlmann, M., Carpentier, J.-L., Van Obberghen, E., Freychet, P., Thamm, P., et al. 1982. Internalized insulin receptors are recycled to the cell surface in rat hepatocytes. *Proc. Natl. Acad. Sci. USA* 79:5921–25

52. Felig, P. 1981. The endocrine pancreas: diabetes mellitus. In *Endocrinology and Metabolism*, ed. P. Felig, J. D. Baxter, A. E. Broadus, L. A. Frohman, pp. 776–82. New York: McGraw-Hill

53. Fine, R. E., Goldenberg, R., Sorrentino, J., Herschman, H. R. 1981. Subcellular structures involved in internalization and degradation of epidermal growth factor. *J. Supramol. Struct.* 15:235–51

53a. Galloway, C. J., Dean, C. E., Marsh, M., Rudnick, G., Mellman, I. 1983. Acidification of macrophage and fibroblast endocytic vesicles *in vitro. Proc. Natl. Acad. Sci. USA* 80:3334–38

54. Gavin, J. R. III, Roth, J., Neville, D. M. Jr., De Meyts, P., Buell, D. N. 1974. Insulin-dependent regulation of insulin receptor concentrations: a direct demonstration in cell culture. *Proc. Natl. Acad. Sci. USA* 71:84–88

55. Geuze, H. J., Slot, W. J., Strous, G. J. A. M. 1983. The pathway of the asialoglycoprotein-ligand during receptor-mediated endocytosis: a morphological study with colloidal gold/ligand in the human hepatoma cell line Hep G2. *Eur. J. Cell Biol.* 32:38–44

56. Geuze, H. J., Slot, J. W., Strous, G. J. A. M., Lodish, H. F., Schwartz, A. 1982. Immunocytochemical localization of the receptor for asialoglycoprotein in rat liver cells. *J. Cell Biol.* 92:865–70

57. Geuze, H. J., Slot, W. J., Strous, G. J.

A. M., Lodish, H. F., Schwartz, A. L. 1983. Intracellular site of asialoglycoprotein receptor-ligand uncoupling: double-label immunoelectron microscopy during receptor-mediated endocytosis. *Cell* 32: 277–87

58. Geuze, H. J., Slot, J. W., Strous, G. J. A. M., Peppard, J., Von Figura, K., et al. 1984. Intracellular receptor sorting during endocytosis: comparative immunoelectron microscopy of multiple receptors in rat liver. *Cell* 37:195–204

59. Goldstein, J. L., Anderson, R. G. W., Brown, M. S. 1979. Coated pits, coated vesicles, and receptor-mediated endocytosis. *Nature* 271:679–85

59a. Goldstein, J. L., Brown, M. S. 1977. The low density lipoprotein pathway and its relation to atherosclerosis. *Ann. Rev. Biochem.* 46:897–930

60. Gonzalez-Noriega, A., Grubb, J. H., Talkad, V., Sly, W. S. 1980. Chloroquine inhibits lysosomal enzyme pinocytosis and enhances lysosomal enzyme secretion by impairing receptor recycling. *J. Cell Biol.* 85:839–52

61. Gorden, P., Carpentier, J.-L., Cohen, S., Orci, L. 1978. Epidermal growth factor: morphological demonstration of binding, internalization and lysosomal association in human fibroblasts. *Proc. Natl. Acad. Sci. USA* 75:5025–29

62. Green, A., Olefsky, J. M. 1982. Evidence for insulin-induced internalization and degradation of insulin receptors in rat adipocytes. *Proc. Natl. Acad. Sci. USA* 79:427–31

63. Grigorescu, F., White, M. F., Kahn, R. C. 1983. Insulin binding and insulin-dependent phosphorylation of the insulin receptor solubilized from human erythrocytes. *J. Biol. Chem.* 258:13708–16

64. Haigler, H. T., McKanna, J. A., Cohen, S. 1979. Direct visualization of the binding and internalization of a ferritin conjugate of epidermal growth factor in human carcinoma cells A-431. *J. Cell Biol.* 81:382–95

65. Haimes, H. B., Stockert, R. J., Morell, A. G., Novikoff, A. B. 1981. Carbohydrate-specified endocytosis: localization of ligand in the lysosomal compartment. *Proc. Natl. Acad. Sci. USA* 78:6936–39

66. Handley, D. A., Arbeeny, C. M., Eder, H. A., Chien, S. 1981. Hepatic binding and internalization of low density lipoprotein-gold conjugates in rats treated with 17 α-ethinylestradiol. *J. Cell Biol.* 90:778–87

67. Harford, J., Bridges, K., Ashwell, G., Klausner, R. D. 1983. Intracellular dissociation of receptor-bound asialogly-

coproteins in cultured hepatocytes. *J. Biol. Chem.* 258:3191–97

68. Harford, J., Wolkoff, A. W., Ashwell, G., Klausner, R. D. 1983. Monensin inhibits intracellular dissociation of asialoglycoproteins from their receptor. *J. Cell Biol.* 96:1824–28

69. Heaton, J. H., Gelehiter, T. D. 1981. Desensitization of hepatoma cells to insulin action. *J. Biol. Chem.* 256:12257–62

70. Helenius, A., Kartenbeck, J., Simons, K., Fries, E. 1980. On the entry of Semliki Forest virus into BHK-21 cells. *J. Cell Biol.* 84:404–16

71. Helenius, A., Mellman, I., Wall, D., Hubbard, A. 1983. Endosomes. *Trends Biochem. Sci.* 8:245–50

72. Hinkle, P. N., Tashjian, A. H. Jr. 1975. Thyrotropin-releasing hormone regulates the number of its own receptors in the GH3 strain of pituitary cells in culture. *Biochemistry* 14:3845–51

73. Hopkins, C. R. 1983. Intracellular routing of transferrin and transferrin receptors in epidermoid carcinoma A431 cells. *Cell* 35:321–30

74. Hopkins, C. R., Trowbridge, I. S. 1983. Internalization and processing of transferrin and the transferrin receptor in human carcinoma A431 cells. *J. Cell Biol.* 97:508–21

75. Hornick, C. A., Jones, A. L., Renaud, G., Hradek, G., Havel, R. J. 1984. Effect of chloroquine on low-density lipoprotein catabolic pathway in rat hepatocyte. *Am. J. Physiol.* 246:6187–94

76. Horvat, A., Li, E., Katsoyannis, P. G. 1975. Cellular binding sites for insulin in rat liver. *Biochim. Biophys. Acta* 382:609–20

77. Houslay, M. D. 1981. Membrane phosphorylation: a crucial role in the activation of insulin, EGF, and pp 60^Src? *Biosci. Rep.* 1:19–34

78. Iwanij, V. 1980. Intracellular pathway of ^{125}I-glucagon in the rat liver. *J. Cell Biol.* 87:172a

79. Izzo, J. L., Roncone, A. M., Helton, D. L., Izzo, M. J., 1979. Subcellular distribution of intraportally injected ^{125}I-labeled insulin in rat liver. *Arch. Biochem. Biophys.* 198:97–109

80. Josefsberg, Z., Posner, B. I., Patel, B., Bergeron, J. J. M. 1979. The uptake of prolactin into female rat liver. *J. Biol. Chem.* 254:209–14

81. Joseph, K. C., Seung, U. K., Stieber, A., Gonatas, N. K. 1978. Endocytosis of cholera toxin into neuronal GERL. *Proc. Natl. Acad. Sci. USA* 75:2815–19

82. Kahn, C. R., Neville, D. M. Jr., Roth, J.

1973. Insulin-receptor interaction in the obese-hyperglycemic mouse. *J. Biol. Chem.* 248:244–50

83. Kaplan, J. 1980. Evidence for reutilization of surface receptors for α2 macroglobulin. Protease complexes in rabbit alveolar macrophages. *Cell* 19:197–205

84. Kasuga, M., Fujita-Yamaguchi, Y., Blithe, D. L., Kahn, C. R. 1983. Tyrosine-specific protein kinase activity is associated with the purified insulin receptor. *Proc. Natl. Acad. Sci. USA* 80:2137–41

85. Kasuga, M., Fujita-Yamaguchi, Y., Blithe, D. L., White, M. F., Kahn, R. C. 1983. Characterization of the insulin receptor kinase purified from human placental membranes. *J. Biol. Chem.* 258:10973–80

85a. Kasuga, M., Karlsson, F. A., Kahn, C. R. 1982. Insulin stimulates the phosphorylation of the 95,000-dalton subunit of its own receptor. *Science* 215:185–87

85b. Kasuga, M., Zick, Y., Blithe, D. L., Crettaz, M., Kahn, C. R. 1982. Insulin stimulates tyrosine phosphorylation of the insulin receptor in a cell-free system. *Nature* 298:667–69

85c. Kasuga, M., Zick, Y., Blithe, D. A., Karlsson, F. A., Häring, H. U., et al. 1982. Insulin stimulation of phosphorylation of the β-subunit of the insulin receptor formation of both phosphoserine and phosphotyrosine. *J. Biol. Chem.* 257:9891–94

86. Kay, D. G., Khan, M. N., Posner, B. I., Bergeron, J. J. M. 1984. ^{125}I-insulin in hepatic Golgi fractions: application of the diaminobenzidine (DAB)-shift protocol. *Biochem. Biophys. Res. Commun.* 123:1144–48

87. Khan, R. J., Khan, M. N., Bergeron, J. J. M., Posner, B. I. 1984. Prolactin internalization into rat liver Golgi fractions: differential effects of uptake into liver endocytic components: Reduced sensitivity to chloroquine. *Biochim. Biophys. Acta,* in press

88. Khan, M. N., Posner, B. I., Khan, R. J., Bergeron, J. J. T. 1982. Internalization of insulin into rat liver Golgi elements: evidence for vesicle heterogeneity and the path of intracellular processing. *J. Biol. Chem.* 257:5969–76

89. Khan, M. N., Posner, B. I., Verma, A. K., Khan, R. J., Bergeron, J. J. M. 1981. Intracellular hormone receptors: evidence for insulin and lactogen receptors in a unique vesicle sedimenting in lysosome fractions of rat liver. *Proc. Natl. Acad. Sci. USA* 78:4980–84

90. King, A. C., Hernaez-Davis, L., Cuatrecasas, P. 1980. Lysosomotropic amines inhibit mitogenesis induced by growth factors. *Proc. Natl. Acad. Sci. USA* 78:717–21

91. Krupp, M. N., Connolly, D. T., Lane, M. D. 1982. Synthesis, turnover, and down-regulation of epidermal growth factor receptors in human A431 epidermoid carcinoma cells and skin fibroblasts. *J. Biol. Chem.* 257:11489–96

92. Krupp, M., Lane, M. D. 1981. On the mechanism of ligand-induced down-regulation of insulin receptor level in the liver cell. *J. Biol. Chem.* 256:1689–94

93. LaBadie, J. H., Chapman, K. P., Aronson, M. N. Jr. 1975. Glycoprotein catabolism in rat liver. *Biochem. J.* 152:271–79

94. Lai, W. H., Guyda, H. J. 1984. Characterization and regulation of epidermal growth factor receptors in human placental cell cultures. *J. Clin. Endocrinol. Metab.* 58:344–52

95. Lai, W. H., Guyda, H. J., Bergeron, J. J. M. 1984. Binding and internalization of epidermal growth factor in human term placental cells: possible relationship to biological response. Submitted for publication

96. Lesniak, M. A., Roth, J. 1976. Regulation of receptor concentration by homologous hormone. *J. Biol. Chem.* 251:3720–29

97. Lev-Ran, A., Hwang, D., Josefsberg, Z., Barseghian, G., Kemeny, M., et al. 1984. Binding of epidermal growth factor (EGF) and insulin to human liver microsomes and Golgi fractions. *Biochem. Biophys. Res. Commun.* 119:1181–85

97a. Maciag, T. 1982. The human epidermal growth factor receptor-kinase complex. *Trends Biochem. Sci.* 7:197–98

98. Marsh, M., Helenius, A. 1980. Adsorptive endocytosis of Semliki Forest virus. *J. Mol. Biol.* 142:439–54

99. Martin-Perez, J., Siegmann, M., Thomas, G. 1984. EGF, PGF$_{2\alpha}$ and insulin induce the phosphorylation of identical S6 peptides in Swiss mouse 3T3 cells. *Cell* 36:287–94

100. McKanna, J. A., Haigler, H. T., Cohen, S. 1979. Hormone receptor topology and dynamics: morphological analysis using ferritin-labeled epidermal growth factor. *Proc. Natl. Acad. Sci. USA* 76:5689–93

101. Mellman, I. S., Plutner, H., Steinman, R. M., Unkeless, J. C., Cohn, Z. A. 1983. Internalization and degradation of macrophage Fc receptors during receptor-mediated phagocytosis. *J. Cell Biol.* 96:887–95

102. Mellman, I., Plutner, M., Ukkonen, P. 1984. Internalization and rapid recycling

of macrophage Fc receptors tagged with monovalent antireceptor antibody: possible role of a prelysosomal compartment. *J. Cell Biol.* 98:1163–69

103. Mello, R. J., Brown, M. S., Goldstein, J. L., Anderson, R. G. W. 1980. LDL receptors in coated vesicles isolated from bovine adrenal cortex: binding sites unmasked by detergent treatment. *Cell* 20:829–37

103a. Merion, M., Schlesinger, P., Brooks, R. M., Moehring, J. M., Moehring, T. J., et al. 1983. Defective acidification of endosomes in Chinese hamster ovary cell mutants "cross-resistant" to toxins and viruses. *Proc. Natl. Acad. Sci. USA* 80:5315–19

104. Merion, M., Sly, W. S. 1983. The role of intermediate vesicles in the adsorptive endocytosis and transport of ligand to lysosomes by human fibroblasts. *J. Cell Biol.* 96:644–50

105. Mock, E. J., Niswender, G. D. 1983. Differences in the rate of internalization of ^{125}I-labeled human chorionic gonadotrophin luteinizing hormone and epidermal growth factor of ovine luteal cells. *Endocrinology* 113:259–64

106. Moellman, G. E., Varga, J. M., Godawska, E. W., Lambert, D. T., Lerner, A. B. 1978. Compartmentalized action of melanotropin (MSH): the role of endocytosis in the hormonal activation of tyrosinase in murine melanoma cells. *J. Cell Biol.* 79:196a

107. Moxon, L. A., Wild, A. E. 1976. Localisation of proteins in coated micropinocytotic vesicles during transport across rabbit yolk sac endoderm. *Cell Tiss. Res.* 171:175–93

108. Mukherjee, C., Caron, M. G., Lefkowitz, R. J. 1975. Catecholamine-induced subsensitivity of adenylate cyclase associated with loss of β-adrenergic receptor binding sites. *Proc. Natl. Acad. Sci. USA* 72:1945–49

109. Mullock, B. M., Hinton, R. H., Dobrota, M., Peppard, J., Orlans, E. 1979. Endocytic vesicles in liver carry polymeric IgA from serum to bile. *Biochim. Biophys. Acta* 587:381–91

110. Oka, J. A., Weigel, P. H. 1983. Microtubule-depolymerizing agents inhibit asialo-orosomucoid delivery to lysosomes but not its endocytosis or degradation in isolated rat hepatocytes. *Biochim. Biophys. Acta* 763:368–76

111. Pastan, I. H., Willingham, M. C. 1981. Journey to the center of the cell: role of the receptosome. *Science* 214:504–9

112. Pastan, I. H., Willingham, M. C. 1981. Receptor-mediated endocytosis of hormones in cultured cells. *Ann. Rev. Physiol.* 43:239–50

113. Pastan, I. H., Willingham, M. C. 1983. Receptor mediated endocytosis coated pits, receptosomes and the Golgi. *Trends Biochem. Sci.* 8:250–54

114. Pearse, B. M. F. 1982. Coated vesicles from human placenta carry ferritin, transferrin and immunoglobulin G. *Proc. Natl. Acad. Sci. USA* 79:451–55

115. Petruzzelli, L. M., Ganguly, S., Smith, C. J., Cobb, M. H., Rubin, C. S., et al. 1982. Insulin activates a tyrosine-specific protein kinase in extracts of 3T3-L1 adipocytes and human placenta. *Proc. Natl. Acad. Sci. USA* 79:6792–96

116. Pezzino, V., Vigneri, R., Pliam, N. B., Goldfine, I. D. 1980. Rapid regulation of plasma membrane insulin receptors. *Diabetologia* 19:211–15

117. Pilch, P. F., Shia, M. A., Benson, R. J., Fine, R. E. 1983. Coated vesicles participate in the receptor-mediated endocytosis of insulin. *J. Cell Biol.* 93:133–38

118. Posner, B. I., Bergeron, J. J. M., Josefsberg, Z., Khan, M. N., Khan, R. J., et al. 1981. Polypeptide hormones: intracellular receptors and internalization. *Rec. Prog. Horm. Res.* 37:539–82

119. Posner, B. I., Gonzalez, R. M., Guyda, H. J. 1980. Intracellular (Golgi) receptors for insulinlike peptides in rat liver. *Can. J. Biochem.* 58:1075–81

120. Posner, B. I., Josefsberg, Z., Bergeron, J. J. M. 1979. Intracellular polypeptide hormone receptors: characterization and induction of lactogen receptors in the Golgi apparatus of rat liver. *J. Biol. Chem.* 254:12494–99

121. Posner, B. I., Josefsberg, Z., Bergeron, J. J. M. 1978. Intracellular polypeptide hormone receptors: Characterization of insulin binding sites in Golgi fractions from the liver of female rats. *J. Biol. Chem.* 253:4067–73

122. Posner, B. I., Khan, M. N., Bergeron, J. J. M. 1982. Endocytosis of peptide hormones and other ligands. *Endocr. Rev.* 3:280–98

123. Posner, B. I., Patel, B. A., Khan, M. N., Bergeron, J. J. M. 1982. Effect of chloroquine on the internalization of ^{125}I-insulin into subcellular fractions of rat liver. *J. Biol. Chem.* 257:5789–99

124. Posner, B. I., Patel, B., Verma, A. K., Bergeron, J. J. M. 1980. Uptake of insulin by plasmalemma and Golgi subcellular fractions of rat liver. *J. Biol. Chem.* 255:735–41

125. Posner, B. I., Verma, A. K., Patel, B. A., Bergeron, J. J. M. 1982. Effect of colchicine on the uptake of prolactin and insulin into Golgi fractions of rat liver. *J. Cell Biol.* 93:560–67

126. Pricer, W. E. Jr., Ashwell, G. 1976.

Subcellular distribution of a mammalian hepatic binding protein specific for asialoglycoproteins. *J. Biol. Chem.* 251:7539–44

127. Quintart, J., Courtoy, P. J., Baudhuin, P. 1984. Receptor-mediated endocytosis in rat liver: purification and enzymic characterization of low density organelles involved in uptake of galactose exposing proteins. *J. Cell Biol.* 98: 877–84

128. Renston, R. H., Maloney, D. G., Jones, A. L., Hradek, G. T., Wong, K. Y., et al. 1980. Bile secretory apparatus: evidence for a vesicular transport mechanism for proteins in the rat, using horseradish peroxidase and ^{125}Insulin. *Gastroenterology* 78:1373–88

129. Riordan, J. R., Mitchell, L., Slavik, M. 1974. The binding of asialoglycoprotein to isolated Golgi apparatus. *Biochem. Biophys. Res. Commun.* 59:1373–79

130. Rodewald, R. 1973. Intestinal transport of antibodies in the newborn rat. *J. Cell Biol.* 58:189–211

131. Rosen, O. M., Herrera, R., Olowe, Y., Petruzzelli, L. M., Cobb, M. H. 1983. Phosphorylation activates the insulin receptor tyrosine protein kinase. *Proc. Natl. Acad. Sci. USA* 80:3237–40

132. Roth, R. A., Cassell, D. J. 1983. Insulin receptor: evidence that it is a protein kinase. *Science* 219:299–301

133. Schwab, M., Thoenen, H. 1977. Selective trans-synaptic migration of tetanus toxin after retrograde axonal transport in peripheral sympathetic nerves: a comparison with nerve growth factor. *Brain Res.* 122:459–74

134. Serravezza, J. C., Endo, F., DeHaan, R. L., Elsas, L. J. II. 1983. Insulin-induced receptor loss reduces responsiveness of chick heart cells to insulin. *Endocrinology* 113:497–507

135. Silverstein, S. C., Steinman, R. M., Cohn, Z. A. 1977. Endocytosis. *Ann. Rev. Biochem.* 46:669–722

136. Soderquist, A. M., Carpenter, G. 1983. Developments in the mechanism of growth factor action: activation of protein kinase by epidermal growth factor. *Fed. Proc.* 42:2615–20

137. Soll, A. H., Kahn, C. R., Neville, D. M. Jr. 1975. Insulin binding to liver plasma membranes in the obese hyperglycemic (ob/ob) mouse. Demonstration of a decreased number of functionally normal receptors. *J. Biol. Chem.* 250:4702–7

138. Soll, A. H., Kahn, C. R., Neville, D. M. Jr., Roth, J. 1975. Insulin receptor deficiency in genetic and acquired obesity. *J. Clin. Invest.* 56:769–80

139. Srikant, C. B., Freeman, D., McCorkle, K., Unger, R. H. 1977. Binding and

biologic activity of glucagon in liver cell membranes of chronically hyperglucagonemic rats. *J. Biol. Chem.* 252:7434–36

140. Stahl, P., Schlesinger, P. H., Segardson, E., Rodman, J. S., Lee, Y. C. 1980. Receptor-mediated pinocytosis of mannose glycoconjugates by macrophages: characterization and evidence for receptor recycling. *Cell* 19:207–15

141. Standaert, M. L., Pollet, R. J. 1984. Equilibrium model for insulin-induced receptor down-regulation: Regulation of insulin receptors in differentiated BC3H-1 myocytes. *J. Biol. Chem.* 259:2346–54

142. Standaert, M. L., Schimmel, S. D., Pollet, R. J. 1984. The development of insulin receptors and responses in the differentiating nonfusing muscle cell line BC3H-1. *J. Biol. Chem.* 259:2337–45

143. Steer, C. J., Ashwell, G. 1980. Studies on a mammalian hepatic binding protein specific for asialoglycoproteins. *J. Biol. Chem.* 255:3008–13

144. Steinman, R. M., Mellman, I. S., Muller, W. A., Cohn, Z. A. 1983. Endocytosis and the recycling of plasma membrane. *J. Cell Biol.* 96:1–27

145. Sternberger, L. A., Petrali, J. P., Joseph, S. A., Meyer, H. G., Mills, K. R. 1978. Specificity of the immunocytochemical luteinizing hormone-releasing hormone receptor reaction. *Endocrinology* 102: 63–73

146. St. Hilaire, R. J., Jones, A. L., Hradek, G. T., Kim, Y. S. 1981. A quantitative electron microscopic and biochemical analysis of hepatic uptake and processing of epidermal growth factor (EGF). *Gastroenterology* 80:1347 (Abstr.)

147. Stockem, W. 1966. Die reaktion von Amoeba Proteus auf verschiedene markietungssubstanzen. *Zeitschrift fuer Zellforschung* 74:372–400

148. Stockem, W., Wohlfarth-Botterman, K. E. 1969. Pinocytosis (endocytosis). In *Handbook of Molecular Cytology*, ed. A. Lima-de-Faria, pp. 1373–1400. Amsterdam: North Holland

149. Stockert, R. J., Haines, H. B., Morrell, A. G., Novikoff, P. M., Novikoff, A. B., et al. 1980. Endocytosis of asialoglycoprotein-enzyme conjugates by hepatocytes. *Lab. Invest.* 43:556–63

150. Straubinger, R. M., Hong, K., Friend, D. S., Papahadjopoulos, D. 1983. Endocytosis of liposomes and intracellular fate of encapsulated molecules: encounter with a low pH compartment after internalization in coated vesicle. *Cell* 32:1069–79

151. Tanabe, T., Pricer, W. E. Jr., Ashwell, G. 1979. Subcellular membrane topology and turnover of a rat hepatic binding

protein specific for asialoglycoproteins. *J. Biol. Chem.* 254:1038–43
152. Tolleshaug, H. 1984. Intracellular segregation of asialo-transferrin and asialofetuin following uptake by the same receptor system in suspended hepatocytes. *Biochim. Biophys. Acta* 803:182–90
153. Tolleshaug, H., Berg, T., Frolich, W., Norum, K. R. 1979. Intracellular localization and degradation of asialofetuin in isolated rat hepatocytes. *Biochim. Biophys. Acta* 585:71–84
154. Tycho, B., Maxfield, F. R. 1982. Rapid acidification of endocytic vesicles containing α2-macroglobulin. *Cell* 28:643–51
154a. Van Obberghen, E., Kowalski, A. 1982. Phosphorylation of the hepatic insulin receptor: Stimulating effect of insulin on intact cells in a cell-free system. *FEBS Letts.* 143:179–82
154b. Van Obberghen, E., Rossi, B., Kowalski, A., Gazzano, H., Ponzio, G. 1983. Receptor-mediated phosphorylation of the hepatic insulin receptor: Evidence that the M_r 95,000 receptor subunit is its own kinase. *Proc. Natl. Acad. Sci. USA* 80:945–49
155. Via, D. P., Willingham, M. C., Pastan, I., Gotto, A. M. Jr., Smith, L. C. 1982. Co-clustering and internalization of low-density lipoproteins and α2-macroglobulin in human skin fibroblasts. *Exp. Cell Res.* 141:15–22
156. Wall, D. A., Wilson, G., Hubbard, A. L. 1980. The galactose-specific recognition system of mammalian liver: the route of ligand internalization in rat hepatocytes. *Cell* 21:79–83
157. Walsh, R. J., Posner, B. I., Patel, B. 1984. Binding and uptake of [125]iodoprolactin by epithelial cells of the rat choroid plexus: An in vivo autoradiographic analysis. *Endocrinology* 114:1496–505
158. Warshawsky, H., Goltzman, D., Rouleau, M. F., Bergeron, J. J. M. 1980. Direct in vivo demonstration by radioautography of specific binding sites for calcitonin in skeletal and renal tissues of rat. *J. Cell Biol.* 85:682–94
159. Williams, R. H. 1981. The endocrine pancreas and diabetes mellitus: Physiology of insulin secretion. In *Textbook of Endocrinology,* ed. R. H. Williams, pp. 728–34. New York: W. B. Saunders. 6th ed.
160. Willingham, M. C., Hanover, J. A., Dickson, R. D., Pastan, I. 1984. Morphological characterization of the pathway of transferrin endocytosis and recycling in human KB cells. *Proc. Natl. Acad. Sci. USA* 81:175–79
161. Willingham, M. C., Maxfield, F. R.,

Pastan, I. 1980. Receptor-mediated endocytosis of α2–macroglobulin in cultured fibroblasts. *J. Histochem. Cytochem.* 28:818–23
162. Willingham, M. C., Maxfield, F. R., Pastan, I. H. 1979. α2-Macroglobulin binding to the plasma membrane of cultured fibroblasts. *J. Cell Biol.* 82:614–25
163. Willingham, M. C., Pastan, I. 1980. The receptosome: an intermediate organelle of receptor-mediated endocytosis in cultured fibroblasts. *Cell* 21:67–77
164. Willingham, M. C., Pastan, I. H. 1982. Transit of epidermal growth factor through coated pits of the Golgi system. *J. Cell Biol.* 94:207–12
165. Willingham, M. C., Pastan, I. 1983. Formation of receptosomes from plasma membrane–coated pits during endocytosis: analysis by serial sections with improved membrane labeling and preservation techniques. *Proc. Natl. Acad. Sci. USA* 80:5617–21
165a. Willingham, M. C., Pastan, I. H., Sahagian, G. G. 1983. Ultrastructural immunocytochemical localization of the phosphomannosyl receptor in Chinese hamster ovary (CHO) cells. *J. Histochem. Cytochem.* 31:1–11
166. Willingham, M. C., Pastan, I. H., Sahagian, G. G., Jourdian, G. W., Neufeld, E. P. 1981. Morphologic study of the internalization of a lysosomal enzyme by the mannose-6-phosphate receptor in cultured Chinese hamster ovary cells. *Proc. Natl. Acad. Sci. USA* 78:6967–71
167. Wolkoff, A. W., Klausner, R. D., Ashwell, G., Harford, J. 1984. Intracellular asialoglycoproteins and their receptor: a prelysosomal event subsequent to dissociation of the ligand-receptor complex. *J. Cell Biol.* 98:375–81
168. Zeitlin, P. A., Hubbard, A. L. 1982. The surface distribution and intracellular fate of asialoglycoproteins: A morphological and biochemical study of isolated rat hepatocytes and monolayer cultures. *J. Cell Biol.* 92:634–47
169. Zick, Y., Grunberger, G., Podskalny, J. M., Moncada, U., Taylor, S. I., et al. 1983. Insulin stimulates phosphorylation of serine residues in soluble insulin receptors. *Biochem. Biophys. Res. Commun.* 116:1129–35
170. Zick, Y., Kasuga, M., Kahn, R. C., Roth, J. 1983. Characterization of insulin-mediated phosphorylation of the insulin receptor in a cell-free system. *J. Biol. Chem.* 258:75–80
171. Zick, Y., Whittaker, J., Roth, J. 1983. Insulin stimulated phosphorylation of its own receptor. *J. Biol. Chem.* 258:3431–34

Ann. Rev. Physiol. 1985. 47:405–24

INTRACELLULAR MEDIATORS OF INSULIN ACTION

Kang Cheng and Joseph Larner

Department of Pharmacology, University of Virginia School of Medicine, Charlottesville, Virginia 22908

INTRODUCTION

Membrane signaling via novel peptide or peptide-like mediators is a new and rapidly developing field in hormone action. This review is therefore by nature descriptive, because only a relatively small number of experiments have been done. However, the fact that a wide variety of intracellular sites (Table I) can be controlled by hormonal mediator in broken-cell systems in a similar manner to hormone action in intact cells is already impressive progress. Furthermore, two classes of hormones with previously unknown mechanisms of action, insulin and the lactogenic hormones prolactin, human growth hormone, and ovine placental lactogen have been shown to act by this mechanism. These two advances, as well as the evidence indicating the peptide nature of mediator, are stressed in this review and are responsible for solidly establishing this as a novel area of investigation in the field of biocommunications and mechanisms of hormone action.

JUSTIFICATION FOR AN INSULIN MEDIATOR

Is Insulin Internalization and/or Degradation Required for Insulin Action?

Specific binding sites for insulin have been found on several intracellular organelles, and it is known that receptor-bound insulin can be internalized by various target cells (40). However, the process of internalization appears to be too slow to explain rapid insulin effects on membrane transport processes as well as on enzyme activation and inactivation, both of which are observed

405

0066-4278/85/0315-0405$02.00

within seconds after hormone addition (75, 140). At this time insulin is clearly localized outside the cell (40). Recently, it has been reported that insulin-stimulated amino acid transport in hepatocytes can be dissociated from hormone internalization (83). Several laboratories have demonstrated that when lysosomotropic agents were added to intact rat adipocytes, degradation of internalized insulin was completely inhibited, while insulin's actions on glucose transport, cyclic AMP (cAMP) phosphodiesterase activation, and inhibition of lipolysis were unaffected (43, 90, 122). These results suggest that lysosomal degradation products of insulin are not involved in at least these actions of insulin.

On the other hand, it has been suggested that internalization of insulin may be needed to elicit its inhibitory effect on endogenous protein degradation (30). Furthermore, it was reported that insulin itself directly stimulated the mRNA efflux from isolated nuclei (112) and activated nucleotide triphosphatase in isolated nuclear envelopes (102). Verification of these very interesting observations is awaited with interest. Their significance will require further study, particularly with regard to mediator formation. It certainly is conceivable that internalized insulin together with receptor could continue to produce mediator inside the cell. Because internalization and degradation of the hormone do not appear to be necessary for at least some of its rapid initial actions, a signal or mediator would appear to be necessary.

Another argument for a mediator requirement in insulin action is the two-way dissociation of certain insulin actions observed in our own and in other laboratories. For example, Huijing et al (49) reported that, in the perfused rat heart, insulin was able to enhance glucose transport under conditions where it no longer acted to activate glycogen synthase. Conversely, Eboué-Bonis et al (31) demonstrated in rat diaphragm that with the use of N-ethylmaleimide (NEM), a sulfhydryl-blocking agent, the effect of insulin to enhance glucose transport was abolished, while the ability of insulin to activate glycogen synthase was retained. These dissociations argued for a chemical mediator, although the argument at that time was not, of course, conclusive.

Thus, three lines of evidence, indirect and direct, support the hypothesis that insulin is not required to enter cells to mediate at least several of its rapid biological effects.

Insulin-Like Effects of Trypsin and Other Proteolytic Enzymes

Rieser and Rieser (105) first demonstrated that the proteolytic enzyme trypsin, at low concentrations, has "insulin-like" activities when added to rat diaphragms, including stimulation of sugar and amino acid transport and glycogen synthesis. Weis & Narahara (138) reported that trypsin, like insulin, when added to isolated frog sartorius muscles produced an increase in the V_{max} for 3-0-methylglucose transport without altering the apparent K_m. Trypsin added to isolated rat adipocytes rapidly stimulates glucose transport (68, 74), glucose oxidation (68, 70, 71, 74), lipogenesis (70, 74), glycogen synthase activity state (68), and, more slowly, pyruvate dehydrogenase activity state (68). It also inhibits hormone-induced lipolysis (70, 71). The effects of trypsin were blocked by soybean trypsin inhibitor (70). Diisopropyl fluorophosphate-treated trypsin and Nα-p-tosyl-L-lysine chloromethyl ketone–treated trypsin, both devoid of proteolytic activity, were incapable of mimicking insulin's actions. Kono and colleagues (73) have shown that trypsin-stimulated glucose transport in rat adipocytes is mediated through the same mechanism as insulin, namely via the translocation of glucose transporters from an intracellular site to the plasma membrane. At higher concentrations of trypsin, the insulin-like effect of trypsin disappeared, and insulin failed to stimulate glucose transport and to inhibit lipolysis in these trypsin-treated adipocytes (70). However, these cells still remained intact and retained a normal glucose-transport system. Furthermore, after the proteolytic action of trypsin was stopped by soybean trypsin inhibitor, the insulin responsiveness of these cells returned progressively. Further evidence that the proteolytic enzymes trypsin or thrombin initiate their intracellular actions on growth promotion by acting on the cell surface was provided by the elegant experiments of Cunningham and colleagues. They demonstrated convincingly that trypsin (13) or thrombin (14) immobilized on polystyrene beads causes proliferation of cultured quiescent chick-embryo fibroblasts. Furthermore, even the action produced by soluble trypsin is inhibited by immobilized soybean trypsin inhibitor, indicating that soluble trypsin may act at the cell surface. Interestingly, the possibility of generation (by protease action) of mediators, which then initiate cell division and escape from contact growth inhibition, was suggested in the original paper describing this phenomenon (10). Very recently, it was demonstrated that trypsin, like insulin, stimulated the phosphorylation of the β-subunit of the insulin receptor, not only in a partially purified preparation from rat adipocytes, but also in a highly purified insulin receptor from human placenta (126). These results suggest that a site of trypsin action on intact cells is the insulin receptor. The proteolytic action of trypsin on the insulin receptor may be sufficient to generate a signal from the receptor itself or from other components in the cell membrane that then mimic intracellular insulin actions. The generation of insulin-like but not insulin-identical mediator by trypsin action on intact cells and plasma membranes will be discussed later.

Insulin-Like Effects of Anti-Insulin Receptor Antibodies

Kahn et al (60) first reported that antibodies to the insulin receptor present in sera of patients with type B syndrome of insulin resistance and acanthosis nigricans inhibited binding of ^{125}I-insulin to its receptor and stimulated 2-deoxy-D-glucose transport, as well as oxidation of ^{14}C-glucose to [14]CO_2 and conversion of ^{14}C-glucose to lipid and glycogen in isolated adipocytes. Interestingly, the monovalent Fab' fragment of the antireceptor antibody retained its ability to inhibit ^{125}I-insulin binding but lost its bioactivity (61). However, the bioactivity of the Fab' fragment could be restored by the addition of anti-F(ab')$_2$ antisera that cross-links the Fab'-receptor complexes. In the same report, it was demonstrated that antiinsulin antibodies added to suboptimal concentrations of insulin enhanced the biological activity of insulin. These results suggested but did not prove that receptor cross-linking or aggregation may be important for insulin action. Alternative explanations of the data have been given (87). In addition to the insulin-like effects mentioned above, antireceptor antibodies also stimulated glycogen synthase (81), pyruvate dehydrogenase activity state (6), lipoprotein lipase activity (131), and acetyl CoA carboxylase activity (6). These antibodies also inhibited phosphorylase activity (81) and epinephrine-induced lipolysis (55). Although antireceptor antibodies were internalized and degraded by target cells through the same mechanism as receptor-bound insulin (41), it seems unlikely that two different polypeptides, insulin and antireceptor antibodies (see also next section on concanavalin A), would generate an identical or similar degradation product, which would then produce all of these insulin effects.

Generation of Insulin Mediator from Plasma Membrane Systems

Direct evidence demonstrating the involvement of a mediator in insulin's action came from Jarett's laboratory. These investigators demonstrated that addition of insulin to a plasma membrane–mitochondria mixture resulted in a decreased phosphorylation of the α subunit of mitochondrial pyruvate dehydrogenase (116) with a concomitant increase in its activity state (115). The effect at physiological concentrations of insulin to activate pyruvate-dehydrogenase activity-state in this broken-cell system was next shown to require the presence of plasma membranes. Two insulin mimickers, concanavalin A and anti-insulin receptor antibody, also stimulated pyruvate-dehydrogenase activity-state in this system. Because none of these agents was effective on mitochondria in the absence of membranes, these results strongly supported the hypothesis that a mediator is generated by insulin (as well as by concanavalin A and anti–insulin receptor antibody) acting on plasma membranes. This mediator then activates mitochondrial pyruvate dehydrogenase by dephosphorylation. Additional information on insulin mediator(s) from our laboratory and others will be discussed later.

FAILURE OF THE KNOWN SECOND MESSENGERS TO EXPLAIN INSULIN ACTIONS

Cyclic AMP (cAMP)

Because insulin can antagonize certain actions of hormones, such as glucagon, that act via cAMP generation, it was hypothesized that insulin mediated its intracellular actions by decreasing cAMP concentration. However, there are several instances in which the actions of insulin can be dissociated from its ability to decrease cAMP concentration. In muscle, it was first demonstrated by Larner and colleagues that glycogen synthase was activated by insulin, while cAMP concentration was either unaffected (24) or actually increased (39). These results have been confirmed by others (18, 127). In hepatocytes, it has been reported that the ability of insulin to suppress the stimulation of gluconeogenesis by glucagon or epinephrine is not affected by the removal of extracellular Ca^{++}, while its effect of lowering cAMP concentration is abolished (19). In adipocytes, the antilipolytic action of insulin was observed under conditions in which cAMP concentration was unaffected (34, 58). In conclusion, a decrease in the intracellular concentration of cAMP by insulin under certain conditions may explain some, but not all, of the effects of insulin.

Cyclic GMP (cGMP)

Insulin has been shown to cause a transient increase in the concentration of cGMP in fat and liver cells (52). Although the physiological significance of these increased cGMP concentrations is still not clear, it is highly unlikely that cGMP is the second messenger for insulin. First, other agents such as carbamylcholine, A23187, norepinephrine, and fatty acids also elevate cGMP concentrations in both fat and liver cells without the characteristic effects of insulin (33, 52, 124). Secondly, the rise in cGMP with insulin is markedly diminished in fat cells incubated in a Ca^{2+}-free medium, but the metabolic effects of insulin remain essentially unchanged (33).

Calcium

As mentioned earlier, certain insulin effects such as activation of glycogen synthase (80), stimulation of glucose oxidation (8), and inhibition of lipolysis (33) do not require the presence of extracellular Ca^{2+}. Certainly, this does not completely rule out the possibility that intracellular insulin actions are mediated by Ca^{2+}. In fact, a rise of cytoplasmic Ca^{2+} as the result of insulin-induced release of Ca^{2+} from the plasma membranes has been proposed to mediate the hormone's action in muscle (20) and fat (69). However, there are several weak points in this hypothesis. First, the reported effects of insulin on Ca^{2+} fluxes and binding to subcellular fractions could result in either an increase or a decrease in intracellular free Ca^{2+} (26). Secondly, even if insulin does increase cytoplasmic Ca^{2+} concentrations, this would oppose rather than mimic some of insulin's actions. A rise in cytoplasmic Ca^{2+} would certainly favor an activation of phosphorylase rather than the inactivation observed with insulin (63, 99). Furthermore, in hepatocytes, insulin has been shown to inhibit the stimulatory effects of phenylephrine on glycogenolysis and gluconeogenesis that are considered to be mediated through a rise of cytoplasmic Ca^{2+} (7).

H_2O_2

Extracellularly added H_2O_2 mimics the effects of insulin on glucose transport and oxidation (27, 28), incorporation of glucose into lipid (16, 92), inhibition of hormone-stimulated lipolysis (16, 85), and stimulation of pyruvate dehydrogenase (92) in isolated adipocytes. Insulin also stimulates intracellular adipocyte peroxide production through the activation of the plasma membrane–bound NADPH oxidase (91, 96). Thus, endogenous peroxide may play a role in the mechanism of insulin action (91). However, recent studies by de Haen and colleagues (95) indicate that the effect of insulin on adipocyte peroxide production may be the result of changes in free fatty-acid concentrations. Therefore, the possibility of peroxide being a second messenger for intracellular insulin actions is rather unlikely. H_2O_2 has little or no ability to activate glycogen synthase in the absence of glucose (79) or to enhance receptor phosphorylation (S. Tamura & J. Larner, unpublished observation).

INSULIN MEDIATOR(S)

It was first demonstrated by Larner and his colleagues in 1974 that insulinized rabbit skeletal muscle contained increased cAMP-dependent protein kinase inhibitor activity compared to control muscle (78). This inhibitor differed from the inhibitors described by Murad et al (97) and by Walsh et al (134) and thus appeared novel. In 1979, we reported that gel filtration of rat-muscle extracts on Sephadex G-25 columns revealed one fraction (fraction II) with an apparent molecular weight of 1000–1500 that inhibited cAMP-dependent protein kinase and stimulated glycogen synthase phosphoprotein phosphatase (77). Both activities were increased by insulin. In collaboration with Jarett, we demonstrated that the same fraction also stimulated pyruvate dehydrogenase in adipocyte mitochondria (57). Because fraction II mimicked insulin action on three cell-free enzyme systems, we proposed that this fraction contained insulin mediator (77). Because it was free of nucleotide, exhibited absorbance at 230 nm, and was ionic in character we suggested that the mediator was a peptide or peptide-like compound. At about the same time, Jarett's group succeeded in generating a low-molecular-weight factor from adipocyte plasma membranes in response to insulin that stimulated mitochondrial pyruvate dehydrogenase through the activation of the phosphatase (66). Since then, several laboratories have either confirmed or made new observations on this insulin mediator and have extended the experimental approach to other hormones. The biological actions and properties of the insulin mediator will be discussed in detail in following sections.

Biological Actions of Insulin Mediators

Insulin mediator has been isolated from rat skeletal muscle (77), rat adipocytes (67, 68), rat hepatoma cells (100), human IM-9 lymphocytes (56), and plasma membranes of rat adipocytes (4, 66, 114, 143) and liver (1, 109, 123). Its biological actions on enzymes and intact cells are summarized in Table 1. Except for the $Ca^{2+}+Mg^{2+}$–ATPase, which is inhibited by insulin while it is stimulated by insulin mediator, the rest of the insulin mediator effects are similar to those produced by insulin in vivo. The opposing effects of insulin and its mediator on $Ca^{2+}+Mg^{2+}$–ATPase are most likely due to the generation of "antimediator" in excess amount in the cell-free system (93).

Furthermore, most of the enzymes listed in Table 1 are regulated by phosphorylation. Clearly, in the cell insulin promotes phosphorylation as well as dephosphorylation (2). The effects of insulin mediator on some enzymes have been demonstrated to be mediated through the phosphorylation mechanism. Obviously, further studies on other enzymes are needed in order to support or deny the hypothesis that phosphorylation-dephosphorylation is the general mechanism for the action of insulin mediator to mediate its intracellular effects. Of particular interest are the effects of insulin mediator to depress hormone-stimulated adenylate cyclase, and to activate insulin-sensitive cAMP phosphodiesterase. These actions of insulin mediator on the enzymes catalyzing the synthesis and degradation of cAMP together with the action of mediator to inhibit cAMP-dependent protein kinase now explain satisfactorily for the first time the action of insulin to decrease elevated cAMP concentrations in some systems (11).

Evidence for Multiple Insulin Mediators

Numerous reports of biological actions of insulin that are reversed at increased insulin concentrations have appeared. The antilipolytic action of the hormone in fat cells at low or moderate insulin concentrations becomes lipolytic at increased insulin concentrations (72, 119). The action of insulin to inhibit hormone-stimulated adenylate cyclase at lower concentrations becomes stimulatory at higher concentrations (45, 51). Crude insulin mediator preparations have been shown to have a biphasic dose-response curve on Ca^{2+} uptake by mitochondria (130), glycogen synthase phosphoprotein phosphatase (77), pyruvate dehydrogenase phosphatase (109, 114, 115), adenylate cyclase (111), acetyl CoA carboxylase (110), and glucose-6-phosphatase (123). These biphasic effects of insulin mediator on cell-free enzyme systems can be explained by the presence of two antagonistic, biologically active materials in the crude mediator preparation.

Direct evidence for the existence of more than one insulin mediator was first demonstrated by Cheng et al (17). When crude insulin mediator that had a biphasic dose-response curve on glycogen synthase phosphatase was further purified by high-voltage paper electrophoresis, a glycogen synthase phosphoprotein phosphatase stimulator was separated from a glycogen synthase phosphoprotein phosphatase inhibitor. The former inhibited cAMP-dependent protein kinase, whereas the latter stimulated cAMP-dependent protein kinase in

Table 1 "Insulin-like" effects of insulin mediator in cell-free and intact cell systems

	Effect on activity by		Enzyme activity regulated by phosphorylation-dephosphorylation mechanism	Regulation of the phosphorylation state by	
	Insulin	Insulin mediator		Insulin	Insulin mediator
(a) Cell-free systems					
Cytoplasm					
Cyclic AMP-dependent protein kinase	↓ (94, 98, 118, 133)	↓ (77)			
Glycogen synthase	↑ (132)	↑ (77)	yes (37)	↓ (106)	↓ (77)
Acetyl CoA carboxylase	↑ (42, 84)	↑ (110)	yes (12)	↑ (9, 142)	↑ (111)
Cell membrane					
Adenylate cyclase–hormone stimulated	↓ (45, 51)	↓ (111)	yes (21, 82)		
(Ca^{+2}, Mg^{+2})-ATPase	↓ (101)	↑ (93)			
(Na^+, K^+)-ATPase	↑ (104)	↑ (50)			
Endoplasmic reticulum					
Cyclic AMP phosphodiesterase	↑ (86, 144)	↑ (64)	yes (89)		
Glucose-6-phosphatase	↓ (120)	↓ (123)	yes (3)		

Mitochondria				
Pyruvate dehydrogenase	↑ (22, 59, 139)	↑ (115)	yes (103)	
Ca^{+2} transport	↑ (29)	↑ (130)	↓ (48)	↓ (116)
Nucleus				
Transcription of β-casein gene	↑ (32)			
RNA synthesis	↑ (121)	↑ (46)		↑ (107)
Ribosome				
Phosphorylation of ribosomal protein S 6			↑ (44)	
(b) Intact cell systems				
Rat adipocyte				
Hormone-stimulated AMP concentration	↓ (11)	↓ (143)		
Lipogenesis	↑ (141)	↑ (143)		
Antilipolysis	↑ (34)	↑ (143)		
Cultured rat hepatocyte				
Lipogenesis	↑ (35)	↑ (15)		
Down-regulation of insulin receptor	↑ (108)	↑ (15)		

the absence of cAMP. The separation of these two mediators can explain not only the biphasic response of insulin mediator in crude preparations, but also the fact that insulin has been shown to increase certain intracellular protein phosphorylations along with its pattern of decreasing protein phosphorylations. More recently, Saltiel et al (111) have separated the stimulatory and the inhibitory mediator activities of pyruvate dehydrogenase phosphatase by differential ethanol extraction of crude preparations. The generation of both activities from plasma membranes is insulin dose–dependent, with the generation of the stimulatory mediator occurring at lower insulin concentrations than the inhibitory activity. In this context, it is of interest that two papers from Jarett's lab have reported data indicating that single rather than multiple mediators are produced in certain specific cell lines. In the H-4 hepatoma, only the pyruvate dehydrogenase stimulatory mediator was observed (100), whereas in the IM-9 lymphocyte, only the pyruvate dehydrogenase inhibitory mediator (56) was found. Generation of mediator and "antimediator" with similar chemical characteristics suggests the further possibility that insulin action may generate more than two similar mediators. Our recent data that highly purified cAMP-dependent protein kinase inhibitor and mitochondrial pyruvate dehydrogenase stimulator have nonoverlapping biological activities further supports the idea of multiple insulin mediators.

Physical and Chemical Properties of Insulin Mediators

All of the insulin mediators obtained from various sources by different laboratories appear to be heat- and acid-stable substances that are not or are poorly absorbed to charcoal and have M_rs in the range of 1000–3000, as judged by gel filtration at acid pH (66, 77, 109, 100). When mediator is gel-filtered at neutral pH, it has a two-fold greater M_r, suggesting association or aggregation (100, 114). Several laboratories have demonstrated that low concentrations of trypsin stimulated the production of insulin-like but not insulin-identical mediator from either plasma membrane (4, 113) or intact adipocytes (68). Furthermore, the generation of mediator by insulin is inhibited by several protease inhibitors (113). These results suggest that proteolytic action is involved in the formation of insulin mediator and could explain the insulin-like actions of trypsin on intact cell systems (10, 13, 68, 70, 71, 73, 74, 138).

Although the exact structure of insulin mediator is not known, the fact that its activity was destroyed by proteases (113, 123, 143) and neuraminidase (5) suggests that it might be a glycopeptide. Interestingly, it is known that neuraminidase, at high concentrations, abolishes the effects of insulin on glucose transport and lipolysis, without affecting hormone binding (25). The dissociation of insulin binding from its intracellular actions by neuraminidase may be the result of the destruction of the precursor of insulin mediator on the plasma membranes by the enzyme. Several phospholipids have been shown to be present in partially purified insulin mediator (88) and to have insulin-like actions on pyruvate dehydrogenase and cAMP phosphodiesterase (65, 88). The significance of these observations is not clear at present, although it is recognized that insulin does regulate phospholipid metabolism (36). Undoubtedly, purification of insulin mediator to homogeneity in sufficient quantity to allow determination of its structure is the most urgently needed work in this field. Recent preliminary amino acid composition data on two highly purified mediators, namely cAMP-dependent protein kinase inhibitor and mitochondrial pyruvate dehydrogenase stimulator have been presented (17a). The insulin-dependent cytoplasmic mediator of Ca^{+2} transport in mitochondria was reported to contain 42 amino acids as well as carbohydrate and organic phosphate (38).

Effect of Diet, Fasting, and Diabetes Mellitus on Insulin-Mediator Generation

Adipocytes prepared from rats fed a high-fat diet have a decreased number of insulin receptors (54) and diminished glucose transport activation by insulin (53) compared to adipocytes from rats fed a high-carbohydrate diet. Begum et al (4, 5) have, in an excellant series of papers, demonstrated that plasma membranes from fat and liver of rats fed high-fat diets generate less pyruvate dehydrogenase phosphatase stimulatory mediator than those from rats fed high-carbohydrate diets. The mitochondria from these preparations did not differ in their response to mediator. Because trypsin as well as insulin were both less effective in generating stimulatory mediator from plasma membranes derived from high fat–fed rats, it was suggested that fat feeding results in a decrease of insulin mediator precursor molecules on the plasma membrane (4). Analogous experiments have been reported using human skin fibroblasts from a patient with severe insulin resistance associated with leprechaun disease relative to those from a control patient (23). Generation of pyruvate dehydrogenase phosphatase stimulatory mediator by insulin from a liver particulate fraction was also shown to be markedly depressed in fasting and diabetic rats (1). However, refeeding and then insulin treatment restored the ability of insulin to generate chemical mediator.

Cyclic AMP Antagonist

Wasner (135–137), in a series of papers, has reported the isolation of a cAMP antagonist from rat hepatocytes incubated either with insulin or epinephrine. The generation of the cAMP antagonist by epinephrine in hepatocytes was mediated through stimulation of α-adrenergic receptors. No detectable cAMP antagonist was isolated from hepatocytes incubated without hormone. Interestingly, even in the presence of hormone, hepatocytes isolated from indomethacin-treated rats failed to generate the cAMP antagonist. However, synthesis of the cAMP antagonist was restored by adding prostaglandin E_1 to the hepato-cytes. Because PGE_1 itself is not a cAMP antagonist, these results suggested that PGE_1 is involved in the synthesis of or is part of the cAMP antagonist. The cAMP antagonist was routinely assayed by its ability to inhibit cAMP-dependent protein kinase (135). Crude preparations were also shown to inhibit adenylate cyclase (136), to stimulate phosphoprotein (histone P) phosphatase (135), and to activate pyruvate dehydrogenase (136). Certainly, its biological actions on cell-free enzyme systems are very similar to those produced by insulin mediator peptides described earlier. However, the chemical properties of these two substances are distinctly different. For example, the peptide mediator is most stable at acid pH (3–6) where the cAMP antagonist is most unstable (H. K. Wasner, personal communication). No data has been presented to indicate that the cAMP antagonist is produced from cell membranes. A M_r of 500 was estimated for the antagonist by gel filtration on Sephadex G-15 columns. A structure involving a prostaglandin conjugated to inositol phos-phate has recently been proposed (137). Undoubtedly further studies are needed in order to understand the relationship of these two different compounds and their roles in insulin action.

PUTATIVE PROLACTIN PEPTIDE MEDIATOR

It is well known that prolactin, together with insulin and adrenal corticoste-roids, stimulate the synthesis of milk proteins and the transcription of their corresponding mRNAs in midpregnant mammary tissue in organ culture sys-tems (32). Recently, using the same approach developed for the study of the insulin mediator, Teyssot et al (129) demonstrated that when prolactin was added to a microsomal fraction containing prolactin receptors from lactating rabbit mammary gland or from liver, a soluble factor was generated that stimulated β-casein gene transcription in isolated mammary-gland cell nuclei. Other lactogenic hormones, including human growth hormone and ovine placental lactogen, had the same effect. Of the other hormones tested, includ-ing bovine growth hormone, which was inactive, only insulin was active in this system. Generation of this prolactin mediator is membrane-specific, i.e. only membranes containing prolactin receptors are capable of generating mediator upon the addition of prolactin. The mediator was reported to have a M_r of about 1000, as determined by Sephadex G-25 chromatography (128). The fact that this mediator is heat stable and is inactivated by trypsin suggests again that this soluble factor is a peptide. Stimulation of β-casein gene transcription by the factor appears to be mediated through activation of a nuclear phosphoprotein phosphatase, because its effect was blocked by phosphatase inhibitors (47). Because both insulin and prolactin mediators share some common properties, it is tempting to speculate that both hormones may have the same or similar intracellular mediators.

HORMONAL EFFECTS OF MEDIATOR
ON INTACT CELLS

Although insulin mediator has been shown to display several insulin-like activities in cell-free systems, it is very important to be able to demonstrate that insulin mediator is also capable of mimicking the actions of insulin on intact cell systems. Ho and colleagues (143) isolated insulin mediator from adipocyte plasma membranes treated with insulin. Gel filtration on Sephadex G-25 columns, led to an estimated M_r of 1000. When mediator was added to intact adipocytes, it mimicked insulin action by decreasing hormonally elevated cAMP concentrations, as well as by stimulating lipogenesis and antilipolysis. These insulin-like actions are unlikely to result from contamination by insulin, because they are not inhibited by insulin antibody. Insulin mediator isolated from liver particulate fractions also stimulated lipid synthesis and down-regulated insulin-receptor concentrations in primary cultures of isolated rat hepatocytes (15). Interestingly, putative prolactin mediator also stimulates β-casein gene transcription in isolated mammary cells (117). These results from three laboratories clearly indicate that both insulin and prolactin mediators can enter cells by an unknown mechanism and carry out at least some of their intracellular actions. Furthermore, these actions of mediator on intact cell systems greatly strengthen their position as mediators. Mediators will thus also serve as useful probes to further compare with hormone actions in intact cells.

CONCLUSIONS

We have presented the evidence indicating that the action of insulin involves the formation of a mediator. The experimental data directly demonstrating the formation and multiple insulin-like effects of mediator on cell membrane, mitochondria, ribosome, smooth ER, cytosol, and nucleus have been detailed. The generation by insulin of two or more similar mediator molecules has been discussed, and finally the preliminary data indicating that these mediators are oligopeptides or glycopeptides in nature have been presented. The theoretical advantages of a mechanism involving the formation of more than one mediator from precursors in the membrane are two-fold. First, multiple mediators provide the opportunity for the amplification that is needed to transmit information from the receptor present at the cell surface at an active (liganded) concentration of $\sim 10^{-12}$–10^{-10} M to the catalytic components within the cell, present at concentrations of $\sim 10^{-8}$–10^{-6} M. Second, multiple mediators can explain insulin's pleiotypic program that occurs in all subcellular locations at varying times from seconds to hours. The concept of several mediators serves well as a basis for understanding so complex a problem in biocommunication.

We have not discussed the possible interrelationship between the proposed proteolytic formation of mediator and receptor phosphoryation that has recently been demonstrated (62). Hormone-activated proteolysis leading to mediator formation and phosphorylation may be unrelated, or they may be causally interrelated. We favor the latter hypothesis (125). Time and further experiments will tell whether this is the case.

ACKNOWLEDGMENTS

We thank Roberta Sugg and Vickie Loeser for their assistance in preparation of the manuscript. The authors' work in this area is supported by research grants AM 14334 and AM 22125 from the National Institutes of Health and a research grant from the Thomas F. Jeffress & Kate Miller Jeffress Memorial Trust.

Literature Cited

1. Amatruda, J. M., Chang, C. L. 1983. Insulin resistance in the liver in fasting and diabetes mellitus: The failure of insulin to stimulate the release of a chemical modulator of pyruvate dehydrogenase. *Biochem. Biophys. Res. Commun.* 112:35–41

2. Avruch, J., Alexander, M. C., Palmer, J. L., Pierce, M. W., Nemenoff, R. A., et al. 1982. Role of insulin-stimulated protein phosphorylation in insulin action. *Fed. Proc.* 41:2629–33

3. Begley, P. J., Craft, J. A. 1981. Evidence for protein phosphorylation as a regulatory mechanism for hepatic microsomal glucose-6-phosphatase. *Biochem. Biophys. Res. Commun.*, 103:1029–34

4. Begum, N., Tepperman, H. M., Tepperman, J. 1982. Effect of high fat and high carbohydrate diets on adipose tissue pyruvate dehydrogenase and its activation by a plasma membrane–enriched fraction and insulin. *Endocrinology* 110:1914–21

5. Begum, N., Tepperman, H. M., Tepperman, J. 1983. Effects of high fat and high carbohydrate diets on liver pyruvate dehydrogenase and its activation by a chemical mediator released from insulin-treated liver particulate fraction: Effect of neuraminidase treatment on the chemical mediator activity. *Endocrinology* 112: 50–58

6. Belsham, G. J., Brownsey, R. W., Hughes, W. A., Denton, R. M. 1980. Anti–insulin receptor antibodies mimic the effects of insulin on the activities of pyruvate dehydrogenase and acetyl-CoA carboxylase and on the specific, protein phosphorylation in rat epididymal fat cells. *Diabetologia* 18:307–12

7. Blackmore, P. F., Assimacopoulos-Jeannet, F., Chan, T. M., Exton, J. H. 1979. Studies on α-adrenergic and gluca-gon actions in normal and calcium-depleted hepatocytes. *J. Biol. Chem.* 254:2828–34

8. Bonne, D., Belhadj, O., Cohen, P. 1977. Modulation by calcium of the insulin action and of the insulin-like effect of oxytocin on isolated rat lipocytes. *Eur. J. Biochem.* 75:101–05

9. Brownsey, R. W., Denton, R. M. 1982. Evidence that insulin activates fat-cell acetyl-CoA carboxylase by increased phosphorylation at a specific site. *Biochem. J.* 202:77–86

10. Burger, M. M. 1970. Proteolytic enzymes initiating cell division and escape from contact inhibition of growth. *Nature* 227:170–71

11. Butcher, R. W., Sneyd, J. G. T., Park, C. R., Sutherland, E. W. 1966. Effect of insulin on adenosine 3',5'-monophosphate in the rat epididymal fat pad. *J. Biol. Chem.* 241:1651–53

12. Carlson, C. A., Kim, K.-H. 1973. Regulation of hepatic acetyl coenzyme A carboxylase by phosphorylation and dephosphorylation. *J. Biol. Chem.* 248:378–80

13. Carney, D. H., Cunningham, D. D. 1977. Initiation of chick cell division by trypsin action at the cell surface. *Nature* 268:602–6

14. Carney, D. H., Cunningham, D. D. 1978. Cell surface action of thrombin is sufficient to initiate division of chick cells. *Cell* 14:811–23

15. Caro, J. F., Folli, F., Cecchin, F., Sinha, M. K. 1983. Chemical mediator of insulin action stimulates lipid synthesis and down regulates the insulin receptors in primary cultures of rat hepatocytes. *Biochem. Biophys. Res. Commun.* 115: 375–82

16. Cascieri, M. A., Mumford, R. A., Katzen, H. M. 1979. The role of H_2O_2 formation in the insulin-like and insulin-

antagonistic effects on fat cells of w-Aminoalkyl glycosides. *Arch. Biochem. Biophys.* 195:30–44

17. Cheng, K., Galasko, G., Huang, L., Kellogg, J., Larner, J. 1980. Studies on the insulin mediator II. Separation of two antagonistic biologically active materials from fraction II. *Diabetes* 29:659–61

17a. Cheng, K., Thompson, M., Schwartz, C., Malchoff, C., Tamura, S., et al. 1984. In *Molecular Basis of Insulin Action*, ed. M. P. Czech, in press. New York: Plenum

18. Chiasson, J.-L., Dietz, M. R., Shikama, H., Wootten, M., Exton, J. H. 1980. Insulin regulation of skeletal muscle glycogen metabolism. *Am. J. Physiol.* 239:E69–74

19. Claus, T. H., Pilkis, S. J. 1976. Regulation by insulin of gluconeogenesis in isolated rat hepatocytes. *Biochim. Biophys. Acta* 421:246–62

20. Clausen, T. 1975. The effect of insulin on glucose transport in muscle cells. *Curr. Top. Membr. Transp.* 6:169–226

21. Constantopoulos, A., Najjar, V. A. 1973. The activation of adenylate cyclase: II. The postulated presence of (A) adenylate cyclase in a phospho (Inhibited) form (B) a dephospho (Activated) form with a cyclic adenylate stimulated membrane protein kinase. *Biochem. Biophys. Res. Commun.* 53:794–99

22. Coore, H. G., Denton, R. M., Martin, B. R., Randle, P. J. 1971. Regulation of adipose tissue pyruvate dehydrogenase by insulin and other hormones. *Biochem. J.* 125:115–27

23. Craig, J. W., Locker, E. F., Elders, M. J. 1982. Multiple defects in insulin-resistant fibroblasts. *Diabetes* 31(Supp. 2):124A

24. Craig, J. W., Rall, T. W., Larner, J. 1969. The influence of insulin and epinephrine on adenosine 3',5'-phosphate and glycogen transferase in muscle. *Biochim. Biophys. Acta* 177:213–19

25. Cuatrecasas, P., Illiano, G. 1971. Membrane sialic acid and the mechanism of insulin action in adipose tissue cells. *J. Biol. Chem.* 246:4938–46

26. Czech, M. P. 1977. Molecular basis of insulin action. *Ann. Rev. Biochem.* 46:359–84

27. Czech, M. P., Lawrence, J. C., Lynn, W. S. 1974. Evidence for electron transfer reactions involved in the Ca^{2+}-dependent thiol activation of fat cell glucose utilization. *J. Biol. Chem.* 249:1001–6

28. Czech, M. P., Lawrence, J. C. Jr., Lynn, W. S. 1974. Evidence for the involve-

ment of sulfhydryl oxidation in the regulation of fat cell hexose transport by insulin. *Proc. Natl. Acad. Sci. USA* 71:4173–77

29. Dorman, D. M., Barritt, G. J., Bygrave, F. L. 1975. Stimulation of hepatic mitochondrial calcium transport by elevated plasma insulin concentrations. *Biochem. J.* 150:389–95

30. Draznin, B., Trowbridge, M. 1982. Inhibition of intracellular proteolysis by insulin in isolated rat hepatocytes. *J. Biol. Chem.* 257:11988–93

31. Eboué-Bonis, D., Chambout, A. M., Volfin, P., Clauser, H. 1967. Selective action of N-ethylmaleimide on the stimulation by insulin of the metabolism of surviving diaphragms. *Biol. Soc. Chim. Biol.* 49:415–31

32. Elias, J. J. 1980. The role of prolactin in normal mammary gland growth and function. *Horm. Proteins Peptides* 8:37–74

33. Fain, J. N., Butcher, F. R. 1976. Cyclic guanosine 3':5'-monophosphate and the regulation of lipolysis in rat fat cells. *J. Cyc. Nuc. Res.* 2:71–78

34. Fain, J. N., Rosenberg, L. 1972. Antilipolytic action of insulin on fat cells. *Diabetes* 21:414–25

35. Fain, J. H., Scow, R. O., Urgoiti, E. J., Chernick, S. S. 1965. Effect of insulin on fatty acid synthesis in vivo and in vitro in pancreatectomized rats. *Endocrinology* 77:137–49

36. Farese, R. V., Larson, R. E., Sabir, M. A. 1981. Insulin acutely increases phospholipids in the phosphatidate-inositide cycle in rat adipose tissue. *J. Biol. Chem.* 257:4042–45

37. Friedman, D. L., Larner, J. 1963. Studies on UDPG-α-glucan transglucosylase III. Interconversion of two forms of muscle UDPG-α-glucan transglucosylase by a phosphorylation-dephosphorylation reaction sequence. *Biochem.* 2:669–75

38. Gainutdinov., M. K., Turakulov, Y. K., Akhmatov, M. S., Lavina, I. I. 1978. Isolation of a cytoplasmatic regulator mediating the action of hormones on mitochondria. *Khim. Prirodn. Soedin.* 1:116

39. Goldberg, N. D., Villar-Palasi, C., Sasko, H., Larner, J. 1967. Effects of insulin treatment on muscle 3',5'-cyclic adenylate levels in vivo and in vitro. *Biochim. Biophys. Acta* 148:665–72

40. Goldfine, I. D. 1981. Effects of insulin on intracellular functions. *Biochem. Actions Horm.* 8:273–305

41. Gorden, P., Carpentier, J.-L., Freychet, P., Orci, L. 1980. Internalization of

polypeptide hormones. *Diabetologia* 18: 263–74

42. Halestrap, A. P., Denton, R. M. 1973. Insulin and the regulation of adipose tissue acetyl-coenzyme A carboxylase. *Biochem. J.* 132:509–17

43. Hammons, G. T., Jarett, L. 1980. Lysosomal degradation of receptor-bound ^{125}I-labeled insulin by rat adipocytes. *Diabetes* 29:475–86

44. Haselbacher, G. K., Humbel, R. E., Thomas, G. 1979. Insulin-like growth factor: Insulin or serum increase phosphorylation of ribosomal protein S6 during transition of stationary chick embryo fibroblasts into early G_1 phase of the cell cycle. *FEBS Lett.* 100:185–90

45. Hepp, K. D., Renner, R. 1972. Insulin action on the adenyl cyclase system: Antagonism to activation by lipolytic hormones. *FEBS Lett.* 20:191–94

46. Horvat, A. 1980. Stimulation of RNA synthesis in isolated nuclei by an insulin-induced factor in liver. *Nature* 286:906–8

47. Houdebine, L. -M., Djiane, J., Teyssot, B., Devinoy, E., Kelly, P. A., et al. 1984. Preparation and assay of prolactin intracellular relay acting on milk protein genes. *Meth. Enzym.* In press

48. Hughes, W. A., Brownsey, R. W., Denton, R. M. 1980. Studies on the incorporation of [^{32}P] phosphate into pyruvate dehydrogenase in intact rat fat cells. *Biochem. J.* 192:469–81

49. Huijing, F., Nuttall, F. Q., Villar-Palasi, C., Larner, J. 1969. A dissociation in the action of insulin on transport and transferase conversion. *Biochim. Biophys. Acta* 177:204–12

50. Huisman, W. H., Dahms, A. S. 1982. Insulin-dependent release of a possible insulin mediator from rat liver plasma membranes. *Abstr. 12th Int. Cong. Biochem.* Perth, Australia

51. Illiano, G., Cuatrecasas, P. 1971. Modulation of adenylate cyclase activity in liver and fat cell membranes by insulin. *Science* 175:906–8

52. Illiano, G., Tell, G. P. E., Siegel, M. I., Cuatrecasas, P. 1973. Guanosine 3':5'-cyclic monophosphate and the action of insulin and acetyl choline. *Proc. Natl. Acad. Sci. USA* 70:2443–47

53. Ip, C., Tepperman, H. M., Dewitt, J., Tepperman, J. 1976. The effect of diet fat on rat adipocyte glucose transport. *Horm. Metab. Res.* 9:218–22

54. Ip, C., Tepperman, H. M., Holohan, P., Tepperman, J. 1976. Insulin binding and insulin response of adipocytes from rats adapted to fat feeding. *J. Lipid Res.* 17:588–99

55. Jacobs, S., Chang, K.-J., Cuatrecasas,

P. 1978. Antibodies to purified insulin receptor have insulin-like activity. *Science* 200:1283–84

56. Jarett, L., Kiechle, F. L., Popp, D. A., Kotagal, N., Gavin, J. R. III. 1980. Differences in the effect of insulin on the generation by adipocytes and IM-9 lymphocytes of a chemical mediator which stimulates the action of insulin on pyruvate dehydrogenase. *Biochem. Biophys. Res. Commun.* 96:735–41

57. Jarett, L., Seals, J. R. 1979. Pyruvate dehydrogenase activation in adipocyte mitochondria by an insulin-generated mediator from muscle. *Science* 206: 1407–08

58. Jarett, L., Steiner, A. L., Smith, R. M., Kipnis, D. M. 1972. The involvement of cyclic AMP in the hormonal regulation of protein synthesis in rat adipocytes. *Endocrinology* 90:1277–84

59. Jungas, R. L. 1970. Effect of insulin on fatty acid synthesis from pyruvate, lactate, or endogenous sources in adipose tissue: Evidence for the hormonal regulation of pyruvate dehydrogenase. *Endocrinology* 86:1368–75

60. Kahn, C. R., Baird, K., Flier, J. S., Jarett, L., Baird, B. 1977. Effects of autoantibodies to the insulin receptor on isolated adipocytes. *J. Clin. Invest.* 60:1094–106

61. Kahn, C. R., Baird, K. L., Jarett, D. B., Flier, J. S. 1978. Direct demonstration that receptor crosslinking or aggregation is important in insulin action. *Proc. Natl. Acad. Sci. USA* 75:4209–13

62. Kasuga, M., Karlsson, F. A., Kahn, C. R. 1982. Insulin stimulates the phosphorylation of the 95,000-dalton subunit of its own receptor. *Science* 215:185–87

63. Khoo, J. C. 1976. Ca^{2+}-dependent activitation of phosphorylase by phosphorylase kinase in adipose tissue. *Biochim. Biophys. Acta* 422:87–97

64. Kiechle, F. L., Jarett, L. 1981. The effect of an insulin-sensitive chemical mediator from rat adipocytes on low K_m and high K_m cyclic AMP phosphodiesterase. *FEBS Lett.* 133:279–82

65. Kiechle, F. L., Jarett, L. 1983. Phospholipids and the regulation of pyruvate dehydrogenase from rat adipocyte mitochondria. *Mol. Cell. Biochem.* 56:99–105

66. Kiechle, F. L., Jarett, L., Kotagal, N., Popp, D. A. 1981. Partial purification from rat adipocyte plasma membranes of a chemical mediator which stimulates the action of insulin on pyruvate dehydrogenase. *J. Biol. Chem.* 256:2945–51

67. Kiechle, F. L., Jarett, L., Popp, D. A., Katogal, N. 1980. Isolation from rat adipocytes of a chemical mediator for

insulin activation of pyruvate dehydrogenase. *Diabetes* 29:852–55

68. Kikuchi, K., Schwartz, S., Creacy, S., Larner, J. 1981. Independent control of selected insulin-sensitive cell membrane and intracellular functions. *Mol. Cell. Biochem.* 37:125–30

69. Kissebah, A. H., Hope-Gill, H., Vydelingum, N., Tulloch, B. R., Clarke, P. V., et al. 1975. Mode of insulin action. *Lancet* 1:144–47

70. Kono, T. 1969. Destruction and restoration of the insulin effector system of isolated fat cells. *J. Biol. Chem.* 244:5777–84

71. Kono, T., Barham, F. W. 1971. Insulin-like effects of trypsin on fat cells. *J. Biol. Chem.* 246:6204–9

72. Kono, T., Barham, F. W. 1973. Effects of insulin on the levels of adenosine 3':5'-monophosphate and lipolysis in isolated rat epididymal fat cells. *J. Biol. Chem.* 248:7417–26

73. Kono, T., Robinson, F. W., Blevens, T. L., Ezaki, O. 1982. Evidence that translocation of the glucose transport activity is the major mechanism of insulin action on glucose transport in fat cells. *J. Biol. Chem.* 257:10942–47

74. Kuo, J. F., Dill, I. K., Holmlund, C. E. 1967. Comparisons of the effects of *Bacillus subtilis* protease, type VIII (subtilopeptidase A), and insulin on isolated adipose cells. *J. Biol. Chem.* 242:3659–64

75. Larner, J., Cheng, K., Schwartz, C., Dubler, R., Creasy, S., et al. 1981. Chemical mechanism of insulin action via proteolytic formation of mediator peptides. *Mol. Cell. Biochem.* 40:155–61

76. Deleted in proof

77. Larner, J., Galasko, G., Cheng, K., De Paoli-Roach, A. A., Huang, L., et al. 1979. Generation by insulin of a chemical mediator that controls protein phosphorylation and dephosphorylation. *Science* 206:1408–10

78. Larner, J., Huang, L. C., Brooker, G., Murad, F., Miller, T. B. 1974. Inhibition of protein kinase in insulin treated muscle. *Fed. Proc.* 33:261

79. Lawrence, J. C., Larner, J. 1978. Activation of glycogen synthase in rat adipocytes by insulin and glucose involves increased glucose transport and phosphorylation. *J. Biol. Chem.* 253:2104–13

80. Lawrence, J. C., Larner, J. 1978. Effects of insulin, methoxamine, and calcium on glycogen synthase in rat adipocytes. *Mol. Pharm.* 14:1079–91

81. Lawrence, J. C. Jr., Larner, J., Kahn, C.

R., Roth, J. 1978. Autoantibodies to the insulin receptor activate glycogen synthase in rat adipocytes. *Mol. Cell. Biochem.* 22:153–57

82. Layne, P., Constantopoulos, A., Judge, J. F. X., Rauner, R., Najjar, V. A. 1973. The occurance of fluoride-stimulated membrane phosphoprotein phosphatase. *Biochem. Biophys. Res. Commun.* 53:800–5

83. LeCam, A., Maxfield, F., Willingham, M., Pastan, I. 1979. Insulin stimulation of amino acid transport in isolated rat hepatocytes is independent of hormone internalization. *Biochem. Biophys. Res. Commun.* 88:873–81

84. Lee, K. H., Thrall, T., Kim, K.-H. 1973. Hormonal regulation of acetyl CoA carboxylase effect of insulin and epinephrine. *Biochem. Biophys. Res. Commun.* 54:1133–40

85. Little, S., de Haen, C. 1980. Effects of hydrogen peroxide on basal and hormone-stimulated lipolysis in perfused rat fat cells in relation to the mechanism of action of insulin. *J. Biol. Chem.* 255:10888–95

86. Loten, E. G., Assimacopoulos-Jeannet, F. D., Exton, J. H., Park, C. R. 1978. Stimulation of a low-K_m phosphodiesterase from liver by insulin and glucagon. *J. Biol. Chem.* 253:746–57

87. Lyen, K. R. 1983. Insulin does not aggregate its own receptor. *Diabetologia* 24:304–5

88. Macaulay, S. L., Kiechle, F. L., Jarett, L. 1982. Phospholipids as possible chemical mediators of insulin action on low K_m cAMP phosphodiesterase. *Fed. Proc.* 41:1082

89. Marchmont, R. J., Houslay, M. D. 1981. Characterization of the phosphorylated form of the insulin-stimulated cyclic AMP phospodiesterase from rat liver plasma membranes. *Biochem. J.* 195:653–60

90. Marshall, S., Olefsky, J. M. 1980. The endocytotic-internalization pathway of insulin metabolism: Relationship to insulin degradation and activation of glucose transport. *Endocrinology* 107:1937–45

91. May, J. M., de Haen, C. 1979. Insulin-stimulated intracellular hydrogen peroxide production in rat epididymal fat cells. *J. Biol. Chem.* 254:2214–19

92. May, J. M., de Haen, C. 1979. The insulin-like effect of hydrogen peroxide on pathways of lipid synthesis in rat adipocytes. *J. Biol. Chem.* 254:9017–21

93. McDonald, J. M., Pershadsingh, H. A., Kiechle, F. L., Jarrett, L. 1981. Parallel stimulation in adipocytes of the plasma

membrane Ca^{2+}-transport/(Ca^{2+} + Mg^{2+})-ATPase system and mictochondrial pyruvate dehydrogenase by a supernatant factor derived from isolated plasma membranes. *Biochem. Biophys. Res. Commun.* 100:857–64

94. Mor, M. A., Vila, J., Ciudad, C. J., Guinovart, J. J. 1981. Insulin inactivation of rat hepatocyte cyclic AMP-dependent protein kinase. *FEBS Lett.* 136:131–34

95. Muchmore, D. B., Little, S. A., de Haen, C. 1982. Counterregulatory control of intracellular hydrogen peroxide production by insulin and lipolytic hormones in isolated rat epididymal fat cells: A role of free fatty acids. *Biochem.* 21:3886–92

96. Mukherjee, S. P., Lynn, W. S. 1977. Reduced nicotinamide adenine dinucleotide phosphate oxidase in adipocyte plasma membrane and its activation by insulin. *Arch. Biochem. Biophys.* 184:69–76

97. Murad, F., Rall, T. W., Vaughan, M. 1969. Conditions for the formation, partial purification, and assay of an inhibitor of adenosine 3',5'-monophosphate. *Biochim. Biophys. Acta* 192:430–45

98. Northrup, T. E., Krezowski, P. A., Palumbo, P. J., Kim, J. K., Hui, Y. S. F., et al. 1979. Insulin inhibition of hormone-stimulated protein kinase systems of rat renal cortex. *Am. J. Physiol.* 236:E649–54

99. Ozawa, E., Hosoi, K., Ebashi, S. 1967. Reversible stimulation of muscle phosphorylase by low concentrations of calcium ions. *J. Biochem.* 61:531–33

100. Parker, J. C., Kiechle, F. L., Jarett, L. 1982. Partial purification from hepatoma cells of an intracellular substance which mediates the effects of insulin on pyruvate dehydrogenase and low-K_m cyclic AMP phosphodiesterase. *Arch. Biochem. Biophys.* 215:339–44

101. Pershadsingh, H. A., McDonald, J. M. 1979. Direct addition of insulin inhibits a high affinity Ca^{2+}-ATPase in isolated adipocyte plasma membranes. *Nature* 281:495–97

102. Purrello, F., Vigneri, R., Clawson, G. A., Goldfine, I. D. 1982. Insulin stimulation of nucleoside triphosphatase activity in isolated nuclear envelopes. *Science* 216:1005–7

103. Reed, L. J. 1981. Regulation of mammalian pyruvate dehydrogenase complex by a phosphorylation-dephosphorylation cycle. *Curr. Top. Cell. Reg.* 18:95–129

104. Resh, M. D., Nemenoff, R. A., Guidot-ti, G. 1980. Insulin stimulation of (Na^+, K^+)-adenosine triphosphatase-dependent $^{86}Rb^+$ uptake in rat adipocytes. *J. Biol. Chem.* 255:10938–45

105. Rieser, P., Rieser, C. H. 1964. Anabolic responses of diaphragm muscle to insulin and to other pancreatic proteins. *Proc. Soc. Exp. Biol. Med.* 116:669–71

106. Roach, P. J., Rosell-Perez, M., Larner, J. 1977. Muscle glycogen synthase in vivo state: Effects of insulin administration on the chemical and kinetic properties of the purified enzyme. *FEBS Lett.* 80:95–98

107. Rosen, O. M., Rubin, C. S., Cobb, M. H., Smith, C. J. 1981. Insulin stimulates the phosphorylation of the ribosomal protein S6 in a cell-free system derived from 3T3-L1 adipocytes. *J. Biol. Chem.* 256:3630–33

108. Roth, J., Kahn, C. R., Lesniak, M. A., Gorden, P., De Meyts, P. 1975. Receptors for insulin, NSILA-s, and growth hormone: Applications to disease states in man. *Rec. Prog. Horm. Res.* 31:95–139

109. Saltiel, A., Jacobs, S., Siegel, M., Cuatrecasas, P. 1981. Insulin stimulates the release from liver plasma membranes of a chemical modulator of pyruvate dehydrogenase. *Biochem. Biophys. Res. Commun.* 102:1041–47

110. Saltiel, A. R., Doble, A., Jacobs, S., Cuatrecasas, P. 1983. Putative mediators of insulin action regulate hepatic acetyl CoA carboxylase activity. *Biochem. Biophys. Res. Commun.* 110:789–95

111. Saltiel, A. R., Siegel, M. I., Jacobs, S., Cuatrecasas, P. 1982. Putative mediators of insulin action: Regulation of pyruvate dehydrogenase and adenylate cyclase activities. *Proc. Natl. Acad. Sci. USA* 79:3513–17

112. Schumm, D. E., Webb, T. E. 1981. Insulin-modulated transport of RNA from isolated liver nuclei. *Arch. Biochem. Biophys.* 210:275–79

113. Seals, J. R., Czech, M. P. 1980. Evidence that insulin activates an intrinsic plasma membrane protease in generating a secondary chemical mediator. *J. Biol. Chem.* 255:6529–31

114. Seals, J. R., Czech, M. P. 1981. Characterization of a pyruvate dehydrogenase activator released by adipocyte plasma membranes in response to insulin. *J. Biol. Chem.* 256:2894–99

115. Seals, J. R., Jarett, L. 1980. Activation of pyruvate dehydrogenase by direct addition of insulin to an isolated plasma membrane/mitochondria mixture: Evidence for generation of insulin's second

messenger in a subcellular system. *Proc. Natl. Acad. Sci. USA* 77:77–81

116. Seals, J. R., McDonald, J. M., Jarett, L. 1979. Insulin effect on protein phosphorylation of plasma membranes and mitochondria in a subcellular system from rat adipocytes. *J. Biol. Chem.* 254:6691–96

117. Servely, J. L., Teyssot, B., Houdebine, L. M., Delouis, C., Djiane, J., et al. 1982. Induction of β-casein mRNA accumulation by the putative prolactin second messenger added to the culture medium of cultured mammary epithelial cells. *FEBS Lett.* 148:242–46

118. Shen, L. C., Villar-Palasi, C., Larner, J. 1970. Hormonal alteration of protein kinase sensitivity to 3',5'-cyclic AMP. *Physiol. Chem. Physics* 2:536–44

119. Solomon, S. S., Brush, J. S., Kitabchi, A. E. 1970. Antilipolytic activity of insulin and proinsulin on ACTH and cyclic nucleotide-induced lipolysis in the isolated adipose cell of rat. *Biochim. Biophys. Acta* 218:167–69

120. Speth, M., Schulze, H.-U. 1981. Hormone-induced effects on the rat liver microsomal glucose-6-phosphatase system in vitro. *Biochem. Biophys. Res. Commun.* 99:134–41

121. Steiner, D. F. 1966. Insulin and the regulation of hepatic biosynthetic activity. *Vit. Horm.* 24:1–61

122. Suzuki, K., Kono, T. 1979. Internalization and degradation of fat cell–bound insulin. *J. Biol. Chem.* 254(19):9786–94

123. Suzuki, S., Toyota, T., Suzuki, H., Goto, Y. 1984. A putative second messenger of insulin action regulates hepatic microsomal glucose-6-phosphatase. *Biochem. Biophys. Res. Commun.* 118:40–46

124. Takeda, M., Nakaya, Y. 1976. Effect of guanosine 3':5'-monophosphate on glucose oxidation and epinephrine-stimulated lipolysis in isolated rat epididymal fat cells. *J. Biochem.* 80:717–22

125. Tamura, S., Brown, T. A., Whipple, J. H., Fujita-Yamaguchi, Y., Dubler, R. E., et al. 1984. A novel mechanism for the insulin-like effect of vanadate on glycogen synthase in rat adipocytes. *J. Biol. Chem.* 259:6650–58

126. Tamura, S., Fujita-Yamaguchi, Y., Larner, J. 1983. Insulin-like effect of trypsin on the phosphorylation of rat adipocyte insulin receptor. *J. Biol. Chem.* 258:14749–52

127. Tarui, S., Saito, Y., Fujimoto, M., Okabayashi, T. 1976. Effects of insulin on diaphragm muscle independent of the variation of tissue levels of cyclic AMP

and cyclic GMP. *Arch. Biochem. Biophys.* 174:192–98

128. Teyssot, B., Djiane, J., Kelly, P. A., Houdebine, L.-N. 1982. Identification of the putative prolactin second messenger activating β-casein gene transcription. *Biol. Cell* 43:81–88

129. Teyssot, B., Houdebine, L.-M., Djiane, J. 1981. Prolactin induces release of a factor from membranes capable of stimulating β-casein transcription in isolated mammary cell nuclei. *Proc. Natl. Acad. Sci. USA* 78:6729–33

130. Turakulov, Y. K., Gainutdinov, M. K., Lavina, I. I., Akhmov, M. S. 1977. Insulin-dependent cytoplasmic regulator of the transport of Ca^{2+} ions in liver mitochondria. *Rep. Acad. Sci. U.S.S.R.* 234:1471–74

131. Van Obberghen, E., Spooner, P. M., Kahn, C. R., Chernick, S. S., Garrison, M. M., et al. 1979. Insulin-receptor antibodies mimic a late insulin effect. *Nature* 280:500–2

132. Villar-Palasi, C., Larner, J. 1960. Insulin-mediated effect on the activity of UDPG-glycogen transglucosylase of muscle. *Biochim. Biophys. Acta* 39:171–73

133. Walaas, O., Walaas, E., Gronnerod, O. 1972. Effect of insulin and epinephrine on cyclic AMP–dependent protein kinase in rat diaphragm. *Israel J. Med. Sci.* 8:353–57

134. Walsh, D. A., Ashby, C. D., Gonzalaz, C., Calkins, D., Fischer, E. H., et al. 1971. Purification and characterization of a protein inhibitor of adenosine 3',5'-monophophate-dependent protein kinases. *J. Biol. Chem.* 246:1977–85

135. Wasner, H. K. 1975. Regulation of protein kinase and phosphoprotein phosphatase by cyclic AMP and cyclic AMP antagonist. *FEBS Lett.* 57:60–63

136. Wasner, H. K. 1981. Biosynthesis of cyclic AMP antagonist in hepatocytes from rats after adrenalin or insulin stimulation. *FEBS Lett.* 133:260–64

137. Wasner, H. K. 1983. Prostaglandylinositol cyclic phosphate, a second messenger of insulin. *Abstr. 2nd Int. Symp. Ins. Recp.* Rome, Italy

138. Weis, L. S., Narahara, H. T. 1969. Regulation of cell membrane permeability in skeletal muscle. *J. Biol. Chem.* 244:3084–91

139. Weiss, L., Loffler, G., Schirman, A., Weiland, O. 1971. Control of pyruvate dehydrogenase interconversion in adipose tissue by insulin. *FEBS Lett.* 15:229–31

140. Whitesell, R. R., Gliemann, J. 1979.

Kinetic parameters of transport of 3-0-methylglucose and glucose in adipocytes. *J. Biol. Chem.* 254:5276–83

141. Winegrad, A. I., Renold, A. E. 1958. Studies on rat adipose tissue in vitro: I. Effects of insulin on the metabolism of glucose, pyruvate, and acetate. *J. Biol. Chem.* 233:267–72

142. Witters, L. A. 1981. Insulin stimulates the phosphorylation of acetyl-CoA car-

boxylase. *Biochem. Biophys. Res. Commun.* 100:872–78

143. Zhang, S.-R., Shi, Q.-H., Ho, R. 1983. Cyclic AMP-lowering mediator of insulin. *J. Biol. Chem.* 258:6471–76

144. Zinman, B., Hollenberg, C. H. 1974. Effect of insulin and lipolytic agents on rat adipocyte low-K_m cyclic adenosine 3':5'-monophosphate phosphodiesterase. *J. Biol. Chem.* 249:2182–87

Ann. Rev. Physiol. 1985. 47:425-42
Copyright © 1985 by Annual Reviews, Inc. All rights reserved

THE NATURE AND REGULATION OF THE RECEPTORS FOR INSULIN-LIKE GROWTH FACTORS

Matthew M. Rechler

Section on Biochemistry of Cell Regulation, Laboratory of Biochemical Pharmacology, National Institute of Arthritis, Diabetes, and Digestive and Kidney Diseases, National Institutes of Health, Bethesda, Maryland 20205

S. Peter Nissley

Endocrinology Section, Metabolism Branch, National Cancer Institute, National Institutes of Health, Bethesda, Maryland 20205

INTRODUCTION

The two insulin-like growth factors IGF-I and IGF-II[1] are chemically similar to each other as well as to insulin (60). The IGFs and insulin elicit the same biological responses (e.g. stimulation of fibroblast DNA synthesis and of adipose cell glucose metabolism), typically nonadditively, suggesting convergence of their effector pathways. Competitive binding experiments showed that IGF receptors were distinct from insulin receptors (11, 26, 31) and that two subtypes of IGF receptors existed that differed in their affinity for IGF-I and IGF-II and in their reactivity with insulin (41, 43). Although the receptors for IGFs and insulin preferentially bound the homologous ligand, insulin receptors also had weak affinity for IGFs, and one subtype of IGF receptor (type I) had a weak affinity for insulin.

---

[1]For simplicity, we will refer to IGF-I and IGF-II from human plasma as prototypes of the two major families of IGFs. We consider IGF-I, somatomedin C (21), and basic somatomedin (2) to be chemically and/or functionally identical. MSA (multiplication-stimulating activity) is the rat homolog of IGF-II (25) and functionally interchangeable with it.

425

0066-4278/85/0315-0425$02.00

Recently, covalent cross-linking of [125]Iodine-labeled IGFs to receptors has clearly established that the two subtypes of IGF receptors defined by binding specificity also differ in structure (16, 28, 43). The subunit organization of type I IGF receptors, which bind insulin, is quite similar to that of insulin receptors, whereas type II IGF receptors have a structure different from both of the other receptors. This parallelism of type I receptors and insulin receptors is supported by other independent lines of evidence, including reactivity with antireceptor antibodies, autophosphorylation by receptor tyrosine kinase, and biosynthesis. This review will consider selected aspects of the characterization of type I and type II receptors, including receptor structure, phosphorylation, and regulation. More comprehensive reviews have been published recently (34, 40).

IDENTIFICATION OF IGF-RECEPTOR SUBTYPE

IGF receptors have been identified by the binding of tracer concentrations of ^{125}I-labeled IGF-I or IGF-II. Formal demonstration that the observed binding is to an IGF receptor depends upon preferential competitive inhibition of radioligand binding by unlabeled IGF-I and IGF-II. It is important to note that although the IGF-receptor subtypes tend to have preferential affinity for IGF-I (type I) or IGF-II (type II), without exception they have 10–100% affinity for the other peptide.[2] Because of this extensive cross-reactivity, we prefer the designations type I and type II receptors rather than the potentially misleading nomenclature of IGF-I and IGF-II receptors.

Although some cell and membrane preparations possess only type I or type II IGF receptors, quite commonly both receptor subtypes coexist on the same cells. In these cases radiolabeled IGF-I or IGF-II may distribute between the two receptor subtypes, depending upon their relative affinities and concentrations, so that the observed competition profiles may be a composite of binding to both receptors.

Affinity cross-linking techniques have provided a powerful ancillary technique to help identify the IGF receptor subtype to which a given ligand binds. Typically, radiolabeled IGF is covalently cross-linked (e.g. with the bifunctional reagent, disuccinimidyl suberate) to receptors on intact cells or membranes and then the solubilized radioligand-receptor complexes are analyzed by sodium dodecyl sulfate–polyacrylamide gel electrophoresis (SDS-PAGE) and

---

[2]In addition to IGF-I and IGF-II, the only other peptide hormones or growth factors that interact significantly with the IGF receptors are insulin and proinsulin, and even this interaction is limited to type I IGF receptors. ^{125}I-IGF tracer binding also may be inhibited by specific IGF-carrier proteins. ^{125}I-IGF-carrier protein complexes may bind poorly to receptors and remain in the supernate with unbound radioligand when cells or membranes are recovered by centrifugation.

autoradiography. Type I IGF receptors, typically labeled with ^{125}I-IGF-I, have a $M_r > 300,000$ when disulfide bonds are left intact and a $M_r = 130,000$ after reduction of disulfide bonds (4, 6, 16, 28). The type I receptor has a higher affinity for IGF-I than IGF-II; it also binds insulin at high concentrations. Type II IGF receptors, typically labeled with ^{125}I-IGF-II, have a $M_r = 260,000$ after disulfide reduction and a $M_r = 220,000$ without reduction, consistent with the presence of intrachain disulfide bonds and the absence of disulfide bridges to other membrane proteins (16, 27, 28). Type II receptors prefer IGF-II to IGF-I and do not bind insulin.

Despite the major insights into IGF-receptor structure that have come from affinity cross-linking studies, it also is important to appreciate the limitations of this approach. For example, because only binding subunits are identified, cross-linking by itself cannot provide a complete description of receptor structure. Convincing evidence that type I IGF receptors possessed a 90,000–98,000-dalton β-subunit, in addition to the 130,000-dalton α(binding) subunit, was obtained only when biosynthetically labeled and surface-labeled receptors were immunoprecipitated with monoclonal antibodies (see below). Ultimately, physical characterization of purified receptors is required. A second potential difficulty is that, for both theoretical and technical reasons, cross-linked receptors may not accurately reflect the total receptor population in the preparation. To minimize the likelihood of cross-linking multiple proteins, experimental conditions are chosen such that a small percentage [e.g. 0.5–1% (58)] of the total ligand-receptor complexes are cross-linked. This introduces a major uncertainty as to whether the visible 0.5–1% represents the invisible 99–99.5%. Furthermore, when both IGF-receptor subtypes are present, it has been implicitly assumed that cross-linking of ^{125}I-IGF-I, for example, to type I and type II receptors proceeds with equal efficiency (28). This assumption seems to be valid in some but not all cases. For example, cross-linking underrepresents ^{125}I-IGF-I type II IGF receptor complexes in BC$_3$H-1 mouse myocytes (7). Cross-linking results should be compared with results of competitive binding studies with tracer radioligand and with the bound radioactivity in the cross-linking experiments (e.g. 10, 41). Inhibition by high concentrations of insulin is especially useful. Lack of inhibition of ^{125}I-IGF-I binding by insulin should correlate with the autoradiographic presence of 260,000/220,000-dalton complexes rather than 130,000/300,000-dalton complexes.

Identification of cross-linked ^{125}I-IGF-receptor complexes can positively establish the presence of type I and/or type II receptors in a preparation. For example, this may help differentiate whether ^{125}I-IGF binding that is not inhibited by insulin represents binding to an IGF carrier protein ($M_r = 30,000$–40,000) subunit (8) or a type II IGF receptor. By themselves, however, cross-linking studies are insufficient to establish either the absence of a particular receptor subtype or the relative proportions of type I and type II receptors.

PHYSICAL CHARACTERIZATION OF IGF RECEPTORS

Type I Receptor

Initial affinity-labeling experiments showed that without reduction of disulfide bonds the ^{125}I-IGF-I–receptor complexes were large (>300,000 daltons (4, 6, 16, 28). After reduction of disulfide bonds, only 130,000-dalton complexes of radioligand and α subunit were evident. Evidence for the existence of a β subunit in the type I IGF receptor has come from immunoprecipitation of biosynthetically labeled or surface-labeled receptors by monoclonal antibodies specifically directed against the type I receptor (12, 24). In addition to a labeled α subunit, an intensely labeled 92,000–98,000-dalton species also was present in the immunoprecipitate (β subunit).

Type I receptors have not been purified to homogeneity. Type I receptors have been solubilized from plasma membrane preparations (4, 5, 51). Based on a Stokes radius of 7.2 nm (4), a sedimentation coefficient of 11S, and the partial specific volume of the insulin receptor, the M_r of the IGF-I receptor was calculated to be 402,000 (5).

Thus, results of affinity cross-linking experiments, biosynthetic labeling, and hydrodynamic measurements have demonstrated that the type I receptor is a heteromeric structure made up of α ($M_r = 130,000$) and β ($M_r = 92,000$–98,000) subunits connected by disulfide bonds. The exact stoichiometry of the α and β subunits remains to be determined.

Type II Receptor

Affinity-labeling experiments in which radiolabeled IGF-II was covalently cross-linked to intact cells or membranes and analyzed by SDS-PAGE, indicated that the M_r of the radioligand-receptor complex was 260,000 (16, 27, 28). This conclusion has now been confirmed in studies characterizing the type II receptor purified to near homogeneity from rat placenta (36) and Swarm rat chondrosarcoma cells (1). Type II receptors were solubilized with detergent from 100,000 × g membrane preparations and further purified by affinity chromatography using IGF-II Sepharose. The receptor was identified at all stages of the purification procedure by its ability to bind radiolabeled IGF-II. The major component in the purified receptor preparation had a M_r of 250,000 as determined by SDS-PAGE and silver staining.

When radiolabeled IGF-II was covalently cross-linked to the purified receptor preparations, the radiolabeled IGF-II complexed to the 250,000-dalton species (1, 36). The binding affinity (2×10^9 M^{-1}) and specificity of the purified receptor preparations approximated the binding affinity and specificity of the receptor on intact cells or membrane preparations (1, 36). The experimental binding capacity of the purified receptor for IGF-II determined by Scatchard analysis was half the value calculated assuming 1:1 binding stoichiometry (1, 36), consistent with the presence of impurities, inactive receptor, or perhaps simply reflecting the limitation of Scatchard analysis for determining binding capacity.

Perdue and coworkers (37, 54) also have determined the molecular weight of solubilized type II receptors from rat placenta using two other approaches. In the first method (37), a series of hydrodynamic measurements were made on the solubilized receptor to determine Stokes radius (7.2 nm), sedimentation coefficient (9.9S), and partial specific volume (0.72 cm^{3}g^{-1}); a M_r of 290,000 was calculated. The second approach (54) utilized PAGE under nondenaturing conditions. By comparing the mobility of the radiolabeled IGF-II–receptor complex at each of 6–7 gel concentrations with the mobility of seven standard proteins (Ferguson-Hedrick plot), a M_r of 250,000 was calculated for the IGF-II receptor.

Together these results lead to the conclusion that the type II receptor is a large monomeric species of M_r = 250,000. The purified 250,000-dalton receptor is sufficient to bind IGF-II. Detergent-solubilized receptor examined under nondenaturing conditions also has a M_r of 250,000, indicating that this represents the size of the native receptor complex.

PHOSPHORYLATION OF IGF RECEPTORS

Type I Receptor

Jacobs et al (13) demonstrated IGF-I–dependent phosphorylation of the β subunit of the type I receptor in intact IM-9 lymphocytes. The ATP pool of IM-9 cells was prelabeled with [^{32}P]H$_3$PO$_4$ before short exposure to IGF-I. The labeled cells were solubilized, and glycoproteins were isolated on a wheat germ lectin–Sepharose column. Type I receptors were immunoprecipitated with monoclonal antibodies specific for the type I receptor, and the immunoprecipitate was analyzed by SDS-PAGE and autoradiography. Phosphorylation of a 92,000–98,000-dalton species (β subunit) was increased in the cells exposed to IGF-I. Insulin at higher concentrations also stimulated the phosphorylation of this protein.

Jacobs et al (13) also were able to demonstrate IGF-I–dependent phosphorylation of a 92,000–98,000-dalton species using a partially purified receptor preparation. IM-9 cells were solubilized, and receptors were partially purified by wheat germ lectin–affinity chromatography. The receptor preparation was incubated with IGF-I and then with [γ^{32}P]ATP. After immunoprecipitation with monoclonal antibody (see below), phosphorylated species were analyzed by SDS-PAGE. Phosphorylation of the β subunit was enhanced by as little as

2.5 ng ml^{-1} IGF-I. Phosphoamino acid analysis indicated that phosphorylation occurred on tyrosine residues. Tyrosine phosphorylation in the type I receptor also was demonstrated when receptor prepared by wheat germ lectin–affinity chromatography and immunoprecipitation was incubated with [γ-^{32}P]ATP, suggesting that the tyrosine-specific kinase activity was intrinsic to the receptor or tightly associated with it (13).

Using a partially purified mixture of IGF and insulin receptors from human placenta, Rubin et al (48) demonstrated an IGF-I–dependent phosphorylation of a 90,000-dalton species. The concentration of IGF-I (3 nM) required for half-maximal stimulation of phosphorylation approximated the concentration of IGF-I (4 nM) required for half-maximal inhibition of ^{125}I-IGF-I binding to the IGF receptor, suggesting that the type I IGF receptor, rather than the insulin receptor, was the mediator of the IGF-I–stimulated phosphorylation. A monoclonal antibody directed against the type I IGF receptor (24) immunoprecipitated the phosphorylated 90,000-dalton species, suggesting that it represented the β subunit of the type I receptor. Interestingly, a monoclonal antibody directed against the insulin receptor also immunoprecipitated a 90,000-dalton phosphorylated species following incubation with 22 nM IGF-I. Because IGF-I at concentrations below 50 nM has minimal interaction with the insulin receptor, this latter result suggests that phosphorylation of the β subunit of the insulin receptor may be mediated by interaction of IGF-I with the type I IGF-I receptor.

Zick et al (61) partially purified IGF receptors from a rat-liver cell line (BRL-3A2) that has type I and type II IGF receptors but few insulin receptors. They demonstrated IGF-I-dependent phosphorylation of a 98,000-dalton membrane protein that was a part of a $M_r > 300,000$ complex. When the IGF receptor preparation was incubated with IGF-I, [γ-^{32}P]ATP, and a synthetic tyrosine-containing polymer [poly(glu, tyr) 4:1], phosphorylation of the artificial substrate was observed. IGF-II and insulin were active at higher concentrations. Thus, the receptor preparation possessed IGF-I–dependent tyrosine-kinase activity.

The results of these phosphorylation experiments directly parallel earlier results for the insulin receptor and are consistent with the β subunit of the type I receptor having intrinsic tyrosine-kinase activity capable of phosphorylating the type I receptor and other substrates. Obviously, it is important to confirm these results with IGF receptor purified to homogeneity.

Recently, tumor-promoting phorbol esters have been shown to stimulate the phosphorylation of the β subunit of the type I receptor in intact IM-9 lymphocytes (14). Because phorbol esters directly activate protein kinase C, presumably the effect of phorbol esters on type I IGF receptor phosphorylation is via kinase C. In the case of the stimulation of insulin receptor phosphorylation by phorbol ester, at least some of the phosphorylated sites were distinct from those sites phosphorylated in response to insulin. Kinase C–mediated phosphorylation of the type I receptor represents another potential mechanism for the control of receptor function.

As with other receptors, it is not known what role phosphorylation of the type I IGF receptor itself or of other substrates plays in receptor function and IGF-I action.

Type II Receptor

We recently provided preliminary evidence that the type II receptor is phosphorylated in intact cells (9). Rat embryo fibroblasts, H-35 hepatoma cells, and BRL-3A2 rat liver cells were incubated with $[^{32}P]H_3PO_4$ to label the ATP pool, and then IGF-II was added. The cells were solubilized with detergent; glycoproteins were purified on a wheat germ lectin–Sepharose column and analyzed by SDS-PAGE and autoradiography. Among the phosphorylated bands were species having the size of the IGF-II receptor ($M_r = 210,000$ without reduction, 250,000 with reduction). Importantly, the 250,000-dalton species bound to an IGF-II–Sepharose affinity column and was eluted with a low-pH, high-salt buffer after extensive washing with a high-salt buffer. The MSA affinity column purified 250,000-dalton species was more heavily labeled in BRL-3A2 rat liver cells after treatment with IGF-II, whereas phosphorylation of this species was not IGF-dependent in rat embryo fibroblasts. Because rat embryo fibroblasts produce IGF-II while BRL-3A2 cells do not, these results suggest that in rat embryo fibroblasts, endogenously produced IGF-II may stimulate phosphorylation of the type II receptor.

Phosphorylation of the type II receptor could not be demonstrated when solubilized receptors from BRL-3A2 cells were incubated with IGF and [γ-^{32}P]ATP (61), suggesting that the type II receptor does not possess intrinsic protein-kinase activity. Thus in contrast to phosphorylation of the type I IGF receptor, type II IGF–receptor phosphorylation is only seen in intact cells (9, 61). The significance of type II–receptor phosphorylation remains to be determined.

REGULATION OF IGF RECEPTORS

Downregulation of the Type I Receptor

Rosenfeld et al (46) reported that preincubation of IM-9 lymphocytes with IGF-I resulted in 50% reduction of ^{125}I-IGF-I binding. Scatchard analysis of the binding data suggested that the downregulation of IGF-I binding was accounted for by a decrease in receptor number rather than a change in binding affinity. The ability of IGF-I, IGF-II, and insulin to decrease the number of type I IGF receptors was proportional to their relative potency in inhibiting binding of ^{125}I-IGF-I to IM-9 cells (IGF-I > IGF-II > insulin), suggesting that downregulation depended upon receptor occupancy. Similarly, IGF-I and insulin were shown to downregulate type I IGF receptors on monolayer cultures of human skin fibroblasts (45).

The BC_3H-1 mouse muscle cell line possesses both type I and type II IGF receptors. Prolonged incubation of BC_3H-1 cells with IGF-I, IGF-II, or insulin resulted in decreased binding of IGF-I (7). Scatchard analysis of IGF-I binding data before and after downregulation suggested that the decreased binding resulted from a decrease in binding affinity for IGF-I. Upon more detailed examination, however, it appears that the apparent decrease in affinity for IGF-I is the result of selective downregulation of type I IGF receptors (having a higher affinity for IGF-I), with sparing of type II IGF receptors (which have a lower affinity for IGF-I). Interestingly, the type II IGF receptors in Swarm rat chondrosarcoma cells (50) and HTC cells (10) also are not downregulated.

Acute Upregulation of the Type II IGF Receptor by Insulin: Rapid Translocation of Cycling Receptors to the Cell Surface

Brief (2–3 minutes) incubation of isolated rat adipocytes with insulin caused a marked increase in IGF-II binding to type II IGF receptors (20, 35, 49). Insulin was active at 10^{-10} M, a concentration similar to that required for stimulation of glucose oxidation. IGF-II binding also was increased by proinsulin and by agonistic autoantibodies to the insulin receptor; inactive monovalent Fab fragments of these antibodies blocked the insulin-stimulated increase in IGF-II binding (20). These results suggested that these molecules acted via the insulin receptor in a manner parallel to the activation of glucose transport.

Did the increase in IGF-II binding to intact adipose cells after treatment with insulin reflect an increase in the binding affinity or an increase in the concentration of type II IGF receptors? Initial experiments on intact cells and isolated membranes provided conflicting results. King et al (20) performed Scatchard analysis of IGF-II-binding data obtained after incubation with rat adipocytes at 24°C. Insulin increased IGF-II receptor affinity but caused no increase in receptor number. Kinetic studies of IGF-II binding supported the conclusion that insulin increased receptor affinity; however, the association constant (K_a) derived from kinetic studies was 40-fold higher than that obtained by Scatchard analysis of equilibrium-binding data. Oppenheimer et al (35) also reported that insulin caused an increase in receptor affinity without a change in receptor number, based on Scatchard analysis of IGF-II binding to intact adipocytes. However, Scatchard analysis of IGF-II binding to isolated membrane fractions from control cells and from insulin-stimulated cells demonstrated no change in binding affinity, but rather a reciprocal translocation of type II IGF receptors from the low-density microsomal fraction to the plasma membrane fraction. The authors chose to dismiss the findings on isolated membranes as an artifactual redistribution of receptors occurring during homogenization, perhaps because of insulin-induced changes in membrane environment.

Recently, Wardzala et al (57) have confirmed the previous discrepant effects of insulin in intact cells and membranes and have used a novel experimental strategy to resolve the issue. They have used 1 mM KCN during the IGF-II–binding incubation to block receptor cycling. It became apparent that adipose cells have a large intracellular pool of unoccupied type II IGF receptors. In the absence of KCN, type II receptors recycle and IGF-II accumulates, presumably intracellularly. In the presence of KCN, bound IGF-II is confined to the cell surface. Because previous binding studies with intact adipose cells were performed at 24°C in the absence of KCN, receptor recycling and intracellular accumulation of ligand undoubtedly occurred, thereby invalidating the use of Scatchard analysis, which assumes a simple, reversible binding reaction.

Wardzala et al (57) then compared IGF-II binding to insulin-treated cells and control adipose cells in the presence of KCN. Under these conditions, insulin increases the number of type II IGF receptors without affecting their affinity for IGF-II. These results were confirmed in subcellular membrane fractions: receptor number increased in plasma membranes from insulin-treated adipose cells, accompanied by a reciprocal decrease in receptor number in low-density microsomes. Thus, the increased binding of IGF-II to adipose cells treated with insulin appears to involve a redistribution of type II IGF receptors cycling between an intracellular pool of receptors and the plasma membrane. It is of interest that insulin induces a similar translocation of glucose transporters to the surface of adipose cells with similar rapid kinetics and at comparably low concentrations.

The functional significance of insulin-induced upregulation of type II IGF receptors is unknown, because no biological response has been assigned to this receptor. It will be of interest to determine whether the stimulation of IGF-II binding by insulin described in L6 rat myoblasts (3) and H-35 rat hepatoma cells (35) arises by similar mechanisms.

FURTHER COMPARISON BETWEEN THE TYPE I IGF RECEPTOR AND THE INSULIN RECEPTOR

From the preceding discussion, many similarities between type I IGF receptors and insulin receptors are apparent in structure and organization, peptide specificity, tyrosine autophosphorylation, and downregulation. In this section we review other properties that have been examined to determine the full extent of their homologies.

Immunoreactivity

Studies using a group of human sera containing circulating polyclonal autoantibodies to the insulin receptor, and others using mouse monoclonal antireceptor antibodies, indicate that type I IGF receptors and the insulin receptor share related but not identical antigenic determinants. Kasuga et al (18) observed that each of seven sera from patients with autoantibodies to the insulin receptor also reacted significantly with type I IGF receptors in human placenta and/or IM-9 lymphoid cells in immunoprecipitation or binding inhibition assays. The rank order of potency of five sera was the same for inhibition of the binding of radiolabeled IGF-I or insulin. One of the sera, however, showed a selective decrease in reactivity with the type I receptor: it effectively immunoprecipitated cross-linked and surface-iodinated insulin receptors, but did not significantly immunoprecipitate cross-linked type I IGF receptors. Jonas et al (15) reported similar quantitative differences in the ability of some of the same sera to immunoprecipitate placental insulin and type I IGF receptors.

Discrimination between insulin receptors and type I IGF receptors by some of the autoimmune sera clearly supported the conclusion that the two receptors were immunologically distinct. Reactivity of these polyclonal sera with the two receptors might represent true immunologic relatedness or simply reflect the coexistence of two antibody populations in the antisera, one directed against the insulin receptor and the other against the type I receptor.

Recent studies with monoclonal antireceptor antibodies unequivocally demonstrate the presence of related antigenic determinants on the two receptors. Kull et al (24) raised monoclonal antibodies to insulin receptors and type I IGF receptors by immunizing mice with solubilized receptor preparations from human placental membranes that had been extensively purified by lectin-Sepharose and insulin-Sepaharose affinity chromatography. Interestingly, in view of the antibodies generated, although the two receptors copurified through the initial steps, insulin-binding activity but not IGF-I–binding activity remained in the urea eluate of the insulin-Sepharose column. Thus, the immunogen contained insulin receptors alone, or insulin receptors plus denatured type I IGF receptors. The three resulting monoclonal antibodies immunoprecipitated both insulin receptors and type I IGF receptors labeled with ^{125}I-insulin and ^{125}I-IGF-I, respectively. One antibody preferentially precipitated insulin receptors, whereas the other two were more effective in immunoprecipitating type I IGF receptors. These results clearly demonstrate that monoclonal antibodies are capable of recognizing determinants on both insulin receptors and type I IGF receptors. The fact that different antibodies have different affinities for the two receptors suggests that either the determinants or their microenvironment are different.

Roth et al (47) have generated a monoclonal antibody that inhibits insulin binding to human insulin receptors and examined its ability to inhibit IGF-I binding to type I IGF receptors. Mice were immunized with intact human lymphoid cells (IM-9) that possess insulin receptors and type I IGF receptors but lack type II IGF receptors (40, 42). The resulting monoclonal antibody did inhibit both insulin and IGF-I binding to human IM-9 cells and placental membranes. It had a 300-fold greater affinity for the insulin receptor than for the type I IGF receptor. This suggests that insulin receptors and type I IGF receptors also are antigenically related at or near their binding sites.

Although it has been less extensively investigated, monoclonal and polyclonal antibodies to the insulin receptor do not appear to recognize determinants on type II IGF receptors: binding of labeled IGF-II is not inhibited (10, 43, 47), and ligand-receptor complexes are not precipitated (18).

Physical Characteristics

Although insulin receptors and type I IGF receptors appeared similar in size, more precise analysis has revealed differences in isoelectric point and in the size of both α and β subunits. The isoelectric point of the type I IGF receptor solubilized from human placental membranes and examined without cross-linking was 4.6, whereas the placental insulin receptor had an isoelectric point of 4.2 (51). Differences in α and β subunit size were reported by Kull et al (24) after immunoprecipitating surface-iodinated receptors in human placental membranes and IM-9 lymphoid cells with monoclonal antibodies to insulin receptors and type I IGF receptors. The β subunit of both type I receptors had a M_r of 92,000–98,000, compared with a M_r of 90,000 for the β subunit of the insulin receptor. The α subunit of the type I IGF receptor in placenta was slightly smaller ($M_r = 132,000$) than the placental insulin receptor α subunit ($M_r = 135,000$). This difference was not seen in IM-9 cells. Stuart et al (52) have used simultaneous double-label affinity cross-linking of human placental type I IGF receptors (labeled with ^{125}I-IGF-I) and insulin receptors (labeled with ^{131}I-insulin) to demonstrate that the IGF receptor α subunit was at least 8000 daltons smaller than the insulin receptor α subunit (134,000 vs 142,000 daltons). Differences in ligand size would only increase this difference. The relative contributions of the protein and carbohydrate moieties to these differences in electrophoretic mobility and charge are not known.

Biosynthesis

Jacobs et al (12) labeled cultured human lymphoid cells (IM-9) with [^{35}S]methionine in the presence and absence of monensin, an inhibitor of post translational protein processing. Labeled cells were solubilized, and glycoproteins were immunoprecipitated with monoclonal antibodies specific for insulin receptors and type I IGF receptors (see above). In the presence of monensin, synthesis of mature α and β subunits of both the insulin receptor and the type I IGF receptor was inhibited, and a new 180,000-dalton species accumulated. In analogy with more extensive studies of insulin receptor biosynthesis, the 180,000-dalton polypeptide is thought to represent a biosynthetic precursor of the α and β subunits. When unlabeled monensin-treated cells were affinity labeled with ^{125}I-insulin, a radiolabeled 180,000-dalton species was precipitated by insulin receptor antibodies but not by antibodies to the type I IGF receptor. This suggested that although both insulin receptors and type I IGF receptors appear to be synthesized as 180,000-dalton precursor molecules, each receptor has a distinct precursor polypeptide.

Genetics

It has been appreciated recently that certain rare genetic disorders characterized by clinical insulin resistance appear to arise from profoundly impaired insulin binding to insulin receptors, which can be demonstrated in permanent cell cultures (e.g. skin fibroblasts, lymphocytes) established from these patients (53). In two such patients, an associated defect in IGF-I binding to type I IGF receptors has been described (30, 55). The defect appears to be selective, because unrelated receptors for epidermal growth factor are spared (55). It results in a selective functional impairment of IGF-stimulated IGF receptor–mediated stimulation of glucose uptake (22). Although it is possible that the concurrent defects in both receptors are coincidental, alternatively it may reflect a lesion in a component common to both receptors or some additional level of interaction between the receptors.

ROLE OF IGF RECEPTORS IN MEDIATING BIOLOGIC RESPONSES

Because insulin and the IGFs can produce the same biologic responses at appropriate concentrations, and because many cell types possess insulin receptors and the two types of IGF receptors, it frequently has been difficult to determine which receptor is mediating a particular response. IGF-I and IGF-II bind to all three receptors, and their responses might potentially be mediated by any or all of them. Insulin binds to insulin receptors and type I IGF receptors, but not to type II receptors, excluding the latter from consideration as a mediator of the biological responses to insulin.

Attempts to assess the relative contributions of the three receptors to an observed response have included: (a) determination of the receptors present on the cell type and the binding affinities of the three peptide ligands; (b) determination of the biological dose response for insulin, IGF-I, and IGF-II; and, most directly, (c) selective blockade of insulin receptors with Fab fragments of antireceptor antibodies. (Similar blocking antibodies are not yet available for type I and type II IGF receptors.) Although it was initially proposed that acute metabolic effects of insulin and the IGFs were mediated by insulin receptors, and that chronic growth effects (DNA synthesis and cell multiplication) induced by both classes of peptides were mediated by the IGF receptors, it now is abundantly clear that this is an oversimplification and that there are as many exceptions as examples of the rule. Some examples of how these principles are applied follow.

Rat adipose cells possess insulin receptors and type II IGF receptors but lack type I receptors (19, 28). Insulin stimulates glucose oxidation at 50-fold lower concentrations than are required for IGFs (19, 60), suggesting that insulin and most probably IGF act through the insulin receptor. This was demonstrated directly by King et al (19) using Fab fragments of anti-insulin receptor IgG to selectively inhibit binding to insulin receptors without affecting type II IGF receptors. The antireceptor Fab fragments inhibited the stimulation of glucose oxidation induced by both insulin and IGF-II, strongly suggesting that IGF-II as well as insulin acted via the insulin receptor.

In other tissue types, IGFs appear to stimulate glucose transport and metabolism via IGF receptors. Evidence is based on a greater biological potency of IGFs (relative to insulin) than could be accounted for by simple cross-reaction with the insulin receptor. Examples include mouse muscle (38) and human skin fibroblasts (22). Yu & Czech (58) recently have reached a similar conclusion in rat soleus muscle from studies correlating the dose response for hexose and amino acid transport with the dose response for inhibition of affinity labeling of the receptor. However, in this study, the ED_{50} for IGF-II biological effect and for the inhibition of insulin binding by IGF-II were similar (i.e. insulin was $\sim$ 50-fold more potent than IGF-II for both effects), so that it is possible that IGF-II acts via the insulin receptor. If this possibility could be excluded, the results would favor the authors' interpretation that IGF-II is acting via the type I rather than the type II IGF receptor.

Chick embryo fibroblasts possess type I IGF receptors and insulin receptors but lack type II IGF receptors (17, 41). The relative and absolute potencies of IGF-I, IGF-II, rat IGF-II, insulin, and proinsulin in stimulating [³H]thymidine incorporation into DNA correlate closely with the affinity of these peptides for the type I IGF receptor (33, 41, 59, 60). By contrast, the concentration of insulin required to stimulate DNA synthesis greatly exceeds the concentrations required for interaction with the insulin receptor. Thus, in chick embryo fibroblasts, the IGFs, insulin, and proinsulin appear to stimulate DNA synthesis by acting through the type I IGF receptor.

Similarly, both classes of peptides appear to exert growth-promoting effects through IGF receptors rather than insulin receptors in human (19) and Chinese hamster (56) fibroblasts, rabbit lens (44), and neonatal rat islet β-cells (39). In human fibroblasts, blockade of insulin receptors with anti-receptor Fab fragments had no effect on insulin- or IGF-II–stimulated DNA synthesis, confirming that the insulin receptor did not participate in this stimulation (19). By contrast, convincing evidence that insulin acts as a mitogen through the insulin receptor has been presented in H-35 rat hepatoma cells (23, 29), F-9 teratocarcinoma cells (32), and other cell types.

Although certain responses in some tissues may be mediated solely by insulin receptors or IGF receptors, not uncommonly the same response is elicited by parallel activation of insulin receptors by insulin and IGF receptors by IGFs. Examples include the stimulation of glucose uptake and α-aminoisobutyric acid (AIB) transport in human fibroblast (22) and mouse myocyte (7) cultures.

POSTBINDING REGULATION OF AN IGF RECEPTOR–MEDIATED RESPONSE BY INSULIN

The fact that IGFs and insulin activate the same biological responses, and that typically the maximal effects of optimal concentrations of the hormones are not additive, strongly suggests convergence of their effector pathways. Consistent with this concept is the presence of symmetrical functional defects in IGF receptor–mediated and insulin receptor–mediated response pathways in fibroblasts from a patient with leprechaunism: impaired stimulation of glucose uptake by both peptides, with sparing of IGF- and insulin-stimulated AIB transport via both receptors (22).

Recently, Heaton et al (10) presented evidence suggesting that in a rat hepatoma cell line (HTC), insulin might regulate a step distal to hormone binding that is common to the actions of insulin and IGFs. When HTC cells are incubated with insulin, the enzyme tyrosine aminotransferase (TAT) is induced after 2–6 hr of incubation. When the incubation is continued for 24 hr, however, TAT levels return to basal and incubation of the cells with fresh insulin or IGF-II fails to induce TAT, suggesting desensitization to the effects of both hormones. HTC cells possess insulin receptors and type I and type II IGF receptors. In untreated cells, insulin induced TAT via the insulin receptor, whereas IGFs induce TAT via one or both IGF receptors. Insulin downregulates insulin receptors by 50%, but neither the extent of receptor loss nor the kinetics of recovery of binding and stimulation indicate that downregulation of insulin binding is sufficient to account for the observed desensitization. Insulin does not downregulate type I or type II IGF receptors, so that the desensitization of TAT induction by IGFs also must occur by a postbinding mechanism.

SUMMARY AND CONCLUSIONS

1. Two subtypes of IGF receptors have been identified. **Type I IGF receptors** have a $M_r > 300,000$ and are composed of disulfide-linked 130,000-dalton (α) and ~90,000-dalton (β) subunits. The α subunit binds hormone; the β subunit appears to have intrinsic tyrosine kinase activity and to be autophosphorylated. Type I receptors preferentially bind IGF-I but also bind IGF-II and, more weakly, insulin. **Type II IGF receptors** consist of a 250,000-dalton protein that contains internal disulfide bonds but is not linked to other membrane components. Type II receptors bind IGF-II with higher affinity than IGF-I. They do not interact with even very high concentrations of insulin.

2. Type I IGF receptors and insulin receptors are homologous structures.

They have similar subunit structure. Both receptors bind IGFs and insulin. They have similar (but not identical) antigenic determinants. Both receptors are downregulated by IGFs and insulin. Both receptors are affected in certain patients with genetically determined insulin resistance.

3. Type II IGF receptors do not appear to be homologous to type I receptors. They differ in structure, peptide binding specificity, and antigenic determinants. Type II receptors do not appear to be downregulated. Although type II receptors appear to be phosphorylated in intact cells, they do not possess intrinsic tyrosine protein-kinase activity.

4. Insulin acutely upregulates type II IGF receptors in intact rat adipose cells by effecting a redistribution of receptors cycling between a large intracellular pool and the plasma membrane.

5. Insulin and the IGFs elicit the same biological responses, either by cross-reacting with one of the receptors for the heterologous ligand or by concurrent activation of convergent effector pathways by binding to the homologous receptor. Which mechanism is utilized appears to depend more on the tissue than on the biological response.

6. Insulin desensitizes rat hepatoma cells to the actions of insulin and IGFs, mediated by both insulin and IGF receptors, by mechanisms distal to hormone binding and possibly common to IGF and insulin effector pathways.

Literature Cited

1. August, G. P., Nissley, S. P., Kasuga, M., Lee, L., Greenstein, L. A., Rechler, M. M. 1983. Purification of an insulin-like growth factor II receptor from rat chondrosarcoma cells. *J. Biol. Chem.* 258:9033–36

2. Bala, R. M., Bhaumick, B. 1979. Purification of a basic somatomedin from human plasma Cohn fraction IV-1, with physicochemical and radioimmunoassay similarity to somatomedin-C and insulin-like growth factor I. *Can. J. Biochem.* 57:1289–98

3. Benedict, M. P., Florini, J. R. 1982. Effects of serum deprivation on the interaction of MSA and myoblasts: nonphysiologic binding characteristics. *Program of the Endocrine Society*. Abstr. 319

4. Bhaumick, B., Bala, R. M., Hollenberg, M. D. 1981. Somatomedin receptor of human placenta: solubilization, photolabeling, partial purification, and comparison with insulin receptor. *Proc. Natl. Acad. Sci. USA* 78:4279–83

5. Bhaumick, B., Armstrong, G. D., Hollenberg, M. D., Bala, R. M. 1982. Characterization of the human placental receptor for basic somatomedin. *Can. J. Biochem.* 60:923–32

6. Chernausek, S. D., Jacobs, S., Van Wyk, J. J. 1981. Structural similarities between human receptors for somatomedin C and insulin; analysis by affinity labeling. *Biochemistry* 20:7345–50

7. DeVroede, M. A., Romanus, J. A., Standaert, M. L., Pollet, R. J., Nissley, S. P., Rechler, M. M. 1984. Interaction of insulin-like growth factors with a nonfusing mouse muscle cell line: binding, action, and receptor down-regulation. *Endocrinology* 114:1917–29

8. Grizzard, J. D., D'Ercole, A. J., Wilkins, J. R., Moats-Staats, B. M., Williams, R. W. 1984. Affinity-labeled somatomedin-C receptors and binding proteins from the human fetus. *J. Clin. Endocrinol. Metab.* 58:535–42

9. Haskell, J. F., Nissley, S. P., Rechler, M. M., Sasaki, N., Greenstein, L. A., Lee, L. 1984. Evidence for phosphorylation of the type II insulin-like growth factor (IGF) receptor in cultured cells. *Program 7th Int. Cong. Endocrinol., Quebec*, Abstr. 931, p. 726. Amsterdam: Excerpta Medica Int. Cong. Ser. 652

10. Heaton, J. H., Krett, N. L., Alvarez, J. M., Gelehrter, T. D., Romanus, J. A., Rechler, M. M. 1984. Insulin regulation of insulin-like growth factor action in rat

hepatoma cells. *J. Biol. Chem.* 259: 2396–402

11. Hintz, R. L., Clemmons, D. R., Underwood, L. E., Van Wyk, J. J. 1972. Competitive binding of somatomedin to the insulin receptor of adipocytes, chondrocytes, and liver membranes. *Proc. Natl. Acad. Sci. USA* 69:2351–53

12. Jacobs, S., Kull, F. C., Cuatrecasas, P. 1983. Monensin blocks the maturation of receptors for insulin and somatomedin C: identification of receptor precursors. *Proc. Natl. Acad. Sci. USA* 80:1128–31

13. Jacobs, S., Kull, F. C., Earp, H. S., Svoboda, M., Van Wyk, J. J., Cuatrecasas, P. 1983. Somatomedin-C stimulates the phosphorylation of the β-subunit of its own receptor. *J. Biol. Chem.* 258:9581–84

14. Jacobs, S., Sahyoun, N. E., Saltiel, A. R., Cuatrecasas, P. 1983. Phorbol esters stimulate the phosphorylation of receptors for insulin and somatomedin-C. *Proc. Natl. Acad. Sci. USA* 80:6211–13

15. Jonas, H. A., Baxter, R. C., Harrison, L. C. 1982. Structural differences between insulin and somatomedin-C/insulin-like growth factor I receptors revealed by autoantibodies to the insulin receptor. *Biochem. Biophys. Res. Commun.* 109: 463–70

16. Kasuga, M., Van Obberghen, E., Nissley, S. P., Rechler, M. M. 1981. Demonstration of two subtypes of insulin-like growth factor receptors by affinity cross-linking. *J. Biol. Chem.* 256:5305–8

17. Kasuga, M., Van Obberghen, E., Nissley, S. P., Rechler, M. M. 1982. Structure of the insulin-like growth factor receptor in chicken embryo fibroblasts. *Proc. Natl. Acad. Sci. USA* 79:1864–68

18. Kasuga, M., Sasaki, N., Kahn, C. R., Nissley, S. P., Rechler, M. M. 1983. Antireceptor antibodies as probes of insulin-like growth factor receptor structure. *J. Clin. Invest.* 72:1459–69

19. King, G. L., Kahn, C. R., Rechler, M. M., Nissley, S. P. 1980. Direct demonstration of separate receptors for growth and metabolic activities of insulin and multiplication-stimulating activity (an insulin-like growth factor) using antibodies to the insulin receptor. *J. Clin. Invest.* 66:130–40

20. King, G. L., Rechler, M. M., Kahn, C. R. 1982. Interactions between receptors for insulin and the insulin-like growth factors on adipocytes. *J. Biol. Chem.* 257:10001–6

21. Klapper, D. G., Svoboda, M. E., Van Wyk, J. J. 1983. Sequence analysis of somatomedin-C: Confirmation of identity with insulin-like growth factor I. *Endocrinology* 112:2215–17

22. Knight, A. B., Rechler, M. M., Romanus, J. A., Van Obberghen-Schilling, E. E., Nissley, S. P. 1981. Stimulation of glucose incorporation and amino acid transport by insulin and an insulin-like growth factor in fibroblasts with defective insulin receptors cultured from a patient with leprechaunism. *Proc. Natl. Acad. Sci. USA* 78:2554–58

23. Koontz, J. W., Iwahashi, M. 1981. Insulin as a potent, specific growth factor in a rat hepatoma cell line. *Science* 211:947–49

24. Kull, F. C., Jacobs, S., Su, Y-F., Svoboda, M. E., Van Wyk, J. J., Cuatrecasas, P. 1983. Monoclonal antibodies to receptors for insulin and somatomedin-C. *J. Biol. Chem.* 258:6561–66

25. Marquardt, H., Todaro, G. J., Henderson, L. E., Oroszlan, S. 1981. Purification and primary structure of a polypeptide with multiplication-stimulating activity from rat liver cell cultures. *J. Biol. Chem.* 256:6859–65

26. Marshall, R. N., Underwood, L. E., Voina, S. J., Foushee, D. B., Van Wyk, J. J. 1974. Characterization of the insulin and somatomedin-C receptors in human placental cell membranes. *J. Clin. Endocrinol. Metab.* 39:283–92

27. Massagué, J., Guillette, B. J., Czech, M. P. 1981. Affinity labeling of multiplication-stimulating activity receptors in membranes from rat and human tissues. *J. Biol. Chem.* 256:2122–25

28. Massagué, J., Czech, M. P. 1982. The subunit structures of two distinct receptors for insulin-like growth factor I and II and their relationship to the insulin receptor. *J. Biol. Chem.* 257:5038–41

29. Massagué, J., Blinderman, L. A., Czech, M. P. 1982. The high-affinity insulin receptor mediates growth stimulation in rat hepatoma cells. *J. Biol. Chem.* 257:13958–63

30. Massagué, J., Freidenberg, G. F., Olefsky, J. M., Czech, M. P. 1983. Parallel decreases in the expression of receptors for insulin and insulin-like growth factor I in a mutant human fibroblast line. *Diabetes* 32:541–44

31. Megyesi, K., Kahn, C. R., Roth, J., Froesch, E. R., Humbel, R. E., et al. 1974. Insulin and nonsuppressible insulin-like activity (NSILA-s): evidence for separate plasma membrane receptor sites. *Biochem. Biophys. Res. Commun.* 57:307–15

32. Nagarajan, L., Anderson, W. B. 1982. Insulin promotes the growth of F9 embryonal carcinoma cells apparently by

acting through its own receptor. *Biochem. Biophys. Res. Commun.* 106:974–80

33. Nissley, S. P., Rechler, M. M., Moses, A. C., Short, P. A., Podskalny, J. M. 1977. Proinsulin binds to a growth peptide receptor and stimulates DNA synthesis into chick embryo fibroblasts. *Endocrinology* 101:708–16

34. Nissley, S. P., Rechler, M. M. Insulin-like growth factors: biosynthesis, receptors, and carrier proteins. In *Hormonal Proteins and Peptides,* ed. C. H. Li, in press. New York: Academic

35. Oppenheimer, C. L., Pessin, J. E., Massagué, J., Gitomer, W., Czech, M. P. 1983. Insulin action rapidly modulates the apparent affinity of the insulin-like growth factor II receptor. *J. Biol. Chem.* 258:4824–30

36. Oppenheimer, C. L., Czech, M. P. 1983. Purification of the type II insulin-like growth factor receptor from rat placenta. *J. Biol. Chem.* 258:8539–42

37. Perdue, J. F., Chan, J. K., Thibault, C., Radaj, P., Mills, B., Daughaday, W. H. 1983. The biochemical characterization of detergent-solubilized insulin-like growth factor II receptors from rat placenta. *J. Biol. Chem.* 258:7800–11

38. Poggi, C., Le Marchand-Brustel, Y., Zapf, J., Froesch, E. R., Freychet, P. 1979. Effects and binding of insulin-like growth factor I in the isolated soleus muscle of lean and obese mice: comparison with insulin. *Endocrinology* 105:723–30

39. Rabinovitch, A., Quigley, C., Russell, T., Patel, Y., Mintz, D. H. 1982. Insulin and multiplication stimulating activity (an insulin-like growth factor) stimulate islet β-cell replication in neonatal rat pancreatic monolayer cultures. *Diabetes* 31:160–64

40. Rechler, M. M., Nissley, S. P. 1984. Receptors for insulin-like growth factors. In *Receptors for Polypeptide Hormones,* ed. B. I. Posner, in press. New York: Dekker

41. Rechler, M. M., Zapf, J., Nissley, S. P., Froesch, E. R., Moses, A. C., et al. 1980. Interactions of insulin-like growth factors I and II and multiplication stimulating activity with receptors and serum carrier proteins. *Endocrinology* 107:1451–59

42. Rechler, M. M., Podskalny, J. M., Nissley, S. P. 1976. Interaction of multiplication-stimulating activity with chick embryo fibroblasts demonstrates a growth receptor. *Nature* 259:134–36

43. Rechler, M. M., Kasuga, M., Sasaki, N., DeVroede, M. A., Romanus, J. A., Nissley, S. P. 1983. Properties of in-sulin-like growth factor subtypes. In *Insulin-like Growth Factors/Somatomedins: Basic Chemistry, Biology and Clinical Importance,* ed. E. M. Spencer, pp. 459–90. New York: W. de Gruyter

44. Reddan, J. R., Dziedzic, D. C. 1982. Insulin-like growth factors, IGF-I, IGF-2 and somatomedin C trigger cell proliferation in mammalian epithelial cells cultured in a serum-free medium. *Exper. Cell Res.* 142:293–300

45. Rosenfeld, R. G., Dollar, L. A. 1982. Characterization of the somatomedin-C/insulin-like growth factor I (SM-C/IGF-I) receptor on cultured human fibroblast monolayers: regulation of receptor concentrations by SM-C/IGF-I and insulin. *J. Clin. Endocrinol. Metab.* 55:434–40

46. Rosenfeld, R. G., Hintz, R. L., Dollar, L. A. 1982. Insulin-induced loss of an insulin-like growth factor-I receptor on IM-9 lymphocytes. *Diabetes* 31:375–81

47. Roth, R. A., Maddux, B., Wong, K. Y., Styne, D. M., Van Vliet, G., et al. 1983. Interactions of a monoclonal antibody to the insulin receptor with receptors for insulin-like growth factors. *Endocrinology* 112:1865–67

48. Rubin, J. B., Shia, M. A., Pilch, P. F. 1983. Stimulation of tyrosine-specific phosphorylation *in vitro* by insulin-like growth factor I. *Nature* 305:438–40

49. Schoenle, E., Zapf, J. Froesch, E. R. 1976. Binding of non-suppressible insulin-like activity (NSILA) to isolated fat cells: evidence for two separate membrane acceptor sites. *FEBS Lett.* 67:175–79

50. Stevens, R. L., Austen, K. F., Nissley, S. P. 1983. Insulin induced increase in insulin binding to cultured chondrosarcoma chondrocytes. *J. Biol. Chem.* 258:2940–44

51. Stuart, C. A., Brosnan, P. G., Furlanetto, R. W. 1984. The somatomedin-C receptor of human placenta. *Metabolism* 33:90–96

52. Stuart, C. A., Pietrzyk, R., Siu, A. K. Q., Furlanetto, R. W. 1984. Size discrepancy between somatomedin-C and insulin receptors. *J. Clin. Endocrinol. Metab.* 58:1–5

53. Taylor, S. I., Samuels, B., Roth, J., Kasuga, M., Hedo, J. A., et al. 1982. Decreased insulin binding in cultured lymphocytes from two patients with extreme insulin resistance. *J. Clin. Endocrinol. Metab.* 54:919–30

54. Thibault, C., Chan, J. K., Perdue, J. F., Daughaday, W. H. 1984. Insulin-like growth factor receptors: molecular radius and molecular weight determination using quantitative polyacrylamide gel elec-

trophoresis. *J. Biol. Chem.* 259:3361–67

55. Van Obberghen-Schilling, E. E., Rechler, M. M., Romanus, J. A., et al. 1981. Receptors for insulin-like growth factor I are defective in fibroblasts cultured from a patient with leprechaunism. *J. Clin. Invest.* 68:1356–65

56. Van Obberghen-Schilling, E., Pouysségur, J. 1983. Mitogen-potentiating action and binding characteristics of insulin and insulin-like growth factors in Chinese hamster fibroblasts. *Exper. Cell Res.* 147:369–78

57. Wardzala, L. J., Simpson, I. A., Rechler, M. M., Cushman, S. W. 1984. Potential mechanism of the stimulatory action of insulin on insulin-like growth factor II binding to the isolated rat adipose cell: apparent redistribution of receptors recycling between a large intracellular pool and the plasma membrane. *J. Biol. Chem.* 259:8378–83

58. Yu, K-T., Czech, M. P. 1984. The type I insulin-like growth factor receptor medi-

ates the rapid effects of multiplication-stimulating activity on membrane transport systems in rat soleus muscle. *J. Biol. Chem.* 259:3090–95

59. Zapf, J., Schoenle, E., Froesch, E. R. 1978. Insulin-like growth factors I and II: some biological actions and receptor binding characteristics of two purified constituents of nonsuppressible insulin-like activity of human serum. *Eur. J. Biochem.* 87:285–96

60. Zapf, J., Froesch, E. R., Humbel, R. E. 1981. The insulin-like growth factors (IGF) of human serum: chemical and biological characterization and aspects of their possible physiological role. *Curr. Top. Cell. Reg.* 19:257–309

61. Zick, Y., Sasaki, N., Rees-Jones, R. W., Grunberger, G., Nissley, S. P., Rechler, M. M. 1984. Insulin-like growth factor-I (IGF-I) stimulates tyrosine kinase activity in purified receptors from a rat liver cell line. *Biochem. Biophys. Res. Commun.* 119:6–13

Ann. Rev. Physiol. 1985. 47:443–67

ACTIONS OF INSULIN-LIKE GROWTH FACTORS

E. R. Froesch, Chr. Schmid, J. Schwander, and J. Zapf

Metabolic Unit, University Hospital, CH-8091 Zurich, Switzerland

INTRODUCTION

Three different lines of research and three entirely different observations have led to the discovery of the insulin-like growth factors (IGFs).

In 1957, Salmon & Daughaday carried out an important experiment (44). They observed that serum stimulated the incorporation of ^{35}S into incubated cartilage. Serum of hypophysectomized rats was devoid of this sulfation activity. It could not be reconstituted by addition of growth hormone to the incubation medium but reappeared after administration of growth hormone to hypophysectomized rats (44). These observations led Daughaday to postulate that growth hormone itself does not stimulate growth processes in vitro and in vivo, but rather induces the formation of factors that mediate the message of growth hormone. These factors—first called sulfation factors, later somatomedins—lead to sulfation of cartilage in vitro, which reflects growth in vivo. As we shall see, this hypothesis has been proven to be valid.

Most cultured cells need serum to grow. Several growth factors in serum are responsible for growth-promoting effects, an aspect that will be discussed below in more detail. In 1972, Pierson & Temin extracted factors from serum, which they called multiplication-stimulating activity (MSA) (37). These factors had molecular weights below 10,000. When added to culture medium, they stimulated cells to replicate. Later it was found that cultured liver cells secrete MSA into the culture medium (10). This was the first demonstration that MSA is produced in the liver and that MSA may lead to autocrine stimulation of the same cells by which it is secreted.

The third road towards the discovery of insulin-like growth factors departed from an entirely different observation: Serum exerts insulin-like effects on

443

0066-4278/85/0315-0443$02.00

insulin target tissues such as muscle and adipose tissue. These effects are much greater than would be expected on the basis of the insulin content of serum. Furthermore, the insulin effects of serum are not suppressed by the addition of anti-insulin serum, contrary to the effects of insulin (15). The molecules in serum responsible for these insulin-like effects (originally termed NSILA) were searched for and finally identified as insulin-like growth factors I and II (42, 43). The major steps leading to the discovery of these two growth factors have been reviewed recently (20).

Somatomedins, multiplication-stimulating activity, and insulin-like growth factors are members of one big family of polypeptide hormones. All of these polypeptide hormones do not exist in serum or in other body fluids in the free form, but are bound to specific carrier proteins (61). These serum-binding proteins appear to be the same for these various factors. IGFs, somatomedins, and MSA act via IGF receptors and cross-react to some extent with the insulin receptor (40, 41). In the bound form they do not appear to readily bind to the insulin or IGF receptor (35, 63). This is the reason why IGF can be present in human serum in concentrations of up to 1 μg ml^{-1} without causing hypoglycemia. However, a few ng of the free hormone have marked growth-promoting effects (65). In other words, insulin-like growth factors are present in serum in great excess. Serum probably serves as a storage pool. In this respect these polypeptide hormones are similar to the thyroid and steroid hormones, which are also bound to specific carrier proteins.

CHEMISTRY OF INSULIN-LIKE GROWTH FACTORS

In the introduction we have superficially presented the various insulin-like growth factors. So far, two of them, IGF I and IGF II, have been chemically characterized. Their structures have been elucidated by Rinderknecht & Humbel (42, 43). IGF I and IGF II are homologous peptides, and they are structurally related to insulin (2). They consist of an A-domain homologous to the A-chain of insulin and a B-domain homologous to the B-chain of insulin. In the A- and B-regions the homology between IGFs and insulin is approximately 45%. In contrast to insulin, the C-domains are retained in IGF I and II and they consist of 12 and 8 amino acids, respectively. An additional D-domain extends from the C-terminal end of the A-chain. The structural relationship between the IGFs, the somatomedins, and MSA has been elucidated in the last few years: Somatomedin C is identical with IGF I (26). MSA purified from conditioned buffalo rat liver cell medium is homologous to IGF II (28). It is fair to state that the three different lines of research, the somatomedin line, the MSA line, and the NSILA-IGF line, have led to the discovery of the same polypeptide hormones. It is possible, but by no means proven, that somatomedin A may be different from somatomedin C and that other insulin-like growth factors may be present in human serum (7). The major somatomedins are IGF I and IGF II because these two factors make up more than 90% of the total extractable small molecular insulin-like noninsulin material of serum. It is also likely that these two factors are of paramount physiological importance for regenerative processes of tissues of mesodermal origin, wound healing and growth of cartilage and bone.

The homology between insulin-like growth factors and insulin indicates that these two hormones are the product of a gene duplication that may have taken place about 600 million years ago (2). The precursor molecule of insulin and IGF has not yet been detected. The gene duplication that led to the diversion of IGF into IGF I and IGF II took place about 300 million years ago, i.e. with the appearance of the mammals on earth.

Figure 1 shows the receptor- and the anitibody-binding regions of insulin projected on the three-dimensional model of the IGF molecule. Whereas the structural similarity in the receptor-binding region between insulin and IGF is considerable, the more hydrophilic sequences of the antibody-binding region are rather different. This explains the biological similarities and the lack of immunological cross-reactivity.

ARE IGFs HORMONES? ORIGIN, SYNTHESIS, AND SECRETION OF IGF

The hepatic origin of the IGFs has long been suspected, but had not been proven until a few years ago (1, 7, 22, 39, 45). Difficulties in depicting the origin of the IGFs have to do with the large concentrations of IGF in serum and the low

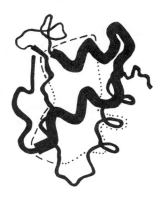

PROPOSED RECEPTOR BINDING
REGION OF INSULIN PROJECTED
ON THE 3-DIMENSIONAL MODEL
OF IGF I

ANTIBODY BINDING REGIONS
OF INSULIN PROJECTED ON THE
3-DIMENSIONAL MODEL OF IGF I

Figure 1 The antibody-binding regions of insulin and of IGF do not appear to overlap at all. There are as yet no insulin antibodies cross-reacting with IGF and vice versa. IGF antibodies recognize the C-loops and their extensions towards the A- and B-domains (from 2).

concentrations in tissues. Extraction procedures and immunohistochemistry of all kinds of tissues failed to identify a tissue as a probable source of IGFs. In this respect the IGFs are completely different from most polypeptide hormones. The latter are synthesized in endocrine cells. Most of them are stored in the form of granules. These granules are rapidly secreted into the blood stream when the endocrine cell is told to do so, and, therefore, the hormone levels in plasma vary rapidly and over a wide range. This is entirely different in the case of the IGFs. The concentration of IGFs does not undergo diurnal variations and is very stable in any given subject under constant nutritional and endocrine conditions.

The mode of synthesis and secretion of IGF by the liver has been elucidated by Schwander et al in our laboratory (55). We used the cyclically perfused rat liver to study IGF synthesis and secretion and compared it with the synthesis and secretion of albumin. The secretion of rat IGF from the perfused rat liver is a steady, slow process that parallels albumin secretion. When ^{35}S-cysteine is added to the perfusion medium, this amino acid is readily incorporated into the IGF molecule. After 20–30 min the secreted IGF molecule contains measurable quantities of ^{35}S-cysteine and after about 1 hr the specific radioactivity of the secretory product reaches a plateau (Figure 2). This can be interpreted to mean that there is no or only very little preformed, stored IGF in liver cells. It is, therefore, also rather unlikely that there are large amounts of IGF precursor molecules stored in the liver. Quite on the contrary, IGF is synthesized rapidly from amino acids and is readily secreted. These processes of IGF synthesis and secretion are paralleled by those of albumin synthesis and secretion (55). Mayer & Schalch (29) have reached the same conclusions using cultured rat liver cells. IGFs may also be produced by other cells and tissues in minor quantities (see 65 for review). Based on calculations of the production of rat IGF by the isolated liver and of the half-life of infused and injected human IGFs, one can conclude that more than 90% of the total IGF is secreted by the liver.

The liver is also the source of the IGF-binding protein (1, 55). Schwander et al have shown that IGF and its binding protein are secreted independently of each other. Livers of hypophysectomized rats secrete no measurable quantities of IGF but near-normal amounts of its binding protein (Figure 3). This makes it unlikely that IGF and the binding protein have common precursors (55).

It is absolutely remarkable to what extent the modes of synthesis and processing of IGF and insulin, such closely related polypeptide hormones, have diverged during a relatively short time of evolution. Insulin is synthesized in the B cells of the islets of Langerhans in the pancreas and stored in the form of B granules. These granules are expulsed into the blood by exocytosis when the plasma glucose concentration rises and, therefore, insulin concentrations in the blood increase rapidly and fall rapidly again according to the need of the

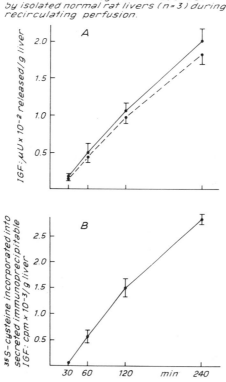

Figure 2 Rat IGF release was determined by two assays using the serum-binding protein (61) and lipogenesis in isolated fat cells from U-^{14}C-glucose (62). The secreted IGF was immunoprecipitated with IGF I antibodies, and the ^{35}S-cysteine that had been incorporated was counted in the precipitate. Synthesis and secretion of IGF are linear and parallel processes, and the specific radioactivity of the IGF molecule forms a plateau already after 60 min of recirculation (from 55).

organism, which changes from second to second. In contrast to insulin, IGF secretion is a steady, slow process leading to a constant level of IGF in serum that is much higher than that of insulin because most or all of the IGF is bound to its binding proteins (see 65 for review). The major regulatory factors of the IGF concentrations in serum are growth-hormone levels (66), nutrition, adequate insulin secretion, and probably also adequate thyroid function, without which growth-hormone secretion is decreased. Only IGF I appears to be absolutely dependent on growth hormone (66). Pituitary dwarfs with a complete deficiency of growth hormone secretion have extremely low levels of IGF I. However, their IGF II levels are 200–300 instead of 600 ng ml^{-1}, i.e. about one third to one half of the normal concentration. We do not know why this amount of IGF II does not suffice to stimulate normal growth processes. Probably

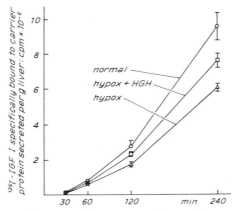

Figure 3 The binding protein concentration was measured by covalent cross-linking of ^{125}I–IGF I to the binding protein. The mean of two dilutions in duplicate is given, expressed as counts per minute of ^{125}I–IGF I bound/g liver. All *points* represent the mean values of three experiments ± SD. The concentration of secreted binding protein was significantly different in all three groups (p < 0.02) at 240 min of perfusion (from 55). Hypox = hypophysectomized; HGH = human growth hormone.

IGF II is much less active in stimulating growth than IGF I. IGF II has one-third the potency of IGF I in stimulating DNA synthesis in human fibroblasts (see Figure 4) and one-fifth the potency in rat osteoblasts (Figure 5) (50). It is possible that these IGF II concentrations are sufficient to sustain tissue repair and regenerative processes.

CIRCULATING FORMS OF INSULIN-LIKE GROWTH FACTORS

As mentioned above, insulin-like growth factors circulate in plasma in the bound form with M_rs of approximately 50,000 and 150,000, respectively (see 24, 65 for review). In the bound form, IGF does not cross-react with the insulin receptor and does not exert insulin-like effects (35, 63). When cartilage or chondrocytes are incubated in serum, thymidine and sulfate incorporation is stimulated according to the IGF content of the serum. It is not known whether the tissues dissociate IGF from the binding complex so that free IGF can then interact with the IGF receptor, or whether the whole IGF-carrier complex interacts with the receptor. Simple dissociation of IGF from the binding complex could occur at low pH. Under this condition the noncovalent

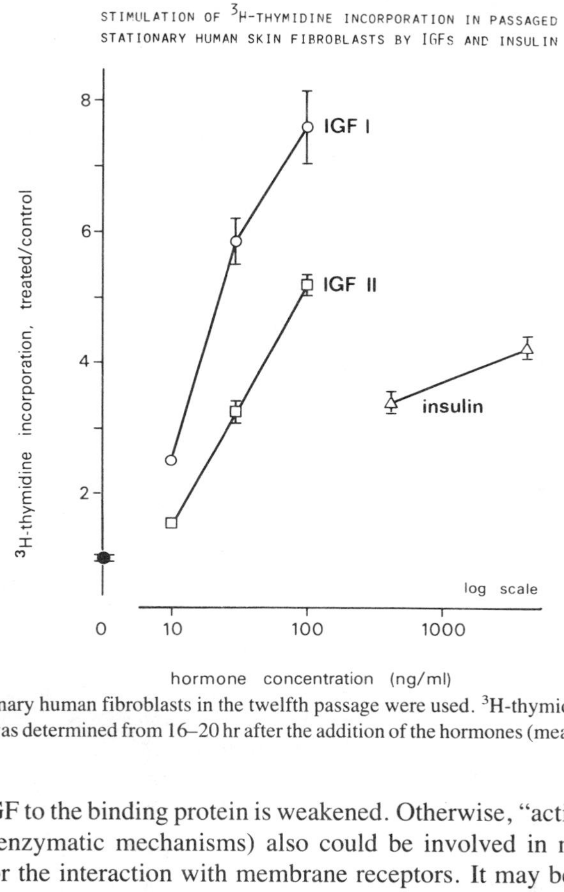

STIMULATION OF ^{3}H-THYMIDINE INCORPORATION IN PASSAGED STATIONARY HUMAN SKIN FIBROBLASTS BY IGFs AND INSULIN

Figure 4 Stationary human fibroblasts in the twelfth passage were used. ^{3}H-thymidine incorporation into DNA was determined from 16–20 hr after the addition of the hormones (mean ± SEM, n = 12).

binding of IGF to the binding protein is weakened. Otherwise, "active mechanisms" (e.g. enzymatic mechanisms) also could be involved in making IGF accessible for the interaction with membrane receptors. It may be of interest that cerebrospinal fluid contains only the 50K but none of the 150K complex. There appears to be much less IGF present in cerebrospinal fluid than would be expected from the high content of the 50K binding protein (U. Widmer & J. Zapf, unpublished observations).

INSULIN-LIKE EFFECTS OF IGF

IGF elicits classical insulin effects on all target tissues of insulin: IGF increases glucose metabolism of adipose tissue (16). It stimulates glucose transport as demonstrated by means of 3-O-methylglucose efflux and influx (62). Lipid, glycogen, and protein synthesis are also stimulated by IGF. IGF inhibits lipolysis in the same way as insulin, enhances low K_m phosphodiesterase

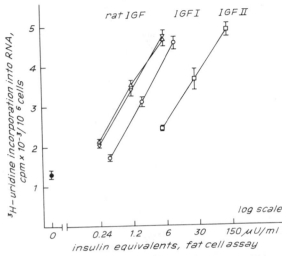

Stimulation of ³H-uridine incorporation into RNA of cultured rat calvaria cells by human IGF I (○), IGF II (□), and by rat IGF preparations partially purified from serum (▽) and from liver perfusion (△). Mean ± SD of triplicates.

Figure 5 The potencies of human IGF I and II and of two preparations of impure rat IGF were compared with respect to ³H-uridine incorporation in cultured primary rat calvaria cells. Rat IGF was partially purified from rat serum (56) and also from the medium of perfused normal rat livers (55). Rat IGF is three times more potent than IGF I and the latter five times more potent than IGF II. These results are compatible with the respective potency ratios obtained in in vivo infusion experiments in hypophysectomized rats (54). The experimental conditions are described in detail in (47).

activity, and inhibits calcium ATPase (E. Schoenle, unpublished observations). The IGFs are one-fifth to one-hundredth as potent in exerting all of these effects on adipose tissue as insulin, and there is reason to believe that the effects are elicited by interaction with the insulin receptor (67). In binding experiments, IGF competes for the insulin receptor with a K_d that corresponds to the concentration of IGF needed for half-maximal stimulation of glucose uptake of adipose tissue (for review see 65). In contrast, IGF binds with a much higher affinity to its own adipocyte receptor. After intraperitoneal injection to rats together with U-^{14}C-glucose, IGF stimulates glucose incorporation into glycogen in the adjacent tissues (16).

IGF mimics all of the in vitro effects of insulin on the soleus muscle of mice. The best-studied effects comprise the following stimulations: glucose transport as demonstrated by 2-deoxyglucose accumulation, glycolysis as demonstrated by increased lactate formation, and glycogen and protein synthesis. IGF is about 5–10% as potent as insulin on mouse soleus muscle (38). In the perfused rat heart preparation, IGF simulates all effects of insulin with a potency of about 25% of that of insulin (34). Glucose transport and lactate formation are stimulated at low IGF concentrations. At much higher concentrations the contractility of the rat heart is increased by IGF as well as by insulin (3). The concentration of these hormones required to enhance contractility appears to be the same as that required for half-maximal saturation of the insulin receptor (3). Taken together with the binding data, it would appear that IGF stimulates glucose uptake and glycolysis in the rat heart via the IGF receptor, whereas half-maximal occupation of the insulin receptor is required for stimulation of contractility (3).

Liver cells have IGF receptors, mainly IGF II receptors. Therefore, liver plasma membranes are used for an efficient and quite specific radioreceptor assay for IGF II (8, 58, 60). Because it is notoriously difficult to demonstrate insulin effects on liver cells, little is known about effects of IGFs on the liver. It has been demonstrated that chick embryo liver cells respond to IGF in the same way as to insulin (59): IGF stimulates the synthesis of RNA, protein, and glycogen. It is likely, but has not been demonstrated unequivocally, that hepatic cells of other species respond similarly to IGF.

HYPOGLYCEMIC EFFECTS OF IGF IN VIVO

Impure preparations of IGF (NSILA-s) injected intravenously as a bolus provoke a rapid fall of the blood sugar (16). These earlier studies have now been repeated with pure IGF I and IGF II (Zapf & Froesch, manuscript in preparation). Both hormones were injected intravenously together with anti-insulin serum in order to block possible effects of endogenous insulin and together with $U^{14}C$-glucose in order to trace the fate of glucose. IGF I and IGF II lead to acute hypoglycemia, with a nadir between 15 and 30 min. (Fig. 6). The rate of removal of injected ^{14}C-glucose from the blood is enhanced under the influence of IGF, and ^{14}C-radioactivity is recovered in the classical insulin target tissues in the form of glycogen in muscle and lipids in adipose tissue. It is of particular interest that muscle in vivo is much more sensitive to IGF than adipose tissue. This is in keeping with the in vitro results where IGF was 50–100 times less potent than insulin on adipose tissue, 10–20 times less potent on soleus muscle, and 3–5 times less potent on the rat heart (see 65 for review). The IGF effects on muscle in vivo subside 30–45 min after intravenous injection of the hormone. Despite the fact that the half-life of injected unlabeled IGF in the normal rat is 3–4 hr, it is to be expected that IGF has only short-lasting effects on insulin target tissues. First of all, insulin-like effects of IGF after intravenous injection are demonstrable only with large amounts of IGF that override the binding capacity of the carrier proteins. Only part of the

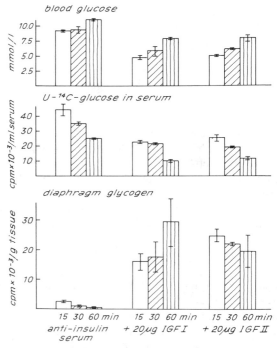

Effects of i.v. IGF I and IGF II on blood glucose and incorporation of i.v. U-14C-glucose in hypox rats after 15, 30 and 60 minutes. (n = 2, range)

Figure 6 IGF I and IGF II were injected i.v. into hypophysectomized (hypox) rats in doses of 20 μg together with anti-insulin serum (neutralizing capacity of 100 m units) and 1 μCi of U-^{14}C-glucose. The rats were killed after 15, 30, and 60 min, and blood glucose and ^{14}C in serum and in glycogen of the diaphragm were determined. The IGFs led to a rapid fall of the blood sugar in spite of the blocking of the effects of insulin with anti-insulin serum. The injected U-^{14}C-glucose disappeared rapidly from the serum under the influence of the IGFs and appeared in the glycogen of the diaphragm. The latter parameter is stimulated to a much greater extent than lipogenesis in adipose tissue by IGFs (Zapf & Froesch, manuscript in preparation).

IGF is bound by the free sites on the binding proteins. The IGF that is not bound crosses the blood barrier into the interstitial fluid and thereby gains access to the target cells. So far, available evidence suggests that free IGF has a much shorter half-life than IGF bound to the small and large molecular binding protein. Dissociation of IGF from the binding protein is likely to occur, but the concentrations of free IGF reached in the interstitial fluid appear to be so small that no insulin-like effects are elicited. The half-life of i.v. injected unlabeled IGF is 3–4 hr in normal rats. IGF II is considerably less hypoglycemic than IGF I (Zapf & Froesch, manuscript in preparation).

GROWTH-PROMOTING EFFECTS OF INSULIN-LIKE GROWTH FACTORS

MSA, somatomedins, and IGFs have been shown to be potent growth-promoting stimuli for many different cultured cells in vitro. Impure preparations of NSILA-s containing varying amounts of IGF I and II were tested in primary chick embryo fibroblast cultures by Morell & Froesch (36). In these early experiments it was shown that fibroblasts that had been kept in serum-free medium for 48 hr synthesized more DNA under the influence of NSILA-s and replicated faster.

Later, similar experiments were carried out with pure IGF I and IGF II: Both are equipotent stimulators of DNA synthesis and cell replication in primary chick embryo fibroblast cultures (62). Chick embryo fibroblasts appear to have only one IGF membrane receptor, which recognizes IGF I and IGF II with about the same affinity. Passaged human fibroblasts and transformed fibroblast lines of mammals are also stimulated by IGF I and II to synthesize DNA and to replicate (see Figure 4) (18). In all of these cell systems, IGFs do not substitute for serum even at large concentrations. They stimulate DNA synthesis and cell replication less than the platelet-derived growth factor and other growth factors that are much more potent mitogens than IGF (47, 50). All effects of small concentrations of IGF on cultured fibroblasts are mimicked by unphysiologically high concentrations of insulin. The effects of IGF and of insulin are not additive and appear to be mediated through the same receptor, whereas the effects of IGF and of platelet-derived growth factor on DNA synthesis are additive. It is likely that the growth-promoting effects of serum can be mimicked by the two major growth-promoting stimuli of serum, i.e. IGF and platelet-derived growth factor (PDGF). Both of these factors are present in blood in large concentrations, IGF stored in complexed form with its serum-binding protein and platelet-derived growth factor stored in the platelets. PDGF reaches the cells as soon as platelets attach to the wall of the blood vessels and release their contents. Stiles and coworkers have studied the qualitative effects of IGF and of other factors and have put forth the interesting hypothesis that insulin and IGFs are "progression" factors, whereas platelet-derived and similar growth factors render these cells "competent" to respond to the progression factors (56). In view of our recent findings, according to which IGF promotes differentiation more markedly than replication of undifferentiated mesodermal cells, the hypothesis of Stiles appears to hold true only for some transformed cells but probably not for primary cultured cells of mesodermal origin and not for cellular differentiation and organization of organs in the whole body.

Recently, these studies on growth parameters and replication have been extended to smooth muscle cells (B. Pfeiffle, personal communication), chondrocytes (17, 21), and bone cells (47, 48), which all respond to IGF I and IGF II with increased cellular replication and/or enhanced formation of matrix. Evidence is accumulating that in these cell systems the IGFs may be important for cell replication, cell differentiation, and the production of specific cellular products.

GROWTH-PROMOTING EFFECTS OF THE IGFs IN VIVO

Many clinical and animal studies point to a relationship between growth and IGF I levels. Thus, in patients with acromegaly, IGF I levels are about 3-fold higher than in normal subjects (64, 66). Pituitary dwarfs have low levels of IGF I, which rise into the normal range when they are treated with growth hormone (32). The rise of the IGF serum concentration goes along with growth. Markedly decreased IGF levels have been determined after hypophysectomy in the following animal species: the rat (25), the dog (11), and the minipig (M. Becker, unpublished observations). Rats bearing growth hormone–producing tumors have very high levels of somatomedin C/IGF I and grow rapidly (4). After excision of the tumor, growth hormone and IGF levels fall, and the animals stop growing. In the dog, acromegaly is not a rare disease and goes along with increased levels of IGF I (12). Such dogs are cured by hypophysectomy or drugs that decrease growth hormone secretion and IGF levels in plasma. In all of these situations, IGF I levels parallel the growth-hormone concentration, i.e. one cannot discriminate whether growth hormone or IGF is responsible for excessive or diminished growth. There are, however, two experiments of nature that seem to indicate that IGF rather than growth hormone is directly related to growth:

1. The pygmies living in Central Africa are of small stature and rarely exceed 145 cm (about 4′7″) in height. Negroes of the Bantu grouping live in the small area side by side with the pygmies, but do not mingle with them and are much taller. Nutritional and environmental factors do not explain the small size of the pygmies, who do not suffer from malnutrition. The response of plasma growth hormone to various stimuli in pygmies was studied 15 years ago and found to be normal. In particular, pygmies have normal resting plasma growth hormone concentrations (31). Nevertheless, pygmies display hypoglycemic unresponsiveness after exogenous insulin and insulinopenia after an i.v. arginine infusion or after an oral glucose load similar to GH-deficient dwarfs (30). Similar to this latter group of patients, IGF I levels are very low, but in contrast to GH-deficient dwarfs, they do not rise in response to administered growth hormone (33). The riddle of the small size of the pygmies appears to have been solved: They are small because they have low plasma levels of IGF I. They do not synthesize normal amounts of IGF I despite normal levels of active growth hormone.

2. The second example has to do with dogs, in which inbreeding to produce a particular predetermined size is fashionable. Thus, three different kinds of poodles are bred: the standard, miniature, and toy. They belong to the same race of dogs but are differently inbred. Eigenmann and coworkers measured growth hormone and IGF I levels in groups of these three differently sized poodles and found normal growth-hormone levels and responses in all three groups, high levels of IGF I in the standard poodle, intermediate levels in the miniature poodle, and very low IGF I levels in the toy poodle (13). It would, of course, be very interesting to treat toy poodles with IGF I in order to see whether they grow bigger. This experiment has not yet been carried out because sufficient amounts of IGF I are not yet available.

GROWTH-PROMOTING EFFECTS OF SUBCUTANEOUSLY ADMINISTERED IGF

The question whether or not pituitary growth hormone has direct growth-promoting effects on cartilage and bone has not been solved in a definitive manner (23). Hypophysectomized animals who have stopped growing show a clear-cut growth spurt when they receive growth hormone. Growth-hormone treatment has become the routine therapy for pituitary dwarfs.

Growth hormone leads, among other things, to a rise of the serum levels of IGF I, which might well mediate the effects of growth hormone (32). Isaksson et al injected growth hormone directly into the growth plate of one leg of hypophysectomized rats and compared the epiphyseal width on both sides. These investigators found that locally administered growth hormone led to an increase of the epiphyseal width and concluded that under these circumstances growth hormone has a direct effect on cartilage (23). In our laboratory a more physiological route of growth hormone and IGF administration was used (14, 53). Because IGF plasma levels are rather constant and do not change rapidly, we decided to infuse IGF subcutaneously with the help of osmotic Alza minipumps. Two doses of IGF I, 43 μg and 103 μg per day, and one dose of IGF II, 131 μg per day, were infused during 6 days into hypophysectomized rats. For comparison 12.5 and 25 mU, respectively, of growth hormone were administered to two groups of hypophysectomized rats by the same route. IGF had marked growth-promoting effects (14, 53). The body weight rose (Figure 8), the tibial epiphyseal width increased (Figure 8), and thymidine incorporation into costal cartilage, which was taken from the animals after 6 days of infusion and incubated in vitro, was enhanced.

These effects were highly significant. They were elicited by slow subcutaneous infusions of IGF I, and they were dose-dependent. IGF II was much less potent than IGF I (54). This is in keeping with the effects of IGF I and

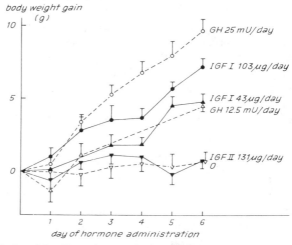

Longitudinal control of body weight gain in untreated hypox rats (▽) and hypox rats treated with IGF I 103μg/day (●), IGF I 43μg/day (▲), IGF II 131μg/day (▼), GH 12.5 mU/day (△) and GH 25mU/day (○).

Figure 7 The body weight of hypophysectomized rats receiving IGF or growth hormone (GH) by infusions with subcutaneously implanted osmotic Alza minipumps during 6 days increases linearly. 103 μg of IGF I per day are almost as potent as 25 mU of growth hormone. The two lower doses of these two hormones had similar and comparable effects on the body weight. IGF II was without a significant effect (from 53).

IGF II on rat calvaria cells in vitro, where the potency ratio is about 5 : 1 in favor of IGF I (47, 50). In addition, the efficacy of IGF I was compared with that of endogenous rat IGF present in the serum of these hypophysectomized rats under the influence of subcutaneously infused growth hormone. Assuming that the major growth factor in these hypophysectomized rats under growth hormone administration was endogenous rat IGF, this latter insulin-like growth factor appeared about twice as potent as IGF I (54). This potency ratio is again compatible with that found in vitro on rat calvaria cells, where rat IGF was 2–3-fold more effective than IGF I (see Figure 5) (50). These results demonstrate in a definitive manner that the somatomedin hypothesis of Salmon & Daughaday (44) is valid: Growth hormone stimulates the liver to synthesize and secrete insulin-like growth factors that, in turn, stimulate replication of chondrocytes and osteoblasts and matrix formation by these cells. Whether or not growth hormone has additional effects on these cell systems superimposed on those of IGF cannot be decided on the basis of these results.

However, we found that growth hormone does have distinct effects on the form in which IGF circulates in serum. Growth hormone–deficient rats and

Tibial epiphyseal width of hypophysectomized rats after a 6 days' SC infusion of 0.9% Na Cl (a), hGH (b), IGF II (c) and IGF I (d).

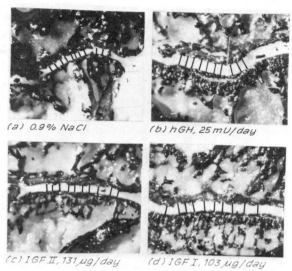

(a) 0.9% NaCl   (b) hGH, 25 mU/day

(c) IGF II, 131 μg/day   (d) IGF I, 103 μg/day

Figure 8 The tibial epiphyseal width was measured in hypophysectomized rats 6 days after the infusion of NaCl, human growth hormone (hGH), IGF I, and IGF II. The effects of IGF I and hGH are comparable, whereas those of IGF II are still significant but less important (from 54).

men lack the large-M_r IGF-binding protein in serum (5, 25, 36a). When serum of the IGF-infused rats was investigated with respect to the two binding proteins, the large-M_r binding protein was still lacking. This is in contrast to growth-hormone treatment, which leads to the reappearance of the large-M_r binding protein. All of the IGF present in the serum of IGF-infused rats circulates in the form of a 50K complex, whereas in the growth hormone–infused rats the endogenous rat IGF circulates mostly in the form of the big 150K complex. It is to be expected that the diffusion of IGF into the interstitial space and the accessibility of IGF to the various membrane receptors is quite different whether it is bound to the small or to the large-M_r binding protein. One piece of evidence for different handling of IGF is the finding that the half-life of infused IGF in hypophysectomized rats is in the order of 20 min, whereas it is about ten-fold longer, i.e. ~4 hr, in normal rats or growth hormone–treated hypophysectomized rats (Zapf & Froesch, manuscript in preparation). In this way growth hormone might modulate the accessibility of IGF in a very distinct manner, the impact of which is not yet fully understood.

EFFECTS OF IGFs ON DIFFERENTIATION OF MESENCHYMAL CELLS

Evidence is accumulating that IGFs have distinct effects on the differentiation of cells of mesodermal origin. The data stem from three different cell systems in three different species and were obtained with human IGFs. It has been shown that insulin in pharmacological concentrations favors the differentiation of myoblasts and the formation of myotubes in primary cultures of chick embryonic cells (9). Schmid et al carried out similar experiments with very low concentrations of IGF. Chick cells from the body walls were seeded in the total absence of serum in minimum essential medium supplemented with 650 mg liter^{-1} of human serum albumin.

Growth factors, when present, were added to the medium in which the cells were dispersed, and the medium was changed every other day. In the presence of IGF I or II, more myotubes were observed, and their number reached a maximum after 3–5 days (Figure 9a, 9b) (51). After that time myotubes start contracting and detach from the dishes. The total cell number was not increased drastically in the presence of IGF, and in particular, fibroblasts did not replicate to any great extent. In order to ascertain that the cells seen on the dishes were really muscle cells, acetylcholinesterase activity was determined as a marker enzyme. Acetylcholinesterase activity rose to a maximum 3–5 days after IGF addition, in parallel with the appearence of myotubes and to much higher levels than could be accounted for by the increase of the number of cells (Figure 10) (51). IGF I and IGF II were equipotent in stimulating myoblast differentiation and myotube formation. This finding must be interpreted in view of the fact that chick cells appear to have only one IGF receptor, which has approximately the same affinity for IGF I as for IGF II.

The second observation concerns colony formation of erythroid cells from embryonic mouse liver and adult mouse bone marrow. The major factor that stimulates growth and differentiation of erythroid cells is erythropoietin. IGF I was tested on colony formation and found to be a potent growth and colony formation factor. The effect on colony formation depended on the dose of IGF and occurred within the "physiological" concentration range of the hormone (27) (Figure 11).

The third and most recent observation concerns osteoblast-like (i.e. calvaria) cells of newborn rats. These cells together with chondrocytes are responsible for growth until maturation and for regeneration of bone and new matrix formation throughout adulthood. Primary calvaria cells can be cultured and can be used as a model to study the influence of hormones on more or less "pure" bone cell cultures. The cells were characterized by their alkaline phosphatase activity and their response to parathyroid hormone with respect to cAMP formation. When the cultures reach confluence, ^{3}H-thymidine incorporation into DNA decreases, and their content of alkaline phosphatase tends to in-

PRIMARY CHICK EMBRYO CELLS (NO GROWTH FACTORS)

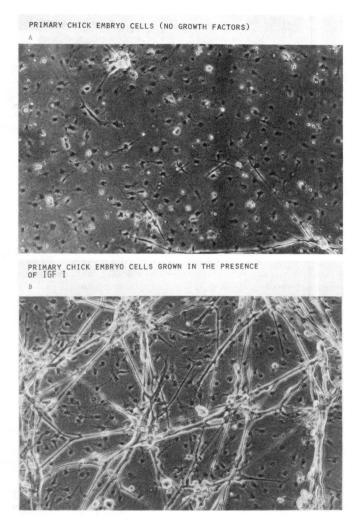

PRIMARY CHICK EMBRYO CELLS GROWN IN THE PRESENCE
OF IGF I

Figure 9a and 9b Cells from the body walls of 10-day-old chicken embryos were plated in MEM-Eagle medium at a density of 1.4×10^6 cells per dish (Falcon, 35 mm diameter). Human serum albumin was present (65 mg liter^{-1}). These pictures are phase contrast photomicrographs taken of these cells after 3 days of culture, in 9a without any additions and in 9b with the addition of 100 ng ml^{-1} of IGF I. Myotubes are very prominent in the dish where IGF I was present (Figure 9b) (from 51).

crease. Most growth factors, like serum, lead to an increased frequency of replication, and alkaline phosphatase activity per cell decreases or does not change. Such cellular responses are considered typical for growth factors that act mainly as mitogens. In the case of the IGFs we observe a different behavior

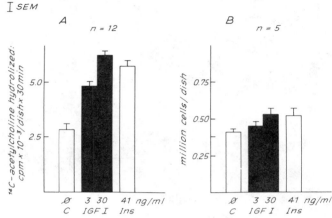

Figure 10 The same cells as described in Figure 9 were used. The cell number was determined (*B*) and compared with a marker enzyme of muscle, acetylcholine esterase activity (*A*). After 4 days IGF I leads to a small increase of the cell number and to a disproportionate increase in ACE activity. Both effects are dose-dependent and are also produced by insulin (Ins). These data indicate that IGF preferentially promotes differentiation of myoblasts. Modified from (51).

of osteoblast-like cells: The number of cells increases only to a modest extent, but the cells appear to become and remain highly differentiated (Figure 12) (48).

Besides IGF I, triiodothyronine (T_3) had clear-cut effects on differentiation. When grown in the presence of T_3, the cell number remained unchanged, and the cells were sensitized toward the action of parathyroid hormone with respect to ornithine decarboxylase induction (52). It is likely that matrix formation is also influenced by IGF I and T_3. The major endocrine factors stimulating growth, the formation and differentiation of bone, appear, therefore, to be the IGFs and thyroid hormones. We have not had the opportunity to study the bone growth factors, which may be local, possibly autocrine growth factors. In view of our results on growth of hypophysectomized rats in vivo, IGF I is much more active than IGF II. In any case, IGF I appears to be a prerequisite in vivo and in vitro for orderly growth and differentiation of bone.

CONCLUSIONS AND OUTLOOK

The insulin-like growth factors are close relatives to insulin. A gene duplication approximately 600 million years ago led to the diversion of a precursor molecule of IGF and insulin into these two distinct hormones. Insulin became

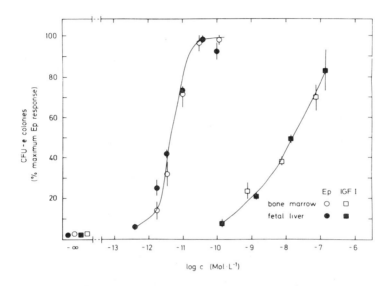

Figure 11 The effects of erythropoetin (Ep) and of IGF I on the formation of erythroid colonies from fetal mouse liver cells and adult bone marrow cells were studied. IGF I in physiological concentrations mimics the effects of Ep (from 27).

responsible for the acute homeostasis of the major energy substrates in the organism, such as glucose, free fatty acids, and ketone bodies. Insulin remained responsible for some major anabolic processes such as the maintenance of the major energy stores (glycogen, fat), amino acid transport into cells, and the synthesis of enzymes and other proteins. All these processes function normally only if the secretion of insulin is regulated in a coordinated fashion, induced from second to second by variations of the glucose concentrations. Therefore, the insulin concentration in plasma fluctuates considerably within short time intervals, according to the requirements of the organism. The IGFs have taken an entirely different physiological function. Their major source is the liver, which synthesizes and secretes the newly formed product readily into the circulation. There, IGF is bound to the serum binding proteins from which they appear to be released by dissociation and binding of IGF to the IGF receptors. IGF concentrations in serum are remarkably constant. The half-life of IGF in the rat is in the order of 4 hr, that of insulin 4–5 min. If nutrition is adequate and if insulin secretion maintains a normal distribution of the sub-

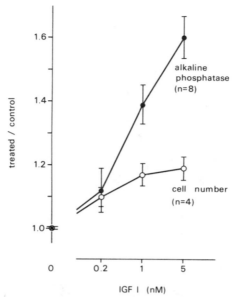

Figure 12 Cells were obtained from calvaria of newborn rats and plated at a density of 0.5 million cells per dish (Falcon, 35 mm diameter) in medium containing 1% fetal calf serum (FCS). The medium was a 1 : 1 mixture of MEM Alpha (Gibco) and Ham's F12. After 1 day the FCS was substituted with lg/liter of human serum albumin (HSA) and IGF I was added. Media were changed on days 1 and 4, and the cells were harvested on day 7. IGF I stimulates cell replication in a dose-dependent manner and has relatively greater effects on the alkaline phosphatase activity, indicating that IGF I acts as a weak mitogen and strongly supports differentiation of osteoblasts (from 48). (mean ± SEM, experiments)

strate flux from resorption in the small intestine, IGF is primarily controlled by growth hormone secretion from the pituitary. Hypophysectomized animals and pituitary dwarfs have very low levels of IGF I that can be stimulated by the administration of growth hormone. Besides these growth hormone–deficient, dwarfed animals and men, there are also some groups of dwarfed individuals who have normal growth hormone secretion, but clearly deficient IGF I secretion. Prominent examples are the pygmies, the Laron dwarfs, and, in the animal kingdom, the toy poodle.

IGF receptors are present in all tissues so far studied. The IGFs cross-react with a relatively poor affinity with the insulin receptor. The postreceptor events after IGF binds to its receptors are not yet understood. IGF leads to a rise of ornithine decarboxylase activity, DNA, RNA, and protein synthesis, and finally also to cell replication. The IGFs appear to be rather weak mitogens compared to other growth factors such as platelet-derived growth factor or fibroblast growth factor. Rather, IGFs have distinct effects on differentiation of cells of mesodermal origin. Thus, it has been shown that erythroid cells, precursors of muscle cells and of osteoblasts, undergo differentiation in the presence of IGFs in the mouse, chick, and rat, respectively.

The question whether the IGFs mediate the message of growth hormone to the major end organs, i.e. cartilage and bone, has been solved. IGF I has been administered to hypophysectomized rats, which grow under the influence of IGF I alone without any other hormone supplementation. However, growth hormone appears to modulate the effects of IGF. Under the influence of growth hormone, IGF is distributed differently among the serum-binding proteins. In this and maybe still other ways the effects of IGF on the target tissues are modulated by growth hormone. Whether or not growth hormone has additional direct effects on these target tissues is not certain at the present time.

Besides these growth-promoting effects, the IGFs also exert insulin-like effects on all target cells of insulin. IGF mimics all effects of insulin on adipose tissue. The IGFs are 50–100 times less active on adipose tissue than insulin, and these effects are mediated by the insulin receptor. IGFs act on striated muscle in the same way as insulin, with an activity ratio of 10 : 1 in favor of insulin. It could be that the IGFs exert all these effects via the IGF receptor. Finally, the IGFs are one-third to one-fifth as active as insulin in stimulating glucose uptake of the perfused rat heart and approximately one-fiftieth as active as insulin in stimulating contractility of the rat heart. It appears that IGF exerts its effects on glucose metabolism via the IGF receptor and those on contractility via the insulin receptor (see Figure 13).

Complementary anabolic action of insulin and IGF

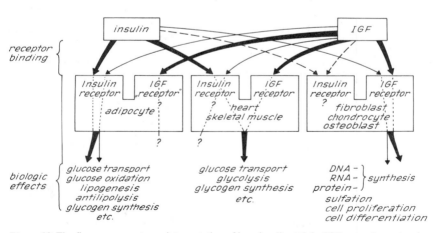

Figure 13 The figure represents our interpretation of how insulin and the IGFs complement each other with regard to growth and anabolic processes in general. Insulin is a prerequisite without which growth processes cannot be initiated because of lack of substrate. IGF appears to have taken over from the common ancestor molecule the regulation of the slow growth processes and the stimulation of the differentiation of some mesenchymal cells (from 65).

The binding of IGF to the serum-binding proteins changes the accessibility of the hormone to the respective cellular receptors. Insulin-like effects of IGF in vivo can be elicited only by bolus injections overriding the binding capacity of the binding proteins so that enough free IGF can reach the insulin target cells.

IGF has not yet become available in sufficient quantities to identify possible therapeutic indications for men and animals. Production of these growth factors by biotechnological means should make it possible to test their therapeutic potential with regard to: growth, wound and fracture healing, stimulation of anabolic processes in catabolic patients, topical application for cartilage and bone restoration, and resolution of metabolic problems in diabetics (19).

Literature Cited

1. Binoux, M., Hossenlopp, P., Lassarre, C., Seurin, D. 1980. Somatomedin production by rat liver in organ culture. I. Validity of the technique. Influence of the released material on cartilage sulphation. Effects of growth hormone and insulin. *Acta Endocrinol.* 93:73–82
2. Blundell, T. L., Bedarkar, S., Rinderknecht, E., Humbel, R. E. 1978. Insulin-like growth factors: A model for tertiary structure accounting for immunoreactivity and receptor binding. *Proc. Natl. Acad. Sci. USA* 75:180–84
3. Borner, F., Froesch, E. R. 1985. Increase of myocardial contractility by insulin and insulin-like growth factor I. *Diabetologia,* submitted for publication
4. Chochinov, R. H., Mariz, I. K., Daughaday, W. H. 1977. Isolation of a somatomedin from plasma of rats bearing growth hormone secreting tumors. *Endocrinology* 100:549–56
5. Copeland, K. C., Underwood, L. E., Van Wyk, J. J. 1980. Induction of immunoreactive somatomedin C in human serum by growth hormone: Dose response relationships and effect on chromatographic profiles. *J. Clin. Endocr. Metab.* 50:690–97
6. Daughaday, W. H., Hall, K., Raben, M. S., Salmon, W. D. Jr., van den Brande, L. J., Van Wyk, J. J. 1972. Somatomedin: Proposed designation for sulfation factor. *Nature* 235:107
7. Daughaday, W. H., Philips, L. S., Herington, A. C. 1975. Somatomedin generation by perfused livers. *Adv. Metab. Disord.* 8:151–57
8. Daughaday, W. H., Trivedi, B., Kapadia, M. 1981. Measurement of insulin-like growth factor II by a specific radioreceptor assay in serum of normal individuals, patients with abnormal growth hormone secretion, and patients

with tumor-associated hypoglycemia. *J. Clin. Endocr. Metab.* 53:289–91
9. Dollenmeier, P., Turner, D. C., Eppenberger, H. M. 1981. Proliferation and differentiation of chick skeletal muscle cells in a chemically defined medium. *Exp. Cell Res.* 135:47–61
10. Dulak, N., Temin, H. J. 1973. A partially puriefed polypeptide fraction from rat liver cell conditioned medium with multiplication stimulating activity for embryo fibroblasts. *J. Cell. Physiol.* 81:153–60
11. Eigenmann, J. E., Becker, M., Kammermann, B., Zapf, J., Leemann, W., Froesch, E. R. 1977. The influence of hypophysectomy of NSILA-s concentrations in the dog. Evidence for partially pituitary independent regulation. *Acta Endocrinol.* 86:498–503
12. Eigenmann, J. E., Eigenmann, R. Y., Rijnberk, A., Van der Gaag, A., Zapf, J., Froesch, E. R. 1983. Progesterone-controlled growth hormone overproduction and naturally occurring canine diabetes and acromegaly. *Acta Endocrinol.* 104:167–76
13. Eigenmann, J. E., Patterson, D. F., Froesch, E. R. 1984. Body size parallels insulin-like growth factor I levels but not growth hormone secretory capacity. *Acta Endocrinol.* 106:448–53
14. Ellis, S., Zapf, J., Froesch, E. R., Humbel, R. E. 1981. Stimulation of body weight increase and epiphyseal cartilage growth in hypophysectomized rats by insulin-like growth factor. *Endocrinology* 108:103 (Abstr.)
15. Froesch, E. R., Bürgi, H., Ramseier, E. B., Bally, P., Labhart, A. 1963. Antibody-suppressible and nonsuppressible insulin-like activities in human serum and their physiologic significance. An insulin assay with adipose tissue of increased precision and specificity. *J. Clin. Invest.* 42:1816–34

16. Froesch, E. R., Müller, W. A., Bürgi, H., Waldvogel, M., Labhart, A. 1966. Nonsuppressible insulin-like activity of human serum. I. Physicochemical properties, extraction and partial purification. *Biochim. Biophys. Acta* 121:360–74

17. Froesch, E. R., Zapf, J., Audhya, T. K., Ben-Porath, E., Segen, B. J., Gibson, K. D. 1976. Nonsuppressible insulin-like activity and thyroid hormones: Major pituitary-dependent sulfation factor for chick embryo cartilage. *Proc. Natl. Acad. Sci. USA* 73:2904–8

18. Froesch, E. R., Zapf, J., Walter, H., Schoenle, E., Rinderknecht, E., Humbel, R. E. 1979. Serum NSILA and IGF: News and riddles. *Horm. Cell Regul.* 3:149–67

19. Froesch, E. R., Zapf, J., Humbel, R. E. 1982. Insulin-like activity, IGF I and II, and the somatomedins. In: *Diabetes Mellitus*, ed. M. Ellenberg, H. Rifkin, pp. 179–201. New York: Med. Exam. Publ.

20. Froesch, E. R. 1983. From NSILA to IGF: A look back on the major advances and breakthroughs. In: *Insulin-Like Growth Factors/Somatomedins*, ed. M. Spencer, pp. 13–29. New York: de Gruyter

21. Guenther, H. L., Guenther, H. E., Froesch, E. R., Fleisch, H. 1982. Effect of insulin-like growth factor on collagen and glycosaminoglycan synthesis by rabbit articular chondrocytes in culture. *Experientia* 38:979–80

22. Haselbacher, G. K., Andres, R. Y., Humbel, R. E. 1980. Evidence for the synthesis of a somatomedin similar to insulin-like growth factor I by chick embryo liver cells. *Eur. J. Biochem.* 111:245–50

23. Isaksson, O. G. P., Jansson, J.-V., Gause, I. A. M., 1982. Growth hormone stimulates longitudinal bone growth directly. *Science* 216:1237–38

24. Kaufmann, U., Zapf, J., Torretti, B., Froesch, E. R. 1977. Demonstration of a specific serum carrier protein of nonsuppressible insulin-like activity in vivo. *J. Clin. Endocrinol. Metab.* 44:160–66

25. Kaufmann, U., Zapf, J., Froesch, E. R. 1978. Growth hormone dependence of nonsuppressible insulin-like activity (NSILA) and of NSILA-carrier protein. *Acta Endocrinol.* 87:716–27

26. Klapper, D. G., Svoboda, M. E., van Wyk, J. J. 1983. Sequence analysis of somatomedin C: Confirmation of identity with insulin-like growth factor I. *Endocrinology* 112:2215–17

27. Kurtz, A., Jelkmann, W., Bauer, Ch. 1982. A new candidate for the regulation of erythropoiesis. *FEBS Lett.* 149:105–8

28. Marquardt, H., Todaro, G. J., Henderson, L. E., Oroszlan, S. 1981. Purification and primary structure of a polypeptide with multiplication-stimulating activity from rat liver cell cultures. *J. Biol. Chem.* 256:6859–65

29. Mayer, P. W., Schalch, D. S. 1983. Somatomedin synthesis by a subclone of buffalo rat liver cells: Characterization and evidence for immediate secretion of de novo synthesized hormone. *Endocrinology* 113:588–95

30. Merimee, T. J., Rimoin, D. L., Rabinovitz, D., Cavalli-Sforza, L. L., McKusick, V. A. 1968. Metabolic studies in the African pygmy. *Transact. Assoc. Am. Physicians* 81:221–30

31. Merimee, T. J., Rimoin, D. L., Cavalli-Sforza, L. L. 1972. Metabolic studies in the African pygmy. *J. Clin. Invest.* 51:395–401

32. Merimee, T. J., Zapf, J., Froesch, E. R. 1982. Insulin-like growth factor(s) (IGFs) in pygmies and subjects with the pygmy trait: Characterization of the metabolic actions of IGF I and IGF II in man. *J. Clin. Endocr. Metab.* 55:1081–88

33. Merimee, T. J., Zapf, J., Froesch, E. R. 1981. Dwarfism in the pygmy: An isolated deficiency of insulin-like growth factor I. *New Engl. J. Med.* 305:965–68

34. Meuli, C., Froesch, E. R. 1975. Effects of insulin and of NSILA on the perfused rat heart: Glucose uptake, lactate production and efflux of 3-0-methylglucose. *Eur. J. Clin. Invest.* 5:93–9

35. Meuli, C., Zapf, J., Froesch, E. R. 1978. NSILA-carrier protein abolishes the action of nonsuppressible insulin-like activity (NSILA-s) on perfused rat heart. *Diabetologia* 14:255–59

36. Morell, B., Froesch, E. R. 1973. Fibroblasts as an experimental tool in metabolic and hormone studies. II. Effects of insulin and nonsuppressible insulin-like activity (NSILA-s) on fibroblasts in culture. *Eur. J. Clin. Invest.* 3:119–23

36a. Moses, A. C., Nissley, S. P., Cohen, K. L., Rechler, M. M. 1976. Specific binding of a somatomedin-like polypeptide in rat serum depends on growth hormone. *Nature* 263:137–40

37. Pierson, R. W., Temin, H. M. 1972. The partial purification from calf serum of a fraction with multiplication-stimulating activity for chicken fibroblasts in the cell culture and with non-suppressible insulin-like activity. *J. Cell. Physiol.* 79:319–30

38. Poggi, C., Le Marchand-Brustel, Y., Zapf, J., Froesch, E. R., Freychet, P.

1979. Effects and binding on insulin-like growth factor I (IGF I) in the isolated soleus muscle of lean and obese mice: Comparison with insulin. *Endocrinology* 105:723–30

39. Rechler, M. M., Eisen, H. J., Higa, O. Z., Nissley, S. P., Moses, A. C., et al. 1979. Characterization of a somatomedin (insulin-like growth factor) synthesized by fetal rat liver organ cultures. *J. Biol. Chem.* 254:7942–50

40. Rechler, M. M., Zapf, J., Nissley, S. P., Froesch, E. R., Moses, A. C., et al. 1980. Interactions of insulin-like growth factors I and II and multiplication-stimulating activity with receptors and serum carrier proteins. *Endocrinology* 107:1451–59

41. Rechler, M. M., Kasuga, M., Sasaki, N., De Vroede, M. A., Romanus, J. A., Nissley, S. P. 1983. Properties of insulin-like growth factor receptor subtypes. See Ref. 20, pp. 459–90

42. Rinderknecht, E., Humbel, R. E. 1978. The amino acid sequence of human insulin-like growth factor I and its structural homology with proinsulin. *J. Biol. Chem.* 253:2769–76

43. Rinderknecht, E., Humbel, R. E. 1978. Primary structure of human insulin-like growth factor II. *FEBS Lett.* 89:283–86

44. Salmon, W. D. Jr., Daughaday, W. H. 1957. A hormonally controlled serum factor which stimulates sulfate incorporation by cartilage in vivo. *J. Lab. Clin. Med.* 49:825–36

45. Schalch, D. S., Heinrich, U. E., Draznin, B., Johnson, C. J., Miller, L. L. 1979. Role of the liver in regulating somatomedin activity: Hormonal effects on the synthesis and release of insulin-like growth factor and its carrier protein by the isolated perfused rat liver. *Endocrinology* 104:1143–51

46. Schlumpf, U., Heimann, R., Zapf, J., Froesch, E. R. 1976. Nonsuppressible insulin-like activity and sulfation activity in serum extracts of normal subjects, acromegalics, and pituitary dwarfs. *Acta Endocrinol.* 81:28–42

47. Schmid, C., Steiner, Th., Froesch, E. R. 1983. Insulin-like growth factors stimulate synthesis of nucleic acids and glycogen in cultured calvaria cells. *Calcif. Tissue Int.* 35:578–85

48. Schmid, Ch., Steiner, Th., Froesch, E. R. 1985. Triiodothyronine increases the responsiveness of cultured bone cells to parathyroid hormone. *Endocrinology,* submitted for publication

49. Schmid, Ch., Steiner, Th., Froesch, E. R. 1983. Stimulation of glycogen synthesis in osteoblast-like cells by PTH and IGF. See Ref. 20, pp. 441–45

50. Schmid, Ch., Steiner, Th., Froesch, E. R. 1983. IGF-effects on and binding to rat calvaria cells in culture. See Ref. 20, pp. 421–29

51. Schmid, Ch., Steiner, Th., Froesch, E. R. 1983. Preferential enhancement of myoblast differentiation by insulin-like growth factors (IGF I and IGF II) in primary cultures of chicken embryonic cells. *FEBS Lett.* 161:117–21

52. Schmid, Ch., Steiner, Th., Froesch, E. R. 1984. Triiodothyronine (T_3) favors ornithine decarboxylase induction by parathyroid hormone (PTH) in cultured bone cells. *Experientia* 40:613 (Abstr.)

53. Schoenle, E., Zapf, J., Humbel, R. E., Froesch, E. R. 1982. Insulin-like growth factor I stimulates growth in hypophysectomized rats. *Nature* 296:252–53

54. Schoenle, E., Zapf, J., Hauri, Ch., Steiner, Th., Froesch, E. R. 1985. Comparison of in vivo effects of insulin-like growth factors (IGF) I and II and growth hormone (GH) in hypophysectomized rats. *Acta Endocrinol.* In press

55. Schwander, J., Hauri, C., Zapf, J., Froesch, E. R. 1983. Synthesis and secretion of insulin-like growth factor and its binding protein by the perfused rat liver: Dependence on growth hormone status. *Endocrinology* 113:297–305

56. Stiles, C. D., Capone, G. T., Scher, C. D., Antoniades, H. N., van Wyk, J. J., Pledger, W. J. 1979. Dual control of cell growth by somatomedins and platelet-derived growth factor. *Proc. Natl. Acad. Sci. USA* 76:1279–83

57. Suzuki, F., Kato, Y., Hiraki, Y., Canalis, E., Raisz, L. G. 1983. Action of growth factors on chondrocytes: Discovery of local somatomedins in fetal bovine cartilage. See Ref. 20, pp. 431–36

58. Widmer, U., Zapf, J., Froesch, E. R. 1982. Is extrapancreatic tumor hypoglycemia associated with elevated levels of insulin-like growth factor II? *J. Clin. Endocr. Metab.* 55:833–39

59. Widmer, U., Schmid, Ch., Zapf, J., Froesch, E. R. 1985. Effects of insulin-like growth factors on chick embryo hepatocytes. *Acta Endocrinol.* In press

60. Widmer, U., Zapf, J., Froesch, E. R., Kew, M. D. 1983. Insulin-like growth factor (IGF) levels measured by radioimmunoassay (RIA) and radioreceptorassay (RRA) in various forms of tumor hypoglycemia. See Ref. 20, pp. 317–23

61. Zapf, J., Waldvogel, M., Froesch, E. R. 1975. Binding of nonsuppressible insulin-like activity to human serum: Evidence for a carrier protein. *Arch. Biochem. Biophys.* 168:638–45

62. Zapf, J., Schoenle, E., Froesch, E. R. 1978. Insulin-like growth factors I and II:

Some biological actions and receptor binding characteristics of two purified constituents of nonsuppressible insulin-like activity of human serum. *Eur. J. Biochem.* 87:285–96

63. Zapf, J., Schoenle, E., Jagars, G., Sand, I., Grunwald, J., Froesch, E. R. 1979. Inhibition of the action of nonsuppressible insulin-like activity on isolated rat fat cells by binding to its carrier protein. *J. Clin. Invest.* 63:1077–84

64. Zapf, J., Morell, B., Walter, H., Laron, Z., Froesch, E. R. 1980. Serum levels of insulin-like growth factor (IGF) and its carrier protein in various metabolic disorders. *Acta Endocrinol.* 95:505–17

65. Zapf, J., Froesch, E. R., Humbel, R. E. 1981. The insulin-like growth factors (IGF) of human serum: Chemical and biological characterization and aspects of their possible physiological role. *Curr. Top. Cell. Regul.* 19:257–309

66. Zapf, J., Walter, H., Froesch, E. R. 1981. Radioimmunological determination of insulin-like growth factors I and II in normal subjects and in patients with growth hormone disorders and extrapancreatic tumor hypoglycemia. *J. Clin. Invest.* 68:1321–30

67. Zapf, J., Schoenle, E., Waldvogel, M., Sand, I., Froesch, E. R. 1981. Effect of trypsin treatment of rat adipocytes on biological effects and binding of insulin-like growth factor. Further evidence for the action of insulin-like growth through the insulin receptor. *Eur. J. Biochem.* 113:605–9

Ann. Rev. Physiol. 1985. 47:469–82

THE NATURE AND REGULATION OF THE RECEPTORS FOR PITUITARY GROWTH HORMONE

J. P. Hughes

Department of Life Science, Indiana State University, Terre Haute, Indiana 47809

H. G. Friesen

Department of Physiology, University of Manitoba, Winnipeg, Manitoba, Canada R3E 0W3

INTRODUCTION

Although more than a decade has passed since development of a radioreceptor assay for growth hormone (GH) (43), characterization of the GH receptor has only recently progressed beyond rather superficial binding studies. This relatively slow progress in characterization of the receptor can be attributed in large part to the problem of defining an in vitro biological response to GH. In fact, usage of the term "GH receptor" is, in most cases, technically incorrect because GH-binding sites in only a few tissues have been shown to mediate GH action. Other problems that have plagued characterization of the GH receptor include the presence of multiple forms of the receptor/hormone, some overlap between the binding specificities of GH and prolactin (PRL) receptors, and a lack of specific biochemical techniques for identification of the GH receptor.

Some of the problems outlined above have been partially resolved by the recent introduction of new in vitro systems in which to characterize the function of the GH receptor and by the use of new technologies for identification/ purification of the GH receptor. The impact, both current and future, of these new developments is emphasized in this summary. Constraints on chapter length do not permit discussion of receptor purification or of the many factors

469

0066-4278/85/0315-0469$02.00

that regulate GH receptor number/affinity. For a more comprehensive treatment of these subjects and of GH receptors in general, the reader is directed to a
recent review (34).

CHARACTERIZATION OF RECEPTOR FUNCTION: IN VITRO SYSTEMS

Identification of in vitro responses to GH has been difficult despite the wide
variety of processes regulated by GH in vivo. Part of the difficulty is that some
of the responses to GH are indirect effects mediated by GH-dependent factors
(10, 69) rather than effects directly linked to activation of the GH receptor. In
recent studies, however, specific binding of GH has been correlated with
metabolic responses in primary cultures of adipocytes (15, 26), with developmental responses in a fibroblast cell line (58, 61), and with growth responses in
primary cultures of chondrocytes (14, 49).

Adipocytes

It has long been documented that GH regulates carbohydrate and lipid metabolism (1, 21); however, these metabolic actions of GH have only recently been
correlated with receptor binding (26). Using cultured adipocytes, investigators
(26) have found that the various metabolic responses to GH occur at different
levels of receptor occupancy. These data may suggest that the diverse actions of
GH are mediated by different "second messengers" or even through different
GH receptors. An alternative explanation is that some of the effects attributed
to GH may be due to contaminants present in GH preparations (17–19);
however, this proposal is a point of some controversy (23, 24). Thus, final
interpretation of the data on receptor occupancy vs metabolic response must
await resolution of the controversy regarding which actions are mediated
through the GH receptor. In any event, primary cultures of adipocytes show
promise as an in vitro system in which to examine the early events, perhaps
multiple, that follow activation of the GH receptor.

3T3 Fibroblasts

Cultured preadipose 3T3 fibroblasts undergo conversion to adipocytes when
exposed to insulin and to an adipogenic factor(s) that is present in the sera of
most animals (41, 65, 67, 68). Recent studies (28, 55, 62) have clearly shown
that GH is at least one if not the serum factor. The possibility of additional
factors has been raised by the finding that anti-GH antisera do not totally
eliminate the adipogenic activity of bovine or rat sera (62). Moreover, there is
no apparent correlation between GH-receptor number/affinity and the susceptibility of 3T3 lines to adipose conversion (61). If GH is the primary adipogenic
factor, then these data (61) raise the interesting possibility that events im-

mediately following activation of the receptor may differ in the various 3T3 cell lines. After conversion to adipocytes, 3T3-F442A cells still bind GH; thus, these cells may prove to be a convenient source of adipocytes for metabolic studies similar to those outlined for primary cultures of adipocytes. Future studies with this cell line should provide valuable information on the role of the receptor in mediating the effects of GH on differentiation and possibly on regulation of metabolic events.

Chondrocytes

Stimulation of chondrocyte proliferation in vivo generally has been considered to be an indirect action of GH mediated by somatomedins (10, 69). In a recent study (36), however, in vivo injection of hGH directly into the epiphyseal cartilage of hypophysectomized rats stimulated local chondrocyte proliferation. Moreover, binding sites for hGH have been identified on rabbit ear chondrocytes (14), although it is not entirely clear from the data whether the sites are specific for somatotrophic or for lactogenic hormones. A direct effect of hGH on chondrocytes in primary cultures has been demonstrated by Madsen and coworkers (49). Using chondrocytes isolated from rabbit ear and from rat rib, these investigators (49) showed that hGH stimulates thymidine uptake in vitro under serum-free conditions. Ovine PRL did not stimulate thymidine uptake in this study; however, the highest concentration of ovine PRL used in the study was only two-fold higher than the minimally effective dose of hGH. At a slightly higher concentration, ovine PRL might have stimulated thymidine uptake, because an earlier binding study (14) has shown that ovine PRL is only five-fold less active than hGH in inhibiting binding of [^{125}I]hGH to chondrocytes. Stimulation of thymidine uptake in response to hGH may yet prove to be an indirect effect mediated by growth factors released from the chondrocytes in vitro; however, even this eventuality would not alter the fact that hGH acts directly on chondrocytes. If it can be demonstrated conclusively that hGH is acting via GH receptors, then primary cultures of rabbit chondrocytes may prove to be an excellent system in which to study the role of the GH receptor in mediating the growth-promoting actions of GH. Moreover, the GH receptor in this system could be further characterized using a monoclonal antibody specific for the rabbit GH receptor (74; see section on Monoclonal Antibody).

Future Directions

At present, hormonal regulation of cell proliferation and/or differentiation is poorly understood. However, the focus of future research in this area has been sharpened by studies on covalent modification of existing proteins and on regulation of protein synthesis. The possibility that cell proliferation is regulated in part by tyrosine phosphorylation has recently received considerable attention because it has been demonstrated that tyrosine-specific protein kinase activity is associated with receptors for several growth factors (7, 37, 60, 81) and with some viral oncogenes (35). Moreover, it appears that some oncogenes stimulate growth by virtue of the fact that they code for growth factors or even for aberrant growth-factor receptors (50). Although kinase activity has not yet been demonstrated for the growth hormone receptor, tyrosine phosphorylation may prove to be one of the early events that follows activation of the receptor. Regulation by GH of mRNA/protein synthesis has been studied with some success by using two-dimensional electrophoresis to examine products of in vitro translations (70). This approach is particularly powerful because it provides information on individual proteins, and it opens the possibility of isolating and cloning GH-dependent mRNAs. Spiegelman et al (78) have used this type of approach to examine differentiation-dependent proteins in 3T3 cells. In these experiments, labeled cDNA synthesized from the total mRNA of preadipocytes and adipocytes was hybridized to DNA from bacterial colonies containing cloned adipocyte cDNAs. DNA from colonies containing differentiation-dependent cloned cDNAs hybridized more strongly with cDNA from adipocytes than from preadipocytes. Thus, using this technique, it was possible to identify clones of genes for specific proteins. It can be appreciated that this hybrid selection technique could be used to isolate genes for GH-dependent proteins in 3T3 cells or in virtually any other cell responsive to GH. Future studies of tyrosine-specific protein phosphorylation and protein synthesis should provide valuable data on the role of the receptor in mediating the actions of GH on cell proliferation/differentiation.

RECEPTORS FOR DIFFERENT FORMS OF GH

20K Variant

The 20K variant of hGH (45, 46) possesses substantial growth-promoting activity (45, 56, 77), but the variant lacks some of the early insulin-like effects of hGH (16). Despite high growth-promoting activity, 20K hGH is relatively ineffective in inhibiting [^{125}I]hGH (22K) binding to GH receptors in liver membranes from rats and rabbits (72, 84). Lewis et al (72) and Wohnlich & Moore (84) have interpreted these binding data to indicate the presence of novel receptors for 20K. However, a subsequent study (32) of 20K hGH binding has suggested that, in rabbit liver, 20K hGH is bound with high affinity by a subset of the receptors that bind 22K hGH rather than by novel GH receptors. Despite their differences, all of these binding studies (32, 72, 84) suggest that GH is bound by multiple receptors or at least multiple forms of one receptor. It is possible, therefore, that the growth-promoting and insulin-like actions of 22K hGH are mediated by different receptors and that 20K hGH cannot activate the receptor that mediates the insulin-like effects.

Two-Chain Forms

Modified forms of GH with a cleavage(s) in the portion of the molecule comprised by amino-acid residues 133–146 have been identified in pituitary extracts (75) and generated using various enzymes (5, 44, 54). Cleavage of the GH molecule in this region produces a two-chain form that consists of an amino-terminal fragment linked by a disulfide bond to a smaller carboxy-terminal fragment. Further treatment of these forms with reducing and carboxy-methylating agents produces complexes of noncovalently linked fragments (13, 22, 25). Not all proteolytic cleavages decrease GH activity; rather, several investigators (5, 44, 75) have identified cleaved forms of GH with enhanced biological activities. Thus, in some cases, cleavage may increase binding of GH to its receptor. This possibility is further suggested by preliminary data (33) that indicate that cleavage of GH enhances binding to receptor. Cleavage of GH also may selectively alter binding to different GH receptors. In at least one case (22) the potency of a cleaved form relative to that of intact GH varied according to the response studied (e.g. glucose oxidation vs delayed lipolysis). The investigators have speculated (22) that these apparent changes in relative potency indicate the presence of multiple classes of GH receptors. Further-more, Maciag et al (48) have reported a cleaved form that, unlike intact GH, stimulates incorporation of sulfate. Thus, proteolytic cleavage of the GH molecule may be necessary for expression of some of the actions of GH, and these actions may be mediated by separate GH receptors.

GH Fragments

For the most part, fragments of GH have shown little or no activity in standard radioreceptor assays (for review see 40). This is true even for fragments that show growth-promoting activity in bioassays (40). It is unlikely, therefore, that the biologically active fragments of GH that have been described recently (2, 47, 59, 85) will inhibit [^{125}I]GH binding in a standard radioreceptor assay. However, it is possible that one or more of these peptides may bind to receptors that also recognize intact GH.

BIOCHEMICAL CHARACTERIZATION

Chemical Composition

A number of studies have clearly shown that the GH receptor is an integral membrane protein. Lectin-receptor interactions further suggest that GH recep-tors contain a carbohydrate component (29, 79) that is associated with the extracellular domain of the receptor in conjunction with the GH-binding site. However, a role for carbohydrate moieties in maintenance of the binding site has not been established. Cleavage of sialic acid residues with neuraminidase does not inhibit GH-receptor interaction (4, 29, 79), and conflicting results have been obtained with galactosidase (4, 29). Phospholipids also appear to be relatively unimportant for binding of GH to its receptor because phospholipase C decreases binding only slightly if at all (4, 79), and receptor in partially purified preparations binds GH with high affinity despite the absence of a normal phospholipid environment (79, 82). However, even if carbohydrate and lipid are not required for GH binding, it is possible that these components participate in events that follow hormone-receptor interaction.

Subunit Structure

Analysis of the GH receptor by gel filtration (52, 79, 82) has shown that Triton-solubilized receptor elutes with a M_r of 200,000–300,000 (Table 1). This technique probably overestimates the M_r of the GH receptor because it does not take into account the amount of Triton bound to receptor. If it is assumed that Triton accounts for approximately one third of the receptor-detergent complex, as has been suggested for other receptors (38, 53, 63, 64, 76), then the approximate M_r of the GH receptor under nondenaturing conditions would range from 130,000 to 200,000. This estimate of M_r is consistent with recent data obtained using cross-linking techniques to identify GH receptors on rat hepatocytes (11), rat adipocytes (8), and IM-9 lymphocytes (31) (Table 1). Under reducing conditions on SDS-electrophoresis, the M_rs of these receptors ranged from 108,000 to 112,000. In the absence of reducing agents, however, the GH receptor identified on rat hepatocytes migrated as a higher-M_r species (11), suggesting that this GH receptor interacts via interchain disulfide bonds with other receptor or perhaps nonreceptor proteins.

In contrast to the relatively high M_rs obtained for human and rat GH receptors in cross-linking studies, M_rs in the range of 50,000–67,000 have been obtained for the rabbit GH receptor in microsomal membranes (27, 31, 80) (Table 1). Similar M_rs were obtained in the absence of reductants; thus, the low-M_r species identified in microsomal membranes did not result from disruption of disulfide-linked moities. In contrast to cross-linking studies, a high M_r was obtained for the rabbit GH receptor by gel filtration (79, 82). These data suggest that the GH-binding moiety identified in cross-linking studies is only a subunit of the GH receptor. Because subunit dissociation is effected by SDS in the absence of reducing agents, it is unlikely that the subunits composing the microsomal GH receptor are covalently linked. A subunit structure for the rabbit GH receptor is further suggested by recent data obtained in our laboratory (J. P. Hughes & H. G. Friesen, unpublished data) using plasma membranes prepared from rabbit liver. Cross-linking of human or rat GH to the plasma membranes primarily identified a 97,000-dalton receptor that was

Table 1 Molecular weights obtained for GH receptors from different species

Source of receptors	Techniques used for molecular weight determinations		
		SDS-electrophoresis (ref.)	
	Gel filtration (ref.)	Unreduced	Reduced
Rabbit liver	200K–300K[a] (79, 82)	50K–67K[a] (27, 31, 80)	50K–67K[a] (27, 31, 80)
		97K[b] (unpublished data)	56K[b] (unpublished data)
Rat hepatocytes	—[d]	300K[c] (11)	108K[c] (11)
Rat adipocytes	—	94K–103K[c] (8)	112K[c] (8)
IM-9 Lymphocytes	>200K[a] (52)	108K[c] (31)	108K[c] (31)

Receptor identified in [a]microsomal membranes, [b]plasmalemma, or [c]whole cells.
[d]No data available.

composed of disulfide-linked subunits. Moreover, at least one of the subunits was similar in size (56,000 daltons) to the GH receptor identified in microsomal membranes prepared from rabbit liver (31, 80) (Table 1). Thus, the data appear to suggest that the GH receptor in intracellular membranes (microsomal membranes) is composed of noncovalently linked subunits, whereas the receptor on the cell surface (plasma membranes) is primarily composed of disulfide-linked subunits. This difference between intracellular and cell surface receptors in rabbit liver suggests that disulfide linkages may play a role in the function of the GH receptor as has been suggested for other receptors (3, 9, 20, 42, 51, 57). These different forms of the rabbit GH receptor also may account, in part, for data (see below) that suggest the presence of two GH receptors in rabbit liver membranes.

MULTIPLE GH RECEPTORS

Although conclusive evidence for or against multiple GH receptors is not yet available, several lines of evidence suggest this possibility. One line of evidence stems from the marked differences in binding observed when two or more GH tracers are used to characterize GH receptors in the same rabbit liver membrane preparation (30, 32). These differences in binding were examined recently in a study (32) that used rat GH, the 20K variant of hGH and 22K hGH. In this study (32), rat GH, 20K hGH and 22K hGH were equipotent in inhibiting the binding of ^{125}I-labeled rat GH to rabbit liver, but rat GH and 20K hGH were far less active than 22K hGH in inhibiting the binding of 22K [^{125}I]hGH to the same membrane preparation. The lower potencies of rat GH and 20K hGH in inhibiting binding of the latter tracer could not be explained by the small number of lactogenic receptors in the membrane preparation; thus, it was proposed (32) that rat GH and 20K bind to only a subset of the GH receptors that bind 22K hGH. Evidence in support of multiple classes of receptors also has been obtained from studies (22, 48) that have examined the binding characteristics/biological actions of cleaved forms of GH (see Receptors for Different Forms of GH). In one of the studies (22), the potencies of cleaved forms relative to those of intact GH were dependent upon the biological end point of the assay system. For example, a plasmin digest of hGH was ten-fold more active than hGH in producing delayed lipolysis but one-tenth as active in stimulating glucose oxidation. These results led to the suggestion (22) that different classes of receptors may be associated with the various actions of GH. Finally, there are data (73) that suggest that the monoclonal antibody specific for rabbit GH receptor preferentially binds to a subset of GH receptors in rabbit liver membranes. Thus, the existence of multiple receptors is suggested by several lines of evidence.

MONOCLONAL ANTIBODIES

Another problem encountered in studies of GH receptor function is the general lack of specific agonists and antagonists. Many GH preparations contain PRL as a contaminant (the opposite is true for PRL preparations), and thus it is difficult to define conclusively receptor specificity. Moreover, GH receptors are not totally specific when heterologous hormones (hormones from other species) are used (30, 82). In addition to the lack of highly specific GH agonists, there are no naturally occurring or synthetic GH antagonists. This is unfortunate because, as demonstrated in many neurotransmitter systems, antagonists greatly facilitate study of receptor function. Some of these problems have been resolved, at least for the rabbit GH receptor, through the use of hybridoma technology (74).

Anti–GH Receptor Antibody

The monoclonal antibody generated against the rabbit GH receptor (74) blocks binding of hormone to the receptor; thus, it is probable that the antibody binds in or near the active site of the GH receptor. The site recognized by the antibody is specific to the rabbit GH receptor in that the antibody does not block binding to human or rat GH receptors or binding to the rabbit PRL receptor. The high specificity characteristic of this monoclonal antibody is not shared by polyclonal antisera (83) in that these latter antibodies recognized GH receptors from many species. It also appears that the monoclonal antibody differentiates between forms of the GH receptor (73). Preliminary results (74) suggest that the antibody is an IgE, which is consistent with the fact that the antibody does not bind to Protein A (J. S. A. Simpson, J. P. Hughes & H. G. Friesen, unpublished results). It is necessary, therefore, to block IgE receptors in some membrane preparations to prevent sequestration of the anti–GH receptor antibody (J. S. A. Simpson, J. P. Hughes & H. G. Friesen, unpublished results). The high specificity of the monoclonal antibody in conjunction with its availability in almost unlimited quantities can be exploited in a wide variety of studies. Preliminary data (74) have shown that the monoclonal antibody is effective for purification of the GH receptor by affinity chromatography. The use of this antibody rather than hGH as the coupled ligand in affinity chromatography allows a one-step separation of GH receptors from PRL receptors. Data on the agonist/antagonist properties of the antibody are not yet available; however, on the basis of results obtained with other receptors (12, 39, 71), it is probable that Fab fragments of the antibody will act as GH antagonists in biological systems, whereas the intact antibody may have the properties of an agonist. Irrespective of whether it acts as an agonist or an antagonist, the monoclonal antibody should facilitate study of GH receptor function.

Anti-GH Antibodies

Retegui et al (66) and Cadman et al (6) have used monoclonal antibodies specific for hGH to examine hormone binding to the GH receptor. Although several antibodies were capable of blocking hGH binding to receptors, none could distinguish separate sites on hGH for binding to GH and PRL receptors. It is unlikely, therefore, that these antibodies will be of value for the more rigorous task of identifying separate classes of GH receptors. The data (6, 66) may indicate that GH and PRL receptors recognize overlapping regions on the GH molecule; however, it is also possible that antibodies, by virtue of their size, are unsuitable as probes in this type of study.

SUMMARY

Recent developments have contributed greatly to our understanding of GH receptor structure and function; however, much remains to be done. One of the first priorities should be to elucidate the early events that follow activation of the GH receptor. The in vitro systems outlined in this review show promise in this regard; however, all three systems require further characterization. Future studies of the GH receptor in these and other systems will undoubtedly be facilitated by the monoclonal antibody generated against the GH receptor and by recently described cross-linking methodologies. Despite these recent advances, however, it is likely that detailed characterization of receptor structure and function awaits cloning of the GH-receptor gene(s).

ACKNOWLEDGMENTS

We are grateful to Laura Bakken for secretarial assistance. This work was supported by US Public Health Service Grants AM 32989 and HD 07843 and by MRC Canada.

Literature Cited

1. Altszuler, N. 1974. Actions of growth hormone on carbohydrate metabolism. In *Handbook of Physiology*, Endocrinology, Section 7, ed. E. Knobil, W. H. Sawyer, 4(2):233–52. Washington DC: Am. Physiol. Soc. 601 pp.
2. Armstrong, J. M., Bornstein, J., Bromley, J. O., Macaulay, S. L., Ng, F. M. 1983. Parallel insulin-like actions of human growth hormone and its part sequence hGH 7–13. *Acta Endocrinol.* 102:492–98
3. Ben-Haim, D., Landau, E. M., Silman, I. 1973. The role of a reactive disulfide bond in the function of the acetylcholine receptor at the frog neuromuscular junction. *J. Physiol.* 234:305–25
4. Blossey, H. 1979. Studies on the molecular architecture and the composition of the GH receptor from rabbit liver. *Horm. Metab. Res.* 11:616–21
5. Bunner, D. L., Lewis, U. J., Vanderlaan, W. P. 1979. Comparative potency of subtilisin-cleaved and intact human growth hormone measured in growth hormone-deficient human subjects. *J. Clin. Endocrinol. Metab.* 48:293–96
6. Cadman, H. F., Wallis, M., Ivanyi, J. 1982. The effects of monoclonal antibodies against human growth hormone

on hormone-receptor interactions. *FEBS Lett.* 137:149–52

7. Carpenter, G. 1983. The biochemistry and physiology of the receptor-kinase for epidermal growth factor. *Mol. Cell. Endocrinol.* 31:1–19

8. Carter-Su, C., Schwartz, J., Kikuchi, G. 1984. Identification of a high affinity growth hormone receptor in rat adipocyte membranes. *J. Biol. Chem.* 259:1099–104

9. Czech, M. P., Lawrence, J. C. Jr., Lynn, W. S. 1974. Evidence for the involvement of sulfhydryl oxidation in the regulation of fat cell hexose transport by insulin. *Proc. Natl. Acad. Sci. USA* 71:4173–77

10. Daughaday, W. H., Hall, K., Raben, M. S., Salmon, W. D., Van den Brande, J. L., Van Wyk, J. J. 1972. Somatomedin: proposed designation for sulfation factor. *Nature* 235:107

11. Donner, D. 1983. Covalent coupling of human growth hormone to its receptor on rat hepatocytes. *J. Biol. Chem.* 258:2736–43

12. Dusanter-Fourt, I., Djiane, J., Kelly, P. A., Houdebine, L. M., Teyssot, B. 1984. Differential biological activities between mono- and bivalent fragments of antiprolactin receptor antibodies. *Endocrinology* 114:1021–27

13. Eden, S., Kostyo, J. L., Schwartz, J. 1982. Ability of growth hormone fragments to compete with ^{125}I-iodinated human growth hormone for specific binding to isolated adipocytes of hypophysectomized rats. *Biochim. Biophys. Acta* 721:489–91

14. Eden, S., Isaksson, O. G. P., Madsen, K., Friberg, U. 1983. Specific binding of growth hormone to isolated chondrocytes from rabbit ear and epiphyseal plate. *Endocrinology* 112:1127–29

15. Fagin, K. D., Lackey, S. L., Reagen, C. R., DiGirolamo, M. 1980. Specific binding of growth hormone by rat adipocytes. *Endocrinology* 107:608–15

16. Frigeri, L. G., Peterson, S. M., Lewis, U. J. 1979. The 20,000-dalton structural variant of human growth hormone: lack of some early insulin-like effects. *Biochem. Biophys. Res. Commun.* 91:778–82

17. Frigeri, L. G. 1980. Absence of in vitro dexamethasone-dependent lipolytic activity from highly purified growth hormone. *Endocrinology* 107:738–43

18. Frigeri, L. G., Robel, G., Stebbins, N. 1982. Bacteria derived human growth hormone lacks lipolytic activity in rat adipose tissue. *Biochem. Biophys. Res. Commun.* 103:1041–46

19. Frigeri, L. G., Khoo, J. C., Robel, G. 1983. Absence of lipolytic activity from purified human growth hormone in cultured 3T3-L1 adipocytes. *Horm. Res.* 17:197–201

20. Goldman, J. M., Hadley, M. E. 1972. Sulfhydryl requirement for alpha adrenergic activity and melanophore stimulating hormone (MSH) action on melanophores. *J. Pharmacol. Exp. Ther.* 182:93–100

21. Goodman, H. M., Schwartz, J. 1974. Growth hormone and lipid metabolism. See Ref. 1, pp. 211–32.

22. Goodman, H. M., Kostyo, J. L. 1981. Altered profiles of biological activity of growth hormone fragments on adipocyte metabolism. *Endocrinology* 108:553–58

23. Goodman, H. M., Grichting, C. 1983. Growth hormone and lipolysis: a reevaluation. *Endocrinology* 113:1697–702

24. Goodman, H. M. 1984. Biological activity of bacterial derived human growth hormone in adipose tissue of hypophysectomized rats. *Endocrinology* 114:131–35

25. Graf, L., Li, C. H., Cheng, C. H. K., Jibson, M. D. 1981. Two contiguous thrombin fragments of human somatotropin form a functionally active recombinant, but the two homologous fragments from sheep hormone do not. *Biochemistry,* 20:7251–58

26. Grichting, G., Levy, L. K., Goodman, H. M. 1983. Relationship between binding and biological effects of human growth hormone in rat adipocytes. *Endocrinology* 113:1111–20

27. Haeuptle, M. T., Aubert, M. L., Djiane, J., Kraehenbuhl, J. P. 1983. Binding sites for lactogenic and somatogenic hormones from rabbit mammary gland and liver. *J. Biol. Chem.* 258:305–14

28. Hayashi, I., Nixon, T., Morikawa, M., Green, H. 1981. Adipogenic and anti-adipogenic factors in the pituitary and other organs. *Proc. Natl. Acad. Sci. USA* 78:3969–72

29. Herington, A. C., Elson, D. 1979. Interaction between the hepatic growth hormone receptor and concanavalin A. *Mol. Cell Endocrinol.* 16:91–97

30. Hughes, J. P. 1979. Identification and characterization of high and low affinity binding sites for growth hormone in rabbit liver. *Endocrinology* 105:414–20

31. Hughes, J. P., Simpson, J. S. A., Friesen, H. G. 1983. Analysis of growth hormone and lactogenic binding sites cross-linked to iodinated human growth hormone. *Endocrinology* 112:1980–85

32. Hughes, J. P., Tokuhiro, E., Simpson, J. S. A., Friesen, H. G. 1983. 20K is bound

with high affinity by one rat and one of two rabbit growth hormone receptors. *Endocrinology* 113:1904–6

33. Hughes, J. P., Hughes, E. F. 1984. Cleavage of growth hormone by rabbit liver plasmalemma enhances binding. *J. Biol. Chem.* In press

34. Hughes, J. P., Elsholtz, H. P., Friesen, H. G. 1984. Growth hormone and prolactin receptors. In *Polypeptide Hormone Receptors,* ed. B. I. Posner. New York: Marcel Dekker. In press

35. Hunter, T. 1982. Phosphotyrosine—a new protein modification. *Trends Biochem. Sci.* 7:246–49

36. Isaksson, O. G. P., Jansson, J. O., Gause, I. A. M. 1982. Growth hormone stimulates longitudinal bone growth directly. *Science* 216:1237–39

37. Jacobs, S., Kull, F. C. Jr., Earp, H. S., Svoboda, M. E., Van Wyk, J. J., Cuatrecasas, P. 1983. Somatomedin-C stimulates the phosphorylation of the β-subunit of its own receptor. *J. Biol. Chem.* 258:9581–84

38. Jaffe, R. C. 1982. Hydrodynamic characterization of the Triton X-100 solubilized lactogenic hormone receptor of rat liver. *Biochemistry* 21:2936–39

39. Kahn, C. R. 1979. The role of insulin receptors and receptor antibodies in states of altered insulin action. *Proc. Soc. Exp. Biol. Med.* 162:13–21

40. Kostyo, J. L., Wilhelmi, A. E. 1976. Conference on the structure-function relationships of pituitary growth hormone: a report. *Metabolism* 25:105–24

41. Kuri-Harcuch, W., Green, H. 1978. Adipose conversion of 3T3 cells depends on a serum factor. *Proc. Natl. Acad. Sci. USA* 75:6107–9

42. Kwock, L., Wallach, D. F. H., Hefter, K. 1976. Involvement of sulfhydryl groups in the action of insulin and radiation on thymocyte Na$^+$-dependent amino acid transport. *Biochim. Biophys. Acta* 419:93–103

43. Lesniak, M. A., Roth, J., Gorden, P., Gavin, J. R. III. 1973. Human growth hormone radioreceptor assay using cultured human lymphocytes. *Nature New Biol.* 241:20–21

44. Lewis, U. J., Pence, S. J., Singh, R. N. P., Vanderlaan, W. P. 1975. Enhancement of the growth-promoting activity of human growth hormone. *Biochem. Biophys. Res. Commun.* 67:617–24

45. Lewis, U. J., Dunn, J. T., Bonewald, L. F., Seavey, B. K., Vanderlaan, W. P. 1978. A naturally occurring structural variant of human growth hormone. *J. Biol. Chem.* 253:2679–87

46. Lewis, U. J., Bonewald, L. F., Lewis, L.

J. 1980. The 20,000-dalton variant of human growth hormone: location of the amino acid deletions. *Biochem. Biophys. Res. Commun.* 92:511–16

47. Lostroh, A. J., Krahl, M. E. 1978. Synthetic fragment of human growth hormone with hyperglycemic properties: residues 44–77. *Diabetes* 27:597–98

48. Maciag, T., Forand, F., Ilsley, S., Cerundolo, J., Greenlee, R., et al. 1980. The generation of sulfation factor activity by proteolytic modification of growth hormone. *J. Biol. Chem.* 255:6064–70

49. Madsen, K., Friberg, U., Roos, P., Eden, S., Isaksson, O. 1983. Growth hormone stimulates the proliferation of cultured chondrocytes from rabbit ear and rat rib growth cartilage. *Nature* 304:545–47

50. Marx, J. L. 1984. Oncogene linked to growth factor receptor. *Science* 223:806

51. Marzullo, G., Hine, B. 1980. Opiate receptor function may be modulated through an oxidation-reduction mechanism. *Science* 208:1171–73

52. McGuffin, W. L. Jr., Gavin, J. R. III, Lesniak, M. A., Gorden, P., Roth, J. 1976. Water-soluble specific growth hormone binding sites from cultured human lymphocytes: preparation and partial characterization. *Endocrinology* 98:1401–7

53. Meunier, J. C., Olsen, R. W., Changeux, J. P. 1972. Studies on the cholinergic receptor protein from *Electrophorus electricus*. Effect of detergents on some hydrodynamic properties of the receptor protein in solution. *FEBS Lett.* 24:63–68

54. Mills, J. B., Gennick, S. E., Kostyo, J. L. 1983. Fragments of human growth hormone produced by digestion with bromelain. *Biochim. Biophys. Acta* 742:169–74

55. Morikawa, M., Nixon, T., Green, H. 1982. Growth hormone and the adipose conversion of 3T3 cells. *Cell* 29:783–89

56. Mosier, H. D. Jr., Lewis, U. J. 1982. The 20,000-dalton variant of human growth hormone: effect of bioassayable somatomedin activity in serum. *Horm. Metab. Res.* 14:440–41

57. Mukherjee, S. P., Mukherjee, C. 1981. Role of sulfhydryl oxidation in adipocyte plasma membrane surface in the response of adenylate cyclase to isoproterenol and glucagon. *Biochim. Biophys. Acta* 677:339–49

58. Murphy, L. J., Vrhovsek, E., Lazarus, L. 1983. Characterization of specific growth hormone binding sites in mouse fibroblasts. *Endocrinology* 113:750–57

59. Ng, F., Henderson, T., Bromley, J., Bornstein, J. 1983. Modulation of hepatic insulin receptors by a human growth hormone fragment (hGH 6–13). *Mol. Cell. Endocrinol.* 30:63–71

60. Nishimura, J., Huang, J. S., Duel, T. F. 1982. Platelet-derived growth factor stimulates tyrosine-specific protein kinase activity in swiss mouse 3T3 cell membranes. *Proc. Natl. Acad. Sci. USA* 79:4303–7

61. Nixon, T., Green H. 1983. Properties of growth hormone receptors in relation to the adipose conversion of 3T3 cells. *J. Cell. Physiol.* 115:291–96

62. Nixon, T., Green, H. 1984. Contribution of growth hormone to the adipogenic activity of serum. *Endocrinology* 114:527–32

63. Poullet, R. J., Haase, B. A., Standaert, M. L. 1981. Characterization of detergent-solubilized membrane proteins. Hydrodynamic and sedimentation equilibrium properties of the insulin receptor of the cultured human lymphoblastoid cell. *J. Biol. Chem.* 256:12118–26

64. Rae-Venter, B., Dao, T. L. 1983. Hydrodynamic properties of rat hepatic prolactin receptors. *Arch. Biochem. Biophys.* 222:12–21

65. Reed, B. C., Kaufmann, S. H., Mackall, J. C., Student, A. K., Lane, M. D. 1977. Alterations in insulin binding accompanying differentiation of 3T3-L1 preadipocytes. *Proc. Natl. Acad. Sci. USA* 74:4876–80

66. Retegui, L. A., De Meyts, P., Peña, C., Masson, P. L. 1982. The same region of human growth hormone is involved in its binding to various receptors. *Endocrinology* 111:668–76

67. Rubin, C. S., Lai, E., Rosen, O. M. 1977. Acquisition of increased hormone sensitivity during in vitro adipocyte development. *J. Biol. Chem.* 252:3554–57

68. Rubin, C. S., Hirsch, A., Fung, C., Rosen, O. M. 1978. Development of hormone receptors and hormonal responsiveness in vitro. *J. Biol. Chem.* 253:7570–78

69. Salmon, W. D., Daughaday, W. H. 1957. A hormonally controlled serum factor which stimulates sulfate incorporation by cartilage in vitro. *J. Lab. Clin. Invest.* 49:825–36

70. Seelig, S., Mariash, C. N., Topliss, D. J., Oppenheimer, J. H. 1983. Growth hormone acts at a pretranslational level in hepatocyte cultures. *Biochem. Biophys. Res. Commun.* 115:882–87

71. Shiu, R. P. C., Elsholtz, H. P., Tanaka, T., Friesen, H. G., Gout, P. W., et al.

1983. Receptor-mediated mitogenic action of prolactin in a rat lymphoma cell line. *Endocrinology* 113:159–65

72. Sigel, M. B., Thorpe, N. A., Kobrin, M. S., Lewis, U. J., Vanderlaan, W. P. 1981. Binding characteristics of a biologically active variant of human growth hormone (20K) to growth hormone and lactogen receptors. *Endocrinology* 108:1600–3

73. Simpson, J. S. A., Hughes, J. P., Friesen, H. G. Monoclonal antibody to rabbit growth hormone receptor: binding characteristics and evidence for two receptors. In *Hormone Receptors and Receptor Diseases,* ed. H. Imura, H. Kuzuya, pp. 35–44. Amsterdam: Excerpta Medica

74. Simpson, J. S. A., Hughes, J. P., Friesen, H. G. 1983. A monoclonal antibody to the growth hormone receptor of rabbit liver membranes. *Endocrinology* 112:2137–41

75. Singh, R. N. P., Seavey, B. K., Rice, V. P., Lindsey, T. T. 1974. Modified forms of human growth hormone with increased biological activities. *Endocrinology* 94:883–91

76. Smigel, M., Fleischer, S. 1977. Characterization of Triton X-100–solubilized prostaglandin E binding protein of rat liver plasma membranes. *J. Biol. Chem.* 252:3689–96

77. Spencer, E. M., Lewis, L. J., Lewis, U. J. 1981. Somatomedin-generating activity of the 20,000-dalton variant of human growth hormone. *Endocrinology* 109:1301–2

78. Spiegelman, B. M., Frank, M., Green, H. 1983. Molecular cloning of mRNA from 3T3 adipocytes. *J. Biol. Chem.* 258:10083–89

79. Tsushima, T., Sasaki, N., Imai, Y., Matsuzaki, F., Friesen, H. G. 1980. Characteristics of solubilized human-somatotropin-binding protein from the liver of pregnant rabbits. *Biochem. J.* 187:479–92

80. Tsushima, T., Murakami, H., Wakai, K., Isozaki, O., Sato, Y., Shizume, K. 1982. Analysis of hepatic growth hormone binding sites of pregnant rabbit crosslinked to ^{125}I-labelled human growth hormone. *FEBS Lett.* 147:49–53

81. Van Obberghen, E., Rossi, B., Kowalski, A., Gazzano, H., Ponzio, G. 1983. Receptor-mediated phosphorylation of the hepatic insulin receptor: evidence that the M_r 95,000 receptor subunit is its own kinase. *Proc. Natl. Acad. Sci. USA* 80:945–49

82. Waters, M. J., Friesen, H. G. 1979. Puri-

fication and partial characterization of a nonprimate growth hormone receptor. *J. Biol. Chem.* 254:6815–25

83. Waters, M. J., Friesen, H. G. 1979. Studies with anti-growth hormone receptor antibodies. *J. Biol. Chem.* 254:6826–32

84. Wohnlich, L., Moore, W. V. 1982. Binding of a variant of human growth hormone to liver plasma membranes. *Horm. Metab. Res.* 14:138–41

85. Yudaev, N. A., Pankov, Yu. A., Keda, Yu. M., Sazina, E. T., Osipova, T. A., et al. 1983. The effect of synthetic fragment 31–44 of human growth hormone on glucose uptake by isolated adipose tissue. *Biochem. Biophys. Res. Commun.* 110:866–72.

Ann. Rev. Physiol. 1985. 47:483–499

MODE OF ACTION OF PITUITARY GROWTH HORMONE ON TARGET CELLS

Olle G. P. Isaksson, Staffan Edén, and John-Olov Jansson

Department of Physiology, University of Göteborg, Box 33031, 400 33 Göteborg, Sweden

INTRODUCTION

Although the results of growth hormone (GH) action on somatic growth are easily recognized, the site and the cellular mechanism(s) behind these effects of the hormone are unclear. One of the major obstacles in the exploration of the mechanisms of action of GH at the cellular level has been the lack of concordance between in vivo and in vitro effects. Administration of GH in vivo to GH-deficient animals or man results in a marked stimulation of chondrogenesis and myogenesis, resulting in accelerated somatic growth (for reviews see 11, 16, 59, 61, 88). However, when added in vitro to explants of cartilage or incubated muscle preparations, GH exerts small and inconsistant effects on growth-associated parameters (59). This discrepancy between the in vivo and in vitro effects of GH plus the identification and subsequent chemical characterization of GH-dependent plasma peptides—in this review called somatomedin(s) or insulin-like growth factors—has led to the concept that GH stimulates cell proliferation indirectly via somatomedins. According to the somatomedin hypothesis, GH has no direct effects on cartilage but instead stimulates chondrogenesis and subsequent growth by increasing the level of somatomedins. These in turn stimulate several growth-associated parameters in cartilage and other tissues. The somatomedins are synthesized and released primarily from the liver in response to GH (16, 48). The aim of this review is to discuss the role of direct effects of GH at the cellular and tissue level resulting in the physiological effects attributed to GH action. There will be a special emphasis on recent studies suggesting direct effects of GH on differentiation and proliferation of its target cells.

483

0066-4278/85/0315-0483$02.00

DEVELOPMENT OF GH DEPENDENCE

Growth and development during fetal and early postnatal life proceeds at a normal or near-normal rate in the absence of pituitary GH. In primates, hypophysectomy of the fetus in utero (monkey) or congenital absence of the pituitary gland (man) does not result in a decrease of fetal length or weight at birth (93, 102). Moreover, GH-deficient children born of GH-deficient mothers are of normal weight and length, clearly demonstrating that fetal growth in primates is independent of GH (95). In the rabbit, decapitation of fetuses in utero does not interfere with fetal growth (54). However, hypophysectomy of lambs in utero has been reported to result in slight retardation of fetal growth, suggesting that fetal growth in this species is partly GH-dependent. In a carefully designed study, Walker and coworkers (110) examined the pituitary dependence of postnatal growth in the rat by hypophysectomizing rats at different ages. Following hypophysectomy, growth was only slightly decreased in animals younger than ten days of age. Thereafter, the rate of growth progressively decreased and ceased completely (in terms of body weight) 28 days after birth, demonstrating the gradual increase in GH dependence of postnatal growth.

The Snell-Smith mouse represents another example of GH-independent growth. These mice do not secrete GH or TSH, due to a recessive gene defect. Despite this, they grow at a near-normal rate during the first week of postnatal life. Their growth rate then gradually delines and reaches a standstill one month after birth (101).

The progressive decrease in growth rate of GH-deficient subjects or rats during early postnatal life suggests that GH responsiveness develops gradually. Indeed, such an increase in responsiveness to GH as a function of age has been demonstrated both in vivo as well as in vitro in isolated tissues (3, 37, 84). The mechanism(s) for this progressive increase in GH dependence and responsiveness postnatally is not known. Interestingly, the number of somatogenic binding sites is low in ovine liver membranes during the fetal and neonatal period. A few days after birth the number of binding sites begins to increase and, for older lambs and adult sheep, the characteristic high binding capacity is soon reached (29). A similar increase in GH binding in liver membranes as a function of age has been demonstrated in the rat (71). Thus, it is possible that the development of GH dependence and responsiveness is intimately coupled to the development of GH receptors. Paradoxically, compared to prepubertal GH levels, plasma levels are elevated during late fetal life and in the early postnatal period in many species (30). The physiological significance of the increased plasma levels of GH during this period of GH-independent growth is not readily apparent.

GH STIMULATES POSTNATAL GROWTH BY INCREASING THE NUMBER OF CELLS

The growth of different tissues during postnatal life is mainly a process of cell multiplication or, as in the case of skeletal muscle, formation of multinucleated myotubes from myoblasts (11, 79, 83). Because GH dependence develops during this developmental process, it is obvious that GH—directly or indirectly—influences the rate of cell multiplication and differentiation in different organs. In normal rats, the number of nuclei, which reflect the DNA content in skeletal muscle, increases dramatically from the neonatal period to the period of sexual maturation, after which the increase of nuclei eventually ceases (12). The increment in the number of nuclei in human skeletal muscle during the corresponding stage of development is even more pronounced (10). The normal increase of muscle DNA content with time does not occur under conditions of GH deficiency (9). As a result, the DNA content in muscle of pituitary dwarfs is considerably lower than in normal individuals of the same age (11). In the rat, hypophysectomy at day 21 results in a decrease of DNA content in skeletal muscle with time, suggesting that the loss rate of nuclei is higher than their rate of formation (9). Administration of GH normalizes this situation, i.e. it increases the DNA content both in man and in the rat. Besides skeletal muscle, GH has also been shown to increase the DNA content and the rate of DNA synthesis in the liver, kidney, heart, and adipose tissue of hypophysectomized rats, demonstrating that GH stimulates DNA synthesis in many tissues (35). The brain is one notable exception that is not influenced by GH. DNA synthesis in the brain is not decreased after hypophysectomy or increased by GH replacement therapy (35).

SOMATOMEDIN HYPOTHESIS OF GH ACTION

Considerable evidence has accumulated to suggest that the effect of GH on different growth processes, particularly skeletal growth, is mediated by GH-dependent plasma factors—somatomedins—that are produced mainly in the liver in response to GH (16, 48, 88). The main basis for this theory is the fact that most investigators have failed to demonstrate stimulatory effects of GH in vitro on cartilage metabolism, whereas somatomedin(s), when added in vitro, stimulate a number of processes that are associated with both cell multiplication and growth. Although somatomedins undoubtly stimulate a number of cellular processes in vitro, their postulated mediator role for GH action in vivo is still controversial. Accordingly, earlier efforts to demonstrate stimulatory effects by different somatomedin preparations on longitudinal bone growth were essentially negative (25, 49, 108). However, evidence in favor of the somatomedin hypothesis of GH action comes from the recent demonstration that continuous administration of the insulin-like growth factor IGF-1/Sm-C to hypophysectomized rats, via implanted osmotic minipumps, increased tibial epiphysial width and ^{3}H-thymidine incorporation into costal cartilage (97). However, the magnitude of the effects observed was small and comparable to those of 12.5–25 mU continuously infused hGH day^{-1}; this represents the lower part of the dose-response curve for the effect of GH on longitudinal bone growth in hypophysectomized rats (107).

The difficulty in demonstrating stimulatory effects of GH in vitro on cartilage could be due to the fact that cartilage is not a target tissue for GH and that the effect of GH in vivo on chondrogenesis is indeed mediated by insulin-like growth factors produced elsewhere. However, it is necessary to consider alternative possibilities, e.g. that the culture conditions usually employed for studying long-term effects of GH in vitro could be unfavorable for the expression of GH effects but satisfactory for growth factors of the somatomedin class. Such a difference could be due to the fact that GH and insulin-like growth factors influence different metabolic pathways or stimulate cells in different phases of the cell cycle. The in vitro requirements for these processes may be different. Another possibility which will be discussed below is that GH only acts on a few not fully differentiated cells in a tissue, and that this activation process requires special in vitro conditions.

Indeed, there are earlier reports in the literature suggesting direct effects of GH on cartilage. Phillips and coworkers (87) found that administration of small doses of GH to hypophysectomized rats stimulated cartilage metabolism without a concomitant increase in plasma somatomedin activity. Direct stimulatory effects of GH in vitro on the mitotic index in condylar cartilage of the rat mandible have also been documented after culture for several days in the presence of serum (86, 104).

DIRECT EFFECTS OF GH ON LONGITUDINAL BONE GROWTH

Longitudinal bone growth is the result of cell proliferation of chondrocytes in the epiphyseal growth plate. After hypophysectomy the rate of cell proliferation decreases and concomitantly the epiphyseal plate narrows. Replacement therapy with GH restores the rate of cell proliferation and the width of the growth plate. The increase in width of the growth plate of hypophysectomized rats following initiation of GH replacement therapy is proportional to the logarithm of the GH dose given and forms the basis for the classical tibia test for bioassay of GH activity in vivo (28).

Determination of the width of the growth plate usually gives a good estimate of the *rate* of longitudinal bone growth. However, the tibia test does not measure accumulated longitudinal bone growth. By using the intravital marker tetracycline, which is incorporated into newly formed bone, the accumulated longitudinal bone growth can be specifically and accurately determined (45, 46, 107).

We have explored the possibility of a direct effect of GH on cartilage growth by injecting GH locally in vivo into the epiphyseal growth plate of the proximal tibia of anesthetized hypophysectomized rats. Our investigations showed that local administration of human GH stimulated longitudinal bone growth of the leg injected, as measured by the tetracycline method (52). Moreover, an increase in the width of the cartilage growth plate of the leg injected has also been observed, suggesting that chondrogenesis was stimulated (50). The effect was specific for GH, because injection of saline or ovine prolactin caused no such stimulation. Local injection of 0.5 µg hGH twice, with a two-day interval, caused a significant acceleration of longitudinal bone growth (O. Isaksson, J-O. Jansson, unpublished observations). If given systemically, this dose of GH is a subthreshold dose, suggesting that GH given locally must interact with cells in or close to the growth plate to produce its effect. Recently, local injection of hGH into the growth plate of the proximal tibia of *normal* rats has been found to stimulate longitudinal bone growth of the injected leg (106). These investigators found that injection of 100 µg of hGH in two separate doses, with a two-day interval, stimulated longitudinal bone growth by approximately 10% compared to the contralateral leg. The authors suggest that local treatment with GH might have therapeutic potential for the treatment of local growth disorders.

IN VITRO EFFECTS OF GH ON CULTURED CHONDROCYTES

Chondrocytes isolated from rabbit ear and epiphyseal plates have specific binding sites for GH (18). These receptors show half-maximal binding at hGH concentrations of 10–20 ng ml^{-1}. This concentration frequently can be recorded in the plasma during episodes of GH secretion in the rabbit (13) and, therefore, is well within the physiological range. Specific binding of ^{125}I-hGH to cultured chondrocytes isolated from rabbit growth plates and articular cartilage has recently been observed also in another laboratory (90). These investigators made the additional observation that the specific binding of ^{125}I-hGH, expressed per 100 µg DNA as the percentage of total radioactivity, was very low for hGH compared to the binding of insulin-like growth factors. Possibly the number of GH receptors per chondrocyte is small. However, this observation may also reflect the fact that GH only binds to a small percentage of cells at a defined stage of differentiation, as suggested below.

GH has also been shown to stimulate DNA synthesis in cultured chondrocytes from rabbit ear and rat rib growth cartilage (70). In these experiments the cells were first cultured in the presence of newborn calf serum to allow a period of rapid cell proliferation. Then the cells were incubated in serum-free medium (MCDB-104) with or without GH. The stimulatory effect of GH was dose-dependent, and a clear stimulation was seen with 50 ng ml^{-1} of hGH both for rabbit ear and rat rib growth cartilage. The finding that GH in vitro under specific experimental conditions has the capacity to stimulate DNA synthesis in cultured chondrocytes has recently been confirmed (M. T. Corvol, personal communication).

SITE OF ACTION OF GH IN THE EPIPHYSEAL GROWTH PLATE

The chondrocytes in the growth plate show a strict organization in a fascicular pattern oriented longitudinally in the direction of growth. At the top of the growth plate (towards the epiphysis) there is a resting or germinal zone of cells (prechondrocytes?). The germinal zone is the stem cell area of the growth plate. Cells from this layer differentiate and enter the proliferative zone, where they undergo limited multiplication during the process of normal growth. Subsequently, these cells mature and enter the hypertrophic cell zone before eventually becoming calcified and being incorporated into metaphyseal bone (45, 55, 56).

What cells in the growth plate are the target cells for GH action? To study whether GH preferentially binds to chondrocytes at a defined stage of differentiation in the growth plate, the binding of ^{125}I-hGH was investigated in the growth plate during incubation of rat rib growth plates in the absence and presence of excessive amounts of unlabeled hGH (O. Isaksson, S. Edén, A. Lindahl, K. Madsen, manuscript in preparation). The incubation period was followed by repeated washings in buffer medium, and the localization of radioactivity in the growth plate was then determined by autoradiography. In growth plates incubated with ^{125}I-hGH, a distinct zone of radioactivity could be localized at the very top of the growth plate, corresponding to the germinal cell zone. No radioactivity was found in the proliferative and hypertrophic cell zones, suggesting that these cells do not bind GH. No distinct localization of radioactivity was found in growth plates that had been incubated with the tracer plus an excessive amount of hGH. This finding that GH mainly binds to the cells in the germinal zone of the growth plate might explain why epiphyseal growth plates do not accumulate radioactivity after injection of ^{125}I-hGH to hypophysectomized rats (73). Moreover, this finding suggests that cells in the germinal zone of the growth plate are the primary target cells for GH in the growth plate, as previously suggested by Green and coworkers (42). Their suggestion was based on their findings that GH stimulates the differentiation of preadipose cells and myoblasts. Cells in the germinal zone of the growth plate are probably prechondrocytes and would thus be at the same stage of differentiation as preadipocytes and myoblasts. However, it remains to be shown that GH stimulates the differentiation of prechondrocytes in vitro before this hypothesis has been validated.

DIRECT EFFECTS OF GH ON CELL PROLIFERATION IN NONSKELETAL TISSUE

A number of reports show that GH promotes growth and development of many tissues that have no apparent relationship to skeletal and muscle tissue. Golde and coworkers utilized clonal assays to study the in vitro effects of GH and other polypeptide hormones on the colony-forming activity of erythropoietin-stimulated hematopoietic progenitor cells (31–34, 74). The number of colony-forming units of bone marrow or peripheral blood stem cells were studied in a suspension culture stabilized with methyl-cellulose. GH was found to stimulate the number of erythroid colonies in a species-specific manner, as indicated by the fact that bovine GH was ineffective for human but effective for murine erythroid proliferation. Thus, the in vitro differences in responsiveness closely paralleled the classical in vivo observations of growth-promoting effects by GH from different species (57). The stimulatory effect of GH observed by Golde and coworkers was dose-dependent, and concentrations of GH in the nanogram range produced significant effects. This stimulatory effect of GH on cell colony formation was independent of serum factors, because the effect was also observed in serum-free medium.

The same group of investigators were also able to demonstrate an in vitro species-specific effect of GH on the colony formation of normal human peripheral blood T progenitor cells. GH did not stimulate granulopoiesis, suggesting that only erythropoiesis and lymphopoiesis are under direct pituitary control (74).

Smooth muscle is another tissue that responds directly in vitro to GH with a stimulation of growth (63–65). The effect was studied in rabbit aorta explants consisting primarily of smooth muscle cells. ^{3}H-thymidine incorporation was stimulated, and the number of mitotic cells in the preparation increased. GH also increased the DNA content and the tissue mass of the cultured explants, showing that GH indeed increased the number of cells. A concentration of 1–2 ng hGH per ml medium was effective, and represents a concentration of GH well within the physiological range (23).

Rat pancreatic B-cells appear to be direct target cells for GH, because it has been demonstrated that GH stimulates their ^{3}H-thymidine incorporation and DNA content in culture (80, 91). The stimulatory effect was most pronounced in serum-free medium and was independent of the glucose concentration. The insulin-like growth factor, multiplication-stimulating activity (MSA), also stimulated B-cell replication but the maximal effect was less than for GH. In combination, MSA and GH produced additive effects, suggesting that the effect of GH was not dependent upon MSA (91). The direct effect of GH on islet cell growth might contribute to the well-known hyperinsulinaemia associated with conditions of GH overproduction.

In his investigations into the balance between different hormonal systems, Selye (100) injected GH intracutaneously or subcutaneously to normal rats. He found that this treatment intensely stimulated the proliferation of fibroblasts, suggesting that GH interacted with fibroblasts at the site of GH injection. These initial observations have been subsequently confirmed, and GH has been shown to stimulate human fibroblasts in tissue culture (15). The mechanism for the stimulatory effect of GH on fibroblasts has not yet been elucidated, but it has been found that hGH augments "the rate of entry" of DNA synthesis in cultured human fibroblasts, provided that platelet-poor plasma from a hypopituitary individual was also present in the culture medium (15). Interestingly, GH in vitro stimulates the production of IGF-1/Sm-C in fibroblasts derived from human skin and lung (6, 14). GH also augments the production of IGF-I in rat fibroblasts, an effect which seems to be dependent on the rat donor age, because it has been demonstrated that GH has this effect in fibroblasts from 25-day-old rats but not in those from fetal rats (1).

EFFECT OF GH ON CELL DIFFERENTIATION

A most significant contribution to the understanding of the cellular mechanism of action of GH has recently come from experiments by Green and coworkers (for review see 42). These investigators have studied the factors regulating adipose conversion in cloned preadipose lines derived from 3T3 cells. In early studies it was shown that preadipose cells grow exponentially in the presence of a high concentration of fetal calf serum (41). However, when the rate of growth of preadipose cells is inhibited by decreasing the amount of fetal calf serum to $\sim 1\%$, the preadipose cells come to a resting state and eventually convert to adipose cells (62). The differentiation of preadipose cells to adipocytes is a consequence of a reorganized pattern of gene expression and leads to extensive alteration in enzyme activities and cell composition (103).

The adipose conversion is stimulated by as yet unidentified factors in the plasma and by pituitary growth hormone (47, 76). The effect of GH is dose-dependent, and a concentration of hGH as low as 0.5 ng ml^{-1} was effective (76). Biosynthetic hGH is as effective as native hGH, excluding the possibility that a pituitary contaminant could be a contributing factor to the effect observed. Moreover, the effect on adipose conversion is highly specific for GH, because no other characterized growth factor or hormone tested promotes adipose conversion (75, 82). GH receptors have been identified on different preadipose cell lines (81). Interestingly, not all cell lines that have receptors for GH respond to GH in vitro, in terms of differentiation; this suggests that susceptibility to adipose conversion is determined at a site(s) distal to the GH receptor (81). GH accounts for about half the adipogenic activity in fetal bovine serum, and this activity can be neutralized by antibodies to GH (82). The identity of factors in serum other than GH that promote adipose conversion is still unclear.

Recently, Green and coworkers (83) demonstrated that GH in vitro stimulates the differentiation of multinucleated muscle cells from myoblasts in a cloned muscle line. By analogy with preadipose cells, the GH effect was very specific and was elicited by hormone concentrations in the nanogram range.

METABOLIC EFFECTS OF GH

The relationship between short- and long-term effects of GH is unclear. Consequently, it is not known whether the different effects of GH are due to activation of the same receptor and reflect the same initial cellular event, or whether there is one hormone-receptor interaction for each response produced or group of responses. A distinct possibility is that the receptor population of GH is heterogenous, leading to activation of different metabolic pathways. Indeed, different fragments of GH produced by enzymatic digestion of GH have different profiles of biological activity in vitro, suggesting that there are different structural requirements for the different effects of GH (39, 58, 92). Alternatively, these results could be explained by the fact that the different effects of GH are due to activation of different sites on the same, single receptor (39). In any case, conclusive biological data supporting or reflecting the existence of physically distinct GH receptors is still missing.

The metabolic effects of GH can be classified as insulin-like and insulin-antagonistic. Accordingly, the lipolytic and diabetogenic effects of GH are the result of the insulin-antagonistic effects of GH. The fact that the same hormone can produce two apparently antagonistic effects is paradoxical. Therefore, the hypothesis that different variants of the GH molecule cause the different metabolic effects has been raised repeatedly (68). Different variants of GH from the pituitary gland have been isolated, varying both in terms of size and charge (44, 58, 68). Recently, Frigeri (24) reported that highly purified hGH obtained from clinical grade hGH did not contain lipolytic activity, suggesting that the lipolytic activity was due to a pituitary contaminant. However, when the same preparation was tested in another laboratory, it exerted a clear lipolytic effect. Consequently, it was suggested that the test system used by Frigeri (24) may not have been adequate for detecting lipolytic activity (38). In addition, bacterially synthesized GH, that should be free of pituitary peptides that might contaminate hGH, also has lipolytic activity in vitro (36). Further-more, injection of biosynthetic hGH into normal adult humans produces the same spectrum of effects as native hGH, clearly confirming that the insulin-antagonistic effect of GH is an intrinsic property of the molecule (96).

GH exerts transient insulin-like effects in tissues from hypophysectomized rats, from animals injected with antiserum to GH, and from young fasted animals (2, 3, 60, 84, 99). One of the common denominators for these animal models is that plasma GH was eliminated or suppressed. This suggests that endogenous GH usually prevents the expression of the insulin-like effect of GH. The insulin-like effect of GH is transient, however, and is followed by a period of homologous refractoriness. The tissues appear to become "normal-ized," in the sense that GH no longer exerts insulin-like effects. The develop-ment of refractoriness to its own insulin-like effect can be used as a specific and sensitive bioassay for GH activity. In fact, GH concentrations less than 10 ng ml^{-1} have been confirmed to induce refractoriness in adipose tissue in vitro (43, 69).

The molecular events involved in the insulin-like effects of GH are presently unknown. It has been shown that GH, like insulin, stimulates dephosphoryla-tion of hormone-sensitive lipase (HSL) in adipocytes, thereby suggesting that insulin and GH share the same metabolic pathway for the antilipolytic effect distal to HSL (8). Earlier reports showed that freshly isolated adipocytes from normal rats, that usually are refractory to the insulin-like effect of GH, have a significant number of GH receptors, suggesting that refractoriness to the insulin-like effect of GH cannot be explained by depletion of GH receptors (43). Edén and colleagues in 1982 published evidence that the number of GH-specific binding sites in adipocytes isolated from normal and hypophysectomized rats increased with incubation time, indicating that addi-tional binding sites were developed or unmasked during the preincubation period (20). However, Grichting and coworkers (43) found that binding of GH to adipocytes responsive to the GH insulin-like effect was indistinguishable from binding to responsive cells. One can conclude that this question, whether alterations in the number and binding characteristics of GH receptors are involved in the development and maintenance of GH refractoriness, needs to be clarified further.

Administration of pharmacologically high amounts of GH or excessive GH secretion undoubtedly results in decreased carbohydrate tolerance and hyperin-sulinemia (5, 21, 40), demonstrating that GH exerts insulin-antagonistic or diabetogenic effects under these conditions. However, this fact does not exclude the possibility that the insulin-like effect could have a physiological function in normal subjects. Recent experiments have demonstrated that refrac-toriness to the insulin-like effect is rapidly reversible both in vivo and in vitro. Thus, administration of rGH antibodies to normal rats reversed refractoriness within a 3-hr period both in adipose tissue and in skeletal muscle (26, 98, 99). There again, incubation of adipocytes or skeletal muscle in vitro for 3 hr also reversed the refractoriness (3, 20, 43). The recognition that GH's secretory pattern is episodic or pulsatile in nature, with a periodicity of 3–4 hr in male rats (17, 72, 105), coupled to the fact that the time course for maintenance of GH refractoriness has approximately the same duration, also suggests that the insulin-like effect of GH might have a physiological role. In fact, there are experimental data suggesting that endogenous GH regulates protein, as well as carbohydrate metabolism, on an hour-to-hour basis in normal rats (53, 99).

EARLY CELLULAR EVENTS IN RESPONSE TO GH ACTION

It is now generally accepted that binding of GH to receptors in the plasma membrane is the primary event in the action of GH on target cells. GH receptors have been identified in isolated cells of many different organs, including the liver, lymphopoietic tissue, adipose tissue, connective tissue, and cartilage (19, 22, 27, 67, 78, 89). Although progress has been made in understanding the interaction between GH and its receptor, knowledge is meager concerning the cellular events following GH-receptor interaction and the expression of the effects of GH on various cell functions.

Alterations in cyclic nucleotide metabolism might be involved in the early action of GH on target cells. The observation that inhibitors of cyclic nucleotide phosphodiesterase blocked the insulin-like effect of GH, but not that of insulin, in vitro was the first finding that suggested a role for cyclic nucleotides in the intracellular action of GH. (85, 94). Efforts to demonstrate decreased tissue levels of cAMP and cGMP in muscle after addition of GH in vitro have been unsuccessful (2, 51). However, in the perfused rat heart and in epididymal fat pads, GH causes a rapid decrease in the cAMP level (77). GH also inhibits adenylate cyclase activity in the diaphragm and heart of young normal or hypophysectomized rats, after both in vivo and in vitro administration (4). These investigators also found that addition of nanomolar concentrations of GH directly to the muscle membranes in the adenylate cyclase assay produced an inhibitory effect, provided the GTP analog, Gpp(NH)p, also was present. Their observations suggest that the GH inhibition of adenylate cyclase activity is caused by a direct GH interaction with components of the plasma membrane. In this regard, GH inhibition of glucagon and fluoride-stimulated adenylate cyclase activation has also been demonstrated in the liver from hypophysectomized rats (66). Of course, it is possible that cGMP also might have a role in GH action, because it has been reported that GH in vitro increases cytoslic guanylate cyclase activity in the liver (109).

As yet, there is no compelling evidence that a decrease in the cellular level of cAMP is important for the GH effect, with the possible exception of the antilipolytic effect of GH in adipose tissue (7). In this tissue GH inhibits protein kinase within 3 min, a response most probably due to the prior decrease in cAMP level. However, it is presently unclear whether changes in cyclic nucleotide metabolism have any relation to the other effects of GH and, in addition, the role of cAMP in the growth-promoting effect of GH is totally unknown. A better understanding of the cellular mechanisms controlling cell proliferation and differentiation is required before a rational approach can be taken to clarify the specific mechanism of action of GH.

SUMMARY AND CONCLUSIONS

Normal postnatal somatic growth becomes progressively dependent on GH with time. In contrast to other hormones, GH is the only hormone known to produce a dose-dependent stimulation of postnatal growth. Most of the effects attributed to GH action appear to be the result of a direct effect of GH on cells in different peripheral tissues, including cartilage. In addition to the growth-stimulating effect, GH has the intrinsic properties of being able to exert both insulin-like and insulin-antagonistic effects in adipose tissue and skeletal muscle. These two apparently antagonistic effects seem to be explained by the stage of responsiveness of the target cells to GH, which is determined by the previous influence of endogenous GH. An inhibition of adenylate cyclase with a concomitant decrease in intracellular cAMP might be an important early cellular event in the course of GH action, but it is not known whether or how this change in nucleotide metabolism relates to the various expressed effects of the hormone.

The recognition that GH directly interacts with chondrocytes in cartilage suggests that alterations in the concentration of circulating somatomedins cannot be the only factor regulating skeletal growth. The recent discovery by Green and coworkers (42) demonstrating that GH specifically stimulates the differentiation of cloned preadipose cells and myoblasts in tissue culture may be a major breakthrough in the understanding of the mechanism of action of the growth-promoting effect of GH. Green (42) has proposed that GH directly stimulates terminal differentiation of cells in many different tissues including epiphyseal plate cartilage. The finding that GH binds specifically to cells in the resting cell zone but not to differentiated chondrocytes in the growth plate suggests that prechondrocytes in the growth plate are the target cells for GH action.

If it is correct that GH directly stimulates the differentiation of prechondrocytes, we suggest that, during the process of chondrocyte differentiation in the growth plate, the genes that code for growth factors of the somatomedin class, such as IGF-I, are expressed. As a consequence, the clonal expansion of the chondrocytes in the proliferative zone of the growth plate that occurs in vivo during the process of normal growth is the result of this *local* production of growth factors.

ACKNOWLEDGMENTS

This work was supported by a grant from the Swedish Medical Research Council (No. B84–04X–04250–11B), and by KabiVitrum AB Stockholm, Sweden.

Literature Cited

1. Adams, S. O., Nissley, S. P., Handwerger, S., Rechler, M. M. 1983. Developmental patterns of insulin-like growth factor-I and -II synthesis and regulation in rat fibroblasts. *Nature* 302:150–53
2. Ahrén, K., Albertsson-Wikland, K., Isaksson, O., Kostyo, J. L. 1976. Cellular mechanisms of the acute stimulatory effect of growth hormone. In *Growth Hormone and Related Peptides*, ed. A. Pecile, E. E. Müller, 381:94–103. Amsterdam: Excerpta Medica
3. Albertsson-Wikland, K., Isaksson, O. 1976. Development of responsiveness of young normal rats to growth hormone. *Metabolism* 25:747–59
4. Albertsson-Wikland, K., Rosberg, S. 1982. Inhibition of adenylate cyclase activity in muscles by growth hormone. *Endocrinology* 111:1855–61
5. Altzuler, N. 1974. Actions of growth hormone on carbohydrate metabolism. In *Handbook of Physiology*, ed. E. Knobil, W. H. Sawyer, 2:233–52. Washington DC: Am. Physiol. Soc. Vol. 4
6. Atkison, P. R., Weidman, E. R., Bhaumick, B., Bala, R. M. 1980. Release of somatomedin-like activity by cultured WI-38 human fibroblasts. *Endocrinology* 106:2006–12
7. Birnbaum, R. S., Goodman, H. M. 1976. Studies on the mechanism of the antilipolytic effect of growth hormone. *Endocrinology* 99:1336–45
8. Björgell, P., Rosberg, S., Isaksson, O., Belfrage, P. 1984. The anti-lipolytic, insulin-like effect of growth hormone is caused by a net decrease of hormone-sensitive lipase phosphorylation. *Endocrinology*. 115:1151–56
9. Cheek, D. B., Graystone, J. E. 1969. The action of insulin, growth hormone, and epinephrine on cell growth in liver, muscle, and brain of the hypophysectomized rat. *Pediat. Res.* 3:77–88
10. Cheek, D. B., Hill, D. E. 1970. Muscle and liver cell growth: role of hormones and nutritional factors. *Fed. Proc.* 29:1503–9

11. Cheek, D. B., Hill, D. E. 1974. Effect of growth hormone on cell and somatic growth. See Ref. 5, pp. 159–85.
12. Cheek, D. B., Holt, A. B., Hill, D. E., Talbert, J. L. 1971. Skeletal muscle cell mass and growth: the concept of the deoxyribonucleic acid unit. *Pediat. Res.* 5:312–28
13. Chihara, K., Minamitani, N., Kaji, H., Kodama, H., Kita, T., Fujita, T. 1983. Human pancreatic growth hormone–releasing factor stimulates release of growth hormone in conscious unrestrained male rabbits. *Endocrinology* 113:2081–85
14. Clemmons, D. R., Underwood, L. E., van Wyk, J. J. 1981. Hormonal control of immunoreactive somatomedin production by cultured human fibroblasts. *J. Clin. Invest.* 67:10–19
15. Clemmons, D. R., van Wyk, J. J. 1981. Somatomedin-C and platelet-derived growth factor stimulate human fibroblast replication. *J. Cell. Physiol.* 106:361–67
16. Daughaday, W. H. 1981. Growth hormone and the somatomedins. In *Endocrine Control of Growth*, ed. W. H. Daughaday, pp. 1–24. New York: Elsevier
17. Edén, S. 1979. Age- and sex-related differences in episodic growth hormone secretion in the rat. *Endocrinology* 105:555–60
18. Edén, S., Isaksson, O. G. P., Madsen, K., Friberg, U. 1983. Specific binding of growth hormone to isolated chondrocytes from rabbit ear and epiphyseal plate. *Endocrinology* 112:1127–29
19. Edén, S., Kostyo, J. L., Schwartz, J. 1982. Ability of growth hormone fragments to compete with ^{125}I-iodinated human growth hormone for specific binding to isolated adipocytes of hypophysectomized rats. *Biochim. Biophys. Acta* 721:489–91
20. Edén, S., Schwartz, J., Kostyo, J. L. 1982. Effects of preincubation on the ability of rat adipocytes to bind and re-

spond to growth hormone. *Endocrinology* 111:1505–12

21. Engel, F. L., Kostyo, J. L. 1964. Metabolic actions of pituitary hormones. In *The Hormones,* ed. G. Pincus, K. V. Thimann, E. B. Astwood, 5:69–158. New York: Academic

22. Fagin, K. D., Lackey, S. L., Reagan, C. R., DiGirolamo, M. 1980. Specific binding of growth hormone by rat adipocytes. *Endocrinology* 107:608–15

23. Finkelstein, J. W., Roffwarg, H. P., Boyar, R. M., Kream, J., Hellman, L. 1972. Age-related change in the twenty-four-hour spontaneous secretion of growth hormone. *J. Clin. Endocrinol. Metab.* 35:665–70

24. Frigeri, L. G. 1980. Absence of in vitro dexamethasone-dependent lipolytic activity from highly purified growth hormone. *Endocrinology* 107:738–43

25. Fryklund, L., Uthne, K., Sievertsson, H. 1974. Identification of two somatomedin A active polypeptides and in vivo effects of a somatomedin A concentrate. *Biochem. Biophys. Res. Commun.* 61:957–62

26. Gause, I., Edén, S., Jansson, J.-O., Isaksson, O. 1983. Effects of in vivo administration of antiserum to rat growth hormone on body growth and insulin responsiveness in adipose tissue. *Endocrinology* 112:1559–66

27. Gavin, J. R. III, Saltman, R. J., Tollefsen, S. E. 1982. Growth hormone receptors in isolated rat adipocytes. *Endocrinology* 110:637–43

28. Geschwind, I. I., Li, C. H. 1954. The tibia test for growth hormone. In *Hypophyseal Growth Hormone, Nature and Actions,* ed. R. W. Smith, O. H. Gaebler, C. N. H. Long, pp. 28–53. New York: McGraw-Hill

29. Gluckman, P. D., Butler, J. H., Elliott, T. B. 1983. The ontogeny of somatotropic binding sites in ovine hepatic membranes. *Endocrinology* 112:1607–12

30. Gluckman, P. D., Grumbach, M. M., Kaplan, S. L. 1981. The neuroendocrine regulation and function of growth hormone and prolactin in the mammalian fetus. *Endocrine Rev.* 2:363–95

31. Golde, D. W. 1979. In vitro effects of growth hormone. In *Growth Hormone and Other Biologically Active Peptides,* ed. A. Pecile, E. E. Müller, 495:52–62. Amsterdam: Excerpta Medica

32. Golde, D. W. 1980. Growth factors. *Ann. Internal Med.* 92:650–62

33. Golde, D. W., Bersch, N., Kaplan, S. A., Rimoin, D. L., Li, C. H. 1980. Peripheral unresponsiveness to human growth hormone in Laron dwarfism. *New Engl. J. Med.* 303:1156–59

34. Golde, D. W., Bersch, N., Li, C. H. 1977. Growth hormone: Species-specific stimulation of erythropoiesis in vitro. *Science* 196:1112–13

35. Goldspink, D. F., Goldberg, A. L. 1975. Influence of pituitary growth hormone on DNA synthesis in rat tissues. *Am. J. Physiol.* 228:302–9

36. Goodman, H. M. 1984. Biological activity of bacterial derived human growth hormone in adipose tissue of hypophysectomized rats. *Endocrinology* 114:131–35

37. Goodman, H. M., Coiro, V. 1981. Induction of sensitivity to the insulin-like action of growth hormone in normal rat adipose tissue. *Endocrinology* 108:113–19

38. Goodman, H. M., Grichting, G. 1983. Growth hormone and lipolysis: A reevaluation. *Endocrinology* 113:1697–702

39. Goodman, H. M., Kostyo, J. L. 1981. Altered profiles of biological activity of growth hormone fragments on adipocyte metabolism. *Endocrinology* 108:553–58

40. Goodman, H. M., Schwartz, J. 1974. Growth hormone and lipid metabolism. See Ref. 5, pp. 211–31

41. Green, H., Kehinde, O. 1976. Spontaneous heritable changes leading to increased adipose conversion in 3T3 cells. *Cell* 7:105–13

42. Green, H., Morikawa, M., Nixon, T. 1984. A dual effector theory of growth hormone action. In *Human Growth Hormone Symposium,* in press. New York: Plenum

43. Grichting, G., Levy, L. K., Goodman, H. M. 1983. Relationship between binding and biological effects of human growth hormone in rat adipocytes. *Endocrinology* 113:1111–20

44. Hanson, L. Å., Roos, P., Rymo, L. 1966. Heterogeneity of human growth hormone preparations by immuno-gel filtration and gel filtration electrophoresis. *Nature* 212:948–49

45. Hansson, L. I. 1967. Daily growth in length of diaphysis measured by oxytetracycline in rabbit normally and after medullary plugging. *Acta Orthoped. Scand.* (Suppl. 101):34–84

46. Hansson, L. I., Menander-Sellman, K., Stenström, A., Thorngren, K.-G. 1972. Rate of normal longitudinal bone growth in the rat. *Calc. Tiss. Res.* 10:238–51

47. Hayashi, I., Nixon, T., Morikawa, M., Green, H. 1981. Adipogenic and anti-adipogenic factors in the pituitary and

other organs. *Proc. Natl. Acad. Sci. USA* 78:3969–72

48. Herington, A. C., Cornell, H. J., Kuffer, A. D. 1983. Recent advances in the biochemistry and physiology of the insulin-like growth factor/somatomedin family. *Int. J. Biochem.* 15:1201–10

49. Holder, A. T., Spencer, E. M., Preece, M. A. 1981. Effect of bovine growth hormone and a partially pure preparation of somatomedin on various growth parameters in hypopituitary dwarf mice. *J. Endocrinol.* 89:275–82

50. Isaksson, O. G. P., Edén, S., Albertsson-Wikland, K., Jansson, J.-O., Friberg, U., Madsen, K. 1984. Direct action of growth hormone on cartilage metabolism. See Ref. 42, in press

51. Isaksson, O., Gimpel, L. P., Ahrén, K., Kostyo, J. L. 1974. Growth hormone and cyclic AMP in rat diaphragm muscle. *Acta Endocrinol.* 77(Suppl. 191):73–80

52. Isaksson, O. G. P., Jansson, J.-O., Gause, I. A. M. 1982. Growth hormone stimulates longitudinal bone growth directly. *Science* 216:1237–39

53. Isaksson, O., Nutting, D. F., Kostyo, J. L., Reagan, C. R. 1978. Hourly variations in plasma concentrations of growth hormone and insulin and in amino acid uptake and incorporation into protein in diaphragm muscle of the rat. *Endocrinology* 102:1420–28

54. Jost, A. 1952. Hormonal factors in the development of the fetus. *Cold Spring Harb. Symp. Quant. Biol.* 19:167–81

55. Kember, N. F. 1978. Cell kinetics and the control of growth in long bones. *Cell Tissue Kinet.* 11:477–85

56. Kember, N. F., Walker, K. V. R. 1971. Control of bone growth in rats. *Nature* 229:428–29

57. Knobil, E., Hotchkiss, J. 1964. Growth hormone. *Ann. Rev. Physiol.* 26:47–74

58. Kostyo, J. L. 1974. The search for the active core of pituitary growth hormone. *Metabolism* 23:885–99

59. Kostyo, J. L., Isaksson, O. 1977. Growth hormone and regulation of somatic growth. In *Int. Rev. Physiol., Reproductive Physiology II*, 13:255–74

60. Kostyo, J. L., Nutting, D. F. 1973. Acute in vivo effects of growth hormone on protein synthesis in various tissues of hypophysectomized rats and their relationship to the levels of thymidine factor and insulin in the plasma. *Horm. Metab. Res.* 5:167–72

61. Kostyo, J. L., Nutting, D. F. 1974. Growth hormone and protein metabolism. See Ref. 5, pp. 187–210

62. Kuri-Harcuch, W., Green, H. 1978. Adipose conversion of 3T3 cells depends on a serum factor. *Proc. Natl. Acad. Sci. USA* 75:6107–9

63. Ledet, T. 1976. Growth hormone stimulates the growth of arterial medial cells in vitro. *Diabetes* 25:1011–17

64. Ledet, T. 1981. Diabetic macroangiopathy and growth hormone. *Diabetes* 30:(Suppl. 2):14–17

65. Ledet, T., Vuust, J. 1980. Arterial procollagen type I, type III, and fibronectin. Effects of diabetic serum, glucose, insulin, ketone, and growth hormone studied on rabbit aortic myomedial cell cultures. *Diabetes* 29:964–70

66. Leppert, P., Guillory, J., Russo, L. J., Moore, W. V. 1981. In vivo effect of human growth hormone on hepatic adenylate cyclase activity. *Endocrinology* 109:990–92

67. Lesniak, M. A., Gorden, P., Roth, J., Gavin, J. R. III, 1974. Binding of ^{125}I human growth hormone to specific receptors in human cultured lymphocytes: characterization of the interaction and a sensitive radioreceptor assay. *J. Biol. Chem.* 249:1661–67

68. Lewis, U. J., Singh, N. P., Tutwiler, G. F., Sigel, M. B., Vanderlaan, E. F., Vanderlaan, W. P. 1980. Human growth hormone: a complex of proteins. *Recent Prog. Horm. Res.* 36:477–508

69. Lindahl, A., Edén, S., Albertsson-Wikland, K., Isaksson, O., Kostyo, J. L. 1983. Relationship between the biological and immunological activities of growth hormone circulating in normal rats. *Endocrinology* 112:2054–58

70. Madsen, K., Friberg, U., Roos, P., Edén, S., Isaksson, O. 1983. Growth hormone stimulates the proliferation of cultured chondrocytes from rabbit ear and rat rib growth cartilage. *Nature* 304:545–47

71. Maes, M., de Hertogh, R., Watrin-Granger, P., Ketelslegers, J. M. 1983. Ontogeny of liver somatotropic and lactogenic binding sites in male and female rats. *Endocrinology* 113:1325–32

72. Martin, J. B. 1976. Brain regulation of growth hormone secretion. In *Frontiers in Neuroendocrinology*, ed. L. Martini, W. F. Ganong, 4:129–68. New York: Raven

73. Mayberry, H. E., van den Brande, J. L., van Wyk, J. J., Waddell, W. J. 1971. Early localisation of ^{125}I-labeled human growth hormone in adrenals and other organs of immature hypophysectomized rats. *Endocrinology* 88:1309–17

74. Mercola, K. E., Cline, M. J., Golde, D. W. 1981. Growth hormone stimulation

of normal and leukemic human T-lymphocyte proliferation in vitro. *Blood* 58:337–40

75. Morikawa, M., Green, H., Lewis, U. J. 1984. Activity of human growth hormone and related polypeptides on the adipose conversion of 3T3 cells. *Mol. Cell. Biol.* 4:228–31

76. Morikawa, M., Nixon, T., Green, H. 1982. Growth hormone and the adipose conversion of 3T3 cells. *Cell* 29:783–89

77. Mowbray, J., Davies, J. A., Bates, D. J., Jones, C. J. 1975. Growth hormone, cyclic nucleotides and the rapid control of translation in heart muscle. *Biochem. J.* 152:583–92

78. Murphy, L. J., Vrhovsek, E., Lazarus, L. 1983. Identification and characterization of specific growth hormone receptors in cultured human fibroblasts. *J. Clin. Endocrinol. Metab.* 57:1117–24

79. Nadal-Ginard, B. 1978. Commitment, fusion and biochemical differentiation of a myogenic cell line in the absence of DNA synthesis. *Cell* 15:855–64

80. Nielsen, J. H. 1982. Effects of growth hormone, prolactin, and placental lactogen on insulin content and release, and deoxyribonucleic acid synthesis in cultured pancreatic islets. *Endocrinology* 110:600–6

81. Nixon, T., Green, H. 1983. Properties of growth hormone receptors in relation to the adipose conversion of 3T3 cells. *J. Cell. Physiol.* 115:291–96

82. Nixon, T., Green, H. 1984. Contribution of growth hormone to the adipogenic activity of serum. *Endocrinology* 114:527–32

83. Nixon, B. T., Green, H. 1984. Growth hormone promotes the differentiation of myoblasts and preadipocytes generated by azacytidine treatment of 10T 1/2 cells. *Proc. Natl. Acad. Sci. USA* 81:3429–32

84. Nutting, D. F. 1976. Ontogeny of sensitivity to growth hormone in rat diaphragm muscle. *Endocrinology* 98:1273–83

85. Payne, S. G., Kostyo, J. L. 1970. Inhibition by theophylline of the stimulatory effects of growth hormone on amino acid transport and protein synthesis in muscle. *Endocrinology* 87:1186–91

86. Petrovic, A., Stutzmann, J. 1980. Hormone somatotrope: Modalités d'action sur la croissance des diverses variétés de cartilage. *Path. Biol.* 28:43–58

87. Phillips, L. S., Herington, A. C., Daughaday, W. H. 1974. Hormone effects on somatomedin action and somatomedin generation. In *Advances in Human Growth Hormone Research*, ed. S.

Raiti, pp. 50–67. DHEW Pub. No. (NIH) 74–612. Washington DC: DHEW

88. Phillips, L. S., Vassilopoulou-Sellin, R. 1980. Somatomedins. *New Engl. J. Med.* 302:371–80

89. Posner, B. I. 1976. Characterization and modulation of growth hormone and prolactin binding in mouse liver. *Endocrinology* 98:645–54

90. Postel-Vinay, M. C., Corvol, M. T., Lang, F., Fraud, F., Guyda, H., Posner, B. 1983. Receptors for insulin-like growth factors in rabbit articular and growth plate chondrocytes in culture. *Exp. Cell. Res.* 148:105–16

91. Rabinovitch, A., Quigley, C., Rechler, M. M. 1983. Growth hormone stimulates islet B-cell replication in neonatal rat pancreatic monolayer cultures. *Diabetes* 32:307–12

92. Reagan, C. R., Kostyo, J. L., Mills, J. B., Gennick, S. E., Messina, J. L., et al. 1981. Recombination of fragments of human growth hormone: altered activity profile of the recombinant molecule. *Endocrinology* 109:1663–71

93. Reid, J. D. 1960. Congenital absence of the pituitary gland. *J. Pediat.* 56:658–64

94. Rillema, J. A., Kostyo, J. L., Gimpel, L. P. 1973. Inhibition of metabolic effects of growth hormone by various inhibitors of cyclic nucleotide phosphodiesterase. *Biochim. Biophys. Acta* 297:527–39

95. Rimoin, D. L., Merimee, T. J., McKusick, V. A. 1966. Growth hormone deficiency in man: an isolated, recessively inherited defect. *Science* 152:1635–37

96. Rosenfeld, R. G., Wilson, D. M., Dollar, L. A., Bennet, A., Hintz, R. L. 1982. Both human pituitary growth hormone and recombinant DNA-derived human growth hormone cause insulin resistance at a postreceptor site. *J. Clin. Endocrinol. Metab.* 54:1033–38

97. Schoenle, E., Zapf, J., Humbel, R. E., Froesch, E. R. 1982. Insulin-like growth factor I stimulates growth in hypophysectomized rats. *Nature* 296:252–53

98. Schwartz, J. 1980. Enhanced sensitivity to insulin in rats treated with antibodies to rat growth hormone. *Endocrinology* 107:877–83

99. Schwartz, J. 1982. Rapid modulation of protein synthesis in normal rats by specific neutralization and replacement of growth hormone. *Endocrinology* 111:2087–90

100. Selye, H. 1955. Effect of somatotropic hormone (STH) upon inflammation. In

Hypophyseal Growth Hormone, Nature and Actions, ed. R. W. Smith, O. H. Gaebler, C. N. H. Long, pp. 123–37. New York: McGraw-Hill

101. Smeets, T., van Buul-Offers, S. 1983. A morphological study of the development of the tibial proximal epiphysis and growth plate of normal and dwarfed Snell mice. *Growth* 47:145–59

102. Smith, P. E. 1954. Continuation of pregnancy in rhesus monkeys *(Macaca mulatta)* following hypophysectomy. *Endocrinology* 55:655–64

103. Spiegelman, B., Green, H. 1980. Control of specific protein biosynthesis during the adipose conversion of 3T3 cells. *J. Biol. Chem.* 255:8811–18

104. Stutzmann, J., Petrovic, A. 1980. Regulation intrinseque de la vitesse de croissance du cartilage condylien de la mandibule. *Path. Biol.* 28:9–16

105. Tannenbaum, G. S., Martin, J. B. 1976. Evidence for an endogenous ultradian rhythm governing growth hormone secretion in the rat. *Endocrinology* 98:562–70

106. Thorngren, K.-G., Aspenberg, P. 1984. Local bone growth stimulation with growth hormone in the normal rat. *Acta Orthoped. Scand.* In press

107. Thorngren, K.-G., Hansson, L. I. 1974. Bioassay of growth hormone I. Determination of longitudinal bone growth with tetracycline in hypophysectomized rats. *Acta Endocrinol.* 75:653–68

108. Thorngren, K.-G., Hansson, L. I., Fryklund, L., Sievertsson, H. 1977. Human somatomedin A and longitudinal bone growth in the hypophysectomized rat. *Mol. Cell. Endocrinol.* 6:217–21

109. Vesely, D. L. 1981. Human and rat growth hormones enhance guanylate cyclase activity. *Am. J. Physiol.* 240:E79–82

110. Walker, D. G., Simpson, M. E., Asling, C. W., Evans, H. M. 1950. Growth and differentiation in the rat following hypophysectomy at 6 days of age. *Anat. Record.* 106:539–54

CELL AND MEMBRANE PHYSIOLOGY

Introduction, Joseph F. Hoffman, *Section Editor*

The theme of the articles presented in this year's section on Cell and Membrane Physiology is carrier-mediated membrane transport. Although carrier-mediated processes come in many varieties, they all serve to transport and exchange ions and/or molecules in highly selective and specific ways between cells and their environment. Carrier-mediated processes can be either passive, i.e. promoting level or downhill movement, or active, in the sense of utilizing energy to force movement uphill against an electropotential gradient. Critical distinction among many of the various types of processes is formally difficult, but operational and phenomenological criteria have been successfully developed to describe and study a variety of transport systems. Downhill transport processes may occur without specific interaction of the transported species with membrane components, such as might happen in the electrodiffusion of an ion through an aqueous pore containing fixed charges. On the other hand, passage of a transported species across a membrane through a channel or by a carrier evidently involves not only specific and selective interaction but also depends on changes in the configurational state(s) of the membrane components comprising that transport pathway.

Channels, last year's section topic, seem to behave in ways that are clearly different from carriers, in that they operate faster (open and closed states) and permit the passage of many more ions during the open state than do carrier-mediated processes. And, as already mentioned, carriers are coupled to energy sources either directly, as is the case for active cation transport, or indirectly, as in cotransport or countertransport mechanisms. Important for the articles that follow is the fact that the molecular elements responsible for carrier or channel transport are specific proteins that span the membrane domain. The various

501

articles, then, are concerned, where possible, with characterizing the different membrane processes in terms of molecular mechanisms of ligand interaction and transport and in surveying the current status of that particular field regarding such aspects as identification, isolation, reconstitution, structure, and composition of the molecular components involved. Because of space limitations only a selected few of the many types of transport systems could be reviewed. Perhaps in the future it will be possible to survey other types of carrier-mediated transport mechanisms.

Ann. Rev. Physiol. 1985. 47:503–17

THE GLUCOSE TRANSPORTER OF MAMMALIAN CELLS

Thomas J. Wheeler

Department of Biochemistry, University of Louisville School of Medicine, Louisville, Kentucky 40292

Peter C. Hinkle

Section of Biochemistry, Molecular, and Cell Biology, Division of Biological Sciences, Cornell University, Ithaca, New York 14853

INTRODUCTION

Most mammalian cells take up glucose by facilitated diffusion catalyzed by an integral membrane protein. The transporter carries glucose alone, driven by its concentration gradient, and is different from the Na^+-linked glucose transporter present in kidney and intestine. Human erythrocytes have unusually high glucose-transport activity, corresponding to fetal erythrocytes of other mammals, and have been studied in detail for many years (see 9, 50, 51, 72, 105 for reviews). Recent work has focused on studies of identification, kinetics, and regulation of the transporter in erythrocytes and other cells. We will review recent progress on these questions and point to a mechanism of glucose transport consistent with the findings.

IDENTIFICATION, RECONSTITUTION, AND CHARACTERIZATION

Reconstitution

The most general approach to identification of a transporter is incorporation of the solubilized protein into liposomes (see 42). Once the conditions for such incorporation, or reconstitution, have been found, the procedure can be used to assay the transporter during chromatographic purification steps. Transport assays with liposomes are as convenient as binding assays and insure that an active transporter is studied. It is necessary, however, to demonstrate substrate specificity and specific inhibitor sensitivity of the reconstituted system, because nonspecific increases in permeability can also occur when proteins are incorporated into liposomes.

The first reconstitution studies of the red cell glucose transporter (55, 56) used Triton X-100, freeze-thaw or sonication reconstitution methods, and DEAE-cellulose chromatography for purification. The active fraction was a broad band at 55,000 daltons on SDS–polyacrylamide gel electrophoresis, a part of band 4.5. Transport was assayed by influx of ^{14}C-D-glucose, with ^{14}C-L-glucose (which is not a substrate) as a control. Transport was inhibited by cytochalasin B (56), phloretin (101), $HgCl_2$ (56), and other inhibitors. The purified protein bound 0.5 mol of cytochalasin B per mol protein competitively with glucose (90). In some preparations, octaethylene-glycol-n-dodecyl ether (6) or octylglucoside (7) have been substituted for Triton X-100. Using octylglucoside, 0.7 mol of cytochalasin B bound per mol of transporter, indicating a probable stoichiometry of 1:1 (7). In other studies the glucose transporter has been reconstituted by cholate (5, 34) or deoxycholate (24) dialysis, sonication (53, 55), or a reverse-phase (15) method. A fraction enriched in band 4.5 was purified by "transport specificity fractionation" (34), in which 0.8 M glucose leaves liposomes containing the transporter, changing their density and allowing separation. We were not able to reproduce this effect, however, and believe it unlikely to have worked by the mechanisms described, because 0.8 M glucose is 50-fold higher than the K_m for net flux and would enter primarily by nonspecific mechanisms. Reconstitution of Triton X-100 extracts of red cells into a planar membrane has also been reported (75) that was consistent with band 4.5 containing the active fraction.

The specific activity of the purified, reconstituted band-4.5 protein is 5–15% of that expected for a fully active transporter (5, 101). This could be due to loss of activity or inefficient reconstitution. From cytochalasin B binding and transport data for liposomes reconstituted by cholate solubilization and gel filtration, it was concluded that each transporter active in binding was also functional in transport, but with a low rate (5). On the other hand, our analysis of results using the freeze-thaw procedure (81, 101) indicates that, with this procedure, transporters with normal transport activity are reconstituted with low efficiency.

Different reconstitution procedures have used different phospholipids, but little systematic characterization has been made. The freeze-thaw method (56) gave best results with soybean phospholipids or mixtures of phosphatidylcholine (PC) and phosphatidylethanolamine (PE) (P. F. Kamp & P. C. Hinkle, unpublished observations). Either of the two lipids could be saturated, but not both, and when saturated lipids were used the activity was lower with longer fatty acids. Because single lipids gave no activity, the effects of phase transitions without phase separation of lipid mixtures could not be investigated. However, it was concluded that a fluid membrane was necessary for activity. Similar observations were made using solubilized adipose cell membrane (68), although the nonspecific, cytochalasin B–insensitive transport was two thirds of the total transport activity because of the crude fractions used. Other reconstitution procedures used erythrocyte lipids (53), dioleoyl-PC (5), or egg-PC plus cholesterol (34). In a recent systematic study of the erythrocyte glucose transporter reconstituted by a reverse-phase method (15), which produces active liposomes using only PC, a variety of saturated PCs gave activity (A. Carruthers & D. L. Melchior, personal communication). Surprisingly, activity was also obtained below the phase transition with distearoyl-PC, but not with dipalmitoyl-PC or dimyristoyl-PC. A study of the effects of altering the lipid composition of erythrocytes on glucose transport showed that depletion of cholesterol or replacement of outer monolayer PC with dipalmitoyl-PC or dioleoyl-PC had little or no effect on activity at 20°C (4).

The isolated transporter is a glycoprotein (56) with characterized amino acid composition (90). The carbohydrate can be labeled from the external medium (35). Treatment with endo-β-galactosidase sharpens the band on SDS-gels to an apparent M_r of 46,000 (35), but does not reduce transport activity (101). Tryptic peptide maps of the protein show identical peptides from all parts of the broad band and some peptides in common with band 7, but not with band 3 (82). The isolated transporter is not completely pure, however, and has been shown to contain the nucleoside transporter in addition to the glucose transporter (106).

Recently it was reported that reconstitution of octylglucoside-solubilized red cell membranes gave best activity with a 100,000-dalton (band 3) fraction (89). Transport was measured by including glucose oxidase inside the vesicles and measuring oxygen uptake. The specific activities reported were higher than those reported earlier (101) by 75- and 180-fold, using band-4.5 and band-3 fractions, respectively. The only inhibitor used was phloretin at 1.6 mM. At such high levels phloretin cannot be considered a specific inhibitor of glucose transport, because it inhibits the nonspecific permeability of hydrophilic molecules (73). Sugar specificity could not be tested because of the enzyme assay, and transport was not inhibited by cytochalasin B (R. Langdon, personal communication). Thus it is likely that the results are due to a nonspecific permeability pathway created by the procedure. The membrane fractions were prepared from ghosts without first washing away peripheral membrane proteins, which we found increases nonspecific permeability in reconstitution studies (D. C. Sogin, unpublished observations).

Covalent Labeling

Several covalent labels have been used in attempts to identify the glucose transporter of human red cells, including sugar derivatives, cytochalasin B, and protein reagents whose reactivity with the transporter is modulated by sugars or other ligands. The sugar affinity labels used were glucosyl isothiocyanate (94) and maltosyl isothiocyanate (71). The glucose label reacted with many membrane proteins, although the highest activity per slice of SDS-polyacrylamide gel was at 100,000 daltons (band 3). This region also contains the most protein and could have been labeled nonspecifically. The maltosyl isothiocyanate affinity label, which is not transported, inhibited glucose transport and labeled almost exclusively band 3. The reaction was partially inhibited by glucose or cytochalasin B. The isolated transporter at 55,000 daltons is a very broad band, however, and could easily be missed. It also forms dimers in SDS under some conditions.

Labeling studies using modulation of the reactivity of general protein reagents have identified several polypeptides. Band 4.5 was labeled by glutathione maleimide (12) in a reaction inhibited by cytochalasin B or glucose, and by 1-fluoro-2,4-dinitrobenzene (FDNB) in a reaction inhibited by cytochalasin B or maltose (65, 87). D-Glucose enhanced the labeling of 200,000-dalton (52, 87) and 90,000-dalton (87) polypeptides by FDNB. Apparently several erythrocyte membrane proteins bind sugars, and polypeptides labeled by this procedure are not necessarily related to the glucose transporter. The cytochalasin B site was clearly associated with band 4.5, however.

The most recent labeling method is to add ^{3}H-cytochalasin B and use ultraviolet light to cause a covalent reaction between the inhibitor and its binding site (16, 85). Band 4.5 was labeled in a glucose-reversible reaction, confirming that the glucose transporter is a polypeptide of about 50,000 daltons. The peak of the action spectrum for labeling was at 280 nm, where cytochalasin B does not have significant absorbance, indicating that the protein becomes activated by the light and reacts with the label (23). Under optimal conditions, 8% of the transporter molecules could be labeled, which is high efficiency for photolabeling.

Possible Proteolysis, Native Structure

The reconstitution and labeling studies have clearly shown that a polypeptide in band 4.5 is active in glucose transport and binds cytochalasin B competitively with D-glucose. It has been proposed, however, that this polypeptide is a proteolytic fragment of the native glucose transporter (71, 75). Two experiments strongly contradict this suggestion. The photolabeling with cytochalasin B described above (16, 85) was done under conditions where the proposed proteolysis would not occur and did not label a higher-M_r polypeptide. Studies with antibodies against the isolated 55,000-dalton polypeptide did not react with higher-M_r species on SDS-polyacrylamide gels, as they would if the 55,000-dalton polypeptide were a fragment (8, 92). Band 3, which is predominantly the anion transporter, does form a fragment at 55,000 daltons on proteolysis, but this fragment is a sharper band on SDS gels than the glucose transporter, and peptide analysis indicates it is different (82).

The molecular weight of the native transporter is not certain. Freeze-fraction electron microscopy of the reconstituted transporter revealed 62 Å particles on the fracture face, which were not present in liposomes of the same lipid without protein, suggesting the native form may be a dimer (41). Results from sucrose gradient centrifugation of the isolated transporter in Triton X-100 are also consistent with a dimer (107). Electron radiation inactivation of glucose transport and cytochalasin B binding indicates a 185,000-dalton target size (19) consistent with a tetramer of the band-4.5 polypeptide.

It has been claimed that the number of transporters can be determined solely from the kinetic parameters and the thickness of the cell membrane (13, 49), which would allow calculation of the M_r of a purified preparation. These calculations take the maximum permeability of the membrane in cm per sec and calculate a turnover number based on the distance the glucose travels in crossing the membrane. However, the turnover number is not simply a rate of diffusion across the membrane but is a function of the molecular mechanism of the transporter, so the results of such calculations are not valid.

Identification in Other Cells

The transporter in several other cells has been identified using photolabeling with cytochalasin B and/or cross-reactivity with antibodies against the purified human erythrocyte transporter. The transporters that have been identified include HeLa (92), human placenta (46, 48), rat adipocyte (66, 88, 102) and skeletal muscle (58), and chick embryo fibroblast (74, 80, 88). In all cases polypeptides with M_rs of 40,000 to 60,000 were identified, similar to the M_r of the eythrocyte transporter. In one case (80) a higher-M_r polypeptide (82,000) was also identified, but this was probably a dimer artifact in the SDS.

Work is also proceeding on the purification and reconstitution of transporters from various cells. The rat adipocyte transporter has been reconstituted (79, 86, 93) and partially purified (17), as has the bovine thymocyte transporter (83). Effects of phospholipid composition on the reconstituted LM cell transporter have been studied (3). The transporters from bovine heart and rat skeletal muscle have also been reconstituted (100).

Regulation

The techniques of reconstitution, antibody cross-reactivity, and measurement of glucose-reversible cytochalasin B binding have proven useful in investigating some aspects of the regulation of the transporter, particularly its stimulation by insulin. In adipose and muscle cells, glucose transport is increased manyfold by insulin. The effect is probably explained by the transporter recruitment hypothesis proposed independently by two groups, based on assay of the transporter by reconstitution (93) and by cytochalasin B binding (20). The transporters are recruited to the plasma membrane from a vesicle fraction when insulin is present and return when insulin is withdrawn. Subsequent studies with antibodies against the band-4.5 glucose transporter from human erythrocytes showed that a cross-reacting polypeptide was present in adipose cells that moved from a vesicle fraction to the plasma membrane upon addition of insulin (66, 102). Studies with muscle cells indicate a similar mechanism (97). Other mechanisms of regulation of transport activity may occur (e.g. 57). In addition, two polypeptides have been found to be induced by glucose starvation (e.g. 99) that are stress or "heat shock" proteins, probably not related to glucose transport.

KINETICS AND MECHANISMS

Erythrocytes

Transport kinetics in human erythrocytes have been studied primarily by light-scattering assays of net sugar movement or by assays using radioactive sugars. Several types of experiments are possible with sugar on one side of the membrane or on both sides (see 27). A useful framework for examining the kinetics is the carrier model in which no assumptions are made about symmetry or about equal mobilities of loaded and unloaded carriers (78). Although carrier models originally envisioned a protein moving from one side of the membrane to the other, they are kinetically identical to alternating conformation models (96), in which a binding site is alternately exposed to the two sides of the membrane:

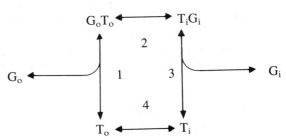

Here G_o and G_i represent glucose outside and inside the cell and T_o and T_i the outward- and inward-facing conformations of the transporter, respectively. Equations describing sugar movement for various conditions have been derived (e.g. 27).

Two features of erythrocyte glucose transport that are explained by this model are asymmetry and exchange acceleration. Asymmetry can arise if the two conformations differ in their probability or affinity for glucose. Because the structure of the transporter protein is different on the two sides of the membrane, inward- and outward-facing conformations are certainly different, and asymmetry is not unexpected. However, because the transporter does not concentrate glucose on one side of the membrane, the model requires that the ratio of K_ms for the two directions of transport be equal to the ratio of V_{max}s. Erythrocytes show asymmetric kinetics with efflux having a 3- to 4-fold higher V_{max} and a 4- to 15-fold higher K_m than uptake (54, 63, 70). Equilibrium exchange, measured with radioactive tracer at equal net concentrations of glucose on the two sides of the membrane, has higher K_m and V_{max} values than net flux (26, 63, 69). Faster exchange than net flux is explained by the model if the rate-limiting step in net flux is the conformational change of the empty transporter (step 4), a step that can be bypassed in exchange.

Both of these features have been observed with the purified reconstituted transporter. The transporter is reconstituted with various degrees of scrambling of orientation, depending on the reconstitution procedure (6, 101). Trypsin, which inactivates the transporter only at a site on the inner side of the erythrocyte membrane, can be used to determine the degree of scrambling and also to generate transporters with only one active orientation. These transporters show about a four-fold asymmetry of both V_{max} and K_m values for net flux (101), thus obeying the model, although the K_ms (0.4 and 1.7 mM for uptake and efflux, respectively) were lower than in erythrocytes (1.6 and 7–25 mM). In addition, equilibrium exchange has a high K_m (about 30 mM), similar to values obtained with erythrocytes, and exchange is faster than net flux. The average degree of exchange acceleration was much higher for the reconstituted transporter (30-fold) than for erythrocytes (4-fold). The lower net flux K_ms and higher exchange acceleration seen with the reconstituted transporter might arise if the experimental procedure underestimates K_m and V_{max} under net flux conditions. Alternatively, the differences could be due to altered properties of the transporter itself or to differences in its lipid environment. Interestingly, transport in erythrocytes shows greater exchange acceleration and a lower uptake K_m (0.2 mM) at 0°C (63). Thus the reconstituted transporter at 25°C behaves like the native transporter at lower temperatures.

Two major lines of evidence from experiments with erythrocytes have seemed inconsistent with the carrier model. First, if the K_m for efflux is taken as 25 mM (54), the asymmetry for K_m is much greater than that for V_{max}. Second, in infinite-*cis* experiments, in which inhibition of net flux of saturating glucose is measured, low K_m values are observed for both efflux [1.7 mM (84)] and uptake [2.8 mM (40)]. According to the model, these numbers should be asymmetric to the same extent as the net flux parameters. However, the infinite-*cis* uptake K_m appears to reveal a "high-affinity" site at the inner surface, leading some workers to reject the carrier model.

Both of these points rely on K_ms determined from integrated rate equations applied to transport progress curves rather than initial rates, and this might be a source of error. For such equations to be applied, the transport must be uniform in most of the cells and behave ideally throughout the experiment. One suggested source of anomalous kinetic results is the anomerization of glucose (9, 36), which would be particularly important in such experiments. Glucose consists of α and β anomers, which equilibrate slowly compared to transport [k = 0.01 min $^{-1}$ at 20°C and pH 7.4, calculated from data in (76)], and the β anomer is a much better transport substrate (28). Studies with transport inhibitors also indicate a preference for the β configuration (11). Mutarotase, which could accelerate the equilibration of anomers, is apparently not present in erythrocytes (28). In efflux experiments, β glucose would be preferentially depleted within the cell, producing an erroneously high K_m. In infinite-*cis* uptake, β glucose would be preferentially enriched inside the cell, producing a K_m that would be lower than for the equilibrium mixture. We note that in efflux experiments, much lower K_ms have been observed when initial rates were used rather than integrated rate equations (32, 70). In experiments using initial rates and equilibrated mixtures of anomers, much smaller errors will be observed, although the observed parameters will be composites of those for the two anomers.

Several factors have been reported to influence the observed kinetics in erythrocytes and should be considered when results from different experiments are compared to each other and to models. Fresh and outdated blood show differences in kinetics, with nearly a two-fold increase in the exchange K_m upon aging of the cells (98). The uptake V_{max} was reported to be lowered by ATP depletion (47), whereas hemolysis and resealing with ATP or ADP restored the activity. An effect on photolabeling with cytochalasin B was also observed. Phosphorylation of membrane proteins was proposed as a mechanism for these effects. The presence of low-molecular-weight cytoplasmic factors has also been shown to influence the kinetics of transport of erythrocytes, ghosts, and inside-out vesicles (14). Removing or adding back these factors altered kinetic parameters in various transport experiments. The authors concluded that the transporter is symmetric in the absence of the factors. However, directional symmetry was not shown directly, and our experiments with the reconstituted transporter (101) indicate that the isolated transporter has asymmetric kinetics.

Several alternative models have been proposed to account for the discrepancies between kinetics in erythrocytes and the carrier model. The tetramer model (64) is symmetric and thus cannot account for the asymmetry of net flux. A model involving paired antiparallel carriers (25) predicts both high- and low-affinity sites on both sides of the membrane, but the evidence of this is unconvincing. A symmetric pore model involving rate-limiting formation and breakdown of a complex between glucose and hemoglobin (72) was rejected when asymmetric transport was observed in ghosts with 95% of the hemoglobin removed (18). The most recent model, the allosteric pore (43), involves three "subunits" (or kinetic compartments), negative cooperativity, and asymmetry. Conflicting results regarding negative cooperativity of equilibrium exchange have been reported (44, 98). The fact that the purified transporter is a single polypeptide that spans the bilayer argues against models involving different kinds of subunits (25, 43).

Information relating to the structure and mechanism of the transporter has come from both binding studies with the purified transporter and inhibition and inactivation studies with erythrocytes. Various inhibitors act competitively with glucose but differ as to which side of the membrane they act on (see 105). Sugars with alkyl groups at C-6 or C-1 inhibit only from the outside or inside, respectively (10); phloretin inhibits from the outside (60); and cytochalasin B inhibits from the inside (21). However, when the binding of cytochalasin B to the purified transporter is examined, glucose and all inhibitors tested (maltose, 6-O-propylgalactose, 4,6-O-ethylideneglucose, propyl β-glucopyranoside, phloretin, and diethylstilbestrol) were competitive with cytochalasin B (36, 91). These results indicate that of the various ligands, only one binds at a time, in support of an alternating conformation model. The same conclusion was reached from inhibition studies in erythrocytes (61). Models in which substrate sites are exposed simultaneously on the two sides of the membrane (43, 64, 72) are thus unlikely.

The results do not indicate more than a single site for substrates and competitive inhibitors, although the site has two major conformations (outward- and inward-facing). In addition, depending on which ligand is bound, minor conformational changes occur. Changes in the fluorescence of the transporter upon binding of ligands have been reported (37); these may prove useful in further characterization of the conformational changes. The binding of ligands can alter the reactivity of the transporter with covalent labels. Opposite effects on reactivity produced by ligands bound from the inside has been interpreted as evidence for two different internal sites for glucose and cytochalasin B (59). However, the results could also be explained by different conformations induced by different ligands bound at a single site. Crystallographic studies of the cytochalasins have indicated that cytochalasin B binds because it assumes a structure similar to glucose (39), and thus is likely to bind at the glucose site.

Other Cells

The rat adipocyte has been studied extensively (33). Assay of transport in this cell is difficult because the intracellular volume is very small (about 2% of the packed volume) and the cells equilibrate rapidly. However, a rapid assay technique (103) has been used in most recent studies. In order to avoid the complications of intracellular metabolism, 3-O-methylglucose, which is transported but not metabolized, has generally been used as a substrate.

Several groups have obtained kinetic results that were consistent with a symmetric carrier model without exchange acceleration (67, 95, 103). However, in only one of these (95) was net flux directly measured in both directions, and here variations of as much as five-fold in parameters were reported. In another case (67), the authors cite as a major argument for symmetry the equality of K_m values for exchange uptake and exchange efflux, but these are necessarily equal for any model whether or not it is symmetric. These studies indicate differences between the rat adipocyte and the human erythrocyte transporter, with the former showing much less asymmetry and exchange acceleration. However, the data do not appear to be sufficient to rule out a smaller (up to two-fold) degree of asymmetry. One group (29, 30) reported anomalous kinetics with 2-deoxyglucose, a sugar that is phosphorylated but not metabolized further. A model was proposed including two symmetric carriers connected by an aqueous pore, with the second carrier rate-limiting for deoxyglucose (31).

Experiments indicating a similarity between the rat adipocyte and human erythrocyte transporters include antibody cross-reactivity (66, 102) (see above) and inhibition studies with alkyl sugars (45). Sugars substituted at the C-4, C-6 end inhibit from outside only; C-1 glucosides inhibit only at the inside. The same result is seen with erythrocytes (10). Thus the same asymmetry of the structure of the binding site is seen in both cells, although little or no kinetic asymmetry is seen in adipocytes.

A number of cell lines (Novikiff rat hepatoma, HeLa, mouse L- and P388 leukemia, Chinese hamster ovary) show symmetric kinetics with exchange faster than net flux by 1.5- to 14-fold (38, 77). The degree of exchange acceleration varied among batches of cells, leading the authors to propose that the rate-determining movement of the unloaded transporter is possibly a site for regulation. In rat thymocytes (104) and giant squid axons (1, 2), asymmetry (10- or 4-fold, respectively) was observed but not exchange acceleration. Thus various kinetic patterns are seen in different cells. Nearly all the results are consistent with a carrier model, but the degrees of asymmetry and exchange acceleration vary.

SUMMARY AND CONCLUSIONS

The glucose transporter is now identified but may have modifications or other subunits that control its activity. The kinetics and inhibitor binding studies are consistent with the carrier model with different degrees of asymmetry and a single binding site that varies in specificity depending on the conformation of the protein. The physical structure could actually be quite different from the usual diagrams (rocking bananas), however, and could function as a monomer or higher oligomer. The binding site, or filter, that gives specificity could be in the middle as usually depicted; alternatively it could be entirely on the cytoplasmic side, where the protein is trypsin sensitive, and hydrophobic helices could span the membrane forming a simple channel. Possible restrictions on structures in the membrane from the hydrophobic nature of transmembrane segments of membrane proteins (62) may favor a globular domain outside the membrane as the binding site. Such speculations will have to await more structural information about the transporter.

Literature Cited

1. Baker, P. F., Carruthers, A. 1981. Sugar transport in giant axons of *Loligo. J. Physiol.* 316:481–502
2. Baker, P. F., Carruthers, A. 1981. 3-O-Methylglucose transport in internally dialyzed giant axons of *Loligo. J. Physiol.* 316:503–25
3. Baldassare, J. J. 1983. Enhancement of the reconstituted glucose transport activity from LM cells by phosphatidylethanolamine. *J. Biol. Chem.* 258:10223–26
4. Baldassare, J. J., Fisher, G. J., Henderson, P. A., Ladenson, R. C. 1983. Effects of alterations of membrane lipid composition on the activity of the glucose transporter from intact human erythrocytes. *Fed. Proc.* 42:2195 (Abstr.)
5. Baldwin, J. M., Gorga, J. C., Lienhard, G. E. 1981. The monosaccharide transporter of the human erythrocyte. Transport activity upon reconstitution. *J. Biol. Chem.* 256:3685–89
6. Baldwin, J. M., Lienhard, G. E., Baldwin, S. A. 1980. The monosaccharide transport system of the human erythrocyte. Orientation upon reconstitution. *Biochim. Biophys. Acta* 599:699–714
7. Baldwin, S. A., Baldwin, J. M., Lienhard, G. E. 1982. Monosaccharide transporter of the human erythrocyte. Characterization of an improved preparation. *Biochemistry* 21:3836–42
8. Baldwin, S. A., Lienhard, G. E. 1980. Immunological identification of the human erythrocyte monosaccharide transporter. *Biochem. Biophys. Res. Commun.* 94:1401–8
9. Baldwin, S. A., Lienhard, G. E. 1981. Glucose transport across plasma membranes: facilitated diffusion systems. *Trends Biochem. Sci.* 6:208–11
10. Barnett, J. E. G., Holman, G. D., Chalkley, R. A., Munday, K. A. 1975. Evidence for two asymmetric conformational states in the human erythrocyte sugar-transport system. *Biochem. J.* 145:417–29
11. Barnett, J. E. G., Holman, G. D., Munday, K. A. 1973. Structural requirements for binding to the sugar-transport system of the human erythrocyte. *Biochem. J.* 131:211–21
12. Batt, E. R., Abbott, R. E., Schachter, D. 1976. Impermeant maleimides. Identification of an exofacial component of the human erythrocyte hexose mechanism. *J. Biol. Chem.* 251:7184–90
13. Carruthers, A. 1983. Sugar transport in giant barnacle muscle fibres. *J. Physiol.* 336:377–96
14. Carruthers, A., Melchior, D. L. 1983. Asymmetric or symmetric? Cytosolic modulation of human erythrocyte hexose transfer. *Biochim. Biophys. Acta* 728:254–66
15. Carruthers, A., Melchior, D. L. 1984. A rapid method of reconstituting human erythrocyte sugar transport proteins. *Biochemistry* 23:2712–18
16. Carter-Su, C., Pessin, J. E., Mora, R., Gitomer, W., Czech, M. P. 1982. Photoaffinity labeling of the human erythrocyte D-glucose transporter. *J. Biol. Chem.* 257:5419–25
17. Carter-Su, C., Pillion, D. J., Czech, M. P. 1980. Reconstituted D-glucose transport from the adipocyte plasma membrane. Chromatographic resolution of transport activity from membrane glycoproteins using immobilized concanavalin A. *Biochemistry* 19:2373–85
18. Challiss, J. R. A., Taylor, L. P., Holman, G. D. 1980. Sugar transport asymmetry in human erythrocytes—the effect of bulk haemoglobin removal and the addition of methylxanthines. *Biochim. Biophys. Acta* 601:155–66
19. Cuppoletti, J., Jung, C. Y., Green, F. A.

1981. Glucose transport carrier of human erythrocytes. Radiation target size measurement based on flux inactivation. *J. Biol. Chem.* 256:1305–6

20. Cushman, S. W., Wardzala, L. J. 1980. Potential mechanism of insulin action on glucose transport in the isolated rat adipose cell. Apparent translocation of intracellular transport systems to the plasma membrane. *J. Biol. Chem.* 255:4758–62

21. Devés, R., Krupka, R. M. 1978. Cytochalasin B and the kinetics of inhibition of biological transport. A case of asymmetric binding to the glucose transporter. *Biochim. Biophys. Acta* 510:339–48

22. Deleted in proof

23. Deziel, M., Pegg, W., Mack, E., Rothstein, A., Klip, A. 1984. Labelling of the human erythrocyte glucose transporter with [³H]-labeled cytochalasin B occurs via protein photoactivation. *Biochim. Biophys. Acta* 772:403–6

24. Edwards, P. A. 1977. Reconstitution of glucose-transporting vesicles from erythrocyte membranes disaggregated in detergent. *Biochem. J.* 164:125–29

25. Eilam, Y. 1975. Two-carrier models for mediated transport. I. Theoretical analysis of several two-carrier models. *Biochim. Biophys. Acta* 401:349–63

26. Eilam, Y., Stein, W. D. 1972. A simple resolution of the kinetic anomaly in the exchange of different sugars across the membrane of the human red blood cell. *Biochim. Biophys. Acta* 266:161–73

27. Eilam, Y., Stein, W. D. 1974. Kinetic studies of transport across red blood cell membranes. In *Methods in Membrane Biology,* ed. E. D. Korn, 2:283–354. New York: Plenum

28. Faust, R. G. 1960. Monosaccharide penetration into human red blood cells by an altered diffusion mechanism. *J. Cell. Comp. Physiol.* 56:103–21

29. Foley, J. E., Foley, R., Gliemann, J. 1980. Rate-limiting steps of 2-deoxyglucose uptake in rat adipocytes. *Biochim. Biophys. Acta* 599:689–98

30. Foley, J. E., Foley, R., Gliemann, J. 1980. Glucose-induced acceleration of deoxyglucose transport in rat adipocytes. Evidence for a second barrier to sugar entry. *J. Biol. Chem.* 255:9674–77

31. Foley, J. E., Gliemann, J. 1981. Glucose transport in isolated rat adipose cells. *Int. J. Obesity* 5:679–84

32. Ginsburg, H. 1978. Galactose transport in human erythrocytes. The transport mechanism is resolved into two simple asymmetric antiparallel carriers. *Biochim. Biophys. Acta* 506:119–35

33. Gliemann, J., Rees, W. D. 1983. The insulin-sensitive hexose transport system in adipocytes. *Curr. Top. Membr. Transp.* 18:339–79

34. Goldin, S. M., Rhoden, V. 1978. Reconstitution and 'transport specificity fractionation' of the human erythrocyte glucose transport system. A new approach for identification and isolation of membrane transport proteins. *J. Biol. Chem.* 253:2575–83

35. Gorga, F. R., Baldwin, S. A., Lienhard, G. E. 1979. The monosaccharide transporter from human erythrocytes is heterogeneously glycosylated. *Biochem. Biophys. Res. Commun.* 91:955–61

36. Gorga, F. R., Lienhard, G. E. 1981. Equilibria and kinetics of ligand binding to the human erythrocyte glucose transporter. Evidence for an alternating conformation model for transport. *Biochemistry* 20:5108–13

37. Gorga, F. R., Lienhard, G. E. 1982. Changes in the intrinsic fluorescence of the human erythrocyte monosaccharide transporter upon ligand binding. *Biochemistry* 12:1905–8

38. Graff, J. C., Wohlhueter, R. M., Plagemann, P. G. W. 1981. Hexose transport in Novikoff rat hepatoma cells. A simple carrier with directional symmetry, but variable relative mobilities of loaded and empty carrier. *Biochim. Biophys. Acta* 641:320–33

39. Griffin, J. F., Rampal, A. L., Jung, C. Y. 1982. Inhibition of glucose transport in human erythrocytes by cytochalasins: A model based on diffraction studies. *Proc. Natl. Acad. Sci. USA* 79:3759–63

40. Hankin, B. L., Lieb, W. R., Stein, W. D. 1972. Rejection criteria for the asymmetric carrier and their application to glucose transport in the human red blood cell. *Biochim. Biophys. Acta* 288:114–26

41. Hinkle, P. C., Sogin, D. C., Wheeler, T. J., Telford, J. N. 1979. Studies of the glucose transporter from human erythrocytes reconstituted in liposomes. In *Function and Molecular Aspects of Biomembrane Transport,* ed. E. Quagliariello, F. Palmieri, S. Papa, M. Klingenberg, pp. 487–94. Amsterdam: Elsevier/North Holland

42. Hokin, L. E. 1981. Reconstitution of 'carriers' in artificial membranes. *J. Membr. Biol.* 60:77–93

43. Holman, G. D. 1980. An allosteric pore model for sugar transport in human erythrocytes. *Biochim. Biophys. Acta* 599:203–11

44. Holman, G. D., Busza, A. L., Pierce, E. J., Rees, W. D. 1981. Evidence for negative cooperativity in human erythrocyte

sugar transport. *Biochim. Biophys. Acta* 649:503–14

45. Holman, G. D., Rees, W. D. 1982. Side-specific analogues for the rat adipocyte sugar transport system. *Biochim. Biophys. Acta* 685:78–86

46. Ingermann, R. L., Bissonnette, J. M., Koch, P. L. 1983. D-glucose-sensitive and -insensitive cytochalasin B binding proteins from microvillus plasma membranes of human placenta. Identification of the D-glucose transporter. *Biochim. Biophys. Acta* 730:57–63

47. Jacquez, J. A. 1983. Modulation of glucose transport in human red blood cells by ATP. *Biochim. Biophys. Acta* 727:367–78

48. Johnson, L. W., Smith, C. H. 1982. Identification of the glucose transport protein of the microvillous membrane of human placenta by photoaffinity labelling. *Biochem. Biophys. Res. Commun.* 109:408–13

49. Jones, M. N., Nickson, J. K. 1980. Identifying the monosaccharide transport protein in the human erythrocyte membrane. *FEBS Lett.* 115:1–8

50. Jones, M. N., Nickson, J. K. 1981. Monosaccharide transport proteins of the human erythrocyte membrane. *Biochim. Biophys. Acta* 650:1–20

51. Jung, C. Y. 1975. Carrier-mediated glucose transport across human red cell membranes. In *The Red Blood Cell*, ed. D. M. Surgenor, pp. 705–51. New York: Academic. 2nd ed.

52. Jung, C. Y., Carlson, L. M. 1975. Glucose transport carrier in human erythrocyte membranes. Dinitrophenylation of a membrane component modified by D-glucose. *J. Biol. Chem.* 250:3217–20

53. Kahlenberg, A., Zala, C. A. 1977. Reconstitution of D-glucose transport in vesicles composed of lipids and intrinsic protein (zone 4.5) of the human erythrocyte membrane. *J. Supramol. Struct.* 7:287–300

54. Karlish, S. J. D., Lieb, W. R., Ram, D., Stein, W. D. 1972. Kinetic parameters of glucose efflux from human red blood cells under zero-*trans* conditions. *Biochim. Biophys. Acta* 255:126–32

55. Kasahara, M., Hinkle, P. C. 1976. Reconstitution of D-glucose transport catalyzed by a protein fraction from human erythrocytes in sonicated liposomes. *Proc. Natl. Acad. Sci. USA* 73:396–400

56. Kasahara, M., Hinkle, P. C. 1977. Reconstitution and purification of the D-glucose transporter from human erythrocytes. *J. Biol. Chem.* 253:7384–90

57. Kashiwagi, A., Huecksteadt, T. P., Foley, J. E. 1983. The regulation of glucose transport by cAMP stimulators via three different mechanisms in rat and human adipocytes. *J. Biol. Chem.* 258:13685–92

58. Klip, A., Walker, D., Ransome, K. J., Schroer, D. W., Lienhard, G. E. 1983. Identification of the glucose transporter in rat skeletal muscle. *Arch. Biochem. Biophys.* 226:198–205

59. Krupka, R. M., Devés, R. 1980. Evidence for allosteric inhibition sites in the glucose carrier of erythrocytes. *Biochim. Biophys. Acta* 598:127–33

60. Krupka, R. M., Devés, R. 1980. Asymmetric binding of steroids to internal and external sites in the glucose carrier of erythrocytes. *Biochim. Biophys. Acta* 598:134–44

61. Krupka, R. M., Devés, R. 1981. An experimental test for cyclic *versus* linear transport models. The mechanism of glucose and choline transport in erythrocytes. *J. Biol. Chem.* 256:5410–16

62. Kyte, J., Doolittle, R. F. 1982. A simple method for displaying the hydropathic character of a protein. *J. Mol. Biol.* 157:105–32

63. Lacko, L., Wittke, B., Kromphardt, H. 1972. Zur kinetik der glucose-aufnahme in erythrocyten. Effekt der trans-konzentration. *Eur. J. Biochem.* 25:447–54

64. Lieb, W. R., Stein, W. D. 1970. Quantitative predictions of a noncarrier model for glucose transport across the human red cell membrane. *Biophys. J.* 10:585–609

65. Lienhard, G. E., Gorga, F. R., Orasky, J. E. Jr., Zoccoli, M. A. 1977. Monosaccharide transport system of the human erythrocyte. Identification of the cytochalasin B binding component. *Biochemistry* 16:4921–26

66. Lienhard, G. E., Kim, H. H., Ransome, K. J., Gorga, J. C. 1982. Immunological identification of an insulin-responsive glucose transporter. *Biochem. Biophys. Res. Commun.* 105:1150–56

67. May, J. M., Mikulecky, D. C. 1982. The simple model of adipocyte hexose transport. Kinetic features, effect of insulin, and network thermodynamic computer simulations. *J. Biol. Chem.* 257:11601–08

68. Melchior, D. L., Czech, M. P. 1979. Sensitivity of the adipocyte D-glucose transport system to membrane fluidity in reconstituted vesicles. *J. Biol. Chem.* 254:8744–47

69. Miller, D. M. 1968. The kinetics of selective biological transport. IV. Assessment of three carrier systems using the erythrocyte monosaccharide transport data. *Biophys. J.* 8:1339–52

70. Miller, D. M. 1971. The kinetics of selective biological transport. V. Further data on the erythrocyte monosaccharide transport system. *Biophys. J.* 11:915–23

71. Mullins, R. E., Langdon, R. G. 1980. Maltosyl isothiocyanate: an affinity label for the glucose transporter of the human erythrocyte membrane. 2. Identification of the transporter. *Biochemistry* 19:1205–12

72. Naftalin, R. J., Holman, G. D. 1977. Transport of sugars in human red cells. In *Membrane Transport in Red Cells*, ed. J. C. Ellory, V. L. Lew, pp. 257–300. New York: Academic

73. Owen, J. D., Solomon, A. K. 1972. Control of nonelectrolyte permeability in red cells. *Biochim. Biophys. Acta* 290:414–18

74. Pessin, J. E., Tillotson, L. G., Yamada, K., Gitomer, W., Carter-Su, C., et al. 1982. Identification of the stereospecific hexose transporter from starved and fed chicken embryo fibroblasts. *Proc. Natl. Acad. Sci. USA* 79:2286–90

75. Phutrakul, S., Jones, M. N. 1979. The permeability of bilayer lipid membranes on the incorporation of erythrocyte membrane extracts and the identification of the monosaccharide transport proteins. *Biochim. Biophys. Acta* 551:188–200

76. Pigman, W., Anet, E. F. L. J. 1972. Mutarotations and actions of acids and bases. In *The Carbohydrates, Chemistry and Biochemistry*, ed. W. Pigman, D. Horton, IA:165–94. New York: Academic. 642 pp. 2nd ed.

77. Plagemann, P. G. W., Wohlheuter, R. M., Graff, J., Erbe, J., Wilkie, P. 1981. Broad specificity hexose transport system with differential mobility of loaded and empty carrier, but directional symmetry, is common property of mammalian cell lines. *J. Biol. Chem.* 256:2835–42

78. Regen, D. M., Morgan, H. E. 1964. Studies of the glucose-transport system in the rabbit erythrocyte. *Biochim. Biophys. Acta* 79:151–61

79. Robinson, F. W., Blevins, T. L., Suzuki, K., Kono, T. 1982. An improved method of reconstitution of adipocyte glucose transport activity. *Anal. Biochem.* 122:10–19

80. Salter, D. W., Baldwin, S. A., Lienhard, G. E., Weber, M. J. 1982. Proteins antigenically related to the human erythrocyte glucose transporter in normal and Rous sarcoma virus transformed chicken embryo fibroblasts. *Proc. Natl. Acad. Sci. USA* 79:1540–44

81. Sase, S., Anraku, Y., Nagano, M., Osumi, M., Kasahara, M. 1982. Random distribution of the glucose transporter of human erythrocytes in reconstituted liposomes. *J. Biol. Chem.* 257:11100–5

82. Sase, S., Takata, K., Hirano, H., Kasahara, M. 1982. Characterzation and identification of the glucose transporter of human erythrocytes. *Biochim. Biophys. Acta* 693:253–61

83. Schraw, W. P., Regen, D. M. 1983. Reconstitution of the D-glucose transporter of bovine thymocyte plasma membrane: partial purification of transport activity by chromatography on agarose lentil lectin and agarose ethanethiol. *Arch. Biochem. Biophys.* 220:214–24

84. Sen, A. K., Widdas, W. F. 1962. Determination of the temperature and pH dependence of glucose transfer across the human erythrocyte membrane measured by glucose exit. *J. Physiol.* 160:392–403

85. Shanahan, M. F. 1982. Cytochalasin B. A natural photoaffinity ligand for labeling the human erythrocyte glucose transporter. *J. Biol. Chem.* 257:7290–93

86. Shanahan, M. F., Czech, M. P. 1977. Purification and reconstitution of the adipocyte plasma membrane D-glucose transport system. *J. Biol. Chem.* 252:8341–43

87. Shanahan, M. F., Jacquez, J. A. 1978. Differential labeling of components in human erythrocyte membranes associated with the transport of glucose. *Membr. Biochem.* 1:239–67

88. Shanahan, M. F., Olson, S. A., Weber, M. J., Lienhard, G. E., Gorga, J. C. 1982. Photolabeling of glucose-sensitive cytochalasin B binding proteins in erythrocyte, fibroblast, and adipocyte membranes. *Biochem. Biophys. Res. Commun.* 107:38–43

89. Shelton, R. L. Jr., Langdon, R. G. 1983. Reconstitution of glucose transport using human erythrocyte band 3. *Biochim. Biophys. Acta* 733:25–33

90. Sogin, D. C., Hinkle, P. C. 1978. Characterization of the glucose transporter from human erythrocytes. *J. Supramol. Struct.* 8:447–53

91. Sogin, D. C., Hinkle, P. C. 1980. Binding of cytochalasin B to human erythrocyte glucose transporter. *Biochemistry* 19:5417–20

92. Sogin, D. C., Hinkle, P. C. 1980. Immunological identification of the human erythrocyte glucose transporter. *Proc. Natl. Acad. Sci. USA* 77:5725–29

93. Suzuki, K., Kono, T. 1980. Evidence that insulin causes translocation of glucose transport activity to the plasma membrane from an intracellular storage site. *Proc. Natl. Acad. Sci. USA* 77:2542–45

94. Taverna, R. D., Langdon, R. G. 1973. D-glucosyl isothiocyanate, an affinity label for the glucose transport proteins of the human erythrocyte membrane. *Biochem. Biophys. Res. Commun.* 54:593–99

95. Taylor, L. P., Holman, G. D. 1981. Symmetrical kinetic parameters for 3-O-methyl-D-glucose transport in adipocytes in the presence and in the absence of insulin. *Biochim. Biophys. Acta* 642:325–35

96. Vidaver, G. A. 1966. Inhibition of parallel flux and augmentation of counter flux shown by transport models not involving a mobile carrier. *J. Theor. Biol.* 10:301–6

97. Wardzala, L. J., Jeanrenaud, B. 1981. Potential mechanism of insulin action on glucose transport in the isolated rat diaphragm. Apparent translocatation of intracellular transport units to the plasma membrane. *J. Biol. Chem.* 256:7090–93

98. Weiser, M. B., Razin, M., Stein, W. D. 1983. Kinetic tests of models for sugar transport in human erythrocytes and a comparison of fresh and cold-stored cells. *Biochim. Biophys. Acta* 727:379–88

99. Welch, W. J., Garrels, J. I., Thomas, G. P., Lin, J. J-C., Feramisco, J. R. 1983. Biochemical characterization of the mammalian stress proteins and identification of two stress proteins as glucose- and Ca^{2+}-ionophore–regulated proteins. *J. Biol. Chem.* 258:7102–11

100. Wheeler, T. J., Hauck, M. A. 1984. Reconstitution of the glucose transporter from heart and skeletal muscle. *Fed. Proc.* 43:1573 (Abstr.)

101. Wheeler, T. J., Hinkle, P. C. 1981. Kinetic properties of the reconstituted glucose transporter from human erythrocytes. *J. Biol. Chem.* 256:8907–14

102. Wheeler, T. J., Simpson, I. A., Sogin, D. C., Hinkle, P. C., Cushman, S. W. 1982. Detection of the rat adipose cell glucose transporter with antibody against the human red cell glucose transporter. *Biochem. Biophys. Res. Commun.* 105:89–95

103. Whitesell, R. R., Gliemann, J. 1979. Kinetic parameters of transport of 3-0-methylglucose and glucose in adipocytes. *J. Biol. Chem.* 254:5276–83

104. Whitesell, R. R., Tarpley, H. L., Regen, D. M. 1977. Sugar-transport kinetics of the rat thymocyte. *Arch. Biochem. Biophys.* 181:596–602

105. Widdas, W. F. 1980. The asymmetry of the hexose transfer system in the human red cell membrane. *Curr. Top. Membr. Transp.* 14:165–223

106. Wu, J-S. R., Kwong, F. Y. P., Jarvis, S. M., Young, J. D. 1983. Identification of the erythrocyte nucleoside transporter as a band 4.5 polypeptide. Photoaffinity labeling studies using nitrobenzylthioinosine. *J. Biol. Chem.* 258:13745–51

107. Zoccoli, M. A., Baldwin, S. A., Lienhard, G. E. 1978. The monosaccharide transport system of the human erythrocyte. Solubilization and characterization on the basis of cytochalasin B binding. *J. Biol. Chem.* 253:6923–30

Ann. Rev. Physiol. 1985. 47:519–33

KINETICS AND MECHANISM OF ANION TRANSPORT IN RED BLOOD CELLS

Michael L. Jennings

Department of Physiology and Biophysics, The University of Iowa, Iowa City, Iowa 52242

INTRODUCTION

The transport of HCO_3 and Cl across the red blood cell membrane takes place as an obligatory one-for-one exchange, the physiological function of which is to facilitate CO_2 transport and excretion. The anion exchange is catalyzed by a protein known as band 3, the 95,000-dalton integral membrane protein of red cells. In the past several years there have been significant advances in understanding of several aspects of band 3 structure and function (see 43, 52, 55, 83, 90). This review will be confined primarily to recent work in three areas: (a) the physiological role of Cl-HCO_3 exchange, (b) kinetic models of the anion exchange process, and (c) the relation between band 3 structure and anion exchange.

ROLE OF Cl-HCO_3 EXCHANGE IN CO_2 EXCRETION

In the systemic capillaries, CO_2 enters the capillary lumen by simple diffusion. It then diffuses into the red cell and is very rapidly converted to $HCO_3 + H^+$ by carbonic anhydrase. The increased intracellular HCO_3 concentration provides

---

[a]*Abbreviations used*   DIDS: 4,4'-diisothiocyanostilbene-2,2'-disulfonate; H₂DIDS: 4,4'-diisothiocyanodihydrostilbene-2,2'-disulfonate; DNDS: 4,4'-dinitrostilbene-2,2'-disulfonate; NAP-taurine: N-(4-azido-2-nitrophenyl)-2-aminoethanesulfonate; DBDS: 4,4'-dibenzamido-2,2'-disulfonate; DIOSPITC: 2,6-di-iodosulfophenylisothiocyanate; PG: phenylglyoxal; PITC: phenylisothiocyanate; PLP: pyridoxal-5'-phosphate; APMB: 2-(4'-aminophenyl)-6-methylbenzenethiazol-3',7-disulfonate; pCMBS: para-chloromercuribenzenesulfonate.

519

0066-4278/85/0315-0519$02.00

the driving force for the efflux of HCO_3 in exchange for extracellular Cl. In this manner, CO_2 in the systemic capillaries is converted largely into plasma HCO_3, the form in which it is carried to the lungs. In the pulmonary capillaries, CO_2 is released into alveolar air by the reversal of all the above steps.

Although the overall process of CO_2 transport was described many years ago (72), it is only recently that the quantitative contribution of red cell Cl-HCO_3 exchange has been studied in detail (11, 12, 52, 90). The half-time for net Cl-HCO_3 exchange under physiological conditions is about 100 msec (90); this is sufficient time for 90% completion of the exchange during the usual capillary transit time. Under some conditions, e.g. salicylate poisoning, the Cl-HCO_3 exchange is not complete by the time the cell is through the capillary (13). The theoretical consequences of this are that a given rate of CO_2 excretion should require a larger mixed venous/alveolar P_{CO_2} gradient and a larger tissue/blood P_{CO_2} gradient (11, 90). Would total inhibition of red cell Cl-HCO_3 exchange have catastrophic consequences? It is difficult to see why it should. A moderate increase in alveolar ventilation would increase the mixed venous/alveolar P_{CO_2} gradient enough to offset the decrease in CO_2 release caused by lack of Cl-HCO_3 exchange. An advantage conferred by the exchange, in addition to its effect on CO_2-carrying capacity, is the prevention of the large post-capillary pH transients described by Crandall and coworkers (12).

KINETICS OF BAND 3–CATALYZED ANION EXCHANGE

Substrate Specificity

In addition to Cl and HCO_3, many other anions (e.g. Br, SO_4, PO_4) are transported by way of band 3 (15, 43, 47a, 63, 75, 77). The rates of transport of these anions vary over a $> 10^4$-fold range (see 43), with Cl and HCO_3 transported most rapidly. This selectivity is caused mainly by variations in the translocation rates of the anions rather than variations in affinity of binding to transport sites. Thus, the binding sites for transported anions are rather non-selective, with anions as dissimilar as Cl and SO_4 binding with apparent affinities of the same order of magnitude (27, 43, 60, 77). Lactate, pyruvate, and other substituted monocarboxylates are transported by a kinetically distinct pathway (17) that involves a protein other than band 3 (17, 35).

Obligatory Exchange

A remarkable feature of band 3–catalyzed Cl and HCO_3 transport is that the transport consists almost entirely of an obligatory one-for-one exchange. The chloride conductance, estimated in a variety of ways (see 43), is about 10^{-4}-fold that predicted from ^{36}Cl-Cl exchange rates. Conductive chloride fluxes, although of much lower magnitude than exchange fluxes, are also catalyzed by band 3 (44); the conductive flux represents an altered catalytic cycle with at least one very slow step (22, 39, 45).

Kinetic Models of the Exchange

The fact that the anion transport consists mainly of an obligatory exchange implies that one complete catalytic cycle must involve two anions. By analogy to two-substrate enzymes (9), the catalysis could be of either of two kinds. In a ping-pong mechanism, only one anion is bound to the system at a time, and intracellular and extracellular anions take turns crossing the membrane. In a simultaneous (74) mechanism, an intracellular anion and an extracellular anion bind to band 3 in either a random or preferred order, and then are transported by some set of concerted steps involving both anions.

Several groups have published kinetic studies designed to distinguish between these two classes of mechanisms. The ping-pong mechanism requires that the transport protein exist in either of two stable conformations, which can be denoted "inward facing" and "outward facing." This is not a requirement of simultaneous mechanisms. Passow and coworkers (64, 65) and Rothstein and coworkers (25), using slowly (or non-) penetrating inhibitors of anion transport, have shown that there are distinct band 3 protein conformations that can reasonably be identified as "inward facing" and "outward facing." For example, stilbenedisulfonate derivatives (e.g. DIDS[1], H$_2$DIDS) are not transported appreciably, but they are potent inhibitors of band 3–mediated anion transport (7). They inhibit transport competitively (78) by binding with high affinity (and in some compounds, subsequently reacting covalently) to a site accessible only from the extracellular medium (40). Trapping another nonpenetrating disulfonic acid, APMB, inside resealed ghosts inhibits transport and changes the conformation around an amino group at the outward-facing stilbenedisulfonate site (65). This transmembrane effect could result from APMB binding to the inward-facing conformation and, by mass action, recruiting more transporters away from the outward-facing state.

Another kind of experiment that has been used to distinguish ping-pong from simultaneous mechanisms involves the effects of the *trans* anion on the kinetics of the tracer flux of a given *cis* anion. Gunn & Fröhlich (27) measured the ^{36}Cl-Cl exchange flux at fixed intracellular Cl and varying extracellular Cl concentration. The exchange flux, for a given Cl$_i$, is half-maximal at an extracellular Cl concentration equal (by definition) to K$_{1/2 \text{ out}}$. The K$_{1/2 \text{ out}}$ is lower at smaller intracellular Cl concentrations, as predicted by the ping-pong model (27). A related kind of experiment is to measure the rate of exchange of Cl for a very slowly transported anion (e.g., sulfate or phosphate). The K$_{1/2 \text{ in}}$ for Cl efflux into an all-phosphate medium is more than ten-fold smaller than the K$_{1/2 \text{ in}}$ for Cl-Cl exchange, as is predicted by the ping-pong model (31). Simultaneous models do not in general predict an effect of *trans* anion on K$_{1/2}$.

The ping-pong mechanism implies that the proportions of inward- and outward-facing transport systems depend on the intrinsic asymmetry of the protein (see below) and on the concentrations of substrates and inhibitors on each side of the membrane. For example, if the Cl concentration is large inside the cell, and if there is no rapidly penetrating anion in the extracellular medium, virtually all the transporters should be recruited, by mass action, to the outward-facing conformation (14, 43). Several competitive and noncompetitive inhibitors of anion transport, including H_2DIDS (24), niflumic acid (47), NAP-taurine (46), and DNDS (21, 31), are more potent in the presence of an outward Cl gradient. These effects of the Cl gradient are further evidence of distinct inward- and outward-facing conformations.

Because band 3 is such an abundant membrane protein, it is possible to prepare resealed red cell ghosts in which the number of moles of intracellular ^{36}Cl exceeds the number of moles of band 3 by only about three-fold. When these ghosts are resuspended at 0°C in a high-SO_4 medium that is devoid of Cl, HCO_3, or other rapidly penetrating anion, there is a rapid ($t_{1/2} < 10$ sec) loss of about 10^6 Cl ions per ghost, with a much slower further efflux (31). This rapid Cl efflux very likely represents the Cl lost during a partial catalytic cycle: internal binding, outward translocation, and extracellular release. The amount of Cl released is slightly less than the number of band 3 polypeptides per ghost. This result supports the ping-pong mechanism by showing that anion efflux and extracellular release can take place in the absence of anion influx.

Salhany & Rauenbuehler (75) have pointed out that the above "half turnover" experiments do not rule out all mechanisms that involve a ternary complex among the protein and the two anions that are exchanged in one catalytic cycle. They have proposed a model that is very similar to the simple ping-pong mechanism but in which the extracellar anion binds *before* the release of the anion that has just been transported outward.

Self-Inhibition

As the concentration of a given substrate anion (e.g. Cl, SO_4, Br) is raised on both sides of the membrane to concentrations exceeding 150–200 mM, the unidirectional flux of that anion actually decreases (14, 15, 27, 43, 77). The inhibitory binding site is termed the "modifier site" (15, 43, 91); its relation to the transport site(s) is not yet clear (46, 55, 91).

pH Dependence

The pH dependence of band 3-catalyzed anion fluxes has been examined over a very wide range of extracellular pH (23, 26a, 50, 60a, 62, 90, 90a). Lowering the extracellular pH below 7.4 strongly activates SO_4 influx into Cl-loaded cells (60a). The bound proton is cotransported with the SO_4 (30); the overall exchange is thus electroneutral. Milanick & Gunn (60) have shown that bound

SO_4 affects the pK for H binding, bound H affects the K_m for SO_4 binding, and the order of binding of the two ions is random. It is likely that the same extracellular H titration ($pK_A \sim 5$) that activates SO_4 influx also inhibits Cl-Cl exchange (60). An interesting recent finding is that in dansylated resealed ghosts, the pH dependence of SO_4 transport closely resembles that of Cl exchange in native membranes (50).

The self-exchange flux of chloride is independent of both extracellular and intracellular pH (at 0°C) between pH 7 and 10 (23, 90, 90a). This has been demonstrated in resealed red cell ghosts, where the distribution of anions is not strongly affected by pH (23). Raising the extracellular pH from 10 to 11 accelerates the Cl-Cl exchange flux (at 330 mM Cl) slightly; this acceleration probably results from deactivation of a self-inhibitory site (90, 90a, 91). Further increase in extracellular pH inhibits the flux according to a titration curve of pK 12 (90). Less is known about H^+ titrations on the intracellular side of band 3. A titratable group of pK < 7 is inhibitory to both Cl and SO_4 transport (60b, 77).

Functional Asymmetry of Anion Exchange

At a fixed intracellular Cl concentration of 100 mM, extracellular Cl activates the Cl-Cl exchange flux with a $K_{1/2}$ of about 2 mM at 0°C (27). If extracellular Cl is fixed and large, intracellular Cl activates the exchange flux with a $K_{1/2}$ of about 50 mM (27). This asymmetry could be caused by a true asymmetry in the binding affinities of Cl to transport sites on the two sides of the membrane. It is also possible that the unimolecular rate constant for inward translocation is larger than that for outward translocation. Such an asymmetry would reflect a free energy difference between the inward and outward facing conformations of the band 3-chloride complex. Either an asymmetry in the translocation rate constants or in the true binding constants could cause the observed asymmetry in the $K_{1/2}$ for Cl exchange. Under most conditions, the majority of the transporters appear to face inward; the exact magnitude of the asymmetry is uncertain (see 46, 47). For Cl, the asymmetry is believed to be caused by asymmetric translocation rate constants (47); for Br, however, the translocation rate constants appear to be reasonably symmetric (27).

STRUCTURE OF THE BAND 3 PROTEIN

Subunit Structure

There is considerable evidence that band 3 is a dimer or tetramer in the membrane (71, 82, 88). Although some models of coupled transport depict the substrate moving along the interface between (or among) subunits of an oligomer (42), this does not appear to be how band 3 functions. The stoichiometry of stilbenedisulfonate binding is one molecule per polypeptide

(37, 48, 79), and each subunit is capable of carrying out anion transport even if the adjacent subunit has been irreversibly inhibited by DIDS or H_2DIDS (48, 53, 54, 79, 89). There is evidence, however, that binding of a bulky stilbenedisulfonate (e.g. DBDS) to one subunit can inhibit binding to the adjacent subunit (53–55). Also, Boodhoo & Reithmeier (4) showed recently that monomeric band 3, immobilized on a derivatized Sepharose column, does not bind stilbenedisulfonates with high affinity. This suggests that intersubunit interactions are necessary for the stability of the stilbenedisulfonate site. [Further discussions of possible relations between transport and band 3 subunit structure are in (33, 55, and 90).]

Cytoplasmic Domain

The N-terminus of band 3 is contained in a water-soluble 43,000-dalton cytoplasmic domain that can be cleaved from the inner surface of band 3 by proteolysis with trypsin or chymotrypsin under very mild conditions (84, 85). The cytoplasmic domain can be cleaved from the membrane without major effect on band 3–catalyzed anion transport (26, 49). The function of this domain is to bind the cytoskeleton (1). It also binds glycolytic enzymes (83) and hemoglobin (76); the physiological significance of this binding is not yet clear. Because this review is concerned with the anion transport function of band 3, the cytoplasmic domain will not be considered further.

Membrane Domain

The C-terminal 60% of band 3 is tightly, hydrophobically associated with the membrane. This material, the membrane domain, is heterogeneously glycosylated (29), and its molecular weight is about 52,000. In general terms, it is probable that the membrane domain of band 3 resembles the structure proposed for bacteriorhodopsin (28), in which there are several membrane-crossing α-helical segments connected by short hydrophilic stretches. The evidence for this, in the case of band 3, is that the membrane domain is highly α-helical (R. A. F. Reithmeier, personal communication), and the fragments remaining after very vigorous proteolysis of unsealed membranes have a size (~ 4000 daltons) appropriate for a single passage through the bilayer (66). There is also one 72-residue fragment (see below) whose sequence is known and is very suggestive of two hydrophobic crossing strands connected by a hydrophilic segment (5). It is not yet clear what fraction of the mass of the membrane domain consists of this kind of structure.

In Situ Proteolysis of the Membrane Domain

Considerable effort has been devoted to identifying and localizing sites of in situ proteolysis and chemical modification of the membrane domain. The rationale for this work is to place restrictions on the possible ways in which the polypeptide may be arranged in the membrane (see Figures 1 and 2). Extracellular chymotrypsin, thermolysin, or pronase, acting on intact cells, can cleave band 3 at a site that is located about 17,000 daltons from the N-terminus of the membrane domain (18, 84, 85). The chymotrypsin cleavage does not appreciably inhibit anion exchange (8), and both cleavage products are integral and appear to remain associated with each other following the proteolysis (37, 71).

Papain, acting on intact cells, cleaves the outer surface of band 3 at three additional sites (34, 36, 51) and inhibits anion exchange (34, 37, 58). Two of the cleavage sites are within 6 residues of the chymotrypsin cleavage site, and the third is 72 residues further toward the C-terminus of band 3 (36). The latter cleavage is very likely responsible for the inhibitory action of papain on anion exchange (36). This inhibition results from a ten-fold reduction of the unimolecular rate constant for the efflux step in the catalytic cycle (34). Papain also lowers the affinity of reversible binding of stilbenedisulfonates (34, 51) and flufenamic acid (10). It was formerly believed that extracellular papain releases 5000–10,000 daltons of material from the membrane (34, 37). This is not true; the 7000-dalton papain cleavage product is hydrophobically associated with the membrane (36).

Treatment of unsealed membranes with proteolytic enzymes has revealed several other cleavage sites. Chymotrypsin, at much higher concentrations than

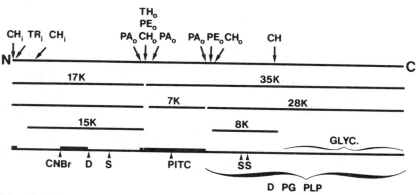

Figure 1 Sites of intracellular *(i)* and extracellular *(o)* proteolysis of the membrane domain of band 3 by chymotrypsin *(CH)*, trypsin *(TR)*, thermolysin *(TH)*, pepsin *(PE)*, and papain *(PA)*. The integral fragments produced by chymotrypsin *(17K, 35K)* or papain *(16.5K, 7K, 28K)* digestion of intact cells and subsequent trypsin treatment of ghosts are shown, as are the *15K* and *8K* fragments that have been identified following vigorous chymotrypsin digestion of unsealed membranes. The lower portion of the figure indicates the locations of sulfhydryls *(S)*, carbohydrate *(GLYC)*, and the sites of chemical modification by H$_2$DIDS *(D)*, pyridoxal phosphate *(PLP)*, phenylglyoxal *(PG)*, and phenylisothiocyanate *(PITC)*. The thickened lines indicate regions of known sequence. See text for references.

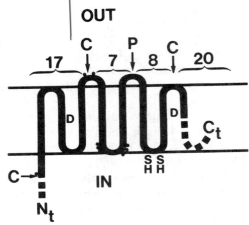

Figure 2   Two-dimensional model of the folding of the membrane domain of band 3. Proteolytic cleavage sites for chymotrypsin *(C)* and papain *(P)* are indicated. The covalent attachment sites *(D)* for the two ends of the H_2DIDS molecule must be about 20 Å apart. The D site in the C-terminal 28,000 daltons has not been localized further in the primary structure. The *dots* signify known positions of positive charge in the band 3 sequence (5, 34, 36, 59).

those used to cleave the cytoplasmic domain, removes about 20 residues from the N-terminus of the membrane domain (68). High bilateral chymotrypsin concentrations also degrade the 35,000 dalton fragment to one of 8,000 daltons plus several smaller peptides that have not been identified (20). The 8,000-dalton peptide has been localized in the primary structure: its N-terminus is about 220 residues from the N-terminus of the membrane domain (67).

Pepsin digestion of unsealed membranes produces a 8000–10,000-dalton membrane-bound fragment that is derived from band 3 (5, 86). A major recent achievement in the study of band 3 structure is the sequencing of 72 residues of this fragment by Brock et al (5). This is the most extensive sequence known for the membrane domain of band 3. Subsequent sequence data from Jennings et al (36) on the chymotryptic and papain fragments have localized the Brock et al (5) fragment in the primary structure: it has a common N-terminus with the 35,000-dalton chymotryptic fragment (Figure 1).

Sites of Chemical Modification

Several sites of chemical modification, some of significance to band 3 function, have been at least partially localized in the primary structure. One major reactive lysine residue is that which reacts covalently with H_2DIDS at neutral pH (7, 8). This is very likely the same lysine that reacts rapidly with dinitrofluorobenzene (64, 73), isothiocyanobenzenesulfonate (18), and DIOSPITC (59). This lysine is definitely located in the 17,000-dalton chymotryptic fragment (26). Data on the more precise location are conflicting, but it is located at least 9000 daltons from the N-terminus (59, 68). Although this lysine reacts covalently with transport inhibitors, it does not necessarily have an essential role in the transport itself (32, 64).

Several other lysine residues are known to be in contact with the extracellular water. The most N-terminal of these is on the N-terminal CNBr peptide of the 17,000-dalton fragment (36a). This peptide ($M_r \sim 6000$) must therefore cross the membrane. Because Mawby & Findlay (59) have shown that the polypeptide immediately C-terminal to this CNBr peptide is extremely hydrophobic, it is probable that the 17,000-dalton fragment crosses the membrane at least three times.

Other exofacial lysines are located three residues from the C-terminus of the 17,000-dalton fragment (34) and four residues from the N-terminus of the 35,000-dalton chymotryptic fragment (5, 36). Neither of these has any known role in the transport. There is one exofacial lysine in the 35,000-dalton fragment that appears to be important for anion transport. This lysine reacts with H_2DIDS at pH > 8; this produces a covalent cross-link between the 17,000- and 35,000-dalton fragments (37, 38). Reductive methylation of this lysine inhibits Cl transport by about 75%, even though the methylated lysine retains its charge (32). It is probable that the same lysine reacts with pyridoxal phosphate (58, 61), which is an inhibitor of anion transport (6). The exact location of this lysine is not yet known, but it is within 28,000 daltons of the C-terminus of band 3 (36, 58, 61).

Brock et al (5) have shown that there is a group of three lysines and three arginines that probably are at the inner membrane surface of the peptic fragment that they sequenced. One of these lysines reacts with phenylisothiocyanate under conditions in which this agent inhibits transport (5, 41, 80). The only other lysine that has been localized to the inner surface is the N-terminus of the membrane domain (when chymotrypsin is used to cleave the cytoplasmic domain). When trypsin is used instead, the adjacent bond is cleaved and this lysine remains attached to the cytoplasmic domain (59).

The membrane domain has three cysteine residues. Two of these are reactive with N-ethylmaleimide and are exposed to the intracellular water (69). They are located quite close to each other in the 8,000-dalton peptide that remains after exhaustive chymotrypsin treatment of unsealed membranes (67). The third sulfhydryl does not react with NEM under most conditions, but it is labeled by pCMBS (81). It is located about 5000 daltons from the C-terminus of the 17,000-dalton fragment (67). The sulfhydryls have no known role in anion transport.

Weith and coworkers (2, 3, 92) and Zaki (95, 96) have demonstrated that arginine-selective reagents inhibit band 3–mediated anion transport. There are apparently two reactive arginines that can be labeled from the extracellular medium (3). Both are in the 35,000-dalton chymotryptic fragment, but not in the 8000–10,000-dalton pepsin fragment (3). Because the latter is now known to be at the N-terminus of the 35,000-dalton peptide (36), the modified arginines must be within 25,000 daltons of the band 3 C-terminus.

As discussed above, chloride transport is inhibited by H^+ binding to a group that has $pK_a \sim 5$ (60). The low temperature dependence of this pK_a suggests that the titratable group is a carboxylate (90). Consistent with this is the finding by Wieth and coworkers (2, 90) that water-soluble carbodiimides inhibit band 3–catalyzed chloride transport. The modified carboxyl group(s) resides in the 35,000-dalton chymotryptic fragment, but not in the 28,000-dalton papain subfragment (2).

Lactoperoxidase-catalyzed iodination has been used in several laboratories to label band 3. The tyrosine adjacent to the extracellular chymotrypsin cleavage site can be iodinated by extracellular lactoperoxidase (29), as can the tyrosine in position 70 of the Brock et al (5) peptic fragment. There are several sites of iodination at the cytoplasmic surface of the membrane domain (19, 57, 94). Another potentially useful label for the cytoplasmic surface of the membrane domain is phosphorylation. The major site of phosphorylation is Tyrosine 8 in the cytoplasmic domain (16), but it has been reported that there is also significant phosphorylation in regions that are now known to be in the membrane domain (19). Waxman (87), however, did not detect phosphorylation in the membrane domain.

POSSIBLE MECHANISMS OF ANION EXCHANGE

Despite recent advances in the understanding of band 3 structure, detailed molecular models of the anion transport mechanism are still necessarily speculative. There is considerable evidence (see above) that the concept of "inward facing" and "outward facing" conformations is applicable to band 3. There may of course be stable intermediate conformations, in which the anion has access to neither aqueous solution. Such conformations are proposed in "zipper"-type models of the anion exchange (5, 93), which postulate that the transport pathway consists of a series of ion pairs (e.g.. side chains of lysine or arginine associated with glutamate or aspartate side chains). The anion is transported by successively exchanging places with the protein-bound negative charges. Because the exchange cannot occur in the absence of a transported anion, the mechanism gives rise to ping-pong kinetics.

Other structural models of the anion exchange pathway postulate an aqueous channel that goes partway through the membrane and is interrupted by the permeability barrier (e.g. 55). As yet, too little is known about band 3 sequence and structure to evaluate the likelihood of an aqueous cavity. However, the stilbenedisulfonate binding site, although accessible only from the extracellular water, apparently lies considerably below the outer surface of the membrane (56, 70). This is consistent with the existence of a significant aqueous cavity at the outer aspect of band 3.

It is clear that several regions of the primary structure of the membrane domain are important for transport. The stilbenedisulfonate site is probably made up of regions of all the major proteolytic fragments identified in Figure 1 and 2. A phenylglyoxal-modified arginine, in the C-terminal half of the membrane domain (3), is especially likely to have an essential role in transport. The transport must involve conformational changes in the protein-anion complex, the detailed nature of which is not yet known.

ACKNOWLEDGMENT

The author is grateful to P. A. Knauf, R. B. Gunn, and R. A. F. Reithmeier for providing unpublished data. Financial support was from NIH RCDA K04 AM01137.

Literature Cited

1. Bennett, V., Stenbuck, P. J. 1980. Association between ankyrin and the cytoplasmic domain of band 3 isolated from the human erythrocyte membrane. *J. Biol. Chem.* 255:6424–32

2. Bjerrum, P. J. 1983. Identification and location of amino acid residues essential for anion transport in red cell membranes. In *Structure and Function of Membrane Proteins,* ed. E. Quagliariello, F. Palmieri, pp. 107–15. Amsterdam: Elsevier

3. Bjerrum, P. J., Wieth, J. O., Borders, C. L. 1983. Selective phenylglyoxalation of functionally essential arginyl residues in the erythrocyte anion transport protein. *J. Gen. Physiol.* 81:453–84

4. Boodhoo, A., Reithmeier, R. A. F. 1984. Characterization of matrix-bound band 3, the anion transport protein from human erythrocyte membranes. *J. Biol. Chem.* 259:785–90

5. Brock, C. J., Tanner, M. J. A., Kempf, C. 1983. The human erythrocyte anion transport protein. *Biochem. J.* 213:577–86

6. Cabantchik, Z. I., Balshin, M., Breuer, W., Rothstein, A. 1975. Pyridoxal phosphate: an anionic probe for protein amino groups exposed on the outer and inner surface of intact human red blood cells. *J. Biol. Chem.* 250:5130–36

7. Cabantchik, Z. I., Rothstein, A. 1974. Membrane proteins related to anion permeability of human red blood cells. I. Localization of disulfonic stilbene binding sites in proteins involved in permeation. *J. Membr. Biol.* 15:207–26

8. Cabantchik, Z. I., Rothstein, A. 1974. Membrane proteins related to anion permeability of human red blood cells. II. Effects of proteolytic enzymes on disulfonic stilbene sites of surface proteins. *J. Membr. Biol.* 15:227–48

9. Cleland, W. W. 1963. The kinetics of enzyme-catalyzed reactions with two or more substrates or products. I. Nomenclature and rate equations. *Biochim. Biophys. Acta* 67:104–37

10. Cousin, J.-L., Motais, R. 1982. Inhibition of anion transport in the red blood cell by anionic amphiphilic compounds. I. Determination of the flufenamate-binding site by proteolytic dissection of the band 3 protein. *Biochim. Biophys. Acta* 687:147–55

11. Crandall, E. D., Bidani, A. 1981. Effects of RBC HCO_3/Cl exchange kinetics on lung CO_2 exchange: theory. *J. Appl. Physiol.* 50:265–71

12. Crandall, E. D., Mathew, S. J., Fleischer, R. S., Winter, H. I., Bidani, A. 1981. Effects of inhibition of RBC HCO_3/Cl$^-$ exchange on CO_2 excretion and downstream pH disequilibrium in isolated rat lungs. *J. Clin. Invest.* 68: 853–62

13. Crandall, E. D., Winter, H. I., Schaeffer, J. D., Bidani, A. 1982. Effects of salicylate on HCO_3/Cl exchange across the human erythrocyte membrane. *J. Membr. Biol.* 65:139–45

14. Dalmark, M., 1975. Chloride transport in human red cells. *J. Physiol.* 250:39–64

15. Dalmark, M. 1976. Effects of halides and bicarbonate on chloride transport in human red blood cells. *J. Gen. Physiol.* 67:223–34

16. Dekowski, S. A., Rybicki, A., Drickamer, K. 1983. A tyrosine kinase associated with the red cell membrane phosphorylates band 3. *J. Biol. Chem.* 258:2750–53

17. Deuticke, B. 1982. Monocarboxylate transport in erythrocytes. *J. Membr. Biol.* 70:89–103

18. Drickamer, L. K. 1976. Fragmentation of the 95,000 dalton transmembrane polypeptide in human erythrocyte membranes. Arrangement of the fragments in the lipid bilayer. *J. Biol. Chem.* 251:5115–23

19. Drickamer, L. K. 1977. Fragmentation of the band 3 polypeptide from the human erythrocyte membranes. Identification of regions likely to interact with the lipid bilayer. *J. Biol. Chem.* 252:6909–17

20. DuPre, A. M., Rothstein, A. 1981. Inhibition of anion transport associated with chymotryptic cleavages of red blood cell band 3 protein. *Biochim. Biophys. Acta* 646:471–78

21. Fröhlich, O. 1982. The external anion binding site of the human erythrocyte anion transporter: DNDS binding and competition with chloride. *J. Membr. Biol.* 65:111–23

22. Fröhlich, O., Leibson, C., Gunn, R. B. 1983. Chloride net efflux from intact erythrocytes under slippage conditions. Evidence for a positive charge of the anion binding/transport site. *J. Gen. Physiol.* 81:127–52

23. Funder, J., Wieth, J. O. 1976. Chloride transport in human erythrocytes and ghosts: a quantitative comparison. *J. Physiol.* 262:679–98

24. Furuya, W., Tarshis, T., Law, F.-Y., Knauf, P. A. 1984. Transmembrane effects of intracellular chloride on the inhibitory potency of extracellular H$_2$DIDS: evidence for two conformations of the transport site of the human erythrocyte anion exchange protein. *J. Gen. Physiol.* 83:657–81

25. Grinstein, S., McCulloch, L., Rothstein, A. 1979. Transmembrane effects of irreversible inhibitors of anion transport in red blood cells. Evidence for mobile transport sites. *J. Gen. Physiol.* 73:493–514

26. Grinstein, S., Ship, S., Rothstein, A. 1978. Anion transport in relation to proteolytic dissection of band 3 protein. *Biochim. Biophys. Acta* 507:294–304

26a. Gunn, R. B., Dalmark, M., Tosteson, D. C., Wieth, J. O. 1973. Characteristics of chloride transport in human red blood cells. *J. Gen. Physiol.* 61:185–206

27. Gunn, R. B., Fröhlich, O. 1979. Asymmetry in the mechanism for anion exchange in human red blood cell membranes. *J. Gen. Physiol.* 74:351–74

28. Henderson, R., Unwin, P. N. T. 1975. Three-dimensional model of purple membrane obtained by electron microscopy. *Nature* 257:28–32

29. Jenkins, R. E., Tanner, M. J. A. 1977. The structure of the major protein of the human erythrocyte membrane. Characterization of the intact protein and major fragments. *Biochem. J.* 161:139–47

30. Jennings, M. L. 1976. Proton fluxes associated with erythrocyte membrane anion exchange. *J. Membr. Biol.* 28:187–205

31. Jennings, M. L. 1982. Stoichiometry of a half-turnover of band 3, the chloride transport protein of human erythrocytes. *J. Gen. Physiol.* 79:169–85

32. Jennings, M. L. 1982. Reductive methylation of the two 4,4'-diisothiocyanodihydrostilbene- 2,2'-disulfonate-binding lysine residues of band 3, the human erythrocyte anion transport protein. *J. Biol. Chem.* 257:7554–59

33. Jennings, M. L. 1984. Oligomeric structure and the anion transport function of human erythrocyte band 3 protein. *J. Membr. Biol.* 80:105–19

34. Jennings, M. L., Adams, M. F. 1981. Modification by papain of the structure and function of band 3, the erythrocyte anion transport protein. *Biochemistry* 20:7118–23

35. Jennings, M. L., Adams-Lackey, M. 1982. A rabbit erythrocyte membrane protein associated with L-lactate transport. *J. Biol. Chem.* 257:12866–71

36. Jennings, M. L., Adams-Lackey, M., Denney, G. H. 1984. Peptides of human erythrocyte band 3 protein produced by extracellular papain cleavage. *J. Biol. Chem.* 259:4652–60

36a. Jennings, M. L., Nicknish, J. S. 1984. Erythrocyte band 3 protein: evidence for multiple membrane-crossing segments in the 17,000-dalton chymotryptic fragment. *Biochemistry.* In press

37. Jennings, M. L., Passow, H. 1979. Anion transport across the erythrocyte membrane, in situ proteolysis of band 3 protein, and cross-linking of proteolytic fragments by H$_2$DIDS. *Biochim. Biophys. Acta* 554:498–519

38. Kampmann, L., Lepke, S., Fasold, H., Fritzsch, G., Passow, H. 1982. The kinetics of intramolecular cross-linking of the

band 3 protein in the red blood cell membrane by 4,4'-diisothiocyano dihydrostilbene-2,2'-disulfonic acid (H$_2$DIDS). *J. Membr. Biol.* 70:199–216

39. Kaplan, J. H., Pring, M., Passow, H. 1983. Band-3 protein-mediated anion conductance of the red cell membrane. Slippage vs ionic diffusion. *FEBS Lett.* 156:175–79

40. Kaplan, J. H., Scorah, K., Fasold, H., Passow, H. 1976. Sidedness of the inhibitory action of disulfonic acids on chloride equilibrium exchange and net transport across the human erythrocyte membrane. *FEBS Lett.* 62:182–85

41. Kempf, C., Brock, C., Sigrist, H., Tanner, M. J. A., Zahler, P. 1981. Interaction of phenylisothiocyanate with human erythrocyte band 3 protein. II. Topology of phenylisothiocyanate binding sites and influence of p-sulfophenylisothiocyanate on phenylisothiocyanate modification. *Biochim. Biophys. Acta* 641:88–98

42. Klingenberg, M. 1981. Membrane protein oligomeric structure and transport function. *Nature* 290:449–54

43. Knauf, P. A. 1979. Erythrocyte anion exchange and the band 3 protein: Transport kinetics and molecular structure. *Curr. Top. Membr. Transp.* 12:249–363

44. Knauf, P. A., Fuhrmann, G. F., Rothstein, S., Rothstein, A. 1977. The relationship between anion exchange and net anion flow across the human red blood cell membrane. *J. Gen. Physiol.* 69:363–86

45. Knauf, P. A., Law, F., Marchant, P. J. 1983. Relationship of net chloride flow across the human erythrocyte membrane to the anion exchange mechanism. *J. Gen. Physiol.* 81:95–126

46. Knauf, P. A., Law, F.-Y., Tarshis, T., Furuya, W. 1984. Effects of the transport site conformation on the binding of external NAP-taurine to the human erythrocyte anion exchange system: evidence for intrinsic asymmetry. *J. Gen. Physiol.* 83:683–701

47. Knauf, P. A., Mann, N. A. 1984. Use of niflumic acid to determine the nature of the asymmetry of the human erythrocyte anion exchange system. *J. Gen. Physiol.* 83:703–25

47a. Ku, C.-P., Jennings, M. L., Passow, H. 1979. A comparison of the inhibitory potency of reversibly acting inhibitors of anion transport on chloride and sulfate movements across the human red cell membrane. *Biochim. Biophys. Acta* 553:132–41

48. Lepke, S., Fasold, H., Pring, M., Passow, H. 1976. A study of the relationship between inhibition of anion exchange and binding to the red blood cell membrane of 4,4'-diisothiocyanostilbene-2,2'-disulfonic acid (DIDS) and its dihydro derivative (H$_2$DIDS). *J. Membr. Biol.* 29:147–77

49. Lepke, S., Passow, H. 1976. Effects of incorporated trypsin on anion exchange and membrane proteins in human red blood cell ghosts. *Biochim. Biophys. Acta* 455:353–70

50. Lepke, S., Passow, H. 1982. Inverse effects of dansylation of red blood cell membrane on band 3 protein-mediated transport of sulphate and chloride. *J. Physiol.* 328:27–48

51. Lieberman, D. M., Reithmeier, R. A. F. 1983. Characterization of the stilbenedisulfonate binding site of the band 3 polypeptide of human erythrocyte membranes. *Biochemistry* 22:4028–33

52. Lowe, A. G., Lambert, A. 1983. Chloride-bicarbonate exchange and related transport processes. *Biochim. Biophys. Acta* 694:353–74

53. Macara, I. G., Cantley, L. C. 1981. Interactions between transport inhibitors at the anion binding sites of the band 3 dimer. *Biochemistry* 20:5095–105

54. Macara, I. G., Cantley, L. C. 1981. Mechanism of anion exchange across the red cell membrane by band 3: Interactions between stilbenedisulfonate and NAP-taurine binding sites. *Biochemistry* 20:5695–701

55. Macara, I. G., Cantley, L. C. 1983. The structure and function of band 3. In *Cell Membranes, Methods and Reviews*, ed. E. Elson, W. Frazier, L. Glaser, 1:41–87. New York: Plenum

56. Macara, I. G., Kuo, S., Cantley, L. C. 1983. Evidence that inhibitors of anion exchange induce a transmembrane conformational change in band 3. *J. Biol. Chem.* 258:1785–92

57. Markowitz, S., Marchesi, V. T. 1981. The carboxyl-terminal domain of human erythrocyte band 3. *J. Biol. Chem.* 256:6463–68

58. Matsuyama, H., Kawano, Y., Hamasaki, N. 1983. Anion transport activity in the human erythrocyte membrane modulated by proteolytic digestion of the 38,000-dalton fragment in band 3. *J. Biol. Chem.* 258:15376–81

59. Mawby, W. J., Findlay, J. B. C. 1982. Characterization and partial sequence of di-iodosulphophenyl isothiocyanate-binding peptide from human erythrocyte anion transport protein. *Biochem. J.* 205:465–75

60. Milanick, M. A., Gunn, R. B. 1982. Proton-sulfate co-transport. Mechanism of H$^+$ and sulfate addition to the chloride

transporter of human red blood cells. *J. Gen. Physiol.* 79:87–113

60a. Milanick, M. A., Gunn, R. B. 1984. Proton-sulfate cotransport: External proton activation of sulfate influx into human red blood cells. *Am. J. Physiol.* In press

60b. Milanick, M. A., Gunn, R. B. 1984. Asynchrony in the proton and anion transport sites on band 3 determined by proton inhibition of chloride exchange. Submitted for publication

61. Nanri, H., Hamasaki, N., Minakami, S. 1983. Affinity labeling of erythrocyte band 3 protein with pyridoxal 5 phosphate. Involvement of the 35,000-dalton fragment in anion transport. *J. Biol. Chem.* 258:5985–89

62. Obaid, A. L., Crandall, E. D. 1979. HCO_3/Cl exchange across the human erythrocyte membrane: effects of pH and temperature. *J. Membr. Biol.* 50:23–41

63. Obaid, A. L., Leininger, T. F., Crandall, E. D. 1980. Exchange of HCO_3 for monovalent anions across the human erythrocyte membrane. *J. Membr. Biol.* 52:173–79

64. Passow, H., Fasold, H., Gärtner, E. M., Legrum, B., Ruffing, W., Zaki, L. 1980. Anion transport across the red blood cell membrane and the conformation of the protein in band 3. *Ann. NY Acad. Sci.* 341:361–83

65. Passow, H., Zaki, L. 1978. Studies on the molecular mechanism of anion transport across the red blood cell membrane. In *Molecular Specialization and Symmetry in Membrane Function*, ed. A. K. Solomon, M. Karnovsky, pp. 229–50. Cambridge, MA/London: Harvard Univ. Press

66. Ramjeesingh, M., Gaarn, A., Rothstein, A. 1984. Pepsin cleavage of band 3 produces its membrane-crossing domains. *Biochim. Biophys. Acta* 769:381–89

67. Ramjeesingh, M., Gaarn, A., Rothstein, A. 1983. The locations of the three cysteine residues in the primary structure of the intrinsic segments of band 3 protein, and implications concerning the arrangement of band 3 protein in the bilayer. *Biochim. Biophys. Acta* 729:150–60

68. Ramjeesingh, M., Gaarn, A., Rothstein, A. 1980. The location of a disulfonic stilbene binding site in band 3, the anion transport protein of the red blood cell membrane. *Biochim. Biophys. Acta* 599:127–39

69. Rao, A. 1979. Disposition of the band 3 polypeptide in the human erythrocyte membrane. *J. Biol. Chem.* 254:3503–11

70. Rao, A., Martin, P., Reithmeier, R. A. F., Cantley, L. C. 1979. Location of the stilbenedisulfonate binding site of the human erythrocyte anion-exchange system by resonance energy transfer. *Biochemistry* 18:4505–16

71. Reithmeier, R. A. F. 1979. Fragmentation of the band 3 polypeptide from human erythrocyte membranes. Size and detergent binding of the membrane-associated domain. *J. Biol. Chem.* 254:3054–60

72. Roughton, F. J. W. 1935. Recent work on carbon dioxide transport by the blood. *Physiol. Rev.* 15:241–96

73. Rudloff, V., Lepke, S., Passow, H. 1983. Inhibition of anion transport across the red cell membrane by dinitrophenylation of a specific lysine residue at the H_2DIDS binding of the band 3 protein. *FEBS Lett.* 163:14–21

74. Sachs, J. R. 1977. Kinetic evaluation of the Na-K pump reaction mechanism. *J. Physiol.* 273:489–514

75. Salhany, J. M., Rauenbuehler, P. B. 1983. Kinetics and mechanism of erythrocyte anion exchange. *J. Biol. Chem.* 258:245–49

76. Sayare, M., Fikiet, M. 1981. Cross-linking of hemoglobin to the cytoplasmic surface of human erythrocyte membranes. *J. Biol. Chem.* 256:13152–58

77. Schnell, K. F., Gerhardt, S., Schöppe-Fredenburg, A. 1977. Kinetic characteristics of the sulfate self-exchange in human red blood cells and red blood cell ghosts. *J. Membr. Biol.* 30:319–50

78. Shami, Y., Rothstein, A., Knauf, P. A. 1978. Identification of the Cl^- transport site of human red blood cells by a kinetic analysis of the inhibitory effects of a chemical probe. *Biochim. Biophys. Acta* 508:357–63

79. Ship, S., Shami, Y., Breuer, W., Rothstein, A. 1977. Synthesis of tritiated 4,4'-diisothiocyano-2,2'-stilbene disulfonic acid ([³H]DIDS) and its covalent reaction with sites related to anion transport in human red blood cells. *J. Membr. Biol.* 33:311–23

80. Sigrist, H., Kempf, C., Zahler, P. 1980. Interaction of phenylisothiocyanate with human erythrocyte band 3 protein. I. Covalent modification and inhibition of phosphate transport. *Biochim. Biophys. Acta* 597:137–44

81. Solomon, A. K., Chasan, B., Dix, J. A., Lukacovic, M. F., Toon, M. R., Verkman, A. S. 1983. The aqueous pore in the red cell membrane: band 3 as a channel for anions, cations, nonelectrolytes, and water. *Ann. NY Acad. Sci.* 414:97–124

82. Steck, T. L. 1972. Cross-linking the major proteins of the isolated erythrocyte membrane. *J. Mol. Biol.* 66:295–305

83. Steck, T. L. 1978. The band 3 protein of the human red cell membrane: A review. *J. Supramolec. Struct.* 8:311–24

84. Steck, T. L., Koziarz, J. J., Singh, M. K., Reddy, G., Köhler, H. 1978. Preparation and analysis of seven major, topographically defined fragments of band 3, the predominant transmembrane polypeptide of human erythrocyte membranes. *Biochemistry* 17:1216–22

85. Steck, T. L., Ramos, B., Strapazon, E. 1976. Proteolytic dissection of band 3, the predominant transmembrane polypeptide of the human erythrocyte membrane. *Biochemistry* 15:1154–61

86. Tanner, M. J. A., Williams, D. G., Kyle, D. 1979. The anion-transport protein of the human erythrocyte membrane. Studies on fragments produced by pepsin digestion. *Biochem. J.* 183:417–27

87. Waxman, L. 1979. The phosphorylation of the major proteins of the human erythrocyte membrane. *Arch. Biochem. Biophys.* 195:300–14

88. Weinstein, R. S., Khodadad, J. K., Steck, T. L. 1980. The band 3 protein intramembrane particle of the human red blood cell. In *Membrane Transport in Erythrocytes, A. Benzon Symp. 14*, ed. U. V. Lassen, H. H. Ussing, J. O. Wieth, pp. 35–50. Copenhagen: Munksgaard

89. Wieth, J. O. 1979. Bicarbonate exchange through the human red cell membrane determined with [^{14}C] bicarbonate. *J. Physiol.* 294:521–39

90. Wieth, J. O., Andersen, O. S., Brahm, J., Bjerrum, P. J., Borders, C. L. Jr. 1982. Chloride-bicarbonate exchange in red blood cells: physiology of transport and chemical modification of binding sites. *Phil. Trans. R. Soc. London Ser. B* 299:383–99

90a. Wieth, J. O., Bjerrum, P. J. 1982. Titration of transport and modifier sites in the red cell anion transport system. *J. Gen. Physiol.* 79:253–82

91. Wieth, J. O., Bjerrum, P. J. 1983. Transport and modifier sites in capnophorin, the anion transport protein of the erythrocyte membrane. See Ref. 2, pp. 95–106

92. Wieth, J. O., Bjerrum, P. J., Borders, C. L. Jr. 1982. Irreversible inactivation of red cell chloride exchange with phenylglyoxal, an arginine-specific reagent. *J. Gen. Physiol.* 79:283–312

93. Wieth, J. O., Bjerrum, P. J., Brahm, J., Andersen, O. S. 1982. The anion transport protein of the red cell membrane. A zipper mechanism of anion exchange. *Tokai J. Exp. Clin. Med.* 7(Suppl.):91–101

94. Williams, D. G., Jenkins, R. E., Tanner, M. J. A. 1979. Structure of the anion-transport protein of the human erythrocyte membrane. Further studies on the fragments produced by proteolytic digestion. *Biochem. J.* 181:477–93

95. Zaki, L. 1981. Inhibition of anion transport across red blood cells with 1,2-cyclohexanedione. *Biochem. Biophys. Res. Commun.* 99:243–51

96. Zaki, L. 1983. Anion transport in red blood cells and arginine specific reagents. I. Effect of chloride and sulfate ions on phenylglyoxal sensitive sites in the red blood cell membrane. *Biochem. Biophys. Res. Commun.* 110:616–24

Ann. Rev. Physiol. 1985. 47:535–44

ION MOVEMENTS THROUGH THE SODIUM PUMP

Jack H. Kaplan

Department of Physiology G4, University of Pennsylvania, Philadelphia, Pennsylvania 19104

INTRODUCTION

In the last decade, the burgeoning interest in membrane proteins and the development of new techniques for their isolation and characterization have resulted in an enormous increase in our knowledge of the sodium pump as a membrane protein. At the same time, more extensive studies on the transport characteristics of the system have enhanced our understanding of the sodium pump as an ion-transporting system. In the last several years, the sodium pump has been the subject of many reviews. These include: the reaction mechanism (6, 10, 18, 44); Na activation of enzymatic activity and transport (27); characteristics of cardiac glycoside binding (15); ligand interactions (39); and enzyme distribution in the renal tubule (25). The papers presented at three meetings dedicated to the sodium pump are also an excellent source of detailed studies of the system during the last decade (2, 22, 53).

THE ALBERS-POST MODEL

Most mechanistic studies on the sodium pump have been interpreted on the basis of a scheme that resulted from the pioneering studies of Albers and coworkers (1) and Post et al (42). Na pump enzyme is phosphorylated by ATP in the presence of Na and Mg to yield an acid-stable phosphoenzyme ($E_1 \sim P$), rapidly cleaved by ADP and relatively insensitive to K ions. $E_1 \sim P$ is in equilibrium with $E_2 P$, which is insensitive to the addition of ADP and rapidly cleaved by K ions. Evidence also exists (24) for two forms of dephosphoenzyme, the first, E_1, having a high affinity for Na ions, the second, E_2, having a higher affinity for K ions. Thus the model can be viewed as a cycle composed of

535

0066-4278/85/0315-0535$02.00

two sets of equilibria between a pair of phosphoenzymes ($E_1 \sim P$ and $E_2 P$) and a pair of dephosphoenzymes (E_1 and E_2). Since the pump can work in the absence of extracellular Na (Na_o) and in the absence of intracellular K (K_i), Na_i is responsible for the activation of phosphorylation to $E_1 \sim P$ and K_o for the activation of hydrolysis of $E_2 P$.

TRANSPORT PATHWAYS

The transport modes described in this section have been observed in red blood cells or in resealed red cell ghosts. The biochemical reactions underlying these transport pathways have generally been characterized in studies on partially purified enzyme from a variety of sources having high specific activities. Although the overall reaction mechanism for all sodium pumps independent of source will be very similar, significant differences do exist, observed as differences in cation affinity, response to temperature, or the relative contributions of the various transport modes to the overall pump operation. Recent studies using resealed red cell ghosts or vesicles from red cells on the Na-ATPase (4), ATP:ADP exchange (26, 29) and [18][O]P_i:water exchange (33) have characterized the transport and biochemical reactions in the same system. The low pump density in human red blood cells (about 250 copies per cell) limits the extent to which biochemical investigations can be pursued in this system. The recent characterization of reconstituted proteoliposomes containing purified Na,K-ATPase enzyme (34) and of tight vesicles of known orientation (14) from renal outer medulla (which contain a high concentration of the enzyme) make it likely that transport, biochemical, and structural studies may now be pursued in the same system.

Na:K Exchange

The exchange of Na_i for K_o is the major physiological mode of the sodium pump. Three Na ions are expelled for every two K ions taken up at the expense of one molecule of ATP, and an electric potential is generated by the pump. By greatly increasing the normal transmembrane ionic gradients, it is possible to drive a reverse exchange, i.e. $Na_o:K_i$, with the concomitant synthesis of ATP. Recent studies have exploited pump reversal and have shown a strong voltage dependence on the reverse electrogenic pump current (11). The direction of the effect (inward current declines as the cell is made more negative) led the authors to suggest that either the pump operates in series with a voltage-sensitive gate or that a rate-limiting step in the reverse pump cycle is inhibited by negative membrane potentials.

The biochemical activity underlying the $Na_i:K_o$ exchange is the Na,K-ATPase activity. The earlier observations that ATPase activity measured in the presence of Na with low (μM) levels of ATP is inhibited by K ions and that this inhibition is converted to an activation with higher levels of ATP was elegantly accounted for in the studies of Post et al (43). This work laid the basis for the subsequent investigation of occluded cation enzyme forms (discussed below) and the central importance of these forms in the pump mechanism. Briefly, following dephosphorylation by K ions, a form of the enzyme, often denoted $E_2(K)$ is produced, in which the K ion is very tightly bound. The conversion of this form to one in which K can be released rapidly to the cell interior is stimulated by ATP acting at a site with relatively low affinity (~ 100 μM) compared to the site at which ATP binds prior to phosphorylation (on E_1) with a high affinity (~ 0.1 μM). Thus the equilibrium between E_1 and E_2, the dephosphoenzyme forms, can be regulated not only by Na and K ions, but also by ATP, which shows a difference in apparent affinity of some three orders of magnitude. Recent studies have pointed to the involvement of pH in the $E_1 \rightleftharpoons E_2$ equilibrium, where H^+ binding to the E_2 form takes place, and release as $E_2 \rightarrow E_1$ occurs (51, 52). The consequences for transport of this pH effect on the dephosphoenzyme equilibrium have not yet been systematically investigated, although a recent report describes the complete inhibition of active transport when the intracellular pH is lowered to pH 6.8 (45).

A recent extension of the Albers-Post model based on studies using fluorescent nucleotides attempts to explicitly identify the steps at which ion loading and unloading take place (37). It is proposed that Na ions leave at the outside surface from an E_2P form, after the conformational transition $E_1 \sim P \rightarrow E_2P$ has occurred. Earlier models have Na_o leaving from $E_1 \sim P$, and De Weer has recently argued in favor of this view (10). There is no unequivocal evidence that enabled $E_1 \sim P$ or $E_2 P$ to be selected as the form with sites available for Na_o. Studies on the Na activation of ATP:ADP exchange (see below) in red cell membranes supply some evidence that E_2P does have sites at the external surface for Na ions. Effects of Na on ATP:ADP exchange that are known to occur at the external surface at 37°C are not evident at 0°C, when $E_2 P$ levels are insignificant (32, 54).

It seems likely that the Na,K-ATPase is a ping-pong mechanism with respect to the substrates Na and K, i.e. Na_i binds to the internal sites, activates phosphorylation, and is released before K_o binds to the external sites and dephosphorylates the enzyme. K is then released at the inside before Na_i binds and before a new cycle is started. The partial enzymatic reactions, Na-dependent phosphorylation, K-promoted dephosphorylation, Na-dependent ATP:ADP exchange, and K-dependent exchange of ^{18}O atoms between P_i and water (8) and the existence of the pump in two major conformations E_1 and E_2 promoted by either Na ions or K ions, all support this mechanism. The "partial" transport reactions Na:Na exchange in the absence of K_o and K:K exchange in the absence of Na_i provide confirmation of this mechanism from transport studies. Some observations, however, have been regarded as incompatible with a consecutive or ping-pong formalism and have been considered to support a simultaneous model. These include an apparent lack of effect of P_i on K and ATP affinities (16) and the effects of the transported cation on one side of the membrane on the affinity for the *trans* cation (46). Recently, it has been shown that P_i does have an effect on K and ATP affinities, and it has been pointed out by Sachs (47) that the observations on the trans effects of cations cannot be regarded as unequivocal proof for a simultaneous model. Recent results showing that the apparent affinity for K depends upon ATP (13) also support the ping-pong reaction mechanism. However, it has been pointed out (48) that the form of the enzyme bearing ATP and P_i that is thought to be the intermediate for K:K exchange may not be present in the normal reaction cycle (because there is evidence that P_i is released before ATP binds), and then it is possible that K:K exchange may be a side reaction, and thus its properties cannot be used as support for the ping-pong reaction mechanism.

Although the majority of investigators utilize the Albers-Post model, the involvement of phosphoenzyme intermediates during Na:K exchange has been questioned, and an alternative model proposed (49, 50). Recently, some experimental support was provided for this view, and it was proposed that the usual phosphoenzyme intermediates are not kinetically competent in the Na,K-ATPase cycle (41).

Uncoupled Na Efflux

When red cells are suspended in media containing no Na or K ions (e.g. in choline or Mg), a ouabain-sensitive efflux of Na is observed that has a high affinity for Na_i and for ATP. The stoichiometry of this transport is close to three Na ions transported per molecule of ATP hydrolyzed. Studies using resealed ghosts have established that the associated Na-ATPase is inhibited by low Na_o and then stimulated as Na_o is elevated (19). In preparations of partially purified enzyme, the Na-activation curve shows three phases (3, 38). In the range 0–3 mM Na the ATPase is activated, at 3–10 mM Na a plateau or slight inhibition is seen, and as Na is increased, the ATPase activity rises. Combining the results of these studies we can assign these three phases to, in order of increasing [Na], activation by Na_i related to the Na_i requirement for phosphorylation, an inhibition due to Na_o, and a stimulation due to Na_o. The inhibition by Na_o has been claimed to be due to an effect of Na_o in slowing the dephosphorylation rate of the phosphoenzyme (presumably $E_2 P$), the activation due to a stimulation of the dephosphorylation rate (3). A question remaining from these studies was whether the activation of Na-ATPase by Na_o was associated with an influx of Na ions, i.e. whether the flux was still "uncoupled" at high Na_o. Studies in red cell vesicles suggest that an ATP-dependent Na:Na exchange occurs (5). Na_o may be exerting its effects via a weak K-like effect at the outside surface. The inhibition of Na-ATPase by K_o is probably due to the formation of occluded K,

$E_2(K)$, which at low [ATP] builds up because K release is rate-limiting. The observation that when [ATP] is increased from 5 μM to 1 mM the rate of Na-ATPase is increased by 2.5-fold was taken to be support for an apparent high affinity for ATP (38). If the apparent affinity for ATP is less than 1 μM, the question remains: Why does the rate increase with [ATP]? Perhaps there is an involvement of Mg or, even in the absence of K ions, ATP also plays a role in the ATPase cycle at a site of low affinity.

The possibility that the sodium pump may act as a neutral salt pump has recently been raised (12). In an extension of studies of the electrogenicity of $Na_i:K_o$ exchange in red cells (23), it was found that a ouabain-sensitive efflux of anions accompanied "uncoupled" Na efflux. If the anion movements are not indirectly linked via an electrical potential generated by the pump, then the possibility exists of an anion movement through the pump complex.

Na:Na Exchange

When red cells are suspended in K-free media, a 1:1 exchange of Na_i for Na_o occurs, which requires the presence of ATP (7) and ADP and proceeds without net ATP hydrolysis. These characteristics suggested that the biochemical reaction accompanying this transport mode was the ATP:ADP exchange (9, 17). In this reaction, enzyme is phosphorylated by ATP and the phosphoenzyme then phosphorylates ADP. The Na activation of ATP:ADP exchange in enzyme preparations shows a similar triphasic activation as that of Na-ATPase (3, 29, 30). Studies in resealed ghosts where the sidedness of this activation could be examined have established many similarities between the cation effects on the ATP:ADP exchange and on Na:Na exchange (26, 29). The studies were performed using caged ATP, a photolabile precursor of ATP, to initiate the intracellular reaction (28). The Na activation curve can be assigned to activation sites for Na_i reflecting the requirement for Na_i in phosphorylation, an inhibitory phase ($Na_o < 5$ mM), and an activating phase of low affinity for Na_o that did not saturate in the physiological range.

The rate of ATP:ADP exchange depends upon the level of $E_1 \sim P$ (ADP-sensitive phosphoenzyme), and high [Na] favors increased $E_1 \sim P:E_2 P$ ratios. Na_o binds to what are unloading sites for Na in the forward cycle and reverses the usual $E_1 \sim P \rightarrow E_2P$ conformational transition. This explanation is supported by observations that either NEM treatment of kidney enzyme (3) or lowering the temperature to 0°C with red cell membranes (32) converts the triphasic Na activation curve of ATP:ADP exchange to a simple hyperbola. In both of these situations the $E_1 \sim P \rightarrow E_2 P$ transition is blocked, and $E_1 \sim P$ is maximal at low [Na].

The studies in resealed ghosts provided information that had not been available from studies in unsided preparations. When Na_o is zero and Na:Na exchange cannot take place, a measureable ATP:ADP exchange activity occurs

(26, 29). The phosphorylation-dephosphorylation cycle occuring through $E_1 \sim$ P turns over in the absence of the associated transport. The biochemical and transport reactions, although linked, are not tightly coupled. It would be of interest to know how the V_{max} of each of these processes compare.

K:K Exchange

K:K exchange transport requires the presence of ATP, nonhydrolyzable ATP analogs (see 18), or ADP (31) in addition to P_i. The requirement for ATP (or ADP) reflects the stimulation of the release of K from the $E_2(K)$ occluded form. The requirement for P_i has been assumed to reflect phosphorylation of the enzyme to yield E_2 P forms associated with K entry steps in the overall cycle. Studies in red cell ghosts measuring $^{18}[O]P_i:H_2O$ exchange using ^{31}P NMR have established that phosphorylation by P_i does indeed take place during K:K (or Rb:Rb) exchange (33). The rate of the exchange of ^{18}O atoms between P_i and water was some 5–10-fold faster than the simultaneously measured K:K exchange, and inhibitors that slow the transport also slow the oxygen exchange (e.g. Na_i + oligomycin). Interestingly, when the rate of K:K exchange was very low (in the absence of ADP), the rate of oxygen exchange was close to the rate in the presence of ADP (33). This implies that rapid phosphorylation-dephosphorylation cycles take place through E_2 P in the absence of the associated transport. The cation exchange and phosphorylation-dephosphorylation reactions are linked but not tightly coupled, a situation previously seen at the E_1 $\sim$ P level for Na:Na exchange.

In resealed red cell ghosts it has also been shown that AsO_4^{3-} will substitute for P_i and support K:K exchange, presumably via an enzyme arsenylation (L. J. Kenney & J. H. Kaplan, unpublished observations); similar substitution of AsO_4^{3-} for P_i has been previously observed in the Ca pump from sarcoplasmic reticulum (40). From studies in resealed ghosts and reconstituted proteoliposomes, it seems likely that ATP and P_i bind to the same intermediate in this transport pathway, i.e. $E_2(K)$. A detailed discussion of the rates of the various transitions and the effects of ligands involved in this pathway has been provided by Karlish & Stein (35). ATP or P_i are able to activate or inhibit K:K exchange via binding to independent sites on $E_2(K)$ and then driving the equilibria towards either E_1 ATP or E_2 P. An alternative mechanism is possible in that inhibition by P_i occurs through competition at the ATP site and vice versa.

Passive Fluxes

These fluxes are exceptional in taking place through the pump apparatus in the absence of the usual pump ligands, i.e. ATP, ADP, P_i, and so on. They were first described in proteoliposomes prepared from purified renal enzyme (36). The fluxes are small but reduce the complexity of the possible cation-ligand interactions so that the system is essentially a facilitated diffusion system (or carrier) for pump cations. The relevance of these small fluxes to sodium pumps in their normal membrane environment has been established by the recent measurement of similar fluxes in resealed red cell ghosts. [86]Rb uptake into ghosts containing only Mg and monovalent cations show similar activation by pump ligands (ADP and P_i) that were observed in proteoliposomes. Interestingly, in the absence of ligands Rb_o shows an apparent affinity of < 50 μM. This implies that contrary to expectation, E_2 in a nonphosphorylated form shows high affinity for Rb at the extracellular surface (L. J. Kenney, J. H. Kaplan, unpublished observations).

OCCLUDED CATIONS AND CONFORMATIONAL TRANSITIONS

Due to space limitations, several areas central to an understanding of the pump mechanism can only be given a cursory consideration. Conformational changes associated with K transport have recently been reviewed (20, 35), as have been the role of occluded ion forms of the Na,K-ATPase (21, 35). There is good evidence that entry of K into an occluded form, $E_2(K)$, can occur from either the cytoplasmic or extracellular compartments and that the coupling of these pathways can provide a satisfactory model for the mechanism of K transport (in Na:K exchange or K:K exchange). Evidence is also presented that Na ions can also be occluded in the $E_1 \sim P$ form of the enzyme (21). Direct detection of occluded Na ions has been difficult, and so far this has only been achieved with either NEM-treated enzyme or chymotrypsin-treated enzyme, both treatments claimed to block the $E_1 \sim P \rightarrow E_2 P$ transition. It has been suggested that occlusion of K ions is a design feature of the sodium pump so that ion leaks through the system are reduced (35). Occlusion may also represent a way in which conformational transitions that are necessary for transport can be tightly coupled to ion-binding events. In order to efficiently couple a conformational transition with ion transport, it is important that if the transition is relatively slow the ion to be transported remains bound to its site for sufficiently long without dissociating into the media. Occlusion represents a way in which reversible binding is made tighter and the ion is prevented from dissociating from its site with a rate constant appropriate to the affinity with which it is initially bound reversibly. In the case of Na, such occlusion occurs as a consequence of phosphorylation (and release of ADP), and $(Na)E_1 \sim P$ is formed. It can then be released to the external medium after $(Na)E_1 \sim P \rightarrow NaE_2 P$.

The ability to measure occluded states, ion binding, and the rates of conformational transitions attest to the progress being made towards understanding the mechanism of the sodium pump. The synthesis here of much of this information is precluded by space limitations. The next major steps in our understanding will take place when electrical effects on the elemental processes can be characterized and when structural information can be combined with our knowledge of the ion movements.

NOTE ADDED IN PROOF   Since this article was completed, several reports have appeared that promise to be of great interest to workers in this field. These include a report on the structural organization of the protein, with data on the unit cell for protomeric and diprotomeric forms and the disposition of the protein between extracellular and cytoplasmic domains (Zampighi, A., Kyte, Freytag, W. 1984. *J. Cell Biol.* 98:1851–64); a detailed characterization of the properties of reconstituted, fully active enzyme in proteoliposomes (Cornelius, F., Skou, J. C. 1984. *Biochim, Biophys. Acta* 772:357–73); and measurements of the rate of release of occluded cations in a sided preparation (Forbush III, B. 1984. *Biophys. J.* A5:76a). The most recent international meeting dedicated to the sodium pump was held in Cambridge, England, in August 1984. The proceedings of this meeting are to be published during the coming year (edited by J. C. Ellory and I. M. Glynn) and will contain the most current account of many aspects of the sodium pump.

ACKNOWLEDGMENTS

I am grateful to Linda J. Kenney for invaluable assistance during the writing of this article. Work described in this review, performed in the author's laboratory, was supported by NIH Grant HL 30315. JHK is a recipient of RCDA K04-HL-01092.

Literature Cited

1. Albers, R. W., Koval, G. J., Siegel, G. J. 1968. Studies on the interaction of ouabain and other cardioactive steroids with Na,K-activated ATPase. *Mol. Pharmacol.* 4:324–36
2. Askari, A., ed. 1974. Properties and functions of (Na$^+$K)-activated adenosine triphosphatase. *Ann. NY Acad. Sci.* 242:1–741
3. Beaugé, L. A., Glynn, I. M. 1979. Sodium ions, acting at high-affinity extracellular sites, inhibit sodium-ATPase activity of the sodium pump by slowing dephosphorylation. *J. Physiol.* 289:17–31
4. Blostein, R. 1979. Side-specific action of Na on (Na,K)-ATPase. *J. Biol. Chem.* 254:6673–77
5. Blostein, R. 1983. Sodium pump catalyzed Na:Na exchange associated with ATP hydrolysis. *J. Biol. Chem.* 248:7948–53
6. Cantley, L. C. 1981. Structure and mechanism of the Na,K-ATPase. *Curr. Top. Bioenerg.* 11:201–307
7. Cavieres, J. D., Glynn, I. M. 1979. Sodium-sodium exchange through the sodium pump, the roles of ATP and ADP. *J. Physiol.* 297:637–45
8. Dahms, A. S., Miara, J. E. 1983. ^{31}P[^{18}O]NMR kinetic analysis of ^{18}O oxygen exchange reaction between P$_i$ and H$_2$O catalyzed by Na,K-ATPase. *Curr. Top. Membr. Trans.* 19:371–75
9. De Weer, P. 1970. Effects of intracellular adenosine-5'-diphosphate and orthophosphate on the sensitivity of sodium efflux from squid axon to external sodium and potassium. *J. Gen. Physiol.* 56:583–620
10. De Weer, P. 1983. Na,K-ATPase: reaction mechanism and ion translocating steps. *Curr. Top. Membr. Trans.* 19:599–623
11. De Weer, P., Rokowski, R. F. 1984. Current generated by backward running

electrogenic sodium pump in squid giant axons. *Nature* 309:450–52

12. Dissing, S., Hoffman, J. F. 1983. Anion-coupled Na efflux mediated by the Na/K pump in human red blood cells. *Curr. Top. Membr. Trans.* 19:693–95

13. Eisner, D. A., Richards, D. E. 1981. The interaction of potassium ions and ATP on the sodium pump of resealed red cell ghosts. *J. Physiol.* 319:403–18

14. Forbush, B. III. 1982. Characterization of right-side-out membrane vesicles rich in (Na$^+$K)-ATPase and isolated from dog kidney outer medulla. *J. Biol. Chem.* 257:12678–84

15. Forbush, B. III. 1983. Cardiotonic steroid binding to Na,K-ATPase. *Curr. Top. Membr. Trans.* 19:167–201

16. Garay, R. P., Garrahan, P. J. 1975. The interaction of adenosine triphosphate and inorganic phosphate with the sodium pump in red cell. *J. Physiol.* 249:51–67

17. Glynn, I. M., Hoffman, J. F. 1971. Nucleotide requirements for sodium:sodium exchange catalyzed by the sodium pump in human red cells. *J. Physiol.* 218:239–56

18. Glynn, I. M., Karlish, S. J. D. 1975. The sodium pump. *Ann. Rev. Physiol.* 37:13–55

19. Glynn, I. M., Karlish, S. J. D. 1976. ATP hydrolysis associated with an uncoupled Na efflux through the sodium pump: evidence for allosteric effects of intracellular ATP and extracellular Na. *J. Physiol.* 256:465–96

20. Glynn, I. M., Karlish, S. J. D. 1982. Conformational changes associated with K transport by Na/K-ATPase. In *Membranes and Transport,* ed. A. N. Martonosi, 1:529–36. New York/London: Plenum. 688 pp.

21. Glynn, I. M., Richards, D. E. 1983. Existence and role of occluded-ion forms of Na,K-ATPase. *Curr. Top. Membr. Trans.* 19:625–38

22. Hoffman, J. F., Forbush, B. III, eds. 1983. *Curr. Top. Membr. Trans.* 19:1–1043

23. Hoffman, J. F., Kaplan, J. H., Callahan, T. J. 1979. The Na:K pump in red cells is electrogenic. *Fed. Proc.* 38:2440–41

24. Jorgensen, P. L. 1977. Purification and characterization of (Na+)-ATPase. VI. Differential tryptic modification of catalytic functions of the purified enzyme in presence of NaCl and KCl. *Biochim. Biophys. Acta* 401:399–415

25. Jorgensen, P. L. 1980. Sodium potassium ion pump in kidney tubules. *Physiol. Rev.* 60:864–917

26. Kaplan, J. H. 1982. Sodium pump mediated ATP:ADP exchange: the sided

effects of sodium and potassium ions. *J. Gen. Physiol.* 80:915–37

27. Kaplan, J. H. 1983. Sodium ions and the sodium pump: transport and enzymatic activity. *Am. J. Physiol.* 245:G327–33

28. Kaplan, J. H., Forbush, B. III, Hoffman, J. F. 1978. Rapid photolytic release of adenosine-5'-triphosphate from a protected ATP analogue:utilization by the Na:K pump of human red blood cell ghosts. *Biochemistry* 17:1929–35

29. Kaplan, J. H., Hollis, R. J. 1980. External Na dependence of ouabain-sensitive ATP:ADP exchange initiated by photolysis of intracellular caged-ATP in human red cell ghosts. *Nature* 288:587–89

30. Kaplan, J. H., Hollis, R. J., Mone, M. D. 1981. The regulation of Na pump-mediated ATP:ADP exchange by extracellular Na ions. In *Advances in Physiological Science,* ed. S. R. Hollan, G. Gardos, B. Sarkadi, 6:293–98. Budapest: Hungarian Academy

31. Kaplan, J. H., Kenney, L. J. 1982. ADP supports ouabain-sensitive K:K exchange in human red blood cells. *Ann. NY Acad. Sci.* 402:292–95

32. Kaplan, J. H., Kenney, L. J. 1984. Temperature effects on sodium pump phosphoenzyme distribution in human red blood cells. *J. Gen. Physiol.* In press

33. Kaplan, J. H., Kenney, L. J., Webb, M. R. 1984. P$_i$ phosphorylation of red cell (Na$^+$K)-ATPase during K:K exchange. *Biophys. J.* 45:159a. (Abstr.)

34. Karlish, S. J. D., Pick, U. 1981. Sidedness of the effects of sodium and potassium ions on the conformational state of the sodium-potassium pump. *J. Physiol.* 312:505–29

35. Karlish, S. J. D., Stein, W. D. 1982. Protein conformational changes in (Na,K)-ATPase and the role of cation occlusion in active transport. *Ann. NY Acad. Sci.* 402:226–38

36. Karlish, S. J. D., Stein, W. D. 1982. Passive Rb fluxes mediated by the (Na,K)-ATPase reconstituted into phospholipid vesicles. *J. Physiol.* 328:295–316

37. Karlish, S. J. D., Yates, D. W., Glynn, I. M. 1978. Conformational transitions between Na-bound and K-bound forms of (Na+K)-ATPase studied with formycin nucleotides. *Biochim. Biophys. Acta* 525:252–64

38. Mardh, S., Post, R. L. 1977. Phosphorylation from adenosine triphosphate of sodium and potassium-activated adenosine triphosphatase. *J. Biol. Chem.* 252:633–38

39. Norby, J. G. 1983. Ligand interactions with the substrate site of Na,K-ATPase:

nucleotides, vanadate, and phosphorylation. *Curr. Top. Membr. Trans.* 19:281–314

40. Pick, U., Bassilian, S. 1983. The effects of ADP, phosphate and arsenate on Ca efflux from sarcoplasmic reticulum vesicles. *Eur. J. Biochem.* 131:393–99

41. Plesner, I. W., Plesner, L., Norby, J. G., Klodos, I. 1981. The steady state kinetic mechanism of ATP hydrolysis catalyzed by membrane bound (Na$^+$K)-ATPase from ox brain. III. A minimal model. *Biochim. Biophys. Acta* 643:483–94

42. Post, R. L., Kume, S., Tobin, T., Orcutt, B., Sen, A. K. 1969. Flexibility of an active center in sodium-plus-potassium adenosine triphosphatase. *J. Gen. Physiol.* 54:306s–26s

43. Post, R. L., Hegyvary, C., Kume, S. 1972. Activation by adenosine triphosphate in the phosphorylation kinetics of sodium and potassium ion transport adenosine triphosphatase. *J. Biol. Chem.* 247:6530–40

44. Robinson, J. D., Flashner, M. S. 1979. The (Na$^+$K)-activated ATPase. Enzymatic and transport properties. *Biochim, Biophys. Acta* 549:145–76

45. Russell, J. M., Boron, W. F., Brodwick, M. S. 1983. Intracellular pH and Na fluxes in barnacle muscle with evidence for reversal of the ionic mechanism of intracellular pH regulation. *J. Gen. Physiol.* 82:47–78

46. Sachs, J. R. 1977. Kinetic evaluation of the Na-K pump reaction mechanism. *J. Physiol.* 273:489–514

47. Sachs, J. R. 1980. The order of release of sodium and addition of potassium in the sodium-potassium pump reaction mechanism. *J. Physiol.* 302:219–40

48. Sachs, J. R. 1983. Evaluation of the reaction mechanism of the sodium pump by steady-state kinetics. *Curr. Top. Membr. Trans.* 19:537–46

49. Skou, J. C. 1975. The (Na$^+$K)-activated enzyme system and its relationship to transport of sodium and potassium. *Q. Rev. Biophys.* 7:401–34

50. Skou, J. C. 1982. The (Na$^+$K)-ATPase: coupling of the reaction with ATP to the reaction with Na and K. *Ann. NY Acad. Sci.* 402:169–84

51. Skou, J. C. 1982. The effect of pH, ATP and of modification with pyridoxal 5-phosphate on the conformational transition between Na-form and K-form of the (Na$^+$K)-ATPase. *Biochim. Biophys. Acta* 688:369–80

52. Skou, J. C., Essman, M. 1980. Effects of ATP and protons on the Na:K selectivity of the (Na$^+$K)-ATPase studied by ligand effects on intrinsic and extrinsic fluorescence. *Biochim. Biophys. Acta* 601:386–402

53. Skou, J. C., Norby, J. G., eds. 1979. Na,K-ATPase, Structure and Kinetics. London: Academic. 549 pp.

54. White, B., Blostein, R. 1982. Comparison of red cell and kidney (Na$^+$K)-ATPase at 0°. *Biochim. Biophys. Acta* 688:685–90

Ann. Rev. Physiol. 1985. 47:545-60

KINETIC PROPERTIES OF THE PLASMA MEMBRANE Na^+-H^+ EXCHANGER

Peter S. Aronson

Departments of Medicine and Physiology, Yale University School of Medicine, New Haven, Connecticut 06510

INTRODUCTION

The plasma membranes of a wide variety of animal cells contain a carrier-mediated transport system that brings about the transmembrane exchange of Na^+ for H^+. This transport system has been identified in virtually every type of cell in which its possible presence has been examined, including ova (25), sperm (23, 60), erythrocytes (12, 13, 32, 42, 55), lymphocytes (20, 21), capillary endothelial cells (7), skeletal muscle cells (1, 2, 18, 39, 56), cardiac muscle cells (16, 43), neuronal cells (34–36), astroglial cells (26), fibroblasts (14, 19, 37, 38, 41, 44, 53), renal tubular cells (9, 27, 40, 46), bladder cells (33), intestinal cells (22, 31, 40) and gall bladder cells (17, 59). Under physiologic conditions, the plasma membrane Na^+-H^+ exchanger (also known as antiporter or countertransporter) mediates the uphill extrusion of H^+ coupled to, and thus driven by, the downhill flow of Na^+ into the cell. This process can subserve a number of physiologic functions in which regulating the cellular uptake of Na^+ or efflux of H^+ is important. Indeed, recent evidence suggests that the plasma membrane Na^+-H^+ exchanger plays a critical role in the regulation of intracellular pH (2, 9, 16, 21, 34, 35, 37, 41, 43, 59), the regulation of cell volume (12, 13, 17, 20, 32, 42, 55), the transepithelial transport of Na^+ and HCO_3^- (4, 9, 22, 27, 31, 40, 59), the initiation of cell growth and proliferation in response to activating stimuli and growth factors (8, 11, 14, 19, 23, 25, 36–38, 44, 49, 50, 53, 60), and the metabolic response to hormones such as insulin (18, 39).

0066-4278/85/0315-0545$02.00

The purpose of this review is to describe the kinetic properties of the plasma membrane Na^+-H^+ exchanger and to relate these kinetic properties to the functioning of this ubiquitous transport system under physiologic conditions.

STOICHIOMETRY

The most direct approach for estimating the coupling ratio of the Na^+-H^+ exchanger is to measure the net flux of Na^+ via the exchanger in one direction and then to compare it with the net flux of H^+ via the exchanger in the opposite direction under the same conditions. In multiple studies utilizing this approach (9, 12, 21, 25, 32, 35, 41), the directly measured ratio of Na^+ (or Li^+) transported per H^+ has ranged from 0.6 to 1.2. In none of these studies was it concluded that the measured ratio differed significantly from 1.0. Nevertheless, the errors were sufficiently large that a 20–50% deviation from a coupling ratio of 1.0 could not be excluded in most cases.

A second approach for evaluating the coupling ratio of the Na^+-H^+ exchanger is to determine whether its operation is associated with a flow of charge across the plasma membrane. In numerous studies employing this approach (1, 2, 8, 12, 16, 20, 21, 36, 38, 56), stimulating or inhibiting Na^+-H^+ exchange has been found to cause no measurable change in the transmembrane electrical-potential difference. From estimates of the Na^+-H^+ exchange fluxes and the membrane resistance provided in at least one such study (1), it is clear that as little as a 10% deviation from a coupling ratio of 1.0 would have caused a detectable shift in the membrane potential. This is likely to have been the case in several of the other studies as well. Thus, the electrically silent operation of the Na^+-H^+ exchanger strongly argues that its coupling ratio is very close to 1.0.

Another approach for examining the question of electroneutrality of the Na^+-H^+ exchanger is to test whether changing the membrane potential alters its rate of ion transport. With only two exceptions, changing the membrane potential has generally been found to have no effect on Na^+-H^+ exchange (12, 27, 30, 31, 33, 38, 40, 46, 47, 59). One exception was a study in which stimulation of amiloride-sensitive Na^+ influx into renal microvillus membrane vesicles resulted from imposing an inside-negative membrane potential (58). However, renal microvillus membranes possess an appreciable H^+ conductance (10, 45, 51), and a possible artifact was that the observed stimulation of Na^+-H^+ exchange resulted not from the voltage per se but from voltage-induced acidification of the intravesicular space. Indeed, in other studies in which renal microvillus membrane vesicles were prepared and equilibrated in higher buffer concentrations (15, 27), Na^+-H^+ exchange was observed to be completely insensitive to changes in the membrane potential. The other exception was a study in which membrane depolarization was found to stimulate Na^+-H^+ exchange in skeletal muscle (1). However, Na^+-H^+ exchange in this study was electrically silent. The dependence on membrane potential therefore must have reflected a direct or indirect effect of voltage on the kinetics of Na$^+$-H$^+$ exchange rather than a coupling ratio not equal to 1.0. In fact, this observation underscores the limitation of testing the voltage-dependence of transport rate as a strategy for determining whether a transport process is electrogenic or electroneutral (3, 52).

The coupling ratio of a transport process such as Na$^+$-H$^+$ exchange can also be estimated using a thermodynamic approach. If its coupling ratio is 1.0, the Na$^+$-H$^+$ exchanger should be at equilibrium and mediate no net fluxes of Na$^+$ and H$^+$ whenever the transmembrane Na$^+$ gradient is balanced by a similarly directed H$^+$ gradient of the same magnitude (i.e. whenever $[Na^+]_o/[Na^+]_i$ is equal to $[H^+]_o/[H^+]_i$) (3). This predicted behavior was actually observed in renal microvillus membrane vesicles in which net Na$^+$ fluxes were measured after imposition of varying transmembrane Na$^+$ and H$^+$ gradients (30). A related observation was made in crayfish neurons (34). During recovery from an intracellular acid load, $[H^+]_i$ declined as $[Na^+]_i$ rose until $[Na^+]_o/[Na^+]_i$ became equal to $[H^+]_o/[H^+]_i$. At that point, recovery of pH$_i$ ceased, just as predicted, if the coupling ratio of the Na$^+$-H$^+$ exchanger were 1.0.

A coupling ratio of 1.0 is, of course, consistent with stoichiometries of 2:2, 3:3, and so on, as well as of 1:1. However, the rate of Na$^+$-H$^+$ exchange has generally been found to be a simple, saturating, Michaelis-Menten function of $[Na^+]_o$ (6, 10, 21–24, 28, 29, 31, 41, 46, 47, 50, 55–57), with a Hill coefficient of 1.0 (24, 57). This is most consistent with the presence of only a single site for binding of external Na$^+$. Similarly, the kinetics of interaction of H$^+$ with the Na$^+$-H$^+$ exchanger suggests the presence of only a single site for binding of external H$^+$ (6, 19, 21, 41, 46, 56). Taken together, these findings strongly imply that the stoichiometry of the plasma membrane Na$^+$-H$^+$ exchanger is actually 1:1 rather than 2:2, 3:3, and so on.

SUBSTRATE SPECIFICITY AND TRANSPORT MODES

Many findings suggest that the plasma membrane Na$^+$-H$^+$ exchanger can function in multiple exchange modes involving Na$^+$, H$^+$ and the alternative substrate, Li$^+$. Inward Na$^+$ gradients stimulate H$^+$ efflux (2, 16, 25–27, 40) and outward H$^+$ gradients stimulate Na$^+$ influx (19, 22, 27, 31, 33, 40), consistent with exchange of external Na$^+$ for internal H$^+$. Outward Na$^+$ gradients stimulate H$^+$ influx (10, 15, 16, 35, 39, 57, 59), indicating exchange of internal Na$^+$ for external H$^+$. Internal Na$^+$ stimulates ^{22}Na influx (5, 47), and external Na$^+$ stimulates ^{22}Na efflux (7, 29, 47), suggesting Na$^+$-Na$^+$ exchange. Inward gradients of Li$^+$, a competitive inhibitor of Na$^+$ influx (29, 47), stimulate H$^+$ efflux (25, 27, 35, 46, 53, 59), consistent with exchange of external Li$^+$ for internal H$^+$. Outward gradients of Li$^+$ stimulate H$^+$ influx (10, 41, 51), indicating exchange of internal Li$^+$ for external H$^+$. These exchanges of external Na^+ for internal H^+ (2, 16, 28, 35, 39, 46), internal Na^+ for external H^+ (35, 37, 39, 42, 43, 49), internal Na^+ for external Na^+ (5, 7), external Li^+ for internal H^+ (22, 24), and internal Li^+ for external H^+ (41) are all sensitive to inhibition by the diuretic drug amiloride, which seems to be a general, nontransported inhibitor of this transport system.

There is some evidence that NH_4^+ may also be a substrate for the Na^+-H^+ exchanger. External NH_4^+ inhibits Na^+ influx (7, 22, 27, 29, 31) in accord with competition at the external transport site (29). Inward NH_4^+ gradients stimulate net H^+ efflux (29), consistent with exchange of external NH_4^+ for internal H^+. External NH_4^+ stimulates Na^+ efflux (7, 29), suggesting exchange of internal Na^+ for external NH_4^+. However, the apparent stimulation of H^+ efflux by inward NH_4^+ gradients can be attributed to nonionic diffusion of NH_3 (48) without necessitating the existence of carrier-mediated NH_4^+-H^+ exchange. Likewise, the ability of inward NH_4^+ gradients to generate inside-alkaline pH gradients could in principle account for inhibition of Na^+ influx and stimulation of Na^+ efflux without invoking a direct interaction of NH_4^+ with the Na^+-H^+ exchanger. Nevertheless, in one study using renal microvillus membrane vesicles (29), external NH_4^+ caused inhibition of Na^+ influx and stimulation of Na^+ efflux under conditions in which NH_4^+-induced pH gradients were prevented. This suggests that NH_4^+ actually can compete at the external transport site and that Na^+-NH_4^+ exchange is a functional mode of the Na^+-H^+ exchanger.

No other cations have as yet been identified for which the Na^+-H^+ exchanger has appreciable affinity. External K^+, Rb^+, and Cs^+ inhibit Na^+ influx via the Na^+-H^+ exchanger weakly (22, 31) or not at all (27, 46). Choline (27) and tetramethylammonium (31) have no effect on Na^+ influx. Moreover, inward gradients of K^+ (21, 26, 27, 32, 35, 41, 53, 59), Rb^+ (21, 59), Cs^+ (21, 59), choline (21, 26, 32, 35, 39, 53), Ca^{2+} (35, 41) and Mg^{2+} (39) fail to promote H^+ efflux under conditions in which H^+ efflux can be stimulated by inward Na^+ gradients. A slow rate of K^+-H^+ exchange in renal microvillus membrane vesicles was observed in one study (10), but electrical coupling of K^+ and H^+ fluxes occurring through independent conductive pathways was not completely excluded. Significant K^+-H^+ exchange could not be demonstrated in other studies employing renal microvillus membrane vesicles (27, 51). In amphibian red cells (12), amiloride-insensitive, electroneutral K^+-H^+ exchange is observed after cell swelling in hypotonic media, and amiloride-sensitive Na^+-H^+ exchange is observed after cell shrinkage in hypertonic media. It has been proposed that both of these exchange processes are mediated by the same "transport moiety" (13), but direct evidence on this point is not yet available.

In most (6, 24, 29, 42, 47, 59) although not all (10, 41) studies, the $K_{1/2}$ for interaction of the Na^+-H^+ exchanger with external Na^+ is several-fold higher than that for interaction with external Li^+. The $K_{1/2}$ for external NH_4^+ has been less extensively examined, but appears to be only slightly less than the $K_{1/2}$ for

Na$^+$ (6, 29). In several preparations, the K$_{1/2}$ for interaction of external H$^+$ with the Na$^+$-H$^+$ exchanger is in the range 10^{-8}–10^{-7} M (6, 19, 21, 41, 46, 56), far lower than the reported K$_{1/2}$ values (10^{-3}–10^{-2} M) for Li$^+$, NH$_4^+$ and Na$^+$. Thus, the apparent selectivity sequence for binding of external cations is H$^+$>>Li$^+$>NH$_4^+$≥Na$^+$>>K$^+$, Rb$^+$, Cs$^+$.

Interestingly, there is a different selectivity sequence for the relative rates of transport of these cations once they are bound. For example, despite the lower apparent affinity for binding of Na$^+$ compared to Li$^+$, the V$_{max}$ for exchange of internal H$^+$ with external Na$^+$ is several-fold higher than the V$_{max}$ for exchange of internal H$^+$ with external Li$^+$ (10, 24, 59). This suggests that the rate-limiting step for entry of bound Li$^+$ (e.g. translocation or debinding at the inner surface of the membrane) is slower than the rate-limiting step for entry of bound Na$^+$. This conclusion is further supported by the observation that ^{22}Na efflux into external Li$^+$ is slower than into external Na$^+$ (7, 29, 42, 46), indicating that exchange of internal Na$^+$ for external Li$^+$ occurs more slowly than Na$^+$-Na$^+$ exchange. Moreover, external Li$^+$ inhibits ^{22}Na efflux measured under conditions in which H$^+$ is the only other exchangeable cation (29, 42), suggesting that exchange of internal Na$^+$ for external Li$^+$ occurs more slowly than exchange of internal Na$^+$ for external H$^+$. Thus, the rate of entry of bound Li$^+$ is also slower than the rate of entry of bound H$^+$. There are conflicting data on the relative rates of entry of bound Na$^+$ compared to H$^+$. External Na$^+$ stimulates ^{22}Na efflux from renal microvillus membrane vesicles more than does a saturating concentration of external H$^+$ (6), indicating that Na$^+$-Na$^+$ exchange is faster than exchange of internal Na$^+$ for external H$^+$. This implies that the rate-limiting step for entry of bound Na$^+$ is faster than that of bound H$^+$. External NH$_4^+$ stimulates ^{22}Na efflux from renal membrane vesicles as much as does external Na$^+$ (29), suggesting that entry of bound NH$_4^+$ must also be faster than bound H$^+$. In contrast, external Na$^+$ modestly inhibits ^{22}Na efflux from dog red cells (42), implying that Na$^+$-Na$^+$ exchange is slower than exchange of internal Na$^+$ for external H$^+$, and thus that entry of externally bound Na$^+$ is slower than entry of bound H$^+$. Taken together, the available data indicate that the rate constants for the rate-limiting step for entry of bound cations vary, and are in either the selectivity sequence Na$^+$ ≈ NH$_4^+$ > H$^+$ > Li$^+$ or the sequence H$^+$ > Na$^+$ > Li$^+$. In either case, transport of bound Li$^+$ appears to be kinetically less favorable than the transport of bound Na$^+$, H$^+$ or NH$_4^+$.

KINETIC MODELS

As already reviewed, the plasma membrane Na$^+$-H$^+$ exchanger has a tightly coupled 1:1 stoichimetry, can bind Li$^+$ and NH$_4^+$ in addition to Na$^+$ and H$^+$, and can function in multiple exchange modes involving these cations (e.g. can mediate Na$^+$-H$^+$, Li$^+$-H$^+$, Na$^+$-Na$^+$, and Na$^+$-NH$_4^+$ exchanges). These properties are easily explained on the basis of a transport protein that can bind a Na^+, H^+, Li^+ or NH_4^+ on one side of the membrane, and exchange it for one or another of these same cations on the opposite side of the membrane. This view of the Na^+-H^+ exchanger as a cation exchanger is illustrated by the kinetic scheme illustrated in the top of Figure 1. What are the possible kinetic routes by which the net exchange of external A_o^+ for internal H_i^+ can take place? By analogy with enzyme kinetics, we can consider A_o^+ and H_i^+ as the substrates for this "reaction," and A_i^+ and H_o^+ as the products. There are six possible ordered cyclic sequences for the steps of A_o^+ and H_i^+ binding, and A_i^+ and H_o^+ debinding. For example, A_o^+ could bind (*step 1* in top of Figure 1) to the free outwardly facing conformation of the transporter, T_o. The transporter could then undergo a conformational change (*step 2*) from the outwardly facing form A^+T_o to the inwardly facing form A^+T_i. Debinding of A_i^+ at the inside (*step 3*) could then be followed by binding of H_i^+ (*step 4*) to the free, inwardly facing form of the transporter, T_i. After a conformational change of the inwardly facing TH_i^+ to the outwardly facing TH_o^+ (*step 5*), H_o^+ could debind (*step 6*), regenerating T_o to start the cycle again. Similarly, the alternative substrate B_o^+ could exchange with H_i^+ via the cycle $1' \rightarrow 2' \rightarrow 3' \rightarrow 4 \rightarrow 5 \rightarrow 6$. Exchange of A_o^+ for A_i^+ could occur through the cycle $1 \rightarrow 2 \rightarrow 3 \rightarrow 3 \rightarrow 2 \rightarrow 1$. Exchange of B_o^+ for A_i^+ could take place via the cycle $1' \rightarrow 2' \rightarrow 3' \rightarrow 3 \rightarrow 2 \rightarrow 1$. Clearly, this kinetic scheme allows for multiple exchange modes involving H^+ and other cations (e.g. A^+, B^+) sharing the transport system. The differences in relative rates of entry of externally bound cations can also be explained by this model. For example, let A^+ correspond to Na^+ and B^+ to Li^+. The slower rate of entry of externally bound Li^+ compared to Na^+ could be explained on the basis that the conformational change of the Li^+-bound transporter (*step 2'*) and/or the debinding of Li^+ (*step 3'*) are slower than the corresponding steps for entry of bound Na^+ (*steps 2 and 3*).

However, other kinetic schemes are also compatible with the ability of the Na^+-H^+ exchanger to perform tightly coupled 1:1 exchanges among H^+ and other cations. For example, the binding of A_o^+ (*step 7* in top of Figure 1) could precede the debinding of H_o^+ (*step 8*), and/or the binding of H_i^+ (*step 9*) could precede the debinding of A_i^+ (*step 10*). Two additional ordered sequences are possible that are not even illustrated in Figure 1, namely A_o^+ on $\rightarrow H_i^+$ on $\rightarrow H_o^+$ off $\rightarrow A_i^+$ off, as well as H_i^+ on $\rightarrow A_o^+$ on $\rightarrow A_i^+$ off $\rightarrow H_o^+$ off. Furthermore, combinations of the six ordered reaction sequences in various schemes with random binding and debinding are possible subject only to the restriction that there can be no reaction cycles permitting uncoupled fluxes of H^+, A^+, or B^+.

In addition, it must be emphasized that what has come to be called the Na^+-H^+ exchanger may actually be a Na^+-OH^- cotransport system. By adding an OH^- to each of the transporter forms just discussed and by replacing

CATION-PROTON EXCHANGE

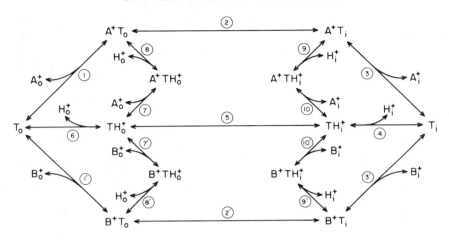

CATION-HYDROXYL COTRANSPORT

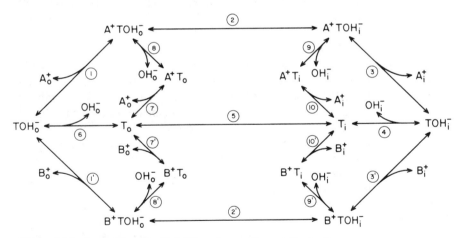

Figure 1 Kinetic models of the Na$^+$-H$^+$ exchanger. See text for details.

the steps of H$^+$ binding and debinding with steps of OH$^-$ debinding and binding, respectively, one can transform the model of cation-proton exchange shown at the *top* of Figure 1 into the model of cation-hydroxyl cotransport shown in the *bottom* of Figure 1. For example, the equivalent of A$_o^+$-H$_i^+$ exchange, namely A$_o^+$-OH$_o^-$ cotransport, can occur with the binding of OH$_o^-$

(step 6) preceding the binding of A_o^+ *(step 1)* and with the debinding of A_i^+ *(step 3)* preceding the debinding of OH_i^- *(step 4)*, as in the cycle $1\to2\to3\to4\to5\to6$. Exchange of A_o^+ for A_i^+ could occur through the cycle $1\to2\to3\to3\to2\to1$, and exchange of B_o^+ for A_i^+ through the cycle $1'\to2'\to3'\to3\to2\to1$. Other ordered sequences are possible, such as the binding of A_o^+ *(step 7)* preceding the binding of OH_o^- *(step 8)*, and/or the debinding of OH_i^- *(step 9)* preceding the debinding of A_i^+ *(step 10)*. Again, two additional ordered sequences are possible that are not illustrated in Figure 1, namely A_o^+ on $\to$ OH_i^- off $\to$ OH_o^- on $\to$ A_i^+ off, as well as A_o^+ on $\to$ A_i^+ off $\to$ OH_o^- on $\to$ OH_i^- off. Once more, schemes with random sequences of binding are possible subject to the restriction that there can be no reaction cycles permitting uncoupled fluxes of OH^-, A^+, or B^+. Thus, despite the convention of referring to the Na^+-H^+ exchanger as a cation-proton exchanger, its transport properties can be equally well explained on the basis of cation-hydroxyl cotransport.

INTERACTION WITH EXTERNAL PROTONS

The purpose of this and the following sections is to define the simplest model of the Na^+-H^+ exchanger that can account for the observed kinetic effects of varying external and internal pH. Only models of this transport system as a cation-proton exchanger will be considered, but the reader should keep in mind that alternative interpretations based on models of cation-hydroxyl cotransport are also possible.

Reducing external pH inhibits exchange of external Na^+ with internal H^+ in several preparations, the results conforming to simple titration curves with pK values in the range 7–8 (6, 19, 21, 46, 56). Graphing of these data as Dixon plots ($1/V$ vs $[H^+]_o$) gives straight lines (6, 21), implying that external protons inhibit by interacting at a single site. Moreover, in the presence of an outward Li^+ gradient, the rate of H^+ influx in fibroblasts increases as external pH is lowered, and the Lineweaver-Burk plot ($1/V$ vs $1/[H^+]_o$) is linear, again suggesting interaction of protons at a single external site (41). As mentioned earlier, the interaction of external Na^+ with the Na^+-H^+ exchanger also follows simple, Michaelis-Menten behavior and is suggestive of a single binding site.

These results can be explained by either one of the two ordered sequences of external binding-debinding reactions shown in the top of Figure 1. If there were higher order dependence on $[Na^+]_o$ and/or $[H^+]_o$, one would have to invoke the presence of additional binding sites or the presence of both pathways (i.e. *steps 1, 6, and 7, 8*) so as to permit a random reaction sequence. Although these possibilities are not excluded by the observed Michaelis-Menten behavior of Na_o^+ and H_o^+, they are not required and so will not be considered further. It might also be noted in this context that a second site for external Li^+ has been proposed based on the finding that Li$^+$ inhibits the V$_{max}$ for Na$^+$-H$^+$ exchange in renal microvillus membrane vesicles (24). Such an effect of Li$^+$ has not been observed in other studies involving renal microvillus membrane vesicles (29) and intact renal cells (47), and thus will also not be considered further.

Is there any basis on which to choose between the two ordered sequences of external binding-debinding reactions illustrated in the top of Figure 1? In the pathway involving nonsimultaneous cation and proton binding *(steps 6 and 1)*, the binding of A$_o^+$ and H$_o^+$ is to the same form of the transporter, T$_o$, and is thus completely mutually exclusive. This entails the prediction that H$_o^+$ should be a purely competitive inhibitor of A$_o^+$ transport and vice versa. Indeed, raising [H$^+$]$_o$ does cause an increase in the K$_{1/2}$ for Na$^+$ with no significant effect on the V$_{max}$ for exchange of external Na$^+$ with internal H$^+$ in such preparations as renal microvillus membrane vesicles (6), kidney cells (46), and fibroblasts (41). In renal microvillus membrane vesicles, raising [H$^+$]$_o$ also increases the K$_{1/2}$ of the Na$^+$-H$^+$ exchanger for interaction with the alternative substrates Li$^+$ and NH$_4^+$ (6). Moreover, raising [Na$^+$]$_o$ causes an increase in the K$_{1/2}$ for H$^+$ with no effect on the V$_{max}$ for exchange of external H$^+$ with internal Li$^+$ in fibroblasts (41). Taken together, these results are quite consistent with the nonsimultaneous reaction mechanism in which H$^+$ and other cations compete for binding to T$_o$.

However, there are other findings that do not fit such a reaction mechanism. The inhibitory effect of H$_o^+$ on the exchange of external Na$^+$ with internal H$^+$ in lymphocytes is of the mixed type (21). Raising [H$^+$]$_o$ reduces the V$_{max}$ for exchange of external Na$^+$ with internal H$^+$ in skeletal muscle cells and has no effect on the K$_{1/2}$ for Na$^+$ (56). Furthermore, in this preparation, raising [Na$^+$]$_o$ has no effect on the K$_{1/2}$ for external H$^+$ (56). Although not consistent with the nonsimultaneous pathway involving mutually exclusive binding of H$_o^+$ and A$_o^+$, these results are consistent with the alternative ordered sequence *(steps 7 and 8 in the top* of Figure 1) involving simultaneous binding of H$_o^+$ and A$_o^+$. This reaction sequence predicts that H$_o^+$ and A$_o^+$ should be mixed type inhibitors of one another, although the effect of each on the other can be almost exclusively on the K$_{1/2}$ or on the V$_{max}$, depending on the relationships among the various rate constants in the reaction cycle [see discussion of product inhibition of bi-bi systems in (54)]. For example, although the possibility of simultaneous binding of A$_o^+$ and H$_o^+$ to form A$^+$TH$_o^+$ would seem to exclude the possibility of purely competitive inhibition, this is not necessarily the case. Suppose the complex A$^+$TH$_o^+$ were highly unstable and had exceptionally high rate constants for dissociation in both directions. Binding of H$_o^+$ to A$^+$T$_o$ *(step 8)* would then serve to knock off A$_o^+$ *(step 7)* and lead to the accumulation of TH$_o^+$. Similarly, binding of A$_o^+$ to TH$_o^+$ *(step 7)* would serve to knock off H$_o^+$ *(step 8)* and lead to the accumulation of A$^+$T$_o$. Raising the concentration of A$_o^+$ could overcome inhibition by H$_o^+$ and vice versa [see discussion of Theorell-

Chance mechanisms in (54)]. Thus, in this example the observed inhibition would be purely competitive.

The simultaneous and nonsimultaneous routes for external cation and proton binding also differ with respect to the predicted behavior of inhibitors. With the exception of one study (24) of renal microvillus membrane vesicles that conflicts with another study employing a similar preparation (28), amiloride has generally been found to be a purely competitive inhibitor with respect to external Na^+ (28, 41, 47, 55, 56). This implies that the binding of amiloride and external Na^+ are mutually exclusive. In the nonsimultaneous reaction mechanism, this would be explained on the basis that amiloride competes for binding to T_o (Figure 1). But this necessarily predicts that the binding of amiloride should also be mutually exclusive with H_o^+. In renal microvillus membrane vesicles, H_o^+ does compete with amiloride in a manner consistent with this prediction (6). However, in fibroblasts, amiloride is a mixed inhibitor with respect to H_o^+ as it inhibits the V_{max} for exchange of external H^+ with internal Li^+ (41). Moreover, in skeletal muscle cells the K_i for amiloride is unaffected by a ten-fold change in $[H^+]_o$ (56). These findings are clearly not in accord with the prediction of the nonsimultaneous reaction mechanism. The simultaneous reaction sequence (*steps 7 and 8 in the top* of Figure 1), by allowing the simultaneous binding of H_o^+ and any inhibitor that competes with A_o^+, can give rise to mixed or noncompetitive effects. However, it should be noted that the simultaneous reaction mechanism can also explain a purely competitive interaction between H_o^+ and such an inhibitor. For example, if the inhibitor-T-H_o^+ complex were highly unstable, then H_o^+ and the inhibitor would serve to knock one another off, just as described earlier for H_o^+ and A_o^+.

Certainly it is possible that Na^+-H^+ exchangers in some tissues have a simultaneous mechanism for external cation and proton binding, whereas other Na^+-H^+ exchangers possess a nonsimultaneous mechanism. However, if all Na^+-H^+ exchangers have a common ordered mechanism, then it must be the simultaneous reaction sequence, because this is the only mechanism that can accommodate all of the observed effects of external protons on the kinetics of Na^+-H^+ exchangers.

INTERACTION WITH INTERNAL PROTONS

In a variety of cell types, raising the concentration of internal H^+ stimulates the rate of Na^+-H^+ exchange (1, 2, 9, 16, 19, 21, 35, 37, 46), an effect due to an increase in V_{max} with little or no change in the $K_{1/2}$ for external Na^+ (22). However, whereas the kinetic effects of external protons can be explained by a simple, ordered reaction mechanism involving a single proton-binding site, the kinetic effects of internal protons cannot be explained by such a mechanism. For example, in renal microvillus membrane vesicles the rate of Na^+ influx by

Na$^+$-H$^+$ exchange has a greater than first order dependence on the internal H$^+$ concentration (5). Similarly, in intact kidney cells (9) and in lymphocytes (21), efflux of H$^+$ in exchange for Na$^+$ has a steeper dependence on internal pH than expected for a simple Michaelis-Menten process. These findings are inconsistent with any ordered reaction mechanism involving only a single binding site for internal protons. In view of the arguments already presented that the stoichiometry of the Na$^+$-H$^+$ exchanger is 1:1, this has led to the proposal that internal H$^+$, independent of its role as a transportable substrate, can act as an allosteric activator of the Na$^+$-H$^+$ exchanger (5). According to this concept, there exist one or more inwardly facing titratable groups, protonation of which causes activation of the transport system. Consistent with this proposal are the additional findings in renal microvillus membrane vesicles that raising [H$^+$]$_i$ stimulates a transport mode not involving the transport of protons, namely Na$^+$-Na$^+$ exchange, and that raising [H$^+$]$_i$ can even stimulate the net efflux of Na$^+$ in exchange for external protons (5).

The presence of a separate and distinct activator site is not, however, the only possible explanation for these apparently anomalous kinetic effects of internal protons. This behavior can alternatively be explained on the basis of a random reaction mechanism for binding of H$_i^+$, as illustrated in the *top* of Figure 1. Because this reaction mechanism includes two different transporter conformations that can bind H$_i^+$, specifically T$_i$ and A$^+$T$_i$, it is predicted that [H$^+$]$_i^2$ terms can appear in the rate equation (54). Thus, the fact that the exchange of external Na$^+$ with internal H$^+$ has a greater than first order dependence on [H$^+$]$_i$ does not necessarily require the existence of a second binding site for H$_i^+$, such as an activator site.

The finding that raising [H$^+$]$_i$ stimulates exchange of internal Na$^+$ with external H$^+$ or with external Na$^+$ can also be explained without invoking the existence of an activator site for H$_i^+$. For example, suppose that the rate constants in both directions at *step 3* in Figure 1 are so small that this limb of the reaction pathway does not functionally exist. The availability of TH$_i^+$ to bind A$_i^+$ at *step 10* would be affected by the equilibrium distribution between TH$_i$ and T$_i$ at *step 4*. Depending on the model parameters, it is possible that as [H$^+$]$_i$ is raised, the stimulatory effect of H$_i^+$ to promote conversion of T$_i$ to TH$_i^+$ *(step 4)* can outweigh the inhibitory effect of H$_i^+$ to retard conversion of A$^+$TH$_i^+$ to A$^+$T$_i$ *(step 9)*. Thus, in at least some range of internal pH, it is possible that raising [H$^+$]$_i$ can stimulate the efflux of A$_i^+$ in exchange for H$_o^+$ or A$_o^+$.

PHYSIOLOGICAL IMPLICATIONS

From a thermodynamic point of view, Na$^+$-H$^+$ exchange is driven by the inwardly directed Na$^+$ gradient (i.e. [Na$^+$]$_o$/[Na$^+$]$_i$) opposed by the inwardly directed H$^+$ gradient (i.e. [H$^+$]$_o$/[H$^+$]$_i$). Knowledge of these gradients allows one to predict the net direction of Na^+-H^+ exchange. That is, when $[Na^+]_o/[Na^+]_i$ exceeds $[H^+]_o/[H^+]_i$, there is net influx of Na^+ in exchange for internal H^+; when $[H^+]_o/[H^+]_i$ exceeds $[Na^+]_o/[Na^+]_i$, there is net efflux of Na^+ in exchange for external H^+. However, thermodynamic considerations are not necessarily of help in predicting how changes in $[Na^+]_o$, $[Na^+]_i$, $[H^+]_o$, and $[H^+]_i$ may affect the rate of Na^+-H^+ exchange when the transport system is poised far from equilibrium. This is best exemplified by the observation that raising $[H^+]_i$ (i.e. reducing $[H^+]_o/[H^+]_i$) can actually stimulate the rate of net Na^+ efflux in exchange for external H^+ (5). In this example, the transport rate becomes faster when the favorable thermodynamic driving force becomes smaller.

Under physiologic conditions, the plasma membrane Na^+-H^+ exchanger is poised far from equilibrium. Due to the active extrusion of Na^+ via the (Na^+K^+)-ATPase, most animal cells maintain an inwardly directed Na^+ gradient of at least 5–10-fold across the plasma membrane. Intracellular H^+ concentration is generally equal to or slightly higher than the extracellular H^+ concentration (48). Thus, there is a large thermodynamic driving force favoring the net entry of Na^+ in exchange for internal H^+. Based on the observed kinetic properties of the Na^+-H^+ exchanger, what can be predicted concerning the relative effects of $[Na^+]_o$, $[Na^+]_i$, $[H^+]_o$, and $[H^+]_i$ in governing its transport rate under physiologic conditions?

The $K_{1/2}$ for external Na^+ at physiologic external pH has been estimated to be 3–50 mM in various preparations (6, 9, 10, 17, 21–24, 28, 31, 41, 46, 50, 55, 56, 59). Because physiologic extracellular Na^+ concentrations greatly exceed these values, it is clear that most Na^+-H^+ exchangers normally operate under conditions of near saturation with respect to external Na^+. Accordingly, changes in $[Na^+]_o$ will have relatively little effect on the rate of Na^+-H^+ exchange.

Because Na^+-H^+ exchangers are relatively saturated with respect to external Na^+ at physiologic external pH, changes in $[H^+]_o$ will have relatively little effect on the rate of Na^+-H^+ exchange in those cases (6, 41, 46) in which external H^+ is a purely competitive inhibitor of Na^+ influx. However, in those cases in which H_o^+ is a mostly or entirely noncompetitive inhibitor (21, 56), changes in $[H^+]_o$ will cause significant changes in the rate of Na^+-H^+ exchange inasmuch as the apparent pK for external protons is 7–8 (6, 19, 21, 46, 56) and therefore is in the physiologic range of extracellular pH.

The dependence of Na^+-H^+ exchange on changes in $[Na^+]_i$ under physiologic conditions has not been extensively examined. However, in one study of lymphocytes (21), reducing $[Na^+]_i$ below physiologic levels was found to significantly stimulate the rate of Na^+-H^+ exchange at any of several values of internal pH. This suggests that under physiologic conditions there is a significant backflux of internal Na^+ in exchange for external H^+ or external Na^+.

Reducing [Na$^+$]$_i$ presumably inhibits Na$_i^+$-H$_o^+$ exchange and promotes the conversion of Na$_o^+$-Na$_i^+$ exchange into Na$_o^+$-H$_i^+$ exchange. Both of these effects would tend to stimulate the net rate of exchange of external Na$^+$ with internal H$^+$. The dependence of the rate of Na$^+$-H$^+$ exchange on [Na$^+$]$_i$ has led to the suggestion that the Na$^+$-H$^+$ exchanger may play a role in the regulation of [Na$^+$]$_i$ (21).

The greater than linear dependence of Na$^+$-H$^+$ exchange on [H$^+$]$_i$ has already been discussed. Whether it reflects the existence of a random mechanism for binding of H$^+$ to its internal transport site, or reflects the presence of an activator site that is separate and distinct from the internal H$^+$ transport site, this finding indicates that [H$^+$]$_i$ is probably the most important factor controlling the rate of Na$^+$-H$^+$ exchange under physiologic conditions. Clearly, this is a kinetic property that would enhance the ability of plasma membrane Na$^+$-H$^+$ exchangers to extrude intracellular acid loads and thereby contribute to the regulation of intracellular pH. In addition, it may be noted that if [H$^+$]$_i$ is the most important factor governing the transport rate of the Na$^+$-H$^+$ exchanger, then altering the apparent affinity for internal H$^+$ is a potential mechanism for regulating the function of this transport system. Indeed, recent evidence suggests that stimulation of the plasma membrane Na$^+$-H$^+$ exchanger by growth factors results from a shift in its sensitivity to intracellular pH (37).

SUMMARY

The plasma membrane Na$^+$-H$^+$ exchanger is a ubiquitous transport system that participates in diverse cell functions involving the cellular uptake of Na$^+$ or extrusion of H$^+$. It has a tightly coupled 1:1 stoichiometry, has affinity for Li$^+$ and NH$_4^+$ in addition to Na$^+$ and H$^+$, and can function in multiple amiloride-sensitive exchange modes involving these cations. These general transport properties may be explained by kinetic models involving either cation-hydroxyl cotransport or actual cation-proton exchange. The most important kinetic property of the Na$^+$-H$^+$ exchanger is its greater than first-order dependence on [H$^+$]$_i$. This property enables the Na$^+$-H$^+$ exchanger to play an important role in the regulation of intracellular pH.

Acknowledgment

The excellent secretarial assistance of Tina DeGennaro is greatly appreciated. The author's work in this area has been supported by U. S. P. H. S. grants AM-17433 and AM-33793, and an Established Investigatorship from the American Heart Association.

Literature Cited

1. Abercrombie, R. F., Roos, A. 1983. The intracellular pH of frog skeletal muscle: its regulation in hypertonic solutions. *J. Physiol.* 345:189–204

2. Aickin, C. C., Thomas, R. C. 1977. An investigation of the ionic mechanism of intracellular pH regulation in mouse soleus muscle fibres. *J. Physiol.* 273: 295–316

3. Aronson, P. S. 1981. Identifying secondary active solute transport in epithelia. *Am. J. Physiol.* 240:F1–11

4. Aronson, P. S. 1983. Mechanisms of active H$^+$ secretion in the proximal tubule. *Am. J. Physiol.* 245:F647–59

5. Aronson, P. S., Nee, J., Suhm, M. A. 1982. Modifier role of internal H$^+$ in activating the Na$^+$-H$^+$ exchanger in renal microvillus membrane vesicles. *Nature* 299:161–63

6. Aronson, P. S., Suhm, M. A., Nee, J. 1983. Interaction of external H$^+$ with the Na$^+$-H$^+$ exchanger in renal microvillus membrane vesicles. *J. Biol. Chem.* 258: 6767–71

7. Betz, A. L. 1983. Sodium transport in capillaries isolated from rat brain. *J. Neurochem.* 41:1150–57

8. Boonstra, J., Moolenaar, W. H., Harrison, P. H., Moed, P., Van Der Saag, P. T., De Laat, S. W. 1983. Ionic responses and growth stimulation induced by nerve growth factor and epidermal growth factor in rat pheochromocytoma (PC 12) cells. *J. Cell Biol.* 97:92–98

9. Boron, W. F., Boulpaep, E. L. 1983. Intracellular pH regulation in the renal proximal tubule of the salamander. Na-H exchange. *J. Gen. Physiol.* 81:29–52

10. Burnham, C., Munzesheimer, C., Rabon, E., Sachs, G. 1982. Ion pathways in renal brush border membranes. *Biochim. Biophys. Acta* 685:260–72

11. Burns, C. P., Rozengurt, E. 1983. Serum, platelet-derived growth factor, vasopressin and phorbol esters increase intracellular pH in Swiss 3T3 cells. *Biochem. Biophys. Res. Commun.* 116: 931–38

12. Cala, P. M. 1980. Volume regulation by Amphiuma red blood cells. The membrane potential and its implications regarding the nature of the ion-flux pathways. *J. Gen. Physiol.* 76:683–708

13. Cala, P. M. 1983. Cell volume regulation by Amphiuma red blood cells. The role of Ca^{2+} as a modulator of alkali metal/H$^+$ exchange. *J. Gen. Physiol.* 82:761–84

14. Cassel, D., Rothenberg, P., Zhuang, Y.-X., Deuel, T. F., Glaser, L. 1983.

Platelet-derived growth factor stimulates Na$^+$-H$^+$ exchange and induces cytoplasmic alkalinization in NR6 cells. *Proc. Natl. Acad. Sci. USA* 80:6224–28

15. Cohn, D. E., Hruska, K. A., Klahr, S., Hammerman, M. R. 1982. Increased Na$^+$-H$^+$ exchange in brush border vesicles from dogs with renal failure. *Am. J. Physiol.* 242:F293–99

16. Deitmer, J. W., Ellis, D. 1980. Interactions between the regulation of the intracellular pH and sodium activity of sheep cardiac Purkinje fibres. *J. Physiol.* 304:471–88

17. Ericson, A.-C., Spring, K. R. 1982. Volume regulation by Necturus gallbladder: apical Na$^+$-H$^+$ and Cl$^-$-HCO$_3^-$ exchange. *Am. J. Physiol.* 243:C146–50

18. Fidelman, M. L., Seeholzer, S. H., Walsh, K. B., Moore, R. D. 1982. Intracellular pH mediates action of insulin on glycolysis in frog skeletal muscle. *Am. J. Physiol.* 242:C87–93

19. Frelin, C., Vigne, P., Lazdunski, M. 1983. The amiloride-sensitive Na$^+$/H$^+$ antiport in 3T3 fibroblasts. *J. Biol. Chem.* 258:6272–76

20. Grinstein, S., Clarke, C. A., Rothstein, A. 1983. Activation of Na$^+$/H$^+$ exchange in lymphocytes by osmotically induced volume changes and by cytoplasmic acidification. *J. Gen. Physiol.* 82: 619–38

21. Grinstein, S., Cohen, S., Rothstein, A. 1984. Cytoplasmic pH regulation in thymic lymphocytes by an amiloride-sensitive Na$^+$/H$^+$ antiport. *J. Gen. Physiol.* 83:341–69

22. Gunther, R. D., Wright, E. M. 1983. Na$^+$, Li$^+$ and Cl$^-$ transport by brush border membranes from rabbit jejunum. *J. Membrane Biol.* 74:85–94

23. Hansbrough, J. R., Garbers, D. L. 1981. Sodium-dependent activation of sea urchin spermatozoa by speract and monensin. *J. Biol. Chem.* 256:2235–41

24. Ives, H. E., Yee, V. J., Warnock, D. G. 1983. Mixed type inhibition of the renal Na$^+$/H$^+$ antiporter by Li$^+$ and amiloride. *J. Biol. Chem.* 258:9710–16

25. Johnson, J. D., Epel, D., Paul, M. 1976. Intracellular pH and activation of sea urchin eggs after fertilisation. *Nature* 262:661–64

26. Kimelberg, H. K., Biddlecome, S., Bourke, R. S. 1979. SITS-inhibitable Cl$^-$ transport and Na$^+$-dependent H$^+$ production in primary astroglial cultures. *Brain Res.* 173:111–24

27. Kinsella, J. L., Aronson, P. S. 1980.

Properties of the Na$^+$-H$^+$ exchanger in renal microvillus membrane vesicles. *Am. J. Physiol.* 238:F461–69

28. Kinsella, J. L., Aronson, P. S. 1981. Amiloride inhibition of the Na$^+$-H$^+$ exchanger in renal microvillus membrane vesicles. *Am. J. Physiol.* 241:F374–79

29. Kinsella, J. L., Aronson, P. S. 1981. Interaction of NH$_4^+$ and Li$^+$ with the renal microvillus membrane Na$^+$-H$^+$ exchanger. *Am. J. Physiol.* 241:C220–26

30. Kinsella, J. L., Aronson, P. S. 1982. Determination of the coupling ratio for Na$^+$-H$^+$ exchange in renal microvillus membrane vesicles. *Biochim. Biophys. Acta* 689:161–64

31. Knickelbein, R., Aronson, P. S., Atherton, W., Dobbins, J. W. 1983. Sodium and chloride transport across rabbit ileal brush border. I. Evidence for Na-H exchange. *Am. J. Physiol.* 245:G504–10

32. Kregenow, F. M., Caryk, T., Siebens, A. Further studies on the volume regulatory response of Amphiuma erythrocytes in hypertonic media—evidence for amiloride-sensitive Na-H exchange. Submitted for publication

33. LaBelle, E. F., Eaton, D. C. 1983. Amiloride-inhibited Na$^+$ uptake into toad bladder microsomes is Na$^+$-H$^+$ exchange. *Biochim. Biophys. Acta* 733: 194–97

34. Moody, W. J. Jr. 1981. The ionic mechanism of intracellular pH regulation in crayfish neurones. *J. Physiol.* 316: 293–308

35. Moolenaar, W. H., Boonstra, J., Van der Saag, P. T., De Laat, S. W. 1981. Sodium/proton exchange in mouse neuroblastoma cells. *J. Biol. Chem.* 256:12883–87

36. Moolenaar, W. H., Mummery, C. L., Van der Saag, P. T., De Laat, S. W. 1981. Rapid ionic events and the initiation of growth in serum-stimulated neuroblastoma cells. *Cell* 23:789–98

37. Moolenaar, W. H., Tsien, R. Y., Van der Saag, P. T., De Laat, S. W. 1983. Na$^+$/H$^+$ exchange and cytoplasmic pH in the action of growth factors in human fibroblasts. *Nature* 304:645–48

38. Moolenaar, W. H., Yarden, Y., De Laat, S. W., Schlessinger, J. 1982. Epidermal growth factor induces electrically silent Na$^+$ influx in human fibroblasts. *J. Biol. Chem.* 257:8502–6

39. Moore, R. D. 1981. Stimulation of Na:H exchange by insulin. *Biophys. J.* 33:203–10

40. Murer, H., Hopfer, U., Kinne, R. 1976. Sodium/proton antiport in brush-border-membrane vesicles isolated from rat

small instestine and kidney. *Biochem. J.* 154:597–604

41. Paris, S., Pouyssegur, J. 1983. Biochemical characterization of the amiloride-sensitive Na$^+$-H$^+$ antiport in chinese hamster lung fibroblasts. *J. Biol. Chem.* 258:3503–8

42. Parker, J. C. 1983. Volume-responsive sodium movements in dog red blood cells. *Am. J. Physiol.* 244:C324–30

43. Piwnica-Worms, D., Lieberman, M. 1983. Microfluorometric monitoring of pH$_i$ in cultured heart cells: Na$^+$-H$^+$ exchange. *Am. J. Physiol.* 244:C422–28

44. Pouyssegur, J., Chambard, J. C., Franchi, A., Paris, S., Van Obberghen-Schilling, E. 1982. Growth factor activation of an amiloride-sensitive Na$^+$/H$^+$ exchange system in quiescent fibroblasts: coupling to ribosomal protein S6 phosphorylation. *Proc. Natl. Acad. Sci. USA* 79:3935–39

45. Reenstra, W. W., Warnock, D. G., Yee, V. J., Forte, J. G. 1981. Proton gradients in renal cortex brush-border membrane vesicles. Demonstration of a rheogenic proton flux with acridine orange. *J. Biol. Chem.* 256:11663–66

46. Rindler, M. J., Saier, M. H. Jr. 1981. Evidence for Na$^+$/H$^+$ antiport in cultured dog kidney cells (MDCK). *J. Biol. Chem.* 256:10820–25

47. Rindler, M. J., Taub, M., Saier, M. H. Jr. 1979. Uptake of ^{22}Na$^+$ by cultured dog kidney cells (MDCK). *J. Biol. Chem.* 254:11431–39

48. Roos, A., Boron, W. F. 1981. Intracellular pH. *Physiol. Rev.* 61:296–434

49. Rothenberg, P., Glaser, L., Schlesinger, P., Cassel, D. 1983. Epidermal growth factor stimulates amiloride-sensitive ^{22}Na uptake in A431 cells. *J. Biol. Chem.* 258:4883–89

50. Rothenberg, P., Glaser, L., Schlesinger, P., Cassel, D. 1983. Activation of Na$^+$/H$^+$ exchange by epidermal growth factor elevates intracellular pH in A431 cells. *J. Biol. Chem.* 258:12644–53

51. Sabolic, I., Burckhardt, G. 1983. Proton pathways in rat renal brush-border and basolateral membranes. *Biochim. Biophys. Acta* 734:210–20

52. Sanders, D., Hansen, U.-P., Gradmann, D., Slayman, C. L. 1984. Generalized kinetic analysis of ion-driven cotransport systems. *J. Membrane Biol.* 77:123–52

53. Schuldiner, S., Rozengurt, E. 1982. Na$^+$/H$^+$ antiport in Swiss 3T3 cells: mitogenic stimulation leads to cytoplasmic alkalinization. *Proc. Natl. Acad. Sci. USA* 79:7778–82

54. Segel, I. H. 1975. *Enzyme Kinetics*. New York: Wiley, 957 pp.

55. Siebens, A. W., Kregenow, F. M. Volume regulatory responses of Amphiuma red cells incubated in anisotonic media. The effect of amiloride. Submitted for publication

56. Vigne, P., Frelin, C., Lazdunski, M. 1982. The amiloride-sensitive Na^+/H^+ exchange system in skeletal muscle cells in culture. *J. Biol. Chem.* 257:9394–400

57. Warnock, D. G., Reenstra, W. W., Yee, V. J. 1982. Na^+/H^+ antiporter of brush border vesicles: studies with acridine orange uptake. *Am. J. Physiol.* 242:F733–39

58. Warnock, D. G., Yee, V. J. 1982. Sodium uptake mechanisms in brush-border membrane vesicles prepared from rabbit renal cortex. *Biochim. Biophys. Acta* 684:137–40

59. Weinman, S. A., Reuss, L. 1982. Na^+/H^+ exchange at the apical membrane of Necturus gallbladder. *J. Gen. Physiol.* 80:299–321

60. Wong, P. Y. D., Lee, W. M., Tsang, A. Y. F. 1981. The effects of extracellular sodium on acid release and motility initiation in rat caudal epididymal spermatozoa in vitro. *Exp. Cell Res.* 131:97–104

Ann. Rev. Physiol. 1985. 47:561–71

SODIUM-CALCIUM EXCHANGE IN PLASMA MEMBRANE VESICLES

Kenneth D. Philipson

Departments of Medicine and Physiology and the American Heart Association, Greater Los Angeles Affiliate, Cardiovascular Research Laboratories, University of California at Los Angeles School of Medicine, Los Angeles, California 90024

INTRODUCTION

The existence of a sodium-calcium exchange mechanism was first inferred from calcium-flux measurements on guinea-pig atria by Reuter & Seitz (47). Subsequently, Na-Ca exchange received much attention due to the critical importance of Ca transport in cellular regulatory pathways. Na-Ca exchange may be essential in mediating several Ca-dependent responses, with the most prominent example being regulation of the cardiac contractile state. In addition, Na-Ca exchange may play a role in maintaining the low cellular Ca level in several tissues. Cells possess multiple Ca-transport mechanisms, however, and unequivocal assignment of a Na or Ca flux to Na-Ca exhange is often not possible in intact tissues. The recent development of techniques for the measurement of Na-Ca exchange in isolated plasma membrane vesicles has greatly facilitated investigations, and this review will focus solely on these studies. Na-Ca exchange has now been described in plasma membrane vesicles from several tissues, but the most detailed measurements have been made using vesicles of cardiac sarcolemma and, to a lesser extent, brain plasma membrane. Reviews describing pioneering studies of Na-Ca exchange in more intact preparations have recently been published (6, 12, 25, 46).

561

0066-4278/85/0315-0561$02.00

METHODOLOGICAL CONSIDERATIONS

Investigations of vesicular Na-Ca exchange received much impetus from Reeves & Sutko (43), who demonstrated a simple technique for the measurement of Na_i-dependent Ca uptake in cardiac sarcolemmal vesicles. Briefly, Na-loaded vesicles are diluted into Na-free medium containing ^{45}Ca, and a rapid exchange of intravesicular Na for extravesicular Ca ensues (see 32 for experimental details). Several authors have shown that the Ca-uptake reaction can be rapidly quenched by the addition of La^{3+} or EGTA, that the transported Ca is intravesicular and not superficially bound, and that the Ca uptake is strictly dependent upon an outwardly directed Na gradient. Cardiac sarcolemmal vesicles demonstrate initial rates for Na_i-dependent Ca uptake of up to 20–30 nmol Ca/mg protein/ s (e.g. 9, 33); these values are comparable to the Ca transport activity of cardiac sarcoplasmic reticular preparations (11). Ca located within vesicles derived from plasma membranes can be readily released by increasing the extravesicular Na concentration via Na_o-dependent Ca efflux, a reverse mode of Na-Ca exchange. Most investigators have chosen to use isotopically labeled Ca with filtration techniques, but vesicular Na-Ca exchange has also been detected using spectroscopic (9, 10, 21) and electrode (10) techniques. In short, it is possible, through a variety of manipulations, to unequivocably attribute a component of Ca flux in isolated plasma membrane vesicles to Na-Ca exchange.

PLASMA MEMBRANE LOCALIZATION

That vesicular Na-Ca exchange activity can be attributed to the plasma membrane and not to membranes from other subcellular organelles has been verified in two ways. Firstly, the level of Na-Ca exchange activity in different membrane fractions correlates with the activity of other plasma membrane markers. Maximal Na-Ca exchange activity correlates with optimal levels of 5'-nucleotidase in brain (49) and smooth muscle (18), (Na^+,K^+)-ATPase in brain (49), and ouabain-binding (43) and K-dependent phosphatase (4) in cardiac-membrane fractions. Secondly, compelling evidence comes from the demonstration that the Na-Ca exchange mechanism and the ATP-dependent Na pump are simultaneously present on the same membrane vesicles. Na that has been actively transported into vesicles by the Na pump can be exchanged with extravesicular Ca (15, 37, 39, 41).

A Na-Ca exchange mechanism has also been described in the mitochondrial inner membrane (8). In contrast to the plasma membrane Na-Ca exchange system, however, this transport pathway is not electrogenic, is of relatively low activity, and can be partially activated by Li as a substitute for Na. It is unlikely that mitochondrial exchange activity significantly interferes with the measurement of plasma membrane Na-Ca exchange.

GENERAL PROPERTIES OF SODIUM-CALCIUM EXCHANGE

Calcium Sites

The apparent $K_m(Ca)$ for the initial rate of Na_i-dependent Ca uptake has been measured several times to be 15–40 µM (5, 37, 38, 40, 43, 45, 49, 55). Caroni et al (9, 10), however, found a much higher affinity (1–2 µM Ca). These authors feel that because Na-Ca exchange is electrogenic (see below), adequate charge compensation is necessary (obtained through the use of valinomycin) for an accurate determination of the Ca affinity. In contrast, however, others (33, 35, 55) find that valinomycin does not change the Ca dependency of the exchange mechanism. In modeling the physiological importance of Na-Ca exchange in mediating cellular Ca efflux, it has been convenient to accept the low $K_m(Ca)$ values of Caroni et al (9, 10). These values, however, have not been reproduced in other laboratories.

The determination of $K_m(Ca)$ is further confounded by two factors. First, the experimental results can be technique-dependent. The presence of EGTA increases the apparent Ca affinity of the exchange mechanism (54). Second, the Ca affinity of the Na-Ca exchanger can be altered in several ways (e.g. by phosphorylation, enzyme treatment, or by the presence of other ions; see below). Thus, it is not possible, at this time, to provide a definitive estimate of Ca affinities for physiological conditions. It should also be noted that most vesicular Na-Ca exchange experiments are arranged to maximize transport activity. Na and Ca are initially present only on opposing membrane surfaces. In vivo, there will be some Na and Ca located both intra- and extracellularly, and the high V_{max} values measured in vitro (especially for cardiac membranes) may not apply.

One apparent shortcoming of Na-Ca exchange experiments using isolated plasma membranes is that the vesicular preparations usually contain a mixture of inside-out (in which the normally cytoplasmic membrane surface faces outward) and right side–out vesicles. Both types of vesicles will participate in the Na_i-dependent Ca uptake reaction (if the vesicles are first preloaded with Na by passive diffusion), and the interpretation of data becomes complicated if the two types of vesicles have different properties. In one study (37) using cardiac sarcolemmal vesicles, this problem was circumvented by preloading only the inside-out vesicles with Na through the action of the ATP-dependent Na pump. This allowed the Na-Ca exchange activity of the inside-out vesicles to be quantitated. It was inferred that the Ca binding sites on the opposing surfaces of the exchange mechanism were symmetrical. That is, the Na-Ca exchange in the two types of vesicles had identical values for the apparent $K_m(Ca)$ and also identical responses to pH and valinomycin.

Na-Ca exchange can be inhibited by divalent and trivalent cations, due to competition with Ca for binding sites (2, 4, 16, 49, 53). In the most detailed study (53), using cardiac sarcolemmal vesicles, the order of divalent cation effectiveness in inhibiting Na_i-dependent Ca influx was Cd > Sr > Ba ~ Mn >> Mg. The effectiveness of the divalent cations was related to their ionic crystal radius as compared with that of Ca. The trivalent cations were much more potent inhibitors (La > Nd > Tm > Y) but appeared to be more effective as their radius increased. At 20 μM Ca, the most effective trivalent cation, La, caused 50% inhibition at about 1 μM, whereas the most potent divalent cation, Cd, caused equal inhibition at about 30 μM. Both Ba and Sr could substitute for Ca and participated in Na-divalent cation exchange, although with lower activity than Ca (52).

Monovalent cations (other than Na and protons) have little effect on the Ca-binding site, and Na_i-dependent Ca uptake proceeds readily in sucrose, choline, K, or Li media (16, 43, 49). Extravesicular Na competitively inhibits Na_i-dependent Ca uptake with a K_i of about 10 mM (45). Hill plot analysis indicates that most of the inhibition could be explained by the interaction of one Na ion with the Ca binding site, although the data also suggest the possible interaction of a second Na with the Ca site at high Na concentrations (45).

Na-Ca exchange is very pH-sensitive in cardiac sarcolemmal vesicles (33, 37, 51, 56) and in membrane vesicles from alkalophilic Bacillus (1). Na_i-dependent Ca uptake is a sigmoidal function of pH. The Ca uptake is markedly inhibited at pH 6 and stimulated at pH 9. This suggests the possible importance of the ionization state of a histidine residue in Na-Ca exchange. It appears that protons and Ca compete for a common binding site on the exchange mechanism (1, 33). The pH sensitivity may be relevant during the negative inotropic response of cardiac muscle to acidosis (33).

Sodium Sites

It is probable that three (or more) Na ions exchange for each Ca ion (see below). Detailed investigation of the Na sites, however, has lagged behind that of the Ca site for technical reasons. Na_i-dependent Ca uptake is experimentally easier to study than Na_o-dependent ^{45}Ca efflux. The alternative use of Na isotopes is not especially useful, due to low isotope specific activity when Na is in the millimolar range. In addition, appropriate spectrophotometric techniques for following rapid Na movements are not currently available and electrode techniques have not been employed.

To study Na_o-dependent Ca efflux (21, 28, 36, 37), vesicles are first preloaded with Ca by passive diffusion, by Na_i-dependent Ca uptake, or by the plasma membrane ATP-dependent Ca pump. The $K_{1/2}(Na)$ has been measured to be 7–32 mM (21, 28, 36) under a variety of conditions. When the initial rates of Na_o-dependent Ca efflux in cardiac vesicles were measured using spectrophotometric techniques (21), the $K_{1/2}(Na)$ values ranged from 21 to 32 mM depending on the method used to preload with Ca. There is a sigmoid dependence of Ca efflux on Na concentration (21, 36), with Hill coefficients ranging from 2.3 to 3.2 (21). This is consistent with the participation of multiple Na ions in the exchange process. Two studies (21, 37) have suggested that the Na sites may have different affinities on the two membrane surfaces of the exchange mechanism.

The Na sites can also be investigated by measuring Ca uptake as a function of the internal Na concentration. After pre-equilibrating cardiac vesicles with varying Na concentrations, the $K_{1/2}(Na)$ for Na_i-dependent Ca uptake had values of 13 and 26 mM (45, 56) with a Hill coefficient of 2.3 (45).

Electrogenicity and Stoichiometry

Substantial evidence indicates that Na-Ca exchange in cardiac sarcolemmal vesicles is electrogenic and that three or more Na ions exchange for each Ca. Vesicular Na-Ca exchange both generates a current and can be affected by imposed membrane potentials. The intravesicular accumulation of tracer quantities of the lipophilic cation tetraphenylphosphonium indicates that an inside-negative membrane potential is generated when Na_i-dependent Ca uptake is activated (10, 44). This is consistent with more positive charge leaving the vesicle (carried by Na) than entering (carried by Ca) with each transport cycle. Because Na_i-dependent Ca uptake involves a net outward movement of positive charge, the production of the inside-negative membrane potential tends to inhibit further Na-Ca exchange. This inhibition can be overcome by using membrane-permeable ions for charge compensation (10) or by producing K-diffusion potentials with valinomycin (4, 10, 24, 27, 30, 33, 35, 37, 44). By altering the internal and external K concentrations in the presence of valinomycin, an imposed membrane potential can be varied according to the Nernst equation. Inside-postitive potentials stimulate Na_i-dependent Ca uptake according to the magnitude of the calculated potential. The extrapolated results indicate that Na-Ca exchange by itself can generate a substantial potential in cardiac sarcolemmal vesicles (35). Valinomycin-induced membrane potentials can also enhance Na_o-dependent Ca efflux (21).

Stimulation of Na-Ca exchange by an imposed membrane potential cannot be explained by a voltage-dependent activation of Ca channels in the sarcolemmal vesicles. The potential-sensitive, Na_i-dependent uptake of Ca involves a substantial ion flux and results in an outwardly directed Ca gradient. Ca accumulation of this magnitude could not result from passive Ca transport through a channel. Likewise, the results cannot be an artifact of any Ca-activated conductance changes that may occur in the membrane.

The unequivocal demonstration of the electrogenicity of the Na-Ca exchange of cardiac sarcolemma has much physiological significance (31). During the prolonged depolarization of the cardiac action potential, Ca influx will occur through Na-Ca exchange and may contribute to the contractile response. Ca efflux (and muscle relaxation) will predominate during repolarization. Thus the properties of Na-Ca exchange are consistent with a role for this transport mechanism in either Ca influx or efflux. The importance of Na-Ca exchange in these processes will depend on intra- and extracellular Na and Ca activities, the stoichiometry of Na-Ca exchange, and the relative activity of Na-Ca exchange as compared with other Ca transport pathways.

Although vesicle experiments can easily detect the electrogenicity of Na-Ca exchange, definitive determination of stoichiometry has been more difficult to achieve. Pitts (41) found that ^{22}Na influx was coupled to ^{45}Ca efflux in cardiac sarcolemmal vesicles at a ratio of 3 to 1. Reeves & Hale (42) have used a thermodynamic approach to determine stiochiometry. These workers observed membrane potential–dependent Ca movements in the initial absence of either a Na or Ca gradient. The Na gradient was then varied to provide the energy to exactly compensate for these Ca movements such that no Ca movement occurred. From the quantitative relationship between membrane potential and the Na equilibrium potential, they calculated a stoichiometry of 3:1. Although further confirmation of this value would be desirable, it is reasonable to accept the coupling ratio of 3:1 as a working hypothesis for modeling purposes.

CALCIUM-CALCIUM EXCHANGE

The Na-Ca exchange mechanism is also able to catalyze Ca-Ca exchange in cardiac (2, 27, 36, 51) and brain (49) membrane vesicles. The stoichiometry of this exchange is 1:1 (2). In contrast to Na-Ca exchange, Ca-Ca exchange requires the presence of a monovalent cation for optimal countertransport (27, 36, 49, 51). Highest activity occurs when the monovalent cation is present on both sides of the vesicle membrane (27, 51). Although there is some disagreement in the literature (27, 36, 49, 51), the sequence for activation of Ca-Ca exchange is approximately K ∼ Rb ∼ Li > Cs > choline. Na can also serve to activate Ca-Ca exchange (27, 36, 51) aside from its ability to participate in Na-Ca exchange. The monovalent cation activating Ca-Ca exchange is not transported by the exchange mechanism (51). Ba and Sr both participate in calcium divalent-cation exchange in sarcolemmal vesicles (53). Surprisingly, Cd is even more potent than Ca in inducing Ca efflux from cardiac membrane vesicles (53), suggesting that Cd can act as a Ca analog on the exchange mechanism.

REGULATION OF SODIUM-CALCIUM EXCHANGE

Regulatory mechanisms affecting Na-Ca exchange have not been elaborated in detail. In cardiac sarcolemmal vesicles, Na-Ca exchange can be modified by pretreatment with different enzymes. For example, experiments with phospholipases give some insight on the interaction of the Na-Ca exchanger with the membrane phospholipid environment. Stimulated (up to ~ 100%) Na-Ca exchange activity occurs after 10–70% of sarcolemmal phospholipid is hydrolyzed by phospholipase C (34). Phospholipase C removes the phosphate-containing head group from phospholipids, and the resultant diacylglycerol forms droplets outside of the membrane bilayer. The phospholipase C preferentially hydrolyzes neutral phospholipids, thus increasing the percentage of the membrane composed of the negatively charged phospholipids phosphatidylinositol and phosphatidylserine. From this result, it was speculated that the stimulation of Na-Ca exchange was due to the greater preponderance of negatively charged phospholipids in the membrane (34). It is surprising that sarcolemmal vesicles demonstrate enhanced Na-Ca exchange transport activity after such harsh enzymatic hydrolysis.

More dramatic effects on Na-Ca exchange activity occur after treatment with phospholipase D (40), which converts other phospholipids to the negatively charged phosphatidic acid. Na-Ca exchange activity in cardiac sarcolemmal vesicles increases up to 400% when about 10% of membrane phospholipid is hydrolyzed to phosphatidic acid. Apparent $K_m(Ca)$ decreases from 18.2 to 6.3 μM, whereas V_{max} increases 75% after enzyme treatment. The results are consistent with the hypothesis that negatively charged phospholipids exert a regulatory effect on Na-Ca exchange. Langer (25) hypothesizes that an increase in Ca bound to the sarcolemmal surface should stimulate Na-Ca exchange, and the effect of phosphatidic acid may be such an example. Langer & Nudd (26) found that phospholipase D treatment of SL membranes increases membrane Ca binding.

The large stimulatory effect of phosphatidic acid on Na-Ca exchange may be relevant to understanding the "phosphatidylinositol response" [for a review, see (3)]. In this phenomenon, breakdown of polyphosphoinositides has been correlated with the Ca influx that accompanies stimulus-response coupling in many tissues. It has been speculated that phosphatidic acid, a breakdown product of polyphosphoinositides, may mediate the Ca influx response. The results cited above (40) provide evidence for a stimulatory role of phosphatidic acid in a well-defined Ca-transport pathway.

Mild treatment of cardiac sarcolemmal vesicles with either a serine or thiol proteinase (39) stimulates Na-Ca exchange by as much as 200%. The affinity of the exchange mechanism for Ca is increased and the apparent $K_m(Ca)$ falls from 22.2 to 8.1 μM, with only a small increase in V_{max}. It is unclear whether the proteinases modify the Na-Ca exchanger itself or other regulatory membrane proteins.

One group (9) finds that the Na-Ca exchange of cardiac sarcolemma can be regulated by phosphorylation/dephosphorylation reactions. The reactions can be catalyzed by a kinase and a phosphatase endogenous to the sarcolemmal membrane. Both the kinase and the phosphatase require both Ca and calmodulin. No cAMP-dependent regulation has been found. Phosphorylated vesicles have both a higher Ca affinity and V_{max} than dephosphorylated vesicles. Because both the activating (phosphorylation) and deactivating (dephosphorylation) reactions were Ca- and calmodulin-dependent, these two regulatory pathways operate simultaneously and antagonistically. Phosphorylation requires less Ca than dephosphorylation, and Caroni & Carafoli (9) speculate that the intracellular Ca concentration will determine the phosphorylation state of the exchanger in vivo. The physiological significance of these complex regulatory steps remains to be unraveled.

ISOLATION AND RECONSTITUTION

Miyamoto & Racker (30) solubilized cardiac sarcolemmal vesicles with cholate in the presence of soybean phospholipids. After dilution and sedimentation, proteoliposomes formed that exhibited five-fold greater Na-Ca exchange activity than the native vesicles. Wakabayashi & Goshima (56) used this technique and found that if the cholate extract was treated with pronase, the proteoliposomes had Na-Ca exchange activity 50-fold greater than the activity of the initial membrane vesicles. They suggested that the pronase eliminates proteins other than the Na-Ca exchanger, although other explanations are possible. Applying these techniques, Hale et al (20) have provided preliminary evidence suggesting that the molecular weight of the Na-Ca exchange protein is 82,000.

PHARMACOLOGY

Na-Ca exchange is insensitive to a wide variety of substances, such as Ca and Na channel blockers (16, 44), ouabain (16), and mitochondrial poisons (16, 49). Na-Ca exchange is inhibited by polymyxin B (38) with moderately high potency and by dibucaine, tetracaine (29), chlorpromazine (10), and amiloride (48) at relatively high concentrations. Recently, amiloride derivatives have begun to attract attention (e.g. 50) as possible specific inhibitors of Na-Ca exchange. Caution is urged in the application of these agents in vivo until their specificity is thoroughly examined.

OTHER TISSUES

In addition to those tissues already mentioned, Na-Ca exchange has also been described in membrane vesicles from kidney (17), skeletal muscle (14), small intestine (13), adrenal medulla (23), liver (22), and sperm flagella (7). The Na-Ca exchange activity is relatively low in all these preparations except the sperm flagella plasma membrane vesicles, which possess the highest Na-dependent Ca uptake capacity (600 nmol Ca/mg protein) so far described. No significant differences in the properties of Na-Ca exchange in vesicles from different tissues have been documented. Apparent differences (19) may be due to comparison of initial rate values in one study with steady-state values in another.

PERSPECTIVES

More detailed kinetic studies of Na-Ca exchange in vesicle preparations should give new insights into the reaction mechanism and the nature of the ion-binding sites. Some experiments are hampered by the rapidity with which intravesicular ion concentrations are altered during the Na-Ca exchange reaction, thereby modifying kinetic properties. Another impediment to investigation is the absence of a stable intermediate such as the phosphorylated intermediate of active ion pumps. Purification of the exchanger protein will allow investigations to begin on a more molecular level. Development of a specific inhibitor is needed to ascertain the physiological significance of Na-Ca exchange. Further correlation of biochemical and physiological studies should also help in this direction. The initial results on the interaction of the Na-Ca exchange mechanism with the surrounding membrane environment indicate that this will also be a fruitful area of investigation.

Literature Cited

1. Ando, A. Yabuki, M. Kusaka, I. 1981. Na^+-driven Ca^{2+} transport in alkalophilic Bacillus. *Biochim. Biophys. Acta* 640:179–84
2. Bartschat, D. K., Lindenmayer, G. E. 1980. Calcium movements promoted by vesicles in a highly enriched sarcolemma preparation from canine ventricle. Calcium-calcium countertransport. *J. Biol. Chem.* 255:9626–34
3. Berridge, M. J. 1984. Inositol triphosphate and diacylglycerol as second messengers. *Biochem. J.* 220:345–60
4. Bers, D. M., Philipson, K. D., Nishimoto, A. Y. 1980. Sodium-calcium exchange and sidedness of isolated cardiac sarcolemmal vesicles. *Biochim. Biophys. Acta* 601:358–71
5. Bersohn, M. M., Philipson, K. D., Fukushima, J. Y. 1982. Sodium-calcium exchange and sarcolemmal enzymes in ischemic rabbit hearts. *Am. J. Physiol.* 242:C288–C295
6. Blaustein, M. P., Nelson, M. T. 1982. Sodium-calcium exchange: its role in the regulation of cell calcium. In *Membrane Transport of Calcium*, ed. E. Carafoli, pp. 217–36. London: Academic
7. Bradley, M. P., Forrester, I. T. 1980. A sodium-calcium exchange mechanism in plasma membrane vesicles isolated from ram sperm flagella. *FEBS Lett.* 121:15–18
8. Carafoli, E. 1982. The transport of calcium across the inner membrane of mitochondrial. See Ref. 6, pp. 109–39
9. Caroni, P., Carafoli, E. 1983. The regulation of the Na^+-Ca^{2+} exchanger of heart sarcolemma. *Eur. J. Biochem.* 132:451–60
10. Caroni, P., Reinlib, L., Carafoli, E. 1980. Charge movements during the Na^+-Ca^{2+} exchange in heart sarcolemmal vesicles. *Proc. Natl. Acad. Sci. USA* 77:6354–58
11. Chamberlain, B. K., Levitsky, D. O., Fleischer, S. 1983. Isolation and characterization of canine cardiac sarcoplasmic reticulum with improved Ca^{2+} transport properties. *J. Biol. Chem.* 258:6602–9
12. Dipolo, R., Beauge, L. 1983. The calcium pump and sodium-calcium exchange in squid axons. *Ann. Rev. Physiol.* 45:313–24
13. Ghijsen, W. E. J. M., DeJong, M. D., Van Os, C. H. 1983. Kinetic properties of Na^+/Ca^{2+} exchange in basolateral plasma membranes of rat small intestine. *Biochim. Biophys. Acta* 730:85–94
14. Gilbert, J. R., Meissner, G. 1982.

Sodium-calcium ion exchange in skeletal muscle sarcolemmal vesicles. *J. Memb. Biol.* 69:77–84

15. Gill, D. L. 1982. Sodium channel, sodium pump, and sodium-calcium exchange activities in synaptosomal plasma membrane vesicles. *J. Biol. Chem.* 257:10986–90

16. Gill, D. L., Grollman, E. F., Kohn, L. D. 1981. Calcium transport mechanisms in membrane vesicles from guinea-pig brain synaptosomes. *J. Biol. Chem.* 256:184–92

17. Gmaj, P., Murer, H., Kinne, R. 1979. Calcium ion transport across plasma membranes isolated from rat kidney cortex. *Biochem. J.* 178:549–57

18. Grover, A. K., Kwan, C. Y., Daniel, E. E. 1981. Na-Ca exchange in rat myometrium membrane vesicles highly enriched in plasma membranes. *Am. J. Physiol.* 240:C175–C182

19. Grover, A. K., Kwan, C. Y., Rangachari, P. K., Daniel, E. E. 1983. Na-Ca exchange in a smooth-muscle plasma membrane-enriched fraction. *Am. J. Physiol.* 244:C158–C165

20. Hale, C. C., Slaughter, R. S., Ahrens, D., Reeves, J. P. 1984. Identification and partial purification of the cardiac sodium-calcium exchange protein. *Proc. Natl. Acad. Sci. USA.* In press

21. Kadoma, M., Froehlich, J., Reeves, J., Sutko, J. 1982. Kinetics of sodium ion–induced calcium ion release in calcium ion–loaded cardiac sarcolemmal vesicles: determination of initial velocities by stopped-flow spectrophotometry. *Biochemistry* 21:1914–18

22. Kraus-Friedmann, N., Biber, J., Murer, H., Carafoli, E. 1982. Calcium uptake in isolated hepatic plasma-membrane vesicles. *Eur. J. Biochem.* 129:7–12

23. Krieger-Brauer, H., Gratzl, M. 1982. Uptake of Ca^{2+} by isolated secretory vesicles from adrenal medulla. *Biochim. Biophys. Acta* 691:61–70

24. Lamers, J. M. J., Stinis, J. T. 1981. An electrogenic Na^+/Ca^{2+} antiporter in addition to the Ca^{2+} pump in cardiac sarcolemma. *Biochim. Biophys. Acta* 640:521–34

25. Langer, G. A. 1982. Sodium-calcium exchange in the heart. *Ann. Rev. Physiol.* 44:435–49

26. Langer, G. A., Nudd, L. M. 1983. Effects of cations, phospholipases, and neuraminidase on calcium binding to "gas-dissected" membranes from cultured cardiac cells. *Circ. Res.* 53:482–90

27. Ledvora, R. F., Hegyvary, C. 1983. Dependence of $Na^+\text{-}Ca^{2+}$ exchange and $Ca^{2+}\text{-}Ca^{2+}$ exchange on monovalent ca-

tions. *Biochim. Biophys. Acta* 729:123–36

28. Michaelis, M. L., Michaelis, E. K. 1981. Ca^{++} fluxes in resealed synaptic plasma membrane vesicles. *Life Sci.* 28:37–45

29. Michaelis, M. L., Michaelis, E. K. 1983. Alcohol and local anesthetic effects on Na^+-dependent Ca^{2+} fluxes in brain synaptic membrane vesicles. *Biochem. Pharmacol.* 32:963–69

30. Miyamoto, H., Racker, E. 1980. Solubilization and partial purification of the Ca^{2+}/Na^+ antiporter from the plasma membrane of bovine heart. *J. Biol. Chem.* 255:2656–58

31. Mullins, L. J. 1979. The generation of electric currents in cardiac fibers by Na/Ca exchange. *Am. J. Physiol.* 236:C103–C110

32. Philipson, K. D. 1984. Methods for measuring sodium-calcium exchange in cardiac sarcolemmal vesicles. In *Methods in Studying Cardiac Membranes*, ed. N. Dhalla, Vol. 1, pp. 147–55. Boca Raton, Fl: CRC Press

33. Philipson, K. D., Bersohn, M. M., Nishimoto, A. Y. 1982. Effects of pH on $Na^+\text{-}Ca^+$ exchange in canine cardiac sarcolemmal vesicles. *Circ. Res.* 50:287–93

34. Philipson, K. D., Frank, J. S., Nishimoto, A. Y. 1983. Effects of phospholipase C on the $Na^+\text{-}Ca^{2+}$ exchange and Ca^{2+} permeability of cardiac sarcolemmal vesicles. *J. Biol. Chem.* 258:5905–10

35. Philipson, K. D., Nishimoto, A. Y. 1980. $Na^+\text{-}Ca^{2+}$ exchange is affected by membrane potential in cardiac sarcolemmal vesicles. *J. Biol. Chem.* 255:6880–82

36. Philipson, K. D., Nishimoto, A. Y. 1981. Efflux of Ca^{2+} from cardiac sarcolemmal vesicles. Influence of external Ca^{2+} and Na^+. *J. Biol. Chem.* 256:3698–702

37. Philipson, K. D., Nishimoto, A. Y. 1982. $Na^+\text{-}Ca^{2+}$ exchange in inside-out cardiac sarcolemmal vesicles. *J. Biol. Chem.* 257:5111–17

38. Philipson, K. D., Nishimoto, A. Y. 1982. Stimulation of $Na^+\text{-}Ca^{2+}$ exchange in cardiac sarcolemmal vesicles by proteinase pretreatment. *Am. J. Physiol.* 243:C191–C195

39. Philipson, K. D., Nishimoto, A. Y. 1983. ATP-dependent Na^+ transport in cardiac sarcolemmal vesicles. *Biochim. Biophys. Acta* 733:133–41

40. Philipson, K. D., Nishimoto, A. Y. 1984. Stimulation of $Na^+\text{-}Ca^{2+}$ exchange in cardiac sarcolemmal vesicles by phospholipase D. *J. Biol. Chem.* 259:16–19

41. Pitts, B. J. R. 1979. Stoichiometry of sodium-calcium exchange in cardiac sarcolemmal vesicles. Coupling to the sodium pump. *J. Biol. Chem.* 254:6232–35

42. Reeves, J. P., Hale, C. C. 1984. The stoichiometry of the cardiac sodium-calcium exchange system. *J. Biol. Chem.* 259:7733–39

43. Reeves, J. P., Sutko, J. L. 1979. Sodium-calcium ion exchange in cardiac membrane vesicles. *Proc. Natl. Acad. Sci. USA* 76:590–94

44. Reeves, J. P., Sutko, J. L. 1980. Sodium-calcium exchange activity generates a current in cardiac membrane vesicles. *Science* 208:1461–64

45. Reeves, J. P., Sutko, J. L. 1983. Competitive interactions of sodium and calcium with the sodium-calcium exchange system of cardiac sarcolemmal vesicles. *J. Biol. Chem.* 258:3178–82

46. Reuter, H. 1982. Na-Ca countertransport in cardiac muscle. In *Membranes and Transport*, ed. A. N. Martonosi, 1:623–31. New York: Plenum

47. Reuter, H., Seitz, N. 1968. The dependence of calcium efflux from cardiac muscle on temperature and external ion composition. *J. Physiol.* 195:451–70

48. Schellenberg, G. D., Anderson, L., Swanson, P. D. 1983. Inhibition of Na^+-Ca^{2+} exchange in rat brain by amiloride. *Molec. Pharmacol.* 24:251–58

49. Schellenberg, G. D., Swanson, P. D. 1981. Sodium-dependent and calcium-dependent calcium transport by rat brain microsomes. *Biochim. Biophys. Acta* 648:13–27

50. Siegel, P. K. S., Cragoe, E. J. Jr., Trumble, M. J., Kaczorowski, G. J. 1984. Inhibition of Na^+/Ca^{2+} exchange in membrane vesicle and papillary muscle preparations from guinea pig hearts by analogs of amiloride. *Proc. Natl. Acad. Sci. USA* 81:3238–42

51. Slaughter, R. S., Sutko, J. L. Reeves, J. P. 1983. Equilibrium calcium-calcium exchange in cardiac sarcolemmal vesicles. *J. Biol. Chem.* 258:3183–90

52. Tibbits, G. F., Philipson, K. D. 1982. Na-dependent alkaline earth metal uptake in cardiac sarcolemmal vesicles. *Fed. Proc.* 41:1240 (Abstr.)

53. Trosper, T. L., Philipson, K. D. 1983. Effects of divalent and trivalent cations on Na^+-Ca^{2+} exchange in cardiac sarcolemmal vesicles. *Biochim. Biophys. Acta* 731:63–68

54. Trosper, T. L., Philipson, K. D. 1984. Stimulatory effect of calcium chelators on Na^+-Ca^{2+} exchange in cardiac sarcolemmal vesicles. *Cell Calcium.* 5:211–22

55. Wakabayashi, S., Goshima, K. 1981. Comparison of kinetic characteristics of Na^+-Ca^{2+} exchange in sarcolemma vesicles and cultured cells from chick heart. *Biochim. Biophys. Acta* 645:311–17

56. Wakabayashi, S., Goshima, K. 1982. Partial purification of Na^+-Ca^{2+} antiporter from plasma membrane of chick heart. *Biochim. Biophys. Acta* 693:125–33

Ann. Rev. Physiol. 1985. 47:573–601

MECHANISM OF CALCIUM TRANSPORT

Giuseppe Inesi

Department of Biological Chemistry, University of Maryland School of Medicine, Baltimore, Maryland 21201

INTRODUCTION

Consistent with the important role of Ca^{2+} in biological control, active transport of this divalent cation has been demonstrated in both plasma and intracellular membranes of eukaryotic cells. With respect to the mechanism of transport, the most informative system is the sarcoplasmic reticulum (SR) membrane, which, by now, serves as a model for active transport and coupled enzyme catalysis. Following the isolation of vesicular fragments of SR membrane (116) and the discovery of their ability to accumulate calcium in the presence of ATP (40, 50, 51), a remarkable number of experimental findings were obtained. *From the structural point of view:* The highly specific protein composition of the SR membrane, consisting of a Ca^{2+}-dependent ATPase that accounts for ~ 50% of the membrane dry weight (49, 64); the ultrastructural localization (7, 17, 33, 49, 52, 60, 66, 74, 118) of the ATPase in the membrane by a combination of biochemical, electron microscopic, and x-ray diffraction methods; the purification (95, 103) of the Ca^{2+}-ATPase and the partial determination of its primary sequence (1, 84, 135); and the formation of bidimensional crystalline arrays of ATPase within the plane of the membrane (9, 36–39). *From the functional point of view:* The 2:1 stoichiometry between ATP hydrolysis and Ca transport (46, 140); the transmembrane Ca^{2+} gradient and its collapse induced by Ca ionophores (119); the phosphorylated enzyme intermediate formed with ATP in the presence of Ca^{2+} (5, 20, 96, 144); the reversal of the pump and the synthesis of ATP (3, 82, 97, 98); the phosphorylation reaction of the enzyme with Pi in the absence of Ca^{2+} (26); the characterization of the partial reactions of the catalytic and transport cycle by equilibrium and kinetic experimentation (44, 70, 83, 137).

0066-4278/85/0315-0573$02.00

The basic experimental facts and the prevailing ideas on the mechanism of Ca transport in SR have been reviewed already (8, 22, 29, 47, 48, 59, 65, 70, 99, 106, 131). I will describe here some of the most important and recent findings and present my own view of the reaction mechanism.

THE SARCOPLASMIC RETICULUM ATPase

Membrane Assembly and Structure

The principal protein of the SR membrane is a Ca^{2+}-dependent ATPase that is densely spaced within the plane of the membrane (49, 64). Its basic structural component is a polypeptide chain of approximately 115,000 daltons (95). Electron microscopic and diffraction studies have demonstrated that the ATPase chain has an amphiphylic character, with a hydrophobic portion inserted into the membrane bilayer and a hydrophylic portion protruding from the cytoplasmic surface of the SR membrane into the aqueous phase (17, 33, 49, 52, 66, 74, 93, 118). Each 115,000-dalton chain crosses the membrane repeatedly, leaving large loops as well as the -N and -C terminals in the cytoplasmic phase, while the joining segments make up the hydrophobic core (1, 84). This disposition is related to the developmental mechanism (2, 108) of ATPase chain integration into smooth endoplasmic reticulum that includes "signal recognition particles" and a noncleaved "signal sequence."

Detailed studies on the structure of the ATPase chain have led to characterization of its tryptic fragments (74, 104, 123, 134) and determination of the amino acid sequence in the polar segments (1, 84, 135). The α-helix content is 30% in the absence of Ca and 38% in the presence of Ca; the β-conformation is 21% in the absence of Ca and 9% in the presence of Ca (43).

Stoichiometry of Catalytic Sites

The number of catalytic sites per protein weight unit can be determined from the phosphorylation levels obtained following incubation of SR ATPase with various substrates in conditions favoring formation of phosphorylated enzyme intermediate and inhibiting its breakdown. The levels most commonly found in the literature correspond to 3–4 nmol per mg of total protein in SR vesicles and are slightly higher in purified ATPase (see 106 for review). A stoichiometry of 3–4 nmol/mg protein is less than expected (i.e. $\sim$ 8 nmol/mg protein) from the appearance of SDS gels in which a band including the $\sim$ 115,000-dalton ATPase chain accounts for most of the protein. This discrepancy has been interpreted as a real difference between the steady-state level of phosphoenzyme and the number of catalytic sites and explained with several hypothesis, including "half the sites" reactivity (41) in the oligomeric relationship of more than one chain. More recently, it was demonstrated that the discrepancy is actually due to the presence of nonspecific protein contaminants in SR vesicles and of denatured protein in preparations purified with ionic detergents. In fact, new methods of ATPase purification by anion exchange columns following solubilization in nonionic detergents, as well as protein analysis by HPLC, have permitted demonstration of a stoichiometric ratio of nearly one between the 115,000-dalton chains and the phosphorylation (catalytic) sites (4). This is in agreement with the stoichiometry obtained by site derivatization with fluorescein isothiocyanate (105). *In conclusion, each 115,000-dalton chain has one catalytic site. All of these sites are reactive, both in SR vesicles and in detergent-treated preparations.*

Stoichiometry of Ca Sites and Mechanism of Binding

Ca binding in the absence of substrate can be measured at equilibrium with the aid of radioactive tracer. In addition to nonspecific binding sites of low affinity (11), the SR ATPase has a class of high affinity ($K_d \cong 10^{-6}$ M) Ca sites that are involved in enzyme activation and transport of the divalent cation. *The stoichiometric ratio of the Ca sites to the catalytic (phosphorylation) sites is 2:1 (71).* Furthermore, equilibrium Ca binding isotherms display a cooperative behavior and competition with respect to protons (58, 71). The degree of cooperativity ($n_H > 3$) observed at low proton concentrations requires interaction of at least four Ca binding domains (58, 138). A protein conformational change, demonstrated by several methods (15, 30, 45, 62, 109), is involved in the mechanism of cooperative interaction (71).

Ca binding to SR ATPase produces a measurable enhancement of intrinsic protein fluorescence that can be utilized for kinetic measurements of Ca binding or dissociation in stopped-flow experiments (10, 34, 42, 45). The kinetics of Ca-dependent fluorescence changes are rather slow, consistent with the occurrence of the conformational change. Furthermore, direct measurements of Ca binding by rapid filtration methods (32) indicate that half of the sites are immediately available for binding, whereas the other half become available more slowly. These findings are supportive of a sequential mechanism (32, 71) consisting of rapid Ca binding to a first site whose occupancy triggers a conformational change that, in turn, renders a second site available for binding as in:

$$E \rightleftharpoons \overset{Ca^{2+}}{E \cdot Ca} \rightleftharpoons E \cdot Ca \rightleftharpoons \overset{Ca^{2+}}{E \cdot Ca_2} \qquad \qquad 1.$$

Equilibrium and kinetic measurements of intrinsic fluorescence changes produced by Ca binding to SR ATPase can be simulated quite satisfactorily (Figure 1) based on this sequential mechanism. The kinetic and equilibrium constants used for these simulations are listed in the legend to Figure 1.

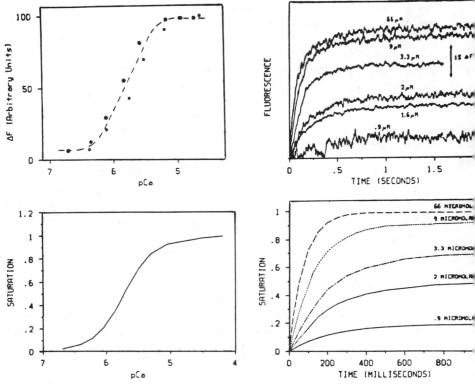

Figure 1   Experimental *(upper panels)* and simulated *(lower panels)* changes in intrinsic fluorescence related to calcium binding as revealed by equilibrium *(left panels)* or kinetic measurements *(right panels)* following addition of Ca to SR ATPase in the absence of ATP (42). The simulated curves were obtained according to Equation 1, assuming $k_1 = 4.25 \times 10^7 \, M^{-1} \, sec^{-1}$, $k_{-1} = 450$ sec^{-1}, $k_2 = 15 \, sec^{-1}$, $k_{-2} = 33 \, sec^{-1}$, $k_3 = 1 \times 10^8 \, M^{-1} \, sec^{-1}$, and $k_{-3} = 18 \, sec^{-1}$.

ATPase Chain Oligomerization

The ATPase chains have a general tendency to aggregate within the membrane plane (7, 94, 112, 118) and follow solubilization with nondenaturing detergents (90–92, 101, 107), raising the possibility that an oligomer of the 115,000-dalton chains may be the basic ATPase unit. In fact, bidimensional crystalline arrays of ATPase chains within the plane of the membrane were obtained in the presence of vanadate (36–39) or phosphate (9). Structural analysis (133) of these arrays indicates that the ATPase chains associate in a dimeric relationship (Figure 2).

The functional implication of such a dimeric association is still somewhat uncertain. Preparations believed to be in a monomeric form have been found to be enzymatically active (18, 19, 80, 87, 90–92, 110). However, doubts have been raised as to whether the detergent-solubilized preparations are really monomeric (122). Presently, two important points are well established: (*a*) All the phosphorylation and Ca sites corresponding to each 115,000-dalton chain are reactive, both in membrane-bound and in solubilized preparations; (b) the degree of Ca-binding cooperativity ($n_H > 3$) observed at low proton concentrations requires interaction of four binding domains, corresponding to two 115,000-dalton chains. This suggests that *the oligomeric association of ATPase chains permits full reactivity of the sites in each monomer, with the added control deriving from cooperative interaction within the dimer.*

COUPLING OF ENZYME AND TRANSPORT ACTIVITIES

The Catalytic and Transport Cycle

It was established by steady-state experimentation that SR vesicles accumulate 2 mol Ca per mol ATP utilized (46, 140). The mechanism of ATP utilization includes a phosphorylated enzyme intermediate that is formed by transfer of the ATP terminal phosphate onto an aspartyl residue of the catalytic site (5, 20, 95, 144). Subsequently, considerable effort has been directed to characterization of pre-steady state events by rapid kinetic experimentation (44, 75, 88, 137). It can be demonstrated (Figure 3) that when ATP is added to SR vesicles preincubated with Ca phosphoenzyme is formed rapidly. Then the 2 mol activating Ca (tightly bound to each mol of enzyme) is rapidly internalized, (i.e. cannot be displaced from the ATPase by La^{3+} added to the reaction medium), and the enzyme undergoes a rather slow decrease in intrinsic fluorescence, leading to Ca^{2+} release inside the vesicles. Finally the phosphorylated intermediate undergoes hydrolytic cleavage, and recycling of the enzyme yields constant rates of Pi production and Ca uptake (42, 72, 76).

At this point it is useful to write down (Scheme 1) a sequence of partial reactions for the catalytic and transport cycle of SR ATPase, which is based on the idea (77) that in order to sustain active transport, the enzyme must reside alternatively in at least two states with different affinity for the transported species and opposite orientation with respect to the plane of the membrane.

This type of scheme was used originally by de Meis & Vianna (29) to describe the reaction cycle of SR ATP, envisioning E as a state with high affinity and outward-oriented calcium sites, and *E as a state with low affinity and inward-oriented sites. Scheme 1 is a modification of the de Meis scheme, inasmuch as the sequential calcium-binding and dissociation mechanism is introduced for the reasons mentioned above (Equation 1). Therefore, Scheme 1 considers three (rather than two) conformational states: E, in the absence of calcium (intrinsic calcium-binding constant $\cong 10^5 \ M^{-1}$); E', following calcium bind-

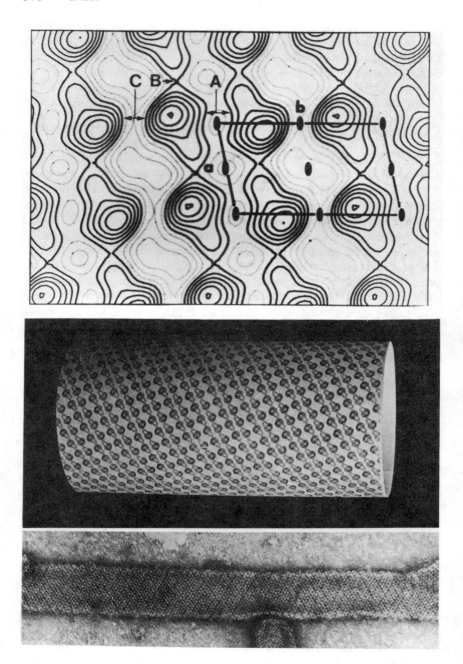

ing (apparent constant for cooperative calcium binding $\cong 10^6$ M^{-1}); and *E, with inward-oriented binding sites in the low-affinity ($> 10^3$ M^{-1}) state, produced by phosphorylation of the catalytic site by the substrate (Figure 4). Other additions pertinent to nucleotide and proton binding were also made. We will refer to and explain Scheme 1 as we proceed through the text. Presently, I will simply point out that the forward rate constants for enzyme phosphorylation with ATP (reaction 1 in Scheme 1) and for hydrolytic cleavage of the phosphoenzyme (reaction 6 in Scheme 1) are $\sim$ 150 (44, 137) and $\sim$ 60 sec^{-1} (72), respectively (25°C, pH 6.8, 80 mM KCl and 5 mM Mg^{2+}). Considering that the phosphorylated intermediate builds up to a level approximating the maximal number of catalytic sites and that the overall turnover is $\sim$ 10 sec^{-1} (75), it can be inferred that an important rate-limiting step must follow formation and precede hydrolytic cleavage of the phosphoenzyme (72).

Kinetic Effects of Ca and ATP

Ca^{2+}, in the μM range, is an absolute requirement for ATPase activity. When the reaction is started by adding ATP and Ca to SR ATPase preincubated with EGTA, the time course of enzyme phosphorylation is slower than that obtained by adding ATP to the enzyme preincubated with calcium (71, 124). Such a time delay is the kinetic expression of the slow mechanism of Ca binding Equation 1 and consequent enzyme activation. One can rationalize that the enzyme must be activated only *after* binding of the second Ca, to insure the 2:1 coupling ratio between Ca transport and ATP hydrolysis.

An interesting kinetic feature of such an activation is that the time course of phosphorylation following addition of ATP and Ca to enzyme preincubated with EGTA (*solid circles* in Figure 5) is significantly faster than the conformational change (*fluorescence signal* in Figure 5) produced by the addition of Ca (in the absence of ATP) to enzyme preincubated with EGTA. One would expect the opposite (enzyme activation before phosphorylation), unless ATP accelerates the Ca-dependent transition as proposed by several investigators (10, 42, 71, 121).

Figure 2   Electron-density maps of Ca^{2+}-ATPase crystals. The density map *(top figure)* was calculated in space group P1 using the averaged structure factors of the low dose data from electron micrographs. *Heavy contours* represent stain-excluding regions (protein); *lighter contours* represent negative stain. The unit cell as drawn contains ATPase dimers clustered around two fold rotation axes at the corner of the unit cells. Dimensions of the unit cell: a = 65 g Å; b = 114.3 Å; γ = 77.5°C. The ribbons of dimers that run parallel to the a axis of the crystal correspond to the right-handed helices in the electron micrograph *(bottom figure)* and in the computer-reconstructed density map folded into a cylinder *(middle figure)*. The observer is looking at the outer surface of the tubule. The bonding regions involved in the formation of dimers (A), dimer chains (B), and extended lattice (C) are indicated. *Top figure* map scale: 0.456 mm/Å. *Middle figure* map scale: 0.0680 mm/Å. *Bottom figure* magnification: $\times$ 150,000. (see 132 for details). This figure was kindly provided by Dr. Anthony Martonosi.

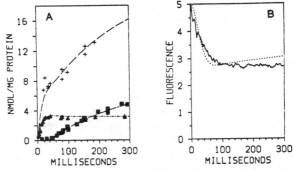

Figure 3   Early phase of phosphoenzyme formation (▲), calcium uptake (+), and P$_i$ production (■) in *A*, and intrinsic fluorescence decrease in *B*, following addition of 10 μM ATP to SR vesicles at 25°C and neutral pH (42). The data in *A* were obtained by quench-flow and the date in *B* by stopped-flow experimentation. The *interrupted lines* fitting the *experimental points* were obtained by a computer simulation based on Scheme 1 (see section on analysis).

In addition to its influence on Ca activation of the nonphosphorylated enzyme, ATP also has an accelerating effect on the evolution of the phosphoenzyme through the catalytic cycle (102, 136). Studies with TNP-nucleotide analogs indicate that this additional effect is likely due to ATP binding in exchange for ADP (111) at the site that is already phosphorylated (rather than binding to an independent site); therefore at this stage ATP is expected to bind with an affinity that is significantly different as compared to that of ATP for the nonphosphorylated catalytic site. In Scheme 1, I have indicated this "secondary" binding by placing ATP in parenthesis, to distinguish it from a strictly "Michaelis" complex. It is likely that in steady state the accelerating effect (68, 113) of the ATP "secondary" binding is on reaction 3 of Scheme 1, although in

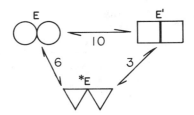

Figure 4   Diagram proposing that the catalytic and transport cycle of SR ATPase includes three (rather than two) main states: *E*, in the absence of Ca^{2+} (intrinsic Ca-binding constant ≅ 10^5 M$^-$), yielding the lowest intrinsic fluorescence; *E'* in the presence of Ca^{2+} (apparent constant for cooperative Ca binding ≅ 10^6 M^{-1}), yielding high intrinsic fluorescence; and **E*, produced by phosphorylation of the catalytic site (Ca sites internally oriented, affinity ≅ < 10^3 M^{-1}), yielding low (slightly higher than *E*) intrinsic fluorescence. The transitions among the three conformational states are indicated with *numbers* identical to those of the corresponding reactions in Scheme 1. The sequential reactions of these three states with ligands and substrates are also listed in Scheme 1.

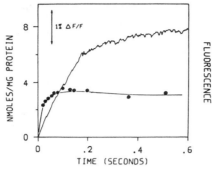

Figure 5 Intrinsic fluorescence rise *(continuous line)* and phosphoenzyme formation *(solid circles)* following addition of Ca alone (fluorescence), or Ca and ATP (phosphoenzyme) to SR ATPase deprived of calcium (42). The fluorescence transient was expected to be faster than the phosphorylation curve, because enzyme activation by Ca must preceed ATP utilization. However, enzyme phosphorylation occurs more rapidly, demonstrating an accelerating effect of ATP on the Ca-induced enzyme transition.

some conditions an accelerating effect of ATP on reaction 10 can also be demonstrated.

State of Ca Binding During the ATPase Cycle

Several types of experimental data indicate that the 2 mol of Ca that produce enzyme activation become "occluded" as a consequence of enzyme phosphorylation by ATP. The exact meaning of "occlusion" is related to the experimental evidence for this phenomenon. Experiments performed at near 0°C have shown that in the occluded state Ca is not easily dissociated from the enzyme following addition of EGTA but is dissociated if ADP is added to promote reversal of the phosphorylation reaction (31, 125, 126). In our laboratory, working at 25°C with the aid of rapid mixing equipment, we have shown that La^{3+} (or EGTA) chases the tightly bound calcium from the ATPase before but not after enzyme phosphorylation with ATP (12, 88); because La^{3+} added a few milliseconds after ATP blocks hydrolytic cleavage of the phosphoenzyme preventing completion of the first cycle, it is clear that Ca is occluded at a stage following enzyme phosphorylation and preceeding hydrolytic cleavage of P_i.

In order to satisfy the vectorial requirements of active transport, Ca^{2+} must be released into the lumen of the vesicles, before hydrolytic cleavage of the phophoenzyme and the beginning of a new enzyme cycle. Furthermore, the inward-oriented sites must release Ca^{2+} with a dissociation constant that is higher than that of the outward-oriented sites, in order to increase the Ca^{2+} concentration in the lumen of the vesicles. Determination of such a dissociation constant is not straightforward, because Ca binding to the low-affinity sites of the phosphoenzyme cannot be measured directly due to interference of other nonspecific low-affinity binding. It could be argued that the Ca^{2+} concentration that produces "back inhibition" of steady-state activity in leaky ATPase preparations reflects the dissociation constant of the low-affinity Ca sites; however, it may also reflect occupancy of the Mg sites. A comparative titration of the Ca sites in the high-affinity (nonphosphorylated enzyme) and low-affinity (phosphorylated enzyme) Ca state was obtained (16) following the spectroscopic signal of Ca occupancy in spin-labeled ATPase (Figure 6). These measurements yield dissociation constants of $\sim 10^{-6}$ and $\sim 10^{-3}$ M for the nonphosphorylated and phosphorylated enzyme, respectively (16, 67).

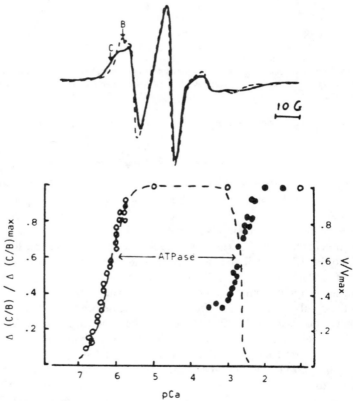

Figure 6 EPR spectra of spin-labeled SR ATPase in the absence *(dotted line)* and the presence *(solid line)* of Ca^{2+} and nucleotide. In the *lower figure* the change in the spectral parameter C/B (○ and ●) and ATPase activity *(broken line)* are plotted as a function of pCa, in the presence of ATP (●) or AMP-PNP (○). Previous to experimentation the SR vesicles were treated with Triton X-100 or sonication to prevent net accumulation of Ca upon addition of ATP. These measurements demonstrated a shift in the Ca affinity of the SR ATPase following enzyme phosphorylation with ATP (67).

Reversal of the Catalytic Cycle

If SR vesicles are filled with Ca by utilization of acetylphosphate (in place of ATP), and then EGTA (to lower the Ca^{2+} concentration in the medium), P_i, and ADP are added, the accumulated Ca is released from the vesicles and a proportional amount of ATP (2 Ca:ATP) is formed (3, 82, 97, 98). Such a reversal of the Ca pump includes formation of a phosphorylated intermediate by incorporation of P_i into the enzyme (97, 143). This phosphoenzyme is chemically equivalent to that formed by utilization of a "high-energy" substrate (i.e. ATP or acetylphosphate) in the forward direction of the pump. In these conditions reversal proceeds through repeated cycles, and the *overall* free-energy requirement for ATP formation is attributed to dissipation of the transmembrane Ca^{2+} gradient.

It is of interest that the enzyme sustains ATP $\rightleftharpoons$ Pi exchange (23) in the presence of high Ca^{2+}, even in preparations that are not able to maintain a transmembrane Ca^{2+} gradient. Furthermore, the enzyme can be phosphorylated with P_i even in the absence of a Ca^{2+} gradient, provided that Ca is removed (by addition of EGTA) from the enzyme. The latter reaction can be demonstrated directly with ^{32}P-P_i (100), or by monitoring H_2O $\rightleftharpoons$ P_i oxygen exchange (81). The difference between the phosphoenzyme formed (E $\sim$ P $\cdot$ Ca_2) with ATP in the presence of Ca and the phosphoenzyme (*E-P) formed wih P_i in the absence of Ca^{2+}, is that the former has a higher phosphorylation potential (i.e. forms ATP upon addition of ADP), and the latter has a low phosphorylation potential. In addition, *E-P Ca_2 has its Ca sites in the low-affinity state, while E $\sim$ P $\cdot$ Ca_2 is in the high-affinity state. Equilibration between the two forms is obtained by adding mM Ca^{2+} to *E-P (reaction 3 in Scheme 1), whereupon addition of ADP leads to formation of ATP (28, 85).

In conditions most commonly used for measurements of ATPase activity (25°C, neutral pH, 80 mM KCl, and 5 mM $MgCl_2$), the equilibrium constant for the phosphorylation reaction of the enzyme with P_i (reaction 6 in Scheme 1) is $\sim$ 1, with $\sim$ 60 sec^{-1} rate constant in the forward and reverse directions (72). Phosphorylation with P_i is favored by low pH and the absence of K^+ (21, 73) and by the presence of organic solvents such as dimethylsulfoxide (25). The effect of pH has been attributed to the catalytic intervention of protein residues dissociating H^+ with a pK near neutrality (73; see also Figure 7). In their dissociated form these residues would withdraw a proton from bound water, thereby assisting nucleophylic attack by the water oxygen on the phosphorus atom and producing hydrolytic cleavage of the phosphoenzyme (*steps 3 and 4* in Figure 7). In their protonated form, these residues would donate a proton to assist formation of leaving water upon P_i condensation with the carboxylate anion of the reactive protein residue (*steps 4 and 3* in reverse cycle in Figure 7). It is of interest that the pK of this residue is in turn influenced by the phosphorylation reaction (73). Concerning the effects of organic solvents, it was pointed out that the free energy required for phosphorylation is dependent, among others, on the presence of water; therefore organic solvents may favor enzyme phosphorylation with Pi, by reducing the water activity in the microscopic environment of the reaction (24, 25, 27).

Charge Displacement and Electrolyte Exchange

Translocation of Ca^{2+} across the membrane will produce charge imbalance if not compensated by movements of other electrolytes. Because the SR membrane is highly permeable to monovalent anions and cations, it is expected that movements of electrolytes through channels that are distinct from the Ca pump

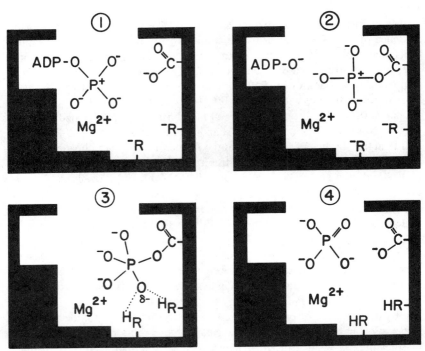

Figure 7 Example of a phosphoryl transfer reaction (ATP terminal phosphate forming a mixed anhydride with an aspartyl residue at the catalytic site) and subsequent hydrolytic cleavage of the phosphoenzyme. Note the general base assisted catalysis, whereby two (or one) protons are withdrawn from water, favoring nucleophylic attack of the water oxygen on the phosphorus atom. This mechanism is consistent with the effect of *specific* derivatization of SR ATPase with dicyclohexylcarbodiimide, that blocks hydrolytic cleavage of the phosphoenzyme and enzyme phosphorylation with P_i without inhibiting Ca-dependent enzyme phosphorylation with ATP (120). This mechanism is also consistent with the pH dependence of these reactions in SR ATPase (73, 102).

will compensate for the electrogenic effect of the Ca^{2+} pump, if any. The question, however, remains whether the Ca^{2+} pump is *intrinsically* electrogenic, or if it includes counter- or co-transport of compensating electrolytes. Early suggestions (83) on a role of Mg^{2+} as a counterion do not appear to be realistic (13). In analogy to the Na^+ pump, K^+ has been suggested as a counterion for the Ca^{2+} pump (14). A special case is that of H^+. There is no question that Ca complexation by the SR ATPase requires participation of a residue dissociating with pK near neutrality, and that Ca and protons exhibit competitive binding in the nonphosphorylated (58) and in the phosphorylated (24) enzyme. Therefore, depending on the pH, binding of Ca to the high-affinity Ca sites releases one proton. It is expected then that when Ca is released on the other side of the membrane, a proton will bind again to the site. In fact, a change in the pK of the participating residue may well be operative in assisting the reduction in Ca affinity of the site as required for active transport. Whether a Ca^{2+} vs H^+ exchange occurs cyclically and is a requirement for the operation of the pump is difficult to demonstrate unambiguously, owing to the high passive permeability of the SR membrane to H^+ and collapse of any putative H^+ gradient through independent channels. The problem of Ca^{2+} vs H^+ exchange has been discussed in detail by Inesi & Hill (69).

THE WORK OF THE PUMP

Free-Energy Utilization

The useful work performed by the SR pump is related to the difference of Ca^{2+} chemical potential in the two compartments delimited by the membrane or, in practice, to the Ca^{2+} gradient across the membrane. In the absence of an electrical potential, the *free-energy* requirement for transport of two Ca ions against this gradient is given by:

$$\Delta G = 2RT \ln \frac{[Ca^{2+}]_{SR\ lumen}}{[Ca^{2+}]_{medium}} \qquad 2.$$

Considering that a concentration ratio of 3–4 orders of magnitude is developed by SR vesicles in vitro at 25°C, 8–11 Kcal per cycle are required when the pump operates at, or near, this level. Early essays on this subject (46–48, 63) established that this requirement is in fact compatible with the ΔG of substrates (i.e. ATP) utilized by the pump. It was also pointed out (63) that if the pump operates with a fixed stoichiometry (Ca:ATP), the pumping *efficiency* will be less than optimal at lower Ca^{2+} gradients due to a lesser free-energy requirement for translocating Ca^{2+} in the face of the same free-energy yield by the substrate. In this case the excess free energy is dissipated as heat or for some other nonaccounted effect. Nearly perfect efficiency is obtained only when the separate free energy contributions of ATP hydrolysis and Ca^{2+} transport are nearly equal and of opposite sign, i.e. the system is near equilibrium. Of course, if the ATP and Ca^{2+} chemical potential charges were actually equal, one would have perfect efficiency, but no net flux. Estimates of this type have been developed by Tanford, who also calculated that in the living skeletal muscle at rest, the Ca^{2+} gradient across the SR membrane and the cytoplasmic concentrations of ATP and its products are close to the values predicted for the equilibrium state of the ATP-driven Ca^{2+} pump (127).

It was demonstrated experimentally (16, 67) that utilization of ATP results in a 3–4 order-of-magnitude reduction in the *affinity* of the ATPase sites for Ca (Figure 6). The free-energy requirement for such a reduction of affinity involving two sites per enzyme is

$$\Delta G = 2RT \ln \frac{K_a^{out}}{K_a^{in}} = 2RT \ln \frac{\sim 10^6 \, M^{-1}}{10^3 \text{ or } 10^2 \, M^{-1}} \cong 8\text{–}11 \text{ Kcal} \qquad 3.$$

This value is equivalent to that obtained from calculations (Equation 2) based on the maximal gradient developed by the pump. This is expected, because the gradient is a consequence of the change in *affinity*. Representation of the pump in terms of change in *affinity* (67) of protein-binding sites is conceptually useful inasmuch as it points out the enzyme's participation and mechanistic role in the energy transfer from ATP to Ca^{2+} chemical potential.

The change in affinity of the Ca-binding sites, which is a key mechanistic feature in the process of energy transduction for active transport, has been discussed by Tanford (128–130) in terms of a *change in the chemical potential of the bound ligand*.

An interesting corollary of this discussion is that, given a set of experimental conditions, the change in Ca-binding affinity is a *constant* resulting from a protein perturbation that produces two discrete states. Therefore, the maximal Ca^{2+} concentration that can be accumulated by the system will be limited (kinetically) by the dissociation constant of the low-affinity state. It should be possible, in principle, to raise this concentration further by increasing the free energy of the coupled substrate; however, such a rise would occur with extremely slow kinetics because the enzyme ceases to be an effective catalyst at Ca^{2+} concentrations exceeding the titration range of the sites in the low affinity state. The fact that in physiological conditions the free energy of ATP is just right to obtain the maximal gradient (i.e. the pump is near equilibrium) is simply an expression of a marvelous biological adaptation, whereby the free energy of ATP hydrolysis, the changes in Ca-binding affinities of the ATPase, and the Ca requirements for control of myofilament activation are well matched.

Free-Energy Changes in the Partial Reactions of the Catalytic and Transport Cycle

A more detailed representation of the catalytic and transport cycle of the SR ATPase is rendered possible by the measurement of equilibrium and rate constants of the partial reactions comprising the cycle (44, 72, 114, 115, 137). Based on known and inferred constants, simulations of the observed kinetics have been carried out to test and illustrate various reaction schemes. Thereby, free-energy diagrams have been constructed (71, 115) calculating the standard free-energy change for each partial reaction from pertinent equilibrium constants. In the standard free-energy diagrams (Figure 8), the enzyme returns to its original energy level after a cycle; the net drop of free energy between the first and the last partial reaction corresponds to the free energy of ATP hydrolysis, which is the free energy input into the cycle. This energy may be recovered to a variable degree by the system, depending on the Ca^{2+} concentrations on the two sides of the membrane (i.e. the gradient).

A multistep mechanism of catalysis and coupled transport includes two types of partial reactions: isomeric transitions that do not entail binding or dissociation of ligands (i.e. $E \rightarrow {}^*E; E \sim P \cdot Ca_2 \rightarrow {}^*E\text{-}P \cdot Ca_2; E \cdot Ca \rightarrow E' \cdot Ca; E \cdot P_i \rightarrow E\text{-}P$), and binding reactions that by their own nature consist of association and dissociation events (i.e. $E + Ca \rightarrow E \cdot Ca; E + ATP \rightarrow E \cdot ATP; E + P_i \rightarrow E \cdot P_i$, and others). In the former case, the equilibrium constant is independent of the choice of standard state

$$(\text{e.g. } K = \frac{[E - P]}{[E \cdot P_i]} = n),$$

and the free energy derived from such a relation ($\Delta G = RT \ln n$) is a standard value that does not need to be corrected for the total concentrations of the two species. On the contrary, the binding reactions undergo second-order equilibration

$$(\text{e.g. } K = \frac{[E \cdot P_i]}{[E] [P_i]} = n \text{ M}^{-1}),$$

and the standard free energy applies only to cases in which the concentration of reagents and products is 1 M. Therefore, the standard free energies of binding reactions must be corrected for the concentration of ligand (see examples in Figure 8) to yield the "basic" (53, 54, 57) free energy that will be operative in a specific set of conditions. This can be done for steady-state conditions (115) in which the concentrations of ligands are maintained approximately constant, but it is more complex for pre–steady state conditions, because in this case the concentrations of ligands are transient. At nearly physiological concentrations of ligands, the basic free energies of the binding and dissociation reactions are

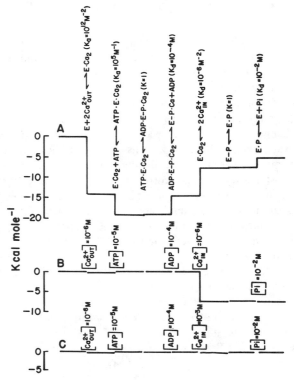

Figure 8 Diagrams of "standard" (*A*) and "basic" (*B* and *C*) free-energy changes for the partial reactions of a "simplified" catalytic and transport cycle of SR ATPase. The number of partial reactions was reduced to a minimal number for the purpose of clarity. The constants are approximative. The concentrations of ligands for *B* and *C* are examples possibly encountered in experimentation with SR vesicles.

much smaller than their standard values. For instance (Figure 8), binding of 2 mol of Ca to 1 mol of enzyme with affinity $\simeq 10^{12}$ M^{-2} yields 16.4 Kcal in standard conditions ([Ca^{2+}] = 1 M), whereas the basic free energy is $\simeq$ zero in the presence of $\sim 10^{-6}$ M Ca^{2+}. On the other hand, dissociation of two Ca ions from 1 mol of enzyme with affinity $\simeq 10^3$ M^{-2} requires 8.2 Kcal in standard condition, but yields 8.2 Kcal of basic free energy in the presence of $\sim 10^{-6}$ M Ca^{2+} (no gradient) and nearly zero basic free energy in the presence of $\sim 10^{-3}$ M Ca^{2+} (maximal gradient). For this reason the utilization of the free energy derived from 1 mol of ATP for transport of 2 mol of Ca (i.e. *efficiency*) is proportional to the Ca^{2+} gradient.

These considerations are also important from the kinetic point of view, because correction of the standard free energies by the ligand concentrations fills the "energy wells" corresponding to the binding reactions. A diagram of "basic" free energies in condition permitting rapid flow of reaction does not display the large variations seen in the standard free-energies diagram. This prevents accumulation of intermediates in the low-energy wells.

"Basic" energy changes, however, do not account for the chemical potentials related to a distribution of enzyme states. In fact, for any of the partial reactions producing a transformation of state a to state b, the basic free energy (ΔG_{ab}) can be corrected for the distribution of states a and b to yield the "gross free-energy" change:

$$\Delta \mu'_{ab} = \Delta G'_{ab} + RT \ln (p_a/p_b)$$

where p_a and p_b are the fractions of enzyme molecules in states a and b, respectively. To this effect, Hill (53, 54, 57) has introduced and defined a statistical method yielding the distribution of states by the use of a grand partition function, which takes into account equilibrium constants, concentration of ligands, and energies of interactions among homologous and heterogeneous species (cooperatively). This statistical analysis has been used for studies of SR properties at equilibrium (58).

The importance of "gross" free energy even for kinetic flow may be appreciated intuitively if one considers the Ca-binding reaction of the ATPase cycle in steady state. Given a binding constant of $10^{12} \, M^{-2}$ for binding of 2 mol of Ca to 1 mol of enzyme, in the presence of $1 \times 10^{-6} \, M \, Ca^{2+}$ the "basic" free energy is zero (see Figure 8B). Therefore, no net binding is expected. Yet, due to a flow of free enzyme produced by the hydrolytic reaction, the equilibrium is displaced and the binding step is continuously presented with free enzyme that renders the "gross" free energy negative and promotes, in fact, forward flow of the overall reaction.

It is noteworthy that even though the values for the "basic" and "gross" energy changes of the partial reactions may be different, the sums of the "basic" and "gross" energies over all reactions of the complete cycyle must be equal, as both correspond to the overall potential of the entire reaction that is only dependent on the concentrations of reactants and products in solution (i.e. the catalyst in its various forms drops out).

An interesting discussion has recently developed as to whether energy transduction for active transport can be traced and localized in one of the partial reactions of the catalytic cycle by following the *standard chemical potential of the bound ligands* (128, 129, 132). It was pointed out (55–57) in this regard that the partial reactions of the cycle involve the enzyme as well as the ligands; although potential changes can be estimated accurately after completion of the cycle, it is impossible to decide at what stage energy is transfered from one ligand (e.g. ATP) to the enzyme and from the enzyme to the other ligand (e.g. Ca). Accordingly, a given chemical potential can be attributed totally to a ligand only when the ligand is in solution, before binding to the enzyme or after dissociating from the enzyme. Having noted these concepts, it must be emphasized that characterization of partial reactions is indeed useful in understanding the mechanism of active transport and coupled enzyme catalysis, inasmuch as it establishes the *sequence* that is necessary for the reactions to accomplish useful work. For instance, we have learned (71, 72, 76) that two Ca ions must bind to an enzyme molecule before the enzyme can be phosphorylated with ATP; these two Ca ions are internalized only as a consequence of enzyme phosphorylation, and the phosphoenzyme is hydrolyzed only after the two Ca ions are released inside the vesicles. This sequence has been very effectively discussed by Jencks (78, 79) in terms of "rules", which are also implied in papers by Tanford (128–132) and Hill (57). It should be understood that these "rules" may not be absolute. For instance, it is conceivable that the phosphoenzyme may undergo hydrolysis even before dissociating Ca, albeit at a very slow rate. Significant flow through "nonideal" routes would reduce the 2:1 coupling ratio of Ca transport to ATP hydrolysis ("slippage of the pump") (8). In fact, experimentally, a perfect 2:1 ratio is rarely obtained, even when passive "leak" of transported Ca is not significant.

Molecular Mechanisms

Turning back to the chemistry of the coupling mechanism, we must first take into account the major role of enzyme phosphorylation, as it is demonstrated experimentally that *transfer of the ATP terminal phosphate onto an aspartyl residue of the catalytic site is followed by internalization of bound Ca (Figure 3) and a reduction in strength of binding* (Figure 6). Another interesting finding is that vanadate binding at the catalytic site (as an analog of a pentacoordinate transition state of phosphate) also inhibits Ca binding (Figure 9). Therefore, occupancy of the phosphorylation site, whether stabilized by covalent or electrostatic interactions, has a determinant influence on the Ca sites. Conversely, Ca occupancy of the transport sites has a determinant influence on the phosphorylation site, because the enzyme • Ca complex can be phosphorylated with ATP but not with P_i, and following Ca dissociation the enzyme can be phosphorylated with P_i but not with ATP. Such a mutual destabilization of phosphate and Ca is not due to actual overlap of the binding sites, because nucleotide occupancy, or chemical derivatizations of the catalytic site producing selective inhibition of enzyme phosphorylation with either P_i or ATP, do not interfere with Ca binding (Table 1). Therefore specific perturbations produced at one site, must be transmitted at some (even very small) distance to produce destabilization of the other site.

With respect to the phosphate (catalytic) site, we know that its physical environment varies greatly, depending on whether the site is actually phosphorylated and whether the Ca sites are occupied or not. This is demonstrated by the very high fluorescence enhancement of the nucleotide analog of TNP-AMP bound (in place of the ADP moiety) at the catalytic site, following

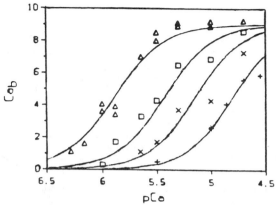

Figure 9   Reduction of the Ca-binding affinity of SR ATPase by vanadate (73). Δ, Control; □, 5 μM vanadate; ×, 20 μM vanadate; +, 100 μM vanadate.

enzyme phosphorylation with P_i in the absence of Ca^{2+}, and to a lesser extent following enzyme phosphorylation with ATP in the presence of Ca^{2+} (36, 111, 139). This effect is due to immobilization of the bound TNP-AMP and a reduced polarity in its environment when the enzyme is phosphorylated. It is likely that changes produced by Ca dissociation contribute to lower the free energy required for P_i utilization to form an acylphosphate at the catalytic site (K p≅ 1), a reaction that is otherwise very unfavorable in solution. Addition of Ca reverses these effects and prevents the phosphorylation reaction with P_i; in this case, ATP is required as a substrate for the phosphorylation reaction.

With respect to Ca destabilization by phosphate, it is noteworthy that occupancy of the catalytic site by a nucleotide analog that is unable to phosphorylate the enzyme (e.g. AMPPNP or AMPPCP) does not interfere with Ca binding (Table 1). Interference is produced when the nucleotide terminal phosphate is transferred to the enzyme. This effect is produced as well by vanadate binding, in virtue of the ability of vanadate to act as stereoanalog of a phosphate transition state. This suggests a significant displacement of the phosphate moiety within its catalytic site, from the binding location within the "Michaelis" complex to its actual phosphorylating position. It is of interest that the Ca sites are affected by occupancy of the phosphate sites, *even in the absence of Ca*. This is demonstrated by phosphorylating the enzyme with P_i in the absence of Ca; the phosphoenzyme so obtained requires mM (rather than μM) Ca^{2+} in order to form ATP upon addition of ADP (28, 85). *Therefore the interdependence of phosphate and Ca sites involves and requires participation of the protein and is present even in the absence of the ligand.* Mutual destabilization is likely to occur by means of structural perturbations possibly producing displacement of carbonyl oxygens, changes in proton dissociation

Table 1 Effect of catalytic site perturbations on Ca binding and enzyme phosphorylation with ATP (in the presence of Ca^{2+}) or Pi (in the absence of Ca^{2+})[a]

Catalytic site perturbation	Ca^{2+} binding	Enzyme phosphorylation	
		with ATP	with P_i
Control	8–10	3–5	4–6
DCC	6–8	3–4	0
FITC	6–8	0	4.5
AMP-PNP	8–10	—	—

[a] Values are expressed in nmol/mg protein. In the appropriate conditions (120), derivatization with DCC (dicyclohexylcarbodiimide) inhibits the Pi reaction but does not effect Ca binding and enzyme phosphorylation with ATP. Derivatization with FITC (Fluorescein isothiocyanate) inhibits the ATP reaction but does not affect Ca binding or the Pi reaction. Catalytic site occupancy by AMP-PNP (an inactive ATP analog) does not affect Ca binding. These measurements, made in the author's laboratory by D. Lewis, demonstrate that various steric obstructions of the catalytic site do not interfere directly with Ca binding.

constants, and/or displacement of bound water. Such perturbations influence Ca complexation by the enzyme, just as protonation of carboxyl groups does for Ca complexation by EGTA.

Because destabilization effects are produced by Ca or vanadate binding, in addition to ATP utilization, it is clear that free energy generated by ligand binding can be utilized to produce protein perturbations. In this case, the net free-energy change produced during equilibration of a pertinent binding reaction includes components related to ligand placement in a stable position (low free-energy level) and to residual motion of the ligand at the binding site, *as well as a positive component related to ligand-induced displacement of the enzyme from its own most stable state* (57). In most cases such displacements are related to local perturbations. On the other hand, a special case is that of *conformational changes,* which are distinguished from *local perturbations* on the basis of extensive propagation of the change through the protein molecule. From the thermodynamic standpoint, two different conformational states may be envisioned as having their own individual energy wells in which each state is most stable, while a local perturbation would simply displace the same state a bit higher from the most stable level in the same energy well. A conformational change of SR ATPase can be demonstrated experimentally (15, 30, 45, 62, 109) following Ca binding to the specific sites involved in enzyme activation and transport of the divalent cation. In analogy to the conformational change produced by oxygen binding to hemoglobin, the ATPase conformational change is ligand (Ca) induced and occurs in the absence of enzyme phosphorylation by the substrate (although it may occur more rapidly in the presence of ATP). This conformational change is undoubtly related to the cooperative mechanism of Ca binding and enzyme activation (71).

It is likely that another conformation state is produced by enzyme phosphorylation, to account for the reduction in affinity and change in orientation of the Ca sites. In fact, bidimensional crystals of ATPase are obtained in the presence of vanadate, which produces a state analogous to membrane phosphorylation; no crystallization is obtained by simply adding Ca, or removing Ca with EGTA.

In conclusion, the central feature of the coupling mechanism is a mutual destabilization of the phosphate and Ca sites (Figure 10). The idea of long-range effects among binding sites occupied by homologous or heterogeneous ligands was originally introduced by Wyman (142) with the formalization of "linked functions and reciprocal effects" as they apply to oxygen and proton binding to hemoglobin. The concept of mutual destabilization has been subsequently discussed in depth (57, 78, 79, 128, 141). *Experimentation* with sarcoplasmic reticulum has permitted *demonstration* of a very important point: mutual destabilization can occur by means of noncovalent binding (vanadate vs Ca binding); *as well as* by covalent interactions (phosphorylation vs Ca binding); then, the energy derived from *both* noncovalent and covalent interactions can be utilized to overcome thermodynamic barriers within the enzyme cycle.

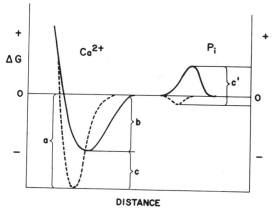

DISTANCE

Figure 10 Hypothetical diagram illustrating reciprocal destabilization of enzyme domains through a conformational change. The standard free energy of binding (electrostatic or covalent) is plotted as a function of distance of the ligands (Ca^{2+} or P_i) from their respective binding domains on the enzyme. A negative ΔG indicates strong binding; a positive ΔG indicates a strong tendency for dissociation (or for EP to breakdown). *a* Is the standard free energy of Ca binding in the absence of a destabilization effect; *b* is the standard free energy of Ca binding taking into account the free energy (*c*) required for the destabilization effect. Note that *c* is utilized to confer a positive ΔG component to the P_i reaction. Experimentally, this destabilization is manifested by a change in the equilibrium constant for the reaction $E + P_i \rightleftharpoons EP$, from > 1 in the absence of Ca^{2+} to $<< 1$ in the presence of Ca^{2+}. Therefore, addition of Ca^{2+} to preformed EP will destabilize (confer "high energy" character to) EP. Conversely, in the presence of Ca, the phosphorylation reaction will require a "high energy" substrate (i.e. ATP). It should be understood that the observed level of *b* does not allow direct estimate of *c*, which can only be inferred indirectly from the free energy required to destabilize the reciprocal site. For this reason, it cannot be argued that a high (observed) free energy of binding is necessarily related to a destabilization (or conformation) effect. Whether destabilization effects occur or not depends on the intrinsic properties of the enzyme.

Finally, it is of interest to consider that the hydrolytic ATPase reaction is not directly instrumental in the coupling mechanism, but it is simply necessary to cleave the phosphoenzyme following Ca release inside the vesicles, thereby permitting repeated cycles of Ca transport.

Analysis of Reaction Mechanisms

Given the complexity of the interdependent reactions comprising the catalytic and transport cycle of SR ATPase, it is difficult to envision intuitively how the system should behave in its detailed functions on the basis of a proposed mechanism. Therefore, without adequate analysis, one falls short of testing if any given mechanism is even possible. The simplest analysis and simulations are those limited to partial reactions of the ATPase cycle. For instance, Ca binding in the absence of ATP has been measured in equilibrium and kinetic conditions, and the experimental results subjected to detailed analysis (Figure 3) (32, 71). Another partial reaction subjected to equilibrium and kinetic analysis is the enzyme phosphorylation with P_i in the absence of Ca (6, 27, 73, 86, 89, 117). Other reactions that cannot be measured at equilibrium were studied by kinetic experimentation, and the pertinent constants were so derived (44, 72, 114, 115, 137). The constants obtained by experimental studies of the partial reactions, together with some assumed values for other constants that are not as yet determined experimentally, have been used to model the experimentally observed, pre–steady state and steady-state kinetic behavior of the entire catalytic and transport system. This type of analysis, although a bit complex, is particularly informative when aimed at simulating multiple and simultaneous kinetic signals such as enzyme phosphorylation, Ca translocation, P_i production, and intrinsic fluorescence transients. An example of this type of simulation (42), based on Scheme 1, is shown in Figure 3. It will be recalled that Scheme 1 is a modification of that originally proposed by de Meis & Vianna, (29) inasmuch as the sequential mechanism of Ca binding is introduced. It is assumed in Scheme 1 that enzyme phosphorylation produces in one step (reaction 3) a reduction in affinity of the Ca site as well as a reversal of the cooperative interaction of the sites. Three distinct states of the enzyme (as opposed to two states proposed by other schemes) are envisioned by this reaction mechanism (Figure 4): E in the absence of Ca^{2+}, E' following cooperative Ca binding, and *E following phosphorylation and loss of Ca affinity.

The highly satisfactory simulation shown in Figure 3 does not prove that the reaction mechanism outlined in Scheme 1 is totally correct, but simply that it is consistent with available experimental data. This simulation is not, by itself, a comprehensive solution. For instance, it does not consider the effects of H^+ and ATP secondary binding. It does not require explicit consideration of functional consequences of possible enzyme dimerization (61). Some of the constants used may be imprecise. Nevertheless, from this modeling we learn that the principal kinetic constraint follows enzyme phosphorylation by ATP and precedes Ca^{2+} release inside the vesicles and hydrolytic cleavage of the phosphoenzyme. Modeling renders it possible to introduce and test the sequential binding mechanism and match it with the requirements of enzyme activation and the kinetics of the entire cycle. It also makes it possible to demonstrate the correct sequence of the partial reactions and reproduce the distribution of the enzyme into the three conformational states revealed by the observed transients of intrinsic fluorescence.

CONCLUSIONS

Vesicular fragments of SR membrane provide a highly favorable system for detailed studies on the mechanism of Ca transport and coupled enzyme catalysis. The specificity of the system, the significant number of measurable intermediate states, and the tight coupling of substrate utilization and cation transport contribute not only to the understanding of SR function, but also to the general subject of energy transduction in biological systems. Equilibrium and kinetic measurements of the partial reactions of the cycle—and related analysis—are quite advanced. As the number of experimentally determined constants increases, analysis and simulations will become more stringent, and a detailed description of the entire catalytic and transport cycle will be obtained in definitive terms. It is clear that the ability of the ATPase protein to sustain positive and negative cooperativity between calcium-calcium and calcium-phosphate sites, respectively, is the basic mechanistic instrument of the Ca pump. The next level of information must be obtained with regard to the chemistry of the catalytic mechanism and to high-resolution molecular structure. Gene identification and recombinant DNA experiments will be undoubtly helpful in studying relationships of structure and function. Future studies must be also directed to control mechanisms, such as those exercised by calmodulin on the Ca^{2+}-ATPase of the erythrocyte membrane and by phosphorylation of accessory proteins on the Ca^{2+}-ATPase of cardiac SR.

Literature Cited

1. Allen, G, Trinnaman, B., Green, N. 1980. The primary structure of the calcium ion-transporting adenosine triphosphatase protein of rabbit skeletal sarcoplasmic reticulum. Peptides derived from digestion with cyanogen bromide, and the sequences of three long extramembranous segments. Biochem. J. 187:591–616

2. Anderson, D., Mostov, K., Blobel, G. 1983. Mechanisms of integration of de novo–synthesized polypeptides into membranes: Signal recognition particle is required for integration into microsomal membranes of calcium ATPase and of lens MP26 but not of cytochrome b5. Proc. Natl. Acad. Sci. USA 80:7249–53

3. Bargolie, B., Hasselbach, W., Makinose, M. 1971. Activation of calcium efflux by ADP and inorganic phosphate. FEBS Lett. 12:267–68

4. Barrabin, H., Scofano, H., Inesi, G.

1984. Adenosinetriphosphatase site stoichiometry in sarcoplasmic reticulum vesicles and purified enzyme. *Biochemistry* 23:1542–48

5. Bastide, F., Meissner, G., Fleischer, S., Post, R. L. 1973. Similarity of the active site of phosphorylation of the ATPase for transport of sodium and potassium ions in kidney to that for transport of calcium ions in sarcoplasmic reticulum of muscle. *J. Biol. Chem.* 248:8385–91

6. Beil, F., Chak, D., Hasselbach, W. 1977. Phosphorylation from inorganic phosphate and ATP synthesis of sarcoplasmic membranes. *Europ. J. Biochem.* 81:151–64

7. Boland, R., Martonosi, A., Tillack, T. 1974. Developmental changes in the composition and function of sarcoplasmic reticulum. *J. Biol. Chem.* 249:612–23

8. Berman, M. 1982. Energy coupling and uncoupling of active calcium transport by sarcoplasmic reticulum membranes. *Biochim. Biophys. Acta* 694:95–121

9. Castellani, L., Hardwicke, P. 1983. Crystalline structure of sarcoplasmic reticulum from scallop. *J. Cell Biology* 97:557–61

10. Champeil, P., Gingold, M., Guillain, F., Inesi, G. 1983. Effect of magnesium on the calcium-dependent transient kinetics of sarcoplasmic reticulum ATPase, studied by stopped flow fluorescence and phosphorylation. *J. Biol. Chem.* 258:4453–58

11. Chevallier, J., Butow, R. 1971. Calcium binding to the sarcoplasmic reticulum of rabbit skeletal muscle. *Biochemistry* 10:2733–37

12. Chiesi, M., Inesi, G. 1979. The use of quench reagents for resolution of single transport cycles in sarcoplasmic reticulum. *J. Biol. Chem.* 254:10370–77

13. Chiesi, M., Inesi, G. 1981. Mg^{++} and Mn^{++} modulation of Ca^{++} transport and ATPase activity in sarcoplasmic reticulum vesicles. *Arch. Biochem. Biophys.* 208:586–92

14. Chiu, V., Haynes, D. 1980. Rapid kinetic studies of active Ca^{++} transport in sarcoplasmic reticulum. *J. Membr. Biol.* 56:219–39

15. Coan, C., Inesi, G. 1977. Calcium dependent effect of ATP on spin-labeled sarcoplasmic reticulum. *J. Biol. Chem.* 252:3044–49

16. Coan, C., Verjovski-Almeida, S., Inesi, G. 1979. Ca^{++} regulation of conformational states in the transport cycle of spin-labeled sarcoplasmic reticulum ATPase. *J. Biol. Chem.* 254:2968–74

17. Deamer, D., Baskin, R. 1969. Ultra-structure of sarcoplasmic reticulum preparations. *J. Cell Biol.* 42:296–307

18. Dean, W., Tanford, C. 1977. Reactivation of lipid-depleted Ca^{++}-ATPase by a nonionic detergent. *J. Biol. Chem.* 252:3551–53

19. Dean, W., Tanford, C. 1978. Properties of a delipidated, detergent-activated Ca^{++}-ATPase. *Biochemistry* 17:1683–90

20. Degani, C., Boyer, P. 1973. A borohydride reduction method for characterization of the acyl phosphate linkage in proteins and its application to sarcoplasmic reticulum adenosine triphosphatase. *J. Biol. Chem.* 248:8222–26

21. deMeis, L. 1972. Phosphorylation of the membranous protein of the sarcoplasmic reticulum: Inhibition by Na^+ and K^+. *Biochemistry* 11:2460–65

22. deMeis, L. 1980. Transport and energy transduction in the sarcoplasmic reticulum. In *Membrane Structure and Function* ed. E. Bittar. New York: Wiley

23. de Meis, L., Carvalho, M., Sorenson, M. 1975. ATP = Pi exchange catalyzed by sarcoplasmic reticulum with and without a Ca^{++} concentration gradient. In *Concepts of Membranes in Regulation and Excitation,* ed. M. Rocha e Silva, G. Suarez-Kurtz, pp. 7–19. New York: Raven

24. deMeis, L., Inesi, G. 1982. ATP synthesis by sarcoplasmic reticulum ATPase following Ca^{++}, pH, temperature, and water activity jumps. *J. Biol. Chem.* 257:1289–94

25. deMeis, L., Martins, O., Alves, E. 1980. Role of water, H^+ and temperature on the synthesis of ATP by the sarcoplasmic reticulum ATPase in the absence of a Ca^{++} gradient. *Biochemistry* 19:4252–61

26. deMeis, L., Masuda, H. 1974. Phosphorylation of the sarcoplasmic reticulum membrane by orthophosphate through two different reactions. *Biochemistry* 13:2057–62

27. deMeis, L., Otero, A., Martins, O., Alves, E., Inesi, G., Nakamoto, R. 1982. Phosphorylation of sarcoplasmic reticulum ATPase by orthophosphate in the absence of a Ca^{++} gradient: Contribution of water activity to the enthalpy and the entropy changes. *J. Biol. Chem.* 257:4993–98

28. deMeis, L., Tume, R. 1977. A new mechanism by which an H^+ concentration gradient drives the synthesis of adenosine triphosphate, pH jump, and adenosine triphosphate synthesis by the Ca^{++}-dependent adenosine triphosphatase of sarcoplasmic reticulum. *Biochemistry* 16:4455–63

29. deMeis, L., Vianna, A. 1979. Energy interconversion by the Ca^{++}-dependent ATPase of the sarcoplasmic reticulum. *Ann. Rev. Biochem.* 48:275–92

30. Dupont, Y. 1976. Fluorescence studies of the sarcoplasmic reticulum calcium pump. *Biochem. Biophys. Res. Commun.* 71:544–50

31. Dupont, Y. 1980. Occlusion of divalent cations in the phosphorylated calcium pump of sarcoplasmic reticulum. *Europ. J. Biochem.* 109:231–38

32. Dupont, Y. 1982. Low-temperature studies of the sarcoplasmic reticulum calcium pump mechanism of calcium binding. *Biochim. Biophys. Acta* 688:75–87

33. Dupont, Y., Harrison, S., Hasselbach, W. 1973. Molecular organization in the sarcoplasmic reticulum membrane studied by X-ray diffraction. *Nature* 244:555–58

34. Dupont, Y., Leigh, J. 1978. Transient kinetics of sarcoplasmic reticulum Ca + Mg ATPase studied by fluorescence. *Nature* 273:396–98

35. Dupont, Y., Pougeois, R. 1983. Evaluation of water acitivity in the free or phosphorylated catalytic site of Ca^{++}-ATPase. *FEBS Lett.* 156:93–98

36. Dux, L., Martonosi, A. 1983. Two-dimensional arrays of proteins in sarcoplasmic reticulum and purified Ca^{++}-ATPase vesicles treated with vanadate. *J. Biol. Chem.* 258:2599–603

37. Dux, L., Martonosi, A. 1983. Ca^{++}-ATPase membrane crystals in sarcoplasmic reticulum: The effect of trypsin digestion. *J. Biol. Chem.* 258:10111–15

38. Dux, L., Martonosi, A. 1983. The regulation of ATPase-ATPase interactions in sarcoplasmic reticulum membrane. I. The effects of Ca^{++}, ATP, and inorganic phosphate. *J. Biol. Chem.* 258:11896–902

39. Dux, L., Martonosi, A. 1983. The regulation of ATPase-ATPase interactions in sarcoplasmic reticulum membrane. II. The influence of membrane potential. *J. Biol. Chem.* 258:11903–7

40. Ebashi, S., Lipman, F. 1962. Adenosine triphosphate-linked concentration of calcium ions in a particular fraction of rabbit muscle. *J. Cell Biol.* 14:389–400

41. Eckert, K., Grosse, R., Levitsky, D., Kuzmin, A., Smirnov, V., Repke, K. 1977. Determination and functional significance of low affinity nucleotide sites of $Ca^{++} + Mg^{++}$–dependent ATPase of sarcoplasmic reticulum. *Acta Biol. Med. Germanica* 36:1–10

42. Fernandez-Belda, F., Kurzmack, M., Inesi, G. 1984. A comparative study of

43. Fronticelli, C., Bucci, E., Shamoo, A. 1984. Solvent perturbation evidence for a two-state system regulated by calcium in sarcoplasmic reticulum ATPase. *Biophys. Chem.* 19:255–58

44. Froehlich, J., Taylor, E. 1975. Transient-state kinetic studies of sarcoplasmic reticulum adenosine triphosphatase. *J. Biol. Chem.* 250:2013–21

45. Guillain, F., Champeil, P., Lacapere, J., Gingold, M. 1981. Stopped-flow and rapid quenching measurement of the transient steps induced by calcium binding to sarcoplasmic reticulum adenosine triphosphatase. *J. Biol. Chem.* 256: 6140–47

46. Hasselbach, W. 1964. Relaxing factor and the relaxation of muscle. *Prog. Biophys. Biophys. Chem.* 14:167–222

47. Hasselbach, W. 1978. The reversibility of the sarcoplasmic calcium pump. *Biochim. Biophys. Acta* 515:23–53

48. Hasselbach, W., Beil, F., Rauch, B. 1979. Sarcoplasmic calcium pump—a model of energy transduction in biological membranes. *Topics Curr. Chem.* 78: 1–56

49. Hasselbach, W., Elfvin, L. 1967. Structural and chemical asymmetry of the calcium-transporting membranes of the sarcotubular system as revealed by electron microscopy. *J. Ultrastructure Res.* 17:598–622

50. Hasselbach, W., Makinose, M. 1961. Die Calciumpumpe der "Erschlaffungsgrana" des Muskels und ihre Abhangigkeit von der ATP-Spaltung. *Biochem. Zeitschrift* 333:518–28

51. Hasselbach, W., Makinose, M. 1963. Uber den Mechanismus des Calciumtransportes durch die Membranen des Sarkoplasmatischen Reticulums. *Biochem. Zeitschrift* 339:94–111

52. Herbette, L., Marquardt, J., Scarpa, A., Blasie, J. 1977. A direct analysis of lamellar X-ray diffraction from hydrated oriented multilayers of fully functional sarcoplasmic reticulum. *Biophys. J.* 20:245–72

53. Hill, T. 1960. *Statistical Thermodynamics.* Reading, MA: Addison-Wesley

54. Hill, T. 1977. *Free Energy Transduction in Biology.* New York: Academic

55. Hill, T. 1983. Derivation of the relation between the linear Onsager coefficients and the equilibrium one-way cycle fluxes of a biochemical kinetic diagram. *Proc. Natl. Acad. Sci. USA* 80:2589–90

56. Hill, T. 1983. Some general principles in

free energy transduction. *Proc. Natl. Acad. Sci. USA* 80:2922–25

57. Hill, T., Eisenberg, E. 1981. Can free energy transduction be localized at some crucial part of the enzymatic cycle? *Quart. Rev. Biophys.* 14:1–49

58. Hill, T., Inesi, G. 1982. Equilibrium cooperative binding of calcium and protons by sarcoplasmic reticulum ATPase. *Proc. Natl. Acad. Sci. USA* 79:3978–82

59. Ikemoto, N. 1982. Structure and function of the calcium pump protein of sarcoplasmic reticulum. *Ann. Rev. Physiol.* 44:297–317

60. Ikemoto, N., Sreter, F., Nakamura, A., Gergely, J. 1968. Tryptic digestion and localization of calcium uptake and ATPase activity in fragments of sarcoplasmic reticulum. *J. Ultrastructure Res.* 23:216–32

61. Ikemoto, N., Garcia, A., Kurobe, Y., Scott, T. 1981. Nonequivalent subunits in the calcium pump of sarcoplasmic reticulum. *J. Biol. Chem.* 256:8593–601

62. Ikemoto, N., Morgan, T., Yamada, S. 1978. Ca^{++}-controlled conformational states in the Ca^{++} transport enzyme of sarcoplasmic reticulum. *J. Biol. Chem.* 253:8027–33

63. Inesi, G. 1971. p-Nitrophenyl phosphate hydrolysis and calcium ion transport in fragmented sarcoplasmic reticulum. *Science* 171:901–3

64. Inesi, G. 1972. Active transport of calcium ion in sarcoplasmic membranes. *Ann. Rev. Biophys. Bioeng.* 1:191–210

65. Inesi, G. 1979. Transport across sarcoplasmic reticulum in skeletal and cardiac muscle. In *Membrane Transport in Biology* ed. G. Giebisch, D. Tosteson, H. Ussing, pp. 357–93 Berlin: Springer-Verlag

66. Inesi, G., Asai, H. 1968. Trypsin digestion of fragmented sarcoplasmic reticulum. *Arch. Biochem. Biophys.* 126:469–77

67. Inesi, G., Coan, C., Verjovski-Almeida, S., Kurzmack, M., Lewis, D. 1978. *Frontiers of Biological Energetics, Vol. 2, Mechanism of Free Energy Utilization for Active Transport of Calcium Ion*, pp. 1129–36 New York: Academic

68. Inesi, G., Goodman, J. J., Watanabe, S. 1967. Effect of diethyl ether on the ATPase activity and calcium uptake of fragmented sarcoplasmic reticulum of rabbit skeletal muscle. *J. Biol. Chem.* 242:4637–43

69. Inesi, G., Hill, T. 1983. Calcium and proton dependence of sarcoplasmic reticulum ATPase. *Biophys. J.* 44:271–80

70. Inesi, G., Kurzmack, M. 1983. The Ca^{++}-dependent ATPase of sarcoplas-

mic reticulum. In Biomembrane Structure and Function, ed. D. Chapman, 4:355–410 London: MacMillan

71. Inesi, G., Kurzmack, M., Coan, C., Lewis, D. 1980. Cooperative calcium binding and ATPase activation in sarcoplasmic reticulum vesicles. *J. Biol. Chem.* 255:3025–31

72. Inesi, G., Kurzmack, M., Kosk-Kosicka, D., Lewis, D., Scofano, H. Guimaraes-Motta, H. 1982. Equilibrium and kinetic studies of calcium transport and ATPase activity in sarcoplasmic reticulum. *Z. Naturforsch.* C 37:685–91

73. Inesi, G., Lewis, D., Murphy, A. 1984. Interdependence of H^+, Ca^{++}, and Pi (or vanadate) sites in sarcoplasmic reticulum ATPase. *J. Biol. Chem.* 259:996–1003

74. Inesi, G., Scales, D. 1974. Tryptic cleavage of sarcoplasmic reticulum protein. *Biochemistry* 13:3298–306

75. Inesi, G., Scarpa, A. 1972. Fast kinetics of adenosine triphosphatase dependent Ca^{++} uptake by fragmented sarcoplasmic reticulum. *Biochemistry* 11:356–59

76. Inesi, G., Watanabe, T., Coan, C., Murphy, A. 1983. The mechanism of sarcoplasmic reticulum ATPase. *Ann. NY Acad. Sci.* 402:515–34

77. Jardetzky, O. 1966. Simple allosteric model for membrane pumps. *Nature* 211:969–70

78. Jencks, W. 1975. Binding energy, specificity, and enzymic catalysis—the Circe effect. *Adv. Enzymol.* 43:219–410

79. Jencks, W. 1980. The utilization of binding energy in coupled vectorial processes. *Adv. Enzymol.* 51:75–106

80. Jorgensen, K., Lind, K., Roigaard-Peterson, H., Moller, J. 1978. The functional unit of calcium-plus-magnesium-ion-dependent adenosine triphosphatase from sarcoplasmic reticulum. *Biochem. J.* 169:489–98

81. Kanazawa, T., Boyer, P. 1973. Occurrence and characteristics of a rapid exchange of phosphate-oxygen catalyzed by sarcoplasmic reticulum vesicles. *J. Biol. Chem.* 248:3163–72

82. Kanazawa, T., Yamada, S., Tonomura, Y. 1970. ATP formation from ADP and a phosphorylated intermediate of calcium-dependent ATPase in fragmented sarcoplasmic reticulum. *J. Biochem.* 68:593–95

83. Kanazawa, T., Yamada, S., Yamamoto, T., Tonomura, Y. 1971. Reaction mechanism of the Ca^{++}-dependent ATPase of sarcoplasmic reticulum from skeletal muscle. V. Vectorial requirements for calcium and magnesium ions of three partial reactions of ATPase: formation and decomposition of a phosphory-

lated intermediate and ATP formation from ADP and the intermediate. *J. Biochem.* 70:95–123

84. Klip, A., Reithmeier, R., MacLennan, D. 1980. Alignment of the major tryptic fragments of the adenosine triphosphatase from sarcoplasmic reticulum. *J. Biol. Chem.* 255:6562–68

85. Knowles, A. Racker, E. 1975. Formation of adenosine triphosphate from Pi and adenosine diphosphate by purified Ca^{2+}-adenosine triphosphatase. *J. Biol. Chem.* 250:1949–51

86. Kolassa, N., Punzengruber, C., Suko, J., Makinose, M. 1979. Mechanism of calcium-independent phosphorylation of sarcoplasmic reticulum ATPase by orthophosphate. *FEBS Lett.* 108:495–500

87. Kosk-Kosicka, D., Kurzmack, M., Inesi, G. 1983. Kinetic characterization of detergent-solubilized sarcoplasmic reticulum adenosinetriphosphatase. *Biochemistry* 22:2559–67

88. Kurzmack, M., Verjovski-Almeida, S., Inesi, G. 1977. Detection of an initial burst of calcium translocation in sarcoplasmic reticulum. *Biochem. Biophys. Res. Commun.* 78:772–76

89. Lacapere, J., Gingold, M., Champeil, P., Guillain, F. 1981. Sarcoplasmic reticulum ATPase phosphorylation from inorganic phosphate in the absence of a calcium gradient: Steady-state and fluorescence studies. *J. Biol. Chem.* 256:2302–06

90. LeMaire, M., Jorgensen, K., Roigaard-Petersen, H., Moller, J. 1976. Properties of deoxycholate solubilized sarcoplasmic reticulum Ca^{++}-ATPase. *Biochemistry* 15:5805–12

91. LeMaire, M., Lind, K., Jorgensen, K., Roigaard, H., Moller, J. 1978. Enzymatically active Ca^{++} ATPase from sarcoplasmic reticulum membranes, solubilized by nonionic detergents. Role of lipid for aggregation of the protein. *J. Biol. Chem.* 253:7051–60

92. LeMaire, M., Moller, J., Tanford, C. 1976. Retention of enzyme activity by detergent-solubilized sarcoplasmic Ca^{++}-ATPase. *Biochemistry* 15:2336–42

93. LeMaire, M., Moller, J., Tardieu, A. 1981. Shape and thermodynamic properties of a Ca^{++}-dependent ATPase: A solution X-ray scattering and sedimentation equilibrium study. *J. Mol. Biol.* 150:273–96

94. Ludi, A., Hasselbach, W. 1983. Excimer formation of ATPase from sarcoplasmic reticulum labeled with N-(3-pyrene)-maleinimide. *Europ. J. Biochem.* 130:5–8

95. MacLennan, D. 1970. Purification and properties of the adenosine triphosphatase from sarcoplasmic reticulum. *J. Biol. Chem.* 245:4508–18

96. Makinose, M. 1969. The phosphorylation of the membrane protein of the sarcoplasmic vesicles during active calcium transport. *Europ. J. Biochem.* 10:74–82

97. Makinose, M. 1972. Phosphoprotein formation during osmo-chemical energy conversion in the membrane of the sarcoplasmic reticulum. *FEBS Lett.* 25:113–15

98. Makinose, M., Hasselbach, W. 1971. ATP synthesis by the reverse of the sarcoplasmic calcium pump. *FEBS Lett.* 12:271–72

99. Martonosi, A. 1972. Transport of calcium by the sarcoplasmic reticulum. In *Metabolic Pathways* ed. L. Hokin, 6:317–49 New York: Academic

100. Masuda, H., deMeis, L. 1973. Phosphorylation of the sarcoplasmic reticulum membrane by orthophosphate. Inhibition by calcium ions. *Biochemistry* 12:4581–85

101. McFarland, B., Inesi, G. 1971. Solubilization of sarcoplasmic reticulum with Triton X-100. *Arch. Biochem. Biophys.* 145:456–64

102. McIntosh, D., Boyer, P. 1983. Adenosine 5'-Triphosphate modulation of catalytic intermediates of calcium ion activated adenosine triphosphatase of sarcoplasmic reticulum subsequent to enzyme phosphorylation. *Biochemistry* 22:2867–75

103. Meissner, G., Conner, G., Fleischer, S. 1973. Isolation of sarcoplasmic reticulum by zonal centrifugation and purification of Ca^{2+}-pump and Ca^{2+}-binding proteins. *Biochim. Biophys. Acta* 298:246–69

104. Migala, A., Agostini, B., Hasselbach, W. 1973. Tryptic fragmentation of the calcium transport system in the sarcoplasmic reticulum. *Z. Naturforsch. C* 28:178–82

105. Mitchinson, C., Wilderspin, A., Trinnaman, B., Green, N. 1982. Identification of a labelled peptide after stoicheiometric reaction of fluorescein isothiocyanate with the Ca^{++}-dependent adenosine triphosphatase of sarcoplasmic reticulum. *FEBS Lett.* 146:87–92

106. Moller, J., Andersen, J., LeMaire, M. 1982. The sarcoplasmic reticulum Ca^{++}-ATPase. *Mol. Cell. Biochem.* 42:83–107

107. Moller, J., Lind, K., Andersen, J. 1980. Enzyme kinetics and substrate stabilization of detergent-solubilized and membraneous $(Ca^{++} + Mg^{++})$–activated ATPase from sarcoplasmic reticulum.

Effect of protein-protein interactions. *J. Biol. Chem.* 255:1912–20

108. Mostov, K., DeFoor, P., Fleischer, S., Blobel, G. 1981. Co-translational membrane integration of calcium pump protein without signal sequence cleavage. *Nature* 292:87–88

109. Murphy, A. 1978. Effects of divalent cations and nucleotides on the reactivity of the sulfhydryl groups of sarcoplasmic reticulum membranes. *J. Biol. Chem.* 253:385–89

110. Murphy, A., Pepitone, M., Highsmith, S. 1982. Detergent-solubilized sarcoplasmic reticulum ATPase. Hydrodynamic and catalytic properties. *J. Biol. Chem.* 257:3551–54

111. Nakamoto, R., Inesi, G. 1984. Studies of the interactions of 2',3'-0-(2,4,6-trinitrocyclohexyldienylidine)-adenosine nucleotides with the sarcoplasmic reticulum $Ca^{++} + Mg^{++}$-ATPase active site. *J. Biol. Chem.* 259:2961–70

112. Napolitano, C., Cooke, P., Segalman, K., Herbette, L. 1983. Organization of cacium pump protein dimers in the isolated sarcoplasmic reticulum membrane. *Biophys. J.* 42:119–25

113. Neet, K., Green, N. 1977. Kinetics of the cooperativity of the Ca^{++}-transporting adenosine triphosphatase of sarcoplasmic reticulum and the mechanism of the ATP interaction. *Arch. Biochem. Biophys.* 178:588–97

114. Pickart, C., Jencks, W. 1982. Slow dissociation of ATP from the calcium ATPase. *J. Biol. Chem.* 257:5319–22

115. Pickart, C., Jencks, W. 1984. Energetics of the calcium-transporting ATPase. *J. Biol. Chem.* 259:1629–43

116. Portzehl, H. 1957. Die Bindung des Erschlaffungfactors von Marsh an die Muskelgrana. *Biochim. Biophys. Acta* 26:373–77

117. Prager, R., Punzengruber, C., Kolassa, N., Winkler, F., Suko, J. 1979. Ionized and bound calcium inside isolated sarcoplasmic reticulum of skeletal muscle and its significance in phosphorylation of adenosine triphosphatase by orthophosphate. *Europ. J. Biochem.* 97:239–50

118. Scales, D., Inesi, G. 1976. Assembly of ATPase protein in sarcoplasmic reticulum membranes. *Biophys. J.* 16:735–51

119. Scarpa, A., Baldassare, J., Inesi, G. 1972. The effect of calcium ionophores on fragmented sarcoplasmic reticulum. *J. Gen. Physiol.* 60:735–49

120. Scofano, H., Barrabin, H., Lewis, D., Inesi, G. 1984. Specific dicyclohexylcarbodiimide inhibition of the E-P + water– E + Pi reaction and ATP-Pi exchange in

sarcoplasmic reticulum ATPase. *Biochemistry*. In press

121. Scofano, H., Vieyra, A., deMeis, L. 1979. Substrate regulation of the sarcoplasmic reticulum ATPase: Transient kinetic studies. *J. Biol. Chem.* 254:10227–31

122. Silva, J., Verjovski-Almeida, S. 1983. Self-association and modification of calcium binding in solubilized sarcoplasmic reticulum adenosinetriphosphatase. *Biochemistry* 22:707–16

123. Stewart, P., MacLennan, D. 1974. Surface particles of sarcoplasmic reticulum membranes: Structural features of the adenosine triphosphatase. *J. Biol. Chem.* 249:985–93

124. Sumida, M., Wang, T., Mandel, F., Froehlich, J., Schwartz, A. 1978. Transient kinetics of Ca^{++} transport of sarcoplasmic reticulum. *J. Biol. Chem.* 253:8772–77

125. Takakuwa, Y., Kanazawa, T. 1979. Slow transition of phoshoenzyme from ADP-sensitive to ADP-insensitive forms in solubilized Ca^{++}, Mg^{++}-ATPase of sarcoplasmic reticulum: evidence for retarded dissociation of Ca^{++} from the phosphoenzyme. *Biochem. Biophys. Res. Commun.* 88:1209–16

126. Takisawa, H., Makinose, M. 1983. Occlusion of calcium in the ADP-sensitive phosphoenzyme of the adenosine triphosphatase of sarcoplasmic reticulum. *J. Biol. Chem.* 258:2986–92

127. Tanford, C. 1981. Equilibrium state of ATP-driven ion pumps in relation to physiological ion concentration gradients. *J. Gen. Physiol.* 77:223–28

128. Tanford, C. 1981. Chemical potential of bound ligand, an important parameter for free energy transduction. *Proc. Natl. Acad. Sci. USA* 78:270–73

129. Tanford, C. 1982. Simple model for the chemical potential change of a transported ion in active transport. *Proc. Natl. Acad. Sci. USA* 79:2882–84

130. Tanford, C. 1982. Steady state of an ATP-driven calcium pump: Limitations on kinetic and thermodynamic parameters. *Proc. Natl. Acad. Sci. USA* 79:6161–65

131. Tanford, C. 1983. Mechanism of free energy coupling in active transport. *Ann. Rev. Biochem.* 52:379–409

132. Tanford, C. 1984. The sarcoplasmic reticulum calcium pump: localization of free energy transfer to discrete steps of the reaction cycle. *FEBS Lett.* 166:1–7

133. Taylor, K., Dux, L., Martonosi, A. 1984. *J. Mol. Biol.* In press

134. Thorley-Lawson, D., Green, N. 1975. Separation and characterisation of tryptic

fragments from the adenosine triphosphatase of sarcoplasmic reticulum. *Europ. J. Biochem.* 59:193–200

135. Tong, S. 1980. Studies on the structure of the calcium dependent ATPase from rabbit skeletal SR. *Arch. Biochem. Biophys.* 203:780–91

136. Verjovski-Almeida, S., Inesi, G. 1979. Fast-kinetic evidence for an activating effect of ATP on the Ca^{++} transport of sarcoplasmic reticulum ATPase. *J. Biol. Chem.* 254:18–21

137. Verjovski-Almeida, S., Kurzmack, M., Inesi, G. 1978. Partial reactions in the catalytic and transport cycle of sarcoplasmic reticulum ATPase. *Biochemistry* 17:5006–13

138. Verjovski-Almeida, S., Silva, J. 1981. Different degrees of cooperativity of the Ca^{++}-induced changes in the fluorescence intensity of solubilized sarcoplasmic reticulum ATPase. *J. Biol. Chem.* 256:2940–44

139. Watanabe, T., Inesi, G. 1982. The use of 2',3'-0-(2,4,6-trinitrophenyl) adenosine 5'-triphosphate for studies of nucleotide interaction with sarcoplasmic reticulum

140. Weber, A. 1966. Energized calcium transport and relaxing factor. In *Current Topics in Bioenergetics,* ed. D. Sanadi, pp. 203–54 New York: Academic

141. Weber, G. 1972. Ligand binding and internal equilibria in proteins. *Biochemistry* 11:864–78

142. Wyman, J. 1964. Linked functions and reciprocal effects in hemoglobin: A second look. *Adv. Prot. Chem.* 19:223–86

143. Yamada, S., Sumida, M., Tonomura, Y. 1972. Reaction mechanism of the Ca^{++}-dependent ATPase of sarcoplasmic reticulum from skeletal muscle. VIII. Molecular mechanism of the conversion of osmotic energy to chemical energy in the sarcoplasmic reticulum. *J. Biochem.* 72:1537–48

144. Yamamoto, T., Tonomura, Y. 1968. Reaction mechanism of the Ca^{++}-dependent ATPase of sarcoplasmic reticulum from skeletal muscle. II. Intermediate formation of phosphoryl protein. *J. Biochem.* 64:137–45

vesicles. *J. Biol. Chem.* 257:11510–16

CARDIOVASCULAR PHYSIOLOGY: NUCLEOTIDE METABOLISM IN THE CARDIOVASCULAR SYSTEM

Introduction, H. V. Sparks, Jr., *Section Editor*

Adenine nucleotides are fascinating and important determinants of cardiovascular function. They play their traditional role in cell energetics, but deserve special attention in this regard because myocardial metabolism is so high even at rest and because vascular smooth muscle uses so little energy as compared to striated muscle. Two of the following reviews deal with the role of adenine nucleotides and creatine phosphate in the regulation of respiration: Drs. Mela-Riker & Bukoski emphasize studies on mitochondrial function; Dr. Jacobus is more concerned with high-energy phosphate metabolism. There are some differences of opinion concerning the signals responsible for regulation of respiration and the role of creatine phosphate, and the reasons for these differences are clearly laid out by the authors. Dr. Jennings reviews the changes in nucleotide metabolism that accompany myocardial ischemia, a crucial subject for those interested in the preservation of ischemic myocardium. Myocardial adenine nucleotide levels are maintained primarily by the purine salvage pathways described by Drs. Manfredi & Holmes. Drs. Butler & Siegman summarize adenine nucleotide metabolism in mechanically efficient vascular smooth muscle, which has given us new insights into muscle energetics.

In addition to their central role in cellular energetics, adenine nucleotides are important extracellular mediators. Dr. Su describes the surface receptors for adenine nucleotides and nucleosides as well as our current understanding of purinergic nerves in the cardiovascular system. Dr. Holmsen summarizes the nucleotide metabolism of platelets, delineating their separate metabolic and messenger functions. Drs. Pearson & Gordon describe how endothelial cells release, degrade, and transport adenine nucleotide and nucleosides. Dr. Rovetto reviews the controversial issue of cellular adenine nucleotide transport in the heart.

As a group, these reviews illustrate the multiplicity of the mechanisms that regulate the extra- and intracellular concentration of adenine nucleotides as well as point out their significance as extracellular messengers.

Ann. Rev. Physiol. 1985. 47:605–16

MYOCARDIAL NUCLEOTIDE TRANSPORT

Michael J. Rovetto

Department of Physiology, University of Missouri School of Medicine, Columbia, Missouri 65212

INTRODUCTION

Generally, adenine nucleotides are thought not to cross cell membranes. Phosphorylated adenosine uptake or release by various cells and tissues, however, is periodically reported (e.g. 8, 10, 12, 18, 52, 58, 61). In some instances these results are not confirmed by additional studies, or there are alternative interpretations not requiring membrane transport. The uncertainty in interpretation of results is due to: (*a*) participation of adenine nucleotides and their metabolites (adenosine, inosine, and hypoxanthine) in numerous intracellular and extracellular reactions; (*b*) bidirectional transmembrane transport processes for the nucleosides (adenosine and inosine); and (*c*) heterogenous cell populations in intact tissues with different nucleoside, and perhaps nucleotide, transport activities. Furthermore, absence of specific inhibitors to delineate between nucleoside and nucleotide transport has retarded resolution of the problem.

Existence of transmembrane nucleotide transport would significantly influence current thinking about regulatory processes in myocardial cells because of the following observations. (*a*) Exogenously added ATP is a more potent vasodilator than adenosine (34), the postulated regulator of coronary blood flow (cf. 2–5); (*b*) Isolated myocardial cells release ATP in sufficient quantities to cause dilation (21); (*c*) Small quantities of ATP appear in the coronary effluent of perfused hearts suggesting release from myocardial purinergic nerves (10, 11) or endothelial cells (52); (*d*) ATP and adenosine differentially affect a number of cell processes, including sympathetic nerve transmitter release (cf. 40, 56).

The importance of nucleotide uptake to cell homeostasis may be to inactivate a potent modulator of cell function. That is, it may subserve an ATP

605

regulatory function or may protect cells against ATP released from damaged cells. ATP uptake also would conserve a molecule that is energetically expensive to synthesize, albeit the major energy cost resides in the purine moiety. Thus, distinguishing between ATP and adenosine movement across cell membranes is an important problem. The goals of this review are to evaluate the evidence supporting myocardial adenine nucleotide translocation and to present some of the problems in measuring this movement.

A distinction is drawn between the terms *transport* and *uptake*. In keeping with the definitions of Plagemann & Wohlhueter (45) transport will be used to refer to selective carrier-mediated movement across the cell membrane. Measurement of this process raises some special problems and can be achieved only when transport is rate-limiting. That is, under conditions that do not allow for significant intracellular accumulation of the transported molecule or metabolite. This is usually achieved experimentally by observing the initial uptake. At later times, as intracellular concentrations increase, subsequent metabolic reactions govern the apparent transport rate. The appropriate term used in most published work to describe nucleoside and nucleotide transmembrane movement is uptake or release. These will be used here to refer to the combined processes of transport and metabolism.

ADENINE NUCLEOTIDE UPTAKE

ATP entry into muscle cells was suggested by the study of Buchthal et al (9), who in 1944 observed ATP-induced contraction in isolated frog muscle fibers. However, later work showed that ATP does not enter these cells (61). In isolated rat soleus muscles incubated with ^{14}C-ATP, the radiolabeled intracellular ATP appears to be greater than when the muscles are incubated with ^{14}C-ADP or ^{14}C-adenosine (13). Chaudry and coworkers present substantial indirect evidence in support of ATP uptake (12–15). They and others (54) find that ATP infusion prolongs the survival period for animals in hemorrhagic shock. ^{14}C-ATP uptake by liver and kidney slices from animals subjected to shock protocols is greater than that into slices from control animals and exceeds free adenosine uptake by these tissues (15). Adenine nucleotides in liver and kidney are restored following prolonged shock by Mg-ATP but not by Mg-ADP, Mg-AMP, or Mg^{++} plus adenosine (14). These results suggest that ATP uptake into tissues occurs and that it is specific for ATP and does not proceed via ATP hydrolysis and uptake of ATP metabolites. These studies do not distinguish between nucleotide uptake per se and uptake of the radiolabeled ATP-derived adenosine. This question is addressed more recently in soleus and diaphragm muscles incubated with 8-^{14}C,α-^{32}P labeled ATP (12). The majority of both labels appears in the ATP fraction. More importantly, the ^{32}P to ^{14}C ratio is 1, indicating uptake of the intact nucleotide molecule. Nonperfused, severely ischemic dog hearts also apparently take up significant amounts of ^{32}P-ATP, although the ^{32}P/^{14}C ratio is less than 1 (17). These results are in sharp contrast to those obtained in guinea-pig hearts (28) and cultured rat myocytes (61). ^{32}P phosphate incorporated into myocyte cell adenine nucleotides is only a fraction of the incorporated ATP-^{14}C adenosine moiety (Table 1). Insensitivity of cultured cells to ATP cannot explain the different results, because similarly cultured myocytes treated with dinitrophenol respond to ATP by increasing contraction rates (25).

In fact, this latter observation by Harary & Slater, is used to support ATP entry into cells, because oligomycin produces an effect similar to that of ATP. It is possible that the different muscle types or conditions account for these contrasting results. But it is more likely that they are due to underestimations of extracellular ^{32}P and ATP, which make it appear that extracellular ATP per se penetrated the cellular space. Thus, when the extracellular fluid of skeletal muscle is not washed free of isotope prior to extraction, but its volume is estimated with raffinose, the ^{32}P/^{14}C ratio is 1 (12). This ratio in hypothermic ischemic cardiac muscle is 50% of that infused into the coronary vasculature, if the extracellular space is not taken into account (17). The ratio is 0.15 when it is assumed that 25% of tissue water is extracellular space (17). As this is probably an underestimation of the size of this space in ischemic tissue, an even lower ratio may be correct. In any event, this value is not greatly different from 0.01 to 0.04 following perfusion of the coronary vasculature with isotope-free buffer (28), or when isolated cells are washed free of extracellular isotope (Table 1) prior to extracting the tissue. The tissue phosphate to purine ratio also does not appear to depend on the nucleotide phosphate which is labeled, as α- and γ-^{32}P are incorporated to the same extent (Table 1). Hence the majority of the adenosine moiety of ATP is taken up into myocardium after phosphate hydrolysis, and ATP uptake, if it occurs at all, represents a very small fraction of the total adenosine uptake.

Table 1 Nucleoside and phosphate uptake into cultured myocytes

Radiolabel	Adenosine uptake (nmol mg^{-1})	32P Uptake (nmol mg^{-1})	^{32}P/^{3}H
^{3}H-Adenosine	66 ± 5	—	—
^{3}H-ATP	132 ± 8	—	—
^{3}H-Adenosine and ^{32}P$_i$	66 ± 5	2.4 ± 0.3	0.04
γ^{32}P-^{3}H ATP	115 ± 10	3.6 ± 0.2	0.03
α^{32}P-^{3}H ATP	108 ± 12	4.8 ± 0.6	0.04

Myocytes from hearts of newborn rats were incubated at 37°C with 10 μM radiolabels for 60 min on the fourth day in culture. They were then rinsed three times with excess cold buffer, extracted with perchloric acid, and then the nucleotides were separated by TLC. The sums of radioactivity in ATP, ADP, and AMP are expressed per mg of cell protein. The 2,8 positions of adenosine and ATP were labeled with ^{3}H. Similar results were obtained with 8-^{14}C adenosine. For each group, n = 6. For additional details see Ref. 59.

NUCLEOTIDE-DERIVED NUCLEOSIDE UPTAKE

Considerable evidence (including that in Table 1) supports enhanced tissue uptake of nucleotide-derived adenosine. In cultured myocytes, the maximum incorporation rate for ATP-derived adenosine is approximately twice that for free adenosine (59, 60). Similar results are obtained in isolated perfused rat hearts, although in this case the differences in uptake rates can be observed only at substrate concentrations below 10 μM (49, 59, 60). Adenosine uptake rates at 50 μM are the same as the maximum ATP-derived adenosine uptake rates observed at 10 μM. As discussed above, Chaudry and coworkers (12–15) have shown ATP-derived nucleoside uptake that exceeds that of free adenosine. There are three possible explanations for the observed differences in free adenosine and nucleotide-derived adenosine uptake rates. Frick & Lowenstein (24) postulate a vectorial transport system for adenosine based on their observations that AMP-derived adenosine is taken up into cardiac tissue in preference to free adenosine, and that 5'nucleotidase inhibition reduces adenosine loss during hypoxia. In this system, adenosine transport is proposed to be coupled to membrane bound 5'nucleotidase. Data consistent with this view have been obtained in the author's laboratory (48). The second possibility is that adenosine is produced in close proximity to the nucleoside transport site and then is transported into the cells on the same carrier as free adenosine. This conclusion is based on recently published results in perfused liver (50), which, like heart, has an abundance of ecto-5' nucleotidase but, unlike heart, synthesizes de novo large quantities of adenosine (46). The third possible explanation is that free adenosine and nucleotide-derived adenosine are preferentially taken up by different cells. As these latter two possibilities offer the simplest explanations for the results, they are considered in greater detail.

A Single Carrier for Adenosine and Adenine Nucleotide-Derived Adenosine

Extensive extracellular metabolism of adenine nucleotides (44) makes it reasonable that adenosine from both sources is transported on the same carrier. Adenosine phosphorylation may simply "protect" it from deamination to inosine and effectively make more adenosine available for transport across cell membranes. This may be achieved by the combination of several factors.

First, phosphorylation would reduce endothelial cell metabolism of adenosine and allow a greater radiolabeled adenosine distribution volume (i.e. the concentration within the interstitial space would approach that in the vascular space). Free adenosine produced within this larger volume would then be subject primarily to transport because of the enzyme and transport kinetics discussed below. It is known that adenosine in the vascular space is subject to transport into endothelial cells (27, 52) and possibly to deamination by an ecto-adenosine deaminase. [Although not reported to occur in coronary endothelial cells, this enzyme appears to be present on pulmonary endothelial cells (27)]. The endothelial cells comprise only a small percentage of the tissue mass, but the membrane surface area is extensive (cf. 44). Additionally, these cells have first access to substrates supplied via the circulation.

Second, phosphorylation would reduce the amount of inosine produced by adenosine deamination and thereby decrease competition between inosine and adenosine for the nucleoside carrier. About 7% of adenosine, at concentrations between 50 and 200 μM, appears as inosine after passing a single time through the coronary vasculature (47). Inhibition produced by this amount of inosine may be small because the affinity of the transport system for inosine in most cells is slightly less than that for adenosine (45). On the other hand, inosine produced within cells and transported out, or produced in the extracellular space near the transport site, may have a considerably higher concentration because of unstirred layers. Inhibition of adenosine transport then would be significant.

Third, the kinetics of enzymes of adenine nucleotide and adenosine metabolism are such that they would increase the distribution volume and limit the inhibitory effects of inosine. The rate-limiting enzyme of ATP hydrolysis, ecto-5' nucleotidase (23, 52), would limit the amount of adenosine available for deamination. For instance, even at a low ATP concentration (10^{-7} M) only 20% of extracellular ATP is converted to adenosine and 66% to AMP (52) (none of the ATP appears as ADP and only 1% remains as ATP). The K_m for adenosine transport is about four-fold lower than that for adenosine deamination (22, 38). Thus, adenosine produced from AMP would be preferentially transported rather than deaminated. The effect would be magnified if AMP is hydrolyzed near the transport site and adenosine is transported as it is produced.

The foregoing discussion does not account for the observation that ATP-derived adenosine uptake in vivo is greater than that of adenosine from AMP or ADP (14). It is likely that the γ phosphate of ATP protects against eventual adenosine deamination by limiting the rate of adenosine production. In perfused kidney, ATP-derived-AMP is hydrolyzed at a slower rate than AMP, particularly at high ATP concentrations (57). This is thought to be due to 5'nucleotidase inhibition by ATP and P_i and to adenylate deaminase inhibition by P_i. A slower hydrolysis rate for ATP than for AMP also is observed in the isolated heart, where 50% of ATP and greater than 70% of AMP (10 μM each) are metabolized to nucleoside and hypoxanthine in a single pass (59). Thus, at the high concentrations used in vivo studies (14) the γ phosphate may extend the half-life of adenosine and give the appearance that ATP is taken up differently than is AMP.

A potential argument against the hypothesis that phosphorylation simply preserves adenosine for subsequent transport is that ADP is a more potent inhibitor of isolated myocardial membrane bound 5'nucleotidase than is ATP (32, 35). Accordingly, ADP should extend the half-life of adenosine as well as or better than ATP. Adenosine from ATP, however, appears to be taken up in preference to that from ADP in kidney, liver, and skeletal muscles (13, 15). Assuming that, in these tissues, ADP is an inhibitor of 5'nucleotidase, the discrepancy may be related to what appears to be differential properties of membrane-bound 5'nucleotidase. The characteristics of this bound enzyme in isolated cardiac sarcolemmal membrane vesicles depend upon whether the vesicles are inside-out or outside-in (30). These findings indicate that there is an ecto- and an endo-membrane–bound enzyme. Thus, 5'nucleotidase preparations used to determine the effects of nucleotides on enzymatic activity (32, 35) may have been mixtures of these enzymes. This issue would be clarified by measurements of the nucleotide inhibition constants of these enzymes in both myocytes and endothelial cells.

Adenosine Uptake Into Different Cells

Selective labeling of different cells with nucleotide-derived and free adenosine may account for the observed differences in their uptake rates. Frick & Lowenstein (24) concluded that free adenosine enters a different cellular nucleotide pool than does AMP-derived adenosine. Although this is supportive evidence for two distinct transport processes, it is not conclusive. The results equally support selective entry of radiolabeled purine into two or more cell types. For the reasons discussed above, free adenosine may preferentially enter endothelial cells, whereas phosphorylation of adenosine may allow greater amounts of it to be taken up by nonendothelial cells. The high adenosine uptake rates from nucleotides may arise because of different affinities for transport in the several types of myocardial cells, the 5'nucleotidase activities in these cells, and/or the absolute numbers of cells exposed to adenosine.

Endothelial cells may be the primary site for removal of circulating adenosine (27, 37, 42), and 5'nucleotidase activity is higher in cultured smooth muscle cells than in endothelial cells (26). Endothelial cells in isolated perfused hearts account for greater than 80% of the adenosine taken up, when adenosine is perfused through the vasculature at concentrations between 10^{-8} and 5×10^{-7} M (37). Only at 10^{-6} M adenosine is there evidence for a substantial amount of adenosine uptake into cells other than endothelial cells. In view of these findings, data originally thought to support adenosine entry into different cellular nucleotide pools (51, 53) may, in fact, represent uptake into one or more cell types. Although the results of these studies are suggestive, they do not directly address the question of whether adenosine and nucleotide-derived adenosine differentially enter different cell types.

Other Considerations

The foregoing considerations of how phosphorylation may affect interstitial adenosine concentrations also reflect on the observed differences in potencies and actions of ATP and adenosine (cf. 40 and the review by Su in this volume). For example, phosphorylation would protect adenosine from metabolism and would maintain adenosine in higher concentrations at the smooth muscle cell membrane. This could account for the greater coronary vasodilation produced by ATP as compared to adenosine (34). In general, some of the effects of ATP and adenosine may be explained by a combination of different concentrations of each, at each of several cell types, and the interaction between the effects produced in these cells. Thus, when free adenosine is administered the highest adenosine concentrations would be achieved at endothelial cell membranes, whereas with ATP, the concentrations of adenosine may be more nearly equal at endothelial, cardiac, and smooth muscle cell membranes. In addition, ATP and adenosine may bind to different receptors (11), which in turn may have different distributions among the several myocardial cell types. The degree to which actions of adenosine and phosphorylated adenosine result from their differential relative concentrations requires further study.

Likewise, the issue of whether nucleotide-derived adenosine is transported on the same or a different carrier than free adenosine is unresolved. Phosphorylated adenosine is not taken up as such, but it is a more effective precursor for cellular nucleotide synthesis than is free adenosine. Uptake of nucleotide-derived adenosine may represent a transport process separate from that for free adenosine, but the available evidence equally supports adenosine preservation by phosphorylation. The difficulty in distinguishing between these reflects on our inability to accurately estimate adenosine concentrations at the transport site. Resolution of this question will require measurements of actual transport in homogeneous systems. This can be accomplished using free cell suspensions that allow rapid separation of cells from the extracellular space and by developing very specific metabolic and transport inhibitors.

NUCLEOTIDE RELEASE

ATP and cyclic adenosine 3',5'-monophosphate release have been reported from a number of tissues under a variety of conditions (cf. 18, 45). Greatest support for cellular release of noncyclic nucleotides, however, comes from studies of chromaffin tissue, nerves, cultured endothelial cells, cultured smooth-muscle cells, and platelets (1, 29, 31, 33, 43, 55). Whether adrenergic nerve terminals release adenine nucleotides in significant amounts is questionable, but ATP involvement in norepinephrine sequestration (cf. 56) make these a possible source for release from myocardial tissue.

Nucleotide efflux may not be viewed as a classical transport process per se but may represent a nonselective increase in membrane permeability or efflux from a very specialized compartment or membrane site. In fact, a membrane Ca^{++}-protein-ATP complex is proposed as the release site in myocytes (19, 58). Before consideration of a mechanism, however, the evidence for nucleotide release from striated muscle tissue will be considered.

Nucleotide release in the absence of Ca^{++} with high K^+ or electrical stimulation is reported to occur in isolated frog skeletal muscle and nerve (1). ATP release also is observed when extra care is taken to minimize damage to the frog nerve muscle preparation and the tissues are isolated for shorter periods of time (8). ATP release is not detected in the preparation if the vasculature is perfused with Ringer's solution prior to isolation (16), suggesting that residual formed blood elements may be the nucleotide source.

In addition to the possibility of cell contamination, quantifying nucleotides in the extracellular milieu is complicated by the presence of Mg^{++}-dependent phosphatases (41). These must be rapidly inactivated, and the cells must be quickly removed from samples used for nucleotide analysis. Even when these precautions are taken, there is little agreement that ATP is released from skeletal muscles. Thus, ATP release reportedly occurs from exercising human forearm muscles (20) but none is detected from ischemic or tetanically contracting blood perfused dog, or non–blood perfused rat, hind limb preparations (6, 7). ATP is detected in the venous effluent from the blood perfused preparations but no consistent differences are detected between resting and contracting muscles (7). These authors concluded that variable degrees of EDTA-induced hemolysis cause ATP release. Thus, divalent cation chelators, added to inhibit phosphatases, increase cell membrane permeability and complicate interpretation of the results from these studies. However, if muscle activity causes ATP release, it should have been detected in vascular effluent from skeletal muscle perfused without cells, but it was not (16). In spite of this finding, a different approach appears to be warranted. Perhaps, venous blood samples should be collected in cold solutions containing specific ATPase, adenosine transport, and 5' nucleotidase inhibitors, and the cells and plasma separated by high speed centrifugation through an organic phase.

Isolated perfused guinea-pig hearts reportedly release ATP in response to hypoxia (39) and to acetylcholine (52). The small quantities released (0.2–0.6 nM) are less than those required to produce measurable coronary flow increases. Rapid ATP hydolysis may cause underestimations of the arterial concentrations at receptor sites. Paddle & Burnstock (39) suggest that ATP is derived from interneurons because its release is not inhibited by adrenergic- or cholinergic-blockade, or nerve section. Schrader et al (52), however, report that atropine completely blocks ATP and other purine release, and the increase in blood flow, in response to acetylcholine.

It is conceivable that the coronary vasodilation and the increase in coronary flow caused by the stimuli in these two studies (39, 52) flushed erythrocytes from the vasculature. Nees et al (36) find that in spite of perfusing the guinea-pig coronary vasculature prior to isolation of endothelial cells, the initial cell preparations are contaminated with erythocytes. We also observe (unpublished observations) that 10 min perfusion of rat hearts fails to remove all erythrocytes, so that upon collagenase treatment, $0.5–3 \times 10^6$ erythrocytes are recovered in the coronary effluent. Contamination of venous samples with as few as 10^3 cells $\cdot$ ml^{-1} would yield 0.1 nM ATP. At the high sensitivities needed to detect ATP arising from the heart, these few cells are not trivial.

On the other hand, this concern may be unwarranted, as Schrader et al (52) did not detect ATP in the coronary effluent of hearts stimulated with β agonists, although in these hearts coronary flow was increased. Furthermore, in some of the experiments (39, 52), ATP was quantified directly in the perfusion medium with firefly-luciferase. This technique likely would not detect ATP in formed elements, but possible contamination of samples with cells or cell debris was not ruled out. The apparent specificity of ATP release for acetylcholine (52), however, provides strong support for ATP release from myocardial tissue. Whether this represents transport per se remains to be determined.

ATP released by the myocardium may arise from any of the cell types contained therein. Cultured vascular endothelial and smooth muscle cells release adenine nucleotides (43). Schrader et al (52) make a case for endothelial cell ATP release in perfused heart because, (a) these cells must be present for acetylcholine to cause vasodilation, and (b) theophylline, an adenosine and adenine nucleotide antagonist, inhibits acetycholine-induced vasodilation. ATP release from the oxygen-dependent myocytes also has been suggested as a means to regulate oxygen delivery (18, 21). The amount of ATP released from isolated myocytes in response to hypoxia, Ca^{++}, and EDTA is of sufficient quantity to cause vasodilation (21). The increased release is unaccompanied by elevations in extracellular lactate dehydrogenase, indicating that a nonspecific increase in membrane permeability does not occur (58). Based upon these results, it is proposed that ATP release is from a membrane surface protein–ATP-Ca^{++} complex (58) and that the signal for release is membrane depolarization (19). This is an intriguing possibility but validation depends upon demonstrating that the stimuli for release do not increase cell membrane permeability to other low molecular weight organic anions and that the ATP is derived from a specific, charge-sensitive ATP pool.

SUMMARY

A thorough consideration of the evidence for striated muscle cell transmembrane nucleotide movement provides only equivocal support for adenine nucleotide specific translocation across cell membranes. It is obvious that nucleotide-derived adenosine is taken up into cells in preference to free adenosine, and it is important to understand why this is so. The potential importance of released nucleotides to cell regulation justify studies to determine the source and release mechanism.

ACKNOWLEDGMENTS

I thank T. Forrester, who graciously provided a preprint of his publication (19) on ATP release, and F. Butson and A. Nelson for assistance in manuscript preparation. The author has been supported by NIH grants HL27336, HL00289, and by the American Heart Association.

Literature Cited

1. Abood, L. G., Koketsu, K., Miyamoto, S. 1962. Outflux of various phosphates during membrane depolarization of excitable tissues. *Am. J. Physiol.* 202:469–74
2. Baer, H. P., Drummond, G. I., eds. 1979. *Physiological and Regulatory Functions of Adenosine and Adenine Nucleotides.* New York: Raven. 438 pp.
3. Berne, R. M. 1980. The role of adenosine in the regulation of coronary blood flow. *Circ. Res.* 47:807–13
4. Berne, R. M., Foley, D. H., Watkinson, W. P., Miller, W. L., Winn, H. R., Rubio, R. 1979. See Ref. 2, pp. 117–26
5. Berne, R. M., Rall, T. W., Rubio, R., eds. 1983. *Regulatory Functions of Adenosine.* The Hague: Martinus Nijhoff. 558 pp.
6. Berne, R. M., Rubio, R., Dobson, J. G. Jr, Curnish, R. R. 1971. Adenosine and adenine nucleotides as possible mediators of cardiac and skeletal muscle blood flow regulation. *Circ. Res.* 28/29(Suppl. I):115–19
7. Bockman, E. L., Berne, R. M., Rubio, R. 1975. Release of adenosine and lack of release of ATP from contracting skeletal muscle. *Pflueger's Arch.* 355: 229–41
8. Boyd, I. A., Forrester, T. 1968. The release of adenosine triphosphate from frog skeletal muscle in vitro. *J. Physiol.* 199:115–35
9. Buchthal, F., Deutsch, A., Knappeis, G. G. 1944. Release of contraction and changes in birefringence caused by adenosine triphosphate in isolated cross striated muscle fibres. *Acta Physiol. Scand.* 8:271–87
10. Burnstock, G. 1977. An assessment of purinergic nerve involvement in vasodilation. In *Mechanisms of Vasodilation,* ed. P. M. Vanhoutte, I. Leusen, pp. 278–84. Basel: Karger. 307 pp.
11. Burnstock, G. 1980. Purinergic receptors in the heart. *Circ. Res.* 46(Suppl. I):175–82
12. Chaudry, I. H., Baue, A. E. 1980. Further evidence for ATP uptake by rat tissue. *Biochim. Biophys. Acta* 628:336–42
13. Chaudry, I. H., Gould, M. K. 1970. Evidence for the uptake of ATP by rat soleus muscle *in vitro*. *Biochem. Biophys. Acta* 196:320–26
14. Chaudry, I. H., Sayeed, M. M., Baue, A. E. 1974. Depletion and restoration of tissue ATP in hemorrhagic shock. *Arch. Surg.* 108:208–11
15. Chaudry, I. H., Sayeed, M. M., Baue, A. E. 1977. Evidence for enhanced uptake of ATP by liver and kidney in hemorrhagic shock. *Am. J. Physiol.* 233:R83–88
16. Dobson, J. G. Jr., Rubio, R., Berne, R. M. 1971. Role of adenine nucleotides, adenosine, and inorganic phosphate in the regulation of skeletal muscle blood flow. *Circ. Res.* 29:375–84
17. Fedelesova, M., Ziegelhoffer, A., Krause, E. G., Wollenberger, A. 1969. Effect of exogenous adenosine triphosphate on the metabolic state of the excised hypothermic dog heart. *Circ. Res.* 24:617–27
18. Forrester, T. 1981. Adenosine or adenosine triphosphate? In *Vasodilation,* ed. P. M. Vanhoutte, I. Leusen, pp. 205–29. New York: Raven. 536 pp.
19. Forrester, T. 1984. Local metabolic influences on the microvasculature in cardiac and skeletal muscle. In *Progress in Microcirculation Research II,* ed. F. C. Courtice, D. G. Garlich, M. A. Perry, Sydney: Comm. Postgrad. Med. Educ., Univ. New South Wales. In press
20. Forrester, T., Lind, A. R. 1969. Identification of adenosine triphosphate in human plasma and the concentration in the venous effluent of forearm muscles before, during and after sustained contractions. *J. Physiol.* 204:347–64
21. Forrester, T., Williams, C. A. 1977. Release of adenosine triphosphate from isolated adult heart cells in response to hypoxia. *J. Physiol.* 268:371–90
22. Fox, I. H., Kelley, W. N. 1978. The role of adenosine and 2'-deoxyadenosine in mammalian cells. *Ann. Rev. Biochem.* 47:655–86
23. Frick, G. P., Lowenstein, J. M. 1976. Studies of 5'-nucleotidase in the perfused rat heart; including measurements of the enzyme in perfused skeletal muscle and liver. *J. Biol. Chem.* 251:6372–78
24. Frick, G. P., Lowenstein, J. M. 1978. Vectorial production of adenosine by 5'-nucleotidase in the perfused rat heart. *J. Biol. Chem.* 253:1240–44
25. Harary, I., Slater, E. C. 1965. Studies in vitro on single beating heart cells. VIII. The effect of oligomycin, dinitrophenol, and ouabain on the beating rate. *Biochim. Biophys. Acta* 99:227–33
26. Hayes, L. W., Goguen, C. A., Stevens, A. L., Magargal, W. W., Slakey, L. L. 1979. Enzyme activities in endothelial cells and smooth muscle cells from swine aorta. *Proc. Natl. Acad. Sci. USA* 76: 2532–35
27. Hellewell, P. G., Pearson, J. D. 1983.

Metabolism of circulating adenosine by the porcine isolated perfused lung. *Circ. Res.* 53:1–7

28. Hoffmann, P. C., Okita, G. T. 1965. Penetration of ATP into the myocardium. *Proc. Soc. Exp. Biol. Med.* 119:573–76

29. Holton, P. 1959. The liberation of adenosine triphosphate on antidromic stimulation of sensory nerves. *J. Physiol.* 145:494–504

30. Lamers, J. M. J., Heyliger, C. E., Panagia, V., Dhalla, N. S. 1983. Properties of 5'-nucleotidase in rat heart sarcolemma. *Biochim. Biophys. Acta* 742:568–75

31. Lollar, P., Owen, W. G. 1981. Active-site-dependent, thrombin-induced release of adenine nucleotides from cultured human endothelial cells. *Ann. NY Acad. Sci.* 370:51–56

32. Lowenstein, J. M., Yu, M-K., Naito, Y. 1983. See Ref. 5, pp. 117–31

33. Mills, D. C. B., Robb, I. A., Roberts, G. C. K. 1968. The release of nucleotides, 5-hydroxytryptamine and enzymes from human blood platelets during aggregation. *J. Physiol.* 195:715–29

34. Moir, T. W., Downs, T. D. 1972. Myocardial reactive hypermia: comparative effects of adenosine, ATP, ADP, and AMP. *Am. J. Physiol.* 222:1386–90

35. Naito, Y., Lowenstein, J. M. 1981. 5'-nucleotidase from rat heart. *Biochemistry* 20:5188–94

36. Nees, S., Gerbes, A. L., Gerlach, E. 1981. Isolation, identification, and continous culture of coronary endothelial cells from guinea pig hearts. *Euro. J. Cell Biol.* 24:287–97

37. Nees, S., Gerlach, E. 1983. See Ref. 5, pp. 347–60

38. Olsson, R. A., Snow, J. A., Gentry, M. K., Frick, G. P. 1972. Adenosine uptake by canine heart. *Circ. Res.* 31:767–78

39. Paddle, B. M., Burnstock, G. 1974. Release of ATP from perfused heart during coronary vasodilation. *Blood Vessel* 11:110–19

40. Paton, D. M. 1979. See Ref. 2, pp. 69–77

41. Pearson, J. D., Carleton, J. S., Gordon, J. L. 1980. Metabolism of adenine nucleotides by ectoenzymes of vascular endothelial and smooth-muscle cells in culture. *Biochem. J.* 190:421–29

42. Pearson, J. D., Carleton, J. S., Hutchings, A., Gordon, J. L. 1978. Uptake and metabolism of adenosine by pig aortic endothelial and smooth-muscle cells in culture. *Biochem. J.* 170:265–71

43. Pearson, J. D., Gordon, J. L. 1979. Vascular endothelial and smooth muscle cells in culture selectively release adenine nucleotides. *Nature* 281:384–86

44. Pearson, J. D., Hellewell, P. G., Gordon, J. L. 1983. See Ref. 5, pp. 333–44

45. Plagemann, P. G. W., Wohlhueter, R. M. 1980. Permeation of nucleosides, nucleic acid bases, and nucleotides in animal cells. *Curr. Top. Membr. Transp.* 14:225–330

46. Pritchard, J. B., O'Connor, N., Oliver, J. M., Berlin, J. M. 1975. Uptake and supply of purine compounds by the liver. *Am. J. Physiol.* 229:967–72

47. Reibel, D. K., Rovetto, M. J. 1979. Myocardial adenosine salvage rates and restoration of ATP content following ischemia. *Am. J. Physiol.* 237:H247–52

48. Rovetto, M. J., Williams, D. O. 1982. A transport system for myocardial cell adenosine efflux. *Fed. Proc.* 41:992 (Abstr.)

49. Rovetto, M. J., Williams, D. O. 1982. The role of myocardial ATP-adenosine transport in cellular loss of adenine nucleotides. *J. Clin. Chem. Clin. Biochem.* 20:411 (Abstr.)

50. Sasaki, T., Abe, A., Sakagami, T. 1983. Ecto-5'-nucleotidase does not catalyze vectorial production of adenosine in the perfused rat liver. *J. Biol. Chem.* 258:6947–51

51. Schrader, J., Gerlach, E. 1976. Compartmentation of cardiac adenine nucleotides and formation of adenosine. *Pflueger's Arch.* 367:129–35

52. Schrader, J., Thompson, C. I., Hiendlmayer, G., Gerlach, E. 1982. Role of purines in acetylcholine-induced coronary vasodilation. *J. Molec. Cell. Cardiol.* 14:427–30

53. Schutz, W., Schrader, J., Gerlach, E. 1981. Different sites of adenosine formation in the heart. *Am. J. Physiol.* 240:H963–70

54. Sharma, G. P., Eiseman, B. 1966. Protective effect of ATP in experimental hemorrhagic shock. *Surgery* 59:66–75

55. Silinsky, E. M., Hubbard, J. I. 1973. Release of ATP from rat motor nerve terminals. *Nature* 243:404–5

56. Stone, T. W. 1981. Physiological roles for adenosine and adenosine 5'-triphosphate in the nervous system. *Neuroscience* 6:523–55

57. Weidemann, M. J., Hems, D. A., Krebs, H. A. 1969. Effects of added adenine nucleotides on renal carbohydrate metabolism. *Biochem. J.* 115:1–10

58. Williams, C. A., Forrester, T. 1983. Possible source of adenosine triphos-

phate released from rat myocytes in response to hypoxia and acidosis. *Cardiovasc. Res.* 17:301–12

59. Williams, D. O. 1981. *Regulation of myocardial purine metabolism: dichotomous systems of adenosine membrane translocation.* PhD thesis. Thomas Jefferson Univ., Philadelphia. 91 pp.

60. Williams, D. O., Rovetto, M. J. 1981. The existence of two adenosine transport systems in myocardial cells. *Fed. Proc.* 40:461 (Abstr.)

61. Woo, Y-T., Manery, J. F., Riordan, J. R., Dryden, E. E. 1977. Uptake and metabolism of purine nucleosides and nucleotides in isolated frog skeletal muscle. *Life Sci.* 21:861–76

Ann. Rev. Physiol. 1985. 47:617–27

NUCLEOTIDE METABOLISM BY ENDOTHELIUM

Jeremy D. Pearson and John L. Gordon

Section of Vascular Biology, M. R. C. Clinical Research Centre, Northwick Park, Harrow, Middlesex, HA1 3UJ, United Kingdom

INTRODUCTION

The vasoactive properties of circulating adenosine and ATP were first recognized half a century ago (22, 23), although it is only in the last decade that the physiological importance of these properties and the classification of purinoceptor-mediated vasoregulation have been investigated in detail (for reviews see 10, 13). As a result of these studies, it became clear that it is also important to understand the mechanisms by which purines are released to the extracellular medium, and the manner in which their effects may be regulated by inactivation or removal from the extracellular milieu. The potentially significant role played by the vascular endothelium in these processes can be inferred from several earlier observations of the rapid catabolism of adenine nucleotides on perfusion through vascular beds and from the demonstration that endothelial cells possess ectoenzymic activities capable of degrading adenine nucleotides to adenosine (see subsequent sections on nucleotide catabolism). More recently it has also been found that adenosine is efficiently removed from the circulation by uptake into endothelial cells (see next section).

The detailed characterization of these processes has been greatly assisted by the availability of cultured endothelial cells: the first publication, in 1973, clearly setting out methods for the isolation, identification, and growth of pure populations of endothelial cells in vitro (38), has led to the culture of endothelium from various species and sites by many research groups, which in turn has produced the realization that endothelial cells play active roles in many aspects of vascular homeostasis (for reviews see 37, 54).

This review focuses on the ability of endothelial cells to catabolize extracellular nucleotides and take up nucleosides. In addition, we address the

617

problem of extracellular release of nucleotides from endothelial cells: although the plasma membrane of endothelial cells (like that of other cells) is in general impermeable to nucleotides, their release can be provoked by a variety of nonlethal stimuli. Other aspects of nucleotide metabolism by endothelial cells, such as the control of the intracellular synthesis and catabolism of ATP and cyclic AMP, which are also likely to be physiologically important but about which rather less is known, are also discussed briefly.

ADENOSINE UPTAKE

In several species, adenosine is substantially removed from circulating blood in vivo on a single passage through various capillary beds (42, 56, 67). These observations imply that neither deamination in plasma [as originally thought; see (15)] nor uptake into blood cells usually constitutes the major pathway for the inactivation of circulating adenosine. A recent study suggests that uptake by blood cells rather than endothelial cells is the main site of removal in the rabbit (14), but the relative importance of red cells and endothelial cells in individual species remains to be determined.

From its position as the first interface between blood and tissue, and the large surface area it exposes to the flowing blood, it is likely that endothelium (particularly in capillary beds) significantly contributes to the measured adenosine uptake. Characterization of the uptake in isolated perfused vascular beds, notably lung and heart, has shown that adenosine is removed from the circulation by a saturable process and converted into intracellular nucleotides (7, 14, 19, 30, 31, 35, 44, 56). The uptake process is potently inhibited by dipyridamole in all species tested except the rat, where the drug is much less effective (35, 42). Estimates of the apparent affinity of the uptake process have varied widely (from 1 to 500 μM), depending on the species and vascular bed employed. As will be discussed below, however, the accurate estimation of kinetic parameters for the membrane adenosine carrier requires experimental conditions (in particular, extremely rapid measurements of uptake) that have not usually been achieved in perfused organ studies, and it is likely that much of the apparent variation in measured affinities is due to the variable contribution of one or more intracellular adenosine metabolic pathways, depending on the experimental methods used.

In earlier studies of perfused tissues no attempt was made to test the hypothesis that endothelial cells are responsible for adenosine clearance. Using indicator dilution techniques, we have measured adenosine uptake in the pig lung relative to an extracellular marker (sucrose) and found an uptake pattern consistent with removal both by the endothelium (apparent $K_m \simeq 35$ μM, $V_{max} \simeq 19$ nmol min^{-1} g^{-1}) and by subendothelial tissue (30). Catravas (14), by using an intravascular marker (indocyanine green or dextran) in indicator dilution studies with the rabbit lung, found an endothelial uptake process with

$K_m \simeq 500 \ \mu M$, $V_{max} = 4 \ \mu mol \ min^{-1} \ g^{-1}$. Recently Nees et al (50) isolated coronary endothelial cells after infusion of radiolabelled adenosine into the guinea-pig heart and were able to conclude that although it makes up < 5% of the total cell population in the heart, endothelium took up > 80% of the radioactivity.

The evidence that endothelial cells contribute significantly to adenosine clearance in perfused tissues is strengthened by the characterization of adenosine uptake by endothelial cells in vitro. Pig aortic or pulmonary endothelial cells efficiently take up adenosine and rapidly convert it to intracellular nucleotides, predominantly ATP (20, 61). In these studies, using incubations of a few minutes or more, two processes can be distinguished: one of high affinity ($K_m = 3 \ \mu M$) and one of lower affinity ($K_m \simeq 250 \ \mu M$). Uptake is powerfully inhibited by dipyridamole or nitrobenzylthioinosine (NBTI). These cells originate from large vessels rather than capillaries, and their metabolic characteristics may have altered in culture, but their rate of adenosine uptake is sufficient to account for most, if not all, of the uptake in the lung, assuming that pulmonary capillary endothelial cells behave similarly [V_{max} for aortic cells in vitro $\simeq 300 \ pmol \ min^{-1}$ per 10^6 cells; $\simeq 10^9$ endothelial cells per 20g piglet lung; V_{max} for endothelial uptake in piglet lung $\simeq 19 \ nmol \ min^{-1} g^{-1}$ (30, 61)].

We have previously discussed the problems in determining the kinetic constants for adenosine transport (65), which arise because of the rapidity with which the cell/medium concentration ratio reaches unity and the multiplicity of intracellular pathways for adenosine metabolism. From the work of Plagemann & Wohlhueter, who first recognized these difficulties and pioneered methods for the accurate measurement of adenosine transport kinetics (reviewed in 68), it seems likely that under the experimental conditions described above the high-affinity process measures the K_m of adenosine kinase, while the lower-affinity process measures the K_m of adenosine deaminase. To date, experiments with cultured endothelial cells have not been performed with an appropriate protocol to determine the true kinetics of adenosine transport. It therefore remains unresolved whether the adenosine carrier in endothelial cells has any features that differentiate it from the fairly broad specificity nucleoside carrier, sensitive to inhibition by dipyridamole or NBTI, present in several other cell types. The estimates for the affinity of adenosine uptake from indicator dilution studies in which rapid sampling techniques were used (cited above) are more likely to measure the K_m of the transport process, but this has not been unequivocally demonstrated.

INTRACELLULAR ADENOSINE METABOLISM

The main products found intracellularly after adenosine uptake by endothelial cells or perfused tissues, as noted above, are adenine nucleotides (mostly ATP). The level of ATP has been determined in cultured coronary endothelial cells (12 μmol g^{-1} = 4 nmol/10^6 cells) and was described by the authors as "extraordinarily high" (50). Comparison with other results, however, indicates that it is similar to that in cultured pig aortic endothelial cells (63) and in several other cell types (e.g. 8, 29, 75), suggesting that it is inappropriate to ascribe any special role to intracellular nucleotide metabolism in the endothelium. The level of ATP in coronary endothelial cells is three-fold higher on a wet-weight basis than that in whole cardiac tissue (50), but this contains substantial amounts of extracellular matrix.

Apart from indirect evidence, from kinetic studies of endothelial adenosine uptake in vitro, and from the description of the metabolic fate of adenosine in the lung with varying substrate concentration or in the presence of enzyme inhibitors (31, 61), there is little known about adenosine kinase and adenosine deaminase in endothelium. The changing pattern of pulmonary intracellular adenosine metabolism with increasing substrate concentration [primarily via adenosine kinase to ATP at low concentration, and at high concentrations (when the kinase is saturated) primarily via adenosine deaminase to inosine and hypoxanthine that are then released extracellularly (31)] is typical of that found in other cell types (4). It is therefore likely that endothelial cells behave similarly. Nees et al have suggested that adenosine deaminase activity is very low in coronary endothelial cells, but estimates (from the same laboratory) for this enzyme activity vary considerably (50, 51).

Two other potential sources of intracellular adenosine should be considered. The first is S-adenosyl-methionine, present in concentrations comparable to those of AMP in the heart and cultured endothelium (50). This can be catabolized via S-adenosyl-homocysteine to yield adenosine, and its potential role as a source of adenosine in cardiac tissue has been explored by Schrader et al (73). The second source is a measurable pool of intracellular adenosine, recently shown to exist in several tissues including the heart, associated with the enzyme S-adenosyl-homocysteine hydrolase (9, 55). It is not clear that this adenosine is available for any metabolic process: it is bound tightly to inactive enzyme (due to suicide inactivation during the formation of adenosine from S-adenosyl-homocysteine) and can be released only slowly.

INTRACELLULAR NUCLEOTIDE CATABOLISM

The degradation of cellular ATP and release of nucleosides (adenosine, inosine, and hypoxanthine) can readily be induced in cultured endothelial cells by brief exposure to hypercapnia, anoxia, H_2O_2, or inhibitors of phosphorylation (3, 50, 51, 64). This release can be selective (i.e. no leakage of high-molecular-weight cell contents occurs) and transient, with no permanent effects on the cells. The metabolic pathways involved have not yet been characterized. In other cell types it seems that catabolism of adenine nucleotides beyond AMP occurs predominantly via AMP deaminase to yield IMP, and hence inosine and hypoxanthine (52, 78), while a small proportion of AMP is dephosphorylated by a cytoplasmic 5'-nucleotidase to produce adenosine (36, 53, 77, 81). The cytosolic 5'-nucleotidase has different properties from plasma membrane 5'-nucleotidase, which is an ectoenzyme and cannot degrade intracellular AMP (reviewed in 59).

In view of the likely physiological role of circulating adenosine released in response to stimuli—in particular, hypoxia in the coronary bed (reviewed in 10)—it is of considerable interest that adenosine derivatives in the perfused heart are released from at least two metabolic compartments (72). These results are consistent with the concept that endothelial cells may be the major source of released adenosine under normoxic conditions (while the myocardial cells are the main source of inosine and hypoxanthine), although after severe ischemia myocardial cells also contribute to the release of adenosine. The experiments of Nees et al (50) described above strengthen the idea that rapid metabolic exchange of adenosine between plasma and tissue in the heart is likely to involve mainly the endothelial cells. These studies suggest (a) that the regulation of endothelial cell adenine nucleotide catabolism is of considerable importance to the physiological response of the whole tissue, and (b) that pathways of nucleotide catabolism may be quantitatively different in endothelial cells from those in myocardial cells.

Another metabolic pathway utilizing intracellular ATP is that which results in the formation of cyclic AMP, an intracellular messenger involved in regulating responses to stimuli in several cell types. Endothelial cells possess receptors for several types of vasoactive agent through which various responses (such as prostacyclin production or the induction of endothelium-dependent vasodilation) can be initiated (e.g. 5, 25, 28, 33, 66, 80). Although the molecular basis of responses to receptor occupation has not yet been fully explored, a rise in cyclic AMP is apparently involved in endothelial responses to catecholamines, prostacyclin, and adenosine—and possibly some other agents, such as acetylcholine, bradykinin, or angiotensin II (1, 2, 12, 27, 32, 46, 48, 71). The results of such studies have not been entirely consistent (perhaps depending on the species and site of endothelial cells used, as well as on the agonist), and the consequences of increases in cyclic AMP are still under debate. For example, it is disputed whether changes in cyclic AMP levels affect endothelial prostacyclin synthesis (1, 34). The perfused heart releases cyclic AMP extracellularly (72); cyclic AMP release from endothelial cells can also be induced in vitro by adenosine (27). Thus the possibility that cyclic AMP, normally thought of as an intracellular messenger in mammalian systems, may function as a signal between vascular cells, or from vascular cells to blood cells, merits further investigation.

EXTRACELLULAR NUCLEOTIDE CATABOLISM

Circulating nucleotides are rapidly catabolized on single passage through a capillary bed; organ-perfusion and indicator-dilution techniques have shown that nucleotides in the vascular lumen are metabolized by endothelial ectoenzymes, and the location of these enzymes at the endothelial plasmalemma has been confirmed cytochemically (e.g. 59, 69, and references therein). The importance of endothelial ectonucleotidases can be judged from the rate of metabolism of bloodborne nucleotides in vitro and in vivo. For example, for exogenous ATP (100 μM) the half life in cell-free plasma is $\simeq$ 30 min, in whole blood $\simeq$ 5 min, and in the microcirculation $<$ 0.1 min (6, 40, 70, 76).

Several workers have noted the presence of ectonucleotidase activity in cultured endothelium (e.g. 16, 17, 20, 21). We demonstrated, by the use of selective inhibitors, that pig aortic endothelial cells express three Ca^{2+} or Mg^{2+}-stimulated ectoenzymes [nucleoside triphosphatase, $K_m(ATP) \simeq 450$ μM; nucleoside diphosphatase, K_m (ADP) $\simeq$ 160 μM; 5'-nucleotidase, $K_m(AMP) \simeq 20$ μM (60)] that together sequentially degrade ATP$\rightarrow$ADP$\rightarrow$AMP$\rightarrow$adenosine. As part of our studies to differentiate between the various ATP and ADP binding sites on endothelium [ectoenzymes and purinoceptors (66)], we have recently studied the stereoselectivity of the ectotriphosphatase and diphosphatase by using optically active analogues with modified sugar or phosphate moieties and concluded that the triphosphatase recognizes the Λ, β,γ-bidentate ATP-Mg^{2+} complex, and the diphosphatase similarly recognizes the Λ, α, β-bidentate complex (18, 62). In contrast, the endothelial P_2 purinoceptor apparently recognizes nucleotide alone (i.e. not complexed with bivalent cation).

Although there is, in general, less detailed information available about the complement of ectonucleotidases on nonvascular cells, it seems that several other cell types possess similar ectoenzymes (for review see 59). The physiological relevance of the enzyme system at the endothelial cell surface is easy to appreciate: ATP, ADP, and adenosine are all potent vasoactive agents, acting at micromolar concentrations at receptors on vascular and blood cells, sometimes with opposing effects, and each compound can be released into the blood stream from various sources (including the endothelium itself—see the following section). The ectoenzymes thus serve to regulate the concentrations of circulating vasoactive purines and hence modulate the biological responses to them.

Other ectoenzymes metabolizing ATP exist at the endothelial cell surface, e.g. nucleoside diphosphate kinase of high activity (60, 65) and pyrophosphatase of modest activity (18). The functions of these enzymes are not yet well understood, but, in common with the ectonucleotidases discussed above, they all operate in the presence of extracellular nucleotides; therefore, discussion of the biological roles of all these enzymes requires an understanding of how nucleotides can arise in plasma. For the purposes of this review, we shall concentrate on endothelium as a potential source of plasma nucleotides.

STIMULATION OF NUCLEOTIDE RELEASE FROM ENDOTHELIUM

It has been known for more than 30 years that high concentrations ($\simeq 100 \mu M$) of adenine nucleotides appear in plasma following trauma (41); the source of these nucleotides was not identified, but blood cells or cells of the vascular wall are likely candidates. Nucleotides are also released into the blood draining from working skeletal muscle, or escaping from a micropuncture in a small artery, where the concentrations in plasma rapidly reach 50 μM (11, 24). Although blood cells may well contribute to this release, nucleotides can also be found in the effluent of organs perfused with blood-free medium (24, 57, 74), suggesting that endothelial cells might be a source of nucleotide release.

Pig aortic endothelial cells in culture release nucleotides when briefly treated with trypsin plus EDTA (the conventional procedure for subculturing cells) or thrombin, which does not detach the cells from their substrate (63). Subsequent studies by the authors revealed that trypsin or EDTA individually induce release of nucleotides. The cells remain viable even if up to 50% of the ATP is released extracellularly; release is selective inasmuch as it is not accompanied by any detectable release of lactate dehydrogenase (45, 63). Because the intracellular ATP concentration is ≥ 5 mM, only a small fractional release is required to generate concentrations of ATP sufficient to affect vascular tone and platelet function.

Our initial studies on nucleotide release from cultured endothelial cells were performed using cells in conventional culture dishes; in experiments with cells grown on plastic microcarrier beads, packed in columns and superfused, we were able to study the time course of the responses and established that nucleotide release was initiated within seconds of exposure to stimuli. Of several neutral proteases tested, neutrophil elastase proved to be the most potent at inducing nucleotide release. This apparently was not a function of the active site of the enzyme (43); rather, it appears to be a function of the enzyme's cationic nature and molecular size, because polylysines of high molecular weight have a similar effect, and the response to these polymers decreases as the size and charge also decrease (49).

Highly cationic proteins released from stimulated neutrophils and platelets can induce vascular permeability and damage endothelium (39, 47). Similarly, the cardiac dysfunction mainly responsible for morbidity and mortality in the hypereosinophilic syndrome is due partly to the effects of eosinophil granule cationic proteins on endothelium (26, 58, 79). Since ATP is a potent vasoactive agent, some of the vascular effects of such cationic proteins may reflect their capacity to induce nucleotide release from endothelium.

CONCLUSIONS

ATP and ADP are powerful vasoactive stimuli that also have opposing effects on platelet function. The capacity of endothelial cells to metabolize adenine nucleotides on their luminal (and, presumably, abluminal) surface is high: in the microcirculation (e.g. of the coronary or pulmonary beds) most exogenous ATP even at high concentrations (up to 1 mM) is metabolized to adenosine in a single passage. Thus, the effects of adenine nucleotides released into the plasma, e.g. by traumatized tissue or by aggregating platelets, are regulated and limited by the local action of endothelial ectonucleotidases.

Adenosine is also a potent vasodilator and inhibits platelet aggregation. Endothelial cells contribute to the removal of adenosine from the plasma, although uptake into other cells in the circulation (e.g. erythrocytes) may be important under certain circumstances. Circulating adenosine is formed either through catabolism of extracellular nucleotides by endothelial ectonucleotidases, or by release from cells after intracellular production. Endothelial cells may contribute significantly to the production of circulating adenosine by either pathway. Finally, selective release of endothelial nucleotides can be induced by diverse stimuli such as neutral proteases, chelation of calcium at the cell surface, and a variety of cationic polymers or proteins.

Thus, a regulatory system exists at the luminal surface of endothelial cells involving the metabolism and transmembrane translocation of adenine nucleotides and adenosine. Endothelial cells also possess receptors for adenine nucleotides (coupled to effector systems that stimulate the production of prostacyclin and that induce endothelium-dependent vasodilation) and for adenosine (coupled to adenylate cyclase). It is becoming increasingly apparent that interactions between adenine derivatives and the luminal surface of vascular endothelium constitute an important means of controlling platelet function and vascular tone.

Literature Cited

1. Adams Brotherton, A. F., Hoak, J. C. 1982. Role of Ca^{2+} and cyclic AMP in the regulation of the production of prostacyclin by the vascular endothelium. *Proc. Natl. Acad. Sci. USA* 79:495–99
2. Ager, A., Gordon, J. L. 1980. Effects of vasoactive and inflammatory agents on cyclic AMP levels in WI38 fibroblasts, endothelial and vascular smooth muscle cells in culture. *Agents Actions* 10:569–72
3. Ager, A., Gordon, J. L. 1984. Differential effects of hydrogen peroxide on indices of endothelial cell function. *J. Exp. Med.* 159:592–603
4. Arch, J. R. S., Newsholme, E. A. 1978. Activities and some properties of 5'-nucleotidase, adenosine kinase and adenosine deaminase in tissues from vertebrates and invertebrates in relation to the concentration and the physiological role of adenosine. *Biochem. J.* 174:965–77

5. Baenziger, N. L., Fogerty, F. J., Mertz, L. F., Chernuta, L. F. 1981. Regulation of histamine-mediated prostacyclin synthesis in cultured human vascular endothelial cells. *Cell* 24:915–23

6. Baer, H.-P., Drummond, G. I. 1968. Catabolism of adenine nucleotides by the isolated perfused cat heart. *Proc. Soc. Exp. Biol. Med.* 127:33–36

7. Bakhle, Y. S., Chelliah, R. 1983. Metabolism and uptake of adenosine in rat isolated lung and its inhibition. *Br. J. Pharmac.* 79:509–15

8. Becker, M. A. 1977. Effects of inosine on purine synthesis in normal and HGPRT-deficient human fibroblasts. In *Purine Metabolism in Man II*, ed. M. M. Müller, E. Kaiser, J. E. Seegmiller. *Adv. Exp. Med. Biol.* 76A:370–75

9. Belloni, F. L., Rubio, R., Berne, R. M. 1984. Intracellular adenosine in isolated rat liver cells. *Pfluegers Arch.* 400:106–8

10. Berne, R. M., Rall, T. W., Rubio, R., eds. 1983. *Regulatory Function of Adenosine*. Boston: Martinus Nijhoff. 558 pp.

11. Born, G. V. R., Kratzer, M. A. A. 1984. Source and concentration of extracellular adenosine triphosphate during haemostasis in rats, rabbits, and man. *J. Physiol.* 354:419–29

12. Buonassisi, V., Venter, J. C. 1976. Hormone and neurotransmitter receptors in an established vascular endothelial cell line. *Proc. Natl. Acad. Sci. USA* 73:1612–16

13. Burnstock, G., ed. 1981. *Purinergic Receptors*. London/New York: Chapman & Hall. 365 pp.

14. Catravas, J. D. 1984. Removal of adenosine from the rabbit pulmonary circulation, in vivo and in vitro. *Circulation Res.* 54:603–11

15. Clarke, D. A., Davoli, J., Phillips, F. S., Brown, G. B. 1952. Enzymatic deamination and vasodepressor effects of adenosine analogues. *J. Pharmac. Exp. Ther.* 106:291–302

16. Cooper, D. R., Lewis, G. P., Lieberman, G. E., Webb, H., Westwick, J. 1979. ADP metabolism in vascular tissue, a possible thromboregulatory mechanism. *Thromb. Res.* 14:901–14

17. Crutchley, D. J., Ryan, U. S., Ryan, J. W. 1980. Effects of aspirin and dipyridamole on the degradation of adenosine diphosphate by cultured cells derived from bovine pulmonary artery. *J. Clin. Invest.* 66:29–35

18. Cusack, N. J., Pearson, J. D., Gordon, J. L. 1983. Stereoselectivity of ectonucleotidases on vascular endothelial cells. *Biochem. J.* 214:975–81

19. Das, D. K., Das, S., Steinberg, H. 1978. Uptake and metabolism of adenosine by the isolated rat lung. *Fed. Proc.* 37:222 (Abstr.)

20. Dieterle, Y., Ody, C., Ehrensburger, A., Stalder, H., Junod, A. F. 1978. Metabolism and uptake of adenosine triphosphate and adenosine by porcine aortic and pulmonary endothelial cells and fibroblasts in culture. *Circulation Res.* 42:869–76

21. Dosne, A. M., Legrand, C., Bauvois, B., Bodevin, E., Caen, J. P. 1978. Comparative degradation of adenylnucleotides by cultured endothelial cells and fibroblasts. *Biochem. Biophys. Res. Commun.* 85:183–89

22. Drury, A. N., Szent-Gyorgi, A. 1929. The physiological activity of adenine compounds with special reference to their action upon the mammalian heart. *J. Physiol.* 68:213–37

23. Fiske, C. H. 1934. The nature of the depressor substance of the blood. *Proc. Nat. Acad. Sci. USA* 20:25–27

24. Forrester, T. 1981. Adenosine or adenosine triphosphate? In *Vasodilation*, ed. P. M. Vanhoutte, I. Leusen, pp. 205–29. New York: Raven

25. Furchgott, R. F. 1983. Role of endothelium in responses of vascular smooth muscle. *Circulation Res.* 53:557–73

26. Gleich, G. J., Frigas, E., Loegering, D. A., Wassom, D. L., Steinmuller, D. 1979. Cytotoxic properties of the eosinophil major basic protein. *J. Immunol.* 123:2925–27

27. Goldman, S. J., Dickinson, E. S., Slakey, L. L. 1983. Effect of adenosine on synthesis and release of cyclic AMP by cultured vascular cells from swine. *J. Cyclic. Nucl. Prot. Phosphoryl. Res.* 9:69–78

28. Gordon, J. L., Martin, W. 1983. Endothelium-dependent relaxation of the pig aorta: relationship to stimulation of ^{86}Rb efflux from isolated endothelial cells. *Br. J. Pharmacol.* 70:531–41

29. Harkness, R. A., Coade, S. B., Mansell, M., Simmonds, R. J. 1982. Nucleotide concentrations in leucocytes and their use in controlling the quality of cell preparations. In *Biochemistry and Function of Phagocytes*, ed. F. Rossi, P. Patriarce, pp. 583–90. New York: Plenum

30. Hellewell, P. G., Pearson, J. D. 1983. Kinetic analysis of prostaglandin $F_{2\alpha}$ and adenosine uptake in the piglet lung. *J. Physiol.* 343:48P. (Abstr.)

31. Hellewell, P. G., Pearson, J. D. 1983. Metabolism of circulating adenosine by the porcine isolated perfused lung. *Circ. Res.* 53:1–7

32. Herbst, T. J., Raichle, M. E., Ferrendelli, J. A. 1979. β-Adrenergic regulation of adenosine-3'-5'-monophosphate concentration in brain microvessels. *Science* 204:330–32

33. Hong, S. L. 1980. Effect of bradykinin and thrombin on prostacyclin synthesis in endothelial cells from calf and pig aorta and human umbilical cord vein. *Thromb. Res.* 18:787–95

34. Hong, S. L. 1983. Inhibition of prostacyclin synthesis in endothelial cells by methylisobutylxanthine is not mediated through elevated cAMP levels. *Biochim. Biophys. Acta.* 754:258–63

35. Hopkins, S. V., Goldie, R. G. 1971. A species difference in the uptake of adenosine by heart. *Biochem. Pharmacol.* 20:3359–65

36. Itoh, R. 1981. Regulation of cytosol 5'-nucleotidase by adenylate energy charge. *Biochim. Biophys. Acta.* 659:31–37

37. Jaffe, E. A., ed. 1984. *Biology of Endothelial Cells.* Boston: Martinus Nijhoff. 448 pp.

38. Jaffe, E. A., Nachman, R. L., Becker, C. G., Minick, C. R. 1973. Culture of human endothelial cells derived from umbilical veins. *J. Clin. Invest.* 52: 2745–56

39. Janoff, A., Zweifach, B. W. 1964. The production of inflammatory changes in the microcirculation by cationic proteins extracted from lysosomes. *J. Exp. Med.* 120:747–64

40. Jørgensen, S. 1956. Breakdown of adenine and hypoxanthine nucleotides and nucleosides in human plasma. *Acta Pharmacol. Tox.* 12:294–303

41. Kalckar, H. M., Lowry, O. H. 1947. The relationship between traumatic shock and the release of adenine compounds. *Am. J. Physiol.* 149:240–45

42. Kolassa, N., Pfleger, K., Tram, M. 1971. Species difference in action and elimination of adenosine after dipyridamole and hexobendine. *Eur. J. Pharmac.* 13:320–25

43. LeRoy, E. C., Ager, A., Gordon, J. L. 1984. Effects of neutrophil elastase and other proteases on porcine aortic endothelial prostaglandin I₂ production, adenine nucleotide release and responses to vasoactive agents. *J. Clin. Invest.* 74:1003–10

44. Liu, M. S., Feinberg, H. 1971. Incorporation of adenosine-8-¹⁴C and inosine-8-¹⁴C into rabbit heart adenine nucleotides. *Am. J. Physiol.* 220:1242–48

45. Lollar, P., Owen, W. G. 1981. Active-site dependent, thrombin-induced release of adenine nucleotides from cultured human endothelial cells. *Ann. NY Acad. Sci.* 307:51–56

46. Makarski, J. S. 1981. Stimulation of cyclic AMP production by vasoactive agents in cultured bovine aortic and pulmonary artery endothelial cells. *In Vitro* 17:450–58

47. Nachman, R. L., Weksler, B., Ferris, B. 1972. Characterization of human platelet vascular permeability-enhancing activity. *J. Clin. Invest.* 51:549–56

48. Nathanson, J. A., Glaser, G. H. 1979. Identification of β-adrenergic sensitive adenylate cyclase in intracranial blood vessels. *Nature* 278:567–69

49. Needham, L. A., Gordon, J. L., Ager, A., LeRoy, E. C. 1984. Endothelial cell responses to neutrophil secretory products. *Proc. 3rd Int. Conf. Biol. Endothelial Cells, Boston,* p. 116 (Abstr.)

50. Nees, S. Gerlach, E. 1983. Adenine nucleotide and adenosine metabolism in cultured coronary endothelial cells: formation and release of adenine compounds and possible functional implications. See Ref. 10, pp. 347–60

51. Nees, S., Willerhausen-Zönnchen, B., Gerbes, A. L., Gerlach, E. 1980. Studies on cultured coronary endothelial cells. *Folia Angiol.* 28:64–68

52. Newby, A. C. 1980. Role of adenosine deaminase, ecto-(5'-nucleotidase) and ecto-(non-specific phosphatase) in cyanide-induced adenosine monophosphate catabolism in rat polymorphonuclear leukocytes. *Biochem. J.* 186:907–18

53. Newby, A. C., Holmquist, C. A., Illingworth, J., Pearson, J. D. 1983. The control of adenosine concentration in polymorphonuclear leucocytes, cultured heart cells and isolated perfused hearts from the rat. *Biochem. J.* 214:317–23

54. Nossel, H. L., Vogel, H. J., eds. 1982. *Pathobiology of the Endothelial Cell.* New York: Academic. 496 pp.

55. Olsson, R. A., Saite, D., Steinhart, C. R. 1982. Compartmentalization of the adenosine pool of dog and rat hearts. *Circulation Res.* 50:617–26

56. Olsson, R. A., Snow, J. A., Gentry, M. K., Frick, G. P. 1972. Adenosine uptake by canine heart. *Circulation Res.* 31: 767–78

57. Paddle, B. M., Burnstock, G. 1974. Release of ATP from perfused heart during coronary vasodilation. *Blood Vessels* 11:110–19

58. Parrillo, J. E., Borer, J. S., Henry, W. L., Wolff, S. M., Fauci, A. S. 1979. The cardiovascular manifestations of the hypereosinophil syndrome. *Am. J. Med.* 67:572–82

59. Pearson, J. D. 1985. Ectonucleotidases: measurement of activities and use of inhibitors. In *Methods Used in Adenosine*

Research, ed. D. M. Paton, in press. New York: Plenum

60. Pearson, J. D., Carleton, J. S., Gordon, J. L. 1980. Metabolism of adenine nucleotides by ectoenzymes of vascular endothelial and smooth muscle cells in culture. *Biochem. J.* 190:421–29

61. Pearson, J. D., Carleton, J. S., Hutchings, A., Gordon, J. L. 1978. Uptake and metabolism of adenosine by pig aortic endothelial and smooth muscle cells in culture. *Biochem. J.* 170:265–71

62. Pearson, J. D., Cusack, N. J., Martin, W. 1984. Discrimination between ecto-ATPase and P_2 purinoreceptors on porcine aortic endothelium. *IX Int. Cong., Int. Union Pharmacol.,* Abstr. Vol. 1913P

63. Pearson, J. D., Gordon, J. L. 1979. Vascular endothelial and smooth muscle cells in culture selectively release adenine nucleotides. *Nature* 281:384–86

64. Pearson, J. D., Gordon, J. L. 1983. Responses of endothelial cells to injury. See Ref. 54, pp. 433–54

65. Pearson, J. D., Hellewell, P. G., Gordon, J. L. 1983. Adenosine uptake and adenine nucleotide metabolism by vascular endothelium. See Ref. 10, pp. 333–45

66. Pearson, J. D., Slakey, L. L., Gordon, J. L. 1983. Stimulation of prostaglandin production through purinoceptors on cultured porcine endothelial cells. *Biochem. J.* 214:273–76

67. Pfleger, K., Seifen, E., Schöndorf, H. 1969. Potentierung der adenosinwirkung am herzen durch inosin. *Biochem. Pharmacol.* 18:43–51

68. Plagemann, P. G. W., Wohlhueter, R. M. 1983. Nucleoside transport in mammalian cells and interaction with intracellular metabolism. See Ref. 10, pp. 179–201

69. Ryan, J. W., Ryan, U. S. 1984. Endothelial surface enzymes and the dynamic processing of plasma substrates. *Int. Rev. Exp. Pathol.* 26:1–43

70. Ryan, J. W., Smith, U. 1971. Metabolism of adenosine 5′-monophosphate during circulation through the lungs. *Trans. Assoc. Am. Physicians* 84:297–306

71. Schafer, A. I., Gimbrone, M. A. Jr., Handin, R. I. 1980. Endothelial cell adenylate cyclase: activation by catecholamines and prostaglandin I_2. *Biophys. Res. Commun.* 96:1640–47

72. Schrader, J., Gerlach, E. 1976. Compartmentation of cardiac adenine nucleotides and formation of adenosine. *Pfluegers Arch.* 367:129–35

73. Schrader, J., Schütz, W., Bardenheuer, H. 1981. Role of S-adenosylhomocysteine hydrolase in adenosine metabolism of mammalian heart. *Biochem. J.* 196:65–70

74. Schrader, J., Thompson, L. T., Hiendlmayer, G., Gerlach, E. 1982. Role of purines in acetylcholine-induced coronary vasodilation. *J. Mol. Cell. Cardiol.* 14:427–30

75. Snyder, F. F., Hershfield, M. S., Seegmiller, J. E. 1977. Purine toxicity in human lymphoblasts. See Ref. 8, pp. 30–39

76. Trams, E. G., Kaufmann, H., Burnstock, G. 1980. A proposal for the role of ecto-enzymes and adenylates in traumatic shock. *J. Theoret. Biol.* 87:609–21

77. Van den Berghe, G., Van Pottelsberghe, C., Hers, H.-G. 1977. A kinetic study of the soluble 5′-nucleotidase of rat liver. *Biochem. J.* 162:611–16

78. Vincent, M. F., Van den Berghe, G., Hers, H.-G. 1982. The pathway of adenine nucleotide catabolism and its control in isolated rat hepatocytes subjected to anoxia. *Biochem. J.* 202:117–23

79. Wassom, D. L., Loegering, D. A., Solley, G. O., Moore, S. B., Schooley, R. T., et al. 1981. Elevated serum levels of the eosinophil granule major basic protein in patients with eosinophilia. *J. Clin. Invest.* 67:651–61

80. Weksler, B. B., Ley, C. W., Jaffe, E. A. 1978. Stimulation of endothelial cell prostacyclin production by thrombin, trypsin and the ionophore A23187. *J. Clin. Invest.* 62:923–30

81. Worku, Y., Newby, A. C. 1983. The mechanism of adenosine production inside rat polymorphonuclear leucocytes. *Biochem. J.* 214:325–30

Ann. Rev. Physiol. 1985. 47:629–43

HIGH-ENERGY PHOSPHATE METABOLISM IN VASCULAR SMOOTH MUSCLE

Thomas M. Butler and Marion J. Siegman

Department of Physiology, Jefferson Medical College, Thomas Jefferson University, 1020 Locust Street, Philadelphia, Pennsylvania 19107

INTRODUCTION

Studies on the energetics of smooth muscle contraction historically have lagged behind those on striated muscle. It is now apparent that through the use of techniques similar to those applied to striated muscle, significant information can be gained concerning the mechanism of transduction of high-energy phosphate breakdown into a mechanical output in smooth muscle. Some aspects of energy metabolism are similar in smooth and striated muscles, but there are certain major differences that are consistent with the functional specialization of the two muscle types. The emphasis of this chapter is to describe the relationships among mechanical output, high-energy phosphate utilization, and intermediary metabolism during smooth muscle contraction.

RELATIONSHIP BETWEEN HIGH-ENERGY PHOSPHATE UTILIZATION AND RECOVERY METABOLISM IN SMOOTH MUSCLE

The phosphagen (ATP and phosphocreatine) content of smooth muscle is rather small compared to the energy demands of the tissue (for review see 9, 53). Largely on these grounds, it has been suggested that there must be a tight coupling between the rate of high-energy phosphate utilization in smooth muscle and the resynthesis of high-energy phosphate by oxidative phosphorylation and glycolysis (62). This does not necessarily imply that there is an immediate adjustment of intermediary metabolism to an energy demand in a

629

0066-4278/85/0315-0629$02.00

normal smooth muscle. A significant breakdown of preformed phosphagen may occur, and the energy derived from such a net phosphagen change can account for a significant fraction of the total energy output of the tissue under particular mechanical conditions.

During a single spontaneous contraction there is a significant decrease in the phosphocreatine (PCr) content, with no measurable change in the ATP or ADP contents of the rat portal vein (36). In order for the PCr content of the muscle to remain constant over the long term, PCr, must be resynthesized mainly by oxidative phosphorylation during the period of rest before the next spontaneous contraction. Although the PCr content of the portal vein is only 2 μmol g^{-1}, a net change in PCr under fully oxygenated conditions can provide more than 80% of the energy requirements during a spontaneous contraction. During a sustained contraction induced by K$^+$ depolarization, there is a decrease of 0.8 μmol g^{-1} at 1 min, and during the subsequent 9 min the PCr content remains constant. The initial decrease in PCr provides about 50% of the total high-energy phosphate demand of the tissue, after which respiration and glycolysis account for the total energy demand.

Similar conclusions concerning the importance of net changes in PCr as an energy source in smooth muscle under nonsteady-state conditions can be drawn from the experiments reported by Butler et al (13) and Siegman et al (74). In the fully oxygenated rabbit taenia coli, the net changes in PCr were between 70% and 80% of the total high-energy phosphate demand during both a 60-sec isometric tetanus and a 35-sec isovelocity shortening.

In the aforementioned studies, PCr was 65–80% of the total creatine content of the tissue under resting conditions. If the creatine kinase reaction were in equilibrium (see 43 for review in skeletal muscle), then the resting muscle would have levels of free ADP below 100 μM. During periods in which there is a high rate of ATP splitting, net PCr breakdown occurs to the extent appropriate for the maintenance of near-equilibrium conditions for the creatine kinase reaction, and can thereby provide a significant fraction of the total energy demand. The rate of oxidative phosphorylation subsequently adjusts to this new energy demand and then provides almost all of the energy requirements during continued contraction (see 53 for review). A correlation has been shown between the calculated free ADP content and the rate of oxygen consumption in the rat portal vein (36). It is tempting to speculate that ADP plays a direct role in the control of respiration in smooth muscle similar to the ADP-stimulated respiration in isolated mitochondria under conditions of saturating substrate and oxygen. Kushmerick (43) has noted, however, that there may be a network of reactions with overlapping reactants and products that exist at near-equilibrium conditions such that the change in one metabolite can effect a change in the concentrations of many. More complex experiments are required to isolate the effect of a change in ADP content on respiration.

An interesting difference seems to exist between the changes in phosphagen content in response to stimulation in the tonic hog carotid artery compared to the more phasic rat portal vein and rabbit taenia coli. Krisanda & Paul (41) report no change in ATP or PCr contents during an isometric contraction initiated by K^+ depolarization. Under these conditions it seems that intermediary metabolism supports the total energy requirements of the tissue from the initiation of the stimulation. Because there was no change in the PCr content of the tissue, the authors conclude that no changes in free ADP concentration occur and that ADP does not play a role in regulation of oxidative phosphorylation. It should be noted, however, that in these muscles at rest, the ratio of PCr to total creatine was a very low 0.34:1, resulting in a correspondingly high calculated value of free ADP concentration. It is possible that the interrelationships among the various energy-supplying reactions may be different in muscles that at rest have a low phosphorylation potential, as evidenced by the fact that most of the total creatine content is present as free creatine rather than phosphocreatine. There is a significant change in the PCr content of the hog carotid artery when the muscle is allowed to shorten at a velocity at which maximum work is performed (42). Evidently the large energy demands associated with shortening exceed the capacity of intermediary metabolism to resynthesize ATP even in tonic smooth muscles.

In spite of its presence in small quantities, phosphocreatine appears to play a pivotal role in the overall energetics of smooth muscle. The content, although low, allows PCr to function optimally as an ATP buffer under conditions where oxidative phosphorylation and glycolysis cannot provide the necessary energy supply. Iyengar et al (40) have found that smooth-muscle creatine kinase has a higher affinity for MgADP than does the skeletal muscle enzyme and that there is a MgADP-mediated increase in PCr binding. Both of these factors would facilitate the role of the enzyme in maintaining ATP concentrations when those of ADP and PCr are low.

The factors that control the total creatine and thereby the phosphocreatine content of a particular muscle remain to be determined. The PCr content is correlated with the amount of creatine kinase activity (10, 39), and it has been suggested that the enzyme content directly determines the phosphocreatine content (39). Considering the importance of net phosphocreatine splitting in normal activity of smooth muscle, it is possible that certain pathological conditions exist whereby there is mismatch between the required and actual rate at which PCr breakdown occurs and ATP is resynthesized. Some recent studies have shown that the total creatine content of smooth muscle can decrease in response to stimulation (36, 74). This would be expected to result in a relatively long-term decrease in the PCr content, and the potential effect of this is not known.

COMPARTMENTALIZATION OF GLYCOLYTIC AND OXIDATIVE METABOLISM

A significant rate of glycolysis with lactate production under fully oxygenated conditions is characteristic of vascular smooth muscle (for review see 53). Under resting conditions, the rate of oxygen consumption and lactate production are often almost equal on a molar basis, resulting in approximately 30% of the ATP supply coming from aerobic glycolysis, but at least 90% of the flux through glycolysis resulting in lactate production (55). Paul (53) has argued that this large lactate production under oxygenated conditions does not result from inadequate tissue oxygenation, or a limitation in oxidative capacity of the muscle. Many studies (26, 33, 66) have shown that the rate of lactate production under aerobic conditions increases in response to stimulation by pharmacological agents as well as by high potassium, without complete removal of sodium ions from the bathing medium. However, when there is complete substitution of K^+ for Na^+, lactate production does not increase during contraction; rather, there is usually a decrease in rate compared to resting conditions. This occurs while the increase in oxygen consumption associated with contraction proceeds as expected (26, 55, 57). The use of ouabain and other procedures that would be expected to interfere with Na^+ - K^+ transport also results in a decrease in the aerobic lactate production with an increase in oxygen consumption proportional to the active force production of the muscle. On the basis of these results, Paul and colleagues (55, 57) postulated that under fully oxygenated conditions, glycolysis with lactate formation provides the ATP required for Na^+ and K^+ transport, while oxidative metabolism is the energy source for the contractile machinery. A study of Hellstrand et al (35a) on the rat portal vein supports this hypothesis in general, but suggests that the compartmentalization is not absolute. Of course, there would not be total separation of the pathways, because it is possible to show a Pasteur effect in smooth muscle (cf. 53).

Lynch and Paul (44) have demonstrated compartmentalization of glycolysis and glycogenolysis in vascular smooth muscle such that glucose taken up from the medium results in lactate formation, whereas glycogen is preferentially oxidized. These data are consistent with the idea that ATP generated from glycolysis and from respiration could provide the energy supply for different processes. Such compartmentalization could result from an association of the glycolytic enzymes with the Na^+ - K^+ pump (55). Another interesting possibility is that creatine kinase might be localized near the contractile elements so that PCr generated by respiration through the proposed PCr shuttle mechanism (see 7 for review) is preferentially used for actin-activated myosin ATPase activity.

GENERAL COMMENTS ON SMOOTH MUSCLE ENERGETICS

The eventual goal of energetics studies on smooth muscle is to determine the overall energy costs of mechanical output under different conditions and to relate these to the underlying reactions. In this way information can be gained concerning the mechanochemical transduction process. Smooth muscle energetics studies published before 1980 have been reviewed in detail (9, 53), and readers are referred to these for discussions and references. For present purposes, only a short summary of this earlier work will be presented.

The striking observation concerning the energetics of smooth muscle is its very low energy demand compared to skeletal muscle. There is a 300–500-fold lower energy input per wet weight of tissue required for maintenance of maximum isometric force in some smooth muscles compared to fast striated muscle. Similarly, as much as a 300-fold difference exists in the energy cost for maintenance of the same force per cross-sectional area in the two types of muscles. Siegman et al (72) have calculated that if all energy usage were due to actin-activated myosin ATPase activity and all myosin were splitting ATP, then on average each myosin would split ATP only every 7.5 sec during maintenance of nearly constant isometric force in the rabbit taenia coli at 18°C. A similar calculation for frog fast skeletal muscle at the same temperature yields a value of 50 msec.

Not surprisingly, there are rather large differences in the energy requirements for isometric force maintenance in different smooth muscles. Hellstrand (32) noted that the energy cost of force production was higher in the rat portal vein than in other more tonic vessels, and myothermic measurements suggest that the rabbit rectococcygenus muscle has a substantially higher rate of energy usage than the rabbit taenia coli (20, 25, 72).

ENERGY USAGE UNDER ISOMETRIC CONDITIONS

Time Course of Energy Usage

Siegman et al (72) found that there was a large change in the rate of chemical energy usage as stimulation duration increased in the rabbit taenia coli under isometric conditions. The suprabasal average rate of energy usage was four-fold higher during the period of force development than when nearly constant force was maintained. This change in rate was not due exclusively to an energy requirement related to work production against the series elasticity. It was also known that there was a very small energy requirement for force output during relaxation. Thus, there were rather large changes in the economy of force production during a single contraction. Similarly, a two-fold decrease in the suprabasal rate of energy usage during a sustained isometric contraction has recently been reported in both hog carotid artery (41a, 54) and rat portal vein (6, 36). A rather large decrease in the rate of energy usage during an isometric contraction seems to be characteristic of most smooth muscles that have been studied. However, Gibbs & Loiselle (25) found no such change in rate of heat production in the rabbit rectococcygeus, but in these experiments contractions were of rather short duration.

Hellstrand (32) showed that in the rat portal vein, force production was associated with a higher steady-state rate of oxygen consumption during a series of spontaneous contractions than during nearly constant force maintenance in a K^+-induced contracture. More recent work suggests that these differences were due primarily to temporal changes in rate of energy usage rather than to differences inherent in the mode of stimulation. During a series of spontaneous contractions, a greater fraction of the total time was spent in the force development phase when economy was low. The ATP utilized per unit tension-time integral ($\int Pdt$) was similar under both stimulation conditions during the period when isometric force was developing (36). There is some conflicting information concerning the effect of the mode of stimulation on the relationship between energy usage and force in the hog carotid artery. Whereas Gluck & Paul (26) found that this relationship was the same when histamine or K^+ depolarization were used, Peterson (64) has reported a 25% greater energy demand for maintenance of the same isometric force during stimulation with histamine than during K^+ depolarization.

Many of these studies suggest that there is some determinant of the relationship between energy usage and force output in smooth muscle under isometric conditions that depends upon duration of stimulation and perhaps also on the mode of stimulation.

Partition into Force-Dependent and Force-Independent Energy Usage

Ideally, if the goal of experiments is to investigate the mechanochemical transduction process, it is necessary to be able to determine what fraction of the total energy usage of the muscle results from actin-activated myosin ATPase activity. Other ATPases, such as those associated with ion pumping, are possibly activated by stimulation, and certain techniques have been used to try to measure the contribution of these processes to the total energy demand. A method applied to skeletal muscle (37, 75) involves decreasing the degree of overlap of thick and thin filaments by stretching the muscle beyond L_o, the length at which maximum isometric force is developed. As the number of crossbridges that can interact with actin decrease, so do both the force output and associated energy requirements of the muscle. At a length where no crossbridge interaction occurs, only the activity of ATPases other than actin-activated myosin ATPase remain. With use of this method, Paul & Peterson (60) estimated the force-independent energy usage to be about 50% of the total energy usage in the bovine mesenteric vein stimulated with epinephrine at L_o. As noted by them, the use of this technique presents difficulties in smooth muscle. Stretching the muscle to long lengths where force output is greatly diminished often causes an irreversible decrease in the force-generating capacity of the muscle measured when the length is returned to L_o. This may be due to a change in the complex arrangement of smooth muscle cells in series and their relationship to the connective tissue matrix as well as to a compromise of intracellular structures. Paul & Peterson (60) did the same type of analysis, using adjustment to lengths less than L_o to vary the force. They found that at the maximally shortened length where no active force was generated, 15–20% of the suprabasal energy usage occurring at L_o remained. Several recent studies in other smooth muscles have shown a proportionality between energy usage and isometric force output at lengths less than L_o and that 20–50% of the suprabasal energy usage at L_o remains at short lengths where no active force is generated (5, 6, 20, 26, 32, 36, 59).

No studies have addressed the question of whether the energy cost of activation processes changes with duration of stimulation, but there is a report that the force-independent energy usage is higher during spontaneous contractions of the rat portal vein than during potassium contractures (32). It is interesting to note that Peterson & Gluck (65) have concluded from a rather complex series of experiments that during potassium-induced contractures, the energy cost of membrane depolarization per se in the hog carotid artery is negligible. They also found no evidence for activation of a calcium-dependent ATPase upon stimulation.

In an effort to investigate the potential time-dependence of energy usage due to activation processes, our laboratories initiated similar experiments to determine the force dependence of energy usage in the rabbit taenia coli at lengths less than L_o. We found no significant change in the high-energy phosphate usage under isometric conditions as force decreased (12, 73). This led to a reevaluation of the concept that force-dependent energy usage could be measured using lengths below L_o.

The assumption inherent in the measurement of force-independent energy usage is that the only mechanism responsible for a decrease in force output is a structurally induced decrease in the number of crossbridges that are interacting. It is not clear that the decrease in isometric force at lengths less than L_o is due only to such a mechanism in any muscle type. Studies on skeletal (70, 71, 76), cardiac (23), and smooth muscle (6) suggest that some of the decrease in force at short lengths results from a decreased activation of the muscle. There is also evidence for the presence of an internal load at short muscle lengths that alters the relationship between crossbridge attachment and external force generation.

Such a mechanism may account for the decrease in maximum shortening velocity observed at short lengths in both skeletal and smooth muscle (22, 27, 38) and the fact that instantaneous stiffness decreases less than active force at lengths shorter than L_o in some smooth and skeletal muscles (8, 46, 49, 67, 73). Finally, there is the potential for a misalignment of contractile filaments and/or cells such that force is generated in an axis other than that measured at very short muscle lengths (73).

It is concluded that the measurement of energy usage at short lengths as a means of estimating force-independent and force-dependent energy usage presents problems. Unless it can be shown that the decrease in force is due only to a decrease in the number of crossbridges interacting at a constant degree of activation of the muscle, then the method is not necessarily appropriate. The observation that energy usage decreases as force decreases is not sufficient validation of the method.

Although there are at present no totally satisfactory methods available to determine the fraction of total energy usage due exclusively to actin-activated myosin ATPase activity, the total rate of energy usage reflects relatively well the underlying crossbridge-related ATPase activity in smooth muscle. The best evidence for this is that under conditions when there are large changes in the average rate of energy usage, there are often similar relative changes in the maximum velocity of shortening (32, 54, 74), which is a generally accepted mechanical measure of crossbridge cycling rate under isometric conditions. Arner & Hellstrand (4, 33, 34) found that in contractions initiated by treatment of the rat portal vein with hypertonic solutions, there was an increase in stiffness and a larger decrease in the maximum velocity of shortening than predicted by the energetics data. As pointed out by the authors, it is likely that there may be factor(s) opposing shortening under hypertonic conditions that would result in measurements of maximum velocity of shortening that under-estimate the actual crossbridge cycling rate under isometric conditions. It seems that the best estimate of relative rate of crossbridge cycling under isometric conditions is gained by measuring both the energy demands of the tissue under isometric conditions and the maximum velocity of shortening. Conclusions concerning changes in the relative rate of crossbridge cycling are strengthened when both measures agree. If they do not show similar changes, then further investigation is required to determine which is the best estimate of crossbridge activity under the particular conditions used.

Force Output and Energy Usage as a Function of External Calcium Concentration

In general, studies of the relationship between force output and energy utiliza-tion under conditions when the calcium content of the bathing medium is varied show a linear relationship between these two variables (5, 6, 11, 32, 63–65). In some cases, in the rat portal vein, there was a slight tendency for a greater relative increase in energy usage than force when force was low than when at higher force levels (5, 32). Other work indicated that stiffness of the smooth muscle also changed in direct proportion to the force output when calcium concentration was varied (63, 67, 73). Because stiffness is thought to be a measure of the number of attached crossbridges, all of these studies were generally interpreted to mean that calcium concentration determined only the number of crossbridges interacting with actin and did not affect the force output and energy utilization per crossbridge. In other words, the economy of force production and crossbridge cycling rate did not depend upon the calcium concentration. More recent experiments, however, have shown that in the both the intact tissue (74) and in skinned fibers (6, 29, 35), there is a nonlinear relationship between energy usage and force output at high calcium concentrations. Although force output reaches a maximum, there are further calcium-dependent increases in the rate of energy usage as calcium concentration is increased. Siegman et al (74) have shown that the maximum velocity of shortening under these conditions agrees well with the measured increases in rate of energy usage. Others have also shown a calcium-dependence of maximum velocity of shortening in both intact and skinned smooth muscles (1, 2, 3, 58) and provided evidence for a direct calcium effect on the rate of crossbridge detachment (28). Such measurements of energy usage and maximum velocity of shortening strongly suggest that there can be calcium-mediated changes in crossbridge cycling rate under isometric conditions in smooth muscle.

Control of Energy Usage and Crossbridge Cycling Rate

A well-known hypothesis explaining how the maximum velocity of shortening and economy of force maintenance are regulated under isometric conditions has been put forward by Murphy and colleagues (see 50 for review). It was based originally on the observation that the decreases in velocity of shortening with duration of stimulation were correlated with decreases in the degree of myosin light chain phosphorylation with no change in the force output from the muscle (21). Because biochemical studies had suggested that phosphorylation of the regulatory light chain of smooth muscle myosin was required for actin-activated myosin ATPase activity (see 31 for review), Murphy and coworkers postulated that only phosphorylated crossbridges cycled at any time during stimulation and that force could be maintained by "latchbridges," which were noncycling or very slowly cycling crossbridges formed when myosin was dephosphorylated. Such "latchbridges" would provide an internal resistance to shortening, giving rise to a decrease in the maximum velocity of shortening. Eventual relaxation of the muscle could occur because the maintenance of these attached but noncycling or very slowly cycling crossbridges required a higher than resting calcium level.

From an energetics point of view the "latchbridge" hypothesis provided an attractive explanation for the observed changes in rate of energy usage and economy of force maintenance with stimulation under isometric conditions. Paul (54) found a good correlation between velocity of shortening and rate of oxygen consumption in the hog carotid artery under conditions in which Dillon et al (21) found a correlation between light chain phosphorylation and shortening velocity. There may be, therefore, a good correspondence between degree of light chain phosphorylation and rate of energy usage in the hog carotid artery.

Butler et al (13) found, however, that there were only relatively small changes in the degree of light chain phosphorylation at times when there was a four-fold change in the average rate of energy usage under isometric conditions in the rabbit taenia coli. Further studies have shown that there is no correlation between the degree of light chain phosphorylation and maximum velocity of shortening during an isometric contraction in the taenia coli (74). The cross-bridge cycling rate, whether measured by high-energy phosphate utilization or by maximum velocity of shortening, can be increased by an increase in the calcium concentration of the bathing medium in the absence of a significant change in the degree of myosin light chain phosphorylation (74). Therefore, under certain conditions in intact smooth muscle, the crossbridge cycling rate can be governed by a calcium-dependent mechanism either independent of or in addition to myosin light chain phosphorylation.

Because the only measure of a "latchbridge" is its effect on the shortening velocity of the muscle, one cannot conclude that changes in shortening velocity are not mediated through the presence of "latchbridges," even if the degree of phosphorylation does not change. The observation that energy usage changes under these conditions does indicate, however, that the rate of cycling of a *phosphorylated crossbridge* can change during an isometric contraction. Because it is apparent that the rate of cycling of a phosphorylated crossbridge depends on the calcium content of the bathing medium, it is tempting to speculate that the duration-dependent variation in crossbridge cycling rate seen during a single tetanic contraction may be mediated through a separate calcium-sensitive regulatory system imposed upon the relatively constant level of myosin light chain phosphorylation (74). Morgan & Morgan (48) have shown that in vascular smooth muscle, pharmacological activation may result in a transient increase in free intracellular calcium that then decays to suprabasal levels. If a similar transient occurs in other smooth muscles, then the observed time-dependent changes in maximum velocity of shortening could be derived from the effects of calcium on phosphorylated myosin (15, 16, 18, 40a, 51, 69) or from other proposed regulatory systems (17, 45, 52, 77).

ENERGY USAGE DURING SHORTENING AND WORK PRODUCTION

Most studies on the energy requirements of shortening in smooth muscle have addressed the question of whether there is a Fenn effect (24). Although the Fenn effect has been variously interpreted (see 47, 68), for present purposes it is taken to mean that a muscle that shortens and does external work utilizes more energy than a muscle under isometric conditions. Hellstrand (32) and Paul & Peterson (61) found no evidence for an increase in the energy requirements of vascular smooth muscle during shortening compared to isometric conditions, but Davey et al (20) found a small increase in the total energy liberation when the rabbit rectococcygeus was subjected to isotonic shortenings. In a detailed study, Butler et al (13) showed that in the rabbit taenia coli, the rate of energy usage during shortening could be increased 2.5-fold compared to isometric conditions if the shortening was initiated during the plateau of an isometric tetanus, a time when the rate of high-energy phosphate usage was quite low. In contrast, there was no measureable difference in the energy cost of contraction between shortening and isometric conditions when the shortening was initiated during the initial phase of the stimulation, a time when the rate of energy usage under isometric conditions was high. The total energy requirements of the shortening were similar in both experimental designs, while the presence or absence of a Fenn effect was dependent on the rate of energy usage prevailing under isometric conditions. There is a preliminary report (42) that a similar three-fold increase in the rate of energy usage above that seen under isometric conditions occurs during shortening from a steady-state isometric contraction in vascular smooth muscle.

Although myothermal measurements show that the total mechanical efficiency of the rabbit rectococcygeus is similar to that of mammalian and amphibian skeletal muscle (20), direct measurements of phosphagen breakdown show that less than 7 kJoule of active external work is performed for each mole of high-energy phosphate used in the rabbit taenia coli (13) and hog carotid artery (42). This represents a much higher chemical energy cost of active external work production than reported for skeletal and cardiac muscle. Possible causes for such a high chemical energy cost of external work production have been addressed in detail by Butler et al (13). It should be noted that whatever the cause of the high energy cost of active external work production in some mammalian smooth muscles, the presence of a large passive tension at the length at which maximum force is generated and association with organs serving a reservoir function enables a rather large amount of external work to be derived from passive mechanical processes. This diminishes to a certain extent the high energy cost of total work production in smooth muscle (13).

ENERGY USAGE DURING STIMULATION AND STRETCH

It has been known for many years that skeletal muscle that is slowly stretched during stimulation develops an active force higher than that during isometric contractions, while the average rate of high-energy phosphate usage is decreased. It has been suggested that such a decrease in energy usage during stimulation and stretch is due to a decrease in the actin-activated myosin ATPase activity that normally occurs under isometric conditions (19). Hanks & Stephens (30) reported that the high-energy phosphate content of smooth muscles that were stretched during stimulation was higher than that in muscles allowed to shorten. However, the quantitative effect of stretch could not be determined because recovery reactions, which were not measured, accounted for most of the energy supply of the muscle.

Butler et al (14) have also investigated the effect of stretch during stimulation of smooth muscle, finding that this mechanical perturbation decreases the average rate of chemical energy usage by 50% during the period of force development, a time at which the rate of energy usage under isometric conditions is high. A greater fractional decrease (80%) in energy usage due to stretch was observed when both the average rate of energy usage and maximum velocity of shortening were increased by a higher concentration of calcium in the bathing medium. No significant change in the rate of energy usage could be demonstrated when the stretch was initiated after the muscle had developed maximum force. This difference in the effect of stretch at various times during stimulation could be more apparent than real, because it is difficult to detect even large fractional differences in very small rates of high-energy phosphate usage.

These results are consistent with the hypothesis that during stimulation and stretch in smooth muscle, crossbridge attachment and force production can occur, even though the actin-activated myosin ATPase activity normally associated with isometric force development is greatly depressed. It is likely that such a small energy requirement for stretch during stimulation plays an important role in the overall energy demand of smooth muscle, because many smooth muscles in situ are activated during periods of stretch. For example, if the muscle were stretched during a time when crossbridge cycling rate and energy usage under isometric conditions were high, there would be a large force output from the muscle without the large energy demand that would be required for force output under normal isometric conditions (14).

ACKNOWLEDGMENTS

We thank Ms. S. U. Mooers for helpful discussions during preparation of the manuscript. We acknowledge support from grants HL 23205 and HL 15835 to the Pennsylvania Muscle Institute. T. M. B. is a recipient of N. I. H. Career Development Award AM 00973.

Literature Cited

1. Aksoy, M. O., Mras, S., Kamm, K. E., Murphy, R. A. 1983. Ca^{++}, cAMP, and changes in myosin phosphorylation during contraction of smooth muscle. *Am. J. Physiol.* 245:C255–C270

2. Arner, A. 1982. Mechanical characteristics of chemically skinned guinea pig taenia coli. *Pfluegers Arch.* 395:277–84

3. Arner, A. 1983. Force-velocity relation in chemically skinned rat portal vein: Effects of Ca^{++} and Mg^{++}. *Pfluegers Arch.* 397:6–12

4. Arner, A., Hellstrand, P. 1980. Contraction of the rat portal vein in hypertonic and isotonic medium: rates of metabolism. *Acta Physiol. Scand.* 110:69–75

5. Arner, A., Hellstrand, P. 1981 Energy turnover and mechanical properties of resting and contracting aortas and portal veins from normotensive and spontaneously hypertensive rats. *Circ. Res.* 48:539–48

6. Arner, A., Hellstrand, P. 1983. Activation of contraction and ATPase activity in intact and chemically skinned smooth muscle of rat portal vein. *Circ. Res.* 53:695-702

7. Bessman, S. P., Geiger, P. J. 1981. Transport of energy in muscle: the phosphorylcreatine shuttle. *Science* 211:448–52

8. Bressler, B. H., Clinch, N. F. 1975. Crossbridges as the major source of compliance in contracting skeletal muscle. *Nature* 256:221–22

9. Butler, T. M., Davies, R. E. 1980. High-energy phosphates in smooth muscle. In *Handbook of Physiology, Section 2: Cardiovascular System, Vascular Smooth Muscle*, ed. D. F. Bohr, A. P. Somlyo, H. V. Sparks, 2:237–52. Bethesda, MD: Am. Physiol. Soc.

10. Butler, T. M., Siegman, M. J. 1976. Chemical changes in rabbit myometrium associated with estrogen treatment. *Fed. Proc.* 35:776 (Abstr.)

11. Butler, T. M., Siegman, M. J. 1983. Chemical energy usage and myosin light chain phosphorylation in mammalian smooth muscle. *Fed. Proc.* 42:57–61

12. Butler, T. M., Siegman, M. J., Mooers, S. U. 1982. Chemical energetics of contraction in mammalian smooth muscle. In *Basic Biology of Muscles: A Comparative Approach*, ed. B. M. Twarog, R. J. C. Levine, M. M. Dewey, pp. 189–201. New York: Raven

13. Butler, T. M., Siegman, M. J., Mooers, S. U. 1983. Chemical energy usage during shortening and work production in mammalian smooth muscle. *Am. J. Physiol.* 244:C234–C242

14. Butler, T. M., Siegman, M. J., Mooers, S. U. 1984. Chemical energy usage during stimulation and stretch of mammalian smooth muscle. *Pfluegers Arch.* 401:391–95

15. Chacko, S., Conti, M. A., Adelstein, R. S. 1977. Effect of phosphorylation of smooth muscle myosin on actin activation and Ca^{++} regulation. *Proc. Natl. Acad. Sci. USA* 74:129–33

16. Chacko, S., Rosenfeld, A. 1982. Regulation of actin-activated ATP hydrolysis by arterial myosin. *Proc. Natl. Acad. Sci. USA* 79:292–96

17. Cole, H. A., Grand, R. J. A., Perry, S. V. 1982. Non-correlation of phosphorylation of the P-light chain and the actin activation of the ATPase of chicken gizzard myosin. *Biochem. J.* 206:319–28

18. Cole, H. A., Patchell, V. B., Perry, S. V. 1983. Phosphorylation of chicken gizzard myosin and the Ca^{++} sensitivity of the actin-activated Mg^{++} ATPase. *FEBS Lett.* 158:17–20

19. Curtin, N. A., Davies, R. E. 1975. Very high tension with very little ATP breakdown by active skeletal muscle. *J. Mechanochem. Cell Motility* 3:147–54

20. Davey, D. F., Gibbs, C. L., McKirdy, H. C. 1975. Structural, mechanical, and myothermic properties of rabbit rectococcygeus muscle. *J. Physiol.* 248:207–30

21. Dillon, P. F., Aksoy, M. O., Driska, S. P., Murphy, R. A. 1981. Myosin phosphorylation and the crossbridge cycle in arterial smooth muscle. *Science* 211:495–97

22. Edman, K. A. P. 1979. The velocity of unloaded shortening and its relation to sarcomere length and isometric force in vertebrate muscle fibres. *J. Physiol.* 291:143–59

23. Fabiato, A., Fabiato, F. 1975. Dependence of the contractile activation of skinned cardiac cells on the sarcomere length. *Nature* 256:54–56

24. Fenn, W. O. 1923. A quantitative comparison between energy liberated and the work performed by the isolated sartorius muscle of the frog. *J. Physiol.* 58:175–203

25. Gibbs, C. L., Loiselle, D. S. 1980. Effect of temperature on mechanical and myothermic properties of rabbit smooth muscle. *Am. J. Physiol.* 238:C49–C55

26. Gluck, E., Paul, R. J. 1977.

The aerobic metabolism of porcine carotid artery and its relationship to isometric force. *Pfluegers Arch.* 370:9–18

27. Gordon, A. R., Siegman, M. J. 1971. Mechanical properties of smooth muscle. I. Length-tension and force-velocity relations. *Am. J. Physiol.* 221:1243–49

28. Guth, K., Junge, J. 1982. Low Ca^{++} impedes crossbridge detachment in chemically skinned taenia coli. *Nature* 300:775–76

29. Guth, K., Mrwa, U. 1982. Maximum force is generated in chemically skinned taenia coli at lower Ca^{++} concentrations than maximum ATPase activity. *Pfluegers Arch.* 394:R44 (Abstr.)

30. Hanks, B. S. R., Stephens, N. L. 1981. Mechanics and energetics of lengthening of active airway smooth muscle. *Am. J. Physiol.* 241:C42–C46

31. Hartshorne, D. J., Siemankowski, R. F. 1981. Regulation of smooth muscle actomyosin. *Ann. Rev. Physiol.* 43:519–30

32. Hellstrand, P. 1977. Oxygen consumption and lactate production of the rat portal vein in relation to its contractile activity. *Acta Physiol. Scand.* 100:91–106

33. Hellstrand, P. 1979. Mechanical and metabolic properties related to contraction in smooth muscle. *Acta Physiol. Scand. Suppl.* 464:1–54

34. Hellstrand, P., Arner, A. 1980. Contraction of the rat portal vein in hypertonic and isotonic medium: mechanical properties and effects of Mg^{++}. *Acta Physiol. Scand.* 110:59–67

35. Hellstrand, P., Arner, A. 1983. Quantitative analysis of ATP turnover in relation to calcium-activated tension in chemically skinned guinea pig taenia coli. *Biophys. J.* 41:247a (Abstr.)

35a. Hellstrand, P. Jorup, C., Lydrup, M. L. 1984.. O_2 consumption, aerobic glycolysis and tissue phosphagen content during activation of the Na^+/K^+ pump in rat portal vein. *Pfluegers Arch.* 401:119–24

36. Hellstrand, P., Paul, R. J. 1983. Phosphagen content, breakdown during contraction, and O_2 consumption in rat portal vein. *Am. J. Physiol.* 244:C250–C58

37. Homsher, E., Mommaerts, W. F. H. M., Ricchiuti, N. V., Wallner, A. 1972. Activation heat, activation metabolism and tension-related heat in frog semitendinosus muscles. *J. Physiol.* 220:601–25

38. Huxley, A. F., Julian, J. 1964. Speed of unloaded shortening in frog striated muscle fibres. *J. Physiol.* 177:60P–61P (Abstr.)

39. Iyengar, M. R. 1984. Creatine kinase as an intracellular regulator. *J. Muscle Res. Cell Motil.* In press

40. Iyengar, M. R., Fluellen, C. E., Iyengar, C. 1982. Creatine kinase from the bovine myometrium: purification and characterization. *J. Mus. Res. Cell Motil.* 3:231–46

40a. Kaminski, E. A., Chacko, S. 1984. Effects of Ca^{+2} and Mg^{+2} on the actin-activated ATP hydrolysis by phosphorylated heavy meromyosin from arterial smooth muscle. *J. Biol. Chem.* 259: 9104–8

41. Krisanda, J. M., Paul, R. J. 1983. Phosphagen and metabolite content during contraction in porcine carotid artery. *Am. J. Physiol.* 244:C385–C390

41a. Krisanda, J. M., Paul, R. J. 1984. Energetics of isometric contraction in porcine carotid artery. *Am. J. Physiol.* 246:C510–C519

42. Krisanda, J. M., Paul, R. J. 1984. The Fenn effect in vascular smooth muscle: phosphagen breakdown during maximum power output in porcine carotid artery. *Biophys. J.* 45:346a (Abstr.)

43. Kushmerick, M. J. 1983. Energetics of muscle contraction. In *Handbook of Physiology, Section 10, Skeletal Muscle,* ed. L. D. Peachey, R. H. Adrian, pp. 189–236. Bethesda, MD: Am. Physiol. Soc.

44. Lynch, R. M., Paul, R. J. 1983. Compartmentalization of glycolytic and glycogenolytic metabolism in vascular smooth muscle. *Science* 222:1344–46

45. Marston, S. B., Trevett, R., Walters, M. 1980. Calcium ion-regulated thin filaments from vascular smooth muscle. *Biochem. J.* 185:355–65

46. Meiss, R. A. 1978. Dynamic stiffness of rabbit mesotubarium smooth muscle: effect of isometric length. *Am. J. Physiol.* 234:C14–C26

47. Mommaerts, W. F. H. M. 1969. Energetics of muscular contraction. *Physiol. Rev.* 49:427–508

48. Morgan, J. P., Morgan, K. G. 1984. Stimulus-specific patterns of intracellular calcium levels in smooth muscle of ferret portal vein. *J. Physiol.* 351:155–67

49. Mulvany, M. J., Warshaw, D. M. 1979. The active tension-length curve of vascular smooth muscle related to its cellular components. *J. Gen. Physiol.* 74:85–104

50. Murphy, R. A., Aksoy, M. O., Dillon, P. F., Gerthoffer, W. T., Kamm, K. E. 1983. The role of myosin light chain phosphorylation in regulation of the crossbridge cycle. *Fed. Proc.* 42:51–56

51. Nag, S., Seidel, J. C. 1983. Dependence on Ca^{++} and tropomyosin of the actin-activated ATPase activity of phosphorylated gizzard myosin in the presence of low concentrations of Mg^{++}. *J. Biol. Chem.* 258:6444–49

52. Nonomura, Y., Ebashi, S. 1980. Calcium regulatory mechanism in vertebrate smooth muscle. *Biomed. Res.* 1:1–14

53. Paul, R. J. 1980. Chemical energetics of vascular smooth muscle. In *Handbook of Physiology, Section 2: Cardiovascular System, Vascular Smooth Muscle,* ed. D. F. Bohr, A. P. Somlyo, H. V. Sparks, 2:201–35. Bethesda, MD: Am. Physiol. Soc.

54. Paul, R. J. 1983. Coordination of metabolism and contractility in vascular smooth muscle. *Fed. Proc.* 42:62–66

55. Paul, R. J. 1983. Functional compartmentalization of oxidative and glycolytic metabolism in vascular smooth muscle. *Am. J. Physiol.* 244:C399–C409

56. Paul, R. J. 1983. The effects of isoproterenol and ouabain on oxygen consumption, lactate production, and the activation of phosphorylase in coronary artery smooth muscle. *Circ. Res.* 52:683–90

57. Paul, R. J., Bauer, M., Pease, W. 1979. Vascular smooth muscle: Aerobic glycolysis linked to sodium and potassium transport processes. *Science* 206:1414–16

58. Paul, R. J., Doerman, G., Zeugner, C., Ruegg, J. C. 1983. The dependence of unloaded shortening velocity on Ca^{++}, calmodulin and duration of contraction in "chemically skinned" smooth muscle. *Circ. Res.* 53:342–51

59. Paul, R. J., Gluck, E., Ruegg, J. C. 1976. Crossbridge ATP utilization in arterial smooth muscle. *Pfluegers Arch.* 361:297–99

60. Paul, R. J., Peterson, J. W. 1975. Relation between length, isometric force, and O_2 consumption rate in vascular smooth muscle. *Am. J. Physiol.* 228:915–22

61. Paul, R. J., Peterson, J. W. 1977. The mechanochemistry of smooth muscles. In *Biochemistry of Smooth Muscle,* ed. N. L. Stephens, pp. 15–39. Baltimore, MD: University Park

62. Paul, R. J., Peterson, J. W., Caplan, S. R. 1973. Oxygen consumption rate in vascular smooth muscle: relation to isometric tension. *Biochem. Biophys. Acta* 305:474–80

63. Peterson, J. W. 1977. Relation of stiffness, energy metabolism, and isometric tension in a vascular smooth muscle. In *Mechanisms of Vasodilatation,* ed. P. M. Vanhoutte, I. Leusen, pp. 79–88. Basel: Karger

64. Peterson, J. W. 1982. Effect of histamine on the energy metabolism of K^+-depolarized hog carotid artery. *Circ. Res.* 50:848–55

65. Peterson, J. W., Gluck, E. 1982. Energy cost of membrane depolarization in hog carotid artery. *Circ. Res.* 50:839–47

66. Peterson, J. W., Paul, R. J. 1974. Aerobic glycolysis in vascular smooth muscle: relation to isometric tension. *Biochem. Biophys. Acta* 357:167–76

67. Pfitzer, G., Peterson, J. W., Ruegg, J. C. 1982. Length dependence of calcium-activated isometric force and immediate stiffness in living and glycerol-extracted vascular smooth muscle. *Pfluegers Arch.* 394:174–81

68. Rall, J. A. 1982. Sense and nonsense about the Fenn effect. *Am. J. Physiol.* 242: H1–H6

69. Rees, D. D., Frederiksen, D. W. 1981. Calcium regulation of porcine aortic myosin. *J. Biol. Chem.* 256:357–64

70. Rudel, R., Taylor, S. 1971. Striated muscle fibers: facilitation of contraction at short lengths by caffeine. *Science* 172:387–88

71. Schoenberg, M., Podolsky, R. J. 1972. Length-force relation of calcium activated muscle fibers. *Science* 176:52–54

72. Siegman, M. J., Butler, T. M., Mooers, S. U., Davies, R. E. 1980. Chemical energetics of force development, force maintenance, and relaxation in mammalian smooth muscle. *J. Gen. Physiol.* 76:609–29

73. Siegman, M. J., Butler, T. M., Mooers, S. U. 1984. Energetic, mechanical, and ultrastructural correlates of the length-tension relationship in smooth muscle. In *Smooth Muscle Contraction,* ed. N. L. Stephens, pp. 189–98. New York: Dekker

74. Siegman, M. J., Butler, T. M., Mooers, S. U., Michalek, A. 1984. Calcium can affect V_{max} without changes in myosin light chain phosphorylation in smooth muscle. *Pfluegers Arch.* 401:385–90

75. Smith, I. C. H. 1972. Energetics of activation in frog and toad muscle. *J. Physiol.* 220:583–99

76. Taylor, S. R., Rudel, R. 1970. Striated muscle fibers: Inactivation of contraction induced by shortening. *Science* 167:282–84

77. Walters, M., Marston, S. B. 1981. Phosphorylation of the calcium ion–regulated thin filaments from vascular smooth muscle. *Biochem. J.* 197:127–39

Ann. Rev. Physiol. 1985. 47:645–63
Copyright © 1985 by Annual Reviews, Inc. All rights reserved

REGULATION OF MITOCHONDRIAL ACTIVITY IN CARDIAC CELLS

Leena M. Mela-Riker

Departments of Surgery and Biochemistry, Oregon Health Sciences University, Portland, Oregon 97201

Richard D. Bukoski

Department of Physiology, Michigan State University, East Lansing, Michigan 48824

INTRODUCTION

The primary role of mitochondria in the myocardium is to supply the cardiac cells with ATP, a necessary source of energy for contraction and for the maintenance of ion homeostasis, protein synthesis, and other important cellular functions. Reducing equivalents from energy fuels enter into the mitochondrial cytochrome chain, ultimately reducing O_2 to form H_2O in a reaction catalyzed by cytochrome oxidase. Energy is conserved at three sites in the electron-transfer chain through the phosphorylation of ADP by the mitochondrial ATPase–ATPsynthetase. The biochemical aspects of the coupling of free energy generated by the respiratory chain to the synthesis of ATP have been recently reviewed (66).

This review centers around the physiologically important aspects of mitochondrial function. These aspects are related to regulation of metabolic activity under physiologic conditions and during fluctuations of need for energy metabolism. The evidence about the possible role of mitochondria in the parallel control of metabolism and coronary flow is discussed. This review does not attempt to provide a description of the detailed biochemical mechanisms of mitochondrial function but rather an emphasis on the physiologically important aspects of the function of mitochondria in cardiac tissue.

645

0066-4278/85/0315-0645$02.00

MITOCHONDRIAL STRUCTURAL AND FUNCTIONAL COMPARTMENTS

It has been estimated that cardiac cells contain 60 mg of mitochondrial protein per gram of tissue, or 40% of the total noncollagenous protein of cardiac tissue (27). Cardiac mitochondria are localized in rows between myofibrils along the total length of the fibrils. This geometry allows a close proximity of the energy-synthesizing compartment of the cell to the energy-utilizing contractile

MITOCHONDRIAL COMPARTMENTS

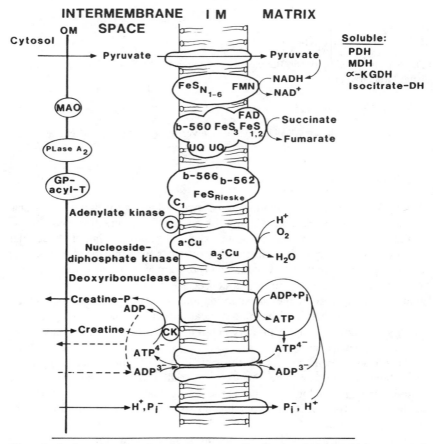

Figure 1   A schematic presentation of the structure and localization of mitochondrial enzymes and translocases. *OM*, outer membrane; *I M*, inner membrane; *FMN*, flavin mononucleotide (NADH dehydrogenase); *FAD*, flavin adenine dinucleotide (succinic dehydrogenase); *FeS*, iron sulfa protein; *UQ*, ubiquinone; *PDH*, pyruvate dehydrogenase; *MDH*, malate dehydrogenase; α-*KGDH*, α-keto-glutarate dehydrogenase.

tissue. Structurally, cardiac mitochondria are tightly packed with cristae, in-foldings of the inner mitochondrial membrane. The protein concentration of these membranes is high and consists mostly of the respiratory chain and the membrane translocase enzymes. The volume of matrix space is small in cardiac mitochondria relative to other tissues. This is necessitated by the limited volume available for the mitochondrial fraction between the muscle fibers.

Mitochondria contain four major compartments: the outer membrane, the inner membrane, the intermembrane space, and the matrix space, which is the space contained within the inner membrane. The *outer membrane* surrounding the mitochondrion provides structural support to the organelle. It is relatively rigid and will rupture during heavy swelling. It contains some essential enzymes such as the mono-amine oxidase, glycerophosphate acyltransferase, and phospholipase A_2 (67).

The outer membrane is relatively porous and does not limit permeability of molecules up to 10,000 daltons. The *intermembrane space,* which is the space between the outer and the inner membrane, provides a controlled compartment for some metabolic enzymes such as adenylate kinase, creatine kinase, nucleoside diphosphate kinase, and deoxyribonuclease (67).

The *inner membrane* is the most active compartment of the mitochondrion. It is selectively permeable and thus controls the transport of essential components into the mitochondrion. This function is accomplished by various carrier systems or translocases such as the adenine nucleotide translocase, the phosphate carrier, the calcium carrier and the substrate transporters, the mono- and dicarboxylate carriers, and the carnitine-acylcarnitine translocase. These carrier or translocase activities are essential for the function of the mitochondrion, because all the enzyme reactions related to ATP synthesis take place in the inner membrane, on its inside surface, or in the matrix space. The cytochromes and nonheme-iron protein components of the electron-transfer chain are imbedded in the inner membrane. The ATPase-ATP synthetase, carnitine-palmitoyltransferase, and some dehydrogenases (succinate dehydrogenase, glycerol-3-phosphate- and β-hydroxybutyrate dehydrogenases, and NADH dehydrogenase) are bound to the inside surface of the inner membrane and some (glutamate-, isocitrate, malate, α-ketoglutarate, and pyruvate dehydrogenases) are in the soluble matrix compartment. The *matrix* also contains other soluble enzymes such as acetyl-CoA acetyl and acyltransferases, aspartate amino-transferase, citrate synthase, phosphoenol pyruvate carboxykinase, and pyruvate carboxylase and membranous binding sites for Ca^{2+} (67).

The structural specificity of the mitochondrial membranes affords important aspects of the compartmentation and regulation of cellular metabolic functions. The adjacency of the respiratory chain components within the limited space of the inner mitochondrial membrane allows rapid transfer of electrons from one component of the chain to the next to allow thermodynamically efficient step functions in the development of the potential energy necessary for the synthesis of ATP. The specific permeability characteristics of the inner membrane provide convenient regulatory steps for the metabolic activities of the cell.

REGULATION OF MITOCHONDRIAL ELECTRON-TRANSFER ACTIVITY

Several laboratories have provided substantial evidence in support of two primary regulatory steps of mitochondrial electron-transfer activity in the heart: the *dehydrogenase activities;* and the *membrane translocase functions*. These enzyme systems provide a logical regulatory step, because the cytochrome components of the fully developed adult respiratory chain exist at concentrations in excess of normal requirements, and the kinetic responses of the cytochromes are significantly faster than those of the flavin-containing dehydrogenases or NADH (10, 40). An important regulatory step is provided by the adeninenucleotide translocase function that regulates the transport of ADP in and ATP out of the mitochondrion (33).

The Regulatory Role of Pyruvate Dehydrogenase Complex

The mammalian pyruvate dehydrogenase (PDH) is an enzyme complex consisting of three catalytic enzymes: pyruvate decarboxylase, dihydrolipoamide acetyltransferase, and dihydrolipoamide dehydrogenase, known as lipoamide dehydrogenase, which is a dimeric protein containing noncovalently attached flavin adenine dinucleotide (FAD) (48–50). The literature on mammalian pyruvate dehydrogenase complex and its metabolic regulation has been recently reviewed (65). The pyruvate decarboxylase catalytic enzyme undergoes *activation-inactivation reactions* via dephosphorylation-phosphorylation of a serine residue of the α-subunit of the $\alpha_2\beta_2$ tetramer (49–51). The phosphorylation resulting in binding of thiamine pyrophosphate and inactivation of PDH is catalyzed by *pyruvate dehydrogenase kinase*. PDH enzyme activation is a result of dephosphorylation catalyzed by a specific *pyruvate dehydrogenase phosphatase*.

The phosphorylation dephosphorylation reactions of PDH, sensitively controlled by various positive and negative effectors, provide an important regulatory mechanism of the active $\leftrightarrow$ inactive PDH enzyme. This step is affected by Ca^{2+}/Mg^{2+}, ATP/ADP ratios, pyruvate concentration, acetyl CoA/CoASH, and NADH/NAD ratios (15).

A second important mechanism of pyruvate dehydrogenase control is provided by the *feedback inhibition of the flux* through the active (dephosphorylated) form of the PDH enzyme (14). Feedback inhibition of flux through the enzyme is caused by high ratios of NADH/NAD, acetyl CoA/CoASH, and by products of fatty acid and branched-chain keto acid oxidation as well as by high branched-chain α-ketoacid concentrations (14, 44).

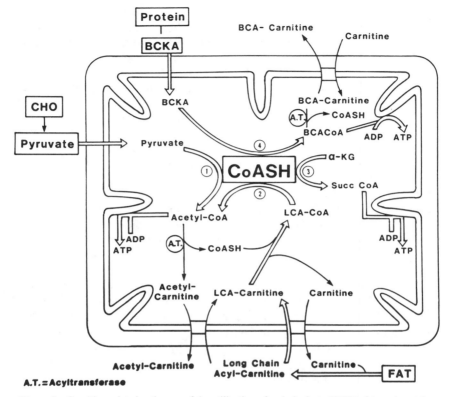

Figure 2   Carnitine related pathways of the utilization of carbohydrate *(CHO)*, fat, and protein-derived fuels.

These two regulatory mechanisms of PDH activity provide convenient cellular control of metabolic activity in the mitochondria on two grounds: (*a*) based on need for ATP synthesis (ATP/ADP ratio); and (*b*) based on availability of various fuels as substrates for the respiratory chain. We discuss in more detail below the control of PDH and other dehydrogenases, possessing similar regulatory mechanisms, by cellular need for synthesis of energy-rich compounds such as ATP.

Utilization of Glucose, Ketone Bodies, and Branched-Chain Amino Acid–Derived Substrates by Mitochondria

In addition to the PDH enzyme complex, cardiac mitochondria contain other complex dehydrogenase enzymes with similar control mechanisms of enzyme activity. These are α-*ketoglutarate dehydrogenase*, β-*hydroxybutyrate dehydrogenase*, and *branched-chain* α-*ketoacid dehydrogenase* enzymes that make the mitochondrial utilization of ketone bodies and amino acid–derived substrates possible (47, 64). Although these dehydrogenases and PDH preferably react with their own specific substrates, they also utilize alternate substrates that act as competitive inhibitors of the dehydrogenase enzyme activity in the presence of its own specific substrate. Thus branched-chain α-ketoacids, β-hydrobutyrate, and acetoacetate are competitive inhibitors of pyruvate dehydrogenase (29). This inhibition provides an explanation for the reduced glucose utilization and pyruvate oxidation during conditions resulting in excessive ketosis and protein catabolism. The increased availability of alternate substrates, ketone bodies, and branched-chain amino acid–derived branched-chain α-ketoacids decrease the utilization of pyruvate. Similarly, pyruvate is a competitive inhibitor of branched-chain α-ketoacid dehydrogenase, thus preventing excessive utilization of branched-chain amino acids as energy fuel under normal nutritional conditions (29, 64). Some pathologic metabolic states such as diabetes, starvation, and protein-wasting syndromes, common after major surgery, trauma, and particularly sepsis, might be a result of reduced pyruvate oxidation due to the availability of excessive amounts of competing substrates (8, 11, 26).

Experimental evidence exists to support this mechanism of inhibition of the active PDH by branched chain α-ketoacids. Walajtys-Rode & Williamson (62) showed that branched-chain α-ketoacids such as α-ketoisovalerate resulted in an inhibition of flux through the active PDH enzyme with no effect on the amount of the active form of the enzyme. This finding suggests that acyl-CoA intermediates of branched-chain α-ketoacids have a direct inhibitory effect on the flux through the active PDH enzyme complex.

β-*Oxidation of Fatty Acids and the Metabolic Role of Carnitine*

Fatty acids and pyruvate provide the major sources of fuel for cardiac mitochondria. Fatty acid oxidation is accomplished by β-oxidation reactions in the mitochondria. Neither long-chain fatty acids nor their CoA esters alone can penetrate through the mitochondrial membrane. *Carnitine,* β-hydroxy-γ-trimethyl ammonium butyrate, is required for the transport of fatty acids across the inner mitochondrial membrane. Long-chain acyl carnitine enters the mitochondria in exchange for free carnitine (6, 25, 55). The availability of fatty acids for β-oxidation in mitochondria is made possible by a sequence of three enzyme-catalyzed reactions: (*a*) Palmitic acid, for example, reacts with cytoplasmic CoA in a palmitoyl-CoA-synthetase and ATP-requiring reaction to form palmitoyl-CoA. (*b*) Palmitoyl-CoA reacts with free carnitine in a reaction catalyzed by carnitine-palmitoyl-transferase of the outer surface of the inner mitochondrial membrane. Carnitine-palmitoyl-carnitine translocase provides the mechanism for transport of the palmitoyl-carnitine into the mitochondrion,

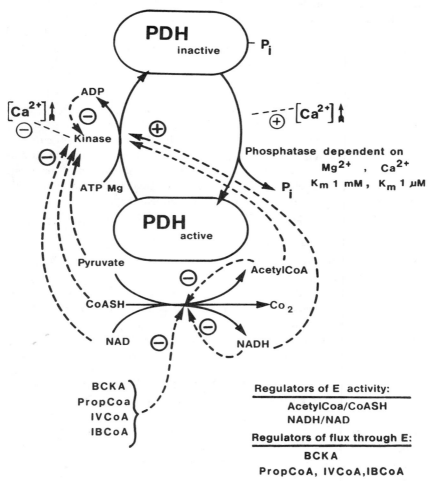

Figure 3   Regulation of pyruvate dehydrogenase *(PDH)* activation and inactivation and flux through the active enzyme. *BCKA,* branched chain α-ketoacid; *PropCoA,* propionyl-CoA; *IVCoA,* isovaleryl-CoA; *IBCoA,* isobutyryl CoA.

where a second carnitine-palmitoyl-transferase located in the inner membrane catalyzes the conversion of palmitoyl-carnitine to palmitoyl CoA, which is metabolized to acetyl CoA in a reaction requiring CoASH. (*c*) The free carnitine released from palmitoyl-carnitine is used for another carnitine-palmitoyl-carnitine translocase reaction.

Carnitine plays an important role in β-*oxidation* via the translocation of long-chain acyl groups into the mitochondrion. Evidence from studies on rat heart mitochondria indicates that the carnitine-acetyl CoA-transferase and carnitine acetylcarnitine translocase systems provide a coupling mechanism for the cytosolic reactions of fatty acid activation and mitochondrial fatty acid oxidation (28). It is also apparent that carnitine has a more *general facilitative effect* on mitochondrial metabolism via its regulation of the acyl CoA/CoASH ratio (4). Utilization of all fuels by mitochondria is dependent on the availability of reduced CoA (CoASH). Oxidation of pyruvate, α-ketoglutarate, fatty acids as well as branched-chain α-ketoacids all depend on a common mitochondrial CoASH pool, thus necessitating a continuous replenishment of this pool. It has been postulated that carnitine is primarily responsible for this replenishment by removing acyl- and acetyl-CoA from the mitochondria as acetylcarnitine (4). It was recently shown that this mechanism of metabolic regulation is defective in inherited disorders of branched-chain amino acid metabolism that are characterized by accumulation of acyl-CoA intermediates and their abnormal organic metabolites (9).

Adenine Nucleotide Translocase

Adenine nucleotide translocase is a mitochondrial inner membrane transport site for ADP and ATP (30, 33). This translocase is necessary for the transport of cytosolic ADP into the mitochondrion and the ATP synthesized in the mitochondria back to the cytosol (33). The phosphate acceptor, ADP^{3-}, enters the mitochondrial matrix in an electrophoretic exchange for the newly formed ATP^{4-}, which is transported out of the matrix. This exchange is catalyzed by the adenine nucleotide translocase, which has a greater affinity for ATP than ADP on the inner side and ADP than ATP at the outer side. Because the extramitochondrial ratio of ATP/ADP is higher than the intramitochondrial ratio, the transfer reaction requires energy and is thought to be linked to the electrochemical gradient that exists across the inner mitochondrial membrane. The function of the adenine nucleotide translocase is an integral part of functional oxidative phosphorylation. The location of the adenine nucleotide specific translocase in the selectively permeable inner mitochondrial membrane provides a convenient control mechanism for the regulation of mitochondrial and cytosolic ATP and ADP levels, as will be discussed below.

In the ischemic heart, lack of sufficient oxygenation prevents complete oxidation of fatty acids and causes accumulation of long-chain acyl CoA esters that are inhibitory to adenine nucleotide translocase activity (55–57). Additions of excess L-carnitine can reverse this inhibition by converting the long-chain acyl CoA esters to long-chain acyl carnitine that can be transported out of the mitochondria. An opposing view has been presented about the ischemic inhibition of adenine nucleotide translocase activity. LaNoue et al (34) argued that the mechanism of that inhibition is via the depletion of the mitochondrial adenine nucleotide pool in ischemia and not via a direct effect on the translocase function.

It is important to note that the activities of carnitine-related reactions involved in the oxidation of fatty acids as well as pyruvate and branched-chain α-ketoacids as fuels are closely linked to the activity of the adenine nucleotide translocase and hence to the availability of ADP for oxidative phosphorylation and ATP synthesis. This linkage provides a parallel and integrated regulation of cellular energy production in the mitochondria by these two important controllers. It has been suggested that thyroid hormone has a rapid direct effect on the rate of oxidative phosphorylation via its action on the adenine nucleotide translocase (41). This conclusion was drawn from experiments on thyroidectomized animals exhibiting a lowered rate of adenine nucleotide translocase, which was restored within 15 min after an injection of triiodothyronine.

IN VIVO CONTROL OF MITOCHONDRIAL RESPIRATION

There is currently considerable controversy about the regulation of mitochondrial respiration in vivo. We will discuss existing evidence about the regulation by (a) oxygen concentration, (b) the cytosolic phosphorylation potential (ratio of $[ATP]/[ADP][P_i]$), or (c) the cytosolic ratio of ATP/ADP, where the activity of the adenine nucleotide translocase is thought to be rate-limiting. In addition, current ideas about the relation of mitochondrial metabolism to the regulation of blood flow in the heart will be discussed. It should be pointed out that although much of the information about in vivo control of mitochondrial respiration in the myocardium was obtained in studies of heart mitochondria, the majority of the work has been carried out in other tissues, and extrapolations have to be made in order to arrive at conclusions about cardiac tissue.

Control of Mitochondrial Respiration by Oxygen

A number of workers have examined the dependence of mitochondrial respiration on oxygen availability. It has been repeatedly demonstrated that mitochondrial respiratory rate is unaffected by O_2 concentration within the normal in vivo range. Sugano et al (59), using isolated pigeon heart mitochondria, showed that the *oxygen concentration required* to provide half-maximal reduction of cytochrome c ranged from 0.27 to 0.03 μM, depending on the metabolic state of the mitochondria. Similarly, the oxygen requirement for half-maximal reduction of NAD^+ varied from 0.08 to 0.06 μM. Oshino et al (46) also examined isolated pigeon heart mitochondria and found that the oxygen requirement for 50% reduction of cytochrome a + a_3 was highly dependent upon the energy state of the mitochondria, but was still less than 1 μM. These findings indicate that mitochondrial respiration is not regulated by the oxygen concentrations that are seen in vivo under normal physiologic conditions.

This conclusion has also been reached by investigators using intact cells. For example, Longmuir (38) measured respiration of isolated liver cells and found an *apparent* K_m *for* O_2 of < 1 μM. In a more recent study, Wilson and coworkers (70, 71) measured the effect of oxygen concentration on the respiration of dispersed rat liver cells and cultured ascites tumor cells. The rate of respiration was unaltered as $[O_2]$ was decreased from 240 μM to 20 μM. At 20 μM, the rate of respiration decreased with an apparent K_m of < 1 μM. They found, however, that the redox state of cytochrome c was sensitive to $[O_2]$ over the entire range. These findings raised the question about the difference of the O_2 dependence of the respiratory rate and oxidative phosphorylation and led to the suggestion that changes in the cellular phosphorylation potential may result in a constant rate of respiration in the face of falling O_2 concentration.

There is some evidence that myocardial energy metabolism is altered by oxygen availability in the intact organ. Gauduel et al (22), using isolated perfused working rat hearts, found that upon changing from a perfusion medium containing red blood cells (hematocrit of 35%) to a cell-free medium, there was a restriction in myocardial oxygen consumption, external work, and the cellular ATP concentration. Similarly, they found a decrease in the rate of oxidative phosphorylation and concluded that in the absence of hemoglobin, the oxygen supply becomes rate-limiting for mitochondrial respiratory activity. From these studies it is clear that although isolated mitochondria are insensitive to varying oxygen concentrations to < 1 μM, in a *more complex system,* such as the isolated perfused rodent heart, a *limited O_2 supply* can result in a substantial metabolic deficit. This limitation might be related to diffusion distances and to inhomogeneity of tissue oxygenation.

Regulation of Mitochondrial Respiration by Cytosolic Phosphorylation Potential[1]

This hypothesis, called the *near equilibrium hypothesis,* has been championed by Wilson and his colleagues and is based upon experiments originally carried out using isolated pigeon heart mitochrondia (16) and later repeated using isolated liver cells (68), ascites tumor cells, and isolated perfused rat liver (69) and rat liver mitochondria (18). They measured the redox potential of the $NAD^+/NADH$ couple and cytochrome c, as well as the extramitochondrial phosphorylation potential in these various systems, and found that the free energy change for the transfer of two reducing equivalents from NADH to cytochrome c was equal to the free energy change for the synthesis of 2 mol of ATP outside of the matrix. It has been concluded from these observations that the reactions are in equilibrium and therefore all of the reactions between the two are in near equilibrium. One important implication of this hypothesis is that the activity of the adenine nucleotide translocase cannot be rate-limiting for

[1]Editor's note: For a contrasting view of this subject, the reader should consult the review by W. Jacobus in this volume, especially pages 709–715.

mitochondrial respiration. Wilson states that the irreversible reduction of O_2 as the terminal reaction in the cytochrome chain is the rate-limiting step of respiration and suggests that as the cytosolic phosphorylation potential decreases, the redox state of the NAD couple and cytochrome c change, resulting in a corresponding increase in the respiratory rate. They conclude therefore that respiration is regulated by the *ratio of [ATP]/[ADP] [P_i] in the cytosol.*

In agreement with this hypothesis, Hassinen & Hiltunen (24) have shown by using surface fluorometry and reflectance spectrometry on isolated crystalloid perfused rat hearts that there is a near equilibrium between the electron carriers and the adenylate system, and thus the near-equilibrium hypothesis also holds for isolated perfused rat hearts. In addition, Wilson et al (72) have recently reported a method for determining the intramitochondrial ratio of free ATP/ ADP using the phosphoenolpyruvate carboxykinase reaction. They found that a significant portion of the ADP within the matrix is bound and that the ratio of free ATP/ADP is higher than or equal to that in the cytosol. This finding indicates that there is an *equilibrium of the ATP/ADP ratio across the mitochondrial inner membrane* and supports the hypothesis that respiration is controlled by the cellular phosphorylation potential.

Adenine Nucleotide Translocase as the Rate-Limiting Step

This hypothesis holds that the rate of mitochondrial respiration is regulated by the activity of the adenine nucleotide translocase. One type of experiment that has provided evidence in support of this hypothesis has been to measure extra- and intramitochondrial ratios of ATP/ADP and correlate them with oxygen consumption. In early work, Davis and coworkers (12, 13) and Kuster et al (32), using isolated rat liver mitochondria, found that at constant [P_i] the respiration rate of isolated mitochondria was proportional to the extramitochondrial ATP/ADP ratio. Furthermore, Davis & Lumeng (12) found that respiration was independent of the intramitochondrial ratio of ATP/ADP. They concluded that the data were consistent with the translocase being rate-limiting for respiratory activity. For example, when the extramitochondrial ATP/ADP ratio is high (~ 100) as during state 4 respiration, ATP competes with ADP for the external carrier site and limits access of the phosphate acceptor to the matrix, thus slowing the rate of oxidative phosphorylation.

In a separate set of experiments, Brawand et al (5), using isolated rat heart mitochondria, measured extra- and intramitochondrial ratios of ATP/ADP as a function of the respiratory state and found that the intramitochondrial ratio of ATP/ADP changes in the same direction as the extramitochondrial ratio. Letko et al (36), using rat liver mitochondria, subsequently found that the intramitochondrial ratio of ATP/ADP correlates well with the mitochondrial respiratory state and raised questions about the validity of the earlier work that showed that there was no correlation of respiratory rate with intramitochondrial ATP/ ADP ratios. Kunz et al (31) carried out a series of experiments with isolated rat liver mitochondria and also found that the rate of respiration responded to the extramitochondrial ratio. However, they measured the rate of respiration during ADP generation within the mitochondrial matrix by inducing citrulline synthesis and found that the rate of respiration was able to respond to the intramitochondrial ATP/ADP ratio. They suggest that the *translocase is the means by which the extramitochondrial ATP/ADP ratio is detected by the matrix* or transformed to the intramitochondrial ratio, which then regulates respiratory rate. The conclusion is also supported by the data of Wanders et al (63), who correlated respiratory activity with intra- and extramitochondrial ATP/ADP ratios during both intra- and extramitochondrial ATP utilization.

All of the experiments that measured intramitochondrial ratios of ATP/ADP used total and not free adenine nucleotide levels. As noted above, Wilson et al (72) recently reported a method for determining the ratio of free intramitochondrial ATP/ADP and found it to be the same as or slightly higher than the extramitochondrial ratio, indicating that there is a rapid equilibration across the membrane. This would question the validity of the conclusions drawn about the direct relation of respiratory rate to intramitochondrial ATP/ADP ratio (5, 12, 13, 31, 36, 63).

Another line of evidence supporting the role of adenine nucleotide translocase as the rate-limiting factor has come from the correlation of respiratory activity with varied activity of the carrier by using the specific inhibitors of the translocase such as atractyloside or its analog carboxyatractyloside (1, 31, 35). Lemasters & Sowers (35) measured oxygen consumption and ATP production by isolated mitochondria as a function of atractyloside concentration and found that the inhibition was directly proportional to the number of occupied carrier sites. These authors concluded that the carrier is rate-limiting for mitochondrial respiration. Forman & Wilson (19), however, recently measured respiration of isolated mitochondria in the presence of carboxyatractyloside and found only a 10% reduction of respiratory activity after occupation of 40–70% of the carrier sites in rat liver mitochondria and 66% in rat heart mitochondria. They concluded that *under conditions where not all of the carrier sites are available for ADP and ATP, the carrier may be rate-limiting; otherwise its activity is in excess* of that required for cellular respiration.

Given the available evidence, we have to conclude that the precise mechanism of the in vivo regulation of mitochondrial respiratory rate has not been firmly established. In light of the recent report by Wilson & Erecinska (72) that the matrix ratio of free ATP/ADP is equal to or higher than that in the extramitochondrial compartment, any conclusions based on the earlier measurements appear to be suspect. The experiments indicating that inhibition of the translocase can decrease the rate of respiration show that this enzyme can be rate-limiting, but it is not clear whether this is ever a case in vivo. Reports that long-chain fatty acyl CoA compounds are inhibitory are not conclusive (1).

We conclude that under normal physiologic conditions, cardiac cells contain excess adenine nucleotide translocase capacity, and this carrier is probably not rate-limiting for mitochondrial respiration. The near-equilibrium hypothesis may hold true and the cytosolic phosphorylation potential may be the regulator for respiration, although the relation of the intramitochondrial ratio of ATP/ADP to respiratory rate needs to be further examined. For a more in-depth discussion, the reader is referred to other recent reviews (17, 60, 61).

The Relationship of Cellular Respiration to Coronary Blood Flow

It has been known for many years that changes in myocardial oxygen consumption (MVO$_2$) are tightly followed by changes in coronary blood flow, i.e. increases in MVO$_2$ result in increases in coronary blood flow. There must therefore be a *metabolic link between mitochondrial respiration and coronary blood flow*. The adenosine hypothesis has been forwarded to explain this phenomenon, and it states that the vasoactive metabolite, adenosine, is released from the myocardium under conditions of increased need for oxygen consumption, resulting in an increase in coronary flow (3). Until recently it was thought that as ATP was hydrolyzed, there was an increase in ADP and hence AMP through the adenylate-kinase reaction. AMP was then believed to be dephosphorylated and vectorially transported out of the cell by an ecto-5'-nucleotidase enzyme (20). Several lines of evidence, however, question the validity of this proposal. It has been demonstrated that there are stores of adenosine bound within the myocardium (45, 54), and Schrader et al (53) demonstrated that adenosine release during hypoxia can be inhibited by infusion of homocysteine thiolactone, a compound that drives newly formed adenosine into S-adenosyl homocysteine (SAH) within the cell through a reaction catalyzed by the enzyme SAH hydrolase. The conclusion can be drawn that there exists within the myocardium an *intracellular source of adenosine* that increases in response to increased respiration.

Using isolated perfused rat hearts, Nuutinen and coworkers (42) have shown increases in coronary flow secondary to hypoxia, increased perfusion pressure, and amytal infusion. They report, however, that only with hypoxia was there an increase in venous adenosine concentration, whereas with all three interventions there was a decrease in the tissue [ATP]/[ADP][P$_i$]. They concluded that *mitochondrial oxidative phosphorylation provides a link* between tissue oxidative metabolism and coronary blood flow, but this link is not adenosine. However, they did not determine whether amytal has a direct vasodilator effect on vascular smooth muscle within the concentration range used. In addition, calculations of conductance made from their data with increased perfusion pressure show only very small changes in conductance, indicating that little if any vasodilation occurred. It is unlikely that an increase in adenosine release could be expected in either of these instances.

In a later study (43), Nuutinen et al examined the effect of dinitrophenol (DNP), an uncoupler of mitochondrial oxidative phosphorylation, and found an increase in coronary flow and an increase in adenosine release, although adenosine concentration in the venous effluent remained unchanged. The increase in coronary flow was accompanied by a decrease in $[ATP]/[ADP][P_i]$. Citing these data and the observation that theophylline did not attenuate the DNP-induced increase in flow, they concluded that $[ATP]/[ADP][P_i]$ and not adenosine mediates or signals the vasodilation. Once again they did not determine whether DNP is a vasodilator in its own right. Because adenosine release occurred, its role in the vasodilation cannot be ruled out. It is becoming apparent that it is not possible to make assumptions about the interstitial concentrations of adenosine based on venous concentrations because of the very active role that the endothelial barrier plays in adenosine metabolism (58). Nuutinen and coworkers have thus provided evidence that mitochondrial oxidative phosphorylation plays a role in signaling for changes in coronary blood flow in response to changes in MVO_2, but they have not ruled out adenosine as the metabolite of primary importance in this response.

Several lines of evidence, including the results of Nuutinen and coworkers described above, led us to examine *isolated heart mitochondria* to determine whether they can *produce adenosine* (7). When isolated mitochondria were incubated with pyruvate and malate as substrates (state 4 respiration), there was a release of adenosine into the medium. The appearance of adenosine was inhibited by the transition from state 4 to state 3 respiration induced by the addition of ADP. Both atractyloside and oligomycin, an inhibitor of the mitochondrial ATPase, also decreased the rate of adenosine production. These observations indicated that mitochondrial adenosine production was regulated by mitochondrial respiration. In support of this was the observation that adenosine production is substrate specific, i.e. greater adenosine production is seen with pyruvate + malate than with glutamate + malate. More recently we demonstrated (Bukoski, Sparks & Mela-Riker, unpublished data) that there is a sarcolemmal 5'-nucleotidase activity associated with the mitochondrial fraction that is only partially removed by treatment with concanavalin A agarose, leaving behind what we believe to be a mitochondrial 5'-nucleotidase enzyme that amounts to approximately 20% of the original activity in the preparation. Concanavalin A agarose–treated mitochondria are still capable of producing adenosine in a reaction dependent on the respiratory state and functional adenine nucleotide translocase.

We propose here that changes in the cytosolic or mitochondrial phosphorylation potential during increased ATP hydrolysis (decreased $[ATP]/[ADP][P_i]$) could result in an increase in AMP (possibly within the matrix) that is subsequently converted to adenosine by the mitochondrial 5'-nucleotidase. The adenosine that is formed could then be exported out of the cell by a sarcolemmal nucleoside carrier to the interstitium, where it could cause vasodilation and increased O_2 delivery to the parenchyma. It remains to be seen whether these mechanisms are operant in the intact myocardium. It may be speculated that a similar system could be functioning within the vascular smooth-muscle cells of the resistance vessels. If there is a functioning 5'-nucleotidase associated with the mitochondria of vascular smooth muscle, these mitochondria would be ideally situated to sense changes in oxygen concentration and to produce adenosine that could conceivably act at the internal adenosine receptor, the "P site," that is thought to exist (37).

MITOCHONDRIAL CREATINE KINASE

Creatine kinase catalyzes the reversible reaction:

$$ATP + creatine \leftrightarrow ADP + creatine\ phosphate\ (CrP) + H^+.$$

Heart-cell creatine-kinase isozymes occur in two compartments: in the mitochondria, and in the cytoplasmic myofibrillar compartment. The mitochondrial compartment contains 30% of the cardiac cell creatine-kinase activity. The mitochondrial creatine kinase is located in the intermembrane space in the immediate vicinity of the adenine nucleotide translocase (52). ATP transported from the mitochondria into the intermembrane space is converted to creatine phosphate and the ADP released is transported back into the mitochondria for further synthesis of ATP (23). Creatine phosphate is a small, easily diffusible molecule that participates in only one reaction (21). Creatine phosphate will thus function as an easily transferable store of energy from the site of its generation, the mitochondria, to the site of its utilization, in the myofibrils. At the myofibrils, cytoplasmic isozyme of creatine kinase converts creatine phosphate to ATP, the immediate energy source for muscle contraction.

A second possible role for the creatine kinase reaction has been proposed (2, 21). Mitochondrial respiration and ATP synthesis are controlled by extramitochondrial ATP/ADP ratio. It has been suggested that the generation of creatine phosphate and ADP by the mitochondrial intermembrane creatine kinase eliminates the necessity for diffusion of ADP over a considerable distance from myofibrils to mitochondria (2). This is particularly important because the intracellular ADP concentration is several orders of magnitude less than the ATP concentration. Thus, the creatine phosphate shuttle provides an effective control of cytoplasmic ADP at a location adjacent to the adenine nucleotide translocase of mitochondrial inner membrane and may influence high-energy phosphate metabolism in the cell. The importance of ADP generated by the mitochondrial creatine kinase reaction has been emphasized by Jacobus, who argues that mitochondrial respiration is controlled solely by the concentration of ADP (see review by Jacobus in this volume).

Jacobus and his collaborators have suggested that there is a multienzyme complex that has preferred access to matrix ATP and that couples creatine phosphate production to oxidative phosphorylation. Conclusive evidence to support this suggestion is lacking.

The existence of the creatine phosphate shuttle from mitochondria to myofibrils has also been shown in experiments on isolated myocytes (39). This evidence is based on the finding that adenine nucleotides are tightly bound to myofibrils, necessitating the phosphorylation of ADP to ATP by the creatine phosphate–dependent creatine kinase of the myofibrils themselves.

SUMMARY

Mitochondria contain four distinct compartments and a selectively permeable inner membrane. These compartments provide an important means of regulation of mitochondrial activity via various carrier and translocase activities. Nutritional substrates derived from glucose, fatty acids, and branched chain amino acids are utilized by mitochondria in a tightly controlled manner. This control is provided by the specific dehydrogenase enzymes and carnitine related reactions and is dependent on cellular needs for energy and availability of various substrates. Several possible in vivo controllers of mitochondrial respiration exist. In this review we have examined: the dependence of mitochondrial function on oxygen availability, the cellular phosphate potential, and the adenine nucleotide translocase activity; the role of adenosine as the regulator of coronary flow providing a link to mitochondrial metabolism; the importance of the creatine-phosphate shuttle and the existence of separate mitochondrial and myofibrillar creatine-kinase enzymes; and the physiologically important mechanisms of the regulation of mitochondrial metabolic activity in the heart.

ACKNOWLEDGMENTS

This work was supported by NIH grants 5 RO1 GM-33267 and 1F32 HL 06777. The authors thank Mrs. Beverly Jensen for her invaluable help in the preparation of the manuscript.

Literature Cited

1. Akerboom, T. P. M., Bookelman, H., Tager, J. M. 1977. Control of ATP transport across the mitochondrial membrane in isolated rat-liver cells. *FEBS Lett.* 74:50–54
2. Altschuld, R. 1980. Interaction between mitochondrial creatine kinase and oxidative phosphorylation. In *Heart Creatine Kinase*, ed. W. E. Jacobus, J. S. Ingwall, pp. 127–32. Baltimore: Williams & Wilkins
3. Berne, R. M. 1963. Cardiac nucleotides in hypoxia: Possible role in regulation of coronary blood flow. *Am. J. Physiol.* 204:317–22
4. Bieber, L. L., Emaus, R., Valkner, K., Farrell, S. 1982. Possible functions of short-chain and medium-chain carnitine acyl-transferases. *Fed. Proc.* 41:2858–62
5. Brawand, F., Folly, G., Walter, P. 1980. Relation between extra- and intramitochondrial ATP/ADP ratios in rat liver mitochondria. *Biochim. Biophys. Acta* 590:285–89
6. Broquist, H. P. 1982. Carnitine

biosynthesis and function. *Fed. Proc.* 41:2840–42

7. Bukoski, R. D., Sparks, H. V., Mela, L. M. 1983. Rat heart mitochondria produce adenosine. *Biochem. Biophys. Res. Comm.* 113:990–95

8. Buse, M. G., Biggers, J. F., Drier, C., Buse, J. F. 1973. The effect of epinephrine, glucagon, and the nutritional state on oxidation of branched chain amino acids and pyruvate by isolated hearts and diaphragms of the rat. *J. Biol. Chem.* 248:697–706

9. Chalmers, R. A., Roe, C. R., Tracey, B. M., Stacey, T. E., Hoppel, C. L., Millington, D. S. 1983. Secondary carnitine insufficiency in disorders of organic acid metabolism: Modulation of acyl-CoA/CoA ratios by L-carnitine *in vivo*. *Biochem. Soc. Trans.* 11:724–25

10. Chance, B., DeVault, D., Legallais, V., Mela, L., Yonetani, T. 1967. Kinetics of electron transfer reactions in biological systems. In *Nobel Symposium 5, Fast Reactions and Primary Processes in Chemical Kinetics*, ed. S. Claesson, pp. 437–68. Stockholm: Interscience

11. Chang, T. W., Goldberg, A. L. 1978. Leucine inhibits oxidation of glucose and pyruvate in skeletal muscle during fasting. *J. Biol. Chem.* 253:3696–701

12. Davis, E. J., Lumeng, L. 1975. Relationships between the phosphorylation potentials generated by liver mitochondria and respiratory state under conditions of adenosine diphosphate control. *J. Biol. Chem.* 250:2275–82

13. Davis, E. J., Davis-van Thienen, W. I. A. 1978. Control of mitochondrial metabolism by the ATP/ADP ratio. *Biochem. Biophys. Res. Comm.* 83:1260–66

14. Davis-van Thienen, W., Davis, E. J. 1981. The effects of energetic steady state, pyruvate concentration, and octanoyl-(-)-carnitine on the relative rates of carboxylation and decarboxylation of pyruvate by rat liver mitochondria. *J. Biol. Chem.* 256:8371–78

15. Denton, R. M., Randle, P. J., Bridges, B. J., Cooper, R. H., Kerbey, A. L., et al. 1975. Regulation of mammalian pyruvate dehydrogenase. *Molec. Cell Biochem.* 9:27–53

16. Erecinska, M., Veech, R. L., Wilson, D. F. 1974. Thermodynamic relationships between the oxidation-reduction reactions and the ATP synthesis in suspensions of isolated pigeon heart mitochondria. *Arch. Biochem. Biophys.* 160:412–21

17. Erecinska, M., Wilson, D. F. 1982. Regulation of cellular energy metabolism. *J. Membr. Biol.* 70:1–14

18. Forman, N. G., Wilson, D. F. 1982. Energetics and stoichiometry of oxidative phosphorylation from NADH to cytochrome c in isolated rat liver mitochondria. *J. Biol. Chem.* 257:12908–15

19. Forman, N. G., Wilson, D. F. 1983. Dependence of mitochondrial oxidative phosphorylation on activity of the adenine nucleotide translocase. *J. Biol. Chem.* 258:8649–55

20. Frick, G. P., Lowenstein, J. M. 1978. Vectorial production of adenosine by 5'-nucleotidase in the perfused rat heart. *J. Biol. Chem.* 253:1240–44

21. Garfinkel, D., Kohn, M. C. 1980. Computer modeling of cardiac energy metabolism. See Ref. 2, pp. 48–62

22. Gauduel, Y., Martin, J. L., Teisseire, B., Duruble, M., Duvelleroy, M. A. 1982. The dependence of cardiac energy metabolism on oxygen carrying capacity. *Biochem. Med.* 28:324–39

23. Gellerich, F., Saks, V. A. 1982. Control of heart mitochondrial oxygen consumption by creatine kinase: The importance of enzyme localization. *Biochem. Biophys. Res. Comm.* 105:1473–81

24. Hassinen, I. E., Hiltunen, K. 1975. Respiratory control in isolated perfused rat heart. Role of the equilibrium relations between the mitochondrial electron carriers and the adenylate system. *Biochim. Biophys. Acta* 408:319–30

25. Hoppel, C. L. 1982. Carnitine and carnitine palmitoyltransferase in fatty acid oxidation and ketosis. *Fed. Proc.* 41:2853–57

26. Hutson, S. M., Cree, T. C., Harper, A. E. 1978. Regulation of leucine and α-ketoisocaproate metabolism in skeletal muscle. *J. Biol. Chem.* 253:8126–33

27. Idell-Wenger, J. A., Grotyohann, L. W., Neely, J. R. 1978. Coenzyme A and carnitine distribution in normal and ischemic hearts. *J. Biol. Chem.* 253:4310–18

28. Idell-Wenger, J. A., Grotyohann, L. W., Neely, J. R. 1982. Regulation of fatty acid utilization in heart. Role of the carnitine-acetyl-CoA transferase and carnitine-acetyl-carnitine translocase system. *J. Molec. Cell Cardiol.* 14:413–17

29. Jackson, R. H., Singer, T. P. 1983. Inactivation of the α-ketoglutarate and pyruvate dehydrogenase complexes of beef heart by branched chain ketoacids. *J. Biol. Chem.* 258:1857–65

30. Krämer, R., Klingenberg, M. 1977. Reconstitution of inhibitor binding properties of the isolated adenosine 5'-diphosphate, adenosine 5'-triphosphate carrier-linked binding protein. *Biochemistry* 16:4954–61

31. Kunz, W., Bohnensack, R., Bohme, G.,

Kuster, U., Letko, G., Schonfeld, P. 1981. Relations between extramitochondrial and intramitochondrial adenine nucleotide systems. *Arch. Biochem. Biophys.* 209:219–29

32. Kuster, U., Bohnensack, R., Kunz, W. 1976. Control of oxidative phosphorylation by the extramitochondrial ATP/ADP ratio. *Biochim. Biophys. Acta* 440:391–402

33. LaNoue, K., Mizani, S. M., Klingenberg, M. 1978. Electrical imbalance of adenine nucleotide transport across the mitochondrial membrane. *J. Biol. Chem.* 253:191–98

34. LaNoue, K. F., Watts, J. A., Koch, C. D. 1981. Adenine nucleotide transport during cardiac ischemia. *Am. J. Physiol.* 241:H663–71

35. Lemasters, J. J., Sowers, A. E. 1979. Phosphate dependence and atractyloside inhibition of mitochondrial oxidative phosphorylation. The ADP-ATP carrier is rate limiting. *J. Biol. Chem.* 254:1248–51

36. Letko, G., Kuster, U., Duszynski, J., Kunz, W. 1980. Investigation of the dependence of the intramitochondrial (ATP)/(ADP) ratio on the respiration rate. *Biochim. Biophys. Acta* 593:196–203

37. Londos, C., Wolff, J., Cooper, D. F. 1983. Adenosine receptors and adenylate cyclase interactions. In *Regulatory Function of Adenosine*, ed. R. M. Berne, T. W. Rall, R. Rubio, pp. 17–32. Boston: Martinus Nijhoff

38. Longmuir, I. S. 1959. Respiration rate of rat-liver cells at low oxygen concentrations. *Biochem. J.* 65:378–82

39. McClellan, G., Weisberg, A., Winegrad, S. 1983. Energy transport from mitochondria to myofibrils by a creatine phosphate shuttle in cardiac cells. *Am. J. Physiol.* 245:C423–27

40. Mela, L. M., Goodwin, C. W., Miller, L. D. 1976. *In vivo* control of mitochondrial enzyme concentrations and activity by oxygen. *Am. J. Physiol.* 231:1811–16

41. Mowbray, J., Corrigall, J. 1984. Short term control of mitochondrial adenine nucleotide translocator by thyroid hormone. *Eur. J. Biochem.* 139:95–99

42. Nuutinen, E. M., Nishiki, K., Erecinska, M., Wilson, D. F. 1982. Role of mitochondrial oxidative phosphorylation in regulation of coronary blood flow. *Am. J. Physiol.* 243:H159–69

43. Nuutinen, E. M., Nelson, D., Wilson, D. F., Erecinska, M. 1983. Regulation of coronary blood flow: effects of 2,4-dinitrophenol and theophylline. *Am. J. Physiol.* 244:H396-H405

44. Olson, M. S., Dennis, S. C., DeBuysere, M. S., Padma, A. 1978. The regulation of pyruvate dehydrogenase in the isolated perfused rat heart. *J. Biol. Chem.* 253:7369–75

45. Olsson, R. A., Saito, D., Steinhart, C. R. 1982. Compartmentalization of the adenosine pool of dog and rat hearts. *Circ. Res.* 50:617–26

46. Oshino, N., Sugano, T., Oshino, R., Chance, B. 1974. Mitochondrial function under hypoxic conditions: The steady states of cytochrome a + a$_3$ and their relation to mitochondrial energy states. *Biochim. Biophys. Acta* 368:298–310

47. Patel, T. B., DeBuysere, M. S., Barron, L. L., Olson, M. S. 1981. Studies on the regulation of the branched chain α-ketoacid dehydrogenase in the perfused rat liver. *J. Biol. Chem.* 256:9009–15

48. Randle, P. J. 1981. Phosphorylation-dephosphorylation cycles and the regulation of fuel selection in mammals. *Curr. Top. Cell Regul.* 18:107–29

49. Randle, P. J., Sugden, P. H., Kerbey, A. L., Radcliffe, P. M., Hutson, N. J. 1978. Regulation of pyruvate oxidation and the conservation of glucose. *Biochem. Soc. Symp.* 43:47–67

50. Reed, L. J. 1981. Regulation of mammalian pyruvate dehydrogenase complex by a phosphorylation-dephosphorylation cycle. *Curr. Top. Cell. Regul.* 18:95–106

51. Robinson, B. H. 1983. Inborn errors of pyruvate metabolism. *Biochem. Soc. Trans.* 11:623–26

52. Saks, V. A., Kupriyanov, V. V., Elizarova, G. V., Jacobus, W. E. 1980. Studies of energy transport in heart cells. The importance of creatine kinase localization for the coupling of mitochondrial phosphorylcreatine production to oxidative phosphorylation. *J. Biol. Chem.* 255:755–63

53. Schrader, J., Schutz, W., Bardenheuer, H. 1981. Role of S-adenosylhomocysteine hydrolase in adenosine metabolism of mammalian heart. *Biochem. J.* 198:65–70

54. Schutz, W., Schrader, J., Gerlach, E. 1981. Different sites of adenosine formation in the heart. *Am. J. Physiol.* 240:H963–70

55. Shug, A. 1979. Control of carnitine-related metabolism during myocardial ischemia. *Texas Reports on Biol. Med.* 39:409–28

56. Shug, A., Shrago, E. 1973. A proposed mechanism for fatty acid effects on energy metabolism of the heart. *J. Lab. Clin. Med.* 81:214–18

57. Shug, A., Shrago, E., Bittar, N., Folts,

J. D., Koke, J. R. 1975. Long chain fatty acyl CoA inhibition of adenine nucleotide translocation in the ischemic myocardium. *Am. J. Physiol.* 228:689–92

58. Sparks, H. V., Manfredi, J. P., Phair, R. D. 1983. A compartmental model of changes in interstitial adenosine associated with increased myocardial adenosine. In *Ca^{2+} Entry Blockers, Adenosine, and Neurohumors,* ed. G. F. Merrill, H. R. Weiss, pp. 189–205. Baltimore: Urban & Schwarzenberg

59. Sugano, T., Oshino, N., Chance, B. 1974. Mitochondrial functions under hypoxic conditions: The steady states of cytochrome c reduction and of energy metabolism. *Biochim. Biophys. Acta* 347:340–58

60. Tager, J. M., Groen, A. K., Wanders, J. A., Duszynski, J., Westerhoff, H. V., Vervoorn, R. C. 1983. Control of mitochondrial respiration. *Biochem. Soc. Trans.* 11:40–43

61. Tager, J. M., Wanders, R. J. A., Groen, A. K., Kunz, W., Bohnensack, R., et al. 1983. Control of mitochondrial respiration. *FEBS Lett.* 151:1–9

62. Walajtys-Rode, E., Williamson, J. R. 1980. Effects of branched chain α-ketoacids on the metabolism of isolated rat liver cells. III. Interactions with pyruvate dehydrogenase. *J. Biol. Chem.* 255:413–18

63. Wanders, R. J. A., Groen, A. K., Meijer, A. J., Tager, J. M. 1981. Determination of the free-energy difference of the adenine nucleotide translocator reaction in rat-liver mitochondria using intra- and extramitochondrial ATP-utilizing reactions. *FEBS Lett.* 132:201–6

64. Waymack, P. P., DeBuysere, M. S., Olson, M. S. 1980. Studies on the activation and inactivation of the branched chain α-ketoacid dehydrogenase in the perfused rat heart. *J. Biol. Chem.* 255:9773–81

65. Wieland, O. H. 1983. The mammalian pyruvate dehydrogenase complex: Structure and regulation. *Rev. Physiol. Biochem. Pharmacol.* 96:123–70

66. Williamson, J. R. 1979. Mitochondrial function in the heart. *Ann. Rev. Physiol.* 41:485–506

67. Wilson, D. F. 1976. Mitochondria. In *Biological Handbooks. I. Cell Biology,* pp. 143–230. Bethesda, MD: FASEB

68. Wilson, D. F., Stubbs, M., Krebs, H. A. 1974. Equilibrium relations between the oxidation-reduction reactions and the adenosine triphosphate synthesis in suspensions of isolated liver cells. *Biochem. J.* 140:57–64

69. Wilson, D. F., Stubbs, M., Oshino, N., Erecinska, M. 1974. Thermodynamic relationships between the mitochondrial oxidation-reduction reactions and cellular ATP levels in ascites tumor cells and perfused rat liver. *Biochemistry* 13:5305–11

70. Wilson, D. F., Erecinska, M., Drown, C., Silver, I. A. 1979. The oxygen dependence of cellular energy metabolism. *Arch. Biochem. Biophys.* 195:485–93

71. Wilson, D. F., Owen, C. S., Erecinska, M. 1979. Quantitative dependence of mitochondrial oxidative phosphorylation on oxygen concentration: A mathematical model. *Arch. Biochem. Biophys.* 195:494–504

72. Wilson, D. F., Erecinska, M., Schramm, V. L. 1983. Evaluation of the relationship between the intra- and extramitochondrial [ATP]/[ADP] ratios using phosphoenolpyruvate carboxykinase. *J. Biol. Chem.* 258:10464–73

Ann. Rev. Physiol. 1985. 47:665–76

EXTRACELLULAR FUNCTIONS OF NUCLEOTIDES IN HEART AND BLOOD VESSELS

Che Su

Department of Pharmacology, Southern Illinois University School of Medicine, P. O. Box 3926, Springfield, Illinois 62708

This chapter will primarily consider findings documented subsequent to recent reviews (17, 72, 75) and proceedings of adenosine symposia (5, 18). Discussion will largely be confined to adenosine and adenine nucleotides, also referred to as purines.

EXTRACELLULAR PURINE LEVELS

The plasma levels of adenosine and adenine nucleotides have remained somewhat elusive. The breakdown of adenosine in blood is rapid, with a half-life of shorter than 10 seconds in human whole blood (48). This is complicated by contribution to the adenosine pool by adenine nucleotides in plasma and blood cells and considerable circadian variation of plasma levels of adenosine and adenine nucleotides (0.1–0.7 μM), at least in the rat (11). In canine arterial blood, plasma adenosine levels of 0.06–0.07 μM were found (51a). The adenosine level in the bovine venous plasma was estimated at ~ 0.5 μM by immediate mixing of blood samples with inorganic phosphate, ethylenediaminetetraacetic acid (EDTA), N6-methyladenosine, and p-chloromercuribenzoate to inhibit 5'-nucleotidase, adenosine deaminase, and xanthine oxidase (53).

Substantially higher plasma adenosine levels were found in unanesthetized, unrestrained rats (79). The arterial blood samples were withdrawn via left carotid arterial catheter into syringes preloaded with heparinized saline contain-

0066-4278/85/0315-0665$02.00

ing dipyridamole. After immediate centrifugation, the supernatant was deproteinated with trichloroacetic acid and neutralized for assay by high pressure liquid chromatography (HPLC). The average basal adenosine concentration was 3.0 μM. This assay (79), however, did not include the equally vasoactive adenine nucleotides that may not be negligible in some vascular beds.

The interstitial purine concentrations in individual organs could vastly differ from the systemic circulating levels, and they remain difficult to assess. The local factors include synthesis and release of adenosine compounds and their inactivation. Within vascular wall, the release can be evoked from adrenergic and nonadrenergic nerves, vascular smooth muscle cells, and endothelial cells (see below).

Vasodilation in cardiac and skeletal muscle functional hyperemia has generally been associated with adenosine (6). However, not all data can be explained by the adenosine hypothesis. The norepinephrine-induced functional hyperemia in the dog heart was not prevented by aminophylline, a purinergic P_1-receptor antagonist that blocked adenosine-induced hyperemia (43). Adenosine release in the isolated guinea pig heart was phasic during metabolically stimulated steady increase in coronary flow (22). Infusion of high concentrations of adenosine to "saturate" its receptors failed to affect exercise hyperemia in the dog gracilis muscle (37). ATP is a more likely candidate, in the views of Forrester (28, 29). ATP is a highly potent dilator at least of the cat pineal vessels, 0.1 nM being effective when applied to the outside of these vessels (30), and this nucleotide is resistant to blockade by methylxanthines. A number of investigators have demonstrated the release of intact ATP from the heart, skeletal muscle, brain synaptosomes, and the Torpedo electric organ (12), although both adenosine and adenine nucleotides may be released from the perfused rabbit heart (31). The source of ATP released from hypoxic myocytes may be the nucleotide-protein-Ca^{2+} complexes in the sarcolemma (84). Forrester (28, 29) reasons that muscle membrane depolarization sets in motion the release of ATP, which acts on the P_2-purinoceptors, and that the widespread ecto-ATPase activity helps localize the nucleotide involvement in blood flow control. Additional data are desirable, for example prevention of functional hyperemia by specific antagonists for ATP such as arylazido aminopropionyl ATP (ANAPP$_3$) (38), because vascular smooth muscle P_2-purinoceptors mediate constriction rather than dilation by ATP (74), although endothelial cells mediate dilation by this nucleotide (see below). Perhaps both the nucleoside and nucleotides participate in functional hyperemia and play somewhat different roles, depending on the vascular bed and physiological state. For the postcontraction hyperemia of skeletal muscle, there is strong evidence that adenosine acts as a mediator (47).

MODES OF ACTION OF PURINES

A recent review (64) discussed the considerable data that adenosine modulates membrane permeabilities to Ca^{2+}, K^+, and Cl^- ions. In some cardiac tissues and vascular smooth muscle, inhibition of Ca^{2+} influx by adenosine results in relaxation. The same investigators have further demonstrated inhibition of inward movement of ^{45}Ca during stimulation by 25 mM K^+ in the cultured vascular smooth muscle monolayers from the rat aorta and porcine carotid arterial strips. They concluded that the diminution of Ca^{2+} influx, rather than increase in cyclic AMP (cAMP), relaxes vascular smooth muscle. Because adenosine elevated ^{45}Ca uptake in undepolarized preparations, an increased Ca^{2+} sequestration within these cells was suggested as another possible mechanism (26). The latter view was supported by another laboratory because nifedipine, a calcium-channel blocker, had no effect on adenosine-mediated relaxation of the isolated rabbit femoral arterial rings. Further, adenosine preferentially relaxed the norepinephrine-induced contraction, whereas nifedipine was more effective against the K^+-induced contraction. Contraction by K^+ is dependent mainly on extracellular Ca^{2+}, and that by norepinephrine on both intra- and extracellular Ca^{2+}. The action of adenosine therefore was suggested to be mediated in part by an intracellular mechanism subsequent to adenosine-receptor occupation (85). The role of the sarcolemmal Na-K pump was investigated in the rabbit coronary and femoral arteries. The adenosine-induced relaxations were attenuated by inhibition of the Na-K pump by ouabain or low Na or K-free solution. In addition, adenosine enhanced the K-induced relaxation. These data are compatible with an enhanced Na-K pump activity contributing directly or indirectly to the relaxant action of adenosine (27). In the guinea-pig atrial muscle as well, adenosine increased the steady-state outward current and ^{42}K efflux, suggestive of activation of the potassium conductance. The hyperpolarizing effect may abbreviate the action potential and, indirectly, inhibit the calcium influx during excitation (42). On the other hand, involvement of cAMP in the adenosine-induced relaxation of bovine coronary arteries was inferred from the activation of cAMP-dependent protein kinase (69).

In a study using enzymatically dispersed ventricular myocytes from bovine and guinea pig hearts, adenosine (up to 0.2 mM) per se had no effect on the action potentials or basal contractility. However, it effectively antagonized the inotropic action of isoproterenol, confirming some previous findings (see 24), and also the electrophysiological stimulant action of this catecholamine. It was interpreted as attenuation of isoproterenol-induced increase in myocardial cAMP, which leads to an enhanced Ca^{2+} influx (4).

The mode of presynaptic action of adenosine was investigated in the isolated guinea pig heart, in which ^{3}H-norepinephrine release was evoked by electrical stimulation or excess K^+. Inhibition of the release by adenosine or acetylcholine was prevented by tetraethylammonium, which prolongs the nerve action potential, at a normal or low Ca^{2+} concentration. From this, it was concluded that these two agents acted by altering electrical properties (e.g. conduction, resting membrane potential, duration of nerve action potential) of sympathetic nerve terminals, which leads to reduction in Ca^{2+} availability for the release process (80). This mode of action is in contrast to the inhibition of norepinephrine release by itself, which seems to affect the Ca^{2+} influx without altering the nerve terminal electrical properties (81). However, inhibition of evoked acetylcholine release from frog motor nerve endings by adenosine and 2-chloroadenosine seems to be mediated by activation of adenylate cyclase (67).

Thus, conflicting views have emerged seemingly awaiting to be reconciled regarding the inhibitory actions of adenosine: reduced Ca^{2+} influx and/or enhanced Ca^{2+} sequestration, increase in cAMP, and stabilization of membrane. It would be interesting to see whether they can totally be attributed to differences in membrane or receptor properties among these sites and whether these are interrelated processes.

Unexpectedly, ATP but not adenosine was found to inhibit acetylcholine release from sympathetic preganglionic nerves of the frog. ATP (0.1 and 0.5 mM) markedly reduced the mean number of acetylcholine quanta released by a nerve impulse, but adenosine (0.4–1 mM), 2-chloroadenosine adenosine (10–100 µM) or α,β-methylene ATP (0.2–0.5 mM), a slowly degradable derivative of ATP, had no effect. On the other hand, the inhibition by ATP (0.2 mM) was antagonized by theophylline (2 mM), suggesting that the receptors do not resemble the P_1 or P_2 type (68). This is a departure from the repeated postulate that the inhibitory effects of ATP are produced by its hydrolysis product, adenosine, acting on P_1 receptors (20, 56, 73). Nor is it consistent with the view that ATP, AMP, and adenosine can act directly on the theophylline-sensitive P_1-receptors at least in the atria and ileal cholinergic nerves of guinea pigs (16, 57).

There is increasing evidence to support the concept of two subtypes, A_1 (or R_i) and A_2 (or R_a, R_s), of cell surface adenosine receptors in the cardiovascular system. The A_1 subtype is associated with inhibition of adenylate cyclase, and the A_2 counterpart often with its stimulation. A_1 receptors have been identified in the atrium and adrenergic and cholinergic nerve terminals (14, 59), including adrenergic nerves in the rabbit portal vein (8). The heart microvessels seem to be equipped with A_2 receptors in view of adenylate cyclase stimulation by adenosine (55). Relaxation of feline cerebral arteries by adenosine was attributed to A_2 receptors linked to cAMP accumulation (25). However, relaxation of the guinea pig aorta by adenosine appeared to be mediated by A_2 receptors, without necessarily stimulating adenylate cyclase, and also by an intracellular site (P site) (15).

As cautioned by Hughes & Stone (39), it may be misleading to refer to purine receptors involved in a functional response as A_1 or A_2. The A_1/A_2 (or R_i/R_a) distinction originally pertained to the modulation of adenylate cyclase activity, which is not necessarily causally related to cardiovascular effects of purines. Possibly purine receptors linked to calcium channels are distinct from those linked to adenylate cyclase. The relationship between these receptor subtypes and the primarily pharmacological P_1 purinoceptor (9) remains ill-defined. It is hoped that the growing ligand binding studies (17) will throw light on adenosine receptor classification.

PURINERGIC NEUROTRANSMISSION AND NEUROMODULATION

The concept of purine-mediated neurotransmission and neuromodulation has recently been reviewed. Within the cardiovascular system, purinergic inhibitory and adrenergic excitatory nerves appear to supply the rabbit portal vein. Purinergic feedback inhibition of norepinephrine release from adrenergic nerves is probably more widespread. It was postulated that ATP or its derivative is coreleased from adrenergic terminals along with norepinephrine by nerve impulses, and in some instances also released from the postsynaptic effector cells following the action of norepinephrine on these cells (75). Release of purines from both vascular adrenergic neuronal and extraneuronal sites was also achieved by ouabain, whereas KCl induced release predominantly from nerve terminals in view of its susceptibility to pretreatment with 6-hydroxydopamine but not phentolamine (45). The adenosine uptake mechanism, probably important for its local inactivation, may differ between the neuronal and extraneuronal compartments because of selective inhibition of the former by papaverine (46).

In the rat portal vein, VIP containing nerve fibers as well as release of VIP by electrical field stimulation was demonstrated (2, 41), and this peptide may be the vasodilator neurotransmitter (40). VIP immunoreactive nerve fibers were also identified in the hepatic portal vein and other blood vessels of the guinea pig (19). In Burnstock's view (9), in the guinea pig portal vein where low ATP levels coexist with norepinephrine in sympathetic nerves, there is no evidence for presynaptic purinergic modulation of norepinephrine release or purinergic transmission. In the rat portal vein, ATP released from sympathetic nerves plays a cotransmitter and neuromodulator role. Finally, in the rabbit portal vein, there is evidence for release of ATP as a transmitter from purinergic nerves and also as a modulator from sympathetic nerves. Although ATP dilated bovine and canine penile arteries, it was not likely the transmitter for the nonadrenergic, noncholinergic vasodilator fibers because hemoglobin blocked vasodilation elicited by nerve stimulation but not by ATP (7). Purinergic innervation in noncardiovascular organs needs further scrutiny.

On the other hand, the cotransmitter role of ATP in the rat and guinea pig vas deferens has been well supported (32, 54, 70). Examples of coexistence of norepinephrine and ATP in sympathetic nerves, either as cotransmitters or as a transmitter and a modulator, include the rabbit aorta and ear artery, and basilar artery and nonvascular tissues of the dog (10). The same investigator has further raised the prospect that purine nucleotides and nucleosides released from nerves may function as trophic factors. As reviewed by Stone (72), adenosine and its derivatives are among the most potent compounds affecting growth-related processes in various cell types.

ENDOTHELIAL PURINE REGULATION

Endothelial cells are known for their efficient uptake and metabolism of adenosine (36). They probably play a biochemical gatekeeper role against adenosine between the blood plasma and vascular interstitial fluid. Additionally, these cells can sequentially hydrolyze ATP to ADP, AMP, and finally to adenosine, by Mg^{2+}-stimulated ectoenzymes, nucleoside triphosphatase, nucleoside diphosphatase, and 5'-nucleotidase (60). Because adenosine inhibits platelet aggregation while ADP induces it, the ecto-ADPase activity has been thought to contribute to endothelial antithrombic properties.

The secretory functions of endothelial cells, too, have attracted much attention in recent years. Pearson & Gordon (61) used cultured porcine aortic endothelial cells to demonstrate liberation of adenine nucleotides by trypsin, thrombin, and collagenase. ADP rapidly accumulates extracellularly before it is degraded to adenosine, although ATP may primarily be released followed by extracellular degradation to ADP. It has subsequently been shown that relaxation of isolated arterial rings by thrombin is abolished by removal of the endothelium (21). The endothelially liberated ADP may thus participate in platelet aggregation and vascular tone regulations.

That ATP and ADP exert most of their arterial relaxing effect through an action on endothelial cells has been well established (33). Evidence points to release of a relaxing factor from these cells through calcium influx, and this factor in turn acts on vascular smooth muscle. AMP and adenosine were thought to cause relaxation of some arteries by acting directly on muscle cells and require no endothelial cells (33). Destruction of endothelium, however, significantly attenuated the adenosine-induced relaxation of the pig aorta (34) and rat aorta and femoral artery (50). ATP, ADP, AMP, and adenosine, but not acetylcholine, induced an increase in ^{86}Rb efflux from preloaded pig aortic endothelial cells. ATP and ADP were equipotent and some 120-fold stronger than AMP and adenosine. Because the ^{86}Rb efflux was abolished by lanthanum, which blocks calcium influx, a calcium-activated efflux of potassium (represented by ^{86}Rb) seems to be associated with the endothelium-dependent relaxation by the adenine compounds (34).

The relaxing factor released by endothelial cells can vary with the stimuli. The possibility of release of adenosine or its nucleotides by acetylcholine was examined in the perfused rabbit pulmonary artery preloaded with ^{3}H-adenosine. Acetylcholine (0.3 and 1 μM) induced a small increase in tritium efflux. However, the purine release was probably insufficient to account for the relaxant effect, as the latter was unaltered by theophylline or dipyridamole (78). A substantial prostacyclin release by ATP (1–300 μM) was achieved using perfused columns of cultured pig aortic endothelial cells on microcarrier beads (35, 62). This suggested that endothelial cells are responsible for the prostacyclin release during perfusion of renal and pulmonary vascular beds with ATP and ADP (65). 2-Methylthio-ATP, a derivative resistant to ATPase, was more potent. ADP was slightly and AMP much less potent, while adenosine was ineffective at 100 μM. The effective concentrations of ATP were comparable with those for its vasodilator action (34), and the released prostacyclin reached 1 ng ml^{-1}. This was well above the minimum level that inhibits platelet aggregation, although prostacyclin did not appear to mediate the ATP-induced relaxation of the canine femoral artery (21).

Thus, as pointed out by Pearson and collaborators (60, 62), endothelial cells with their ectonucleotidases and adenosine uptake system could form a complete cycle for the local control of vascular tone by adenosine; namely, release of ATP or ADP (from endothelial cells, muscle cells, nerve terminals, or platelets), its hydrolysis to another active form, adenosine, and termination of its action by uptake. Prostacyclin release adds a new dimension to the hemostatic and vascular tone regulation by endothelial cells through the nucleotide-nucleoside cycle.

PATHOPHYSIOLOGIC AND THERAPEUTIC IMPLICATIONS

Simply stated, adenosine and adenine nucleotides affect three important processes relevant to circulation: neurotransmission, myocardial and vascular smooth muscle contraction, and platelet aggregation.

The plasma adenosine level in unanesthetized, unrestrained rats is as high as 3 μM (1.6–4.6 μM). The mean arterial pressure was significantly lowered by a small increase in the level by intravenous adenosine infusion, without bradycardia, while the pressure was elevated slightly by an adenosine receptor antagonist, caffeine (79, 83). These results suggest a possible tonic vasodilator function of plasma purines, without discrediting the probably higher interstitial concentrations of purines locally generated, e.g. by sympathetic nerve activity or hypoxia. Within the kidney, sufficient adenosine seems to be produced to decrease the water and sodium excretion and renin release. Accordingly, adenosine has been postulated to mediate a metabolic regulation of the glomerular filtration rate and renin release (58, 71). Of therapeutic interest is the finding that intravenously administered ATP significantly improved the renal function in an induced postischemic acute renal failure in the rat (66).

Many pharmacological effects of theophylline, possibly excepting its anti-asthmatic effects, are probably consequent upon adenosine receptor antagonism (63). The effects of caffeine, too, appear to be associated with the endogenous adenosine. Rats given long-term caffeine administration, which blocked the adenosine-induced hypotension, became more responsive to adenosine after sudden caffeine withdrawal (79). These investigators attribute this to an increase in density or sensitivity of adenosine receptors, which may also be expressed as some of the common aftereffects of caffeine withdrawal such as headaches, because adenosine is a potent cerebral vasodilator. Increase in brain adenosine receptors by chronic caffeine treatment has indeed been demonstrated (52).

Another commonly used agent, dipyridamole, can at therapeutic serum concentrations (1–4 μM) prevent cellular transport of adenosine and its metabolism in whole blood and thus raise its extracellular concentration (48, 49). Diazepam increases human coronary blood flow and potentiates the coronary vasodilator action of adenosine as well as its CNS action. This agent has been found to inhibit the adenosine transport system in the guinea-pig ventricle ($K_i =$ 5–10 μM), possibly accounting for these effects (3).

As a newer approach to reduction of damaging effects of global ischemia during cardiac damage, adenosine deaminase inhibitors have been evaluated. Erythro-9-(2-hydroxy-3-nonyl) adenine (EHNA) and 2'-deoxycoformycin (DCF), given 5 min before ischemia, improved the functional recovery following ischemia in the isolated perfused rat heart (23). The ongoing active interest in adenosine deaminase inhibitors primarily for chemotherapeutic purposes (1) may lead to useful cardiovascular agents.

The adenosine-mediated presynaptic inhibition of adrenergic transmission is diminished in the arteries of spontaneously hypertensive rats (SHR) (44, 51). Additionally, the endothelial cell contribution to adenosine-induced relaxation of the aorta and femoral artery is increased in SHR (50). These anomalies may well help define the hypertensive state (76, 77) and open new avenues to drug therapy of hypertension. Adenosine derivatives have been investigated as potential cardiovascular drugs. Two adenosine analogs [N-cyclohexyl-adenosine (CHA) and adenosine-5'-N-ethylcarboxamine (NECA), 0.1–3.0 mg kg^{-1}] given orally significantly lowered blood pressure in rats (13). Adenosine receptors, as alluded to by Daly (17), and indeed nucleoside and nucleotide mechanisms in a broader sense, apparently are attractive targets for future drugs.

ACKNOWLEDGMENT

This work was supported by NHLBI HL 24683 and American Heart Association grant 83 1048.

Literature Cited

1. Agarwal, R. P. 1982. Inhibitors of adenosine deaminase. *Pharm. Ther.* 17: 399–429
2. Barja, F., Mathison, R. 1982. Adrenergic and peptidergic (substance P and vasoactive intestinal polypeptide) innervation of the rat portal vein. *Blood Vessels* 19:263–72
3. Barker, P. H., Clanachan, A. S. 1982. Inhibition of adenosine accumulation into guinea pig ventricle by benzodiazepines. *Eur. J. Pharmacol.* 78:241–44
4. Belardinelli, L., Isenberg, G. 1983. Actions of adenosine and isoproterenol on isolated mammalian ventricular myocytes. *Circ. Res.* 53(3):287–97
5. Berne, R. M., Rall, T. W., Rubio, R., eds. 1983. *Regulatory Function of Adenosine.* Boston: Martins Nijhoff
6. Berne, R. M., Winn, H. R., Knabb, R. M., Ely, S. F., Rubio, R. 1983. Blood flow regulation by adenosine in heart, brain, and skeletal muscle. See Ref. 5, pp. 293–313
7. Bowman, A., Gillespie, J. S. 1983. Neurogenic vasodilatation in isolated bovine and canine penile arteries. *J. Physiol.* 341:603–16
8. Brown, C. M., Collis, M. G. 1983. Adenosine A₁ receptor mediated inhibition of nerve stimulation–induced contractions of the rabbit portal vein. *Eur. J. Pharmacol.* 93:277–82
9. Burnstock, G. 1983. A comparison of receptors for adenosine and adenosine nucleotides. See Ref. 5, pp. 49–59
10. Burnstock, G. 1983. Recent concepts of chemical communication between excitable cells. In *Dale's Principle and Communication Between Neurones,* ed. N. N. Osborne, pp. 7–35. Oxford/New York: Pergamon
11. Chagoya de Sánchez, V., Hernández-Munoz, R., Díaz-Munoz, M., Villalobos, R., Glender, W., et al. 1983. Circadian variations of adenosine level in blood and liver and its possible physiological significance. *Life Sci.* 33:1057–64
12. Chaudry, I. H. 1982. Does ATP cross the cell plasma membrane? *Yale J. Biol. Med.* 55:1–10
13. Cohen, D. M., Boucher, D. M.,

Olszewski, B. J., Kaplan, H. R. 1983. Effects of adenosine agonists N-cyclohexyladenosine (CHA) and adenosine-5'-N-ethylcarboxamide (NECA) on blood pressure and heart rate in conscious spontaneously hypertensive rats (SHR). *Fed. Proc.* 42:1261
14. Collis, M. G. 1983. Evidence for an A₁-adenosine receptor in the guinea-pig atrium. *Br. J. Pharmacol.* 78:207–12
15. Collis, M. G., Brown, C. M. 1983. Adenosine relaxes the aorta by interacting with an A₂ receptor and an intracellular site. *Eur. J. Pharmacol.* 96:61–69
16. Collis, M. G., Pettinger, S. J. 1982. Can ATP stimulate P₁-receptors in guinea-pig atrium without conversion to adenosine? *Europ. J. Pharmacol.* 81:521–29
17. Daly, J. W. 1982. Adenosine receptors: Targets for future drugs. *J. Med. Chem.* 25:197–207
18. Daly, J. W., Kuroda, Y., Phillis, J. W., Shimizu, H., Ui, M., eds. 1983. *Physiology and Pharmacology of Adenosine Derivatives.* New York: Raven
19. Della, N. G., Papka, R. E., Furness, J. B., Costa, M. 1983. Vasoactive intestinal peptide-like immunoreactivity in nerves associated with the cardiovascular system of guinea pigs. *Neurosci.* 9:605–19
20. De Mey, J., Burnstock, G., Vanhoutte, P. M. 1979. Modulation of the evoked release of noradrenaline in canine saphenous vein via presynaptic receptors for adenosine but not ATP. *Eur. J. Pharmacol.* 55:401–5
21. De Mey, J. G., Claeys, M., Vanhoutte, P. M. 1982. Endothelium-dependent inhibitory effects of acetylcholine, adenosine triphosphate, thrombin and arachidonic acid in the canine femoral artery. *J. Pharmacol. Exp. Ther.* 222:166–73
22. DeWitt, D. F., Wangler, R. D., Thompson, C. I., Sparks, H. V. 1983. Phasic release of adenosine during steady state metabolic stimulation in the isolated guinea-pig heart. *Circ. Res.* 53:636–43
23. Dhasmana, J. P., Digerness, S. B., Geckle, J. M., Ng, T. C., Glickson, J. D., Blackstone, E. H. 1983. Effect of adenosine deaminase inhibitors on the

heart's functional and biochemical recovery from ischemia: A study utilizing the isolated rat heart adapted to ^{31}P nuclear magnetic resonance. *J. Cardiovasc. Pharmacol.* 5:1040–47

24. Dobson, J. G. Jr. 1983. Adenosine reduces catecholamine contractile responses in oxygenated and hypoxic atria. *Am. J. Physiol.* 245:H468–74

25. Edvinsson, L., Fredholm, B. B. 1983. Characterization of adenosine receptors in isolated cerebral arteries of cat. *Br. J. Pharmacol.* 80:631–37

26. Fenton, R. A., Bruttig, S. P., Rubio, R., Berne, R. M. 1982. Effect of adenosine on calcium uptake by intact and cultured vascular smooth muscle. *Am. J. Physiol.* H797–804

27. Foley, D. H. 1984. Diminished arterial smooth muscle response to adenosine during Na-K pump inhibition. *Pfluegers Arch.* 400:85–88

28. Forrester, T. 1981. Adenosine or adenosine triphosphate? In *Vasodilatation*, ed. P. M. Vanhoutte, I. Leusen, pp. 205–29. New York: Raven

29. Forrester, T. 1984. Local metabolic influences on the microvasculature in cardiac and skeletal muscle. In *Progress in Microcirculation Research II*, ed. F. C. Courtice, D. G. Garlick, M. A. Perry. Sydney: Univ. New South Wales. In press

30. Forrester, T., Harper, A. M., MacKenzie, E. T., Thomson, E. M. 1979. Effect of adenosine triphosphate and some derivatives on cerebral blood flow and metabolism. *J. Physiol.* 296:343–55

31. Fredholm, B. B., Hedqvist, P., Lindstrom, K., Wennmalm, M. 1982. Release of nucleosides and nucleotides from the rabbit heart by sympathetic nerve stimulation. *Acta Physiol. Scand.* 116:285–95

32. French, A. M., Scott, N. C. 1983. Evidence to support the hypothesis that ATP is a cotransmitter in rat vas deferens. *Experientia* 39:264–66

33. Furchgott, R. F. 1984. The role of endothelium in responses of vascular smooth muscle to drugs. *Ann. Rev. Pharmacol. Toxicol.* 24:175–97

34. Gordon, J. L., Martin, W. 1983. Endothelium-dependent relaxation of the pig aorta: Relationship to stimulation of ^{86}Rb efflux from isolated endothelial cells. *Br. J. Pharmacol.* 79:531–41

35. Gordon, J. L., Martin, W. 1983. Stimulation of endothelial prostacyclin production plays no role in endothelium-dependent relaxation of the pig aorta. *Br. J. Pharmacol.* 80:179–86

36. Hellewell, P. G., Pearson, J. D. 1983. Metabolism of circulating adenosine by the porcine isolated perfused lung. *Circ. Res.* 53:1–7

37. Hester, R. L., Guyton, A. C., Barber, B. J. 1982. Reactive and exercise hyperemia during high levels of adenosine infusion. *Am. J. Physiol.* 243:H181–86

38. Hogaboom, G. K., O'Donnell, J. P., Fedan, J. S. 1980. Purinergic receptors: Photoaffinity analog of adenosine triphosphate in a specific adenosine triphosphate antagonist. *Science* 208:1273–76

39. Hughes, P. R., Stone, T. W. 1983. Inhibition by purines of the inotropic action of isoprenaline in rat atria. *Br. J. Pharmacol.* 80:149–53

40. Ishii, T., Shimo, Y. 1983. Nonadrenergic inhibitory response in the rat portal vein. *Arch. Intl. Pharmacodyn. Ther.* 261:291–301

41. Järhult, J., Fahrenkrug, J., Hellstrand, P., Uddman, R. 1982. VIP (vasoactive intestinal polypeptide)-immunoreactive innervation of the portal vein. *Cell Tissue Res.* 221:617–24

42. Jochem, G., Neurath, H. 1983. Adenosine activates a potassium conductance in guinea-pig atrial heart muscle. *Experientia* 39:1347–49

43. Jones, C. E., Hurst, T. W., Randall, J. R. 1982. Effect of aminophylline on coronary functional hyperemia and myocardial adenosine. *Am. J. Physiol.* 243:H480–87

44. Kamikawa, Y., Cline, W. H. Jr., Su, C. 1983. Possible roles of purinergic modulation in pathogenesis of some diseases: Hypertension and asthma. See Ref. 18, pp. 189–96.

45. Katsuragi, T., Su, C. 1982. Release of purines and noradrenaline by ouabain and potassium chloride from vascular adrenergic nerves. *Br. J. Pharmacol.* 77:625–29

46. Katsuragi, T., Su, C. 1982. Possible selective inhibition of [^3H]adenosine uptake by papaverine in vascular adrenergic nerves. *Eur. J. Pharmacol.* 79:111–15

47. Kille, J. M., Klabunde, R. E. 1984. Adenosine as a mediator of postcontraction hyperemia in dog gracilis muscle. *Am. J. Physiol.* 246:H274–82

48. Klabunde, R. E. 1983. Dipyridamole inhibition of adenosine metabolism in human blood. *Eur. J. Pharmacol.* 93:21–26

49. Klabunde, R. E. 1983. Effects of dipyridamole on postischemic vasodilation and extracellular adenosine. *Am. J. Physiol.* 244:H273–80

50. Konishi, M., Su, C. 1983. Role of endothelium in dilator responses of spontaneously hypertensive rat arteries. *Hypertension* 5:881–86

51. Kubo, T., Su, C. 1983. Effects of adenosine on [³H]norepinephrine release from perfused mesenteric arteries of SHR and renal hypertensive rats. *Eur. J. Pharmacol.* 87:349–52

51a. Manfredi, J. P., Sparks, H. V. Jr. 1982. Adenosine's role in coronary vasodilation induced by arterial pacing and norepinephrine. *Am. J. Physiol.* 243:H536–45

52. Marangos, P. J., Boulenger, J.-P., Patel, J. 1984. Effects of chronic caffeine on brain adenosine receptors: regional and ontogenic studies. *Life Sci.* 34:899–907

53. McMahon, K. K., Lesniewski, R. R., Fischer, A. G. 1983. Purine nucleoside and purine base concentrations in bovine thyroid and plasma. *Int. J. Biochem.* 15:947–52

54. Meldrum, L. A., Burnstock, G. 1983. Evidence that ATP acts as a cotransmitter with noradrenaline in sympathetic nerves supplying the guinea pig vas deferens. *Eur. J. Pharmacol.* 92:161–63

55. Mistry, G., Drummond, G. I. 1983. Heart microvessels: Presence of adenylate cyclase stimulated by catecholamines, prostaglandins, and adenosine. *Microvasc. Res.* 26:157–69

56. Moody, C. J., Burnstock, G. 1982. Evidence for the presence of P_1-purinoceptors on cholinergic nerve terminals in the guinea-pig ileum. *Eur. J. Pharmacol.* 77:1–9

57. Moody, C. J., Meghji, P., Burnstock, G. 1984. Stimulation of P_1-purinoceptors by ATP depends partly on its conversion to AMP and adenosine and partly on direct action. *Eur. J. Pharmacol.* 97:47–54

58. Osswald, H. 1983. Adenosine and renal function. See Ref. 5, pp. 399–412

59. Paton, D. M. 1981. Structure activity relations of presynaptic inhibition of noradrenergic and cholinergic transmission by adenosine: evidence for action on A_1 receptors. *J. Autonom. Pharmacol.* 1:287–90

60. Pearson, J. D., Carleton, J. S., Gordon, J. L. 1980. Metabolism of adenine nucleotides by ectoenzymes of vascular endothelial and smooth-muscle cells in culture. *Biochem. J.* 190:421–29

61. Pearson, J. D., Gordon, J. L. 1979. Vascular endothelial and smooth muscle cells in culture selectively release adenine nucleotides. *Nature* 281:384–86

62. Pearson, J. D., Slakely, L. L., Gordon, J. L. 1983. Stimulation of prostaglandin production through purinoceptors on cultured porcine endothelial cells. *Biochem. J.* 214:273–76

63. Persson, C. G. A. 1982. Universal adenosine receptor antagonism is neither necessary nor desirable with xanthine antiasthmatics. *Med. Hypothesis* 8:515–26

64. Rubio, R., Knabb, M. T., Tsukada, T., Berne, R. M. 1983. Mechanisms of action of adenosine on vascular smooth muscle and cardiac cells. See Ref. 5, pp. 319–30

65. Schwartzman, M., Raz, A. 1982. Purinergic vs. peptidergic stimulation of lipolysis and prostaglandin generation in the perfused rabbit kidney. *Biochem. Pharmacol.* 31:2453–58

66. Shimizu, K., Tanaka, S., Handa, T., Kawazoe, S., Arao, S., et al. 1983. The effect of adenosine triphosphate-magnesium chloride administration for postischemic acute renal failure (Part 1). *Folia Pharmacol. Japon.* 82:465–74

67. Silinsky, E. M. 1984. On the mechanism by which adenosine receptor activation inhibits the release of acetylcholine from motor nerve endings. *J. Physiol.* 346:243–56

68. Silinsky, E. M., Ginsborg, B. L. 1983. Inhibition of acetylcholine release from preganglionic frog nerves by ATP but not adenosine. *Nature* 305:327–28

69. Silver, P. L., Walus, K., DiSalvo, J. 1984. Adenosine-mediated relaxation and activation of cyclic AMP-dependent protein binase in coronary arterial smooth muscle. *J. Pharmacol. Exptl. Ther.* 228:342–47

70. Sneddon, P., Westfall, D. P. 1984. Pharmacological evidence that adenosine triphosphate and noradrenaline are cotransmitters in the guinea pig vas deferens. *J. Physiol.* 347:561–80

71. Spielman, W. S., Thompson, C. I. 1982. A proposed role for adenosine in the regulation of renal hemodynamics and renin release. *Am. J. Physiol.* 242:F423–35

72. Stone, T. W. 1981. Physiological roles for adenosine and adenosine 5'-triphosphate in the nervous system. *Neuroscience* 6:523–55

73. Stone, T. W. 1983. Purine receptors in the rat anococcygeus muscle. *J. Physiol.* 335:591–608

74. Su, C. 1981. Purinergic receptors in blood vessels. In *Purinergic Receptors,* ed. G. Burnstock, pp. 95–117. London: Chapman & Hill

75. Su, C. 1983. Purinergic neurotransmission and neuromodulation. *Ann. Rev. Pharmacol. Toxicol.* 23:397–411

76. Su, C. 1983. Purinergic regulation of vascular muscle tone. See Ref. 18, pp. 97–101

77. Su, C., Kamikawa, Y., Kawasaki, H., Cline, W. H. Jr. 1983. Presynaptic receptors in hypertension: Contributory to

vasoconstriction. In *Vascular Neuroeffector Mechanisms: 4th Intl. Symp.*, ed. J. A. Bevan, et al, pp. 129–32. New York: Raven

78. Su, C., Katsuragi, T. 1983. Purine release in the blood vessel wall. See Ref. 5, pp. 542–43

79. von Borstel, R. W., Wurtman, R. J., Conlay, L. A. 1983. Chronic caffeine consumption potentiates the hypotensive action of circulating adenosine. *Life Sci.* 32:1151–58

80. Wakade, A. R., Wakade, T. D. 1982. Mechanism of presynaptic actions of adenosine and acetylcholine on noradrenaline release in the guinea pig heart. *Neuroscience* 7:2267–76

81. Wakade, A. R., Wakade, T. D. 1983. Mechanism of negative feedback inhibition of norepinephrine release by alpha-adrenergic agonists. *Neuroscience* 9:673–77

82. Westfall, D. P., Hogaboom, G. K., Colby, J., O'Donnell, J. P., Fedan, J. S. 1982. Direct evidence against a role of ATP as the nonadrenergic, noncholinergic inhibitory neurotransmitter in guinea pig tenia coli. *Proc. Natl. Acad. Sci. USA* 79:7041–45

83. Whitsett, T. L., Manion, C. V., Christensen, H. D. 1984. Cardiovascular effects of coffee and caffeine. *Am. J. Cardiol.* 53:918–22

84. Williams, C. A., Forrester, T. 1983. Possible source of adenosine triphosphate released from rat myocytes in response to hypoxia and acidosis. *Cardiovasc. Res.* 17:301–12

85. Young, M. A., Merrill, G. F. 1982. Comparative effects of adenosine and nifedipine in rabbit vascular smooth muscle. *Can. J. Physiol. Pharmacol.* 61:1057–62

Ann. Rev. Physiol. 1985. 47:677–90

NUCLEOTIDE METABOLISM OF PLATELETS

Holm Holmsen

Department of Biochemistry, University of Bergen, N-5000 Bergen, Norway

PLATELETS

The smallest of the formed elements in blood are the platelets, ranging from 4–7 μ^3 in the animals investigated. They are anucleate and produced by fragmentation of the cytoplasm of the megakaryocytes in the bone marrow; their life in circulation is 5–9 days, depending on the species. Circulating or resting (unstimulated) platelets have a discoid shape and are particularly characterized by an abundance of secretory storage granules; these are subdivided by morphology and contents into dense granules, α-granules, and lysosomes. When activated in the hemostatic and thrombotic processes (initiated by a host of different stimuli), the platelets rapidly change shape from discs to spiny spheres, adhere and aggregate at the site of vascular injury, synthesize prostaglandins and thromboxanes, and secrete the contents of their granules to the extracellular environment.

The platelet responses that are activated during hemostasis and thrombosis have been extensively studied over the last two decades (35, 47). Besides the production of prostaglandins and thromboxanes as well as intracellular protein phosphorylation, the adenine nucleotide metabolism has been found to play a central role in these platelet responses. Firstly, the responses are dependent on ATP[1] availability, probably because energy is utilized both in stimulus-

---

[1] Abbreviations: ADP = adenosine-5'-diphosphate; AMP = adenosine-5'-monophosphate; ATP = adenosine-5'-triphosphate; CTP = cytidine triphosphate; EDTA = ethylenedinitrilotetraacetate; GDP = guanosine-5'-diphosphate; GMP = guanosine-5'-monophosphate; GTP = guanosine-5'-triphosphate; HPLC = high-performance liquid chomatography; IMP = inosine-5'-monophosphate; NMR = nuclear magnetic resonance; P_i = inorganic orthophosphate; PP_i = inorganic pyrophosphate; PRPP = 5'phosphoribosyl-1'-pyrophosphate; UTP = uridine triphosphate.

response coupling and to drive the individual responses. Secondly, a large fraction of the adenine nucleotides are sequestered in the dense granules and released to the environment by exocytosis during platelet secretion. Thirdly, half of the cytoplasmic ADP in platelets is bound to F-actin, and studies of this fraction have given strong evidence for actin treadmilling in an intact cell. Fourthly, ADP is a potent activator of platelet responses and its effects on platelets have been intensively studied. Fifthly, many substances cause elevation of cAMP in platelets, which is accompanied by strong inhibition of platelet responses.

Thus, the adenine nucleotides participate in many aspects of platelet physiology and biochemistry. Acid-soluble guanine, cytidine, and uridine nucleotides are also present in platelets (1, 15, 18, 29, 41, 53, 54, 59, 61) but in markedly smaller amounts than the adenine nucleotides (see Figure 2). They are poorly investigated and only some relevant information about the guanine nucleotides is available. In the present review the compartmentalization and formation/degradation of the adenine nucleotides will be discussed in detail, and the information about the guanine nucleotides is superimposed upon this organizational structure.

The adenine nucleotides exist in three physically distinct compartments in the platelet: in cytoplasm (and mitochondria), bound to F-actin (ADP only), and in the dense granules (Figure 1). The disclosure of these three compartments has been obtained by widely different approaches such as isotope techniques, secretion experiments, subcellular fractionation, study of platelets with the congenital defect "Storage Pool Deficiency," and NMR.

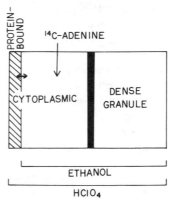

Figure 1 Pools of adenine nucleotides in platelets. A schematical representation of the three nucleotide compartments and how they are differentially extracted by $HClO_4$ and ethanol. Also shown is the distribution of ^{14}C-adenine after it has been taken up by the platelet and converted to adenine nucleotides in the cytoplasmic pool. These labeled nucleotides, as well as those labeled by ^{32}P-P_i and radioactive adenosine (see *Figure 4*), do not exchange easily with the nucleotides in the dense granule pool but equilibrate readily with the protein-bound nucleotide pool. [Taken from (64)].

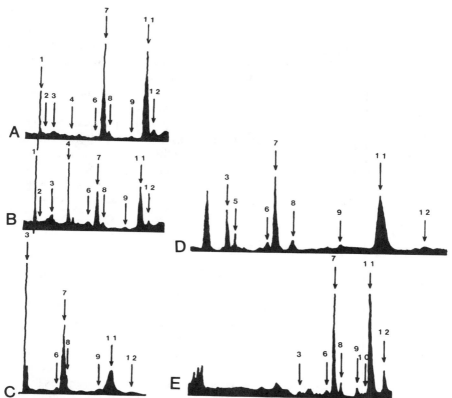

Figure 2   HPLC gradient separation of acid-soluble nucleotides in human platelets. The chromatograms show elution profiles (optical density at 254 nm) of $HClO_4$ extracts during chromatography with linear anion gradients. *A*: extracts of resting platelets in suspension; *B*: the same platelets after treatment with thrombin and sedimentation by centrifugation: Partisil-10 SAX column, 10–700 mM NaH_2PO_4 (15). *C*: extracts of frozen sediments of resting platelets: AS-Pellionex SAX, 1–1000 mM KH_2PO_4 (54). *D*: extracts of resting platelets in suspension: Reeve-Angel Partisil-10 SAX column, 2–500 mM KH_2PO_4. *E*: extracts of frozen, sedimented platelets: Partisil-10 SAX column, 1.5–1000 mM $(NH_4)H_2PO_4$ (18). The identifications of the fractions are: *1* = substances not absorbed to column (e.g. hypoxanthine, serotonin); *2* = start of gradient; *3* = AMP; *4* = IMP; *5* = GMP; *6* = UDP; *7* = ADP; *8* = GDP; *9* = UTP; *10* = CTP; *11* = ATP; *12* = GTP.

The concentrations of the adenine nucleotide have been determined by the firefly luciferin-luciferase methods (43) and by HPLC using anion gradient elution (1, 15, 18, 54, 59) and reversed phase (53). Some chromatograms with the gradient technique from various laboratories are shown in Figure 2, which clearly demonstrates the abundance of adenine nucleotides, the modest amounts of guanine nucleotides, and the negligible amounts of uridine and cytidine nucleotides. Note that the greatest relative peak area variation among the chromatograms is in the AMP peak, which probably reflects differences in the methods for nucleotide extraction. For example, it has been shown that isolation of platelets by centrifugation and freezing the pellet before extraction with $HClO_4$ gave extracts with 3–4-fold higher AMP levels than in extracts obtained by addition of cold $HClO_4$ directly to intact platelets in suspension; the increase in the AMP level corresponded to a lowering of the ATP level (Holmsen, unpublished observations). Apparently, both the physical pressure the platelets experience during centrifugation, as well as breaking the cells open by freezing and thawing before denaturing the catabolic enzymes with acid, cause breakdown of ATP to AMP. However, it is recommended to extract platelet suspensions with two volumes of EDTA-ethanol (43) precooled at $-40°C$, which gives the highest adenylate energy-charge values and preserves the F-actin ADP pool (16).

STORAGE POOL NUCLEOTIDES

The dense granules contain as much as two thirds of the total amount of adenine nucleotides in platelets. These nucleotides, consisting mainly of ATP and ADP, are secreteted to the platelets' environment upon stimulation of the cells and are absent in platelets from patients with storage pool deficiency (45, 48). Most notably, these nucleotides exchange extremely slowly with those in the cytoplasmic pool and do not participate in energy metabolism. These characteristics have been revealed by the lack of incorporation of label into the dense granule nucleotides when intact platelets are incubated with radioisotopes that readily label the cytoplasmic and actin-bound nucleotide pools in vitro; in addition, the metabolic blockers have no effect on the dense granule nucleotides. The ATP/ADP ratio in the dense granules varies greatly in platelets from different species (49) (from 0.7 in man to 5.0 in rabbit). The dense granules are 250–300 nm in diameter and dense in three respects (45): they absorb electrons in unfixed, unstained mounts that make them electron-dense per se, they are the most osmiophilic granules in platelets, and they have the highest specific weight of any platelet organelle (1.21 gm cm^3). The elemental composition of these granules has been sucessfully studied by electron probe analysis (13, 14). In platelets from all species investigated, the dense granules contain ATP, ADP, and serotonin, while the type of divalent cation (Mg and Ca) varies (14, 49). At the extremes are human platelets with almost only Ca and pig platelets with mostly Mg, whereas platelet-dense granules from other species have Ca and Mg in various proportions. Small amounts of the anions GTP, GDP, P_i and PP_i (30% of the amounts of adenine nucleotides) are also present (20). The concentration of the adenine nucleotides and divalent cation within the dense granules are extremely high, i.e. in the 1–2 M (yes, molar!) range, and the granules would be osmotically unstable were the substances in free solution. Recent studies with ^{31}P- and ^{1}H-NMR analyses (62, 63) of dense granules have revealed that the adenine nucleotides and the divalent cations form aggregates, 25,000–30,000 daltons in size. In these aggregates the purine rings of the nucleotides are apparently stacked on top of each other, 55–65 nucleotides per aggregate, and probably linked together by ring-ring interactions and bridges of divalent cations between adjacent polyphosphate groups of the nucleotide subunits. With Mg as the divalent cation (pig platelet dense granules) the aggregates are free in solution at 37°C and produce very distinguishable NMR spectra, whereas the linewidths of the resonances in the spectra increase as the temperature decreases and become indistinguishable below 15°C. Concomitant with this increase in line width, the aggregates separate out as a viscous gel. With Ca as the divalent cation (human platelet–dense granules), the aggregates seem to be an amorphous solid that does not produce NMR signals at any temperature. Our information about the molecular arrangement of the nucleotide-metal storage complex is therefore based on studies of pig platelet–dense granules (62, 63).

Serotonin, the typical amine constituent of platelet-dense granules, is not necessary for the formation of the nucleotide-metal aggregates and does not alter the properties of the aggregates to any large extent when incorporated into them. For example, treatment of piglets with subcutaneous injections of reserpine for several days reduced the serotonin content of the dense granules by 90–95%, with only minor alterations of the NMR characteristics of the aggregates (63). However, the ^{1}H-NMR studies (63) have clearly shown that serotonin is incorporated into the aggregates, positioned with some of the indole ring atoms in 1–2-Å proximity to the purine ring atoms. One can therefore envision that serotonin becomes anchored between adjacent adenosine moieties in the aggregates and with the 5-hydroxyindole ring parallel to the flat purine rings. In being incorporated between these rings, the free motion of 4,6-difluoroserotonin became completely restricted, judged by the marked increase in line width by ^{19}F-NMR (12), suggesting a strong interaction between the indole and adenine rings. It is likely that a similar mechanism is operative in the solid Ca-nucleotide complexes of human platelet–dense granules also. Obviously, the presence of nucleotides and metal in such aggregates within the dense granules explains the osmotic stability of the organelles. It is not known, however, whether the GTP and GDP in the granules can substitute for ATP and ADP or behave differently in the aggregates.

Platelets from patients with the congenital bleeding disorder storage-pool deficiency have no or very little adenine nucleotides and Ca in their dense granules (45, 48, 66). This deficiency is also found in platelets from individuals with the Chediak-Higashi syndrome (10), including numerous animal species

(50–52). Irrespective of origin, such deficient platelets do accumulate serotonin in their granules with the same initial velocity as platelets with normal stores of dense granule constituents, but the deficient platelets have markedly lower capacity for storage of serotonin. These observations suggest that the nucleotide-metal aggregates within the granules participate only in serotonin storage and not directly in granule membrane transport of the amine.

Studies with normal rabbit platelets have shown that the stored ATP in the dense granules exchange slowly with the cytoplasmic nucleotide pool, and equilibrium is obtained within 18 hr (55). In human platelets a much slower exchange was found, and the ATP entering the dense granules, determined as the thrombin-releasable pool, was partially hydrolyzed to ADP (57). Normal rabbit platelets, made storage pool–deficient by thrombin degranulation, did not regain their nucleotides by prolonged incubation in vitro or after reinfusion into the animal (56). Despite the exchange in granules with stored nucleotides, these findings indicate that a net transport of nucleotides across the dense granule membrane does not take place in circulating platelets. It is therefore likely that the nucleotides enter the dense granules at the megakaryocyte stage or during granulogenesis in these precursor cells, a mechanism supported by the finding of uranaffin-staining material in the dense granules of the megakaryocyte (48).

In the above section we have been concerned with the storage of the nucleotides and metal ions. With regard to their origin, that is, their uptake into the dense granules, very little is known. The amounts of secretable ATP correlated very well to that of ADP in platelets from 18 patients with congenital storage-pool deficiency, whereas there was no correlation of secretable nucleotides to secretable Ca (48). This was interpreted to indicate that the cause of the lack of nucleotide-Ca aggregates in the dense granules of storage pool–deficient platelets is due to absense of a functional ATP transport mechanism per se.

METABOLIC POOL NUCLEOTIDES

Soluble Fraction

The cytoplasmic compartment contains one third of the total platelet adenine and guanine nucleotides. These nucleotides are not secreted during platelet secretion (22, 27, 30, 33), are present in normal levels in platelets with storage-pool deficiency (45, 48), give distinct NMR signals (11, 64, 65), and are isotopically labeled when platelets are incubated with radioactive adenine, adenosine, and orthophosphate (30, 33). Radioactive adenine and adenosine are incorporated into the corresponding moieties of the adenine nucleotides (see Figure 4), while $^{32}P_i$ is incorporated only into the energy-rich phosphates of ATP and ADP (22, 26, 27). The ATP/ADP ratio in this compartment is 8–10, as determined by noninvasive NMR studies (65) and by experiments where the nucleotides are extracted under conditions where the binding of ADP to F-actin remains intact, e.g. extraction with organic solvents such as ethanol or acetone (16). The usual extraction of nucleotides from cells, i.e. use of acids (perchloric or trichloroacetic acids), breaks the ADP-actin bond and yield ATP/ADP ratios of 4–5. The cytoplasmic adenine nucleotides are often referred to as "metabolic" or "metabolically active" to designate that they participate in energy metabolism (2). Thus, when platelets are treated with metabolic inhibitors to an extent that they produce less ATP than they consume, the steady-state level of adenine nucleotides decrease, and this decrease is confined exclusively to the cytoplasmic pool (37, 38, 42, 65).

The content of cytoplasmic ATP and ADP is 3.3 and 0.33 μmoles per 10^{11} platelets, respectively. Considering that a human platelet is about 7 μ^3 and that the organelles occupy 30% of this volume, the platelet cytoplasm has 6.7 mM ATP and 0.67 mM ADP. Part of the cytoplasmic pool is obviously present in the mitochondria, but the size of the mitochondrial pool is not known. From labeling studies with radioactive adenine, the level of AMP in the cytoplasmic pool of resting platelets is one tenth of that of ADP, thus 0.07 mM.

The guanine nucleotides in the metabolic compartment are labeled with $^{32}P_i$ (26) and radioactive guanine with a GTP/GDP ratio in ethanol extracts of 7–10. The amounts of the guanylates is about one-eighth of that of the adenylates (H. Holmsen, unpublished observations). In platelets prelabeled with both radioactive guanine and adenine, treatment with substances that lower the adenylate level, such as formaldehyde, produces a profound conversion of ATP to IMP + hypoxanthine at low concentrations without change in the level of GTP (Figure 3A). At higher concentrations of formaldehyde the levels of cytoplasmic ATP and GTP decrease with similar time courses (Figure 3B). Thus, there is not a tight coupling of ATP and GTP utilization; the ATP level can be decreased considerably without change in te GTP level, but below a certain ATP concentration, GTP is also rapidly consumed. These results suggest that the equilibrium for nucleoside diphosphate kinase (GTP = phosphoryl donor, ADP = phosphoryl acceptor) does not favor formation of ATP.

Protein-Bound ADP

The protein-bound ADP is also of a metabolic type because it becomes radioactively labeled when the platelets are incubated with radioactive precursors (15, 16, 25). However, this protein-bound ADP is not readily available to ADP-requiring enzymes (16) and apparently does not give detectable NMR signals (64). The fact that this ADP fraction does become isotopically labeled shows that it exchanges rapidly with the cytoplasmic adenine nucleotides. Thus, actin-bound ADP has the peculiar characteristics of being metabolically unavailable but freely exchangeable. On the other hand, it is readily isolated

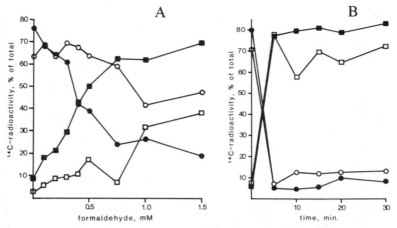

Figure 3 Formaldehyde-induced breakdown of ^{14}C-adenine and ^{14}C-guanine nucleotides in platelets. Two portions of platelet-rich plasma (32) were incubated with 0.4 μM ^{14}C(U)-adenine and 4 μM (8-^{14}C)-guanine, respectively, for 60 min at room temperature. Aliquots of each incubation mixture were then incubated at 37°C with different concentrations of formaldehyde for 10 min (*A*) and with 3 mM formaldehyde for various periods of time (*B*). EDTA-ethanol extracts (43) were made, and the radioactivity of ATP (●), IMP+hypoxanthine (■), GTP (○), and GMP+guanosine (□) were determined after their separation with high-voltage paper electrophoresis (32).

from platelets; it is present in the sediment remaining after extracting platelets with ethanol and can be solubilized from this sediment by perchloric acid. When such sediments are made from platelets prelabeled with radioactive adenine, the specific radioactivity of the sediment-bound ADP is identical to that of the cytoplasmic adenine nucleotides (15), showing that the actin-bound ADP is in complete equilibrium with the cytoplasmic adenine nucleotides. The incorporation of ^{14}C-adenine into the actin pool lags slightly behind incorporation into the cytoplasmic pool, although the maximal rate of incorporation in each pool is identical (17). From this lag it can be calculated that the ADP bound to actin, which amounts to 0.3 μmoles per 10^{11} platelets, turns over every 10 sec in resting platelets at 37°C. This rapid turnover has been explained (17, 47) by treadmilling of actin in platelets: the long F-actin oligomer (consisting of actin monomer-ADP subunits) is constantly polymerized at one end from G-actin-ATP units and depolymerized at the opposite end to free G-actin and ADP, with the same rate for polymerization and depolymerization. Thus, a significant fraction of the large amounts of actin in platelets seems to be in a constant turnover with respect to polymerization/depolymerization, and the treadmill process acts as an ATPase that accounts for about 40% of the consumption of ATP in the resting platelet.

^{32}P$_i$ is incorporated into ethanol-insoluble GDP, indicating the existence of ethanol-resistent, acid-soluble binding of exchangeable GDP to a protein (Daniel & Holmsen, unpublished observations). Such a protein could be tubulin.

NUCLEOTIDE FORMATION AND DEGRADATION

The pathways for adenine nucleotide formation and degradation by platelets are shown in Figure 4. Platelets isolated from blood do not incorporate ^{14}C-glycine into their adenine nucleotides (40), although incorporation of ^{14}C-formate has been reported (46); whether or not de novo synthesis of adenine nucleotides plays an important role in circulating platelets is therefore uncertain. Platelets readily synthesize these nucleotides from preformed adenine (60) and very slowly from hypoxanthine (58) (the so-called salvage pathway). Platelets also make adenine nucleotides from preformed adenosine (39, 61), which is usually present in plasma in submicromolar concentrations due to its high adenosine deaminase activity and the large uptake capacity of the red cells. Adenine and adenosine are converted to AMP, and its adenosine moiety is rapidly distributed among AMP, ADP, and ATP by adenylate kinase. The formation of ATP from ADP by glycolysis and oxidative phosphorylation has been discussed above. As seen in Figure 4, the degradation of adenine nucleotides starts with the deamination of AMP to IMP and ends with the formation of hypoxanthine, which diffuses out of the cell.

Adenine is transported across the platelet plasma membrane by a specific transport system (60). Once inside the cell it reacts with PRPP to yield AMP, a reaction catalyzed by the cytoplasmic adenine phosphoribosyl transferase (31, 40). The rate of the combined transport-phosphoribosylation process is apparently regulated by the intracellular concentration of PRPP (Holmsen, Robkin & Driver, unpublished observations). Phosphoribosylation is very efficient, and no free adenine is accumulated intracellularly. Thus, it is possible that the efficiency of the adenine-AMP conversion creates an outside-to-inside downhill adenine concentration gradient that drives a facilitated diffusion of adenine, although transport by group translocation cannot be excluded (19). Adenine uptake is inhibited by adenosine with a pattern not competitive with but similar to the pattern of inhibition obtained with metabolic blockers (60). It is therefore unlikely that the adenine uptake system and the high K_m adenosine uptake system, which is inhibited by adenine (see below), have anything in common.

Hypoxanthine is taken up by platelets (58) with a transport system different from that for adenine. This purine is converted to IMP by hypoxanthine/guanine phosphoribosyl transferase in the presence of PRPP; IMP is slowly converted to AMP (and GMP) as shown in Figure 4. In platelet lysates, however, hypoxanthine is converted to IMP as efficiently as adenine is con-

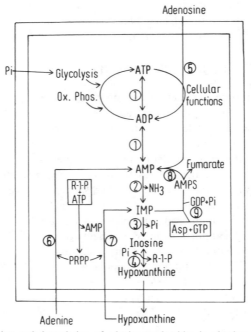

Figure 4 Formation and degradation of adenine nucleotides in platelets. The enzymes that catalyze the individual steps are indicated by the encircled numbers: *1* = Adenylate kinase; *2* = AMP aminohydrolase; *3* = 5'-Nucleotidase; *4* = Purine nucleoside phosphorylase; *5* = Adenosine kinase; *6* = Adenine phosphoribosyl transferase; *7* = Hypoxanthine/Guanine phosphoribosyl transferase; *8* = Adenylosuccinate lyase; *9* = Adenylosuccinate synthetase.

verted to AMP in the presence of PRPP (Holmsen, unpublished observations). The more than 100-fold slower phosphoribosylation of hypoxanthine than adenine by intact platelets demonstrates that this difference in conversion resides at the transport level. The uptake of hypoxanthine is markedly increased by elevating the intracellular PRPP level by treatment of the cells with H_2O_2 (36), indicating that the uptake rate is dependent on the intracellular PRPP level.

Adenosine enters the platelet by two transport mechanisms distinguished by low and high K_m and by the effect of inhibitors (61). The low K_m system transports adenosine at micromolar concentrations and is blocked by papaverine and several other pyrimidopyrimidines. At these levels adenosine is exlusively converted intracellularly to AMP by adenosine kinase in the presence of ATP (31, 39). The high-K_m system is insensitive to these blockers but is inhibited by adenine, and the main product of the transported adenosine intracellularly is inosine, formed by the cytoplasmic adenosine deaminase (31).

Radioactive guanine is taken up by platelets at the same rate as hypoxanthine and subsequently incorporated into GTP, GDP, and GMP in a 8:1:0.5 total radioactivity proportion; the rate of uptake and its K_m are markedly increased by elevation of the PRPP level intracellularly (Daniel & Holmsen, unpublished observations).

In the resting platelet the levels of the cytoplasmic nucleotides are kept fairly constant, because ATP consumption is matched by ATP production, with the individual levels of ATP, ADP, and AMP set at a 100:10:1 proportion through the adenylate kinase equilibrium. During platelet activation (5, 6, 9, 21, 24, 28, 32, 33), metabolic stress (4, 23, 24, 28, 34, 37, 38, 42), and starvation (3, 5), however, consumption exceeds production and the steady-state ATP level decreases. For reasons that are unknown, the further metabolism of the adenine nucleotides is dependent on the condition that causes consumption to exceed production. Thus, during starvation, the lowering of ATP is balanced by accumulation of ADP and, particularly, AMP. In contrast, under the two other conditions there is a slight elevation of the steady-state ADP level and little change in the AMP level, while the there is a massive, transient accumulation of IMP and subsequently of inosine with a final accumulation of hypoxanthine.

The key enzyme in this catabolic route is AMP deaminase, which irreversibly converts AMP to IMP and ammonia; the latter may increase glycolytic flux through its stimulation of phosphofructokinase. Platelet AMP deaminase has been extensively purified (7), and its regulation by substrate AMP, besides the effectors ATP, GTP, phosphate, Na^+, and K^+, has been studied in detail and found to be of a synergistic rather than an allosteric type (7, 8, 44). However, even with a detailed knowledge of the regulation of this enzyme, one can not explain why it is turned on during platelet activation and metabolic stress and turned off during starvation, when there is massive accumulation of substrate AMP and a decrease in the level of the inhibitor ATP. The persistent association of ATP-hypoxanthine conversion with platelet activation to the stage of secretion (24, 32) suggested a tight coupling of the key step in this conversion, AMP deamination, to platelet activation (24). This proved not to be the case because coformycin, a highly specific transition state analog inhibitor of AMP deaminase, failed to inhibit platelet secretion (9).

CONCLUDING REMARKS

In the present review a discussion of the participation of the nucleotides in the platelets' energy metabolism has been deleted, mainly because this participation is not special for these cells, although energy involvement in cellular responses and signal processing is perhaps better understood in platelets than in most cells (23). The existence of the large nucleotide-metal aggregates in the platelet-dense granules may be unique for platelets and represent a mechanism for storing large quantities of nucleotides in osmotically stable granules. The binding of metabolic ADP to F-actin and the simple isolation of the complex by ethanol precipitation offers a new approach to the study of actin treadmilling and the relatively unexplored area of protein-bound nucleotides in intact cells.

Literature Cited

1. Agarwal, K. C., Parks, R. E. Jr., Townsend, L. B. 1979. Adenosine analogs and human platelets. II. Inhibition of ADP-induced aggregation by carboxylic adenosine and imidazole-ring modified analogs. Significance of alterations in the nucleotide pools. *Biochem. Pharmacol.* 28:501–10

2. Akkerman, J. W. N. 1979. Regulation of carbohydrate metabolism in platelets. A review. *Thromb. Haemost.* 39:712–24

3. Akkerman, J. W. N., Gorter, G. 1980. Relation between energy production and adenine nucleotide metabolism in human blood platelets. *Biochim. Biophys. Acta* 590:107–16

4. Akkerman, J. W. N., Gorter, G., Schrama, L., Holmsen, H. 1983. A novel technique for rapid determination of energy consumption in platelets. Demonstration of different energy consumption associated with three secretory responses. *Biochem. J.* 210:145–55

5. Akkerman, J. W. N., Gorter, G., Soons, H., Holmsen, H. 1983. Close correlation between platelet responses and adenylate energy charge during transient substrate depletion. *Biochim. Biophys. Acta* 760:34–41

6. Akkerman, J. W. N., Holmsen, H., Driver, H. A. 1979. Platelet aggregation and Ca^{2+} secretion are independent of simultaneous ATP production. *FEBS Lett.* 100:286–90

7. Ashby, B., Holmsen, H. 1981. Platelet AMP deaminase. Purification and kinetic studies. *J. Biol. Chem.* 256:10519–23

8. Ashby, B., Holmsen, H. 1983. Platelet AMP deaminase: Regulation by MgATP and inorganic phosphate and inhibition by the transition state analog coformycin. *J. Biol. Chem.* 258:3668–72

9. Ashby, B., Wernick, E., Holmsen, H. 1983. Coformycin inhibition of platelet AMP deaminase has no apparent effect on energy metabolism or platelet secretion. *J. Biol. Chem.* 258:321–25

10. Boxer, G. J., Holmsen, H., Robkin, L., Bang, N. U., Boxer, L. A., Baehner, R. L. 1977. Abnormal platelet function in Chediak-Higashi syndrome. *Brit. J. Haematol.* 35:521–23

11. Carroll, R. C., Edelheit, E. B., Schmidt, P. G. 1980. Phosphorus nuclear magnetic resonance of bovine platelets. *Biochemistry* 19:3861–67

12. Costa, J. L., Dobson, C. M., Kirk, K. L., Poulsen, F. M., Valeri, C. R., Vecchione, J. J. 1979. Studies of human platelets by ^{19}F and ^{31}P NMR. *FEBS Lett.* 99:141–46

13. Costa, J. L., Fay, D. D., McGill, M. 1981. Electron probe microanalysis of calcium and phosphorus in dense bodies isolated from human platelets. *Thromb. Res.* 22:399–405

14. Costa, J. L., Smith, M. A., Tanaka, Y., Cushing, R. J. 1981. Phosphorus and divalent cations in dog, rabbit, and human platelet dense bodies as deduced from electron microprobe studies of air-dried whole mounts. *Res. Commun. Chem. Path. Pharmacol.* 32:137–45

15. Daniel, J. L., Molish, I., Holmsen, H. 1980. Radiolabeling of purine nucleotide pools as a method to distinguish among intracellular compartments: Studies on human platelets. *Biochim. Biophys. Acta* 632:444–53

16. Daniel, J. L., Robkin, L., Molish, I., Holmsen, H. 1979. Determination of the ADP concentration available to participate in energy metabolism in an actin-rich cell, the platelet. *J. Biol. Chem.* 254:7870–73

17. Daniel, J. L., Robkin, L., Salganicoff, L., Holmsen, H. 1979. Measurement of the nucleotide exchange rate as a possible determination of the cellular state of actin. In *Motility in Cell Function*, ed. F. A. Pepe, pp. 459–62. New York: Academic

18. D'Souza, L., Glueck, H. I. 1979. Measurement of nucleotide pools in platelets using high pressure liquid chromatography. *Thromb. Haem.* 38:990–1001

19. French, P. C., Sixma, J. J., Holmsen, H. 1974. The uptake of adenine into isolated platelet membranes. *Thromb. Diathes. Haemorrh.* 30:57–64

20. Fukami, M. H., Dangelmaier, C. A., Bauer, J., Holmsen, H. 1980. Secretion, subcellular localization and metabolic status of inorganic pyrophosphate in human platelets. A major constituent of the amine-storing granules. *Biochem. J.* 192:99–105

21. Fukami, M. H., Holmsen, H., Salganicoff, L. 1976. Adenine nucleotide metabolism of blood platelets. IX. Time course of secretion and changes in energy metabolism in thrombin-treated platelets. *Biochim. Biophys. Acta* 444:633–43

22. Holmsen, H. 1965. Collagen-induced release of adenosine diphosphate from blood platelets incubated with radioactive phosphate in vitro. *Scand. J. Clin. Lab. Invest.* 17:239–46

23. Holmsen, H. 1982. Biochemistry of the platelet: Energy metabolism. In *Hemostasis and Thrombosis: Basic Concepts and Clinical Practice,* ed. R. Colman, J. Hirsh, V. Marder, E. Salzman, pp. 431–43. Philadelphia: Lippincott

24. Holmsen, H. 1975. Biochemistry of the platelet release reaction. *CIBA Found. Symp.* 35(NS):175–201

25. Holmsen, H. 1972. Ethanol-insoluble adenine nucleotides in platelets and their possible role in platelet function. *Ann. NY Acad. Sci.* 201:109–21

26. Holmsen, H. 1965. Incorporation in vitro of ^{32}P into blood platelet acid-soluble organophosphates and their chromatographic identification. *Scand. J. Clin. Lab. Invest.* 17:230–38

27. Holmsen, H. 1982. Platelet secretion. See Ref. 23, pp. 390–403

28. Holmsen, H., Akkerman, J. W. N. 1980. On the requirement for ATP availability in platelet responses—a quantitative approach. In *The Regulation of Coagulation,* ed. K. G. Mann, F. B. Taylor, Jr., pp. 409–17. New York: Elsevier/North Holland

29. Holmsen, H., Dangelmaier, C. A., Akkerman, J. W. N. 1983. Determination of levels of glycolytic intermediates and nucleotides in platelets by pulse-labeling with ^{32}P-orthophosphate. *Analyt. Biochem.* 131:266–72

30. Holmsen, H., Day, H. J. 1970. The selectivity of the thrombin-induced platelet release reaction: Subcellular localization of released and retained substances. *J. Lab. Clin. Med.* 75:840–55

31. Holmsen, H., Day, H. J., Pimentel, M. A. 1969. Adenine nucleotide metabolism of blood platelets. V. Subcellular localization and kinetics of related enzymes. *Biochim. Biophys. Acta* 186:244–72

32. Holmsen, H., Day, H. J., Setkowsky, C. 1972. Secretory mechanisms: Behaviour of adenine nucleotides during platelet release reaction induced by adenosine diphosphate and adrenaline. *Biochem. J.* 129:67–82

33. Holmsen, H., Day, H. J., Storm, E. 1969. Adenine nucleotide metabolism of blood platelets. VI. Subcellular localiza-

tion of nucleotide pools with different functions in the platelet release reaction. *Biochim, Biophys. Acta* 186:254–66

34. Holmsen, H., Kaplan, K. L., Dangelmaier, C. A. 1982. Differential energy requirements for platelet responses. A simultaneous study of dense granule, alpha-granule and acid hydrolase secretion, arachidonate liberation, phosphatidyl inositol turnover and phosphatidate formation. *Biochem. J.* 208:9–18

35. Holmsen, H., Karpatkin, S. 1983. Metabolism of platelets. In *Hematology,* ed. W. J. Williams, E. Buetler, A. J. Erslev, M. A. Lichtman, 3:1149–76. New York: McGraw-Hill

36. Holmsen, H., Robkin, L. 1977. Hydrogen peroxide lowers ATP levels in platelets without altering adenylate energy charge and platelet function. *J. Biol. Chem.* 252:1752–57

37. Holmsen, H., Robkin, L. 1980. Effects of antimycin A and 2-deoxyglucose on energy metabolism in washed human platelets. *Thromb. Haem.* 42:1460–72

38. Holmsen, H., Robkin, L., Day, H. J. 1979. Effects of antimycin A and 2-deoxyglucose on secretion in washed human platelets: Differential inhibition of the secretion of acid hydrolases and adenine nucleotides. *Biochem. J.* 182:413–19

39. Holmsen, H., Rozenberg, M. C. 1968. Adenine nucleotide metabolism of blood platelets. I. Adenosine kinase and nucleotide formation from exogenous adenosine and AMP. *Biochim. Biophys. Acta* 155:326–41

40. Holmsen, H., Rozenberg, M. C. 1968. Adenine nucleotide metabolism of blood platelets. III. Adenine phosphoribosyl transferase and nucleotide formation from exogenous adenine. *Biochim. Biophys. Acta* 157:266–79

41. Holmsen, H., Salganicoff, L., Fukami, M. H. 1977. Platelet behaviour and biochemistry. In *The Biochemistry, Physiology and Pathology of Hemostasis,* ed. D. Ogston, B. Bennett, pp. 241–319. Aberdeen: Wiley & Sons

42. Holmsen, H., Setkowsky, C. A., Day, H. J. 1974. Effects of antimycin and 2-deoxyglucose on adenine nucleotides in human platelets. The role of metabolic ATP levels in primary aggregation, secondary aggregation and shape change of human platelets. *Biochem. J.* 144:385–96

43. Holmsen, H., Storm, E., Day, H. J. 1972. Microdetermination of ADP and ATP in blood platelets—a modification of the plasma method. *Analyt. Biochem.* 46:489–501

44. Holmsen, H., Østvold, A.-C., Pimentel, M. A. 1977. Properties of platelet 5'-AMP deaminase. *Thromb. Haem.* 37: 380–95

45. Holmsen, H., Weiss, H. J. 1979. Secretable storage pools in platelets. *Ann. Rev. Med.* 30:119–34

46. Jerushalmy, Z., Patya, M., Boer, P., Sperling, O. 1980. De novo synthesis of purine nucleotides in human blood platelets. *Haemostasis* 9:20–27

47. Karpatkin, S., Holmsen, H. 1983. Composition of platelets. In *Hematology,* ed. W. J. Williams, E. Buetler, A. J. Erslev, M. A. Lichtman, 3:1136–49. New York: McGraw-Hill

48. Lages, B., Holmsen, H., Weiss, H. J., Dangelmaier, C. A. 1983. Thrombin and ionophore A23187–induced dense granule secretion in storage pool deficient platelets: Evidence for impaired nucleotide storage as the primary dense granule defect. *Blood* 61:154–62

49. Meyers, K. M., Holmsen, H., Seachord, C. L. 1982. Comparative study of platelet dense granule constituents. *Am. J. Physiol.* 243:R451–61

50. Meyers, K. M., Holmsen, H., Seachord, C. L., Hopkins, G., Gorham, J. 1979. Characterization of platelets from normal mink and mink with the Chediak-Higashi syndrome. *Am. J. Hematol.* 7:137–46

51. Meyers, K. M., Holmsen, H., Seachord, C. L., Hopkins, G. E., Borchard, R. E., Padgett, G. A. 1979. Storage pool deficiency in platelets from Chediak-Higashi cattle. *Am. J. Physiol.* 237: R239–48

52. Meyers, K. M., Seachord, C. L., Holmsen, H., Prieur, D. J. 1981. Evaluation of the platelet storage pool deficiency in the feline counterpart of the Chediak-Higashi syndrome. *Am. J. Hematol.* 11:241–54

53. Rao, G. H. R., Peller, J. D., White, J. G. 1981. Rapid separation of platelet nucleotides by reversed-phase, isocratic, high-performance liquid chromatography with radially compressed column. *J. Chromat.* 226:466–70

54. Rao, G. H. R., White, J. G., Jachimowicz, A. A., Witkop, C. J. 1974. Nucleotide profiles of normal and abnormal platelets by high-pressure liquid chromatography. *J. Lab. Clin. Med.* 81:839–50

55. Reimers, H. J., Mustard, J. F., Packham, M. A. 1975. Transfer of adenine nucleotides between the releasable and nonreleasable compartments of rabbit blood platelets. *J. Cell Biol.* 67:61–71

56. Reimers, H. J., Packham, M. A., Kinlough-Rathbone, R. L., Mustard, J. F. 1977. Adenine nucleotides in thrombin-degranulated platelets: Effect of prolonged circulation in vivo. *J. Lab. Clin. Med.* 90:490–501

57. Reimers, H. J., Packham, M. A., Mustard, J. F. 1977. Labeling of the releasable adenine nucleotides of washed human platelets. *Blood* 49:89–99

58. Rivard, G. E., Brunst, R. F., McLaren, E. T. 1975. Incorporation of hypoxanthine into adenine and guanine nucleotides by human platelets. *Biochim. Biophys. Acta* 381:144–55

59. Scholar, E. M., Brown, P. R., Parks, R. E. Jr., Calabresi, P. 1973. Nucleotide profiles of the formed elements of human blood determined by high-pressure liquid chromatography. *Blood* 41:927–36

60. Sixma, J. J., Trieshnigg, A. M., Holmsen, H. 1973. Adenine nucleotide metabolism of blood platelets. VIII. Mechanism of adenine uptake by intact cells. *Biochim. Biophys. Acta* 298:3–16

61. Sixma, J. J., Lips, J. P. M., Trieschnigg, A.-M., Holmsen, H. 1976. Transport and metabolism of adenosine in human blood platelets. *Biochim. Biophys. Acta* 443:253–56

62. Ugurbil, K., Fukami, M. H., Holmsen, H. 1984. ^{31}P-NMR studies of nucleotide storage in the dense granules of pig platelets. *Biochemistry* 23:409–16

63. Ugurbil, K., Fukami, M. H., Holmsen, H. 1984. Proton NMR studies of nucleotide and amine storage in the dense granules of pig platelets. *Biochemistry* 23:416–28

64. Ugurbil, K., Holmsen, H. 1981. Nucleotide compartmentation: radioisotopic and nuclear magnetic studies. In *Platelets in Biology and Pathology,* ed. J. L. Gordon, 2:147–77. New York: North Holland Biomedical. 511 pp.

65. Ugurbil, K., Holmsen, H., Shulman, R. G. 1979. Adenine nucleotide storage pools and secretion in platelets as studied by ^{31}P nuclear magnetic resonance. *Proc. Nat. Acad. Sci. USA* 76:2227–31

66. Weiss, H. J. 1980. Congenital disorders of platelet function. *Sem. Hematol.* 17: 228–41

Ann. Rev. Physiol. 1985. 47:691–705

PURINE SALVAGE PATHWAYS IN MYOCARDIUM

John P. Manfredi and Edward W. Holmes

Departments of Medicine and Biochemistry, Duke University, Durham, North Carolina 27710

INTRODUCTION

The biochemical routes through which preformed purine bases and nucleosides are returned to nucleotide pools constitute the purine salvage pathways. In the steady state these salvage pathways, together with the de novo pathway through which purine nucleotides are synthesized from nonpurine precursors, balance the continual loss of purine nucleotides during normal metabolic activity. In myocardium the salvage pathways may be the predominant means by which the purine nucleotide pools are maintained: isolated rat hearts, for instance, synthesize purine nucleotides de novo at 0.02 nmol/min/gm heart (107), while the rates of salvage can be expected to be at least ten-fold higher (61).

Purine salvage in this review refers specifically to the conversion of a purine nucleoside or base to a nucleotide by a single enzyme. The enzymes capable of synthesizing nucleotides from nucleosides and bases are designated salvage enzymes. The salvage pathways will be considered in terms of the substrates and products of these salvage enzymes. In the first section, we will describe the metabolism of purine nucleosides and bases by the salvage enzymes and other, possibly competing enzymes. The second section will be devoted to the enzymatic routes by which the substrates of salvage are produced. In the final section we will consider the possible metabolic fates of the salvaged purines. The biochemical pathways associated with purine salvage are outlined in Figure 1.

0066-4278/85/0315-0691$02.00

691

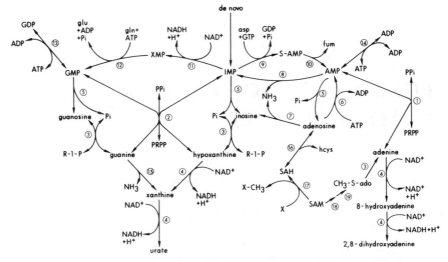

Figure 1   Biochemical pathways associated with purine salvage in mammalian myocardium. "De novo" refers to the synthesis of IMP from nonpurine precursors. Enzymes catalyzing the labeled reactions are: ① adenine phosphoribosyltransferase (EC 2.4.2.7); ② hypoxanthine-guanine phosphoribosyltransferase (EC 2.4.2.8); ③ purine nucleoside phosphorylase (EC 2.4.2.1); ④ xanthine oxidase (EC 1.2.3.2); ⑤ 5'-nucleotidase (EC 3.1.3.5); ⑥ adenosine kinase (EC 2.7.1.20); ⑦ adenosine deaminase (EC 3.5.4.4); ⑧ AMP deaminase (EC 3.5.4.6); ⑨ S-AMP synthetase (EC 6.3.4.4); ⑩ S-AMP lyase (EC 4.3.2.2); ⑪ IMP dehydrogenase (EC 1.2.1.14); ⑫ GMP synthetase (EC 6.3.4.1); ⑬ guanylate kinase (EC 2.7.4.8); ⑭ adenylate kinase (EC 2.7.4.3); ⑮ guanine deaminase (EC 3.5.4.3); ⑯ SAH hydrolase (EC 3.3.1.1); ⑰ homocysteine methyltransferase (EC 2.1.1.10); ⑱ SAM decarboxylase (EC 4.1.1.50); ⑲ aminopropyltransferase (EC 2.5.1.16); ⑳ methylthioadenosine phosphorylase. Reactions catalyzed by xanthine oxidase are written as dehydrogenations, because xanthine oxidase is believed to function as a dehydrogenase in situ (7). Abbreviations: glu, glutamate; gln, glutamine; asp, aspartate; fum, fumarate; Pi, orthophosphate; PPi, pyrophosphate; R-1-P, ribose-1-phosphate; PRPP, 5-phosphoribosyl-1-pyrophosphate; hyc, homocysteine; S-AMP, adenylsuccinate; SAH, S-adenosylhomocysteine; SAM, S-adenosylmethionine; CH_3-S-ado, 5'-methylthioadenosine; X, a methyl group acceptor.

SALVAGE ENZYMES AND METABOLISM OF THEIR SUBSTRATES

Hypoxanthine-Guanine Phosphoribosyltransferase (HGPRT)

Hypoxanthine and guanine are salvaged by HGPRT. HGPRT catalyzes the reversible reaction hypoxanthine (guanine) + PRPP $\rightleftarrows$ IMP (GMP) + PPi, where PRPP signifies 5-phosphoribosyl-1-pyrophosphate, and PPi represents pyrophosphate. Although the enzyme in myocardium has not been extensively studied, the enzyme from other tissues has been found to have the following general characteristics. Its affinities for hypoxanthine and guanine are approximately equal (43, 44) and nearly 1000-fold greater than its affinity for xanthine (40, 43). The equilibrium of the reaction heavily favors nucleotide synthesis, and the enzyme from all tissues exhibits relatively weak pyrophosphorolytic activity (43, 44). As a result, the enzyme can be expected normally to salvage cellular hypoxanthine and guanine to purine nucleotides. Apparent K_ms for guanine range from 1.8 to 4.0 µM among various mammalian tissues, whereas those for hypoxanthine range from 2.4 to 11.0 µM (42–44, 57, 58). PRPP is the sole compound capable of donating the ribose-5-phosphate moiety for IMP synthesis; the apparent K_m for PRPP ranges from 2.4 to 240 µM for the enzyme from different tissues (29, 42, 58, 59). Although the products IMP, GMP, and PPi can inhibit the enzyme (25, 29, 43, 58), the inhibitory constants of each are sufficiently high to suggest that none would be a physiologic effector of the enzyme.

Although the myocardial enzyme has not been isolated, it has been assayed in crude homogenates of heart (25, 26, 42, 57, 65, 75, 102). However, it is risky in the absence of more information to ascribe an enzyme activity in myocardial homogenates to myocytes. In the case of HGPRT, cultured rat myocytes exhibit substantial HGPRT activity (75). This suggests that HGPRT activity in homogenates reflects the enzyme in myocytes, despite the observation that coronary endothelial cells [which comprise only 2–4% of myocardial weight (2, 53)] contain three-fold greater HGPRT activity than myocardium (64). In contrast, the activity of certain other enzymes in crude homogenates can be ascribed, not to the myocytes, but to the coronary endothelium (see below).

Metabolism of Hypoxanthine

Metabolism of cytosolic hypoxanthine could depend on three presumably competing processes: ribosylation by purine nucleoside phosphorylase, degradation by xanthine oxidase, and phosphoribosylation by HGPRT. Although the ribosylation of hypoxanthine by purine nucleoside phosphorylase has not been specifically measured in hearts, incidental results suggest that it is not an important metabolic route: hearts perfused with radiolabeled hypoxanthine neither accumulate (61) nor release (28) significant amounts of radiolabeled inosine. These results cannot be explained by rapid phosphorylation of inosine produced from hypoxanthine, because heart lacks inosine kinase activity (12, 100). Rather, the results are consistent with the concept that purine nucleoside phosphorylase normally functions in situ to phosphorolyze inosine to hypoxanthine, presumably because of the low concentration of ribose-1-phosphate relative to inorganic phosphate. It should also be noted that purine nucleoside phosphorylase activity is not found in myocytes (8, 24, 77, 79) but it is present in coronary endothelial cells (8, 63, 77, 79). It may be concluded that purine nucleoside phosphorylase cannot be a determinant of hypoxanthine removal in myocytes and is an unlikely determinant in nonparenchymal cells.

Xanthine oxidase may also be excluded from myocardial cells. Antibodies raised against xanthine oxidase from milk lipid globules were used to localize the enzyme exclusively to the endothelial cells of bovine heart (37). This study admits the possibility that the low levels of xanthine oxidase activity measured in myocardial homogenates (52, 98) reflects its exclusive presence in endothelium. If this is true, hypoxanthine metabolism in myocytes is restricted to phosphoribosylation via HGPRT, and myocardial production of xanthine and urate is restricted to the endothelium. Such compartmentation of xanthine oxidase provides one explanation for the observation that the bulk of radiolabeled hypoxanthine administered to isolated rat hearts is degraded through xanthine oxidase (28). In the absence of compartmentation this result would be paradoxical, because (a) in rat myocardial homogenates, the activity of HGPRT is more than 200-fold greater than xanthine oxidase (52), and (b) the affinities of the two enzymes for hypoxanthine should be similar, because xanthine oxidase from a number of tissues shows K_m values ranging from 2 to 20 μM (18, 27, 46, 85, 86, 98). If xanthine oxidase is indeed confined to endothelium, preferential catabolism of exogenous hypoxanthine to xanthine and urate could simply reflect the location of endothelium between myocytes and vascular space.

Salvage of cytosolic hypoxanthine by HGPRT may therefore be the only metabolic fate of this purine base in myocytes, and it can be expected to be an important metabolic fate of hypoxanthine in nonparenchymal cells. Phosphoribosylation of hypoxanthine by HGPRT is the route by which exogenous hypoxanthine is incorporated into the myocardial purine nucleotide pool (28, 50, 94, 100). The concentration of PRPP available to HGPRT may be the major factor determining rates of hypoxanthine salvage in isolated rat hearts (28), as has been found in primary cultures of rat skeletal myoblasts (110), in cultured human fibroblasts (111), and in rat hepatoma cells (103).

Metabolism of Guanine

Guanine metabolism in heart has been scarcely studied. Nonetheless, we can presume that the metabolic fate of intracellular guanine might depend on three processes: ribosylation via purine nucleoside phosphorylase, deamination via guanine deaminase, and phosphoribosylation via HGPRT. As is the case for hypoxanthine, purine nucleoside phosphorylase is not likely an important route for guanine removal; it most likely functions to produce guanine by phosphorolysis of guanosine (71). In contrast, guanine deaminase may be an important catabolic enzyme, as is found in rat liver, kidney, and brain (45). Salvage of guanine by HGPRT can also be expected to be an important metabolic fate of guanine, and the rate of salvage should be heavily influenced by the concentration of PRPP.

Adenine Phosphoribosyltransferase (APRT)

Adenine is salvaged by APRT, which catalyzes the reversible reaction adenine + PRPP $\rightleftarrows$ AMP + PPi. Although the enzyme from heart has not been extensively studied, the enzyme from other tissues has been found to possess the following general characteristics. Like HGPRT, the enzyme has relatively weak pyrophosphorolytic activity, and the equilibrium of the reaction strongly favors nucleotide synthesis (33). APRT shows no activity with hypoxanthine or guanine as substrate (92), and PRPP is the only effective sugar donor (23). The enzyme shows an absolute requirement for divalent cations for activity, with Mg^{++} being the most effective (32). Both AMP and PPi inhibit the forward reaction (88), but this is of questionable physiologic significance. APRT will also phosphoribosylate 4-aminoimidazole-5-carboxamide (19), thereby providing a means by which this compound can be introduced into the purine de novo synthetic pathway (93).

Metabolism of Adenine

Myocardial adenine may be metabolized by xanthine oxidase and APRT. It is unlikely that myocardial purine nucleoside phosphorylase could also metabolize adenine, because the enzyme from a number of tissues displays an extremely low affinity for adenine (108). Xanthine oxidase, on the other hand, has been shown to metabolize adenine to 2,8-dihydroxyadenine (105). Although oxidation of adenine to 2,8-dihydroxyadenine has not been shown to occur in heart, the presence of xanthine oxidase in myocardium (52, 98) suggests that this is a possible metabolic route. If, as mentioned above, xanthine oxidase is restricted to endothelial cells, adenine in myocytes will be metabolized exclusively via APRT. In this case, competition between xanthine oxidase and APRT will be confined to endothelial cells.

Regardless of compartmentation of xanthine oxidase, cytosolic adenine can be expected to be salvaged by APRT in both the myocytes and the nonparenchymal cells of the heart. Indeed, the activity of APRT in hearts, which is substantial (16, 52), has been exploited for labeling the adenine nucleotide pool in numerous studies in which hearts are perfused with radiolabeled adenine (e.g. 61, 94, 106). Interpretation of such studies may be complicated by the four-fold greater activity of APRT in coronary endothelium than in myocardium (64) and the three-fold greater adenine nucleotide concentration in endothelial cells compared to myocardium as a whole (65). Although the endothelium accounts for only 2–4% of the mass of the heart (2, 53), such unequal distributions of APRT and adenine nucleotides admit the possibility that the adenine nucleotide pool of the endothelium is disproportionately labeled during perfusion with radioactive adenine.

As with hypoxanthine, the rate at which adenine can be salvaged depends largely on the cytosolic concentration of PRPP. Thus, experimental maneuvers intended to increase the concentration of PRPP available to APRT result in accelerated incorporation of exogenous adenine into myocardial adenine nucleotides (106). The concentration of PRPP may therefore be a limiting factor in myocardial salvage of adenine as well as hypoxanthine.

Adenosine Kinase

Adenosine is salvaged by adenosine kinase. Adenosine kinase is a cytosolic enzyme (12, 84) that catalyzes the reaction adenosine + ATP $\rightleftarrows$ AMP + ADP. The enzyme in heart is kinetically similar to the enzymes in other tissues. It has an absolute requirement for Mg^{++} for activity, probably reflecting that Mg ATP rather than unchelated ATP is the true substrate for the enzyme (10). Both free Mg and free ATP can inhibit the enzyme (10, 69). Reported K_m values for adenosine range from 0.3 to 0.5 μM for the partially purified enzyme (10, 13) and from 0.4 to 1.1 μM for crude preparations of the enzyme (3, 62, 69, 84). Its K_m value for Mg ATP is 0.1 μM (10). Adenosine inhibits the enzyme at concentrations above 2 μM (3, 66). Although inhibition of the myocardial enzyme by ADP and AMP has not been examined, adenosine kinase in other tissues is inhibited by these nucleotides (55, 70).

Metabolism of Adenosine

The metabolic fate of cytosolic adenosine will depend on three enzymes: S-adenosylhomocysteine (SAH) hydrolase, adenosine deaminase, and adenosine kinase. Adenosine, unlike inosine, would not be expected to be phosphorolyzed in heart, because adenosine is an extremely poor substrate for purine nucleoside phosphorylase in other tissues (48, 49, 108). Indeed, no evidence for adenine production could be detected in isolated hearts perfused with adenosine (61, 99). SAH hydrolase, on the other hand, provides a means for removing intracellularly generated adenosine (82). The enzyme is present in the cytosolic fraction of guinea-pig hearts with maximal activities comparable to soluble 5'-nucleotidase and adenosine kinase (82, 84). However, in slices of rat hippocampus, which contains substantial SAH hydrolase activity (9, 80), adenosine incorporation into SAH is normally very low (76). Furthermore, in this preparation an increase in adenosine concentration without a concomitant rise in homocysteine concentration does not significantly increase metabolism of adenosine via SAH hydrolase (76). If heart is similar to brain in this respect, removal of adenosine via SAH hydrolase is not an important metabolic route. This does not, however, address the importance of SAH as a route for production of adenosine (see below).

Adenosine deaminase is another cytosolic enzyme (69, 84) that degrades adenosine. The enzyme is in substantially lower concentrations in guinea-pig coronary endothelium than myocardium, suggesting that deamination of adenosine may be largely relegated to myocytes (65). The activity of adenosine deaminase in dog heart was found to be approximately 50-fold higher than adenosine kinase (69). But the 110-fold lower K_m value of the kinase, together with inhibition of the kinase at high adenosine concentrations, provide an explanation for the preferential phosphorylation of exogenous adenosine at low concentrations and its deamination at high concentrations in blood-perfused dog hearts in situ (69). In contrast, exogenous adenosine has been reported to be mostly deaminated even at low concentrations in isolated, buffer-perfused rat hearts (11). If one assumes blood- and buffer-perfused preparations are not different, the apparent discrepancy between these studies might be explained on the basis of differences in enzyme activities and kinetics among species. For example, the activity of adenosine deaminase relative to adenosine kinase is about 0.3 for mouse heart and 7.0 for rat heart (3); the relative K_m values of the two myocardial enzymes are virtually identical in the two species (3). The metabolic fate of exogenous adenosine may therefore be expected to depend on the species unless demonstrated otherwise.

In all species examined, phosphorylation of adenosine by adenosine kinase is the predominant route by which the purine base of administered adenosine is incorporated into myocardial nucleotides (26, 50, 61, 99). Inhibition of adenosine kinase in situ results in virtually complete inhibition of adenosine incorporation into myocardial purine nucleotides (66). Unlike adenosine, inosine is not phosphorylated in heart (100), and no inosine kinase activity can be detected in homogenates of heart (12).

Guanosine Kinase

Myocardial tissue has not been assayed for guanosine kinase activity. Although a small amount of guanosine kinase activity has been detected in crude homogenates of some nonmyocardial tissues (5, 81), this may actually reflect the combined activities of purine nucleoside phosphorylase and HGPRT (1). If guanosine kinase activity exists, it is not widespread, because some studies have failed to detect any activity in homogenates of other tissues (22, 54). Isolation of a nucleoside kinase specific for guanosine has not been reported, suggesting that phosphorylation of guanosine, if it occurs, would proceed via another, relatively nonspecific, nucleoside kinase. Adenosine kinase, however, is virtually inactive with guanosine as substrate (49, 56). Also, hearts lack inosine kinase activity (12, 100). In myocardium, therefore, no enzymatic mechanism for guanosine phosphorylation is apparent, suggesting that myocardial guanosine is not likely salvaged.

Metabolism of Guanosine

The probable absence of guanosine kinase activity in heart implies that phosphorolysis by purine nucleoside phosphorylase is the only significant metabolic fate of myocardial guanosine. Guanosine is a substrate for purine nucleoside phosphorylase isolated from a variety of tissues (71). The myocardial enzyme can account for the appearance of large quantities of radiolabeled guanine in the effluent perfusate of isolated rabbit hearts perfused with labeled guanosine (94). Significant accumulation of label in the guanine nucleotide pool was observed in this study, presumably reflecting the combined activities of purine nucleoside phosphorylase and HGPRT. It is noteworthy that, despite the substantial production of labeled guanine from the infused guanosine, there was no detectable accumulation of the free base in the heart (94). This can be explained in terms of compartmentation of myocardial purine nucleoside phosphorylase in the blood vessel wall.

PRODUCTION OF SUBSTRATES OF SALVAGE

Production of Hypoxanthine and Guanine

The production of both hypoxanthine and guanine can be accounted for by the activity of myocardial purine nucleoside phosphorylase. The importance of myocardial HGPRT in the production of bases seems unlikely in view of the low activity of the enzyme from other tissues with IMP or GMP as substrate (33, 43, 44); that is, the enzyme has low pyrophosphorolytic activity. Accordingly, because much evidence indicates that purine nucleoside phosphorylase is absent in myocytes (8, 24, 77, 79) but present in endothelium and other cells of the vessel wall (8, 63, 77, 79), production of purine bases in myocardium may be confined to the blood vessel wall.

Production of Adenine

It is not clear how adenine is produced in mammalian cells. Like other mammalian tissues, myocardium does not produce appreciable adenine from adenosine via purine nucleoside phosphorylase (50). The weak pyrophosphorolytic activity of APRT (33) argues against it producing adenine. In some cells, however, adenine can be produced in significant quantities by phosphorolysis of 5'-methylthioadenosine, a metabolite of S-adenosylmethionine (39, 73). The possibility that this enzyme generates adenine in myocardium under normal conditions or during ischemia—when the adenine content of myocardium rises substantially (16)—remains untested.

Production of Adenosine

Adenosine may be produced by S-adenosylhomocysteine (SAH) hydrolase and 5'-nucleotidase. Although the equilibrium of the reaction catalyzed by SAH hydrolase strongly favors synthesis of SAH (14), metabolism of intracellular adenosine by adenosine deaminase and adenosine kinase and metabolism of homocysteine to cystathionine and methionine can be expected to maintain sufficiently low adenosine and homocysteine concentrations to effect continual hydrolysis of SAH. SAH accumulates in various nonmyocardial cells exposed to inhibitors of SAH hydrolase (4, 41, 109), suggesting that catabolism of SAH via SAH hydrolase indeed occurs under normal conditions. Adenosine production via SAH hydrolase has been suggested as a possible route for adenosine production in hypoxic hearts (84). The magnitude of the flux through SAH in hearts has not been measured, however, and the cellular distribution of the myocardial enzyme is unknown.

Adenosine may also be produced by 5'-nucleotidase. Although the membrane-bound 5'-nucleotidase has been thought to metabolize intracellular mononucleotides (20, 21, 78, 83), recent studies indicate the participation of a soluble 5'-nucleotidase in adenosine production in myocytes (84) and in other cell types (17, 35, 36, 67, 96, 104). These studies suggest that the membrane-bound 5'-nucleotidase, which may be exclusively an ecto-enzyme in heart (30) as is true in certain other tissues (15, 67), is dedicated to the hydrolysis of extracellular mononucleotides. However, the dichotomy between intracellular metabolism by a soluble enzyme and extracellular metabolism by a membrane-bound enzyme may be oversimplified. Two classes of membrane-bound 5'-nucleotidase have been described in sarcolemmal vesicles enriched in right-side-out and inside-out orientations, suggesting that a fraction of membrane-bound 5'-nucleotidase may face the cytosol and hydrolyze intracellular mononucleotides (47).

Production of Guanosine

The enzymes potentially involved in guanosine production are purine nucleoside phosphorylase and 5'-nucleotidase. Although guanosine can be produced by purine nucleoside phosphorylase, the myocardial enzyme probably functions to phosphorylyze rather than generate guanosine, as is likely for inosine (71). 5'-Nucleotidase may therefore provide the predominant route through which guanosine is produced in myocardium. This will be particularly true for myocytes if purine nucleoside phosphorylase is restricted to endothelium.

The membrane-bound form of 5'-nucleotidase isolated from rat myocardium has about equal capacities for metabolism of GMP and IMP, which are about half the capacity for AMP hydrolysis (60). The soluble 5'-nucleotidase assayed in homogenates of guinea-pig hearts shows activities with GMP that are about 50% greater than with IMP but only 78% of the activity observed wth AMP (84). These results indicate that both the membrane-bound and soluble 5'-nucleotidase can produce guanosine.

METABOLISM OF PRODUCTS OF SALVAGE

Metabolism of IMP

The fate of IMP formed from the salvage of hypoxanthine by HGPRT will be determined by three enzymes: adenylosuccinate synthetase, IMP dehydrogenase, and 5'-nucleotidase. Adenylosuccinate synthetase catalyzes the conversion of IMP to adenylosuccinate, which can then be converted to AMP via adenylosuccinate lyase. A single study of a crude preparation of the rat myocardial enzyme reports K_m values of 167, 308, and 18 μM for its three substrates IMP, aspartate, and GTP, respectively (52). Although the enzyme in other tissues has been shown to be influenced by several purine nucleotides (89), regulation of the myocardial enzyme has not been studied.

Myocardial IMP dehydrogenase is also uncharacterized. In other tissue, IMP dehydrogenase exhibits lower K_m and equal or higher V_{max} values than adenylosuccinate synthetase (31, 95, 97). If heart is similar in this respect, IMP dehydrogenase can be expected to be tightly controlled, because about 80% of exogenous hypoxanthine incorporated into purine nucleotides appears in the adenine nucleotide pool while 20% appears in the guanine nucleotide pool (28). Cellular compartmentation of adenylosuccinate synthetase or IMP dehydrogenase could also account for a greater incorporation of infused hypoxanthine into adenine than into guanine nucleotides.

Another possible fate of IMP is degradation by cytosolic 5'-nucleotidase to inosine and inorganic phosphate. As discussed in relation to adenosine production, the relative roles of membrane-bound and soluble 5'-nucleotidase in the metabolism of intracellular mononucleotides are unclear. The issue is further clouded by a lack of knowledge about the cellular distribution of the two forms of 5'-nucleotidase. Yet it seems reasonable to presume that in myocytes as in human lymphoblasts (30, 101), intracellular IMP can be degraded to inosine. The only possible fate of the cytosolic inosine thus formed is transport out of the myocyte, because myocytes lack both purine nucleoside phosphorylase (8, 24, 77, 79) and inosine kinase (12, 100). Thus, an inosinate cycle (IMP $\rightarrow$ INO $\rightarrow$ HYPO $\rightarrow$ IMP) like that described in lymphoblasts (101) cannot be expected to exist in myocytes.

Metabolism of GMP

GMP may be consumed by guanylate kinase or 5'-nucleotidase. No evidence has been found for the existence of myocardial GMP reductase, an enzyme that converts GMP to IMP. In isolated hearts perfused with labeled guanosine, for instance, no radioactivity could be detected in IMP or the adenine nucleotide pool, despite significant labeling of guanine nucleotides (94). Nor would HGPRT be expected to provide an important route for catabolism of GMP in view of its weak activity with nucleotides as substrates. Guanylate kinase, on the other hand, provides a means by which substrate entering the GMP pool from guanine via HGPRT or from IMP via IMP dehydrogenase and GMP synthetase can be phosphorylated to high-energy guanine nucleotides. Thus, the expansion of the myocardial GTP pool following maneuvers that accelerate synthesis of IMP (90) reflects the activity of guanylate kinase. The participation of 5'-nucleotidase in the metabolism of GMP is discussed above in the context of guanosine production.

Metabolism of AMP

The fate of AMP will be determined by myokinase, 5'-nucleotidase, and AMP deaminase. Whereas myokinase provides a route by which salvaged bases and nucleosides can be converted to high-energy nucleotides, 5'-nucleotidase and AMP deaminase provide catabolic paths for draining the adenine nucleotide pool. The soluble 5'-nucleotidase isolated from rat liver has been shown to accelerate AMP hydrolysis as adenylate energy charge is lowered over the physiologic range (35). Similar behavior is indicated for the soluble 5'-nucleotidase isolated from rat hearts (51). But the relative importance of soluble and membrane-bound 5'-nucleotidase in the metabolism of cytosolic AMP, as with IMP and GMP, remains uncertain in light of the possible existence of a membrane-bound form on the inner sarcolemmal surface (47).

AMP deaminase is present in heart (6, 68, 87, 91) and, like myokinase and 5'-nucleotidase, is likely present in myocytes (64, 65). The enzyme can account for the small increase in IMP both in rat myocytes subjected to anaerobiosis in the absence of glucose (24) and in rat (74, 78) and rabbit (34) hearts made globally ischemic. However, the failure to observe significant IMP accumulation in dog hearts made globally ischemic (38, 78, 90) and in ischemic rat hearts in some instances (24) suggests the existence of some factor that can prevent substantial IMP production or accumulation during accelerated energy depletion.

Literature Cited

1. Anderson, E. P. 1973. Nucleoside and nucleotide kinases. In *The Enzymes,* ed. P. D. Boyer, 9:49–96. New York: Academic. 586 pp.
2. Anversa, P., Olivetti, G., Melissari, M., Loud, A. V. 1980. Stereological measurement of cellular and subcellular hypertrophy and hyperplasia in the papillary muscle of the adult rat. *J. Mol. Cell. Cardiol.* 12:781–95
3. Arch, J. R. S., Newsholme, E. A. 1978. Activities and some properties of 5'-nucleotidase, adenosine kinase, and adenosine deaminase in tissues from vertebrates and invertebrates in relation to the control of the concentration and physiological role of adenosine. *Biochem. J.* 174:965–77
4. Bader, J. P., Brown, N. R., Chiang, P. K., Cantoni, G. L. 1978. 3-Deazaadenosine, an inhibitor of adenosylhomocysteine hydrolase, inhibits reproduction of Rous sarcoma virus and trans-

formation of chick embryo cells. *Virology* 89:888–94
5. Barankiewicz, J., Jezewska, M. M., Chomczynski, P. 1975. Purine salvage in mammary glands of mice. *FEBS Lett.* 60:384–87
6. Barsacchi, R., Ranieri-Raggi, M., Bergamini, C., Raggi, A. 1979. Adenylate metabolism in the heart. Regulatory properties of rabbit cardiac adenylate deaminase. *Biochem. J.* 182:361–66
7. Battelli, M. G., Della Corte, E., Stirpe, F. 1972. Xanthine oxidase type D (dehydrogenase) in the intestine and other organs of the rat. *Biochem. J.* 126:747–49
8. Borgers, M., Schaper, J., Schaper, W. 1972. Nucleoside phosphorylase activity in blood vessels and formed elements of the blood of the dog. *J. Histochem. Cytochem.* 20:1041–48
9. Broch, O. J., Ueland, P. M. 1980. Regional and subcellular distribution of S-

adenosylhomocysteine hydrolase in the adult rat brain. *J. Neurochem.* 35:484–88

10. deJong, J. W. 1977. Partial purification and properties of rat-heart adenosine kinase. *Arch. Int. Physiol. Biochim.* 85:557–69

11. deJong, J. W. 1972. Phosphorylation and deamination of adenosine by the isolated, perfused rat heart. *Biochim. Biophys. Acta* 286:252–59

12. deJong, J. W., Kalkman, C. 1973. Myocardial adenosine kinase: Activity and localization determined with a rapid, radiometric assay. *Biochim. Biophys. Acta* 320:388–96

13. deJong, J. W., Keijzer, E., Uitendaal, M. P., Harmsen, E. 1980. Further purification of adenosine kinase from rat heart using affinity and ion-exchange chromatography. *Anal. Biochem.* 101:407–12

14. de la Haba, G., Cantoni, G. L. 1959. The enzymatic synthesis of S-adenosyl-L-homocysteine from adenosine and homocysteine. *J. Biol. Chem.* 234:603–8

15. DePierre, J. W., Karnorsky, M. L. 1974. Ecto-enzymes of the guinea pig polymorphonuclear leukocyte. *J. Biol. Chem.* 249:7111–20

16. Deuticke, B., Gerlach, E., Dierkesmann, R. 1966. Abbau freier nucleotide in herz, skeletmuskel, gehirn und leber der ratte bei sauerstoffmangel. *Pfleugers Arch.* 292:239–54

17. Edwards, N. L., Recker, D., Manfredi, J., Rembecki, R., Fox, I. H. 1982. Regulation of purine metabolism by plasma membrane and cytoplasmic 5'-nucleotidase. *Am. J. Physiol.* 243:C270–77

18. Elion, G. B. 1966. Enzymatic and metabolic studies with allopurinol. *Ann. Rheum. Dis.* 25:608–14

19. Flaks, J. G., Erwin, M. J., Buchanan, J. M. 1957. Biosynthesis of the purines. XVI. *J. Biol. Chem.* 228:201–13

20. Frick, G. P., Lowenstein, J. M. 1976. Studies of 5'-nucleotidase in the perfused rat heart. *J. Biol. Chem.* 251:6372–78

21. Frick, G. P., Lowenstein, J. M. 1978. Vectorial production of adenosine by 5'-nucleotidase in the perfused rat heart. *J. Biol. Chem.* 253:1240–44

22. Friedmann, T., Seegmiller, J. E., Subak-Sharpe, J. H. 1969. Evidence against the existence of guanosine and inosine kinases in human fibroblasts in tissue culture. *Exp. Cell. Res.* 56:425–29

23. Gadd, R. E. A., Henderson, J. F. 1970. Studies of the binding of phosphoribosylpyrophosphate to adenine phosphoribosyltransferase. *J. Biol. Chem.* 245:2979–84

24. Geisbuhler, T., Altschuld, R. A., Trewyn, R. W., Ansel, A. Z., Lamka, K., Brierley, G. P. 1984. Adenine nucleotide metabolism and compartmentation in isolated adult rat heart cells. *Circ. Res.* 54:536–46

25. Giacomello, A., Salerno, C. 1978. Human hypoxanthine-guanine phosphoribosyltransferase. *J. Biol. Chem.* 253:6038–44

26. Goldthwaite, D. A. 1957. Mechanisms of synthesis of purine nucleotides in heart muscle extracts. *J. Clin. Invest.* 36:1572–78

27. Greenlee, L., Handler, P. 1964. Xanthine oxidase. VI. *J. Biol. Chem.* 239:1090–95

28. Harmsen, E., de Tombe, P. P., deJong, J. W., Achterberg, P. W. 1984. Enhanced ATP and GTP synthesis from hypoxanthine or inosine after myocardial ischemia. *Am. J. Physiol.* 246:H37–43

29. Henderson, J. F., Brox, L. W., Kelley, W. N., Rosenbloom, F. M., Seegmiller, J. E. 1968. Steady-state kinetics of hypoxanthine-guanine phosphoribosyltransferase. *J. Biol. Chem.* 243:2514–22

30. Hershfield, M. S., Seegmiller, J. E. 1977. Regulation of *de novo* purine synthesis in human lymphoblasts. *J. Biol. Chem.* 252:6002–10

31. Holmes, E. W., Pehlke, D. M., Kelley, W. N. 1974. Human IMP dehydrogenase. Kinetics and regulatory properties. *Biochim. Biophys. Acta* 364:208–17

32. Hori, M., Henderson, J. F. 1966. Purification and properties of adenylate pyrophosphorylase from Ehrlich ascites tumor cells. *J. Biol. Chem.* 241:1406–11

33. Hori, M., Henderson, J. F. 1966. Kinetic studies of adenine phosphoribosyltransferase. *J. Biol. Chem.* 241:3404–8

34. Imai, S., Riley, A. L., Berne, R. M. 1964. Effect of ischemia on adenine nucleotides in cardiac and skeletal muscle. *Circ. Res.* 15:443–50

35. Itoh, R. 1981. Regulation of cytosol 5'-nucleotidase by adenylate energy charge. *Biochim. Biophys. Acta* 659:31–37

36. Itoh, R., Mitsui, A., Tsushima, K. 1967. 5'-Nucleotidase of chicken liver. *Biochim. Biophys. Acta* 146:151–59

37. Jarasch, E.-D., Grund, C., Bruder, G., Heid, H. W., Keenan, T. W., Franke, W. W. 1981. Localization of xanthine oxidase in mammary-gland epithelium and capillary endothelium. *Cell* 25:67–82

38. Jennings, R. B., Reimer, K. A., Hill, M. L., Mayer, S. E. 1981. Total ischemia in dog hearts, *in vitro. Circ. Res.* 49:892–900

39. Kamatani, N., Nelson-Rees, W. A., Carson, D. A. 1981. Selective killing of human malignant cell lines deficient in methylthioadenosine phosphorylase, a purine metabolic enzyme. *Proc. Natl. Acad. Sci. USA* 78:1219–23

40. Kelley, W. N., Rosenbloom, F. M., Henderson, F. J., Seegmiller, J. E. 1967. Xanthine phosphoribosyltransferase in man: Relationship to hypoxanthine-guanine phosphoribosyltransferase. *Biochem. Biophys. Res. Comm.* 28:340–45

41. Kredich, N. M., Hershfield, M. S. 1979. S-adenosylhomocysteine toxicity in normal and adenosine-kinase deficient lymphoblasts of human origin. *Proc. Natl. Acad. Sci. USA* 76:2450–54

42. Krenitsky, T. 1969. Tissue distribution of purine ribosyl- and phosphoribosyltransferases in the Rhesus monkey. *Biochim. Biophys. Acta* 179:506–9

43. Krenitsky, T. A., Papaioannou, R., Elion, G. B. 1969. Human hypoxanthine phosphoribosyltransferase. I. *J. Biol. Chem.* 244:1263–70

44. Krenitsky, T. A., Papaionnou, R. 1969. Human hypoxanthine phosphoribosyltransferase. II. *J. Biol. Chem.* 244:1271–77

45. Kumar, S., Josan, V., Sanger, K. C. S., Tewari, K. K., Krishnan, P. S. 1967. Studies on guanine deaminase and its inhibitors in rat tissues. *Biochem. J.* 102:691–704

46. Lalanne, M., Willemot, J. 1975. Xanthine oxidase from mouse skeletal muscle; purification and kinetic properties. *Int. J. Biochem.* 6:479–84

47. Lamers, J. M. J., Heyliger, C. E., Panagia, V., Dhalla, N. S. 1983. Properties of 5'-nucleotidase in rat heart sarcolemma. *Biochim. Biophys. Acta* 742:568–75

48. Lewis, A. S., Glantz, M. D. 1976. Monomeric purine nucleoside phosphorylase from rabbit liver. *J. Biol. Chem.* 251:407–13

49. Lindberg, B., Klenow, H., Hansen, K. 1967. Some properties of partially purified mammalian adenosine kinase. *J. Biol. Chem.* 242:350–56

50. Liu, M. S., Feinberg, H. 1971. Incorporation of adenosine-8-^{14}C and inosine-8-^{14}C into rabbit heart adenine nucleotides. *Am. J. Physiol.* 220:1242–48

51. Lowenstein, J. M., Yu, M.-K., Naito, Y. 1983. Regulation of adenosine metabolism by 5'-nucleotidases. In *Regulatory Function of Adenosine*, ed. R. M. Berne, T. W. Rall, R. Rubio, pp. 117–31. The Hague: Martinus Nijhoff. 558 pp.

52. Maguire, M. H., Lukas, M. C., Rettie, J.

F. 1972. Adenine nucleotide salvage synthesis in the rat heart; pathways of adenosine salvage. *Biochim. Biophys. Acta* 262:108–15

53. Mall, G., Mattfeldt, T., Rieger, P., Volk, B., Frolov, V. A. 1982. Morphometric analysis of the rabbit myocardium after chronic ethanol feeding—early capillary changes. *Basic Res. Cardiol.* 77:57–67

54. Meikle, A. W., Gotto, A. M., Touster, O. 1967. The metabolism of purine compounds in Ehrlich ascites tumor cells: Evidence for a salvage pathway of inosine metabolism. *Biochim. Biophys. Acta* 138:445–51

55. Meyskens, F. L., Williams, H. E. 1971. Adenosine metabolism in human erythrocytes. *Biochim. Biophys. Acta* 240:170–79

56. Miller, R. L., Adamczyk, D. L., Miller, W. H., Koszalka, G. W., Rideout, J. L., et al. 1979. Adenosine kinase from rabbit liver. II. *J. Biol. Chem.* 254:2346–52

57. Murray, A. W. 1966. Purine-phosphoribosyltransferase activities in rat and mouse tissues and in Ehrlich ascites tumor cells. *Biochem. J.* 100:664–70

58. Murray, A. W. 1966. Inhibition of purine phosphoribosyltransferases from Ehrlich ascites-tumor cells by purine nucleotides. *Biochem. J.* 100:671–74

59. Murray, A. W. 1967. The activities and kinetic properties of purine phosphoribosyltransferases in developing mouse liver. *Biochem. J.* 104:675–78

60. Naito, Y., Lowenstein, J. M. 1981. 5'-Nucleotidase from rat heart. *Biochem.* 20:5188–94

61. Namm, D. H. 1973. Myocardial nucleotide synthesis from purine bases and nucleosides. *Circ. Res.* 33:686–95

62. Namm, D. H., Leader, J. P. 1974. A sensitive analytical method for the detection and quantitation of adenosine in biological samples. *Anal. Biochem.* 58:511–24

63. Nees, S., Gerbes, A. L., Gerlach, E. 1981. Isolation, identification and continuous culture of coronary endothelial cells from guinea-pig hearts. *Eur. J. Cell. Biol.* 24:287–97

64. Nees, S., Gerbes, A. L., Willershausen-Zonnchen, B., Gerlach, E. 1980. Purine metabolism in cultured endothelial cells. In *Purine Metabolism in Man—III. Biochemical, Immunological, and Cancer Research*, ed. A. Rapado, R. W. E. Watts, C. H. M. M. DeBruyn, pp. 25–30. New York: Plenum. 459 pp.

65. Nees, S., Gerlach, E. 1983. Adenine nucleotide and adenosine metabolism in

cultured coronary endothelial cells: Formation and release of adenine compounds and possible functional implications. In *Regulatory Function of Adenosine,* ed. R. M. Berne, T. W. Rall, R. Rubio, pp. 347–55. The Hague: Martinus Nijhoff. 558 pp.

66. Newby, A. C., Holmquist, C. A., Illingworth, J., Pearson, J. F. 1983. The control of adenosine concentration in polymorphonuclear leukocytes, cultured heart cells, and isolated pefused heart from the rat. *Biochem. J.* 214:317–43

67. Newby, A. C., Luzio, J. P., Hales, C. N. 1975. The properties and extracellular location of 5'-nucleotidase of the rat fat-cell plasma membrane. *Biochem. J.* 146:625–33

68. Ogasswara, N., Goto, H., Yamada, Y. 1980. Regulatory properties of AMP deaminase isozymes. See. Ref. 64, pp. 169–75

69. Olsson, R. A., Snow, J. A., Gentry, M. K., Frick, G. P. 1972. Adenosine uptake in canine heart. *Circ. Res.* 31:767–78

70. Palella, T. D., Andres, C. M., Fox, I. H. 1980. Human placental adenosine kinase. *J. Biol. Chem.* 255:5264–69

71. Parks, R. E. Jr., Agawal, R. P. 1972. Purine nucleoside phosphorylase. In *The Enzymes,* ed. P. D. Boyer, 7:483–514. New York: Academic. 959 pp.

72. Deleted in proof

73. Pegg, A. E., Williams-Ashman, H. G. 1969. Phosphate-stimulated breakdown of 5'-methylthioadenosine by rat ventral prostate. *Biochem. J.* 115:241–47

74. Peuhkurinen, K. J., Takala, T. E. S., Nuutinen, E. M., Hassinen, L. E. 1983. Tricarboxylic acid cycle metabolites during ischemia in isolated perfused rat heart. *Am. J. Physiol.* 244:H281–88

75. Ravid, K., Diamant, P., Avi-dor, Y. 1984. Regulation of the salvage pathway of purine nucleotide synthesis by the oxidation state of NAD$^+$ in rat heart cells. *Arch. Biochem. Biophys.* 229:632–39

76. Reddington, M., Pusch, R. 1983. Adenosine metabolism in a rat hippocampal slice preparation: Incorporation into S-adenosylhomocysteine. *J. Neurochem.* 40:285–90

77. Rubio, R., Berne, R. M. 1980. Localization of purine and pyrimidine nucleoside phosphorylases in heart, kidney, and liver. *Am. J. Physiol.* 239:H721–30

78. Rubio, R., Berne, R. M., Dobson, J. G. Jr. 1973. Sites of adenosine production in cardiac and skeletal muscle. *Am. J. Physiol.* 225:938–53

79. Rubio, R., Weidemeier, V. T., Berne, R. M. 1972. Nucleoside phosphorylase: Localization and role in the myocardial distribution of purines. *Am. J. Physiol.* 222:550–55

80. Schatz, R. A., Vunnam, C. R., Sellinger, O. Z. 1977. S-Adenosyl-L-homocysteine in brain. Regional concentrations, catabolism, and the effects of methionine sulfoximine. *Neurochem. Res.* 2:27–38

81. Scholtissek, C. 1968. Nucleotide metabolism in tissue culture cells at low temperatures. III. Studies *in vitro*. *Biochim. Biophys. Acta* 155:14–23

82. Schrader, J., Schutz, W., Bardenheuer, H. 1981. Role of S-adenosylhomocysteine hydrolase in adenosine metabolism in mammalian heart. *Biochem. J.* 196:65–70

83. Schultz, V., Lowenstein, J. M. 1978. The purine nucleotide cycle. *J. Biol. Chem.* 253:1938–43

84. Schutz, W., Schrader, J., Gerlach, E. 1981. Different sites of adenosine formation in the heart. *Am. J. Physiol.* 240:H963–70

85. Skupp, S., Ayvazian, J. H. 1969. Oxidation of 7-methylguanine by human xanthine oxidase. *J. Lab. Clin. Med.* 73:909–16

86. Smythe, H. A. 1977. Xanthine and uric acid as xanthine oxidase inhibitors. *Arth. Rheum.* 20:135–36

87. Solano, C., Coffee, C. J. 1978. Differential response of AMP deaminase isozymes to changes in the adenylate energy charge. *Biochem. Biophys. Res. Comm.* 85:564–71

88. Srivastava, S. K., Beutler, E. 1971. Purification and kinetic studies of adenine phosphoribosyltransferase from human erythrocytes. *Arch. Biochem. Biophys.* 142:426–34

89. Stayton, M. M., Rudolph, F. B., Fromm, H. J. 1983. Regulation, genetics, and properties of adenylosuccinate synthetase: A review. *Curr. Topics Cell. Reg.* 22:104–41

90. Swain, J. L., Sabina, R. L., Hale, P. A., Greenfield, J. C. Jr., Holmes, E. W. 1982. Prolonged myocardial nucleotide depletion after brief ischemia in the open-chest dog. *Am. J. Physiol.* 242:H818–26

91. Takala, T., Hiltunen, J. K., Hassinen, I. E. 1980. The mechanism of ammonia production and the effect of mechanical work load on proteolysis and amino acid catabolism in isolated perfused rat heart. *Biochem. J.* 192:285–95

92. Thomas, C. B., Arnold, W. J., Kelley, W. N. 1973. Human adenine phosphoribosyltransferase. *J. Biol. Chem.* 248:2529–35

93. Thomas, C. B., Meade, J. C., Holmes, E. W. 1981. Aminomidazole carbox-

amide ribonucleotide toxicity: A model for study of pyrimidine starvation. *J. Cell. Physiol.* 107:335–44

94. Tsuboi, K. K., Buckley, N. M. 1965. Metabolism of perfused C^{14}-labelled nucleosides and bases by the isolated heart. *Circ. Res.* 16:343–52

95. Ullman, B., Clift, S. M., Cohen, A., Gudas, L. J., Levinson, B. B., et al. 1979. Abnormal regulation of *de novo* purine synthesis and purine salvage in a cultured mouse T-cell lymphoma mutant partially deficient in adenylosuccinate synthetase. *J. Cell. Physiol.* 99:139–52

96. van den Berghe, G., van Pottelsberghe, C., Hers, H.-G. 1977. A kinetic study of the soluble 5'-nucleotidase of rat liver. *Biochem. J.* 162:611–16

97. Van Der Weyden, M. B., Kelley, W. N. 1974. Human adenylosuccinate synthetase. *J. Biol. Chem.* 249:7282–89

98. Watts, R. W. E., Watts, J. E. M., Seegmiller, J. E. 1965. Xanthine oxidase activity in human tissues and its inhibition by allopurinol (4-hydroxypyrazolo [3,4-d] pyrimidine). *J. Lab. Clin. Med.* 66:688–97

99. Weidemeier, V. T., Rubio, R., Berne, R. M. 1972. Incorporation and turnover of adenosine-U-^{14}C in perfused guinea-pig myocardium. *Am. J. Physiol.* 223:51–54

100. Wiedmeier, V. T., Rubio, R., Berne, R. M. 1972. Inosine incorporation into myocardial nucleotides. *J. Mol. Cell. Cardiol.* 4:445–52

101. Willis, R. C., Kaufman, A. H., Seegmiller, J. E. 1984. Purine nucleotide reutilization by human lymphoblast in lines with aberrations of the inosinate cycle. *J. Biol. Chem.* 259:4157–61

102. Wohlhueter, R. M. 1975. Hypoxanthine phosphoribosyltransferase activity in normal, developing, and neoplastic tissues of the rat. *Eur. J. Cancer* 11:463–72

103. Wohlhueter, R. M., Godfrey, J., Plageman, P. G. W. 1982. The biochemical determinants of hypoxanthine uptake in Novikoff rat hepatoma cells. *J. Biol. Chem.* 257:12691–95

104. Worku, Y., Newby, A. C. 1983. The mechanism of adenosine production in rat polymorphonuclear leucocytes. *Biochem. J.* 214:325–30

105. Wyngaarden, J. B., Dunn, J. T. 1957. 8-Hydroxyadenine as the intermediate in the oxidation of adenine to 2,8-dihydroxyadenine by xanthine oxidase. *Arch. Biochem. Biphys.* 70:150–56

106. Zimmer, H.-G., Gerlach, E. 1978. Stimulation of myocardial adenine nucleotide biosynthesis by pentoses and pentitols. *Pfluegers Arch.* 376:223–27

107. Zimmer, H.-G., Trendelenburg, C., Kammermeier, H., Gerlach, E. 1973. De novo synthesis of myocardial adnenine nucleotides in the rat. *Circ. Res.* 32:635–42

108. Zimmerman, T. P., Gersten, N. B., Ross, A. F., Miech, R. P. 1971. Adenine as substrate for purine nucleoside phosphorylase. *Can. J. Biochem.* 49:1050–54

109. Zimmerman, T. P., Wolberg, G., Duncan, G. S., Elion, G. B. 1980. Adenosine analogues as substrates and inhibitors of S-adenosylhomocysteine hydrolase in intact lymphocytes. *Biochemistry* 19:2252–59

110. Zoref-Shani, E., Sperling, O. 1978. Dependence of the metabolic fate of IMP on the rate of total IMP synthesis. *Biochim. Biophys. Acta* 607:503–11

111. Zoref-Shani, E., Shainberg, A., Sperling, O. 1982. Characterization of purine nucleotide metabolism in primary rat muscle cultures. *Biochim. Biophys. Acta* 716:324–30

Ann. Rev. Physiol. 1985. 47:707–25

RESPIRATORY CONTROL AND THE INTEGRATION OF HEART HIGH-ENERGY PHOSPHATE METABOLISM BY MITOCHONDRIAL CREATINE KINASE

William E. Jacobus

Peter Belfer Laboratory for Myocardial Research, Division of Cardiology, Department of Medicine, and the Departments of Biological Chemistry, and Anesthesiology and Critical Care Medicine, The Johns Hopkins University School of Medicine, Baltimore, Maryland 21205

INTRODUCTION

The chapter on the *"Regulation of Mitochondrial Activity in Cardiac Cells"* by Mela-Riker & Bukoski provides the readers of this volume with a general overview of heart mitochondrial physiology. In my review, attention will be focused directly on the *control and integration* of mitochodrial high-energy phosphate production. The words control and integration have been carefully selected. The control of oxidative phosphorylation is required so that ATP production will be exactly balanced to the high rates of utilization required by contraction. An example will hopefully underscore this need. The rate of ATP turnover in the heart ranges from about 0.66 μmol/s/g tissue (low work) to 2.35 μmol/s/g tissue (high work) (41, 53). The heart contains approximately 10 mM ATP and 25 mM phosphocreatine (79). Therefore, at a normal rate of utilization (1 μmol/s), the total ATP pool turns over six times per minute. Even with the addition of phosphocreatine, the "resting" heart turns over the total high-energy phosphate pool (ATP + PCr) between two and four times per minute. It is for these reasons that ATP production must be under very tight control. There

707

is little margin for error. This brings us to the second concept, integration. The classic view of physiologists has been that ATP is the primary energy source, and phosphocreatine serves as a "reserve," to be called upon during high work conditions. While this may, or may not, be the case in skeletal muscle or brain, it does not appear to be such for heart. As a "reserve" molecule, phosphocreatine would be of very limited value, because it only provides an additional 10 s supply of energy. It appears that the time has come to dispel this previous notion, and begin to view phosphocreatine as perhaps playing a more dynamic role in heart high-energy phosphate metabolism. It therefore is the goal of this chapter to outline a quite different function for phosphocreatine, discussing its potential in the integration or distribution of the high-energy phosphates. These new ideas have evolved from information acquired during the past decade.

The subjects of this review, the integration of high-energy phosphate metabolism and the role of creatine kinase in heart metabolism, represent topics of significant historical interest to both physiologists and biochemists. In a sense, defining the function of phosphocreatine in muscle high-energy phosphate metabolism started an intellectual exchange between these two disciplines that has continued intermittently for more than 70 years. The first participant was Thunberg, who reported in 1911 that creatine stimulated oxygen consumption and CO_2 production in muscle (75). In 1927 Fiske & Subbarow identified the "labile phosphorus" of muscle, named it phosphocreatine, and showed that it decreased during contraction and was restored during recovery (20), all of which preceded the characterization of ATP by a few years (50). The physiological importance of phosphocreatine was immediately recognized (15), especially when Lundsgaard showed that iodoacetate-treated muscle could contract normally in the absence of lactate formation and was accompanied by the breakdown of phosphocreatine (52). On the basis of these results, Lundsgaard postulated that "phosphagen is the substance directly supplying the energy for contraction . . ." In 1934, Lohmann (51) linked ATP and phosphocreatine by demonstrating enzyme-catalyzed phosphoryl group transfer between these two compounds. For a period of time this was called the Lohmann reaction. We now acknowledge this transphosphorylation as the function of creatine kinase (EC 2.7.3.2).

Although quite interesting, it is not really the purpose of this chapter to further review the historical aspects of creatine kinase or phosphocreatine. Nor will it cover the more "biochemical" properties of creatine kinase, including the general concepts of "Energy Transport." These have been adequately reviewed by others (4, 31, 67, 69) and were the subject of a recent symposium (8). This review will focus on new experimental results and theoretical calculations that could alter our view of the integration of heart high-energy phosphate metabolism. The underlying goal of the review is to respond to A. V. Hill's famous "A Challenge to Biochemists" (28) to define the dynamics of high-energy phosphate metabolism in muscle. To approach this, information from two basic areas of cellular bioenergetics will be intertwined. First will be a general discussion of the adenine nucleotide control of mitochondrial respiration, leading to the notion that ADP availability occupies an important regulatory position. On the basis of kinetic and inhibitor studies with isolated heart mitochondria, a case will then be made that the forward rate of the mitochondrial isozyme of creatine kinase (phosphocreatine and ADP producing) may be the dominant reaction controlling myocardial high-energy phosphate production. While these ideas will not fully answer Hill's challenge, they begin to presumably point us in the proper direction.

ADENINE NUCLEOTIDE CONTROL OF RESPIRATION

General Considerations

Shortly after the recognition by Kennedy & Lehninger (37) that mitochondria were the site of oxidative phosphorylation, Siekevitz & Potter (70) and others (38, 46, 56, 60, 61) explored the regulation of cellular respiration, a venture yet to be completed. The reason for this rather extended quest is straightforward. When intact mitochondria are incubated in respiratory medium, oxygen is consumed at an endogenous rate termed State IV. With substrate and Pi present, the addition of ADP (phosphate acceptor), even at micromolar concentrations, results in a marked stimulation of respiration to a near-maximum velocity called State III. From the view of cell physiology, neither State IV or State III are relevant, because the normal rates of tissue oxygen consumption lie between these two in vitro rates. Only under conditions of extreme stress do heart or other tissue oxygen consumption rates ever come close to the maximum respiratory capacity of the tissue (41). Therefore, the biologically important issue is to determine how cells modulate oxygen consumption and high-energy phosphate production to intermediate rates.

In 1955 Chance & Williams (10) suggested that the kinetics of mitochondrial oxidative phosphorylation could be described by the availability of ADP, an idea that predated our knowledge of the adenine nucleotide translocase (40). Klingenberg (39) subsequently postulated that the extramitochondrial phosphorylation potential, [ATP]/[ADP]x[Pi], was the parameter that determined the immediate rates of oxygen consumption. Since that time, this hypothesis has received much experimental and theoretical support (16, 18, 29, 30, 57, 58, 73, 77, 80, 83, 84). In 1973, Slater et al (71) proposed that mitochondrial respiratory control was simply a function of the [ATP]/[ADP] ratio, independent of the tissue content of Pi. This theory has likewise achieved considerable support (5, 6, 11–13, 44, 47, 48, 63, 72). Control by the cytoplasmic phosphorylation potential is based on near-equilibrium thermodynamic considerations, whereas the [ATP]/[ADP] ratio theory is founded on the kinetics of the adenine nucleotide translocase.

The need for these additional theories arose from the biochemical observations that tissue content of ADP appeared to be considerably higher than the estimated apparent K_m of the adenine nucleotide translocase for ADP. For example, the acid-extracted content of ADP in the heart is almost 1.0 mM, whereas the translocase K_m is about 20–30 μM. Under these conditions the translocase would clearly be saturated with ADP, so other control theories were thought to be required. However, recent 31-P NMR data on the in vivo rat brain (1), our own studies on the perfused heart, computer calculations of heart nucleotides (42), and a reestimation of tissue phosphorylation potentials (78) all cast considerable doubt on both of these theories for adenine nucleotide control. The new data (1, 42, 78) all suggest that the concentrations of free ADP in tissues are much lower than that estimated from freeze extraction and potentially fall within the ADP kinetic control range.

Fundamental Approaches

Studies to define the nature of the adenine nucleotide control of respiration have traditionally employed three approaches. In the first, samples were removed from the oxygraph chamber at different points during the State III to State IV transition, the period of "dynamic control" (29, 55). Another approach has been to use specific inhibitors to selectively block the adenine nucleotide translocase and note the results on rates of respiration (11, 47, 73). The third method has been to preincubate mitochondria in medium containing fixed concentrations of ATP and Pi, and initiate steady-state rates of respiration by the graded additions of either an ATPase enzyme or by use of an ADP-generating system like hexokinase (12, 13, 44). A nonexperimental approach has employed computer modeling (5, 6, 18, 54, 83). From these combined techniques, arguments have been generated as to the degree to which mitochondrial respiratory rates are controlled by the extramitochondrial phosphorylation potential, by [Pi], by the kinetics of the translocase, by the [ATP]/[ADP] ratio, by oxygen, by substrate availability, or by the rates of electron transport, exclusively or in some combination (74).

Control by ADP Availability

In our recent work, data were presented for the control of liver mitochondrial respiration, using hexokinase as the ADP-generating system (33). Data are now presented for creatine kinase, using two protocols: constant ATP with variable enzyme, and constant enzyme with variable concentrations of ATP. Under the conditions of a fixed concentration of ATP, with variable creatine kinase, we note that the rate of respiration increases as the log of the phosphorylation potential decreases (Figure 1A). This has been the widely reported observation. Likewise a similar trend is seen with the [ATP]/[ADP] ratio data (Figure 1B). For this parameter, we also note that respiratory rates increase as the [ATP]/

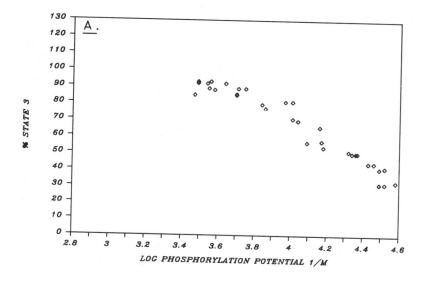

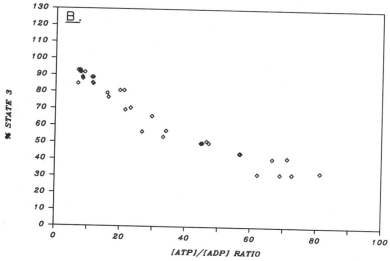

Figure 1   Liver mitochondrial respiration at constant ATP (1.0 mM) and variable skeletal muscle creatine kinase. Respiratory rates were calculated from steady-state rates, with maximum State 3 determined by direct ADP addition. Samples were removed 1.5 min after enzyme addition, extracted and assayed as previously described (33). The oxygraph chamber contained 3.0 mg liver mitochondrial protein. *A*: Log phosphorylation potential vs % State 3 respiratory rates. *B*: [ATP]/[ADP] ratios vs % State 3 respiratory rates. In all cases the concentration of creatine was 20 mM.

[ADP] ratio declines. In other words, the standard approach provides the expected results.

One of the basic assumptions of phosphorylation potential or [ATP]/[ADP] ratio control is that the rates of respiration should correlate to the calculated values for either parameter under all conditions and thus are independent of how the conditions were established. This is the rationale for freeze-extracting tissue, measuring nucleotide levels, calculating ratios, and projecting information on the metabolic status of a tissue (24). However, such does not appear to be the case.

When the liver mitochondrial respiratory studies were conducted under the conditions of a standard activity of added ADP-generating enzyme, whose activity was titrated by varying the concentration of ATP, a markedly different picture is obtained (Figure 2). For several reasons these conditions could be considered more "physiological," because the cell usually operates with relatively fixed concentrations of enzyme and variable concentrations of substrate. When these experimental conditions are employed, we now note an almost mirror-image correlation between respiratory rates and phosphorylation potentials. The rates of respiration increase as the phosphorylation potential increases (Figure 2A). A similar contradictory correlation is seen for the [ATP]/[ADP] ratios (Figure 2B).

In a similar manner, when the control of respiration was studied in heart mitochondria, using the endogenous mitochondrial isozyme of creatine kinase, a similar unique and paradoxical picture was obtained. Because the amount of creatine kinase associated with heart mitochondria is fixed by its intrinsic activity, there was little option but to grade the rates of respiration by alterations in the concentration of ATP, at fixed concentrations of creatine (20 mM) (Figure 3). Similar to the liver data with either hexokinase (33) or creatine kinase (35), with heart mitochondrial creatine kinase we again obtain a direct correlation between respiratory rates and either the log phosphorylation potentials (Figure 3A) or [ATP]/[ADP] ratios (Figure 3B). Thus, there is a clear consistency between the heart and liver data when similar experimental methods are used.

Taken together, these new results strongly suggest that neither the extramitochondrial phosphorylation potential nor the [ATP]/[ADP] ratios could be primary signals *per se* for the regulation of mitochondrial respiration. Some other aspect of the adenine nucleotides must be the controlling feature. In all cases there was a direct and hyperbolic correlation between the rates of respiration and the concentrations of ADP. In other words, the data are consistent with the idea that ADP availability at the translocase is the key regulating parameter, [the concept of respiratory control initially postulated by Chance & Williams (10)].

From the perspective of cell high-energy phosphate metabolism, the direct

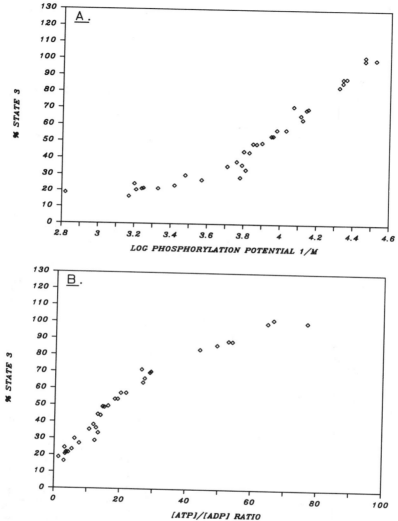

Figure 2 Liver mitochondrial respiration at fixed concentrations of skeletal muscle creatine kinase (0.3 IU) and variable [ATP]. Conditions are the same as in Figure 1 except that the concentrations of ATP were varied from 0.005 mM to 10.0 mM. *A*: Log phosphorylation potential vs % State 3 respiratory rates. *B*: [ATP]/[ADP] ratios vs % State 3 respiratory rates.

regulation of ATP production by ADP availability makes sense. In order to tightly couple the critical balance between energy supply (metabolism) and energy demand (work), heart respiration would best be controlled by a signal indicative of the magnitude of cell labor. In other words, ATP production rates

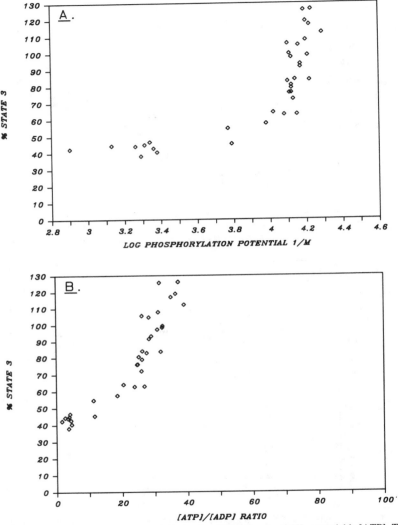

Figure 3   Heart mitochondrial respiration stimulated by endogenous CK_m at variable [ATP]. The oxygraph chamber contained 0.5 mg rat heart mitochondrial protein. Otherwise, all other conditions were as in Figure 2. *A*: Log phosphorylation potential vs % State 3 respiratory rates. *B*: [ATP]/[ADP] ratios vs % State 3 respiratory rates.

should be responsive to changes in the rate of ATP turnover. Clearly, the product of increased cellular "work," whether physical (as in the heart with contraction) or biosynthetic (as in other tissues), is usually the generation of ADP and Pi or, in some cases, AMP and PPi. Therefore, changes in the availability of ADP do in fact directly reflect the steady-state magnitude of energy demand. Our experiments suggest that such changes can act as the primary adenine nucleotide signal to stimulate mitochondrial ATP production.

It is necessary to emphasize at this point that, in the heart, mitochondrial respiration and high-energy phosphate production are probably not controlled by an exclusive step. We have purposely focused on exogenous adenine nucleotide control. However, a unique contribution by Tager's group (25) has been the application of control theory (26, 27, 36, 62) to the regulation of mitochondrial respiration. The important outcome of this work is the documentation that respiratory control is actually a shared process and that the degree of control exerted by a single step is variable with the respiratory rate (25). Under State III conditions, control appears to be primarily exerted by the dicarboxylate carrier and the adenine nucleotide translocase. However, at lower and presumably more physiological rates of respiration, e.g. 50% State III, the rate of the ADP-generating reaction (hexokinase) becomes the dominant control parameter (25). This control by ADP generation is quite consistent with our previous results (33, 35). However, the degree to which other steps—Pi transport, oxygen, transmembrane pH gradients, substrate transport, nucleotide pool sizes, and relative intramitochondrial vs extramitochondrial energy demands—all interact to regulate respiration (3, 9, 17, 21, 22, 43, 45, 49, 68, 81, 82) clearly remains an issue of controversy. It is anticipated that future uses of innovative experimental approaches will yield new data concerning these matters. Such a technique appears to be 31-P NMR. Employing saturation transfer methods, Matthews et al (53) have estimated the flux rates for ATP synthesis and calculated an in vivo ADP/O ratio. This technique now opens the door to much more sophisticated analyses of tissue bioenergetics.

ROLE OF MITOCHONDRIAL CREATINE KINASE

The experimental results outlined above lead to an interesting bioenergetic question. Is it possible that the kinetics of the ADP-ATP translocase are influenced by the site of ADP formation? If this were the case, it could represent a novel form of cellular microcompartmentation. To explore this possibility, the kinetics of ADP-stimulated respiration were studied using three distinct enzymatic systems for ADP formation. In the first, representative of cytoplasmic ADP formation, hexokinase immobilized on agarose beads was used. In the second condition, we employed normal soluble yeast hexokinase for ADP generation. The third system was the endogenous mitochondrial isozyme of creatine kinase, generating ADP in the mitochondrial intermembrane space, rather close to the translocase. In these experiments, heart mitochondria were incubated in sucrose oxygraph medium with succinate as the substrate. Either glucose or creatine, the secondary phosphate acceptors, were present at 20 mM concentrations. The amount of hexokinase added was carefully titrated so that the maximal rates of respiration were not greater than 95% of ADP-stimulated State III. This was crucial, because we did not want hexokinase to produce ADP faster than it could be rephosphorylated. The maximum rates of creatine-stimulated respiration were also about 95% of State III. The reactions were initiated by additions of ATP at different concentrations. After the induction of steady-state respiration, samples were removed and assayed for ADP content. The rates of respiration were then plotted in double-reciprocal format vs 1/[ADP]. The data for the fourth condition were obtained by the direct additions of ADP to the respiratory medium, in the absence of a secondary acceptor. The apparent K_m values for ADP-stimulated respiration, Table 1, were derived from extrapolated kinetic plots. The data of Table 1 show an almost five-fold difference in the apparent K_m for ADP-stimulated respiration, an effect that is dependent upon the site of ADP formation. These results suggest that the adenine nucleotide translocase has the highest affinity for ADP generated by mitochondrial creatine kinase. This is quite consistent with the documentation of the functional coupling of ADP transport from mitochondrial creatine kinase to the adenine nucleotide translocase (23, 54).

In a companion series of experiments, the effects of ATP on the inhibition of ADP-stimulated respiration were determined. The experiments yielded values for K_i, the inhibitory strength of ATP (Table 1). Knowing the ADP K_m values and the ATP K_i values, they can be substituted into the general rate equation for competitive inhibition, known to be the case for the translocase (59). It is then possible to mathematically generate curves for the rates of heart mitochondrial respiration vs [ADP] as influenced by the site of ADP generation (Figure 4). These curves illustrate that heart mitochondrial respiration is most responsive when ADP is generated by the endogenous creatine kinase reaction, and that this enzyme is capable of stimulating respiration to the highest levels. At low concentrations of ADP, the rates of respiration induced by mitochondrial creatine kinase are markedly above those produced by any other generating system. Thus, the data support the idea that, in heart, the forward activity of the mitochondrial creatine kinase reaction (phosphocreatine and ADP formation) may be the dominant reaction controlling the rate of oxidative phosphorylation and thus the rate of tissue oxygen consumption.

Table 1 Apparent K_m and K_i values for ADP-stimulated respiration as a function of the site of ADP formation

	Apparent K_m (μM)	K_i for ATP (mM)
Direct ADP additions	13.2	10.0
Agarose insoluble hexokinase	7.0	10.0
Soluble yeast hexokinase	5.9	10.0
Mitochondrial creatine kinase	2.9	30.0

A second important point relates to fundamental concepts of microcompartmentation (Figure 4) intertwined with issues concerning the "functional" coupling of mitochondrial creatine kinase to the adenine nucleotide translocase. The idea that inner membrane localization is critical for the integration of phosphocreatine production coupled to oxidative phosphorylation was first expressed by Jacobus & Lehninger (32). Thereafter, kinetic studies documenting alterations in the apparent K_m for ATP (34, 64–66), chemical labeling studies (85), and thermodynamic experiments (14) supported the view that there was a unique interaction between mitochondrial creatine kinase and ATP supplied by the adenine nucleotide translocase. These observations have been challenged (2, 7) to some degree. In addition, recent work using translocase inhibitors (54) or pyruvate kinase competition for ADP (23) have shown a unique interaction between the translocase and ADP generated by mitochondrial creatine kinase. A model for these interactions is presented in Figure 5. The concept of "functional coupling" does not in any way include the requirements for *exclusive access* by either ATP or ADP. This is clearly shown in Figure 5, where both endogenous and exogenous nucleotides appear to interact with either the translocase or creatine kinase.

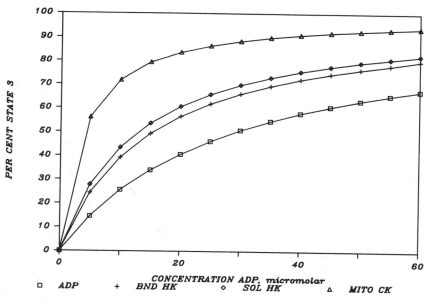

Figure 4   Rates of heart mitochondrial respiration as a function of the location of ADP production. *ADP* is when ADP was pulsed into the oxygraph chamber. *BND HK* is when agarose bound hexokinase and glucose were used as the ADP-generating system. *SOL HK* used soluble yeast kexokinase. *MITO CK* used mitochondrial creatine kinase and creatine. The data were calculated from the kinetic constants of Table 1, using a standard rate equation for one-substrate competitive inhibition.

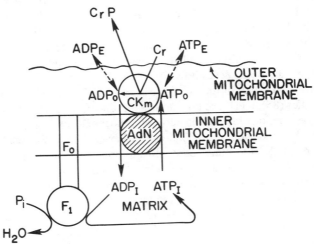

Figure 5 Model for the functional coupling of heart mitochondrial creatine kinase (CK_m) to the inner membrane adenine nucleotide translocase *(AdN)*. F_0 and F_1 represent the inner membrane ATPase.

What is the nature of this effect? Mosbach (55) has stated that the kinetic enhancement of a multistep enzyme system could be explained by four properties of an enzymatic microenvironment. They are: (*a*) enzyme-enzyme proximity; (*b*) the establishment of Nernst unstirred layers; (*c*) other diffusional restrictions; and (*d*) exclusive effects imposed by structured water. For reasons previously detailed (54), we feel that unstirred layers and structured water play only a minor role. Data from our laboratory have also shown that there is no evidence for a concerted or "direct" transfer of the nucleotides (76). In other words, the nucleotides do not need to obligatorily bind to the translocase prior to interaction at the creatine kinase enzymatic active site. More likely, functional coupling is the result of proximity, because the isozyme is bound to the exterior surface of the inner mitochondrial membrane, the membrane also containing the translocase. As a result of this localization, the translocase is positioned to efficiently supply ATP to the active site of mitochondrial creatine kinase, and the enzyme quite effectively recycles ADP back to the carrier. Because the translocase operates by an obligatory exchange mechanism (antiport), these processes would occur almost simultaneously. Therefore, the translocase activity would effectively induce local concentration gradients, resulting in an increase [ATP] and decrease [ADP] in the microenvironment of the enzyme. As a result, the forward direction of the reaction would be strongly favored, and the reversibility of the reaction minimized (ATP and creatine-producing). The magnitude of such local gradients has yet to be determined. It is also quite possible that the outer membrane acts as a moderate barrier for diffusion, thus contributing to "functional coupling" (19).

Independent of its mechanism, "functional coupling" is a very interesting process, because the interaction between the translocase and creatine kinase also potentially represents a unique form of a multienzyme complex. It appears to be the singular example of a transport process coupled to enzymatic catalysis, where the transport system functions both to supply substrate (ATP) and to remove product (ADP). With respect to respiratory control and the maintenance of the reaction exclusively in the forward direction (Figure 5), ADP removal may well be the more important aspect of the coupling. ADP removal decreases the reversibility of the reaction to a degree that, under physiological conditions, has yet to be defined.

ASPECTS OF THE INTEGRATION OF HIGH-ENERGY PHOSPHATE METABOLISM

The fundamental concept of energy transport involves two components, phosphocreatine production by mitochondrial creatine kinase and phosphocreatine utilization to produce the ATP required for myocardial contraction (Figure 6). So far, we have focused only on the left portion of this model, the control of oxidative phosphorylation and the activity of mitochondrial creatine kinase. To complete the picture, a few important points need to be made about the function of the sarcoplasmic isozyme of creatine kinase, CK_3. As reviewed by others (4, 31, 67, 69), it is now known that creatine kinase is bound to the sarcolemmal membrane, the sarcoplasmic reticulum membrane, and intimately associated with the myosin thick filaments as a component of the M line. At these loci, it is believed that phosphocreatine reacts with ADP to locally regenerate "contractile" ATP and creatine. The ATP is used for the requisite steps of ion transport or filament translocation. Creatine recycles to the mitochondria to be transphosphorylated back to phosphocreatine and, thus, control oxidative phosphorylation. In this manner, phosphocreatine serves as a highly specific intermediate transport carrier for cellular high-energy phosphate, whereas creatine functions as the primary sarcoplasmic phosphate acceptor. There is, however, some concern about the general validity of the model presented in Figure 6.

Matthews et al (53) have used 31-P NMR saturation transfer to measure the flux rates of creatine kinase and the rates of ATP turnover in the beating rat heart. They estimate that the rate of ATP-Pi exchange (oxidative phosphorylation) is 2.8 ± 0.3 mmol/s x g dry wt of the heart. On the other hand the rate of ATP-phosphocreatine exchange was 14.6 ± 1.0 mmol/s x g dry wt. These differences in exchange rates are remarkable and interesting. The data suggest that for every turnover of ATP, the status of the adenine nucleotide pool is

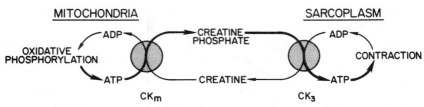

Figure 6 Model for the integration of heart high-energy phosphate metabolism. CK_m and CK_3 are abbreviations for the mitochondrial and sarcoplasmic isozymes of creatine kinase. The flux of high-energy phosphate is indicated by the *dark arrows*.

"checked" more than five times by creatine kinase dephosphorylation and rephosphorylation of ATP and ADP respectively. In other words, creatine kinase makes certain that there is adequate ATP. These data have been interpreted by Matthews et al (53) to indicate that myocardial creatine kinase is in thermodynamic equilibrium with the adenine nucleotide pool. Others have suggested that the data undermine the concept of phosphocreatine Energy Transport, because the kinetics of the reaction appear to reflect the concentrations of free metabolites in the cytoplasmic compartment rather than implying kinetic control exerted by some "functionally coupled" microdomain.

It is possible, however, that having the saroplasmic creatine kinase in thermodynamic equilibrium is precisely what is required for an effective energy-transport system. The equilibrium constant for the creatine kinase reaction (78) can be rearranged in terms of [PCr]/[Cr] and [ATP]/[ADP] ratios. At pH 7.2 [PCr]/[Cr] x 104.7 = [ATP]/[ADP]. As a consequence of this relationship, at cytoplasmic concentrations of 25 mM phosphocreatine, 8.3 mM creatine, and 11.7 mM ATP, the concentration of free ADP will only be 37 μM. This has been well documented for skeletal muscle, brain, and other tissues by Veech et al (78). Viewed one way, the creatine kinase equilibrium operates to maintain a very high [ATP]/[ADP] ratio. Alternatively, it also "amplifies" the metabolic results for changes in [ADP] induced by altered myocardial work (Figure 7). From the theoretical calculations shown in Figure 7, we see that for a 10 μM increase in [ADP], phosphocreatine decreases from 25.0 mM to 23.4 mM, creatine increases from 8.3 mM to 9.9 mM, while ATP would change from 11.67 to 11.66 mM. In other words, micromolar changes in ADP, accompanied by insignificant changes in ATP, are translated by the equilibrium of the creatine kinase reaction to result in large, millimolar, changes in the steady-state concentrations of phosphocreatine and creatine. It is precisely these changes that have perplexed the muscle physiologists for so long (28). Furthermore, it must be noted that both the direction and magnitude of these changes in [PCr] and [Cr] will feedback to the mitochondria to stimulate an increase in the steady-state rate of oxidative phosphorylation. Thus, the cycle is truly complete and the energy-transport system appears to be quite *responsive* to the energetic requirements of heart contraction.

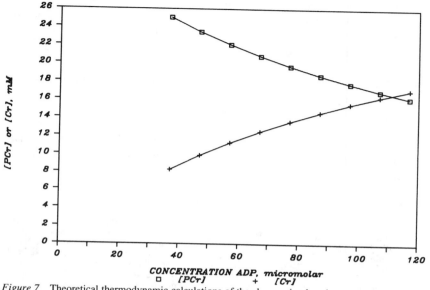

Figure 7   Theoretical thermodynamic calculations of the changes in phosphocreatine [PCr] and creatine [Cr], assuming 11.67 mM ATP, as a function of changes in [ADP]. The data assume that cytoplasmic creatine kinase is in equilibrium. The equilibrium constant was taken from Veech et al (78).

SUMMARY

This review has attempted to integrate three areas of cellular bioenergetics to present a novel and comprehensive view of heart high-energy phosphate metabolism. The goal has been to provide a rational view for the functions of phosphocreatine, creatine, and creatine kinase in the energy metabolism of muscle. The first point is that mitochondrial respiratory control is influenced by changes in the concentration of ADP, stimulating the adenine nucleotide translocase and oxidative phosphorylation. Secondly, as a consequence of the proximity of mitochondrial creatine kinase to the translocase, there appears to be a kinetic preference for ADP generated by the forward creatine kinase reaction. As a result, in heart, it can be viewed that the end product of oxidative phosphorylation is phosphocreatine. Finally, thermodynamic considerations suggest that phosphocreatine plays a major role to maintain or *buffer* the ATP content of the myocardium. Under conditions of increased ATP turnover, large-scale increases in the concentration of ADP, along with major decreases in ATP, are minimized by the creatine kinase equilibrium. The system responds to such a demand with substantial changes in phosphocreatine and creatine, which can kinetically increase the rate of mitochondrial creatine kinase and thus oxidative phosphorylation.

Theoretical enzymologists have long argued whether enzymes are under kinetic or thermodynamic control. Heart creatine kinase may be a unique example where both types of control simultaneously operate in different micro-environments, with mitochondrial creatine kinase kinetically controlled, while the sarcoplasmic isozyme is influenced by equilibrium thermodynamics. Over-all, heart creatine kinase may be a unique example of "kineto-dynamic" metabolic integration.

ACKNOWLEDGMENTS

This work was supported by US Public Health Service Grant HL-20658. The author was an Established Investigator of the American Heart Association when much of this research was conducted.

Literature Cited

1. Ackerman, J. J. H., Grove, T. H., Wong, G. G., Gadian, D. G., Radda, G. K. 1980. Mapping of metabolites in whole animals by ^{31}P NMR using surface coils. *Nature* 283:167–70
2. Altschuld, R. A., Brierley, G. P. 1977. Interaction between the creatine kinase of heart mitochondria and oxidative phosphorylation. *J. Mol. Cell. Card.* 9:875–96
3. Asimakis, G. K., Aprille, J. R. 1980. *In vitro* alteration of the size of the liver mitochondrial adenine nucleotide pool: Correlation with respiratory functions. *Arch. Biochem. Biophys.* 203:307–16
4. Bessman, S. P., Geiger, P. J. 1982. Transport of energy in muscle: The phosphorylcreatine shuttle. *Science* 211:448–52
5. Bohnensack, R. 1981. Control of energy transformation in mitochondria: Analysis by quantitative model. *Biochim. Biophys. Acta.* 634:203–18
6. Bohnensack, R., Kunz, W. 1978. Mathematical model of regulation of oxidative phosphorylation in intact mitochondria. *Acta. Biol. Med. Ger.* 37:97–112
7. Borrebaek, B. 1980. The lack of direct coupling between ATP-ADP translocase and creatine phosphokinase in isolated rabbit heart mitochondria. *Arch. Biochem. Biophys.* 203:827–29
8. Brautbar, N., ed. 1984. *Proc. 2nd Int. Cong. Myocardial and Cellular Bioenergetics and Compartmentation.* New York: Plenum. In press
9. Brawand, F., Folly, G. Walter, P. 1980. Relation between extra- and intramitochondrial ATP/ADP ratios in rat liver mitochondria. *Biochim. Biophys. Acta* 590:285–89
10. Chance, B., Williams, G. R. 1955. Respiratory enzymes in oxidative phosphorylation. *J. Biol. Chem.* 217:385–93
11. Christiansen, E. N., Davis, E. J. 1978. The effects of coenzyme A and carnitine on steady-state ATP/ADP ratios and the rate of long-chain free fatty acid oxidation in liver mitochondria. *Biochim. Biophys. Acta* 502:17–28
12. Davis, E. J., Davis-van Thienen, W. I. A. 1978. Control of mitochondrial metabolism by the ATP/ADP ratio. *Biochem. Biophys. Res. Commun.* 83:1260–66
13. Davis, E. J., Lumeng, L. 1975. Relationships between the phosphorylation potentials generated by liver mitochondria and respiratory state under conditions of adenosine diphosphate control. *J. Biol. Chem.* 250:2275–82
14. DeFuria, R. A., Ingwall, J. S., Fossel, E. T., Dygert, M. K. 1980. Microcompartmentation of the mitochondrial creatine kinase reaction. See Ref. 31, pp. 135–41
15. Eggleton, P., Eggleton, G. P. 1927. The physiological significance of "phosphagen." *J. Physiol.* 63:155–61
16. Erecinska, E., Kula, T., Wilson, D. F. 1978. Regulation of energy metabolism: evidence against a primary role of adenine nucleotide translocase. *FEBS Lett.* 87:139–44
17. Erecinska, M., Stubbs, M., Miyata, Y., Ditre, Wilson, D. F. 1977. Regulation of cellular metabolism by intracellular phosphate. *Biochim. Biophys. Acta* 462:20–35
18. Erecinska, M., Wilson, D. F., Nishiki, K. 1978. Homeostatic regulation of cellular energy metabolism and mitochondrial respiration in rat heart. *Am. J. Physiol.* 234:C82–89

19. Erickson-Viitanen, S., Geiger, P. J., Viitanen, P., Bessman, S. P. 1982. Compartmentation of mitochondrial creatine phosphokinase. II. The importance of mitochondrial membrane for mitochondrial compartmentation. *J. Biol. Chem.* 257:11405–11

20. Fiske, C. H., Subbarow, Y. 1927. The nature of the "inorganic phosphate" in voluntary muscle. *Science* 65:401–3

21. Forman, N. G., Wilson, D. F. 1982. Energetics and stoichiometry of oxidative phosphorylation from NADH to cytochrome c in isolated rat liver mitochondria. *J. Biol. Chem.* 257:12908–15

22. Forman, N. G., Wilson, D. F. 1983. Dependence of mitochondrial oxidative phosphorylation on activity of the adenine nucleotide translocase. *J. Biol. Chem.* 258:8649–55

23. Gellerich, F., Saks, V. A. 1982. Control of heart mitochondrial oxygen consumption by creatine kinase: the importance of enzyme localization. *Biochem. Biophys. Res. Commun.* 105:1473–81

24. Giesen, J., Kammermeier, H. 1980. Relationship of phosphorylation potential and oxygen consumption in isolated perfused rat hearts. *J. Mol. Cell. Cardiol.* 12:891–907

25. Groen, A. K., Wanders, R. J. A., Westerhoff, H. V., van der Meer, R., Tager, J. M. 1982. Quantification of the contribution of various steps to the control of mitochondrial respiration. *J. Biol. Chem.* 257:2754–57

26. Heinrich, R., Rapoport, T. A. 1974. A linear steady-state treatment of enzymatic chains. General properties, control and effector strength. *Eur. J. Biochem.* 42:89–95

27. Heinrich, R., Rapoport, T. A. 1974. A linear steady-state treatment of enzymatic chains. Critique of the crossover theorem and a general procedure to identify interaction sites with an effector. *Eur. J. Biochem.* 42:97–105

28. Hill, A. V. 1950. A challenge to biochemists. *Biochem. Biophys. Acta* 4:4–11

29. Holian, A., Owen, C. S., Wilson, D. F. 1977. Control of respiration in isolated mitochondria: quantitative evaluation of the dependence of respiratory rates on [ATP], [ADP], and [Pi]. *Arch. Biochem. Biophys.* 181:164–71

30. Holian, A., Wilson, D. F. 1980. Relationship of transmembrane pH and electrical gradients with respiration and adenosine 5'-triposphate synthesis in mitochondria. *Biochemistry* 19:4213–21

31. Jacobus, W. E. 1980. Myocardial energy transport: Current concepts of the problem. In *Heart Creatine Kinase: The Integration of Isozymes for Energy Distribution,* ed. W. E. Jacobus, J. S. Ingwall pp. 1–5. Baltimore: Williams & Wilkins

32. Jacobus, W. E., Lehninger, A. L. 1973. Creatine kinase of rat heart mitochondria. Coupling of creatine phosphorylation to electron transport. *Biol. Chem.* 248: 4830–10

33. Jacobus, W. E., Moreadith, R. W., Vandegaer, K. M. 1982. Mitochondrial respiratory control. Evidence against the regulation of respiration by extramitochondrial phosphorylation potentials or by [ATP]/[ADP] ratios. *J. Biol. Chem.* 257:2397–402

34. Jacobus, W. E., Saks, V. A. 1982. Creatine kinase of heart mitochondria: Changes in its kinetic properties induced by coupling to oxidative phosphorylation. *Arch. Biochem. Biophys.* 219:167–78

35. Jacobus, W. E., Vandegaer, K. M., Moreadith, R. W. 1984. Aspects of heart respiratory control by the mitochondrial isozyme of creatine kinase. See Ref. 8. In press

36. Kacser, H., Burns, J. J. 1979. Molecular democracy: Who shares the controls? *Biochem. Soc. Trans.* 7:1149–60

37. Kennedy, E. P., Lehninger, A. L. 1949. Oxidation of fatty acids and tricarboxylic acid cycle intermediates by isolated rat liver mitochondria. *J. Biol. Chem.* 179: 957–72

38. Kielley, W. W., Kielley, R. K. 1951. Myokinase and adenosinetriphosphatase in oxidative phosphorylation. *J. Biol. Chem.* 191:485–500

39. Klingenberg, M. 1961. Zur reversibilitat der oxydativen phosphorylierung. IV. Die beziehung zwischen dem redoxzustand des cytochrome c und dem phosphorylierungspotential des adenosintriphosphates. *Biochem. Z.* 335:263–72

40. Klingenberg, M., Pfaff, E. 1966. Structural and functional compartmentation in mitochondria. In *Regulation of Metabolic Processes in Mitochondria,* ed. J. M. Tager, S. Papa, E. Quagliariello, E. C. Slater, pp. 180–21. New York: American Elsevier

41. Kobayaski, K., Neely, J. R. 1979. Control of maximum rates of glycolysis in rat cardiac muscle. *Circ. Res.* 44:166–75

42. Kohn, M. C., Achs, M. J., Garfinkel, D. 1977. Distribution of adenine nucleotides in the perfused rat heart. *Am. J. Physiol.* 232:R158–63

43. Kunz, W., Bohnensack, R., Bohme, G., Kuster, U., Letko, G., et al. 1981. Relations between extramitochondrial and intramitochondrial adenine nucleotide sys-

tems. *Arch. Biochem. Biophys.* 209:219–29

44. Kuster, U., Bohnensack, R., Kunz, W. 1976. Control of oxidative phosphorylation by the extra-mitochondrial ATP/ADP ratio. *Biochem. Biophys. Acta* 440:391–402

45. Kuster, U., Letko, G., Kunz, W., Duszynsky, J., Bogucka, K., et al. 1981. Influence of different energy drains on the interrelationship between the rate of respiration, protonmotive force and adenine nucleotide patterns in isolated mitochondria. *Biochim. Biophys. Acta* 636:32–38

46. Lardy, H. A., Wellman, H. J. 1952. Oxidative phosphorylations: role of inorganic phosphate and acceptor systems in control of metabolic rates. *J. Biol. Chem.* 195:215–24

47. Lemasters, J. J., Sowers, A. E. 1979. Phosphate dependence and atractyloside inhibition of mitochondrial oxidative phosphorylation. The ADP/ATP carrier is rate-limiting. *J. Biol. Chem.* 254:1248–51

48. Letko, G., Kuster, U. 1979. Competition between extramitochondrial and intramitochondrial ATP-consuming processes. *Acta Biol. Med. Germ.* 38:1379–85

49. Letko, G., Kuster, U., Duszynski, J., Kunz, W. 1980. Investigation of the dependence of the intramitochondrial [ATP]/[ADP] ratio on the respiration rate. *Biochim. Biophys. Acta* 593:196–203

50. Lohmann, K. 1929. Uber die pyrophosphatfraktion im muskel. *Naturwissenschaft* 17:624–25

51. Lohmann, K. 1934. Uber die enzymatische aufsplatung der kreatinphosphorsaure; zugleich ein beitrag zum chemismus der muskelkontraktion. *Biochem. Z.* 271:264–77

52. Lundsgaard, E. 1930. Untersuchungen uber muskelkontraktionen ohne milchsaurebildung. *Biochem. Z.* 217:162–77

53. Matthews, P. M., Bland, J. L., Gadian, D. G., Radda, G. K. 1981. The steady-state rate of ATP synthesis in the perfused rat heart measured by ^{31}P NMR saturation transfer. *Biochem. Biophys. Res. Comm.* 103:1052–59

54. Moreadith, R. W., Jacobus, W. E. 1982. Creatine kinase of heart mitochondria. Functional coupling of ADP transfer to the adenine nucleotide translocase. *J. Biol. Chem.* 257:899–905

55. Mosbach, K. 1978. The microenvironment of immobilized multistep enzyme systems. In *Microenvironments and Metabolic Compartmentation*, ed. P. A.

Srere, R. W. Estabrook, pp. 381–400. New York: Academic

56. Niemeyer, H., Crane, R. K., Kennedy, E. P., Lippmann, F. 1951. Observations on respiration and phosphorylation with liver mitochondria of normal, hypo-, and hyperthyroid rats. *Fed. Proc.* 10:229

57. Nishiki, K., Erecinska, M., Wilson, D. F. 1978. Energy relationships between cystolic metabolism and mitochondrial respiration in rat heart. *Am. J. Physiol.* 234:C73–81

58. Owen, C. S., Wilson, D. F. 1974. Control of respiration by the mitochondrial phosphorylation state. *Archiv. Biochem. Biophys.* 161:581–91

59. Pfaff, E., Klingenberg, M. 1968. Adenine nucleotide translocation of mitochondria. 1. Specificity and control. *Eur. J. Biochem.* 6:66–79

60. Potter, V. R., Recknagel, R. O., Hurlbert, R. B. 1951. Intracellular enzyme distribution: interpretation and significance. *Fed. Proc.* 10:646–53

61. Rabinowitz, M., Stulberg, M. P., Boyer, P. D. 1951. The control of pyruvate oxidation in a cell-free rat heart preparation by phosphate acceptors. *Science* 114:641–42

62. Rapoport, T. A., Heinrich, R., Jacobasch, G., Rapoport, S. 1974. A linear steady-state treatment of enzymatic chains. A mathematical model of glycolysis of human erthrocytes. *Eur. J. Biochem.* 42:107–20

63. Reichert, M., Schaller, H., Kunz, W., Gerber, G. 1978. The dependence on the extramitochondrial ATP/ADP ratio of the oxidative phosphorylation in mitochondria isolated by a new procedure from rat skeletal muscle. *Acta Biol. Med. Ger.* 37:1167–76

64. Saks, V. A., Deppet, E. K., Smirnov, V. N. 1979. Does oxidative phosphorylation increase the rate of creatine phosphate synthesis in heart mitochondria or not? *J. Moll. Cell. Card.* 11:1253–73

65. Saks, V. A., Kupriyanov, G. V., Elizarova, G. V., Jacobus, W. E. 1980. Studies of energy transport in heart cells. The importance of creatine kinase localization for the coupling of mitochondrial phosphorylcreatine production to oxidative phosphorylation. *J. Biol. Chem.* 255:755–63

66. Saks, V. A., Lipina, N. V., Smirnov, V. N., Chazov, E. I. 1976. Studies of energy transport in heart cells. The functional coupling between mitochondrial creatine phosphokinase and ATP-ADP translocase: Kinetic evidence. *Arch. Biochem. Biophys.* 173:34–41

67. Saks, V. A., Rosenshtraukh, L. V.,

Smirnov, V. N., Chazov, E. I. 1978. Role of creatine phosphokinase in cellular function and metabolism. *Can. J. Physiol. Pharmacol.* 56:691–706

68. Schonfeld, P., Kuster, U. 1979. Functional investigations of isolated mitochondria under steady-state conditions by means of a perfusion technique. *Acta Biol. Med. Germ.* 38:1307–14

69. Seraydarian, M. W., Abbott, B. C. 1976. The role of the creatine-phosphorylcreatine system in muscle. *J. Mol. Cell. Cardiol.* 8:741–46

70. Siekevitz, P., Potter, V. R. 1953. Intramitochondrial regulation of oxidative rate. *J. Biol. Chem.* 210:1–13

71. Slater, E. C., Rosing, J., Mol, A. 1973. The phosphorylation potential generated by respiring mitochondria. *Biochim. Biophys. Acta* 292:543–53

72. Stoner, C. D., Sirac, H. D. 1979. Steady-state kinetics of the overall oxidative phosphorylation reaction in heart mitochondria. *J. Bioener. Biomemb.* 11: 113–46

73. Stubbs, M., Vignais, P. V., Krebs, H. A. 1978. Is the adenine nucleotide translocator rate-limiting for oxidative phosphorylation? *Biochem. J.* 172:333–42

74. Tager, J. M., Wanders, R. J. A., Groen, A. K., Kunz, W., Bohnensack, R., et al. 1983. Control of mitochondrial respiration. *FEBS Lett.* 151:1–9

75. Thunberg, T. 1911. Zur kenntnis des Kreatins. *Zent. Physiolog.* 25:915–16

76. Vandegaer, K. M., Jacobus, W. E. 1982. Evidence against direct transfer of the adenine nucleotides by the heart mitochondrial creatine kinase-adenine nucleotide translocase complex. *Biochem. Biophys. Res. Commun.* 109:442–48

77. van der Meer, R., Akerboom, T. P., Groen, A. K., Tager, J. M. 1978. Relationship between oxygen uptake of perfused rat-liver cells and the cytosolic phosphorylation state calculated from indicator metabolites and a redetermined equilibrium constant. *Eur. J. Biochem.* 84:421–28

78. Veech, R. L., Lawson, J. W. R., Cornell, N. M., Krebs, H. A. 1979. Cytosolic phosphorylation potential. *J. Biol. Chem.* 254:6538–47

79. Williamson, J. R., Schaffer, S. W., Ford, C., Safer, B. 1976. Contribution of tissue acidosis to ischemic injury in the perfused rat heart. *Circulation* 53:I3–I14

80. Wilson, D. F., Erecinska, Drown, C., Silver, I. A. 1979. The oxygen dependence of cellular energy metabolism. *Arch. Biochem. Biophys.* 195:485–93

81. Wilson, D. F., Forman, N. G. 1982. Mitochondrial transmembrane pH and electrical gradients: Evaluation of their energy relationships with respiratory rate and adenosine 5-triphosphate synthesis. *Biochemistry* 21:1438–44

82. Wilson, D. F., Owen, C. S., Holian, A. 1977. Control of mitochondrial respiration: A quantitative evaluation of the roles of cytochrome c and oxygen. *Arch. Biochem. Biophys.* 182:749–62

83. Wilson, D. F., Owen, C. S., Erecinska, E. 1979. Quantitative dependence of mitochondrial oxidative phosphorylation on oxygen concentration: a mathematical model. *Arch. Biochem. Biophys.* 195: 494–504

84. Wilson, D. F., Stubbs, M., Veech, R. L., Erecinska, M., Krebs, H. A. 1974. Equilibrium relations between the oxidation-reduction reactions and the adenosine triphosphate synthesis in suspensions of isolated liver cells. *Biochem. J.* 140:57–64

85. Yang, W. C. T., Geiger, P. J., Bessman, S. P., Borrebaek, B. 1977. Formation of creatine phosphate from creatine and ^{32}P-labeled ATP by isolated rabbit heart mitochondria. *Biochem. Biophys. Res. Commun.* 76:882–87

Ann. Rev. Physiol. 1985. 47:727–49

NUCLEOTIDE METABOLISM AND CELLULAR DAMAGE IN MYOCARDIAL ISCHEMIA

Robert B. Jennings and Charles Steenbergen, Jr.

Department of Pathology, Duke University Medical Center, Durham, North Carolina
27710

INTRODUCTION

The heart is dependent on aerobic metabolism for energy production. When coronary arterial flow is reduced to the point that insufficient O_2 is available for oxidative phosphorylation, the myocardium becomes ischemic (49). Although most of the acute biologic changes induced by ischemia occur because of the absolute deficiency of O_2, ischemia cannot be equated with high-flow anoxia or hypoxia, where oxygen deficiency is produced by removing O_2 from the perfusate without reducing the coronary flow rate. The absence of arterial flow during ischemia abolishes substrate delivery and prevents efflux of metabolic end products. Substrate delivery during high-flow hypoxia can be curtailed by removing substrate from the perfusate, but washout of products of metabolism occurs continuously. Because the maximum rate of ATP production from anaerobic glycolysis is less than 10% of the rate of oxidative phosphorylation necessary to sustain cardiac function (72, 137), the onset of ischemia or anoxia will be associated with a marked imbalance between energy production and energy utilization. The concentration of high-energy phosphate compounds in aerobic myocardium is small compared with the rate of ATP utilization; therefore, reserve stores of high-energy phosphates, principally creatine phosphate (CP), are consumed after the onset of anoxia. Contractile work is reduced shortly after aerobic metabolism ceases (39, 42, 132). As a result, the rate of ATP consumption is slowed. Nevertheless, there is a persistent deficit between ADP phosphorylation and ATP hydrolysis that causes net ATP content to decrease as the duration of ischemia or anoxia is prolonged (5, 50, 85, 90, 144).

727

0066-4278/85/0315-0727$02.00

The metabolic, structural, and functional alterations associated with ischemia have been evaluated in a number of different experimental models, including principally, (a) regional ischemia following coronary artery occlusion in vivo (51); (b) total ischemia in excised hearts or myocardium (52, 53, 107, 133); (c) cardioplegia in man or experimental animals (36, 61, 74); and (d) total or low-flow ischemia in isolated perfused hearts or septa (8, 39, 40, 104, 142). In addition, anoxia with or without substrate deprivation and/or metabolic inhibition have been studied in isolated perfused hearts and septa (89, 101, 111, 119, 144), in thin myocardial tissue slices (107), and in isolated myocyte preparations (14, 37).

The time course of metabolic, structural, and functional changes is different in these various models. Some of the variables that influence the rate of change in ischemic injury include the basal metabolic rate, the presence or absence of continued electrical activity, temperature, coronary flow rate, and whether the heart is in situ or has been excised (52, 53). Furthermore, after ligation of a coronary artery in the dog heart in vivo, the changes of injury develop much more rapidly in the subendocardium than in the subepicardium (105). This difference is due primarily to the low collateral flow of the endocardium but unidentified factors also may be involved (26, 105). Thus, duration of ischemia is only one of many variables influencing the severity of ischemic injury that makes comparisons of results obtained from different models and different laboratories difficult.

Ischemic injury traditionally has been divided into *reversible* and *irreversible* or lethal forms (47, 48, 52). These terms have been defined in the context of the in vivo coronary artery occlusion model of myocardial ischemia. Injury is *reversible* if restoration of arterial flow preserves myocyte viability, i.e. if removing the cause of the injury allows the myocyte to survive. Abnormalities may persist for several days in the injured myocytes, but they eventually return to their preischemic state. Injury is *irreversible* if restoration of arterial flow does not prevent cell death. Because reversible abnormalities may not be corrected immediately, unambiguous determination of the reversibility of ischemic injury requires a preparation that does not deteriorate for prolonged periods, so that reversibly injured cells have an opportunity to recover. In in vivo studies designed to define the transition from reversible to irreversible injury, plasma membrane disruption has been found to be a reliable indicator of lethal injury (52), because living myocardium never shows plasma membrane disruption by electron microscopy, while myocardium that cannot be saved by reperfusion invariably demonstrates this lesion. Plasma membrane disruption also can be detected in incubated tissue slices by entry of high-M_r polar compounds such as inulin into the intracellular space and by exit of intracellular proteins, creatine, NAD, and other normally impermeant compounds into the medium (52, 55, 105). Loss of plasma membrane integrity may not be the first alteration that makes ischemic damage irreversible, but it is a readily identifiable indicator that lethal injury has occurred (55).

The focus of this review is on the pathways of adenine nucleotide degradation during anoxia and ischemia, the effects of changes in adenine nucleotide levels on cellular functions such as contractility and maintenance of ion gradients during reversible ischemic injury, and the relationship between adenine nucleotide degradation and irreversible ischemic injury. The effects of ischemia on carbohydrate and lipid metabolism have been reviewed previously (137). There will be no discussion of other nucleotides such as the guanine nucleotides except to indicate that they also are depressed in ischemia (127). Although adenine nucleotide metabolism during myocardial ischemia is the subject of this review, selected data from other organs also will be discussed.

PATHWAYS OF ADENINE NUCLEOTIDE DEGRADATION

Early studies (9, 31, 90, 144) of adenine nucleotide changes during ischemia or anoxia revealed ATP hydrolysis with a transient elevation in ADP content, a more prolonged increase in AMP, followed by production of inosine (INO) and hypoxanthine (HX) (5, 6, 53). Conversion of AMP into INO could occur by two different pathways, one with adenosine (ADO) as an intermediate and the other with inosine monophosphate (IMP) as an intermediate. IMP accumulation is a prominent feature of ischemia in skeletal muscle but occurs to only a limited extent during myocardial ischemia (6), a difference that reflects the relative contents of AMP deaminase in these tissues (78). Thus the predominant pathway of INO production in myocardium appears to involve dephosphorylation of AMP by 5' nucleotidase to form ADO followed by deamination with adenosine deaminase (137).

The changes in adenine nucleotide levels during severe ischemia in vivo in the pentobarbitol-anesthetized open-chest dog heart are shown in Figure 1. ATP falls to one-third of control within 15 minutes. Adenosine is elevated transiently, but even at 10 min, INO is the dominant degradation product. By 40 min, the adenine nucleotide pool (ATP + ADP + AMP) is reduced to less than 40% of control, and INO accounts for about 50% of the adenine nucleotides, nucleosides, and bases. After longer durations of total ischemia, in vitro, HX accumulation becomes more pronounced while INO content declines. Similar results have been obtained by numerous investigators (2, 9, 21, 60, 61, 127, 146).

The regulation of ADO synthesis and degradation has been the focus of much research effort because ADO is a potent vasodilator that may be responsible for coronary vasodilation during myocardial hypoxia or after an episode of ischemia [reviewed in more detail in (7) and (29)]. Myocardial hypoxia increases

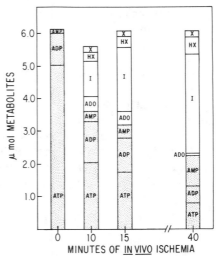

Figure 1 Low-flow ischemia, produced by proximal occlusion of the left circumflex coronary artery in the dog heart, induces the changes in the left ventricular adenine nucleotide pool that are summarized in this diagram. Because the collateral flow of low-flow ischemia ranges from 0–7% of control in this model, the adenine nucleotide pool and its breakdown products are quantitatively recovered after as long as 60 min of ischemia. The distribution of the pool in control nonischemic tissue is plotted at 0 time. ATP is the principal component of the adenine nucleotide pool both in control and reversibly injured myocardium (10 and 15 min of ischemia); during the reversible phase, it falls quickly, reaching 35% of control late in the reversible phase (15 min). ADP is increased significantly after 10 but not after 15 min of ischemia. AMP is increased significantly after all periods of ischemia, as are ADO, INO, HX, and XAN. After 10 and 15 min of ischemia, the ΣAd pool is reduced to 3.5 and 3.25 μmol respectively, and by 40 min, it is only 2.4 μmol/g wet wt. In the early irreversible phase (40 min), ATP is < 10% and ADP is < 50% of control, while AMP is markedly increased. Note that ADO levels fall in the irreversible phase and that INO is the principal nucleotide detected at the time intervals presented. After several hours of severe ischemia, most of the INO is converted to HX. (Reprinted with permission of Raven Press, New York.)

tissue ADO content and ADO release into the effluent (112, 115, 117, 119). Inhibition of ADO deaminase does not completely abolish INO production during hypoxia (64, 109), which may be due to incomplete inhibition of intracellular ADO deaminase; however, these data leave open the possibility that IMP may be the precursor of some of the INO.

According to the adenosine hypothesis (7), ADO produced by oxygen-deficient myocytes must be released into the extracellular space in sufficient amounts to reach vasoactive concentrations in the vicinity of coronary arterioles. Histochemical studies in hearts from various species have revealed that 5' nucleotidase activity is localized primarily in external cell membranes (113). Thus, it has been suggested that hydrolysis of AMP would result in prompt release of ADO into the interstitial space, thereby avoiding further degradation by intracellular ADO deaminase (7). In conflict with this hypothesis, membrane 5' nucleotidase appears to be primarily an ecto-enzyme, accessible to extracellular AMP, but not necessarily intracellular AMP (29). Recently, a soluble cytosolic isoenzyme of 5' nucleotidase has been detected that would allow ADO to be produced throughout the sarcoplasm (79, 120). Inhibition of the membrane-associated nucleotidase during myocardial hypoxia alters neither ADO production nor release into the effluent and its subsequent degradation (120). Inhibition of purine nucleoside transport during myocardial hypoxia resulted in tissue accumulation of ADO and INO, in approximately the same ratio as observed in the effluent in the absence of transport inhibition (120). These data indicate that intracellular ADO can increase substantially despite the presence of intracellular ADO deaminase of high activity.

The V_{max} of cytosolic 5' nucleotidase is much less than that of the membrane-associated enzyme. Although it has been suggested that the activity of cytosolic 5' nucleotidase is sufficient to account for physiologic ADO production (120), it is unlikely to account for all ADO production during ischemia. The flux through 5' nucleotidase during the first 10 min of severe ischemia in vivo in dog heart would be 200–250 nmol/min/g wet wt, based on either ADO, INO, HX, and xanthine (XAN) production or adenine nucleotide (ATP + ADP + AMP) depletion (57). This is greater than the measured capacity of the cytosolic 5' nucleotidase (120); thus, either the activity of the cytosolic enzyme has been underestimated or at least a portion of the sarcolemmal 5' nucleotidase may be accessible to intracellular AMP and may contribute to ADO production in ischemia. Nevertheless, it seems likely that much ADO is produced intracellularly in ischemic myocardium.

ADO deaminase, which converts ADO to INO, is present in cardiac myocytes, pericytes, and endothelial cells (7, 29). Although a small amount of ADO may be catabolized to INO extracellularly (43), the degradation of extracellular ADO predominantly involves transport into the cytosol of myocytes, pericytes, or endothelial cells. This transport is probably not limiting, because ADO is taken up rapidly by a variety of cell types (76, 99, 120) regardless of ATP depletion (99). The fate of intracellular ADO appears to be determined by the ADO concentration and the metabolic status of the cell. Under aerobic conditions, at low ADO concentrations, ADO is converted primarily to AMP by ADO kinase, whereas at higher concentrations deamination to INO predominates (76, 88, 104, 120). Under anaerobic conditions, ADO kinase probably is inhibited by low sarcoplasmic ATP.

Intracellular INO can readily exit into the extracellular space, as indicated by the rapid washout of tissue INO during anoxic perfusion of isolated hearts. INO efflux is stimulated by the concentration gradient produced by the removal of extracellular INO. During low-flow or total ischemia, where diffusion to the systemic circulation is greatly slowed or absent, INO efflux would raise the extracellular concentration and ultimately inhibit further efflux. Thus, because the intracellular compartment is so much larger than the extracellular space, much of the INO produced in the myocytes would be expected to be intracellular during the early phase of low-flow ischemia. During reperfusion, washout of tissue INO far exceeds reincorporation into adenine nucleotides. This may reflect the slow rate of INO conversion to IMP (76).

Hypoxanthine is produced from INO by purine nucleoside phosphorylase. Histochemical studies have revealed that this enzyme is present in pericytes and endothelial cells but not in cardiac myocytes (114); this observation has been confirmed in isolated heart cell preparations, where INO degradation is not observed (37). Although HX is not produced in myocytes, some may be accumulated in these cells due to release of this metabolite from pericytes and endothelial cells with subsequent uptake by myocytes, which possess a HX uptake mechanism (40). Xanthine also is produced during ischemia (23, 53). Xanthine production from HX requires either oxygen or nicotinamide-adenine dinucleotide (NAD), both of which are in low concentration during prolonged ischemia. This accounts for the observation that XAN production is greatest early in the ischemic interval (23, 53). The sites of XAN production will be strongly influenced by the distribution of HX in the ischemic myocardium.

The contents of the adenine nucleotide catabolites, ADO, INO, HX, and XAN, during ischemia are determined by the availability of precursors and the sites and kinetic characteristics of the degradative enzymes discussed above. Tissue ADO increases early during ischemia but ADO never accounts for more than 5% of the total adenine nucleotide pool, i.e., the sum of the adenine nucleotides, nucleosides, and bases (6, 53) (Figure 1) unless anaerobic glycolysis is inhibited (56). INO is the predominant end product of adenine nucleotide degradation during the early phase of ischemia; eventually, i.e. hours later, HX becomes the dominant metabolite (53). Moreover, INO is the major adenine nucleotide catabolite released into the effluent during hypoxia (119, 131) or during ischemia (22, 119).

Although the rate of INO production appears to be determined by the concentration of its immediate precursor, ADO, the relationship between ADO production and AMP concentration is more complex (7, 118). ADO production and ADO content are highest early during the ischemic interval and then decline while AMP levels peak after longer durations of ischemia (Figure 1) (53). AMP is compartmentalized; the cytosolic component of the initial rise in AMP content is presumably due to the action of sarcoplasmic myokinase and is kept small because it is degraded rapidly by either cytosolic or membrane bound 5' nucleotidase. On the other hand, the mitochondrial component of AMP is inaccessible to sarcoplasmic 5' nucleotidase and may account for much of the rise shown at 40 min in Figure 1. Another proposal is that cAMP may be the precursor of a separate AMP pool that is associated with the plasma membrane and would serve as a preferred substrate for membrane-bound 5' nucleotidase (73, 95, 117). cAMP increases early in ischemia due to release of endogenous catecholamines (145). However, the time course of changes in the rates of cAMP synthesis and hydrolysis in ischemic myocardium is unclear, and therefore the importance of this pathway cannot be unambiguously determined. ADO production also may be affected by the regulatory characteristics of membrane-bound and soluble cytosolic 5' nucleotidase. It has been shown that the membrane-bound enzyme is inhibited by ADP and to a lesser extent ATP (29, 79), but if this enzyme is located exclusively on the outside of the plasma membrane, its activity may be unaffected by changes in intracellular metabolite concentrations. However, if a portion of the membrane 5' nucleotidase faces the cytosolic compartment, its activity should be enhanced during prolonged ischemia due to the decline in ATP and ADP contents. In contrast, the soluble cytosolic 5' nucleotidase is activated by both ATP and ADP (79), and therefore the activity of the cytosolic enzyme would be expected to decrease during prolonged ischemia, perhaps contributing to the observed reduction in ADO production late in ischemia despite elevated tissue AMP levels.

In summary, adenine nucleotide degradation during low-flow ischemia occurs rapidly and results primarily in accumulation of INO, a significant proportion of which resides in the sarcoplasm of the myocytes. During reperfusion of reversibly injured tissue, adenine nucleotide levels could be restored to near normal if intracellular INO phosphorylation proceeded more rapidly than INO efflux. However, the capacity of myocytes to convert INO into a nucleotide is limited (76), and most of the INO is washed out of the heart. Thus, ischemia has two deleterious effects on adenine nucleotide metabolism: it lowers the phosphorylation potential which restricts the ability of myocytes to perform maintenance functions that are essential for prolonged viability; and it results in loss of the adenine pool, so that even with reperfusion, adenine nucleotide levels are not restored immediately to their control values.

MYOCARDIAL FUNCTION AND DIMINISHED ATP LEVELS

ATP is essential for myocardial function in that hydrolysis of ATP provides the energy for contraction, the maintenance of ion gradients, and for macromolecular synthesis (137). Myocardial energy demands under normal conditions are high and only can be met by high rates of oxidative phosphorylation (80). During ischemia, the rate of ADP phosphorylation is markedly diminished at the onset of anaerobic conditions and becomes further depressed as the duration of ischemia increases (56). If ATP consumption continues at its preischemic rate, reserves of high-energy phosphate would be depleted within the first minute of ischemia. However, the rate of ATP utilization is reduced in the ischemic cell, with the result that enough ATP is present within the severely ischemic myocytes to maintain certain functions for a significant period of time (Figure 1).

Contractility

The major ATP-utilizing reaction in myocardium is the actin-myosin ATPase, which couples ATP hydrolysis and contraction. Within seconds after the onset of anoxia, contractility declines and the affected tissue essentially becomes acontractile (39, 132). The same response is observed regardless of whether anoxia is induced by cessation of perfusion or by removal of oxygen from the perfusion fluid. The onset of contractile failure is associated temporally with a substantial decline in CP and a quantitatively much smaller decrease in ATP (31, 100, 144). Whether adenine nucleotide changes are of sufficient magnitude and rapidity to cause the abrupt decline in contractile function is unclear (42, 84). However, studies of in vitro preparations of isolated myofibrils (139) and cardiac myocytes with hyperpermeable plasma membranes (25, 81) have shown that contractility is unaffected by changes in ATP concentration between 5 mM and 0.03 mM. Assuming that ATP is evenly distributed in the cellular water, this is a much greater range of ATP concentration than is observed at the time contractility is decreasing early in ischemia. Even if ATP concentration per se does not regulate the actin-myosin ATPase, it is possible that catabolites such as AMP or inorganic phosphate, which show large changes in concentration early during ischemia, might have an inhibitory effect on the ATPase, thereby reducing tension development, or that a fall in phosphorylation potential results in contractile failure (62).

An alternative hypothesis is that acid accumulation is responsible for contractile failure under anoxic conditions (65). It has been shown that intracellular pH declines shortly after the onset of anoxia, regardless of whether anoxia results from cessation of perfusion (16, 65) or removal of oxygen from the perfusate (1, 17). However, it is unclear whether the rate and the magnitude of the pH change is sufficient to account for the rapid decline in tension development during anoxia.

Living reperfused contracting myocardium with a low ATP secondary to an episode of ischemia exhibits depressed contractility for 24 or more hr (44, 140). The explanation for this in vivo phenomenon is unknown. Although an association between myocardial ATP content and ventricular function following oxygen deprivation has been reported (103), accelerated ATP repletion after ischemia did not improve postischemic regional myocardial function (46).

Ion Gradients

Maintenance of ion gradients is an ATP-dependent process. Intracellular Ca and Na concentrations are maintained at levels far below their extracellular concentrations by the sarcolemmal (Na^+,K^+)-ATPase, Ca-ATPases in the plasma membrane and sarcoplasmic reticulum (SR), the mitochondrial Ca pump, and sarcolemmal Na/Ca exchange, which uses the Na gradient established by the (Na^+,K^+)-ATPase. Shortly after the onset of ischemia, interstitial

K concentration increases (41, 45, 66, 67, 142, 143), which might suggest that the (Na^+,K^+)-ATPase is inhibited. However, many investigators have described a plateau in the rise in interstitial K that occurs after 10–15 min of ischemia and lasts until the onset of lethal cell injury (45, 67, 142, 143), at which point it rises to much higher levels because of release of K through the damaged membrane of the dying cells or a K channel activated at 1 mM ATP (94). The initial plateau occurs at an interstitial K of 10–15 mM (45, 66, 67, 142, 143), far below the intracellular K concentration, indicating that a substantial K gradient is maintained during the reversible phase of ischemic injury presumably due to continuing activity of the (Na^+,K^+)-ATPase (67). The fact that intracellular Na activity decreases slightly during the initial 10–15 min of ischemia (66) also suggests that the (Na^+,K^+)-ATPase is active and that a substantial Na gradient is maintained and even increased early during ischemia. The increased interstitial K of early ischemia is probably not solely a function of inhibition of the (Na^+,K^+)-ATPase. The net loss in intracellular K can be accounted for by increased K efflux rather than decreased influx (101). This efflux is probably a volume regulatory response stimulated by the production of intracellular osmotic particles that results in water uptake to maintain osmotic equilibrium (30, 135). Potassium loss is a common response to osmotic swelling in myocytes (96, 97) and other cells (12). Although inhibition of the (Na^+,K^+)-ATPase does not appear to be a feature of early ischemic injury, prolonged oxygen deficiency with (98) or without (55, 82) glycolytic inhibition is associated with increased tissue Na despite intact plasma membranes, suggesting that marked ATP depletion can depress Na/K pump activity.

The effect of energy availability on Ca homeostasis is more difficult to analyze because of the involvement of multiple organelles and membrane systems. The Ca gradient across the plasma membrane is greater than 1000, and is maintained by a Ca-ATPase and Na/Ca exchange (13). As long as the Na gradient is maintained, it seems likely that the Ca gradient could be maintained as well. This concept is supported by the observation that extracellular Ca concentration rises slightly during the initial minutes of myocardial ischemia, in parallel with a slight rise in extracellular Na (30). Nevertheless, cytosolic free Ca concentration could increase early during ischemia without Ca influx if intracellular Ca sequestration sites such as SR and mitochondria released stored Ca. Ca uptake by SR is coupled to ATP hydrolysis, but the ATP dependence of the ATPase of SR is complex. Although the K_m for ATP appears to be less than 50 μM (122), the rate of ATP hydrolysis is decreased by increasing the ADP concentration (122), suggesting that the drop in cytosolic phosphorylation potential that occurs during anaerobic conditions could impair Ca accumulation by SR. SR Ca pump activity is regulated also by cAMP dependent phosphorylation of phospholamban, a microsomal protein (128–130). Phospholamban phosphorylation approximately doubles the velocity of the SR Ca-ATPase at

ATP concentrations above the K_m (128). During the initial phase of ischemia, the rise in cAMP may result in enhanced Ca uptake into the SR, but the progressive fall in phosphorylation potential will ultimately restrict Ca sequestration. Continued electrical activity resulting in release of stored Ca, combined with impaired sequestration, would tend to raise basal cytosolic free Ca concentrations. Furthermore, the SR Ca-ATPase is reversible, and Ca efflux from Ca loaded SR vesicles can be coupled to ATP synthesis in the presence of ADP, inorganic phosphate, and magnesium (24, 130). This process is inhibited by extravesicular Ca concentrations in the μM range. Thus, due to a variety of mechanisms, it is not only possible but likely that SR Ca stores become displaced into the sarcoplasm during prolonged ischemia, but the kinetics and magnitude of this process remain to be determined.

In addition to SR, mitochondria also accumulate Ca, a process that requires ATP or a membrane potential. Studies of mitochondrial Ca transport in a variety of tissues (91, 93) have demonstrated that Ca accumulation is an energy dependent process that becomes impaired when the mitochondrial membrane potential falls. Ca efflux from isolated mitochondria can occur by two mechanisms (92). First, there is Na-induced Ca efflux in heart mitochondria, which is half activated at 8 mM cytosolic Na activity (19). Because the cytosolic Na activity is normally in this range (57, 66, 75) Ca efflux from mitochondria would be expected to be sensitive to increased intracellular Na. The second mechanism is reversal of the Ca uptake pathway, which can occur with collapse of the mitochondrial membrane potential (92, 93). Ca efflux from mitochondria in excess of uptake occurs under a variety of conditions where there is a low mitochondrial membrane potential and a loss of matrix adenine nucleotides (4, 92, 93). Both of these changes would occur eventually during ischemia, but the time course is unknown. Furthermore, the amount of endogenous mitochondrial Ca at the onset of ischemia, i.e. in control tissue, has not been determined unambiguously. Because of binding sites and limited endogenous supplies of Ca^{2+}, even if mitochondria released all matrix Ca early during the ischemic interval, the magnitude of the rise in cytosolic free Ca is unclear (57, 58).

Macromolecular Synthesis and Degradation

Even though myocytes are stable, nondividing cells, all components of the myocyte are continuously turning over (86, 87). Degradation without continued synthesis of replacement components, "turnover without replacement", could be a cause of lethal ischemic injury (52). For instance, internalization of segments of the plasma membrane during pinocytosis without replacement could result in lysis of the membrane. However, rates of turnover of plasma membrane components have not been easy to measure in ischemia. Protein synthesis is an energy-requiring process that is inhibited by anaerobiosis. Although this could be important in ischemic injury, protein degradation also is inhibited during energy-deficient conditions (87). The normal turnover rate for myocardial proteins such as myosin or cytochromes is days; thus, unless degradation of a specific protein is activated during ischemia, proteolysis is unlikely to contribute to early ischemic injury. The effects of ischemia on turnover of other cellular components are less well known, as is the influence of these processes on function and viability.

ADENINE NUCLEOTIDE DEGRADATION AND IRREVERSIBLE ISCHEMIC INJURY

Changes Associated With Lethal Injury

In low-flow regional ischemia, myocardial ATP steadily falls until it reaches 1–2% of control, 60 min after the onset (52). The involved tissue is reversibly injured for about the first 15 min, during which time the ATP has declined by 65% (Figure 1). Irreversible injury develops as the duration of ischemia is extended, but the transition from reversible to irreversible ischemic injury is not sharp. The continuum of changes developing in the severely or totally ischemic myocardium during the transition from the reversible to the irreversible phase include (52, 57): (a) depression of high-energy phosphate content and phosphorylation potential; (b) gradual loss of myocyte glycogen; (c) accumulation of metabolic end products, principally lactate, H^+, AMP, INO, inorganic phosphate, ammonium, and glycolytic intermediates; (d) increased osmolality and cellular edema; and (e) progressive ultrastructural changes. From this large and probably incomplete set of biologic changes, it is not now possible to identify the specific abnormality or abnormalities that cause(s) the transition to irreversibility. Nevertheless, it is possible to define those conditions that analysis shows are invariably associated with the irreversible state. These include: (a) very low levels of high-energy phosphates (creatine phosphate < 1–2% of control, ATP < 10% of control); (b) virtual cessation of anaerobic glycolysis; (c) conversion of > 75% of the adenine nucleotide pool to nucleosides and bases, primarily INO and HX; and (d) characteristic ultrastructural lesions including the formation of mitochondrial amorphous matrix densities and plasma membrane disruption.

A relationship between ATP depletion and lethal myocardial injury has been noted in numerous studies using duration of ischemia or the presence of various pharmacologic agents as the independent variable (10, 50, 53, 108, 116). In general, those agents that preserve ATP during ischemia also decrease the extent of myocardial necrosis. Likewise, cardioplegia and/or hypothermia (36, 61, 74) which reduce the demand for ATP, markedly ameliorate the effects of ischemia on myocyte viability and provide indirect evidence for an association between ATP depletion and cell death.

The importance of ATP to myocyte function and integrity is further emphasized by the comparison between the presence and absence of glucose as a substrate in high-flow anoxia in the isolated perfused heart. As indicated by complete recovery during reoxygenation, no permanent myocyte damage is sustained during 60 or more min of high-flow anoxia with exogenous glucose (136), whereas substrate-free anoxia of shorter duration is associated with massive enzyme release and marked ultrastructural alterations during reoxygenation (32, 33). After an initial burst of glycogenolysis, glycolytic flux is negligible during prolonged substrate-free anoxia. With exogenous glucose in the perfusate, anaerobic glycolysis produces a net of only 2 μmol of ATP per μmol of exogenous glucose converted to lactate, but this apparently is sufficient to maintain cellular integrity. Although these data suggest that the decline in ATP concentration and phosphorylation potential may be the ultimate cause of cell death, they do not indicate the precise quantity of ATP required for viability nor do they imply a mechanism of lethal injury. The minimum myocardial concentration associated with preservation of excellent cardiac contractile function in the whole animal is known to be 3.5 to 4.0 μmol/g wet wt (36, 74).

Determination of the quantitative relationship between loss of ATP and loss of cell viability in regional ischemia in vivo is complicated by the heterogeneous nature of ischemic necrosis and by the likelihood that cell death leads to a rapid hydrolysis of any remaining ATP. Estimates of the minimum level of ATP compatible with viability are 20–40% of the control value (107, 116). These are likely to be overestimates due to the inhomogeneity of ischemia and the need for virtual 100% viability in the sample tested. The lowest estimates have been obtained in excised myocardial preparations late in the reversible phase of injury (53).

Lethal ischemic injury has been studied in tissues other than heart, and there are significant differences in the relationship between ATP depletion and cellular viability in some of these tissues (27, 28) when compared to heart. In brain (68, 69), kidney (138), and liver (15, 63), energy production and energy utilization is imbalanced at the onset of ischemia; a loss of high-energy phosphate compounds, primarily ATP, occurs quickly but does not result in immediate irreversible injury. Ischemic neurons, hepatocytes, and renal tubular cells appear to survive with low ATP longer than myocytes. In each of these tissues as in heart, only small amounts of ATP may be necessary to sustain cellular integrity; if this is true, lethal injury occurs at some time after ATP declines below this level.

The pathogenesis of irreversibility in ischemic injury has not been established. Numerous changes are occurring simultaneously and it has been difficult to develop good objective evidence in support of any hypothesis as to pathogenesis. For this reason, it has been impossible to identify the connection, if any, between ATP depletion and cell death. The hypotheses that have been proposed fall into two broad categories: those that relate ATP depletion to myocyte death while the cells are permamently ischemic, and those that relate irreversibility to defects caused by reperfusion of ischemic myocytes with arterial blood. Even in the latter case, however, myocytes are conditioned by ischemia for a deleterious response to reperfusion.

Pathogenesis of Ischemic Myocyte Death

Cell death occurs quickly in zones of low-flow ischemia and is characterized by the changes noted previously, including principally: (a) depletion of both cellular ATP and the adenine nucleotide pool, acidosis, slowing and eventual cessation of anaerobic glycolysis, and ultrastructural changes; (b) an increase in the osmotic load of the damaged myocytes; (c) disruption of the sarcolemma; and (d) a variety of other changes such as high AMP, INO, HX, NH_4^+, etc. When the foregoing changes are well developed, the injury is irreversible. However, it is not known whether or how any of these changes, or as yet unidentified changes, directly or indirectly cause the injury to become lethal. However, the clear relationship between the release of cellular constituents into the extracellular space and cell death in other cellular systems, and the presence of membrane damage in ischemic injury at or about the time that irreversibility supervenes, suggests this may be the important change in the development of irreversibility in ischemia (52). The changes occurring in zones of moderate or high-flow ischemia in vivo are less well established because of the difficulty of identifying such tissue for study plus the heterogeneous nature of the changes. Therefore the following discussion pertains only to low-flow or total ischemia.

CALCIUM HOMEOSTASIS AND LETHAL INJURY   A rise in sarcoplasmic free $[Ca^{2+}]$ is the critical component of many current hypotheses of the genesis of the irreversible state (28, 52). An increase to 100 μmol could induce cell death by: (a) activation of endogenous proteases that could weaken the sarcolemma or the cytoskeletal supports of the sarcolemma (55, 57); (b) activation of the endogenous phospholipase of the plasmalemma of the sarcolemma with subsequent membrane disruption (52); and (c) disruption of the plasmalemma via development of strong contracture-rigor (33, 57). The calcium-activated neutral protease (CANP) of ventricular muscle affects Z-line and cytoskeletal components (102, 134) but has virtually no activity under physiologic conditions. It requires an ambient Ca concentration of 10^{-4} to 10^{-3} M (134). Similar sarcoplasmic $[Ca^{2+}]$ levels are required for activation of membrane phospholipases in ischemia. However, phospholipase activation seems to occur after, rather than before, membrane damage in ischemia is well developed (126). Each of the above hypotheses requires an increase in $[Ca^{2+}]_i$ from 10^{-7} to 10^{-4} M. Such an increase is possible in severe ischemia but unlikely because of the limited endogenous supplies and the numerous binding sites available to lower the ambient concentration (57). However, an increase in cytosolic $[Ca^{2+}]$ of this magnitude may not be required for CANP activation, since low-calcium-requiring forms have been identified (18, 20, 83), and it has been suggested that CANP activity may be regulated by conversion between high-calcium-requiring and low-calcium-requiring forms (20), and by a protein inhibitor of CANP (18). Further experimental work will be required to determine if CANP participates in the development of ischemic injury.

Release of endogenous Ca^{2+} from the SR and mitochondria may occur late in the reversible phase of ischemia when supplies of sarcoplasmic ATP become limiting for the (Na^+,K^+)-ATPase and the Ca-ATPases of the sarcolemma and SR. The increased sarcoplasmic Ca^{2+} could have the effect of terminally speeding ATP depletion via the Ca ATPase in portions of the myocyte still containing ATP. So far, in total ischemia, no such acceleration of ATP depletion has been detected (53).

Raised cytosolic Ca also could induce the initial reversible increase in diastolic resting tension (contracture) observed in anoxia or ischemia, although the large, irreversible increase in resting tension, seen later, is more likely attributable to the formation of rigor complexes secondary to the virtual absence of ATP (77). The shortening of myofibrils associated with contracture-rigor may be a factor in the loss of structural integrity in lethally injured ischemic myocytes (33). Furthermore, contracture-rigor may compress blood vessels and thus restrict the capacity for reperfusion (35). However, the no-reflow phenomenon in ischemic myocardium appears to develop after irreversible damage already has occurred and thus is unlikely to be a factor in cell death (70).

COMPARISON OF ANOXIA AND ISCHEMIA   Although ATP depletion and raised $[Ca^{2+}]_i$ may be crucial factors in the development of lethal injury, the comparison between ischemia and substrate-free anoxia suggest that these may not be the only factors. ATP depletion occurs in both conditions, and $[Ca^{2+}]_i$ would be expected to rise in both instances, with a greater increase occurring in anoxia than in total ischemia because the increase in $[Ca^{2+}]_i$ is limited in total ischemia by the amount of endogenous Ca, whereas in anoxia, supplies of Ca^{2+} are essentially unlimited. Despite these similarities, ultra-structurally recognizable signs of lethal injury, i.e. plasma membrane fragmentation, appear during ischemia but not during anoxia even with a comparable reduction in tissue ATP (55). Reoxygenation or physical stress is capable of inducing plasma membrane damage after substrate-free anoxia, but ischemia requires no other perturbation to induce a similar degree of injury, suggesting that there are factor(s) present in ischemia and absent during substrate-free anoxia that are important in the development of lethal injury.

One difference between ischemia and substrate-free anoxia that may account for the discrepancy in plasma membrane structural damage is the accumulation of intracellularly produced, osmotically active particles such as lactate, $H_2PO_4^-$, and H^+ in a confined volume during ischemia. In anoxia, or in the presence of metabolic inhibitors, myocytes maintain cell volume (97) because of K^+ efflux as well as through diffusion of metabolically produced osmotic particles out of the tissue. However, K^+ efflux during ischemia is limited by accumulation of released K^+ by the small volume of trapped interstitial fluid; thus, intracellular production of osmotic particles results in increased tissue osmolality, cell swelling, and eventual membrane disruption. Similar changes can be induced by prolonged anoxic incubation, but only by swelling the affected myocytes in hypotonic media. This produces plasma membrane disruption with the same ultrastructural appearance as the fragmented plasma membranes of irreversibly injured ischemic myocardium (125). These results suggest that a defect in the plasma membrane or its cytoskeletal support network develops as a consequence of energy deprivation, either in ischemia or substrate-free anoxia. This defect, per se, does not cause plasma membrane disruption, but it allows the plasmalemma to rupture when it is subjected to cell swelling or mechanical stress secondary to contracture-rigor or resumption of contractile activity during reoxygenation (32).

EFFECTS OF REPERFUSION ON ISCHEMIC MYOCARDIUM   Successful restoration of the arterial flow to reversibly injured ischemic tissue results in preservation of cellular viability and partial restoration of ATP content, but contractile function remains depressed. Creatine phosphate is restored to supernormal levels (127), and the adenylate charge returns to normal in < 3 min. Virtually all of the increase in ATP comes from phosphorylation of the ADP and AMP of the ischemic tissue (57). Further resynthesis of adenine nucleotides occurs very slowly unless substrates for salvage synthesis, such as adenosine, are provided (21, 104, 106, 127). However, accelerated restitution of the adenine nucleotide pool with adenosine infusion does not restore contractility to its preischemic level (46).

Successful reperfusion of myocardium early in the phase defined as irreversible injury, i.e. with low ATP, high lactate, disrupted plasma membranes, and mitochondrial damage, produces striking changes in the damaged myocytes. During reflow, after 40 min of in vivo ischemia, the myocytes swell explosively and exhibit broken subsarcolemmal blebs, massive contraction bands, and mitochondria with calcium phosphate. The Ca for the massive loading is provided by the plasma reperfusing the tissue (121). Moreover, the extracellular Ca is believed to enter the damaged myocytes as a consequence of structural and functional changes induced in the sarcolemma of the myocyte during ischemia. If this hypothesis is correct, reperfusion simply provides an environment in which the "funeral" events of necrosis are accelerated (54, 57, 58, 121).

Although reperfusion is evenly distributed after 40 min of in vivo ischemia, vascular damage induced by ischemia prevents uniform reperfusion after 90 minutes of coronary artery occlusion (70). In the zones which are successfully reperfused at 90 min, contraction-bands form, but mitochondrial Ca^{2+} accumulation does not occur. After 2 hr of ischemia, most of the zone of low-flow ischemia cannot be reperfused.

Because it is known that myocytes subjected to low-flow ischemia without reperfusion eventually die, the question of whether reperfusion itself causes cell injury cannot be answered unless it can be shown that damage observed after reperfusion occurred while the myocytes were still alive, i.e. prior to the onset of true irreversibility. If Ca entry is lethal and is occurring through mechanisms remediable by resumption of oxidative metabolism, then prevention of Ca entry from the plasma by lowering plasma Ca^{2+} during the early phase of reperfusion should prevent cell death in in vivo ischemia. This experiment has never been successfully performed in vivo (3, 110). Attempts to prevent Ca overload in isolated hearts perfused with crystalloidal solutions using enzyme release as an end point have been reported to be successful (141). However, the relationship of the in vitro results to in vivo ischemia remains to be established.

Generation of free radicals in the high O_2 environment of the reactive hyperemia of reperfusion also could kill potentially viable myocytes damaged by ischemia. The ischemic myocardium contains abundant HX as well as some xanthine oxidase. The conversion of HX to XAN can lead to the formation of superoxide and hydroxyl radicals, which are known to damage cell membranes (11, 124). Moreover, the endogenous enzymes that protect against free-radical injury are lost under anoxic conditions, thereby making the tissue more susceptible to injury by free radicals (59). The importance of this mechanism can be inferred from the reported beneficial effect of infusion of free radical scavengers on infarct size, following coronary artery occlusion and reperfusion, and on enzyme release following high-flow hypoxia and reoxygenation (59, 123). However, an observation that tempers enthusiasm for the free-radical hypothesis of reperfusion damage is the fact that membrane damage does not develop late in the reversible phase of ischemic injury when myocardium is reperfused, even though abundant HX is present (Figure 1).

Lastly, reperfusion promotes the development of massive swelling of myocytes irreversibly injured by ischemia. The damaged myocytes swell explosively, presumably because of the response of tissue with high osmolality to reperfusion with 300 mOsm plasma. The large osmotic gradient between the intravascular space and the tissue results in cell swelling that further disrupts myocyte membranes. Moreover, swollen myocytes and endothelial cells in the ischemic reperfused focus may restrict continued arterial flow and thereby induce renewed ischemia—the so-called "no-reflow phenomenon" (70). It is of interest that reperfusion with hypertonic fluid has been shown to have a beneficial effect on the extent of ischemic necrosis, but it is unclear whether this is due to the direct effects of mannitol on the ischemic myocytes or the endothelial cells, or both (71, 135).

SUMMARY

Adenine nucleotide metabolism is greatly altered by myocardial anoxia or ischemia, both of which induce depletion of ATP and of the total adenine nucleotide pool. The depletion occurs at variable rates depending upon the nature of the model and the severity and conditions of the injury. In ischemia, the decrease in both ATP and the adenine nucleotide pool is due to an inadequate rate of production of high-energy phosphate relative to the demand of the heart for energy. In the process of capturing the high-energy phosphate of ADP, AMP is produced via myokinase and is degraded to nucleosides and ultimately to bases. In the early phase of ischemia, ADO and INO are the chief metabolites produced. A small quantity of XAN and large quantities of HX accumulate with time until eventually HX replaces INO as the principal metabolite of the pool.

The biology of myocardial ischemic cell damage in the dog heart is summarized with respect to the depletion of ATP and total adenine nucleotide pool. Myocytes can survive with about 25% of the ATP of control tissue but exhibit a variety of defects that persist for minutes to days. At the onset of irreversibility, the dead tissue invariably exhibits virtually no ATP and a 65% or greater depletion in the total adenine nucleotide pool. It is not known whether these changes in ATP and the pool are directly or indirectly related to the development of irreversibility. In any event, the transition to cell death appears to be gradual.

ACKNOWLEDGMENT

This work was supported in part by grants HL23138 and HL01337 from the National Heart, Lung, and Blood Institute of the National Institutes of Health.

Literature Cited

1. Allen, D. G., Morris, P. G., Orchard, C. H. 1983. A transient alkalosis precedes acidosis during hypoxia in ferret heart. *J. Physiol.* 343:58P–59P
2. Allison, T. B., Ramey, C. A., Holsinger, J. W. Jr. 1978. Transmural gradients of left ventricular tissue metabolites after circumflex artery ligation in dogs. *J. Mol. Cell. Cardiol.* 9:837–52
3. Ashraf, M., White, F., Bloor, C. M. 1978. Ultrastructural influences of reperfusing dog myocardium with calcium-free blood after coronary artery occlusion. *Am. J. Pathol.* 980:423–28
4. Asimakis, G. K., Sordahl, L. A. 1977. Effects of atractyloside and palmitoyl coenzyme A on calcium transport in cardiac mitochondria. *Arch. Biochem. Biophys.* 179:200–10
5. Berne, R. M. 1963. Cardiac nucleotides in hypoxia: possible role in regulation of coronary blood flow. *Am. J. Physiol.* 204:317–22
6. Berne, R. M., Rubio, R., Dobson, J. G.

Jr., Curnish, R. R. 1971. Adenosine and adenine nucleotides as possible mediators of cardiac and skeletal muscle blood flow regulation. *Circ. Res.* 28(Suppl. I):I115–I119

7. Berne, R. M. 1980. The role of adenosine in the regulation of coronary blood flow. *Circ. Res.* 47:807–13

8. Bourdillon, P. D. V., Poole-Wilson, P. A. 1981. Effects of ischaemia and reperfusion on calcium exchange and mechanical function in isolated rabbit myocardium. *Cardiovasc. Res.* XV:121–30

9. Braasch, W., Gudbjarnason, S., Puri, P. S., Ravens, K. G., Bing, R. J. 1968. Early changes in energy metabolism in the myocardium following acute coronary artery occlusion in anesthetized dogs. *Circ. Res.* 23:429–38

10. Braunwald, E., Kloner, R. A. 1982. The stunned myocardium: prolonged, post-ischemic ventricular dysfunction. *Circulation* 66:1146–49

11. Bus, J. S., Cagen, S. Z., Olgaard, M., et al. 1976. A mechanism of paraquat toxicity in mice and rats. *Toxicol. Appl. Pharmacol.* 35:501–13

12. Cala, P. M. 1980. Volume regulation by Amphiuma red blood cells. *J. Gen. Physiol.* 76:683–708

13. Chapman, R. A. 1983. Control of cardiac contractility at the cellular level. *Am. J. Physiol.* 245:H535–52

14. Cheung, J. Y., Leaf, A., Bonventre, J. V. 1984. Mechanism of protection by verapamil and nifedipine from anoxic injury in isolated cardiac myocytes. *Am. J. Physiol.* 246:C323–29

15. Chien, K. R., Abrams, J., Pfau, R. G., Farber, J. L. 1977. Prevention by chlorpromazine of ischemic liver cell death. *Am. J. Pathol.* 88:539–57

16. Cobbe, S. M., Poole-Wilson, P. A. 1980. The time of onset and severity of acidosis in myocardial ischaemia. *J. Mol. Cell. Cardiol.* 12:745–60

17. Cobbe, S. M., Poole-Wilson, P. A. 1980. Tissue acidosis in myocardial hypoxia. *J. Mol. Cell. Cardiol.* 12:761–70

18. Cottin, P., Vidalenc, P. L., Merdaci, N., Ducastaing, A. 1983. Evidence for non-competitive inhibition between two calcium-dependent activated neutral proteinases and their specific inhibitor. *Biochim. Biophys. Acta* 743:299–302

19. Crompton, M., Capano, M., Carafoli, E. 1976. The sodium-induced efflux of calcium from heart mitochondria. *Eur. J. Biochem.* 60:453–62

20. Dayton, W. R., Schollmeyer, J. V., Lepley, R. A., Cortes, L. R. 1981. A calcium-activated protease possibly involved in myofibrillare protein turnover. Isolation of a low-calcium–requiring form of the protease. *Biochim. Biophys. Acta* 659:48–61

21. DeBoer, F. W. V., Ingwall, J. S., Kloner, R. A., Braunwald, E. 1980. Prolonged derangements of canine myocardial purine metabolism after a brief coronary artery occlusion not associated with anatomic evidence of necrosis. *Proc. Natl. Acad. Sci. USA* 77:5471–75

22. deJong, J. W., Verdouw, P. D., Remme, W. J. 1977. Myocardial nucleoside and carbohydrate metabolism and hemodynamics during partial occlusion and reperfusion of pig coronary artery. *J. Mol. Cell. Cardiol.* 9:297–312

23. deJong, J. W., Harmsen, E., deTombe, P. P., Keijzer, E. 1983. Release of purine nucleosides and oxypurines from the isolated perfused rat heart. In *Advances in Myocardiology,* ed. E. Chazov, V. Saks, G. Rona, 4:339–45. New York: Plenum

24. deMeis, L., Vianna, A. L. 1979. Energy interconversion by the Ca^{2+}-dependent ATPase of the sarcoplasmic reticulum. *Ann. Rev. Biochem.* 48:275–92

25. Donaldson, S. K. B., Bond, E., Seeger, L., Niles, N., Bolles, L. 1981. Intracellular pH vs MgATP concentration: relative importance as determinants of Ca-activated force generation of disrupted rabbit cardiac cells. *Cardiovasc. Res.* 15:268–75

26. Dunn, R. B., Griggs, D. M. Jr. 1975. Transmural gradients in ventricular tissue metabolites produced by stopping coronary blood flow in the dog. *Circ. Res.* 37:438–45

27. Farber, E. 1973. ATP and cell integrity. *Fed. Proc.* 32:1534–39

28. Farber, John L. 1982. Biology of disease: membrane injury and calcium homeostasis in the pathogenesis of coagulative necrosis. *Lab. Invest.* 47:114–23

29. Feigl, E. O. 1983. Coronary physiology. *Physiol. Rev.* 63:1–205

30. Friedrich, R., Hirche, H., Kebbel, U., Zylka, V., Bissig, R. 1981. Changes of extracellular Na^+, K^+, Ca^{2+}, and H^+ of the ischemic myocardium in pigs. *Basic Res. Cardiol.* 76:453–56

31. Furchgott, R. F., Gubareff, T. 1958. High energy phosphate content of cardiac muscle under various experimental conditions which alter contractility. *J. Pharm. Exp. Ther.* 124:203–18

32. Ganote, C. E., Seabra-Gomes, R., Nayler, W. G., Jennings, R. B. 1975. Irreversible myocardial injury in anoxic perfused rat hearts. *Am. J. Pathol.* 80:419–50

33. Ganote, C. E. 1983. Contraction band necrosis and irreversible myocardial injury. *J. Mol. Cell. Cardiol.* 15:67–73

34. Garlick, P. B., Radda, G. K., Seeley, P. J. 1979. Studies of acidosis in the ischaemic heart by phosphorous nuclear magnetic resonance. *Biochem. J.* 184:547–54

35. Gavin, J. B., Nevalainen, T. J., Seelye, R. N., Webster, V., Thomson, R. W. 1978. An association between the onset of rigor and loss of vascular competence in early myocardial infarcts. *Pathology* 10:219–25

36. Gebhard, M. M., Bretschneider, H. J., Gersing, E., Preusse, C. J., Schnabel, P. L. A., Ulbrecht, L. J. 1983. Calcium-free cardioplegia-pro. *Eur. Heart J.* 4(Suppl. 4):151–60

37. Geisbuhler, T., Altschuld, R. A., Trewyn, R. W., Ansel, A. Z., Lamka, K., Brierley, G. P. 1984. Adenine nucleotide metabolism and compartmentalization in isolated adult rat heart cells. *Circ. Res.* 54:536–46

38. Gibbs, C. L. 1978. Cardiac energetics. *Physiol. Rev.* 58:174–254

39. Harden, W. R., Barlow, C. H., Simson, M. B., Harken, A. H. 1979. Temporal relationship between onset of cell anoxia and ischemic contractile failure. *Am. J. Cardiol.* 44:741–46

40. Harmsen, E., deTombe, P. P., deJong, J. W., Achterberg, P. A. 1984. Enhanced ATP and GTP synthesis from hypoxanthine or inosine after myocardial ischemia. *Am. J. Physiol.* 246:H37–43

41. Harris, A. S. 1966. Potassium and experimental coronary artery occlusion. *Am. Heart J.* 71:797–802

42. Hearse, D. J. 1979. Oxygen deprivation and early myocardial contractile failure: a reassessment of the possible role of adenosine triphosphate. *Am. J. Cardiol.* 44:1115–21

43. Hellewell, P. G., Pearson, J. D. 1983. Metabolism of circulating adenosine by the porcine isolated perfused lung. *Circ. Res.* 53:1–7

44. Heyndrickx, G. R., Baig, H., Nellens, P., Leusen, I., Fishbein, M. C., Vatner, S. F. 1978. Depression of regional blood flow and wall thickening after brief coronary occlusions. *Am. J. Physiol.* 234:H653–59

45. Hill, J. L., Gettes, L. S. 1980. Effect of acute coronary artery occlusion on local myocardial extracellular K^+ activity in swine. *Circulation* 61:768–78

46. Hoffmeister, H. M., Mauser, M., Schaper, W. 1983. Regional function during accelerated ATP repletion after myocar-dial ischemia. *Circulation* 68(Suppl. III):III193

47. Jennings, R. B., Kaltenbach, J. P., Smetters, G. W. 1957. Enzymatic changes in acute myocardial ischemic injury. *AMA Arch. Path.* 64:10–16

48. Jennings, R. B., Sommers, H. M., Smyth, G. A., Flack, H. A., Linn, H. 1960. Myocardial necrosis induced by temporary occlusion of a coronary artery in the dog. *Arch. Path.* 70:68–78

49. Jennings, R. B. 1970. Myocardial ischemia—observations, definitions and speculations (Editorial). *J. Mol. Cell. Cardiol.* 1:345–49

50. Jennings, R. B., Hawkins, H. K., Lowe, J. E., Hill, M. L., Klotman, S., Reimer, K. A. 1978. Relation between high energy phosphate and lethal injury in myocardial ischemia in the dog. *Am. J. Pathol.* 92:187–214

51. Jennings, R. B., Reimer, K. A. 1979. Biology of experimental, acute myocardial ischemia and infarction. In *Enzymes in Cardiology: Diagnosis and Research,* ed. D. J. Hearse, pp. 21–57. London: Wiley

52. Jennings, R. B., Reimer, K. A. 1981. Lethal myocardial ischemic injury. *Am. J. Pathol.* 102:241–55

53. Jennings, R. B., Reimer, K. A., Hill, M. L., Mayer, S. E. 1981. Total ischemia in dog hearts, *in vitro*: 1. Comparison of high energy phosphate production, utilization, and depletion, and of adenine nucleotide catabolism in total ischemia *in vitro* vs. severe ischemia *in vivo*. *Circ. Res.* 49:892–900

54. Jennings, R. B., Reimer, K. A. 1983. Factors involved in salvaging ischemic myocardium: effect of reperfusion of arterial blood. *Circ.* 68(Suppl. 1):I25–I36

55. Jennings, R. B., Steenbergen, C. Jr., Kinney, R. B., Hill, M. L., Reimer, K. A. 1983. Comparison of the effect of ischemia and anoxia on the sarcolemma of the dog heart. *Eur. Heart J.* 4(Suppl. H):123–37

56. Jennings, R. B., Reimer, K. A., Jones, R. N., Peyton, R. B. 1983. High energy phosphates, anaerobic glycolysis and irreversibility in ischemia. In *Myocardial Ischemia,* ed. J. J. Spitzer, pp. 403–19. New York: Plenum

57. Jennings, R. B., Reimer, K. A., Steenbergen, C. Jr. 1984. Myocardial ischemia and reperfusion: role of calcium. In *Control and Manipulation of Calcium Movement,* ed. J. R. Parratt. New York: Raven. In press

58. Jennings, R. B. 1984. Calcium ions in ischemia. In *Calcium Antagonists and*

Cardiovascular Disease, ed. L. H. Opie, pp. 85–95. New York: Raven

59. Jolly, S. R., Kane, W. J., Bailie, M. B., Abrams, G. D., Lucchesi, B. R. 1984. Canine myocardial reperfusion injury. Its reduction by the combined administration of superoxide dismutase and catalase. *Circ. Res.* 54:277–85

60. Jones, C. E., Thomas, J. X., Parker, J. C., Parker, R. E. 1976. Acute changes in high energy phosphates; nucleotide derivatives and contractile force in ischaemic and non-ischaemic canine myocardium following coronary occlusion. *Cardiovasc. Res.* 10:275–82

61. Jones, R. N., Reimer, K. A., Hill, M. L., Jennings, R. B. 1982. Effect of hypothermia on changes in high energy phosphate production and utilization in total ischemia. *J. Mol. Cell. Cardiol.* 14(Suppl. 3):123–30

62. Kammermeier, H., Schmidt, P., Jungling, E. 1982. Free energy changes of ATP hydrolysis: a causal factor of early hypoxic failure of the myocardium? *J. Mol. Cell. Cardiol.* 14:267–77

63. Kamuke, W., Watanabe, F., Hashimoto, T., Tagawa, K., Ikeda, Y., Nakao, K., Kawashuma, Y. 1982. Changes in cellular levels of ATP and its catabolites in ischemic rat liver. *J. Biochem.* 91:1349–56

64. Katori, M., Berne, R. M. 1966. Release of adenosine from anoxic hearts. *Circ. Res.* 19:420–25

65. Katz, A. M., Hecht, H. H. 1969. The early pump failure of the ischemic heart. *Am. J. Med.* 47:497–502

66. Kleber, A. G. 1983. Resting membrane potential, extracellular potassium activity, and intracellular sodium activity during acute global ischemia in perfused guinea pig hearts. *Circ. Res.* 52:442–50

67. Kleber, A. G. 1984. Extracellular potassium accumulation in acute myocardial ischemia. *J. Mol. Cell. Cardiol.* 16:389–94

68. Kleihues, P., Hossmann, K., Pegg, A. E., Kobayashi, K., Zimmerman, V. 1975. Resuscitation of the monkey brain after one hour of complete ischemia: III. Indications of metabolic recovery. *Brain Res.* 61–73

69. Kleihues, P., Kobayashi, K., Hossmann, K. 1974. Purine nucleotide metabolism in the cat brain after one hour of complete ischemia. *J. Neurochem.* 23:417–25

70. Kloner, R. A., Ganote, C. E., Jennings, R. B. 1974. The "no-reflow" phenomenon after temporary coronary occlusion in the dog. *J. Clin. Invest.* 54:1496–508

71. Kloner, R. A., Reimer, K. A., Willerson, J. T., Jennings, R. B. 1976. Reduction of experimental myocardial infarct size with hyperosmolar mannitol. *Proc. Soc. Exp. Biol. Med.* 151:677–83

72. Kobayashi, K., Neely, J. R. 1979. Control of maximum rates of glycolysis in rat cardiac muscle. *Circ. Res.* 44:166–75

73. Kohn, M. C., Garfinkel, D. 1977. Computer simulation of ischemic rat heart purine metabolism. I. Model construction. *Am. J. Physiol.* 232:H386–93

74. Kübler, W., Spieckermann, P. G. 1970. Regulation of glycolysis in the ischemic and anoxic myocardium. *J. Mol. Cell. Cardiol.* 1:351–77

75. Lado, M. G., Sheu, S.-S., Fozzard, H. A. 1984. Effects of toxicity on tension and intracellular sodium and calcium activities in sheep heart. *Circ. Res.* 54:576–85

76. Liu, M. S., Feinberg, H. 1971. Incorporation of adenosine-8-^{14}C and inosine-8-^{14}C into rabbit heart adenine nucleotides. *Am. J. Physiol.* 220:1242–48

77. Lowe, J. E., Jennings, R. B., Reimer, K. A. 1979. Cardiac rigor mortis in dogs. *J. Mol. Cell. Cardiol.* 11:1017–31

78. Lowenstein, J. M. 1972. Ammonia production in muscle and other tissues: the purine nucleotide cycle. *Physiol. Rev.* 52:382–414

79. Lowenstein, J. M., Yu, M.-K., Naito, Y. 1983. Regulation of adenosine metabolism by 5' nucleotidases. In *Regulatory Function of Adenosine,* ed. R. M. Berne, T. W. Rall, R. Rubio, pp. 117–31. The Hague: Martius Nijhoff

80. Matthews, P. M., Bland, J. L., Gadian, D. G., Radda, G. K. 1981. The steady-state rate of ATP synthesis in the perfused rat heart measured by ^{31}P NMR saturation transfer. *Biochem. Biophys. Res. Commun.* 103:1052–59

81. McClellan, G. B., Winegrad, S. 1978. The regulation of the calcium sensitivity of the contractile system in mammalian cardiac muscle. *J. Gen. Physiol.* 72:737–64

82. McDonald, T. F., MacLeod, D. P. 1973. Metabolism and the electrical activity of anoxic ventricular muscle. *J. Physiol.* 229:559–82

83. Mellgren, R. L. 1980. Canine cardiac calcium-dependent proteases: Resolution of two forms with different requirements for calcium. *FEBS Lett.* 109:129–33

84. Meyer, R. A., Sweeney, H. L., Kushmerick, M. J. 1984. A simple analysis of phosphocreatine shuttle. *Am. J. Physiol.* 246:C365–77

85. Michal, G., Naegle, S., Danforth, W. H., Ballard, F. B., Bing, R. J. 1959. Metabolic changes in heart muscle dur-

ing anoxia. *Am. J. Physiol.* 197:1147–51

86. Millward, D. J. 1980. Protein turnover in skeletal and cardiac muscle during growth and hypertrophy. In *Degradative Processes in Heart and Skeletal Muscle,* ed. K. Wildenthal, pp. 161–99. Amsterdam: Elsevier/No. Holland

87. Morgan, H. E., Chua, B., Beinlich, C. J. 1980. Regulation of protein degradation in heart. See Ref. 86, pp. 87–129

88. Namm, D. H. 1973. Myocardial nucleotide synthesis from purine bases and nucleosides. *Circ. Res.* 33:686–95

89. Neely, J. R., Whitfield, C. F., Morgan, H. E. 1970. Regulation of glycogenolysis in hearts: effects of pressure development, glucose, and FFA. *Am. J. Physiol.* 219:1083–88

90. Neely, J. R., Rovetto, M. J., Whitmer, J. T., Morgan, H. E. 1973. Effects of ischemia on ventricular function and metabolism in the isolated working rat heart. *Am. J. Physiol.* 225:651–58

91. Nicholls, D. G. 1978. The regulation of extramitochondrial free calcium ion concentration by rat liver mitochondria. *Biochem. J.* 176:463–74

92. Nicholls, D. G., Crompton, M. 1980. Mitochondrial calcium transport. *FEBS Lett.* 111:261–68

93. Nicholls, D. G., Scott, I. D. 1980. The regulation of brain mitochondrial calcium-ion transport. *Biochem. J.* 186:833–39

94. Noma, A. 1983. ATP-regulated K^+ channels in cardiac muscle. *Nature* 305:147–48

95. Olsson, R. A., Gentry, M. K., Townsend, R. S. 1973. Adenosine metabolism: properties of dog heart microsomal 5' nucleotidase. *Advan. Exptl. Med. Biol.* 39:27–39

96. Pine, M. B., Borg, T. K., Caulfield, J. B. 1982. Regulation of atrial myocardial cellular volume during exposure to isosmotic high potassium or hyposmotic media. *J. Mol. Cell. Cardiol.* 14:207–21

97. Pine, M. B., Brooks, W. W., Nosta, J. J., Abelmann, W. H. 1981. Hydrostatic forces limit swelling of rat ventricular myocardium. *Am. J. Physiol.* 241:H740–47

98. Pine, M. B., Kahne, D., Jaski, B., Apstein, C. S., Thorp, K., Abelmann, W. H. 1980. Sodium permeability and myocardial resistance to cell swelling during metabolic blockade. *Am. J. Physiol.* 239:H31–39

99. Plagemann, P. G. W., Wohlhueter, R. M. 1983. Nucleoside transport in mammalian cells and interaction with in-tracellular metabolism. See Ref. 79, pp. 179–201

100. Pool, P. E., Covell, J. W., Chidsey, C. A., Braunwald, E. 1966. Myocardial high energy phosphate stores in acutely induced hypoxic heart failure. *Circ. Res.* 19:221–29

101. Rau, E. E., Shine, K. I., Langer, G. A. 1978. Disassociation of energetic state and potassium loss in anoxic mammalian myocardium. *Fed. Proc.* 37:230a

102. Reddy, M. K., Etlinger, J. D., Rabinowitz, M., Fischman, D. A., Zak, R. 1975. Removal of Z-lines and alpha actinin from isolated myofibrils by a calcium-activated neutral protease. *J. Biol. Chem.* 250:4278–84

103. Reibel, D. K., Rovetto, M. J. 1978. Myocardial ATP synthesis and mechanical function following oxygen deficiency. *Am. J. Physiol.* 234:H620–24

104. Reibel, D. K., Rovetto, M. J. 1979. Myocardial adenosine salvage rates and restoration of ATP content following ischemia. *Am. J. Physiol.* 237:H247–52

105. Reimer, K. A., Jennings, R. B. 1979. The "wavefront phenomenon" of myocardial ischemic death. II. The transmural progression of necrosis within the framework of ischemia bed size (myocardium at risk) and collateral flow. *Lab. Invest.* 40:633–44

106. Reimer, K. A., Hill, M. L., Jennings, R. B. 1981. Prolonged depletion of ATP and of the adenine nucleotide pool due to delayed resynthesis of adenine nucleotides following reversible myocardial ischemic injury in dogs. *J. Mol. Cell. Cardiol.* 13:229–39

107. Reimer, K. A., Jennings, R. B., Hill, M. L. 1981. Total myocardial ischemia, *in vitro.* 2. High energy phosphate depletion and associated defects in energy metabolism, cell volume regulation, and sarcolemmal integrity. *Circ. Res.* 49:901–11

108. Reimer, K. A., Jennings, R. B. 1984. Verapamil in two reperfusion models of myocardial infarction: protection of severely ischemic myocardium without limitation of infarct size. *Lab. Invest.* 51: In press

109. Richman, H. G., Wyborny, L. 1964. Adenine nucleotide degradation in the rabbit heart. *Am. J. Physiol.* 207:1139–45

110. Rocco, M. B., Reimer, K. A., Jennings, R. B. 1979. Failure of calcium chelated blood to prevent reperfusion induced indices of irreversible ischemic injury. *Circulation* 59–60:II216

111. Rovetto, M. J., Whitmer, J. T., Neely, J. R. 1973. Comparison of the effects of

anoxia and whole-heart ischemia on carbohydrate utilization in isolated working rat heart. *Circ. Res.* 32:699–711

112. Rubio, R., Berne, R. M. 1969. Release of adenosine by the normal myocardium in dogs and its relationship to the regulation of coronary resistance. *Circ. Res.* 25:407–15

113. Rubio, R., Berne, R. M., Dobson, J. G. Jr. 1973. Sites of adenosine production in cardiac and skeletal muscle. *Am. J. Physiol.* 225:938–53

114. Rubio, V. R., Wiedmeier, T., Berne, R. M. 1972. Nucleoside phosphorylase: localization and role in the myocardial distribution of purines. *Am. J. Physiol.* 222:550–55

115. Rubio, R., Wiedmeier, V. T., Berne, R. M. 1974. Relationship between coronary flow and adenosine production and release. *J. Mol. Cell. Cardiol.* 6:561–66

116. Schaper, J., Mulch, J., Winkler, B., Schaper, W. 1979. Ultrastructural, functional, and biochemical criteria for estimation of reversibility of ischemic injury: a study on the effects of global ischemia on the isolated dog heart. *J. Mol. Cell. Cardiol.* 11:521–41

117. Schrader, J., Gerlach, E. 1976. Compartmentation of cardiac adenine nucleotides and formation of adenosine. *Pfluegers Arch.* 367:129–35

118. Schrader, J. 1983. Metabolism of adenosine and sites of production in the heart. See Ref. 79, 133–56

119. Schrader, J., Haddy, F. J., Gerlach, E. 1977. Release of adenosine, inosine, and hypoxanthine from the isolated guinea-pig heart during hypoxia, flow-autoregulation, and reactive hyperemia. *Pfluegers Arch.* 369:1–6

120. Schutz, W., Schrader, J., Gerlach, E. 1981. Different sites of adenosine formation in the heart. *Am. J. Physiol.* 240:H963–70

121. Shen, A. C., Jennings, R. B. 1972. Kinetics of calcium accumulation in acute myocardial ischemic injury. *Am. J. Path.* 67:441–52

122. Shigekawa, M., Dougherty, J. P., Katz, A. M. 1978. Reaction mechanism of Ca^{2+}-dependent ATP hydrolysis by skeletal muscle sarcoplasmic reticulum in the absence of added alkali metal salts. *J. Biol. Chem.* 253:1442–50

123. Shlafer, M., Kane, P. F., Kirsh, M. M. 1982. Superoxide dismutase plus catalase enhances the efficacy of hypothermic cardioplegia to protect the globally ischemic, reperfused heart. *J. Thorac. Cardiovasc. Surg.* 83:830–39

124. Slater, T. F. 1974. The role of lipid peroxidation in liver injury. In *Pathogenesis and Mechanisms of Liver Cell Necrosis,* ed. D. Keppler, pp. 209–23. Baltimore: University Park Press

125. Steenbergen, C., Jennings, R. B. 1984. Effect of cell swelling on plasma membrane integrity during anoxia in dog heart. *Fed. Proc.* 43:294

126. Steenbergen, C., Jennings, R. B. 1984. Relationship between lysophospholipid accumulation and plasma membrane injury during total *in vitro* ischemia in dog heart. *J. Mol. Cell. Cardiol.* 16:605–21

127. Swain, J. L., Sabina, R. L., McHale, P. A., Greenfield, J. C. Jr., Holmes, E. W. 1982. Prolonged myocardial nucleotide depletion after brief ischemia in the open-chest dog. *Am. J. Physiol.* 242:H818–26

128. Tada, M., Ohmori, F., Yamada, M., Abe, H. 1979. Mechanism of the stimulation of Ca^{2+}-dependent ATPase of cardiac sarcoplasmic reticulum by adenosine 3':5'monophosphate-dependent protein kinase. *J. Biol. Chem.* 254:319–26

129. Tada, M., Katz, A. M. 1982. Phosphorylation of the sarcoplasmic reticulum and sarcolemma. *Ann. Rev. Physiol.* 44:401–23

130. Tada, M., Inui, M. 1983. Regulation of calcium transport by the ATPase-phospholamban system. *J. Mol. Cell. Cardiol.* 15:565–75

131. Takeo, S., Sakanashi, M. 1983. Possible mechanisms for reoxygenation-induced recovery of myocardial high-energy phosphates after hypoxia. *J. Mol. Cell. Cardiol.* 15:577–94

132. Tennant, R., Wiggers, C. J. 1935. The effect of coronary occlusion on myocardial contraction. *Am. J. Physiol.* 112:351–61

133. Thomas, R. A., Rubio, R., Berne, R. M. 1975. Comparison of the adenine nucleotide metabolism of dog atrial and ventricular myocardium. *J. Mol. Cell. Cardiol.* 7:115–23

134. Toyo-Oka, T., Masaki, T. 1979. Calcium-activated neutral protease from bovine ventricular muscle: isolation and some of its properties. *J. Mol. Cell. Cardiol.* 11:769–86

135. Tranum-Jensen, J., Janse, M. J., Fiolet, J. W. T., Krieger, W. J. G., d'Aloncourt, C. N., Durer, D. 1981. Tissue osmolarity, cell swelling and reperfusion in acute regional myocardial ischemia in the isolated porcine heart. *Circ. Res.* 49:364–81

136. Tyberg, J. V., Yeatman, L. A., Parmley, W. W., Urschel, C. W., Sonnenblick, E. H. 1970. Effects of hypoxia on mechanics of cardiac contraction. *Am. J. Physiol.* 218:1780–88

137. Vary, T. C., Reibel, D. K., Neely, J. R. 1981. Control of energy metabolism of heart muscle. *Ann. Rev. Physiol.* 43:419–30

138. Warnick, C. T., Lazarus, H. M. 1981. Recovery of nucleotide levels after cell injury. *Canad. J. Biochem.* 59:116–21

139. Weber, A. 1969. Parallel response of myofibrillar contraction and relaxation to four different nucleoside triphosphates. *J. Gen. Physiol.* 53:781–91

140. Weiner, J. M., Apstein, C. S., Arthur, J. H., Pirzada, F. A., Hood, W. B. 1976. Persistance of myocardial injury following brief periods of coronary occlusion. *Cardiovasc. Res.* 10:678–86

141. Weishaar, R. E., Bing, R. J. 1980. The beneficial effect of a calcium channel blocker diltiazem, on the ischemic-reperfused heart. *J. Mol. Cell. Cardiol.* 12:993–1009

142. Weiss, J., Shine, K. I. 1981. Extracellular potassium accumulation during myocardial ischemia: implications for arrhythmogenesis. *J. Mol. Cell. Cardiol.* 13:699–704

143. Weiss, J., Shine, K. I. 1982. Extracellular K^+ accumulation during myocardial ischemia in isolated rabbit heart. *Am. J. Physiol.* 242:H619–28

144. Williamson, J. R. 1966. Glycolytic Control Mechanisms. II. Kinetics of intermediate changes during the aerobic-anoxic transition in perfused rat heart. *J. Biol. Chem.* 241:5026–36

145. Wollenberger, A., Krause, E.-G., Heier, G. 1969. Stimulation of 3',5'-cyclic AMP formation in dog myocardium following arrest of blood flow. *Biochem. Biophys. Res. Comm.* 36:664–70

146. Wood, J. M., Hanley, H. G., Entman, M. L., Hartley, C. J., Swain, J. A., et al. 1979. Biochemical and morphological correlates of acute experimental myocardial ischemia in the dog. IV. Energy mechanisms during very early ischemia. *Circ. Res.* 44:52–61

RESPIRATORY PHYSIOLOGY: LUNG LIPID METABOLISM

Introduction, Robert E. Forster, II, *Section Editor*

This section deals with the location, metabolism, and processing of lung lipids, particularly the surfactant lipoprotein, an extremely active field of pulmonary research today.

The paper by Dr. Gil reviews the present status of our knowledge of the ultramicroscopic structure of those phospholipids related to lung surfactant. Intracellularly these include the lamellar bodies of the type II cells, and extracellularly these include the myelin figures found in the fluid-filled corners of the alveolar space and the alveolar lining of putative surfactant. Drs. Perelman, Farrell, Engle & Kemnitz review the special aspects of lipid in the developing lung, the topic of earliest clinical concern with surfactant. They pay particular attention to the regulation and timing of surfactant production in the fetal lung and the important role of maternal and fetal endocrines. Dr. King reviews a burgeoning area of pulmonary surfactant physiology, the production, composition, and metabolism of protein associated with lung surfactant (apolipoprotein). There are now known to be a series of such proteins, some of which may be important in the transport of surfactant across the membranes of cells and subcellular particles. The synthesis of surfactant in the adult lung, the substrates, our knowledge of the chemical pathways and of the rate-controlling steps, and the site of synthesis are reviewed by Dr. van Golde. The lung produces not only dipalmitoylphosphatidylcholine but other phospholipids whose functions are at present unknown. Drs. Fisher & Chander summarize present information on the assembly, mechanisms of secretion, and reprocessing of lung surfactant. The lung, with its some 40 different cell types, is clearly a productive arena for the techniques of "cell biology."

751

Ann. Rev. Physiol. 1985. 47:753–63

HISTOLOGICAL PRESERVATION AND ULTRASTRUCTURE OF ALVEOLAR SURFACTANT

Joan Gil

Department of Pathology, Mt. Sinai Medical Center, New York, New York 10029

INTRODUCTION

This article will discuss three elements of surfactant biology in which structural studies are useful: (*a*) the lamellar body of alveolar epithelial type II cells, which is the putative site of intracellular storage of surfactant; (*b*) tubular myelin, a structured fluid (i.e. a liquid crystal) present in the alveolar space of most air-breathing vertebrates; and (*c*) the extracellular alveolar lining of surfactant, which in electron micrographs has never been shown to form a continuous film. The reader is referred to two recent reviews (12, 16) for extensive lists of references.

LAMELLAR BODIES

The lamellar bodies of type II cells play a central role in storage of lipids. Because the interpretation of densely packed lamellar structures is central to any microscopic studies of lipid-rich mixtures, at this point we must review its significance. In vitro studies performed in the 1960s (3, 21, 26, 32, 33) demonstrated that amphiphilic polar lipids—those containing hydrophilic (polar) and hydrophobic domains (fatty-acid chains) in a single molecule—when suspended in water, arrange themselves in parallel lamellae, polar heads against polar heads, hydrophobic chains against hydrophobic chains (Figure 1), resulting in a regular periodicity. In extracellular lipids this may lead to the formation of whorls of concentric lamellae, which electron microscopists call

0066-4278/85/0315-0753$02.00

753

"myelin figures" because of the rather coarse parallelism drawn with the concentric lamellae of nerve myelin. The lamellar body, however, is a unique, highly structured intracellular organelle. Visualization for electron microscopy requires some type of fixation. The basic chemical fixative is OsO_4. In phospholipids, the osmium apparently reacts with the double bonds in the unsaturated fatty chains, but, rather than being bound there, it migrates to and is deposited at the polar groups (26, 32). In a lamella of the type seen in Figure 1 *(left)*, during fixation a linear deposit of osmium will occur over the double row of polar heads, resulting in the formation of electron-dense dark lines with a constant repeat period (Figure 1–3). This is important to electron microscopists because whenever a system of stacked lamellae of appropriate spacing is seen, it can be presumed to represent phospholipids. Work in vitro has raised a perplexing problem: in vitro, only unsaturated lipids react with osmium (26,

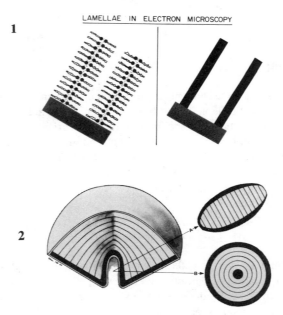

Figure 1   Left panel shows the arrangement proposed for individual phosphatidyl choline molecules in an aqueous lamellar system. Water is confined to the polar domains. *Right panel* shows the electron microscopic appearance after selective deposition of osmium in the polar regions. Lamellae are inserted into the amorphous material shown on *Figure 2*.

Figure 2   Three-dimensional structure of the lamellar body as a bell-shaped system of parallel lamellae that arise from an amorphous dark substance located on the side walls along the limiting membrane. A wedge of the organelle has been removed to show the internal arrangement. *A* and *B* are two frequent views in flat sections resulting from sectioning in the plane shown. See *Figure 6* for frontal view.

33). Because a high percentage of surfactant phospholipids are saturated, the question arises whether surfactant lipids can be fixed and seen at all in osmium-fixed material. Fortunately, the problem is only theoretical because the contents of lamellar bodies and many lipid micelles seen in the alveolar space are osmiophilic.

In chemically fixed lungs, gaps between stacks of lamellae are seen. It had been argued whether this is natural or instead reflects uncontrolled lipid extraction during processing (28), but freeze-fracture studies (15, 20, 22, 27, 29, 30, 34, 37, 43) have revealed that the cavity of the body is completely filled with densely packed lamellae. In freeze-fracture pictures these lamellae are not associated with intramembrane particles (IMP), the kind of small particles that in freeze-fracture micrographs of cell membrane have been interpreted as representing membrane-bound proteins or lipoprotein complexes. The repeat period of the lamellae varies somewhat within the range of 3.5–3.8 nm for the dark band and 3.0–3.5 nm for the lucent interval (6, 14, 29, 30, 35).

The lamellar body has a distinct three-dimensional architecture (10, 34, 38) (Figure 2). Overall the lamellae are bell-shaped and organized around a cylindrical core that often includes a protrusion of the limiting membrane. The lamellae insert into or arise from a thin layer of amorphous, moderately electron-dense material, located along the lateral limiting membrane, but also seen in the core (compare with Figure 1). Sections in different angles result in a variety of morphological appearances, from circumferential (*B*) to longitudinal (*A*) (compare Figure 2 with Figures 3–6). Histochemical localizations of enzymes have always been made in the amorphous material of the core or the periphery. Lamellae do not close laterally and there is no continuity or contact between contiguous lamellae. It is known that lamellar bodies derive from multivesicular bodies (Figure 5) (4, 31), which are organelles related to the lysosomal system. Because of this, the amorphous material occasionally can be

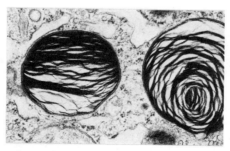

Figure 3   All electron micrographs are of rat or rabbit lungs fixed by vascular perfusion of osmium under Zone II conditions. Compare these lamellar bodies with *views A and B from Figure 2*. Note the areas of insertion of lamellae. The gaps are probably the result of lipid extraction during fixation. 21,600 ×

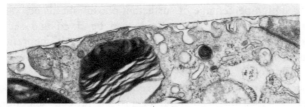

Figure 4   Type II cell with three clearly visible lamellar bodies is covered by an extracellular dark lining of surfactant. 12,750 ×

seen containing a few small vesicles, which suggests that it may be related to the original matrix of the multivesicular body.

It is difficult to decide whether this spectacular three-dimensional arrangement is unique, because there are no other cells with inclusions of concentrated phospholipids in normal mammalian cells. Intracellular osmiophilic lamellae appear, however, in a number of phospholipidoses, and in heterolysosomes. Although those inclusions differ from lamellar bodies, intracellular lipid lamellae unquestionably tend to be bell-shaped.

Finally, morphometric methods have repeatedly been applied to the histological quantitation of the volume of lamellar bodies (9, 23) in the hope that alterations may reflect changes in the rate of synthesis or secretion of surfactant.

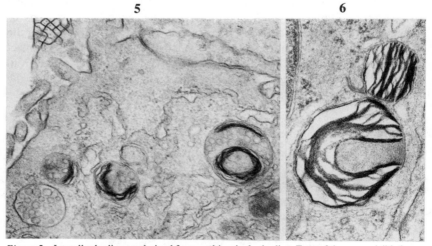

Figure 5   Lamellar bodies are derived from multivesicular bodies. Four of them are visible here; the one to the *left* is devoid of lamellae; the other three are undergoing transformation into lamellar bodies. In the alveolar space, surfactant layer contains some tubulin myelin. 31,365 ×

Figure 6   Compare large lamellar body with *Figure 2*. Smaller lamellar body on top seems to contain a vesicle, a leftover from the multivesicular body stage. 30,345 ×

TUBULAR MYELIN

Tubular myelin (Figures 5, 7–9) is a liquid crystal found inside the alveolar space that, in electron micrographs, often appears as a square lattice, depending on the plane of section. It is a crystal because of its organization, and it is liquid because it adopts the geometry of the crevices and alveolar epithelium that it fills and has a smooth surface against air (Figure 9, *left*). This beautiful structure was already noticed in one of the first published electron microscopic studies of the lung (25). Over the following years, it was redescribed several times under different names. For years, the opinions were split between those who felt that it represented surfactant and those who regarded it as a form of cell debris: the first description and many subsequent observations were based on pathological material. It was named "tubular myelin" by Weibel et al (39) because much of it consists of a system of densely packed, rectangular tubules. Intuitive recognition is immediate: electron micrographs show a square osmiophilic lattice with a side length of 50 nm or alternatively a system of straight or slightly curved parallel lines with a similar spacing. The squares represent cross-sections and the straight parallel lines represent longitudinal arrays longitudinal views of a system of densely packed, rectangular "tubules." High power micrographs reveal that the osmiophilic lines exhibit a double leaflet and that intersections consist of four rectangular L-shaped lines closely apposed to form a cross (Figure 7). The "tubules" are not empty. Weibel had described a longitudinal cylinder in the center of the tubule, which in cross-sections appears as a dark dot (Figure 8) but from other views as many as four small electron-dense points, one in each corner, may be seen. We reported isolation of tubular myelin and found that it has the lipid composition characteristic of surfactant, but for it to become a recognizable entity requires Ca^{++} (10). Others have shown formation of tubular myelin from lamellar bodies (30, 42).

A number of freeze-fracture studies on tubular myelin have been reported (15, 20, 22, 27, 30, 37, 38, 43). One of the most relevant observations is that a number of small particles comparable to IMP are associated with the wall of the tubules, resembling findings in cell membranes; this suggests a lipid-protein association that is not found inside the lamellar bodies (43). In fact, immuno-histochemical studies have revealed specific apoproteins inside tubular myelin (44). However, a precise clarification of the molecular structure of tubular myelin, in particular of the structures in the center of the tubules, has not been presented. Theories on its function widely differ. For some it is simply a reservoir of alveolar surfactant. Our attempts to preserve surfactant in situ (8) revealed tubular myelin frequently filling crevices between the tissue and the air interface (Figure 9), which suggests that it includes the whole surfactant system in the form of a large macromolecular aggregate of variable size.

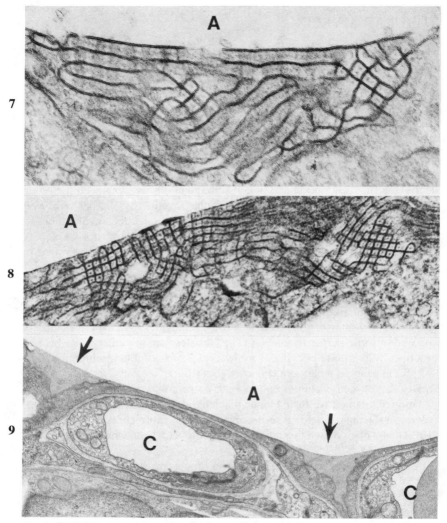

Figure 7 High-power micrography showing tubular myelin. Tubules are sectioned in several directions. Osmiophilic walls of the lattice consist of double leaflets. Notice that there are no crossings of lines in the corners. On the *right* and *top* layer, some material is visible in the center or corners of the tubules. Width or repeat period is in the order of 50 nm. *A* is air space. 77,665 ×

Figure 8 Lower-power micrograph of tubular myelin. Dots visible in the center of some squares. 54,240 ×

Figure 9 Rabbit lung fixed by vascular perfusion. *C* are empty capillaries. *A* is alveolar space. *Left arrow* points at aggregate of tubular myelin filling out completely a crevice in epithelial surface. Note smoothness of interface against air, the result of surface-tension forces. *Right arrow* points at fluid pool similar to the one under the left arrow, but amorphous. 9,600 ×

Recently Thet et al (36), recognizing that tubular myelin is a large molecular aggregate of surfactant that sediments from lung lavage at low speeds, showed that its amount increases during prolonged constant-volume breathing, at the expense of "smaller" forms of surfactant. Others who postulate that surfactant exists as a monolayer lining the whole alveolar epithelium propose that tubular myelin serves as an intermediate to facilitate the otherwise-difficult spreading of the content of lamellar bodies (17). Large amounts of tubular myelin fill alveolar spaces in clearly pathological conditions such as alveolar proteinosis and oxygen poisoning.

FLUID LINING OF ALVEOLAR EPITHELIUM

Despite the overwhelming evidence that considerable amounts of lipid-rich materials can be recovered from the alveolar spaces by lung lavage or homogenization, the alveolar surface appears naked in the common preparations. Weibel & Gil (40) and later Gil & Weibel (8) proposed that surfactant could be preserved in situ by changing the route of administration of the chemical fixatives. Reviews popular at the time had hypothesized that polar lipids would form a continuous monolayer, with the polar groups pointing toward the tissue and hydrophobic fatty acids toward the air like half of one of the lamellae seen on Figure 1. Use of any of the common fixation techniques (filling the alveoli with aqueous aldehyde solutions instilled into the trachea or plunging pieces of tissue into fixatives) would result in reaching the lipid layer with water from its hydrophobic side before fixation, and this would lead to its dislodgement and dispersion into micelles. But if the material could be reached "from behind" (i.e. from the hydrophilic side, by filling the capillaries with fixatives without causing alveolar flooding and impregnating the tissue with fixatives in such a way that tissue and overlying acellular materials became cross-linked before any bulk fluid could enter the air spaces), surfactant would be preserved in situ. A first attempt (40) revealed amounts of tubular myelin stuck to the surface and deep pools of moderately electron-dense fluid between the bulges of neighboring capillaries. Floating on top of these were broken and discontinuous dark lines and stacks of lamellae of a repeat period of 3.8–5.1 nm, compatible with the phospholipid water systems described in the first section. These, therefore, could be identified as free intraalveolar phospholipids, which we interpreted as being part of an artificially broken monolayer that, regardless of the problem of the saturation, had turned out to be osmiophilic. In a second effort with an improved perfusion technique (8), the picture that emerged was one that was soon confirmed by others and has essentially remained unchanged (Figures 9–11). Drawing a parallel with the situation in a Langmuir trough, we described a "base layer," the equivalent of the aqueous hypophase that filled out crevices and pits of the epithelial surface, and an occasional "surface film" seen as a dark line floating on top of the base layer, supposed to represent a monolayer visible because of osmium deposits in the polar heads. The base layer (Figure 9) either appeared to be a floccular fluid or contained osmiophilic dots, osmiophilic whorls, or tubular myelin in different states of organization. Tubular myelin seemed to be buoyant, floating on the surface. Many alveolar pores of Kohn were functionally closed by thin layers of fluid spanning the pore from edge to edge. The alveolar surface of type II cells with its microvilli was always covered in fluid (Figure 4). The surface film (Figures 10–11) appears as an osmiophilic line on top of the base layer over short distances. Sometimes it consists of one leaflet, other times of two; more often it is completely missing.

The technical details of perfusion fixation have been discussed in detail (7). It is required that both inflow and air pressures be well defined, and the osmotic-oncotic pressure must be adjusted to avoid alveolar flooding. In the experience of this author, perfusion under type II conditions is what works best. A number of different, generally simpler, devices for perfusion fixation have been introduced (1, 2, 5). Several authors have undertaken to compare findings in perfusion-fixed lungs with those in lungs fixed by other methods that also would not disturb the air interface. This includes, for instance, immersion of whole lobes (13), rapid freezing followed by freeze-substitution (24, 41), freeze-fracturing (22, 27, 37), and freeze substitution (18, 19)—they showed remarkably similar results.

Additionally to preserving intraalveolar fluids in situ, techniques that do not disturb the air-tissue interface reveal a number of additional functional features of the alveolar surface, in particular the effects of surface tension: evenness of the tissue surfaces, small tissue folds, slit-like deformation of capillaries, and septal pleating (11). Probably the most important contribution of electron microscopy to surfactant research will consist in defining surface-to-volume relationships at different levels of inflation and patterns of tissue deformation during inflation and deflation (11). Theories on surfactant function will have to be compatible with precise knowledge of changes that take place inside the terminal airways during respiratory movements, which can be understood only within the framework of acinus anatomy. The popular proposition that surface concentrations of intraalveolar lipids change with levels of inflation critically depends on incompletely understood anatomic behavior of the terminal airspaces. The literature has never elaborated on how a compression of the surface film in a real alveolus could take place. Morphological studies have never confirmed the existence of a continuous layer. Even in the most satisfactorily fixed lungs, only small parts of the surface are lined by extracellular films. Although the findings described and shown in Figures 4 and 9–11 are reproducible, they require fixation skills and considerable search and never extend over more than a few square microns. The morphological observations can

10

11

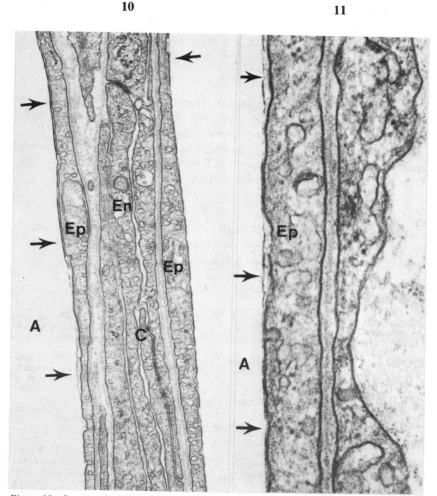

Figure 10   Septum of rabbit lung fixed by vascular perfusion under Zone 2 conditions. Capillary lumen *C* is closed. *A* is alveolar surface. *Arrows* point to clearly extracellular material of variable thickness supposed to represent surfactant preserved in situ. More of it is visible on the *left* than *right* side. Although pictures like these are reproducible, they require considerable search and are not representative of the epithelial surface, which mostly appears smooth and naked. *Ep* is type I epithelium, *En* is endothelial cell. 6,150 ×

Figure 11   Rabbit lung fixed by vascular perfusion. Epithelial type I cell, *Ep*, is lined by an extracellular surface layer of variable thickness. Pictures like this could be interpreted as shallow lateral extensions of the fluid pools seen in *Figure 9*. 72,160 ×

best be interpreted as showing localized pools or accumulations of fluids centered on crevices. The surfaces of these pores extend peripherally in all directions but only over short distances, more like a localized shallow flooding than a continuous lining, and at their edges form a contact angle of near zero with the epithelium—much in the way water of a pond behaves.

SUMMARY

We have discussed the three-dimensional structure of lamellar bodies as visible intracellular storage sites of surfactant. Among the intraalveolar structures, tubular myelin, a liquid crystal, represents a large aggregate of surfactant lipids and proteins of still-unclear significance. Elaborate fixation methods permit visualization in situ of localized pools of fluid that sometimes extend laterally, covering small areas of the alveolar surface.

ACKNOWLEDGMENTS

The author thanks Judith M. McNiff for photographic help and Daniel C. Barrett for typing the manuscript. Work of the author was supported by a National Heart, Lung, and Blood Institute grant, HL-34196.

Literature Cited

1. Callas, G. 1974. A new fixation technique for the electron microscopic study of pulmonary surfactant. *Anat. Rec.* 100:457–64
2. Callas, G. 1982. Osmium vapor fixation of pulmonary surfactant. *Anat. Rec.* 203:301–6
3. Chapman, D., Fluck, D. J. 1966. Physical studies of phospholipids. *J. Cell Biol.* 30:1–11
4. Chevalier, G., Collet, A. J. 1972. *In vivo* incorporation of choline-^{3}H, leucine-^{3}H, and galactose-^{3}H in alveolar type II pneumocytes in relation to surfactant synthesis: a quantitative radioautographic study in mouse by electron microscopy. *Anat. Rec.* 174:289–310
5. Coalson, J. J. 1983. A simple method of lung perfusion fixation. *Anat. Rec.* 205:233–38
6. Douglas, W. H. J., Redding, R. A., Stein, M. 1975. The lamellar substructure of osmiophilic inclusion bodies present in rat type II alveolar pneumonocytes. *Tissue Cell* 7:137–42
7. Gil, J. 1977. Fixation of tissues for electron microscopy under physiological conditions. In *Techniques of Biochemical and Biophysical Morphology,* ed. D. Glick, R. R. Rosenbaum, pp. 19–44. New York: Wiley

8. Gil, J., Weibel, E. R. 1969. Improvements in demonstration of lining layer of lung alveoli by electron microscopy. *Respir. Physiol.* 8:13–36
9. Gil, J., Thurnheer, U. 1971. Morphometric evaluation of ultrastructural changes in type II alveolar cells of rat lung produced by bromhexine. *Respiration* 28:438–56
10. Gil, J., Reiss, O. K. 1973. Isolation and characterization of lamellar bodies and tubular myelin from rat lung homogenates. *J. Cell Biol.* 58:159–71
11. Gil, J., Bachofen, H., Gehr, P., Weibel, E. R. 1979. The alveolar volume to surface area relationship in air- and saline-filled lungs fixed by vascular perfusion. *J. Appl. Physiol: Res. Environ. Exercise Physiol.* 47:990–1001
12. Groniowski, J. A. 1983. Fine structural basis of pulmonary surfactant. *Intern. Rev. Exptl. Path.* 25:183–238
13. Kikkawa, Y. 1970. Morphology of the alveolar lining layer. *Anat. Rec.* 167:389–400
14. Kikkawa, Y., Kaibara, M. 1972. The distribution of osmiophilic lamellae within the alveolar and bronchiolar walls of the mammalian lungs as revealed by osmium-ethanol treatment. *Am. J. Anat.* 134:203–20

15. Kikkawa, Y., Manabe, T. 1978. The freeze-fracture study of alveolar type II cells and alveolar content in the fetal rabbit lung. *Anat. Rec.* 190:627–38
16. Kikkawa, Y., Smith, F. 1983. Cellular and biochemical aspects of pulmonary surfactant in health and disease. *Lab. Invest.* 49:122–39
17. King, R. J., MacBeth, M. C. 1981. Interaction of the lipid and protein components of pulmonary surfactant. Role of phosphatidylglycerol and calcium. *Biochem. Biophys. Acta* 647:159–68
18. Kuhn, C. 1972. A comparison of freeze-substitution with other methods for preservation of the pulmonary alveolar lining layer. *Am. J. Anat.* 133:495–508
19. Kuhn, C., Finke, E. H. 1972. The topography of the pulmonary alveolus: scanning electron microscopy using different fixations. *J. Ultrastruct. Res.* 38:161–73
20. Lauweryns, J. M., Gombeer-Desmecht, M. 1973. Freeze-etching electron microscopy of the lung. *Pathol. Ann.* 8:257–82
21. Luzzati, V., Husson, F. 1962. The structure of the liquid crystalline phases of lipid-water systems. *J. Cell Biol.* 12:207–19
22. Manabe, T. 1979. Freeze-fracture study of alveolar lining layer in adult rat lungs. *J. Ultrastr. Res.* 69:86–97
23. Massaro, G. D., Massaro, D. 1975. Stereologic evaluation of granular pneumocyte lamellar bodies in different species. *Proc. Soc. Exptl. Biol. Med.* 149:333–35
24. Mazzone, R. W., Durand, C. M., West, J. B. 1979. Electron microscopic appearances of rapidly frozen lung. *J. Microsc.* 117:269–84
25. Policard, A., Collet, A., Pregermain, S. 1957. Etude au microscope électronique des figures myéliniques dans les processus inflammatoires. *Bull. Microsc. Appl.* 7:49–53
26. Riemersma, J. C. 1968. Osmium tetroxide fixation of lipids: nature of the reaction product. *Biochim. Biophys. Acta* 152:718–27
27. Roth, J., Winkelmann, H., Meyer, H. W. 1973. Electron microscopic studies in mammalian lungs by freeze-etching. *Exp. Path.* 8:354–62
28. Schock, C., Pattle, R. E., Creasey, J. M. 1973. Methods for electron microscopy of the lamellated osmiophilic bodies of the lung. *J. Microscopy* 97:321–30
29. Smith, U., Smith, D. S., Ryan, J. W. 1972. Freeze-fractured lamellar body membranes of the rat-lung great alveolar cell. *Tissue Cell* 4:457–68
30. Smith, U., Smith, D. S., Ryan, J. W.
1973. Tubular myelin assembly in type II alveolar cells: freeze-fracture studies. *Anat. Rec.* 176:125–28
31. Sorokin, S. P. 1967. A morphological and cytochemical study on the great alveolar cell. *J. Histochem. Cytochem.* 14:884–97
32. Stoeckenius, W. 1962. Some electron microscopical observations on liquid-crystalline phases in liquid-water systems. *J. Cell Biol.* 12:221–29
33. Stoeckenius, W., Mahr, S. C. 1965. Studies in the reaction of osmium tetroxide with lipids and related compounds. *Lab. Invest.* 14:1196–1267
34. Stratton, C. J. 1976. The three-dimensional aspect of mammalian lung multilamellar bodies. *Tissue Cell* 8:693–712
35. Stratton, C. J. 1976. The high-resolution ultrastructure of the periodicity and architecture of lipid-retained and extracted lung multilamellar body laminations. *Tissue Cell* 8:713–28
36. Thet, L. A., Clerch, L., Massaro, G. D., Massaro, D. 1979. Changes in sedimentation of surfactant in ventilated excised rat lungs. Physical alterations in surfactant associated with the development and reversal of atelectasis. *J. Clin. Invest.* 64:600–8
37. Untersee, P., Gil, J., Weibel, E. R. 1971. Visualization of extracellular lining layer of lung alveoli by freeze-etching. *Respir. Physiol.* 13:171–85
38. Weibel, E. R. 1973. Morphological basis of alveolar-capillary gas exchange. *Physiol. Rev.* 53:419–95
39. Weibel, E. R., Kistler, G. S., Töndury, G. 1966. A stereologic electron microscope study of "tubular myelin figures" in alveolar fluids of rat lungs. *Z. Zellforsch* 69:18–27
40. Weibel, E. R., Gil, J. 1968. Electron microscopic demonstration of an extracellular duplex lining layer of alveoli. *Respir. Physiol.* 4:42–57
41. Weibel, E. R., Limacher, W., Bachofen, H. 1982. Electron microscopy of rapidly frozen lungs: a critical evaluation. *J. Appl. Physiol.: Resp. Environ. Exercise Physiol.* 53:516–27
42. Williams, M. C. 1977. Conversion of lamellar body membranes into tubular myelin in alveoli of fetal rat lungs. *J. Cell Biol.* 72:260–77
43. Williams, M. C. 1978. Freeze-fracture studies of tubular myeline and lamellar bodies in fetal and adult rat lungs. *J. Ultrastr. Res.* 64:352–61
44. Williams, M. C., Benson, B. J. 1981. Immunocytochemical localization and identification of the major surfactant protein in adult rat lung. *J. Histochem. Cytochem.* 29:291–305

Ann. Rev. Physiol. 1985. 47:765–74

SYNTHESIS OF SURFACTANT LIPIDS IN THE ADULT LUNG

Lambert M. G. van Golde

Laboratory of Veterinary Biochemistry, State University of Utrecht, P.O. Box 80177, 3508 TD Utrecht, The Netherlands

INTRODUCTION

Pulmonary surfactant prevents alveoli from collapsing at low lung volumes by reducing the surface tension at the alveolar surface. Surfactant deficiency or abnormality occurs, for example, in patients with neonatal (12) and adult (23) respiratory distress syndrome, jeopardizing the structural and functional integrity of the alveoli. Dipalmitoylphosphatidylcholine (DPPC) comprises almost 50% of total surfactant and is undoubtedly its major surface-active component (31). The exact functions of the remaining components, such as unsaturated phosphatidylcholines (PC), phosphatidylglycerols (PG), phosphatidylethanolamines (PE), phosphatidylinositols (PI), cholesterol, and small amounts of specific proteins, are still conjectural (31). The production of surfactant proceeds in the alveolar type II cells, one of the ~ 40 different cell types in lung tissue. The bulk of surfactant components are synthesized in the endoplasmic reticulum and thence transferred, via a still incompletely understood process, to the lamellar bodies. These organelles serve as stores of surfactant before the surfactant is secreted onto the alveolar surface (see review by A. B. Fisher & A. Chander in this volume). It is the purpose of this review to summarize our current understanding of the pathways involved in the biosynthesis of surfactant lipids. The major emphasis will be on the adult lung; a separate review in this volume, by R. H. Perelman, P. M. Farrell, M. J. Engle & J. W. Kemnitz, focuses on the pulmonary surfactant system of the developing lung.

0066-4278/85/0315-0765$02.00

SURFACTANT LIPID SYNTHESIS: GENERAL COMMENTS

Most older studies on surfactant lipid synthesis have been carried out with whole-lung preparations. It is obvious that the results of such studies cannot be directly extrapolated to the alveolar type II cell.

This cell type can now be isolated from adult lung after proteolytic digestion with trypsin or elastase, followed by gradient centrifugation and either differential adherence in primary cultures or centrifugal elutriation (35). So far, only minor differences have been reported between freshly isolated type II cells and cells that have been in primary culture for one day (16, 35, 38). Isolated type II cells and subcellular organelles prepared from these cells (10) are of great value to studies on the pathways of surfactant lipid synthesis and their regulation. However, complementary studies with systems at a higher level of cell and tissue organization will remain necessary.

The type II cell of the mature lung obtains the glycerol backbone of surfactant lipids mainly from circulating glucose (3). Although the type II cell does contain glycerol kinase, glycerol appears to be a minor substrate for the synthesis of surfactant lipids in the adult lung (17). The blood also provides the type II cells with choline and inositol, as well as with an abundant supply of fatty acids. However, recent experiments with ^3H_2O and various carbon sources showed that adult type II cells possess a high capacity of synthesizing fatty acids de novo (33). Interestingly, lactate appeared to be a preferred source of acetyl units. The relative importance of exogenous and endogenously synthesized fatty acids for the production of surfactant lipids by the adult type II cell remains to be established. Active fatty-acid synthesis de novo is probably of vital importance for the rapidly growing and differentiating fetal lung (18).

SYNTHESIS OF SURFACTANT PHOSPHATIDYLCHOLINES

Synthesis De Novo

The synthesis of PC starts with the formation of phosphatidic acid (PA) from either glycerol-3-phosphate or dihydroxyacetone-phosphate (DHAP). The acyl-CoAs required for this conversion are derived from the corresponding free fatty acids by acyl-CoA synthetase. Data on the substrate specificity of this enzyme in whole-lung microsomes are contradictory (11, 39), and no information is available on the specificity of the type II cell acyl-CoA synthetase.

It is likely, but not yet proven, that the formation of PA from glycerol-3-phosphate proceeds in the type II cell via 1-acyl-glycerol-3-phosphate. Experiments with whole-lung microsomes indicate that the lung has the potential to synthesize PA with a significant proportion of dipalmitoyl species (50). The activity of glycerolphosphate acyltransferase in type II pneumocytes appears to be slightly higher than that of whole lung and is localized predominantly in the endoplasmic reticulum (16). Its substrate specificity has so far not been investigated.

An alternative route for the biosynthesis of PA involves the acylation of DHAP followed by reduction of the resulting acyl-DHAP to 1-acyl-glycerol-3-phosphate. Experiments by Mason (34) suggested that up to 60% of PA was synthesized in type II cells via the DHAP pathway.

The synthesis of PC continues with the conversion of PA into diacylglycerols (DG). Four different forms of phosphatidic-acid phosphatase have been identified in whole lung: two cytosolic forms, one requiring aqueous dispersions of PA as substrate and the other depending on membrane-bound PA, and two membrane-associated forms, one utilizing aqueous dispersions of PA and the other membrane-bound PA as substrate. It is likely that the enzyme depending on membrane-bound PA, which resides primarily in the cytosol, is involved in the formation of PC (8, 40). The physiological significance of phosphatidic-acid phosphatases requiring aqueous dispersions of PA is not clear.

The last step in the synthesis of PC requires not only DG but also CDPcholine. This intermediate is synthesized from choline by the sequential action of choline kinase, a cytosolic enzyme, and cholinephosphate cytidylyltransferase, an enzyme present both in the cytosol and in the endoplasmic reticulum. There is recent evidence (45) to suggest that the membrane-bound enzyme is the active form. The conversion of DG into PC in adult lung proceeds in the endoplasmic reticulum. Studies with whole-lung microsomes (28, 46) and with type II cell sonicates (42) have shown that cholinephosphotransferase utilizes disaturated DG equally well as unsaturated DG species. This would imply that DPPC can be synthesized in the type II cell by direct synthesis de novo, provided that sufficient amounts of dipalmitoylglycerol are generated.

Remodeling Mechanisms

Studies with whole lung suggest that DPPC is not only produced by direct synthesis de novo but also by remodeling of PC species that contain palmitate at position 1 and an unsaturated fatty acid at position 2. Two mechanisms have been proposed: (*a*) a deacylation-reacylation cycle, and (*b*) a deacylation-transacylation process [for review see (3)].

Pulse and pulse-chase experiments with type II cells (36, 49) show that unsaturated PC species are indeed converted into disaturated PC (mostly consisting of DPPC). In type II cells, labeled palmitate was incorporated predominantly into the 2 position of disaturated PC but equally into the 1 and 2 position of disaturated DG (42). This enrichment of labeled palmitate at the 2 position of disaturated PC cannot be explained if disaturated PC were synthesized entirely from disaturated DG. The much higher percentage of disaturated species in PC (60%) than in DG (38%) of type II cells (C. A. Crecelius & W. J. Longmore, submitted for publication) supports this idea, if we assume a nonselective utilization of DG species by cholinephosphotransferase (28, 42, 46). However, it should be mentioned that the molecular compositions of DG and PC were not determined in microsomes from type II cells but in sonicates of whole type II cells. Phospholipase A_2 inhibitors diminished the saturation of PC synthesized by type II cells from various labeled precursors (42), whereas phospholipase A_2 activation led to an increased saturation of PC (9). These observations suggest that the remodeling of unsaturated PC may indeed be initiated by phospholipase A_2, removing the unsaturated fatty acid from the 2 position and producing 1-palmitoyl-lysophosphatidylcholine (1-palmitoyl-lysoPC).

There is substantial evidence that the conversion of 1-palmitoyl-lysoPC into DPPC proceeds in the mature type II cell by reacylation rather than by transacylation. Type II cells are highly enriched in lysoPC acyltransferase (2, 16, 27) but not in lysoPC:lysoPC acyltransferase (2) when compared to whole lung. Furthermore, lysoPC acyltransferase of type II cells preferentially utilizes palmitoyl-CoA over unsaturated CoA-esters (2, 15). Injection of rats with labeled *rac*-DL-palmitoyl-lysoPC resulted in the formation of labeled DPPC that consisted almost exclusively of the L-isomer (47), underlining that only lysoPC acyltransferase is involved in the conversion of 1-palmitoyl-lysoPC into DPPC.

The currently available evidence shows that DPPC can be synthesized in the lung both by direct synthesis de novo and by remodeling of unsaturated PC via deacylation-reacylation. The relative importance of these two processes remains to be established.

Do Lamellar Bodies Contribute to Phosphatidylcholine Synthesis?

Although lamellar bodies possess phosphatidic acid phosphatase activity (5), they probably do not contain cholinephosphotransferase (3). Autoradiographical studies also endorse the view that the de novo synthesis of PC proceeds in the endoplasmic reticulum of the type II cells [for review see (3)].

Studies on the pulse-chase labeling of disaturated PC in adenoma type II cells strongly suggested that the endoplasmic reticulum is also the site for the remodeling mechanism (48). On the other hand, it has been recently suggested that an acidic compartment in the type II cell, most probably the lamellar body, also participates in the remodeling pathway (9). Although there is evidence for the presence of phospholipase A in isolated lamellar body preparations (9, 26), it is doubtful whether these organelles contain lysoPC acyltransferase (3). Magoon et al (32) isolated two populations of lamellar bodies that differed in respect to their phospholipid-protein ratio. Evidence was provided that the dense lamellar bodies with the lowest phospholipid-protein ratio developed into light lamellar bodies. The observation that the composition of PC was almost identical in the dense and light organelles strongly argues against an important role of remodeling mechanisms in the maturing lamellar body. Recent pulse-label studies (30) also corroborate the concept that the biogenesis of DPPC proceeds in the endoplasmic reticulum of the type II cells.

Rate-Limiting Steps: Possible Sites for Control

The regulation of the biosynthesis of DPPC in the type II cell has not yet been elucidated. Experiments with type II cells isolated from adult rat lung on the uptake of $[Me\text{-}^{14}C]$choline and its conversion into its metabolites indicated that in these cells the formation of CDPcholine is limited (41). These suggestions were endorsed by measurement of the pool sizes of choline and its metabolites in type II cells (41a). The cholinephosphate pool appeared to be much larger than the choline and CDPcholine pools. Based on thermodynamic calculations it was inferred that both choline kinase and cholinephosphate cytidylyltrans-ferase catalyze nonequilibrium reactions in the type II cells, whereas the cholinephosphotransferase reaction is near its equilibrium. However, the find-ings that labeled choline taken up by the type II cell is rapidly phosphorylated to cholinephosphate and that the cholinephosphate pool is much larger than the choline pool argue against a rate-limiting role of choline kinase. The authors speculate that the formation of surfactant PC is primarily regulated by cho-linephosphate cytidylyltransferase but that under specific conditions choline kinase is regulatory.

Numerous studies have indicated cholinephosphate cytidylyltransferase to be an important target enzyme for the hormonal regulation of surfactant PC synthesis. For extensive discussion of these studies, which were carried out predominantly with the developing lung, the reader is referred to the review by Perelman, Farrell, Engle & Kemnitz in this volume and to several excellent recent reviews (43, 44).

It has been shown that acidic phospholipids (14) and fatty acids (13) activate cytosolic cholinephosphate cytidylyltransferase in the fetal lung. It was sug-gested that this activation was accomplished by conversion of the enzyme from a low-molecular-weight form into a high-molecular-weight form. However, recent studies (45) have made it clear that the microsomal—rather than the cytosolic—cytidylyltransferase controls the rate of PC synthesis. Based on experiments with cultured rat hepatocytes and established cell lines, Vance & Pelech (45) concluded that PC biosynthesis is regulated by translocation of inactive cholinephosphate cytidylyltransferase from the cytosol to the endo-plasmic reticulum, where it is activated. This translocation is thought to be controlled by either reversible phosphorylation of the enzyme or by a direct effect of long-chain fatty acids or acyl-CoAs on the enzyme. It may be important to mention that most studies on the effects of hormones on the activity of this enzyme in the fetal lung have focused on only the cytosolic form of the enzyme.

It has been suggested that phosphatidic-acid phosphatase may control the rate at which DG are produced as substrates for the terminal step of the CDPcholine route. These suggestions are based mainly on changes in activity of the enzyme during development of the lung and on observations that several hormones stimulated the activity of this enzyme. However, in most of these studies phosphatidic-acid phosphatase was measured using aqueous dispersions of PA as substrate [for reviews see (40, 43)].

SYNTHESIS OF PHOSPHATIDYLGLYCEROL AND PHOSPHATIDYLINOSITOL

The pathways leading to PC and those producing PG and PI diverge at the PA branchpoint. Phosphatidate cytidylyltransferase, which commits the utilization of PA to the formation of either PG or PI, occurs both in lung microsomes and mitochondria. However, there is evidence that it is the microsomal activity that is required for surfactant PG or PI formation (5, 22).

CDPdiacylglycerols can be converted into phosphatidylglycerophosphate by glycerolphosphate phosphatidyltransferase. This enzyme is associated primarily with the mitochondria (37, 40). On the other hand, the observations that mitochondrial PG synthesis decreases rather than increases during development of fetal rabbit lung (22) and that the synthesis of microsomal PG was strongly decreased by myo-inositol while that of mitochondrial PG was not affected (20) argue against the mitochondrial origin of surfactant PG. The terminal step in PG biosynthesis involves the dephosphorylation of phosphatidylglycerophosphate by phosphatidylglycerophosphatase. It has been proposed that the dephosphorylation of PA and phosphatidylglycerophosphate are both catalyzed by phosphatidic-acid phosphatase (5), but this suggestion has been recently disputed (8, 40).

PI and PG share CDPdiacylglycerol as a common precursor. The conversion of CDPdiacylglycerol into PI proceeds in the endoplasmic reticulum and is, at least in vitro, reversible (7).

Regulation of Phosphatidylglycerol and Phosphatidylinositol Synthesis

PG starts to appear in surfactant around term, with a concomitant decrease in the percentage of PI. There is general agreement (1, 6, 20) that the availability of myo-inositol is an important factor that modulates the partition of CDPdiacylglycerols between PI and PG synthesis and that the decrease in serum inositol at the end of gestation is probably responsible for the switchover from PI to PG formation. An alternative or additional explanation for the reciprocal relationship between PG and PI in surfactant was proposed by Bleasdale and colleagues (5, 7). According to their hypothesis the increased PC synthesis in late gestation leads to an enhanced level of CMP. This CMP may slow down PI synthesis and thus increase the availability of CDPdiacylglycerol for PG synthesis. Addition of choline to type II cells isolated from adult rat lung increased PC synthesis from labeled glucose. This was accompanied by an increased PG synthesis. However, there was also an increase rather than a decrease in PI formation (1). These observations do not support a CMP-mediated inhibition of PI synthesis as a mechanism to explain the reciprocal relationship between PG and PI synthesis.

SYNTHESIS OF OTHER SURFACTANT LIPIDS

Phosphatidylethanolamine and Phosphatidylserine

There have been few studies on the biosynthesis of PE and phosphatidylserine (PS) in the type II cell, probably because these lipids represent only very minor constituents of surfactant. It is remarkable that surfactant PE hardly contains disaturated species, although this phospholipid shares DG as a common precursor with PC. Probably, disaturated DG are not utilized by ethanolaminephosphotransferase. Recently it was reported that sonicates of type II cells are more active than whole-lung homogenates in converting 1-palmitoyl-lysoPC and 1-palmitoyl-lysoPG into DPPC and dipalmitoylphosphatidylglycerol, respectively. Interestingly, there was hardly any formation of dipalmitoylphosphatidylethanolamine from 1-palmitoyl-lysoPE (19).

As in all mammalian tissues, PS is probably formed in the type II cell by a base-exchange mechanism. Interestingly, PS formation in the developing lung precedes the synthesis of PI and PG (4, 22). It has been speculated that the sequential appearance of these three lipids is critical for normal lung development, possibly by sequentially activating cholinephosphate cytidylyltransferase.

Cholesterol

Studies with perfused isolated lungs of adult rats have shown that endogenous cholesterol synthesis accounts for less than 1% of the total cholesterol used by the lung for surfactant formation. Most of the cholesterol is taken up from circulating LDL or HDL (24). The levels of these lipoproteins in the blood probably regulate the endogenous cholesterol synthesis in the type II cells (25).

CONCLUSIONS

The pathways involved in the formation of the surfactant lipids have been largely elucidated. DPPC, the major surfactant component, can be synthesized both by direct synthesis de novo and by remodeling of unsaturated PC via deacylation-reacylation. The relative importance of both pathways remains to be established. We are only beginning to understand the complex metabolic and hormonal regulatory mechanisms that control surfactant lipid synthesis in the type II cell. Evidence is accumulating that cholinephosphate cytidylyltransferase is an important regulatory enzyme in the production of surfactant PC. The hypothesis that reversible translocation between cytosol and endoplasmic reticulum is a major determinant of the activity of this enzyme is intriguing. The availability of myo-inositol appears to be a principal factor in controlling the partition of the common precursor CDPdiacylglycerol between PG and PI formation.

Evidence is forthcoming that synthesis, secretion, and clearance of surfactant are processes that are inextricably intertwined. If surfactant lipids are indeed taken up efficiently by the alveolar type II cell (21, 29), it will be interesting to investigate how such a re-uptake process and intracellular synthesis of new surfactant lipids are regulated coordinately.

ACKNOWLEDGMENTS

The author is indebted to Dr. J. E. C. Sykes and Dr. J. J. Batenburg for critically reading the manuscript. Studies by the author described in this review were supported in part by the Netherlands Foundation for Chemical Research (S. O. N.), with financial aid from the Netherlands Organization for the Advancement of Pure Research (Z. W. O.) and the Dutch Asthma Foundation (Nederlands Astma Fonds).

Literature Cited

1. Batenburg, J. J., Klazinga, W., van Golde, L. M. G. 1982. Regulation of phosphatidylglycerol and phosphatidylinositol synthesis in alveolar type II cells isolated from adult rat lung. FEBS Lett. 147:71–74

2. Batenburg, J. J., Longmore, W. J., Klazinga, W., van Golde, L. M. G. 1979. Lysolecithin acyltransferase and lysolecithin: lysolecithin acyltransferase in adult rat lung alveolar type II epithelial cells. Biochim. Biophys. Acta 573:136–44

3. Batenburg, J. J., van Golde, L. M. G. 1979. Formation of pulmonary surfactant in whole lung and in isolated type II alveolar cells. In Reviews in Perinatal Medicine, ed. E. M. Scarpelli, E. V. Cosmi, 3:73–114. New York: Raven

4. Benson, B. J., Kitterman, J. A., Clements, J. A., Mescher, E. J., Tooley, W. H. 1983. Changes in phospholipid composition of lung surfactant during development in the fetal lamb. Biochim. Biophys. Acta 753:83–88

5. Bleasdale, J. E., Johnston, J. M. 1982. Phosphatidic acid production and utilization. In Lung Development: Biological and Clinical Perspectives, ed. P. M. Farrell, 1:259–94. New York: Academic

6. Bleasdale, J. E., Tyler, N. E., Busch, F. N., Quirk, J. G. 1983. The influence of myo-inositol on phosphatidylglycerol

synthesis by rat type II pneumonocytes. *Biochem. J.* 212:811–18

7. Bleasdale, J. E., Wallis, P., MacDonald, P. C., Johnston, J. M. 1979. Characterization of the forward and reverse reactions catalyzed by CDP-diacylglycerol: inositol transferase in rabbit lung tissue. *Biochim. Biophys. Acta* 575:135–47

8. Casola, P. G., MacDonald, P. M., McMurray, W. C. C., Possmayer, F. 1982. Concerning the coidentity of phosphatidic acid phosphohydrolase and phosphatidylglycerophosphate phosphohydrolase in rat lung lamellar bodies. *Exp. Lung Res.* 3:1–16

9. Chander, A., Fisher, A. B., Strauss, J. F. 1982. Role of an acidic compartment in synthesis of disaturated phosphatidylcholine by rat granular pneumocytes. *Biochem. J.* 208:651–58

10. Crecelius, C. A., Longmore, W. J. 1983. Phosphatidic acid phosphatase activity in subcellular fractions derived from adult rat type II pneumocytes in primary culture. *Biochim. Biophys. Acta* 750:447–56

11. Das, D. K. 1982. Acyl CoA synthetase from rat lung—Purification and properties. *Lung* 160:207–18

12. Farrell, P. M., Avery, M. E. 1975. Hyaline membrane disease. *Am. Rev. Respir. Dis.* 111:657–88

13. Feldman, D. A., Brubaker, P. G., Weinhold, P. A. 1981. Activation of CTP: phosphocholine cytidylyltransferase in rat lung by fatty acids. *Biochim. Biophys. Acta* 665:53–59

14. Feldman, D. A., Dietrich, J. W., Weinhold, P. A. 1980. Comparison of the phospholipid requirement and molecular form of CTP: phosphocholine cytidylyltransferase from rat lung, kidney, brain, and liver. *Biochim. Biophys. Acta* 620:603–11

15. Finkelstein, J. N., Kramer, C. 1982. Acyltransferase activities in isolated type II alveolar epithelial cells. *Fed. Proc.* 41:668 (Abstr.)

16. Finkelstein, J. N., Maniscalco, W. M., Shapiro, D. L. 1983. Properties of freshly isolated type II alveolar epithelial cells. *Biochim. Biophys. Acta* 762:398–404

17. Fisher, A. B., Chander, A. 1982. Glycerol kinase activity and glycerol metabolism of rat granular pneumocytes in primary culture. *Biochim. Biophys. Acta* 711:128–33

18. Freese, W. B., Hallman, M. 1983. The effect of betamethasone and fetal sex on the synthesis and maturation of lung surfactant phospholipids in rabbits. *Biochim. Biophys. Acta* 750:47–59

19. Funkhouser, J. D., Batenburg, J. J., van Golde, L. M. G. 1981. Acylation of 1-palmitoyl-lysophosphatidylglycerol in alveolar type II cells from rat lung. *Biochim. Biophys. Acta* 666:1–6

20. Hallman, M., Epstein, B. L. 1980. Role of myo-inositol in the synthesis of phosphatidylglycerol and phosphatidylinositol in the lung. *Biochem. Biophys. Res. Commun.* 92:1151–59

21. Hallman, M., Epstein, B. L., Gluck, L. 1981. Analysis of labeling and clearance of lung surfactant phospholipids in rabbit. Evidence of bidirectional surfactant flux between lamellar bodies and alveolar lavage. *J. Clin. Invest.* 68:742–51

22. Hallman, M., Gluck, L. 1980. Formation of acidic phospholipids in rabbit lung during perinatal development. *Pediatr. Res.* 14:1250–59

23. Hallman, M., Spragg, R., Harrell, J. H., Moser, K. M., Gluck, L. 1982. Evidence of lung surfactant abnormality in respiratory failure. Study of bronchoalveolar lavage phospholipids, surface activity, phospholipase activity, and plasma myoinositol. *J. Clin. Invest.* 70:673–83

24. Hass, M. A., Longmore, W. J. 1979. Surfactant cholesterol metabolism of the isolated perfused rat lung. *Biochim. Biophys. Acta* 573:166–74

25. Hass, M. A., Longmore, W. J. 1980. Regulation of lung surfactant cholesterol metabolism by serum lipoproteins. *Lipids* 15:401–6

26. Heath, M. F., Jacobson, W. 1980. The nature of the phospholipases A of lung lamellar bodies. *Pediatr. Res.* 14:846–47

27. Hoehn, S. K., Lesperance, E., Klass, D. J. 1983. Enzymes of phospholipid biosynthesis in rat alveolar type II cells. *Lung* 61:229–34

28. Ide, H., Weinhold, P. A. 1982. Cholinephosphotransferase in rat lung: In vitro formation of dipalmitoylphosphatidylcholine and general lack of selectivity using endogenously generated diacylglycerol. *J. Biol. Chem.* 257:14926–31

29. Jacobs, H., Jobe, A., Ikegami, M., Conaway, D. 1983. The significance of reutilization of surfactant phosphatidylcholine. *J. Biol. Chem.* 258:4156–65

30. Jacobs, H., Jobe, A., Ikegami, M., Jones, S., Miller, D. 1983. Route of incorporation of alveolar palmitate and choline into surfactant phosphatidylcholine in rabbits. *Biochim. Biophys. Acta* 752:178–81

31. King, R. J. 1982. Pulmonary surfactant. *J. Appl. Physiol.* 53:1–8

32. Magoon, M. W., Wright, J. R., Baritussio, A., Williams, M. C., Goerke, J., et al. 1983. Subfractionation of lung surfac-

tant. Implications for metabolism and surface activity. *Biochim. Biophys. Acta* 750:18–31

33. Maniscalco, W. M., Finkelstein, J. N., Parkhurst, A. B. 1983. De novo fatty acid synthesis by freshly isolated alveolar type II epithelial cells. *Biochim. Biophys. Acta* 751:462–69

34. Mason, R. J. 1978. Importance of the acyl dihydroxyacetone phosphate pathway in the synthesis of phosphatidylglycerol and phosphatidylcholine in alveolar type II cells. *J. Biol. Chem.* 253:3367–70

35. Mason, R. J. 1982. Isolation of alveolar type II cells. In *Lung Development: Biological and Clinical Perspectives,* ed. P. M. Farrell, 1:135–50. New York: Academic

36. Mason, R. J., Nellenbogen, J. 1982. Synthesis of saturated phosphatidylcholine and phosphatidylglycerol by freshly isolated rat alveolar type II cells. *Fed. Proc.* 41:1600 (Abstr.)

37. Mavis, R. D., Vang, M. J. 1981. Optimal assay and subcellular location of phosphatidylglycerol synthesis in lung. *Biochim. Biophys. Acta* 664:409–15

38. Miles, P. R., Wright, J. R., Bowman, L., Castranova, V. 1983. Incorporation of [³H]palmitate into disaturated phosphatidylcholines in alveolar type II cells isolated by centrifugal elutriaton. *Biochim. Biophys. Acta* 753:107–18

39. Okuyama, H., Yamada, K., Miyagawa, T., Suzuki, M., Prasad, R., Lands, W. E. M. 1983. Enzymatic basis for the formation of pulmonary surfactant lipids by acyltransferase systems. *Arch. Biochem. Biophys.* 221:99–107

40. Possmayer, F. 1984. Biochemistry of pulmonary surfactant during fetal development and in the perinatal period. In *Pulmonary Surfactant,* ed. B. Robertson, L. M. G. van Golde, J. J. Batenburg, pp. 295–355. Amsterdam: Elsevier

41. Post, M., Batenburg, J. J., Schuurmans, E. A. J. M., van Golde, L. M. G. 1982. The rate-limiting step in the biosynthesis of phosphatidylcholine by alveolar type II cells from adult rat lung. *Biochim. Biophys. Acta* 712:390–94

41a. Post, M., Batenburg, J. J., Smith, B.

T., van Golde, L. M. G. 1984. Pool sizes of precursors for phosphatidylcholine formation in adult rat lung type II cells. *Biochim. Biophys. Acta.* 795:552–57

42. Post, M., Schuurmans, E. A. J. M., Batenburg, J. J., van Golde, L. M. G. 1983. Mechanisms involved in the synthesis of disaturated phosphatidylcholine by alveolar type II cells isolated from adult rat lung. *Biochim. Biophys. Acta* 750:68–77

43. Rooney, S. A. 1983. Biochemical development of the lung. In *The Biological Basis of Reproductive and Developmental Medicine,* ed. J. B. Warshaw, pp. 239–87. New York: Elsevier

44. Smith, B. T. 1984. Pulmonary surfactant during fetal development and neonatal adaptation: hormonal control. See Ref. 40:357–81

45. Vance, D. E., Pelech, S. L. 1984. Enzyme translocation in the regulation of phosphatidylcholine biosynthesis. *Trends Biochem. Sci.* 9:17–20

46. Van Heusden, G. P. H., van den Bosch, H. 1982. Utilization of disaturated and unsaturated phosphatidylcholine and diacylglycerols by cholinephosphotransferase in rat lung microsomes. *Biochim. Biophys. Acta* 711:361–68

47. Van Heusden, G. P. H., Vianen, G. M., van den Bosch, H. 1980. Differentiation between acyl coenzyme A:lysophosphatidylcholine acyltransferase and lysophosphatidylcholine : lysophosphatidylcholine transacylase in the synthesis of dipalmitoylphosphatidylcholine in rat lung. *J. Biol. Chem.* 255:9312–18

48. Voelker, D. R., Snyder, F. 1979. Subcellular site and mechanism of synthesis of disaturated phosphatidylcholine in alveolar type II cell adenomas. *J. Biol. Chem.* 254:8628–33

49. Wykle, R. L., Malone, B., Snyder, F. 1977. Biosynthesis of dipalmitoyl-*sn*-glycero-3-phosphocholine by adenoma alveolar type II cells. *Arch. Biochem. Biophys.* 181:249–56

50. Yamada, K., Okuyama, H. 1979. Possible involvement of acyltransferase systems in the formation of pulmonary surfactant lipid in rat. *Arch. Biochem. Biophys.* 196:209–19

Ann. Rev. Physiol. 1985. 47:775–88

COMPOSITION AND METABOLISM OF THE APOLIPOPROTEINS OF PULMONARY SURFACTANT

Richard J. King

Department of Physiology, University of Texas Health Science Center, San Antonio, Texas 78284

INTRODUCTION

It seems difficult to believe, in light of today's sophisticated morphology, that as recently as 40 years ago pulmonary biologists still thought it possible that gas exchange might occur across capillaries that were directly exposed to the alveolar air (30). With the development of a more realistic viewpoint of alveolar morphology, encompassing an alveolar epithelium with an overlying fluid layer, much older questions (47) concerning the stability of air spaces received renewed interest. Macklin (33), Pattle (37), Clements (9), and Mead (36) and their collaborators asked how it was possible that alveoli were able to resist the collapsing forces that would result from the surface tension of the alveolar air-liquid interface. Pattle and Clements provided partial answers to these questions through their isolation and characterization of a material secreted by alveolar epithelial type II cells, which they then showed to be capable of lowering surface tension to values less than had ever been observed for a biological substance. This material is now generally referred to as pulmonary surfactant. When isolated from alveolar lavage fluid it has been found to be comprised of several lipids, specific apolipoproteins, and carbohydrates (20). The structure is complex and poorly understood (48).

This paper will review information related to the composition and metabolism of this material, focusing on the newer results that are pertinent. Studies on the physicochemical properties and physiological functions of surfactant

0066-4278/85/0315-0775$02.00

will not be developed in detail here. The identification of the lipids in the predominant extracellular pools of surfactant has been largely completed, and the results of newer work have not markedly changed our understanding of this aspect of surfactant composition. However, the description of the associated apolipoproteins in these fractions has undergone some recent refinement because of work using amino acid sequencing and immunological analysis with monoclonal antibodies, and this will be stressed. There is considerably greater ambiguity in the protein composition of surfactant in intracellular sites, because few of the intracellular pools have been isolated, and there is presently little information to include in this review.

COMPOSITION OF PULMONARY SURFACTANT

The two metabolic pools of surfactant that have been most extensively studied are the lamellar bodies, the intracellular pool that is probably the immediate precursor to the extracellular form, and the surfactant fraction purified from alveolar lavage fluid, which includes tubular myelin. The data are obtained from the analyses of fractions that are likely to be heterogeneous. The isolation of the intracellular form, the lamellar bodies, is extremely difficult, and the products may be contaminated with extracellular surfactant, endoplasmic reticulum, and other cellular material (1). Further, metabolic results, as interpreted by Magoon et al (34), suggest that the lamellar bodies may be a continuously evolving metabolic pool. Both "nascent" and "older" lamellar bodies would likely comprise the isolated fractions. The extracellular preparations of surfactant may include recognizable tubular myelin, together with other lamellar forms. In some preparations (22), extensive homogenization is used to provide the best dissociation of extraneous nonsurfactant material from the complex. In these cases the definition of the surfactant fraction is based on the results of surface studies, rather than on morphological criteria. These alternative methods of preparation may result in some differences in composition, particularly with respect to the complement of proteins.

Lipids

Lipids comprise greater than 80% of the pulmonary surfactant (19). The properties and metabolism of these lipids are discussed elsewhere in this volume (see the review by Dr. van Golde), as well as in several other reviews (23, 41, 46). The surfactants obtained from different mammals are similar in composition and are characterized by large amounts of saturated phosphatidylcholine and about 10% phosphatidylglycerol. The fatty acid composition of the phosphatidylglycerol differs between rat and other species, with this phospholipid in rat surfactant being richer in saturated moieties than that of rabbit surfactant. For each species the composition of the lipids in the lamellar bodies is very similar to that of the extracellular surfactant, reinforcing the likelihood that this intracellular pool is the vehicle for the secretion of surfactant into the alveolar fluid.

Proteins in Mature Animals

There is little published information on the composition and identification of the proteins in well-purified and characterized lamellar bodies. I will concentrate, therefore, on findings obtained from surfactants obtained from alveolar lavage fluid.

The proteins associated with a fraction of pulmonary surfactant that has been extensively purified from canine lavage fluid using differential and density gradient centrifugation have been described in previous reviews (19–21). There are two principal nonserum proteins with molecular weights of about 35,000 and 10,000 when the fractions are analyzed under conditions that reduce sulfhydryl bonds. Without reduction, the 35,000-dalton protein forms dimers and higher-molecular-weight forms. There are, in addition, other proteins in much smaller amounts, together with variable quantities of serum albumin. The 35,000-dalton protein can be further defined in isoelectric focusing as a group of 3–5 proteins with isoelectric points of about 4.4, with minor components at about 4.6 (44). The 10,000-dalton protein can be separated into components that are soluble (8) and insoluble (25) in ethanol/diethyl ether (1.3 v/v) at $-15°C$. The soluble protein has been further purified by chromatography with silicic acid using mixtures of chloroform and methanol (8). The results of recent experiments suggest that this protein may affect the reuptake of phospholipid by primary cultures of type II cells (8).

The proteins found in surfactant obtained from rat lavage fluid using the protocol of King & Clements (22) are very similar to those found in canine surfactant (27). However, two proteins, with nominal M_rs of about 38,000 and 32,000, can be resolved, and these may be comparable to the 35,000-dalton group seen in canine surfactant. Without 2-mercaptoethanol, the 38,000-dalton and 32,000-dalton components aggregate to a high-molecular-weight form, suggesting that they are subunits of the same protein. The results of isoelectric focusing show that these proteins are heterogeneous, but the findings from two groups are inconsistent. Sueshi & Benson (44) found that most of the apoproteins had isoelectric points of about 4.4, with minor components detected at 4.6. Katyal & Singh (17) report 11 bands resolved from 3 proteins with M_rs of 38,000, 32,000, and 26,000, and these had isoelectric points ranging from 4.6 to 5.5. Neuraminidase treatment resulted in changes in the pattern seen in isoelectric focusing, suggesting that part of the heterogeneity may be due to differences in carbohydrate groups, rather than to peptide units. In this review, therefore, I will refer to this protein as a singular entity, even though it is comprised of two or more peptide chains that are probably linked by sulfhydryl bonds and may contain several different carbohydrate groups.

It is now established that the 35,000 protein is not derived from serum and is likely to be specifically associated with pulmonary surfactant [most of the evidence for this conclusion is summarized in (10).] Further, a protein with this M_r has been found in the surfactant of every species that has been studied. These include dog (20, 44), rat (17, 27, 44), sheep (24), monkey (17), rabbit (5), chicken (6), human (3, 17, 29), cow (42), and baboon (R. J. King, unpublished results). Recently we have used a method for preparing surfactant that retains a greater proportion of this material in the form of tubular myelin. The procedure is an adaptation of the method used by some to isolate lamellar inclusion bodies (12) and is based on the separation of fractions at the interfaces of discontinuous sucrose density gradients (21). It has several differences from the procedure used in earlier work: sucrose instead of sodium bromide is used to vary density in the gradient; the centrifugation times are shorter; and (perhaps most importantly) the fractions are dispersed by a gentle trituration with a wide-base plastic pipette, rather than with the use of a hand-held homogenizer. The major surfactant fraction, purified from rabbit lung, has a protein-to-phosphorus ratio of 4.2 ± 0.4 (S.E., n = 20). Its composition of lipids is typical of that reported for other surfactants. Further, it has the surface properties expected for this material. At a concentration of 30 μg ml^{-1}, it adsorbs within 25 sec to an air-liquid interface to lower its surface tension to 62 dynes cm^{-1}. This adsorbed material, when compressed at the interface, reduces surface tension to 10 dynes cm^{-1} when its surface concentration is 0.9 μg cm^2. These are the characteristics found in surfactants purified by more extensive procedures. However, the composition of the associated proteins of this fraction differs markedly from that seen in earlier materials. This is shown in Figure 1. There are nearly 20 proteins detectable in this surfactant, of which more than 10 stain intensely with Coomassie blue and are presumed present in relatively high concentration. We used this material to develop polyclonal antiserum in goats, and absorbed the serum with rabbit serum to eliminate their reactivity with serum antigens. Using immunological transfer techniques (45), we then determined those proteins that are not derived from serum. At least 10–12 nonserum proteins are present in these preparations of rabbit surfactant. One must anticipate that even more might be present but are undetected because antibody titers in our antisera are low, or because they are in relatively low concentrations. The protein composition of canine surfactant prepared in this way is very similar to that of the rabbit surfactant seen in Figure 1. As with rabbit surfactant, more than 10 proteins with M_rs ranging from 125 to 10,000 daltons are detectable by staining.

Monoclonal antibodies are now available to some of the proteins in rabbit surfactant. Using standard techniques for monoclonal production, J. B. Base-

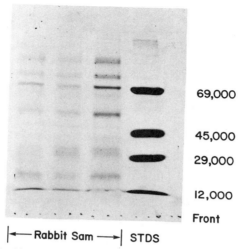

69,000

45,000

29,000

12,000

Front

|←——— Rabbit Sam ———→| STDS

Figure 1 Polyacrylamide gel electrophoresis of three preparations of surfactants prepared from rabbit lavage fluid. Samples were dissolved in 0.15 M lithium diiodosalicylate, 1% SDS, 3 M urea, and 1.4 M 2-mercaptoethanol. Electrophoresis was in 0.1% SDS using slab gels with a 5% acrylamide stacking gel and an 8% separating gel. Abbreviations used: Sam, surface-active material; STDS, standards.

man and I have obtained about 1100 clones from a fusion of spleen cells obtained from mice immunized with rabbit surfactant and with SP2/O myeloma cells, of which about 50 secrete antibodies that react with rabbit surfactant but do not react with rabbit serum. When we further defined their specificites using immunoblots, those that reacted to surfactant tended to fall into three groups, as shown in Figure 2. Some reacted with higher-molecular-weight proteins with nominal M_rs of 135,000 and 125,000 (proteins analyzed under conditions in which sulfhydryl bonds are *not* reduced). Antibodies from other clones reacted with proteins of intermediate size of 78,000, 70,000, and 62,000 daltons; and finally, there is a group of antibodies that reacted to the smaller proteins. These data were obtained from clones that are not established single-cell clones. Thus, the results could be due to heterogeneity in the clones themselves. Alternatively, these proteins may have similar antigenic sites, due either to metabolic processing in vivo or to degradation in vitro.

We have found a few clones that react to *both* the higher- and intermediate-range–molecular-weight proteins. One of these clones has now been subcloned using limiting dilution techniques (35) to establish that it is a single-cell clone. The antibodies secreted by this subclone react principally to the intermediate size apolipoproteins of nominal M_rs of 78,000, 70,000, and 62,000, but there are also weak reactions to the higher-molecular-weight antigens. Because these subclones satisfy the growth characteristics in culture of single-cell popula-

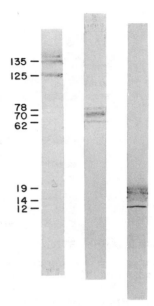

Figure 2   Immunoblots of the proteins in rabbit surfactant reacting with antibodies produced by three clones of hybridoma cells. Electrophoresis was carried out as described in the legend to Figure 1, except that no 2-mercaptoethanol was used. None of these antibodies reacted with rabbit serum. Nominal M_rs are shown in units of 1000 daltons.

tions, we cannot explain the multiplicity of antigen-antibody reactions due to clonal heterogeneity. However, the transfer assays are carried out on materials that are separated in electrophoresis without sulfhydryl reduction, because these monoclonal antibodies do not react with reduced antigens. It is possible that the apparent heterogeneity may be due to the formation of antigen dimers during electrophoresis, because the M_rs of the larger proteins are about twice those of the medium-range group. However, this cannot explain the reactivity of this clone to three proteins (78,000, 70,000, and 62,000) in the same M_r range. These results, therefore, suggest that the same antigenic site may be present on at least three proteins of differing M_rs. It is possible that this heterogeneity may reflect differences in carbohydrate structure rather than amino acid sequence of the peptides, because identical peptides with differing carbohydrate units may migrate at different rates in electrophoresis. This can be investigated using amino acid analyses, but these experiments are not yet completed.

In recent years a protein of $M_r \sim 250,000$ has been found by Lynn and his collaborators in material obtained from the alveolar wash fluid from patients with alveolar proteinosis (38) and from normal human amniotic fluid (3, 39).

These investigators have not attempted to determine the cellular origin or the metabolic function of this protein, but evidence gathered from their laboratory, taken in conjunction with the findings of other workers, suggests that this protein could be a metabolic precursor of some of the apolipoproteins found in preparations of surfactant obtained from both intracellular and extracellular sources. The support for this contention, and its implications, are given in this section.

"Alveolyn," the name given by Lynn to the 250,000-dalton protein, is isolated from the insoluble fraction of the alveolar proteinosis material by gel filtration on a molecular exclusion column, after the reduction and carboxy-methylation of cystine (cysteine) groups and solution of the material in a buffer containing 0.1% sodium dodecyl sulfate. This suggests that 250,000 is probably the approximate minimum M_r, whereas the size of this protein in native material is unknown. Lynn has not reported the percentage of the total protein in the alveolar proteinosis material that is made up of alveolyn, but a photograph of the SDS-polyacrylamide gel electrophoresis of the material from which alveolyn was isolated is shown in Figure 3. It is apparent that alveolyn is barely perceptible even when the gel is markedly overloaded and is likely to

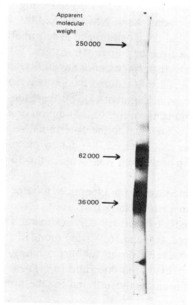

Figure 3 Polyacrylamide gel electrophoresis of delipidated material obtained from the lavage fluid of a patient with alveolar proteinosis. The electrophoresis was carried out in 5% acrylamide gels after reduction and alkylation of the sulfhydryl groups in the protein. Taken from Sahu & Lynn (38) with permission of the authors.

represent only a small percent of the total protein. The major proteins in the alveolar proteinosis material have M_rs of 62,000 and 36,000, but there are smaller amounts of proteins with M_rs of 130,000, 80,000, 36,000, and 26,000. Lynn suggests that all of these proteins are fragments of alveolyn, resulting from the action of a trypsin-like enzyme. Further, his results indicate that the 62,000- and 36,000-dalton proteins in alveolar proteinosis are similar to those proteins of similar M_rs that are found in surfactants from normal animals. The evidence for these conclusions is as follows:

1. A 250,000-dalton protein can be isolated from normal human amniotic fluid using the same methods as those used to isolate alveolyn from alveolar proteinosis material. This protein and alveolyn form a line of identity when reacted to antiserum directed against alveolyn (38). The amino acid compositions of these two proteins are similar, although not identical, and both contain 4-hydroxyproline.
2. Alveolyn, the 62,000-dalton, and the 36,000-dalton glycoproteins react immunologically in a line of identity with antiserum to alveolyn (38). Further, antisera developed against the 62,000-dalton and 36,000-dalton protein react with the 80,000-dalton protein (4).
3. The 80,000-dalton protein can be hydrolyzed using a controlled digestion with trypsin into fragments having M_rs of 62,000, 36,000, 26,000, and 18,000. The amino acid composition and N-terminal of the 36,000-dalton glycoprotein from the alveolar proteinosis material (7) are identical to those of the 36,000-dalton trypsin fragment of the 80,000-dalton protein (4); and the composition of the 62,000-dalton glycoprotein (2) is identical to that of the 62,000-dalton trypsin fragment (4). Further, the sequence of the first five N-terminal amino acids of the 26,000-dalton protein found in alveolar proteinosis material is identical to the N-terminal sequence of the 26,000-dalton trypsin fragment of the 62,000-dalton protein (4). The proposed structural relationship of the four fragments in the 80,000-dalton protein is shown in Figure 4.
4. Alveolyn and its related smaller polypeptides have been found in the media from a clone of human fetal lung cells (40). Proteins of similar M_r are secreted into the media by primary cultures of rat Type II cells (32).
5. Proteins with M_rs of 62,000 and 36,000 are found in the lamellar bodies and lavage fluid from chicken (6) and rabbit (5) lungs, and a 36,000-dalton protein is found in human amniotic fluid (3). These proteins have amino acid compositions similar to those found for the proteins in alveolar proteinosis fluid.

If Lynn's hypothesis is correct—that surfactant-associated proteins derive from alveolyn—then it becomes important to isolate the enzymes responsible for the sequential degradation, determine the sites of action, and probe the

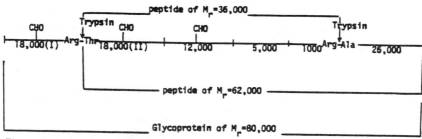

Figure 4 Predicted structure of the protein of M_r 80,000 obtained from alveolar proteinosis material. Taken from Lynn & Bhattacharyya (31) with permission.

physiological consequences of such a metabolic cascade. There is no information on this subject now available. A 36,000-dalton glycoprotein is the major surfactant protein found in surfactant isolated from lavage fluid (20) and is presumably the same protein described by Lynn, but frequently the 62,000-dalton protein (and others) are found in significant amounts. This indicates that the catalysis of alveolyn could have occurred either prior to (or during) secretion, or in the alveolar lumen. However, it is unknown whether alveolyn is present in lamellar bodies. Lynn and coworkers have found both the 62,000-dalton and 36,000-dalton glycoproteins in intracellular fractions enriched in lamellar bodies (5, 6), but the characterization of these intracellular preparations was not extensive. It is possible, therefore, that the lamellar body fraction may have been mixed with surfactant from extracellular sources, and the evidence is not conclusive that the hydrolysis of alveolyn had occurred by the time the surfactant had been packaged into lamellar bodies. The subcellular localization of alveolyn has not been reported, but this will be a difficult task because of the relatively small amount of this protein compared with the other surfactant apolipoproteins, and because of structural similarities that may limit immunological specificity. It is likely that techniques using highly specific monoclonal antibodies will be necessary.

Proteins in Fetal Lung Fluids

There are limited data on the composition of surfactant-associated proteins in fluids derived from the fetal lung. Polyvalent antisera, directed against the nonserum proteins in pulmonary surfactants purified from alveolar lavage fluids, have been used to investigate the appearance of these proteins in human amniotic fluid (29, 43), tracheal fluid from fetal sheep (14), and amniotic fluid and lungs from fetal rats (18).

Surfactant apolipoproteins are detectable in human amniotic fluid by 26 weeks gestational age (43), and their concentration increases about 6-fold (29) to 10-fold (43) by term. This change in concentration is approximately parallel to the increase in surface active phospholipid seen over the same time interval of gestation (29). However apolipoprotein titers, relative to values at full term, may precede the comparable amounts of phospholipid by 1–2 weeks gestational age, although these temporal differences are not of sufficient magnitude to be statistically significant.

The ontogeny of the surfactant apolipoproteins has been investigated in the tracheal fluid from fetal sheep by comparing the changes in concentrations in the apolipoproteins detected by a very sensitive radioimmunoassay to those of phospholipid phosphorus (14). Surfactant apolipoproteins are first detected at 114 days, show a slight rise in concentration at about 117 days, and show a slight decline at about 135 days. However, there are no statistical differences between any of the concentrations of antigen measured during this period. At 137 days, the start of the alveolar period in fetal sheep (term is approximately 147 days), there is an abrupt increase in antigen concentration so that concentrations at term are about 10-fold those seen at the end of the canalicular period. There is a concomitant increase in phospholipid phosphorus, and the ratio of lipid phosphorus to antigen at term is similar to that found in the lavage fluid from adult sheep. However, this ratio is not constant throughout development. Surfactant apolipoproteins are present at the start of the canalicular phase of development, but the amount of phospholipid phosphorus is very low. Thus, the ratio of lipid phosphorus to antigen varies over the period of gestation. It is very low during the canalicular period, but rises abruptly through the transitional period. In a few samples the protein composition of the fetal fluids was studied using polyacrylamide gel electrophoresis. In the alveolar period the tracheal fluids contained both the 35,000-dalton and 10,000-dalton apolipoproteins. Fluids obtained from the canalicular period, however, had only the 35,000-dalton apolipoprotein. The results suggest that the larger protein appears in ovine gestation before that of the smaller apolipoprotein, but detailed metabolic or developmental relationships among the apolipoproteins are unknown.

Katyal & Singh (18) have developed an enzyme-linked immunoassay for a group of three proteins in rat surfactant with M_rs of 26,000, 32,000, and 38,000 and have used it to quantify the concentration of these proteins in fetal rat lungs and amniotic fluid. No antigen could be detected in lung tissue before 17 days gestation. Between 18 and 21 days (term), however, there was a 38-fold increase. Apolipoprotein was first seen in amniotic fluid at 19 days gestation and increased 2–3-fold by term.

The results of all studies show that surfactant-associated proteins appear in fetal fluids at times coincident with the development of the surfactant system. In sheep, low levels of apolipoprotein appear in tracheal fluid before the release of surface active phospholipid, and there is an indication that this may also occur in human fetal development. The results of limited observations suggest that the composition of the surfactant apolipoproteins may also change during development, but the physiological explanation for these findings is unknown.

METABOLISM OF SURFACTANT APOLIPOPROTEINS

There are no recent reports of new studies in this area. Older work (26–28) has been discussed in previous reviews (20, 21), and will, therefore, be summarized briefly.

The 35,000-dalton apolipoprotein of surfactant is maximally labeled in type II cells of rat lung within 15 min after an intravenous injection of radioactive leucine. Radioactivity decreases to about 25% of maximum by 9 hr, and the time rate of change of the labeling in the apolipoprotein is about the same as that of the disaturated phosphatidylcholine (labeled with an intravenous injection of palmitic acid). Both of these components are detectable in surfactant purified from alveolar lavage fluid by 30 min after intravenous injection of the precursors, and the maximal labeling occurs in both components at about the same time. These results suggest that the lipids and this apolipoprotein of surfactant are secreted into the alveolar fluid with similar kinetics. This secretion is likely to occur after the lipid and protein components have been integrated intracellularly into a lipoprotein complex, and incorporated into the lamellar inclusion body, because one or more surfactant proteins can be found in lamellar bodies with immunohistochemical techniques using polyvalent antisera (11). Secretion is probably effected by exocytosis of the surfactant material contained within the lamellar body (48).

The specific activity of the 35,000-dalton apolipoprotein in alveolar surfactant decreases at a more rapid rate than does the specific activity of the saturated phosphatidylcholine. A smaller-molecular-weight protein, of about 10,000 to 12,000 daltons, shows increasing specific activity during this same time period. These results suggest that the lipid and protein components of the complex may be catabolized at different rates using different (and uncertain) mechanisms. The pattern of labeling of the 35,000- and 10,000-dalton proteins is suggestive of a precursor-product relationship, but this has not been verified.

The methods by which surfactant is removed from the alveolar lumen have been actively studied in recent years. Very little surfactant is passed up the airway (13). Both labeled apolipoprotein and saturated phosphatidylcholine are found in alveolar macrophages, but the metabolic clearance of only a small part of the alveolar surfactant can be accounted for in this way (1, 27). Hallman (15) and Jacobs (16) and their colleagues have obtained evidence of the reuptake of a significant amount of the lipids of the extracellular surfactant and its rapid incorporation into surfactant in lamellar bodies. There are no published results on the possible reuptake of the apolipoproteins.

CONCLUSIONS

It is now evident that surfactant material must exist in several intracellular and extracellular compartments. The results of histochemical and biochemical studies suggest that the complex is formed as a lipoprotein prior to its secretion and that the composition of the lipids in lamellar bodies is almost identical to that found in alveolar surfactant (although there are some differences in this composition among species). Comparable information for the proteins is still not available. Details on the intracellular metabolism of surfactant are unknown, and it is uncertain how the components of surfactant are transported to and integrated within the lamellar bodies. The experiments required to examine these intracellular events are technically difficult and are complicated by the apparent reuptake of extracellular surfactant. One must even consider the possibility that the pathways through which the components of surfactant are taken back up from the alveolar fluid and integrated within lamellar bodies may be different from those which synthesize these components de novo. In extracellular sites, tubular myelin, a lipoprotein complex, is a distinctive fraction of the extracellular pool. However, other lamellar forms are found in the alveolar fluid (48), and some have been partially purified (34). Whether all are fractions of the secreted surfactant that have undergone extracellular processing has not been proven. However, similarities in the compositions of the lipids in several of these fractions (34) make this plausible.

ACKNOWLEDGMENTS

Supported by grant number HL 16725, awarded by the National Heart, Lung, and Blood Institute.

Literature Cited

1. Baritussio, A. G., Magoon, M. W., Goerke, J., Clements, J. A. 1981. Precursor-product relationship between rabbit Type II cell lamellar bodies and alveolar surface active material. Surfactant turnover time. *Biochim. Biophys. Acta* 666:382–93
2. Bhattacharyya, S. N., Lynn, W. S. 1977. Studies on structural relationship between two glycoproteins isolated from alveoli of patients with alveolar proteinosis. *Biochim. Biophys. Acta* 494:150–61
3. Bhattacharyya, S. N., Lynn, W. S. 1978. Isolation and characterization of a pulmonary glycoprotein from human amniotic fluid. *Biochim. Biophys. Acta* 537:329–35
4. Bhattacharyya, S. N., Lynn, W. S. 1979. Structural characterization of a glycoprotein isolated from alveoli of patients with alveolar proteinosis. *J. Biol. Chem.* 254:5191–98

5. Bhattacharyya, S. N., Passero, M. A., DiAugustine, R. P., Lynn, W. S. 1975. Isolation and characterization of two hydroxyproline-containing glycoproteins from normal animal lung lavage and lamellar bodies. *J. Clin. Invest.* 55:914–20
6. Bhattacharyya, S. N., Rose, M. C., Lynn, M. G., MacLeod, C., Alberts, M., Lynn, W. S. 1976. Isolation and characterization of a unique glycoprotein from lavage of chicken lungs and lamellar organelles. *Am. Rev. Resp. Dis.* 114:843–50
7. Bhattacharyya, S. N., Sahu, S., Lynn, W. S. 1976. Structural studies on a glycoprotein isolated from alveoli of patients with alveolar proteinosis. *Biochim. Biophys. Acta* 427:91–106
8. Claypool, W. D., Wang, D. L., Chander, A., Fisher, A. B. 1984. "Hydrophobic" surfactant apoproteins and aug-

mentation of phospholipid recycling. *Exp. Lung Res.* 6:215–22

9. Clements, J. A., Brown, E. S., Johnson, R. P. 1958. Pulmonary surface tension and the mucus lining of the lungs: some theoretical considerations. *J. Appl. Physiol.* 12:262–68

10. Clements, J. A., King, R. J. 1976. Composition of surface active material. In *The Biochemical Basis of Pulmonary Function*, ed. R. G. Crystal, pp. 363–87. New York: Marcel Dekker

11. Coalson, J. L., King, R. J. 1984. Immunocytochemical localization of rat surfactant using a gold immunocolloid marker. *Am. Rev. Resp. Dis.* 129:A295

12. Engle, M. J., Sanders, R. L., Longmore, W. J. 1976. Phospholipid composition and acyltransferase activity of lamellar bodies isolated from rat lung. *Arch. Biochem. Biophys.* 173:586–95

13. Fisher, H. K., Hyman, M. H., Ashcraft, S. J. 1979. Alveolar surfactant phospholipids are not cleared via trachea. *Fed. Proc.* 38:1373

14. Gikas, E. G., King, R. J., Mescher, E. J., Platzker, A. C. G., Kitterman, J. A., et al. 1977. Radioimmunoassay of pulmonary surface-active material in the tracheal fluid of the fetal lamb. *Am. Rev. Resp. Dis.* 115:587–93

15. Hallman, M., Epstein, B. L., Gluck, L. 1981. Analysis of labeling and clearance of lung surfactant phospholipids in rabbit. Evidence of bidirectional surfactant flux between lamellar bodies and alveolar lavage. *J. Clin. Invest.* 68:742–51

16. Jacobs, H., Jobe, A., Ikegami, M., Conaway, D. 1983. The significance of reutilization of surfactant phosphatidylcholine. *J. Biol. Chem.* 258:4156–65

17. Katyal, S. L., Singh, G. 1981. Analysis of pulmonary surfactant apoproteins by electrophoresis. *Biochim. Biophys. Acta* 670:323–31

18. Katyal, S. L., Singh, G. 1983. An enzyme-linked immunoassay of surfactant apoproteins. Its application to the study of fetal lung development in the rat. *Pediat. Res.* 17:439–43

19. King, R. J. 1974. The surfactant system of the lung. *Fed. Proc.* 33:2238–47

20. King, R. J. 1982. Pulmonary surfactant. *J. Appl. Physiol.* 53:1–8

21. King, R. J. 1984. Isolation and chemical composition of pulmonary surfactant. In *Pulmonary Surfactant*, ed. L. M. G. van Golde, B. Robertson, J. J. Batenburg. Amsterdam: Elsevier. In press

22. King, R. J., Clements, J. A. 1972. Surface-active materials from dog lung. I. Method of isolation. *Am. J. Physiol.* 223:707–14

23. King, R. J., Clements, J. A. Lipid synthesis and surfactant turnover in the lungs. In *Handbook of Physiology, Respiration*, Vol. 4, ed. A. P. Fishman, A. B. Fisher. Bethesda, MD. Am. Physiol. Soc. In press

24. King, R. J., Gikas, E. G., Ruch, J., Clements, J. A. 1974. The radioimmunoassay of pulmonary surface-active material in sheep lung. *Am. Rev. Resp. Dis.* 110:273–81

25. King, R. J., Klass, D. J., Gikas, E. G., Clements, J. A. 1973. Isolation of apoproteins from canine surface active material. *Am. J. Physiol.* 224:788–95

26. King, R. J., Martin, H., Mitts, D., Holmstrom, F. M. 1977. Metabolism of the apoproteins in pulmonary surfactant. *J. Appl. Physiol.* 42:483–91

27. King, R. J., Martin, H. 1980. Intracellular metabolism of the apoproteins of pulmonary surfactant in rat lung. *J. Appl. Physiol.* 48:812–20

28. King, R. J., Martin, H. M. 1981. Effects of inhibiting protein synthesis on the secretion of surfactant by Type II cells in primary culture. *Biochim. Biophys. Acta* 663:289–301

29. King, R. J., Ruch, J., Gikas, E. G., Platzker, A. C. G., Creasy, R. K. 1975. Appearance of apoproteins of pulmonary surfactant in human amniotic fluid. *J. Appl. Physiol.* 39:735–41

30. Lancet Editorial. 1947. Lining of pulmonary alveoli. *Lancet* 252:68–69

31. Lynn, W. S. 1984. Alveolyn-structure and source. A review. *Exp. Lung Res.* 6:191–96

32. Lynn, W. S., Sahu, S. C., Bhattacharyya, S. N. 1979. Secretory alveolar glycoproteins (alveolyns). In *Le Lavage Broncho-Alveolaire Chez l' Homme*, ed. G. Biserte, J. Chrétien, C. Voisin, INSERM, 84:17–26. Amsterdam: Elsevier

33. Macklin, C. C. 1954. The pulmonary alveolar mucoid film and the pneumonocytes. *Lancet* 266:1099–104

34. Magoon, M. W., Wright, J. R., Baritussio, A., Williams, M. C., Goerke, J. 1983. Subfractionation of lung surfactant. Implications for metabolism and surface activity. *Biochim. Biophys. Acta* 750:18–31

35. McKearn, T. J. 1980. Cloning of hybridoma cells by limiting dilution in fluid phase. In *Monoclonal Antibodies*, ed. R. H. Kennett, T. J. McKean, K. B. Bechtol, p. 374. New York: Plenum

36. Mead, J., Whittenberger, J. L., Radford, E. P. Jr. 1957. Surface tension as a factor in pulmonary volume-pressure hysteresis. *J. Appl. Physiol.* 10:191–96

37. Pattle, R. E. 1955. Properties, function,

and origin of the alveolar lining layer. *Nature* 175:1125–26

38. Sahu, S. C., Lynn, W. S. 1979. Characterization of a high-molecular-weight glycoprotein isolated from the pulmonary secretions of patients with alveolar proteinosis. *Biochem. J.* 177:153–58

39. Sahu, S. C., Lynn, W. S. 1980. A high-molecular-weight alveolar glycoprotein in human amniotic fluid. *Lung* 157:71–79

40. Sahu, S. C., Tanswell, A. K., Lynn, W. S. 1980. A high-molecular-weight alveolar glycoprotein in the cell-free culture medium of human fetal Type II pneumocytes. *Lung* 158:143–50

41. Sanders, R. L. 1982. The composition of pulmonary surfactant. In *Lung Development: Biological and Clinical Perspectives, Vol. 1, Biochemistry and Physiology,* Ed. P. M. Farrell, pp. 193–210. New York: Academic

42. Sawada, H., Kashiwamata, S. 1977. Sodium dodecyl sulfate–disc gel electrophoresis patterns of bovine lung surfactant. *Biochim. Biophys. Acta* 490:44–50

43. Shelley, S. A., Balis, J. U., Paciga, J. G., Knuppel, R. A., Ruffolo, E. H., Bouis, P. J. Jr. 1982. Surfactant "apoproteins" in human amniotic fluid: an enzyme-linked immunosorbent assay for the prenatal assessment of lung maturity. *Am. J. Obst. Gynecol.* 144:224–28

44. Sueishi, K., Benson, B. J. 1981. Isolation of a major apoprotein of canine and murine pulmonary surfactant: biochemical and immunochemical characteristics. *Biochim. Biophys. Acta* 665:442–53

45. Towbin, H., Staehelin, T., Gordon, J. 1979. Electrophoretic transfer of proteins from acrylamide gels to nitrocellulose sheets: Procedure and some applications. *Proc. Natl. Acad. Sci. USA* 76:4350–54

46. van Golde, L. M. G. 1976. Metabolism of phospholipids in the lung. *Am. Rev. Resp. Dis.* 114:977–1000

47. Von Neergaard, K. 1929. Neue auffassungen uber einen grundbegriff der atemmechanik. *Z. Ges. Exptl. Med.* 66:373–94

48. Williams, M. C. 1977. Conversion of lamellar body membrane into tubular myelin in alveoli of fetal rat lung. *J. Cell. Biol.* 72:260–77

Ann. Rev. Physiol. 1985. 47:789–802

INTRACELLULAR PROCESSING OF SURFACTANT LIPIDS IN THE LUNG

Aron B. Fisher and Avinash Chander

Department of Physiology, University of Pennsylvania School of Medicine, Philadelphia, Pennsylvania 19104

INTRODUCTION

Early studies of the lung surfactant system were concerned with its physiological role, physical properties, chemical composition, ultrastructural identification, and biochemical pathways for synthesis. These topics are covered in detail in other chapters of this section. More recently, attention has focused on intracellular transport, assembly, and storage of surfactant components, surfactant secretion, and removal of surfactant from the alveolar space. These can be categorized as cell biology of the surfactant system and are the subjects of this review. This topic will be discussed within the framework of Assembly and Storage of Lung Surfactant Components, Secretion of Lung Surfactant, and Removal and Reprocessing of Lung Surfactant.

ASSEMBLY AND STORAGE OF LUNG SURFACTANT COMPONENTS

It is well accepted that the lamellar bodies of granular pneumocytes represent the intracellular storage site for the lung surfactant (87). The autoradiographic studies of Chevalier & Collet (12) suggested that phospholipids newly synthesized in the endoplasmic reticulum are transferred through the Golgi and packaged into "growing" lamellar bodies. However, the mechanisms for transfer of the principal phospholipid components of lung surfactant from their site of synthesis to the storage organelles have received little attention.

There is also limited information with respect to sites and mechanisms for

789

0066-4278/85/0315-0789$02.00

assembly of the protein components. Autoradiographic studies have suggested that protein components follow a slightly different route of intracellular processing from the lipid (12). Newly synthesized protein labeled with [³H]-leucine was transported from the endoplasmic reticulum through the Golgi apparatus into multivesicular bodies that subsequently fused with lamellar bodies. However, these labeling experiments were not specific for surfactant apoproteins. Therefore, the pathways and mechanisms for intracellular sorting and final assembly of proteins into the definitive secretory product of granular pneumocytes is unresolved.

Phospholipid Exchange Proteins

The general mechanisms by which phospholipids synthesized in endoplasmic reticulum of various cells are transferred to storage or secretory sites have been elucidated in greater detail with identification of a group of proteins called phospholipid exchange proteins (PLEPs) (94, 95). These proteins, which have been best characterized in preparations from liver (2, 47), are found in postmicrosomal supernatant, indicating that they are soluble cytoplasmic components. PLEPs are assayed by their ability to transfer a phospholipid from a donor to an acceptor organelle or artificial vesicle (94). The exchange activity depends on the specific phospholipid and on the nature of donor or acceptor organelles.

The presence of a PLEP in supernatant from lung homogenate was first demonstrated in 1978 (23, 73). This PLEP accelerated transport of phosphatidyl choline (PC) from microsomes to mitochondria, lamellar bodies, or liposomes. It also stimulated phosphatidylinositol (PI) exchange but showed minimal activity towards phosphatidylethanolamine (PE) and essentially no activity towards phosphatidylglycerol (PG) (79). The PC exchange protein from rat lung was demonstrated to be ~ 35,000 daltons under reducing conditions and 32,800 daltons under nondenaturing conditions, suggesting that this protein may be present in a monomeric form (71). It was shown to be rich in glutamic acid and glycine (71). Pool et al (69) demonstrated the presence of this PC-specific PLEP in isolated rat granular pneumocytes. Isoelectric focusing of sheep lung supernatant showed the presence of two subspecies of this PLEP with molecular weights of 21,000 and 22,000, as determined by chromatography on Sephadex and by SDS-PAGE, and with pIs of 7.1 and 5.8, respectively (73).

A second class of specific PLEP was isolated from rat and sheep lungs. This PLEP shows specificity towards PG and has essentially no activity towards PC (88, 90). The detection of this protein was facilitated by gel chromatography of the lung soluble fraction.

Lamellar bodies were shown to be possible acceptor organelles for the PLEPs from lung, although generally microsomes, mitochondria, or liposomes served as better acceptors (23, 24, 71, 79). If surfactant phospholipids are synthesized in the endoplasmic reticulum, a lung PLEP with specificity for transfer of the disaturated form of PC to lamellar bodies should be present but has not yet been demonstrated. Consequently, the precise role of these PLEPs in the assembly of surfactant components remains to be determined.

Lamellar Bodies

Lamellar bodies are regarded as the intracellular storage site for lung surfactant. There is evidence to suggest that these organelles may also have an ancillary role in the biosynthesis of dipalmitoylphosphatidylcholine (DPPC) (11, 22) although this evidence is at present equivocal (4). The study of lamellar bodies has been greatly facilitated by the development of methods for their isolation in relatively high yield and with relatively little contamination by other cell components. Since the original description for the isolation of lamellar bodies from beef lungs (91), lamellar body preparations have been described for rat (21, 28, 66), mouse (4), rabbit (18, 39), pig (33, 82), guinea pig (86), and human (70). Recently, lamellar bodies have been isolated from primary cultures of rat granular pneumocytes (10, 14). The isolation methods have been based on gradient centrifugation of lung homogenates and can be divided into those that utilize sedimentation (28, 66) either on a discontinuous or continuous gradient (29) and those that utilize upward flotation (21, 33). The isopycnic density of the lamellar bodies is approximately 1.06 g ml^{-1} (0.45–0.55 M sucrose) (21, 28, 41).

Examination of isolated lamellar body preparations by transmission electron microscopy has demonstrated morphology similar to lamellar bodies in the intact tissue. The presence of an intact limiting membrane for the isolated lamellar body has been demonstrated (7, 10, 28, 70, 75) and is required for morphologic documentation of an adequate preparation, because synthetic phospholipids in solution can also generate lamellae. Isolated lamellar bodies after disruption demonstrate the in vitro surface activity of natural surfactant (28, 86).

Unfortunately, to date no enzyme activity or other biochemical marker has been identified as unique for lamellar bodies. One parameter that has been considered useful for evaluating purity of preparations is the phospholipid-to-protein ratio (18). In contrast to mitochondria, microsomes, and most other organelles where this ratio is less than one, the phospholipid-to-protein ratio (wt/wt) for lamellar body preparations has been in the range 3–12. Lower values, which have been reported by several investigators (22, 29, 39), may result from contamination with other organelles. Artifactually high values could be generated by the loss of the protein-rich limiting membrane or loss of other protein constituents. The most common contaminant of isolated lamellar body preparations is microsomal protein, which can be detected by measuring NADPH-cytochrome C reductase activity. Although one study showed enrichment of this enzyme, suggesting that it is intrinsic to lamellar bodies (80), other investigations have demonstrated little or no activity (7, 10, 45). Thus, the presence of NADPH-cytochrome C reductase activity in lamellar body preparations can be regarded as evidence for microsomal contamination. Lamellar body preparations are also free of contamination with mitochondrial enzymes (7, 10, 45).

The phospholipid composition of isolated lamellar bodies reflects the composition of the lung surfactant. Of the total lamellar body phospholipid, 70–80% is phosphatidylcholine (10, 21, 28, 75) and 6–14% is phosphatidylglycerol (10, 35, 70, 75). Approximately 75% (range 62–86%) of fatty acids in PC are palmitate (5, 10, 18, 28, 70, 80). Analysis of phosphatidylglycerol composition has yielded more variable results with palmitate, reported generally as 30–60% of fatty acids (7, 10, 35, 70, 80) but with isolated reports of much lower (74) and much higher (75) values. Despite this variability, the data suggest that unlike PC, PG does not exist primarily in the disaturated form.

The protein component of lamellar bodies has not been as well characterized as the phospholipid. Bhattacharyya et al (6) have isolated hydroxyproline containing glycoproteins from lamellar bodies that have characteristics similar to those of a protein isolated by this group from lung lavage. Phizackerly et al (68) showed that approximately 40% of the lamellar body protein consisted of several hydrophobic proteins that could be extracted from lamellar bodies with a mixture of ethanol and ether. These authors suggested that similar proteins were present in the lung lavage material, although this has not yet been demonstrated by structural or immunologic studies of the protein. The hydrophobic proteins that have been isolated from lamellar bodies may be derived in part from the lamellar body–limiting membrane. A protein showing electrophoretic mobility similar to the major surfactant-associated protein (apoprotein A) has also been demonstrated in isolated lamellar bodies (16), further supporting that these organelles are a part of the surfactant system.

Evaluation of isolated lamellar bodies has consistently shown the presence of a large variety of hydrolases that are generally considered to be lysosomal enzymes (5, 7, 18, 29, 39, 40, 41, 62). These studies confirm earlier histochemical studies that demonstrated the presence of acid phosphatase (3, 31, 51, 78), aryl sulfatase B (31), and other nonspecific esterases (89) in lamellar bodies that had been stained in situ. Several studies have demonstrated that acid phosphatase specific activity (expressed per mg protein) of isolated lamellar bodies is enriched over the specific activity in the lung homogenate (10, 18, 39, 41, 82). Lamellar bodies prepared from isolated granular pneumocytes also show enrichment of the acid phosphatase activity (10, 14). The distribution on density centrifigation shows a peak of acid phosphatase activity associated with the lamellar bodies that appears to be clearly distinct from the lysosomal fraction (10, 41). With respect to localization of acid phosphatase activity within the lamellar body, initial morphologic studies indicated a perimembranous distribution (3, 31, 51), whereas a subsequent study suggested predominance in the central core (92). This controversy may be resolved by the model presented by Gil (27), which would suggest that all of the reports are compatible with the perimembranous distribution of acid phosphatase activity.

Other acid hydrolases that have been demonstrated in lamellar bodies include β-glycerophosphatase, arylsulfatase, UDP galactose transferase, β-N-acetylglucosaminidase, β-glucuronidase, and several other minor hydrolases (5, 7, 18, 29, 39, 41). Phosphatidic acid phosphatase (PAPase), an important enzyme in the phospholipid biosynthetic pathway, has been demonstrated in lamellar bodies (14, 16) but may represent acid phosphatase activity. Phospholipases A_1 and A_2 (the enzymes with activity at acidic pH) have also been demonstrated in the organelles (36, 38, 41), but the high-pH, Ca^+-dependent phospholipase A is not present (25). It has been suggested that these phospholipases may have a role in degradation and biosynthesis of surfactant phospholipids (11, 37), although a precise function for these and other hydrolases has not yet been determined.

Maximal activity for these acid hydrolases would require a pH in the acid range, as is commonly associated with lysosomes. Using weakly basic amines, Chander, Reicherter & Fisher (unpublished observations; 11a) have demonstrated that the internal pH of isolated lamellar bodies is approximately 1–2 pH units more acidic than the suspending medium. Maintenance of this pH gradient appears to be ATP-dependent and may, therefore, be a function of a hydrogen-ion pump such as has been described for other acidic organelles. The acidic pH of lamellar bodies may account for the relatively low pH that has been demonstrated for the lung surfactant hypophase (61).

SECRETION OF LUNG SURFACTANT

Recent studies using granular pneumocytes in primary culture have indicated that these cells secrete newly synthesized phosphsolipids as well as other components of the surfactant system (8, 19, 20, 49). Pulse-labeling techniques have permitted determinations of turnover rates of different components of surfactant phospholipids (44–46, 56, 81, 96, 97) after the classical design of Zilversmit (98). These studies have so far been carried out in intact tissue by assuming a simple two-compartment model with lamellar body DSPC as a precursor of surfactant DSPC and assuming that the recoveries of these two pools are quantitative. By this method, a turnover rate of 10.9 hr and secretion rate of 0.12 μmol hr^{-1} for surfactant DSPC has been calculated for adult rats (96). Using a similar model, the corresponding values for alveolar PC of a adult rabbit were calculated to be 3 hr and 3.4 μmol hr^{-1} ($\sim$ 2.5 μmol DSPC hr^{-1}m) (44). These species differences in secretion rates of surfactant phospholipid cannot be explained by differences in body weight, and they await confirmation. Inadequate recoveries of individual phospholipid pools could have distorted these calculations.

The similar labeling kinetics of the protein and DSPC components of surfactant in the lung lavage (48, 50) suggest secretion of both as moieties of surfactant. Furthermore, secretion of surfactant phospholipids and the major surfactant apoprotein were stimulated to a similar degree with isolated granular pneumocytes (19, 20). However, treatment of lung slices with colchicine inhibited DSPC secretion but did not affect the secretion of protein (15). Furthermore, inhibition of protein synthesis using cycloheximide for up to 6 hr did not affect DSPC secretion by isolated type II cells (49). Consequently, these results suggest that the lipid and protein components may be secreted independently rather than as a lipoprotein-like complex. An alternative explanation for the cycloheximide result is that type II cells have sufficient reserves of surfactant-associated protein to maintain normal secretory rates in short-term culture.

Mechanisms of Secretion

Inhibition of secretion of PC and DSPC by in vivo treatment with colchicine suggests involvement of the microtubular system in surfactant secretion (76). Several studies have suggested that cytoskeletal proteins may also be involved in the secretory process. Actin, a component protein of the cytoskeleton, has been demonstrated near the lamellar bodies and plasma membrane, particularly in the microvilli (84). Marino et al demonstrated that cytochalasin B, an inhibitor of cytoskeletal function, decreased DSPC secretion by fetal lung slices (53). Tsilibary et al showed that cytochalasin D disrupted actin microfilaments in microvilli and prevented the depletion of lamellar bodies following isoproterenol in isolated rat lungs (85). These results suggest that actin may be involved in movement and exocytosis of lamellar bodies.

Regulation of Secretion

Evidence for physiological regulation of secretion was first presented by Goldenberg et al (32), who showed that administration of a cholinergic agonist, pilocarpine, to rats caused an increase in size of lamellar bodies located in the apical region of the cell, a decrease in the number of multivesicular bodies, dilatation of the endoplasmic reticulum, and an increased secretion of phospholipids into the alveolar space. Subsequent observations showed that cholinergic agonists and vagal stimulation increased secretion of DSPC (55, 63). This response could be blocked by atropine (55, 63) and also by propranalol and by adrenalectomy (1, 54), suggesting that the cholinergic control of surfactant secretion may be indirect through adrenergic mediation. This is supported by observations with isolated type II cells that showed increased intracellular cGMP when stimulated by cholinergic agonists (8) but no increase in secretion of surfactant phospholipids (8, 19).

Evidence for β-adrenergic regulation of surfactant secretion was presented by Abdellatiff (1), who showed that epinephrine stimulated surfactant secretion

by up to 200% in the isolated perfused lung preparation. β-Adrenergic agonists, isoproterenol and terbutaline, were shown to stimulate DSPC secretion in
vivo (64), in the isolated perfused lung (8, 54), and in isolated granular
pneumocytes in primary culture (8, 19). These effects can be blocked by
propranalol, and can be mimicked by cAMP analogs. (8, 19, 54). Morphometric observations of lungs after isoproterenol show depletion of lamellar
bodies (54), thus supporting a β-adrenergic effect on surfactant secretion.

Several studies have demonstrated that hyperventilation leads to increased
rates of surfactant secretion (58, 63). The effects of hyperventilation were
demonstrated with swimming rats that increased their surfactant secretion as
minute ventilation increased (59). The mechanism for the effect of ventilation
is not clear. Both β-adrenergic and cholinergic mechanisms have been postulated, and propanolol did block the stimulation of secretion (64). Prostaglandins may also play a role, because hyperventilation-induced stimulation of
surfactant secretion was blocked by indomethacin (64). On the other hand,
these effects of inhibitors on increased secretion were not confirmed (57).
Thus, the relative roles of chemical mediators versus physical factors, i.e.
distortion of alveolar septae, in the coordination of ventilation and surfactant
secretion remain to be resolved.

Metabolic factors have also been demostrated in the control of surfactant
secretion, although again data is limited. Intracellular pH may be an important
regulatory factor as alkalosis through hypocapnic perfusion induced depletion
of lamellar bodies (77). This effect may be due in part to effects of pH on
lamellar body formation. Lowered temperature inhibited hyperventilation-
induced surfactant secretion in isolated perfused lung (58) as well as the basal
secretion rate of isolated type II cells in primary culture (49). However, the
effect of temperature may be related to alterations in physical states of the
membrane below the lipid transition temperature. A possible energy requirement for secretion was investigated with hypoxia or 2,4-dinitrophenol in
isolated rat lungs (58). Although neither agent blocked the hyperventilation-
induced increase in surfactant secretion, it is not clear from these studies that
significant alteration of lung energy state was achieved. Although it seems
likely that ATP is involved in surfactant secretion, the precise details remain to
be determined.

REMOVAL AND REPROCESSING OF
LUNG SURFACTANT

The route(s) for surfactant removal have received less study than the pathways
for synthesis and secretion. Alveolar macrophages have been considered as one
of the possible pathways of clearance of surfactant phospholipids. Support for
this hypothesis was provided by the phagocytosis of tubular myelin by these
cells (60), the presence of surfactant phospholipid radioactivity in macrophages

lavaged from prelabeled lungs (17, 48), and accumulation of phospholipids in macrophages during drug-induced phospholipidosis (72). However, uptake by macrophages after instillation of aerosolized radioactive DPPC or sonicated suspensions of biosynthesized surfactant have suggested that only small amounts of surfactant phospholipids are cleared via this pathway (17, 34). Also, only small amounts are cleared by transport up the airways via the mucociliary blanket (26).

An alternative hypothesis for clearance is removal of surfactant phospholipids by the alveolar epithelium. Intratracheal instillation of aerosolized [^{3}H] DPPC or sonicated suspensions of biosynthesized surfactant in rats or rabbits showed that surfactant phospholipids are cleared by lung at a rapid rate (17, 26, 30, 34, 43, 65, 67). Synthetic and biosynthesized phospholipids were taken up by intact lung tissue at similar rates (43). Although some of this radioactivity was accumulated in alveolar macrophages, and a small amount passed into the perfusion medium or blood, the largest percentage of this radioactivity was retained in the lung tissue (17, 30, 34), suggesting a role for lung cells other than alveolar macrophages in the clearance of surfactant phospholipids. An increased rate of removal during hyperventilation suggested that the clearance process is under physiologic control (65). Turnover studies after in vivo labeling have further supported clearance of surfactant phospholipids and recycling of the label. Kinetic analysis has generally revealed a biphasic curve with an early rapid decay phase and a later slower decay phase of the label (44, 96). The later phase possibly results from intermixing, through recycling, of label in extra- and intra-cellular surfactant–associated pools of DSPC.

Autoradiographic studies after intratracheal instillation of aerosolized [^{3}H]DPPC demonstrated the appearance of lipid radioactivity primarily in granular pneuomocytes (26). A role for granular pneumocytes was confirmed by demonstrating the appearance of radioactivity in the isolated lamellar body fraction after instillation of biosynthesized radioactive surfactant phospholipids into the lung (34, 43) or after incubation of lung slices with multilamellar liposomes (83). The ability of granular pneumocytes to internalize phospholipids has been demonstrated with cells in primary culture (9). These cells also internalized a marker for the aqueous compartment of lipid vesicles, indicating that more than simple phospholipid exchange or binding was involved and suggesting that the uptake was by fusion and/or endocytosis. Because the rate of lipid uptake by the isolated cells was low (9), it is possible that additional factors might regulate lipid uptake by these cells in vivo. One such modifier of phospholipid uptake may be a protein component of the lung surfactant. Claypool et al have demonstrated that a hydrophobic protein of lung surfactant significantly stimulates the uptake of lipids by granular pneumocytes in primary culture (13). This protein has a M_r around 10,000 and shows poor reactivity to Lowry's Folin reagent. The uptake of lipids was stimulated in a dose-dependent manner and resulted in proportionately higher uptake of a trypsin-inaccessible (presumably internalized) fraction (13). However, further studies are required to delineate the role of this protein in in vivo clearance and how the structure of this protein is related to the stimulatory effect on phospholipid uptake by granular pneumocytes.

Intracellular Processing

The pathway for processing of surfactant phospholipids in granular pneumocytes after internalization is as yet undetermined. Subcellular fractionation experiments after intratracheal instillation of biosynthesized radioactive surfactant revealed that the specific activity of PC relative to that in lung homogenate was always more than 1 in the lamellar body and almost 0.5 for the microsomal fraction (30). A more recent study has also suggested targetting of recycled surfactant phospholipids into the lamellar bodies (43). However, in another report, the proportion of total radioactivity in the lamellar body fraction, after correction for recoveries of organelles, was only 20% of the total (34). These findings led Hallman and associates (34) to postulate bidirectional surfactant flux between lamellar bodies and the aveolar space and the possible presence of two types of lamellar bodies in the lung. Magoon et al demonstrated light and dense lamellar bodies with large differences in their phospholipid content/mg protein but practically no difference in their phospholipid composition (52). The relationship of these lamellar bodies to surfactant recycling is not yet clear. Although it is possible that recycled radioactivity is present only in lamellar bodies, it is unlikely because studies with other systems [i.e. uptake of lysosomal enzymes by ovarian cells (93) or low density lipoproteins (LDL) by hepatocytes (42)] have shown involvement of compartments that are intermediate between the cell surface receptor and the lysosomes. Further studies using autoradiographic technique or subcellular localization in granular pneumocytes could provide important information on the pathway of internalization of surfactant lipids.

Metabolic Reutilization

Studies using granular pneumoctyes in primary culture to follow the metabolic fate of internalized phosphatidylcholine have suggested significant degradation of this phospholipid in the cell (9). Almost one third of radioactivity from the fatty acyl moiety of PC was in fractions that could arise from degradation of phosphatidylcholine by the action of various phospholipases. In our laboratory using an isolated perfused lung preparation, we have observed the appearance of choline radioactivity from [^{3}H-methyl] dipalmitoylphosphatidylcholine vesicles in water-soluble products that comigrate with authentic choline, choline-phosphate, and CDP-choline on thin-layer chromatography (unpublished observations). Contrary conclusions were reached by Jacobs et al (43), who did not see breakdown of intratracheally administered phosphatidylcholine vesicles labeled with [^{3}H]choline and [^{14}C]palmitic acid. These latter studies showed an initial rapid loss of radioactivity from PC, followed by a slower phase into undetermined pools. It was not determined if this lost radioactivity was recycled into PC or other lipid classes. Studies with isolated granular pneumocytes provided evidence for reutilization of phospholipid degradation products, because a small proportion of fatty acyl radioactivity from DPPC was found in phosphatidylglycerol (9). Based on studies with other systems, the most likely intracellular pathway for these processes is degradation in lysosomes with subsequent transfer of degradation products to the endoplasmic reticulum for reutilization. However, further studies are required to confirm this pathway in the granular pneumocytes.

CONCLUSIONS

Following the initial observations that the alveolar surface contains a lipid-rich material called the lung surfactant, the field of lung cell biology has given evidence of a complex coordination of cellular events that maintain the proper extracellular concentration of this material. Developments in this area have profited greatly from the details of cell biology elucidated in studies of other systems and cell types. Thus, it is increasingly apparent that the epithelial cells of the lung alveolus share and have adapted the general regulatory processes of epithelia to their own purpose in dealing with the air-liquid environment at their surface.

Literature Cited

1. Abdellatif, M. M., Hollingsworth, M. 1980. Effect of oxotremorine and epinephrine on lung surfactant secretion in neonatal rabbits. *Pediatr. Res.* 14: 916–20
2. Akeroyd, R., Moonen, P., Westerman, J., Puyk, W. C., Wirtz, K. W. A. 1981. The complete primary structure of the phosphatidylcholine-transfer protein from bovine liver. *Eur. J. Biochem.* 114:385–91
3. Balis, J. U., Conen, P. E. 1964. The role of alveolar inclusion bodies in the developing lung. *Lab. Invest.* 13:1215–99
4. Baranska, J., Van Golde, L. M. G. 1977. Role of lamellar bodies in the biosynthesis of phosphatidylcholine in mouse lung. *Biochim. Biophys. Acta* 488:285–93
5. Baritussio, A. G., Magoon, M. W., Goerke, J., Clements, J. A. 1981. Precursor-product relationship between rabbit type II cell lamellar bodies and alveolar surface-active material. *Biochim. Biophys. Acta* 666:382–93

6. Bhattacharyya, S. N., Passero, M. A., Di Augustine, R. P., Lynn, W. S. 1975. Isolation and characterization of two hydroxyproline-containing glycoproteins from normal animal lung lavage and lamellar bodies. *J. Clin. Invest.* 55:914–20
7. Boudreau, J., Beauocin, A. R., Nadeau, D. 1983. Sequential isolation of lamellar bodies and surfactant fractions from rat lungs. *Can. Biochem. Cell Biol.* 61:231–39
8. Brown, L. A. S., Longmore, W. J. 1981. Adrenergic and cholinergic regulation of lung surfactant secretion in the isolated perfused rat lung and in the alveolar type II cell in culture. *J. Biol. Chem.* 256:66–72
9. Chander, A., Claypool, W. D. Jr., Strauss, J. F. III, Fisher, A. B. 1983. Uptake of liposomal phosphatidylcholine by granular pneumocytes in primary culture. *Am. J. Physiol.* 245:C397–404
10. Chander, A., Dodia, C. R., Gil, J., Fisher, A. B. 1983 Isolation of lamellar

bodies from rat granular pneumocytes in primary culture. *Biochim. Biophys. Acta* 753:119–29

11. Chander, A., Fisher, A. B., Strauss, J. F. III. 1982. Role of an acidic compartment in synthesis of disaturated phosphatidylcholine by rat granular pneumocytes. *Biochem. J.* 208:651–58

11a. Chander, A., Reicherter, J., Fisher, A. B. 1983. Maintenance of pH gradient by isolated lung lamellar bodies. *Fed. Proc.* 42(5):1278

12. Chevalier, G., Collet, A. J. 1972. In vivo incorporation of choline ^{3}H, leucine-^{3}H and galactose-^{3}H in alveolar type II pneumocytes in relation to surfactant synthesis. A quantitative radioautographic study in mouse by electron microscopy. *Anat. Rec.* 174:289–310

13. Claypool, W. D., Wang, D. L., Chander, A., Fisher, A. B. 1984. An ethanol/ether soluble apoprotein from rat lung surfactant augments liposome uptake by isolated granular pneumocytes. *J. Clin. Invest.* 74:677–84

14. Crecelius, C. A., Longmore, W. J. 1983. Phosphatidic acid phosphatase activity in subcellular fractions derived from adult rat type II pneumocytes in primary culture. *Biochim. Biophys. Acta* 750:447–56

15. Delahunty, T. J., Johnston, J. M. 1976. The effect of colchicine and vinblastine on the release of pulmonary surface active material. *J. Lipid Res.* 17:112–16

16. Delahunty, T. J., Spitzer, H. L., Jimenez, J. M., Johnston, J. M. 1979. Phosphatidate phosphohydrolase activity in porcine pulmonary surfactant. *Am. Rev. Resp. Dis.* 119:75–80

17. Desai, R., Tetley, T. D., Curtis, G. M., Powell, G. M., Richards, R. J. 1978. Studies on the fate of pulmonary surfactant in the lung. *Biochem. J.* 176:455–62

18. DiAugustine, R. P. 1974. Lung concentric laminar organelle. *J. Biol. Chem.* 249:584–93

19. Dobbs, L. G., Mason, R. J. 1979. Pulmonary alveolar type II cells isolated from rats. *J. Clin. Invest.* 63:378–87

20. Dobbs, L. G., Mason, R. J., Williams, M. C., Benson, B. J., Sueishi, K. 1982. Secretion of surfactant by primary cultures of alveolar type II cells isolated from rats. *Biochim. Biophys. Acta* 713:118–27

21. Duck-Chong, C. G. 1978. The isolation of lamellar bodies and their membranous content from rat lung, lamb tracheal fluid and human amniotic fluid. *Life Sci.* 22(22):2025–30

22. Engle, M. J., Sanders, R. L. and Long-more, W. J. 1976. Phospholipid composition and acyltransferase activity of lamellar bodies isolated from rat lung. *Archives of Biochem. and Biophysics* 173:586–595

23. Engle, M. J., van Golde, L. M. G. and Wirtz, K. W. A. 1978. Transfer of phospholipids between subcellular fractions of the lung. *FEBS Letts.* 86:277–281

24. Funkhouser, J. D. and Hughes, E. R., 1983. The lung lamellar body as a functioning membrane in protein-catalyzed phosphatidylcholine transfer. *Arch. Biochem. Biophys.* 221:499–506

25. Garcia, A., Sener, S. F. and Mavis, R. D. 1976. Lung lamellar bodies lack certain key enzymes of phospholipid metabolism. *Lipids* 11: no. 2, 109–112

26. Geiger, K., Gallagher, M. L., and Hedley-Whyte, J. 1975. Cellular distribution and clearance of aerosolized dipalmitoyl lecithin. *J. Appl. Physiol.* 39:759–766

27. Gil, J. 1985. Ultrastructure of the alveolar membrane and lung lipids. *Ann. Rev. Physiol.* 47:753–64

28. Gil, J. and Reiss, O. K. 1973. Isolation and characterization of lamellar bodies and tubular myelin from rat lung homogenates. *J. Cell Biology* 58:152–171

29. Gilder, H., Haschemeyer, R. H., Fairclough G. F. Jr., and Mynarcik, D. C. 1981. Isolation and characterization of lamellar body material from rat lung homogenates by continuous linear sucrose gradients. *J. Lipid Res.* 22:1277–1285

30. Glatz, T., Ikegami, M., Jobe, A. 1982. Metabolism of exogenously administered natural surfactant in the newborn lamb. *Pediatr. Res.* 16:711–15

31. Goldfischer, S., Kikkawa, Y., Hoffman, L. 1968. The demonstration of acid hydrolase activities in the inclusion bodies of Type II alveolar cells and other liposomes in the rabbit lung. *J. Histochem. Cytochem.* 16:102–09

32. Goldenberg, V. E., Buckingham, S., Sommers, S. C. 1969. Pilocarpine stimulation of granular pneumocyte secretion. *Lab. Invest.* 20:147–58

33. Grathwohl, C., Newman, G. E., Phizackerley, P. J. R., Town, M. H. 1979. Structural studies on lamellated osmiophilic bodies isolated from pig lung. *Biochim. Biophys. Acta* 552:509–18

34. Hallman, M., Epstein, B. L., Gluck, L. 1981. Analysis of labeling and clearance of lung surfactant phospholipids in rabbit. *J. Clin. Invest.* 68:742–51

35. Hallman, M., Gluck, L. 1975. Phosphatidylglycerol in lung surfactant. II. Sub-

cellular distribution and mechanism of biosynthesis in vitro. *Biochim. Biophys. Acta* 409:172–91

36. Heath, M. F., Jacobson, W. 1976. Phospholipases A_1 and A_2 in lamellar inclusion bodies of the alveolar epithelium of rabbit lung. *Biochim. Biophys. Acta* 441:443–52

37. Heath, M. F., Jacobson, W. 1980. The action of lung lysosomal phospholipases on dipalmitoyl phosphatidylcholine and its significance for the synthesis of pulmonary surfactant. *Pediat. Res.* 14:254–58

38. Heath, M. F., Jacobson, W. 1980. The nature of the phospholipases A of lung lamellar bodies. *Pediat. Res.* 14:846–47

39. Hoffman, L., 1972. Isolation of inclusion bodies from rabbit lung parenchyma. *J. Cell. Physiol.* 79:65–72

40. Hook, G. E. R. 1978. Extracellular hydrolases of the lung. *Biochemistry* 17:520–28

41. Hook, G. E. R., Gilmore, L. B. 1982. Hydrolases of pulmonary lysosmes and lamellar bodies. *J. Biol Chem.* 257:9211–20

42. Hornick, C. A., Jones, A. L., Renaud, G., Hradek, G., Havel, R. J. 1984. Effect of chloroquine on low-density lipoprotein catabolic pathway in rat hepatocytes. *Am. J. Physiol.* 246:G187–94

43. Jacobs, H., Jobe, A., Ikegami, M., Conaway, D. 1983. The significance of reutilization of surfacant phosphatidycholine. *J. Biol. Chem.* 258:4159–65

44. Jacobs, H., Jobe, A., Ikegami, M., Jones, S. 1982. Surfactant phosphatidylcholine source, fluxes, and turnover times in 3-day-old, 10-day-old, and adult rabbits. *J. Biol. Chem.* 257:1805–10

45. Jobe, A. 1977. The labeling and biological half-life of phosphatidylcholine in subcellular fractions of rabbit lung. *Biochim. Biophys. Acta* 489:440–53

46. Jobe, A., Kirkpatrick, E., Gluck, L. 1978. Labeling of phopholipids in surfactant and subcellular fractions of rabbit lung. *J. Biol. Chem.* 253:3810–16

47. Kamp, H. H., Wirtz, K. W. A., Van Deenen, L. L. M. 1973. Some properties of phospholipid exchange protein purified from beef liver. *Biochim. Biophys. Acta* 318:313–25

48. King, R. J., Martin, H. 1980. Intracellular metabolism of the apoproteins of pulmonary surfactant in rat lung. *J. Appl. Physiol.* 48:812–20

49. King, R. J., Martin, H. M. 1981. Effects of inhibiting protein synthesis on the secretion of surfactant by type II cells in primary culture. *Biochim. Biophys. Acta* 663:289–301

50. King, R. J., Martin, H., Mitts, D., Holstrom, F. M. 1977. Metabolism of the apoproteins in pulmonary surfactant. *J. Appl. Physiol.* 42:483–91

51. Kuhn, C. III. 1968. Cytochemistry of pulmonary alveolar epithelial cells. *Am. J. Pathol.* 53:809–33

52. Magoon, M. W., Wright, J. R., Baritussio, A., Williams, M. C., Goerke, J., et al. 1983. Subfractionation of lung surfactant: implications for metabolism and surface activity. *Biochim. Biophys. Acta* 750:18–31

53. Marino, P. A., Rooney, S. A. 1980. Surfactant secretion in a newborn rabbit lung slice model. *Biochimica et Biophysica.* 620:509–19

54. Massaro, D., Clerch, L., Massaro, G. D. 1982. Surfactant secretion: evidence that cholinergic stimulation of secretion is indirect. *Am. J. Physiol.* 243:C39–45

55. Morgan, T. E., Morgan, B. C. 1973. Surfactant synthesis storage and release by alveolar cells. In *Respiratory Distress Syndrome*, ed. C. A. Villee, D. B. Villee, J. Zuckerman, pp. 117–27. New York: Academic

56. Moriya, T., Kanoh, H. 1974. In vivo studies on the de novo synthesis of molecular species of rat lung lecithin. *Tohoku J. Exp. Med.* 112:241–56

57. Nicholas, T. E., Barr, H. A. 1981. Control of release of surfactant phospholipids in the isolated perfused rat lung. *J. Appl. Physiol.* 51:90–98

58. Nicholas, T. E., Barr, H. A. 1983. The release of surfactant in rat lung by brief periods of hyperventilation. *Resp. Physiol.* 52:69–83

59. Nicholas, T. E., Power, J. H. T., Barr, H. A. 1982. Surfactant homeostasis in the rat lung during swimming exercise. *J. Appl. Physiol.* 53:1521–28

60. Nichols, B. A. 1976. Normal rabbit alveolar macrophages. I. The phagocytosis of tubular myelin. *J. Exp. Med.* 144:906–19

61. Nielson, D. W., Goerke, J., Clements, J. A. 1981. Alveolar subphase pH in the lungs of anesthetized rabbits. *Proc. Natl. Acad. Sci. USA* 78:7119–23

62. Okazaki, T., Johnston, J. M., Snyder, J. M. 1982. Morphogenesis of the lamellar body in fetal lung tissue in vitro. *Biochim. Biophys. Acta* 712:283–91

63. Oyarzun, M. J., Clements, J. A. 1977. Ventilatory and cholinergic control of pulmonary surfactant in the rabbit. *J. Appl. Physiol.* 43:39–45

64. Oyarzun, M. J., Clements, J. A. 1978. Control of lung surfactant by ventilation,

adrenergic mediators, and prostaglandins in the rabbit. *Am. Rev. Resp. Dis.* 117:879–91

65. Oyarzun, M. J., Clements, J. A., Britussio, A. 1980. Ventilation enhances pulmonary alveolar clearance of radioactive dipalmitoyl phosphatidylcholine in liposomes. *Am. Rev. Resp. Dis.* 121:709–21

66. Page-Roberts, B. A. 1972. Preparation and partial characterization of a lamellar body fraction from rat lung. *Biochim. Biophys. Acta* 260:334–38

67. Phizackerley, P. J. R., Newman, G. E., Smith, H., Cooper, J. R. 1983. The reversible detachment and deposition of surfactant and of pulmonary macrophages during bronchopulmonary lavage in the rat. *J. Pathol.* 140:1–7

68. Phizackerley, P. J. R., Town, M. H., Newman, G. E. 1979. Hydrophobic proteins of lamellated osmiophillic bodies isolated from pig lung. *Biochem. J.* 183:731–36

69. Pool, G. L., Bubacz, D. G., Lumb, R. H., Mason, R. J. 1983. Phospholipid-transfer activities in cytosols from lung, isolated alveolar type II cells and alveolar type II cell-derived adenomas. *Biochem. J.* 215:637–42

70. Post, M., Batenburg, J. J., Schuurmans, E. A. J. M., Laros, C. D., van Golde, L. M. G. 1982. Lamellar bodies isolated from adult human lung tissue. *Exp. Lung Res.* 3:17–28

71. Read, R. J., Funkhouser, J. D. 1983. Properties of a non-specific phospholipid-transfer protein purified from rat lung. *Biochim. Biophys. Acta* 752:118–26

72. Reasor, M. J. 1981. Drug-induced lipidosis and the alveolar macrophages. *Toxicology* 20:1–33

73. Robinson, M. E., Wu, L. N. Y., Brumley, G. W., Lumb, R. H. 1978. A unique phosphatidylcholine exchange protein isolated from sheep lung. *FEBS Letts.* 87:41–44

74. Rooney, S. A., Page-Roberts, B. A., Motoyama, E. K. 1975. Role of lamellar inclusions in surfactant production: studies on phospholipid composition and biosynthesis in rat and rabbit lung subcellular fractions. *J. Lipid Res.* 16:418–25

75. Sanders, R. L., Hassett, R. J., Vatter, A. E. 1980. Isolation of lung lamellar bodies and their conversation to tubular myelin figures in vitro. *Anat. Rec.* 198:485–501

76. Sato, T., Akino, T. 1982. Source of lung surfactant phospholipids: comparison of palmitate and acetate as precursors. *Lipids* 17:884–92

77. Shepard, J. W. Jr., Dolan, G. F., Yu, S. Y. 1982. Factors regulating lamellar body volume density of type II pneumocytes in excised dog lungs. *J. Appl. Physiol.* 53:555–62

78. Sorokin, S. P. 1967. A morphologic and cytochemical study on the great alveolar cell. *J. Histochem. Cytochem.* 14:884–97

79. Spalding, J. W., Hook, G. E. R. 1979. Phospholipid exchange between subcellular organelles of rabbit lung. *Lipids* 14:606–13

80. Spalding, J. W., Ortner, M. J., Tombropoulos, E. G., Gilmore, L. B., Hook, G. E. R. 1983. Isolation and characterization of rabbit lung lamellar bodies. *Exp. Lung Res.* 4:171–90

81. Spitzer, H. L., Morrison, K., Norman, J. R., 1968. The incorporation of L-[Me-^{14}C] Methionine and [Me-^{3}H] choline into lung phosphatides. *Biochim. Biophys. Acta* 152:552–58

82. Spitzer, H. L., Rice, J. M., MacDonald, P. C., Johnston, J. M. 1975. Phospholid biosynthesis in lung lamellar bodies. *Biochem. Biophys. Res. Comm.* 66:17–23

83. Tsao, F. H. C. 1979. Use of liposomes in probing the uptake of liposomal phosphatidylcholine by rabbit lung in vitro. *Biochim. Biophys. Acta* 575:234–43

84. Tsilibary, E. C., Williams, M. C. 1983. Actin and secretion of surfactant. *J. Histochem. Cytochem.* 31:1298–304

85. Tsilibary, E. C., Williams, M. C. 1983. Actin in peripheral rat lung: S₁ labeling and structural changes induced by cytochalasin. *J. Histochem. Cytochem.* 31:1289–97

86. Valdivia, E. 1973. Isolation and identification of pulmonary lamellar bodies from guinea pigs. *Prep. Biochem.* 3:19–30

87. van Golde, L. M. G. 1976. Metabolism of phospholipids in lung. *Am. Rev. Resp. Dis.* 114:977–1000

88. van Golde, L. M. G., Oldenbord, V., Post, M., Batenburg, J. J. 1980. Phospholipid transfer proteins in rat lung. *J. Biol. Chem.* 255:6011–13

89. Vatter, A. E., Reiss, O. K., Newman, J. K., Lindquist, K. L., Groeneboer, E. 1968. Enzymes of the lung. I. Detection of esterase with a new cytochemical method. *J. Cell. Biol.* 38:80–98

90. Whitlow, C. D., Pool, G. L., Brumley, G. W., Lumb, R. H., 1980. Protein-catalyzed transfer of phosphatidylglycerol by sheep lung soluble fraction. *FEBS Lett.* 113:221–24

91. Williams, C. H., Vail, W. J., Harris, R. A., Green, D. E. 1971. The isolation and

characterization of the lamellar body of bovine lung. *Prep. Biochem.* 1:37–45

92. Williams, M. C. 1977. Conversion of lamellar body membranes into tubular myelin in alveoli of fetal rat lungs. *J. Cell. Biol.* 72:260–77

93. Willingham, M. C., Pastan, I. H., Sahagian, G. G., Jourdian, G. W., Neufeld, E. F. 1981. Morphologic study of the internalization of a lysosomal enzyme by the mannose-6-phosphate receptor in cultured chinese hamster ovary cells. *Proc. Natl. Acad. Sci. USA* 78:6967–71

94. Wirtz, K. W. A., Kamp, H. H., Van Dennen, L. L. M. 1972. Isolation of a protein from beef liver that specifically stimulates the exchange of phosphatidylcholine. *Biochim. Biophys. Acta* 274:606–17

95. Wirtz, K. W. A., Zilversmit, D. B., 1968. Exchange of phospholipids between liver mitochondria and microsomes in vitro. *J. Biol. Chem.* 243:3596–602

96. Young, S. L., Kremers, S. A., Apple, J. S., Crapo, J. D., Brumley, G. W. 1981. Rat lung surfactant kinetics: biochemical and morphometric correlation. *J. Appl. Physiol.* 51:248–53

97. Young, S. L., Tierney, D. F. 1972. Dipalmitoyl lecithin secretion and metabolism by the rat lung. *Am. J. Physiol.* 222:1539–44

98. Zilversmit, D. B., Entenman, C., Fishler, M. C. 1943. On the calculation of "turnover time" and "turnover rate" from experiments involving the use of labelling agents. *J. Gen. Physiol.* 26:325–31

Ann. Rev. Physiol. 1985. 47:803–22

DEVELOPMENTAL ASPECTS OF LUNG LIPIDS

Robert H. Perelman, Philip M. Farrell, Michael J. Engle, and Joseph W. Kemnitz

Department of Pediatrics and The Primate Center, University of Wisconsin, Madison, Wisconsin 53792

INTRODUCTION

The developmental biochemistry of the lung has been a topic of great interest during the past 15 years because of parallel advances in knowledge from both basic and clinical research. The stimulus for much of the scientific inquiry is the common disease of prematurely delivered newborns known as Respiratory Distress Syndrome (RDS). This disorder, originally called Hyaline Membrane Disease, is the leading cause of neonatal mortality in the United States (89). Ever since Avery & Mead's observations (4) on the surface tension of lung extracts, most investigators have concluded that pulmonary surfactant deficiency accounts for the pathophysiology of RDS, as reviewed elsewhere (32, 35); the supporting evidence indicates that the phospholipids characteristic of pulmonary surfactant are abnormally low in lung parenchyma and broncho-alveolar secretory products. Especially relevant and physiologically important is the presence of decreased total phosphatidylcholine (PC), disaturated PC, and phosphatidylglycerol (PG). These abnormalities occur not only in newborns with RDS but also in fetuses susceptible to the disease upon delivery, as revealed from studies of amniotic fluid (114).

Premature delivery provides the precipitating circumstance for neonatal RDS, i.e. it "sets the stage" for the potentially fatal clinical problem. In a sense, therefore, RDS can be viewed as a disease attributable to incomplete development of the fetal lung at the time of partuition. As a consequence, biochemical immaturity causes collapse of terminal respiratory units that have insufficient surface-active phospholipid. This concept was recognized by Gluck et al (45) from multidisciplinary studies involving rabbits and was later applied to human

803

amniotic fluid. A major advance in perinatal care was thus achieved because of the ability of phospholipid analyses to predict postnatal respiratory function (43, 44). Other relevant research that has "bridged the gap" from the laboratory to the bedside came soon thereafter when Liggins (68) discovered that exogenous glucocorticoids accelerated the maturation of fetal sheep lungs and subsequently that neonatal RDS could be prevented by this approach (69).

Comprehensive investigation of the biology of fetal lung development necessarily involves laboratory animals that in essence serve as models for whatever hypotheses are being tested. It should be emphasized, however, that considerable heterogeneity, biologic variability, and species specificity has been encountered in studies of mice, rats, rabbits, sheep, and monkeys (33). Also, it has been increasingly appreciated that fetal lung metabolism is markedly different from adult lung biochemistry. The fetus develops in a distinctly anaerobic environment and utilizes a special supply of substrates high in glucose, lactate, and amino acids while low in fatty acids. In addition, glycogen accumulates as a unique event in developing pneumocytes in utero and then is depleted concurrent with augmented phospholipid production. Because of the complexity of fetal metabolism, efforts have been made in recent years to isolate lung tissue, either as organ explants (108) or perfused whole lung (85), and to study enriched populations of isolated cells (29), particularly type II pneumocytes that synthesize, store, and secrete surfactant phospholipids. This in vitro approach has made it possible to demonstrate that lactate and stored glycogen (20) can potentially be utilized as precursors for fetal lung phospholipid synthesis.

The Timing of Fetal Lung Development

The morphologic pattern and timing of fetal lung maturation have been assessed according to the three phases recognized in all species and termed the glandular, canalicular, and saccular stages. The marked differences in histologic appearance are especially evident in animals with short gestational periods. In rats, for instance, advances from one stage to the next can occur in 24 hours. On the cellular and subcellular levels, equally impressive changes take place with increasing appearance of lamellar bodies signaling the presence of intracellular surfactant [on days 19–20 in the rat fetus (121, 122) and on day 28 in the rabbit (119)]. The corresponding biochemical changes include increased concentrations of phospholipid occurring very late in the canalicular stage or in the saccular period. The quantitatively most impressive change is a rise in the concentration of total PC and its saturated fraction, which is mainly composed of dipalmitoyl PC. The relative timing of this increase is rather consistent from species to species and occurs on the average when 85–90% of gestation has been completed (33). Furthermore, there is a uniformly close correlation between the rise in PC level and the appearance of surface tension–lowering material in lung parenchyma and in the eventual airspaces (67, 88).

It should be emphasized that lung biochemical maturation with respect to surfactant phospholipid is a relatively late phenomenon during gestation. Because lung surfactant is not generally abundant until the last 12–24 hr in mice, the last 24 hr in rats, the last 10 days in macaques, and the last month of gestation in humans, one can logically assume that the fetal lung is endowed with regulatory mechanisms operating to control the timing of the maturation process and to ensure a "reservoir" of surfactant for the vital extrauterine transition to the air-breathing state.

Factors Altering Fetal Lung Maturation

A list of factors that can change the timing of lung development is presented in Table 1. Many of these were first identified from clinical observations on the epidemiology of neonatal pulmonary surfactant deficiency. Subsequent basic research has been helpful in confirming and clarifying their impact. In most instances, however, the research is still at a descriptive level and has not defined pathobiologic mechanisms nor even the normal physiologic regulator(s) of lung phospholipid metabolism. Genetic factors provide a good example of the rudimentary state of knowledge in this area. Graven & Misenheimer (45a) found in a study of women who had delivered two or more infants weighing 1.25–2.50 kg at birth that if the first baby had RDS, the risk for the subsequent child was 93%, whereas if the first was healthy, only 3% of later infants developed RDS. The implication of a hereditary influence was supported in a similar study by Lankenau (67a) who further observed that the factor was linked to mothers and extended to both maternal half-siblings and first cousins but not to paternal relatives. The basis of this presumably maternal genetic factor has not been investigated except for an unrevealing analysis of four enzymes that catalyze phospholipid biosynthesis in lung tissue obtained from one victim of "familial RDS" (35a).

The major purpose of this article is to review factors that influence fetal lung development, especially those that have effects on phospholipid metabolism. Because the role of the factors listed in Table 1 is not yet known in terms of molecular regulatory mechanisms, our discussion must largely be confined to the descriptive level. It is also necessary to focus our attention on a limited

Table 1 Factors influencing the timing of fetal lung development

Genetic background
Gestational age
Fetal sex
Maternal diabetes mellitus
Hormones
    Corticosteroids
    Other steroids
    Thyroid hormone

number of experimental observations due to space considerations and our desire to be as coherent as possible about this complex topic. As a result, we have chosen to emphasize research on fetal primate development. This has enabled us to avoid a species-by-species comparison that would become confusing. Many reference citations are made to articles that will provide details on other species. In addition, background information is provided on fetal lung biochemistry, to supplement other chapters herein, and on fetal endocrine factors that might influence lung development.

THE DEVELOPMENTAL BIOCHEMISTRY OF LUNG MATURATION

Pathways of Phosphatidylcholine Synthesis

The most important single constituent of the pulmonary surfactant system is disaturated PC. This unusual phospholipid is produced almost exclusively in the mammalian lung via the CDPcholine pathway (30, 37). The enzymatic steps involved in this pathway have been investigated largely in short-gestation species, (84, 101, 102), but the sequence of events leading to disaturated PC is undoubtedly the same in the human and nonhuman primate (30, 37). The CDPcholine pathway is not a simple, straightforward chain of enzymatic activities leading to disaturated PC. In reality, it is a complicated process involving three separate enzymatic sequences. One route is concerned with the production of 1,2-diacylglycerol, most likely utilizing glycerol-3-phosphate as a starting material. Glycerol-3-phosphate is serially acylated to 1,2-diacylglycerol-3-phosphate, or phosphatidic acid. Phosphatidic acid is then dephosphorylated, resulting in a 1,2-diacylglycerol, thus completing one segment in the CDPcholine scheme. Before choline can be joined to 1,2-diacylglycerol it must be activated in another series of enzymatic reactions. Choline is first converted to choline phosphate by choline kinase. The choline phosphate thus formed can then be combined with CTP to make the activated form of choline, CDPcholine. This reaction is catalyzed by choline phosphate cytidylyltransferase. The formation of PC is obtained by transferring the phosphorylcholine of CDPcholine to the 1,2-diacylglycerol previously formed. This final step is carried out by choline phosphotransferase. These two converging pathways are responsible for the net synthesis of PC in lung tissue. The PC produced by this mechanism, however, does not contain the high degree of saturation found in surfactant phospholipids. Thus, acyl rearrangement of pulmonary PC is a necessary third step in producing the final product. Two acyl rearrangement systems have been identified in fetal lung tissue (84, 101, 102). In the first system PC is deacylated in the 2 position by phospholipase A_2 and then reacylated with a saturated fatty acid by lysophosphatidylcholine acyltransferase. The second system also begins with a phospholipase A_2 deacylation, but follows with a transacylation between two molecules of lysophospha-tidylcholine to yield disaturated PC. This last step is accomplished by lysophosphatidylocholine–lysophosphatidylcholine acyltransferase, also known as Marinetti's enzyme. Although studies with adult lung have indicated that Marinetti's enzyme plays only a minor role in the acyl rearrangement of pulmonary PC (9), the question of its importance during late gestation has not been adequately answered.

Substrates for Lung Phospholipid Synthesis

Glucose has been used in a great number of studies probing pulmonary carbohydrate and phospholipid metabolism during gestation. The fetal lung apparently takes up glucose readily and can utilize it for both energy and phospholipid production. This is evidenced by the rapid incorporation of glucose into both the glycerol backbone and fatty acid portion of phospholipids (41, 51) and by the evolution of $^{14}CO_2$ from tissues incubated with radioactive carbohydrate (51, 71, 120). The great majority of these experiments have examined the role of extracellular glucose in lung metabolism. The fetal lung, however, also has recourse to a second pool of glucose, stored intracellularly as glycogen. Both morphologic and biochemical studies have demonstrated that glycogen concentrations in the fetal lung increase until approximately 85%–90% of term, at which time they begin to recede precipitously (64, 71, 88). Enzymes involved in glycogen synthesis and degradation are present in fetal tissues (14, 71), and there is evidence that lysosomal enzymes play a part in pulmonary glycogenolysis (20). The fate of glucose derived from glycogen is not fully understood. The temporal link between glycogen degradation and the increase in surfactant material has led to the belief that glycogen is being used directly for surfactant phospholipid synthesis (64, 71, 88). A recent report by Bourbon et al (21) demonstrating a direct transfer of radiolabelled carbon from glycogen to disaturated PC has considerably strengthened this hypothesis. Utilization of glycogen by the lung may also benefit the fetus by sparing circulating glucose for other tissues such as heart and brain, whose metabolism is more dependent on glucose availability. Although it is clear that both extracellular glucose and glycogen can be used by the fetal lung for a variety of purposes, it is not clear as to the extent to which each source is utilized. A full understanding of carbohydrate metabolism during late gestation cannot be realized until the relative importance of these two substrates is revealed.

The fetal lung can apparently make effective use of three separate pools of precursors for the fatty acid moieties of surfactant phospholipid. Albumin-bound, circulating free fatty acids can be taken up by the lung and used either for esterification to lung phospholipids or oxidation to CO_2 (57, 120). Despite the fact that experimental studies can demonstrate fatty acid utilization by fetal lung, the importance of this substrate in utero may be limited due to the generally low blood levels found during fetal life (25, 90). Another possible source of fatty acids from the circulatory system is triacylglycerols. The lung contains significant lipoprotein lipase activity (52), which makes triacyl-glycerols a potentially valuable resource for fatty acids. Besides using pre-formed fatty acids from the blood, the fetal lung is also equipped to produce fatty acids de novo. The enzymes of fatty-acid synthesis are located in the soluble portion of fetal lung tissue (48) and, like their adult counterparts, produce mainly palmitate as the end product (48). Elongation of fatty acids is not performed to any significant extent in fetal lung (48). Substrates for the de novo synthesis of fatty acids by fetal lung include glucose (41, 51, 104) and perhaps ketone bodies (104) and lactate (99). Lactate is frequently overlooked as a substrate for fetal lung, even though it is present in the fetal circulation in concentrations of approximately 8 mM (42). These high concentrations, cou-pled with the relatively low levels of glucose in fetal blood, may indicate that lactate can substitute for glucose in pulmonary energy generation and fatty-acid synthesis, and there are indications that adult lung may use lactate for lipid synthesis (99). If these results can be extrapolated back to the fetal lung, lactate may be a very important substrate for lung metabolism during late fetal life.

Choline has been widely used as a substrate in investigations of phospholipid metabolism (30, 37). In addition to being vital for PC synthesis, choline is also useful experimentally because of its ready solubility in aqueous systems and because it incorporates so rapidly into the various pulmonary PC fractions. Even though choline is perhaps the most widely used substrate currently, very little is known of choline synthesis in either fetal or adult lung. The only acknowledged source of choline for fetal lung is the blood. Plasma choline concentrations are significantly higher in the fetus and newborn than in the adult (125). Despite being exposed to elevated choline levels, the fetal lung is reported to contain choline concentrations either similar to (13) or lower than (111) the adult lung. This may point to different mechanisms for choline uptake or utilization by the fetal and postnatal lung.

Glycerol has also been administered as a precursor for pulmonary PC synthesis (76) in the lung. When supplied in in vitro systems, glycerol can be incorporated into lung phospholipids; but, because of the low fetal blood concentrations of glycerol (90), its physiological role in late fetal development is most likely a minor one. Glycerol, however, may become important during the neonatal period, when glycerol concentrations are known to increase (90).

THE ENDOCRINOLOGY OF FETAL DEVELOPMENT

Maternal Endocrine Profile

Estrogen and progesterone levels in the pregnant rhesus monkey are discernibly different from those of the nonpregnant monkey within two weeks of concep-tion. These steroids undergo marked fluctuations during weeks 2–6 of pregnancy that correspond initially to stimulation of corpus luteum of conception by chorionic gonadotrophin (mCG) and subsequently to the increasing steroidogenic capacity of the placenta (55). By the sixth week of the rhesus pregnancy, mCG is no longer detectable in the maternal circulation (53), and concentrations of estradiol and estrone are increasing (3, 15, 17, 53). At midpregnancy, blood concentration of estradiol achieves a variable but asymptotic level that is approximately double that seen shortly before ovulation. Progesterone titers in the maternal circulation during mid- and late gestation differ considerably among animals but are typically rather low, i.e. no more than observed during the normal luteal phase of the menstrual cycle (15, 83). Maternal cortisol levels do not change, or increase only slightly, in the rhesus pregnancy (123).

Experimental studies involving the extirpation of endocrine glands and/or fetectomy have established the sites of synthesis of the steroid hormones present in the maternal circulation (16, 23, 55, 115–117). Estrogen is secreted by the placenta, and it is derived from dehydroepiandrosterone sulfate (DHEAS) that is secreted by the fetal adrenal. The placenta is also the primary source of progesterone, which is derived from maternal cholesterol. Cortisol is secreted by the maternal adrenal, and its secretion is normally controlled by ACTH from the maternal pituitary. In contrast to nonpregnant monkeys, however, pregnant monkeys maintain adrenal function following hypophysectomy (and fetectomy), suggesting the presence of an adrenocorticotrophin of placental origin (54).

There are pronounced circadian variations in maternal steroid levels during the third trimester (24, 105, 106). Cortisol, estradiol, and estrone are higher in the morning, whereas progesterone is found in higher concentrations in the evening.

Secretion and metabolism of thyroid hormones during the rhesus pregnancy have been less extensively studied than the steroid hormones. The available evidence indicates that T_3 levels do not change and that total T_4 levels increase, largely because of an increase in T_4-binding proteins (61). Additionally, fasting insulin levels are elevated during the third trimester, and the response to glucose is exaggerated (60a, 92a).

Several differences in maternal endocrinology between the pregnant rhesus and pregnant humans are apparent. For example, the rhesus does not exhibit the large increase in estrogen, progestin, and cortisol concentrations typical of the pregnant woman. Furthermore, the metabolites of these steroids are different between the species. Estriol, a quantitatively major estrogen of the human pregnancy, is not found in the rhesus. Also, pregnanediol is the predominant metabolite of progesterone in the human, whereas androsterone predominates in the rhesus (70).

Although these contrasts between the species are clear, their implications for the regulation of fetal development are not. For example, even though maternal cortisol values are very different during the time of fetal lung maturation, the exposure of the fetus to cortisol may not differ between the species because of differences in serum binding and placental transfer of the hormone, and fetal production of cortisol (10; see below). Most of the additional cortisol seen during the human pregnancy is bound to a serum protein and therefore is less available to placental transfer mechanisms. Estrogen is similarly bound in serum of pregnant women, but not in the pregnant rhesus monkey. Thyroxine, however, is bound in both species. The basis, as well as the significance, of the species differences in binding kinetics of steroid hormones remain to be elucidated.

Fetal Endocrine Profile

There is a marked sex difference in fetal rhesus testosterone levels from approximately day 40 of pregnancy until term (28, 94–96). The sex difference is greatest before day 100. Female fetuses have low but detectable testosterone titers while males' values are variable but 2–4-fold greater than females' (96). The source of the testosterone in the males' circulation is the fetal testis (27, 96). Androstenedione levels are not different between the sexes, but males have higher concentrations of dihydrotestosterone after day 100 (96). Similar sex differences in fetal androgen levels have been reported to occur in the human during early and midpregnancy, but not during the third trimester (1, 98).

Estradiol concentrations in the fetal rhesus circulation are greater in the female than the male only after 150 days of gestation (97). Estrone levels do not differ between the fetal sexes (97). Estradiol values are ten-fold lower in the female fetus than in the maternal circulation, while estrone levels are comparable (97). This appears to be due to the fact that the placenta (the primary source of estrogens for both mother and fetus) selectively secretes estradiol, but not estrone, into the maternal circulation. The placenta is relatively impermeable to estrogens (118).

Female rhesus fetuses have two-fold higher levels of progesterone than male fetuses (49). In the human pregnancy there is not a corresponding sex difference in umbilical vein progesterone levels, but the values for umbilical artery are lower in females than in males, suggesting greater metabolism of progesterone by the female fetus (50).

The fetal adrenals secrete large amounts of cortisol. The metabolic clearance rate for fetal cortisol is high due to placental transport to the maternal circulation and to metabolism to cortisone (65, 77, 78). Most of the cortisone measured in the fetal compartment is derived from transformation of maternal cortisol during the process of placental transport (65, 77). The concentration of cortisol in amniotic fluid increases with gestational age (86). A similar trend for fetal plasma concentration has been reported by some investigators (103) but not by others.

The thyroid gland of the fetal rhesus exhibits secretory activity by midpregnancy. Between days 75 and 150 of pregnancy there is a 50-fold increase in the iodine content of the gland (91, 92). The thyroxine content of the thyroid gland and the serum concentration of thyroxin increase during the third trimester such that by day 150 the blood levels of the hormone are equivalent in the fetal and maternal circulations (10). The placental transfer of thyroxin is limited and seems to be independent of maternal serum levels (5). Thyroid hormone deficiency, induced experimentally, did not affect the lungs as measured at 150 days gestation, but respiratory movements were markedly reduced (61).

Fetal insulin levels are normally about 20% those of the mother during the third trimester and they do not change in response to infusion of substrates; fetuses of diabetic mothers, however, have markedly elevated insulin levels and are responsive to substrate infusion at an earlier age (26, 59, 76a).

INFLUENCES ON THE TIMING OF FETAL LUNG DEVELOPMENT

Gestational Age

Although significant variations in timing occur, pulmonary maturation progresses in an orderly, well defined manner regardless of species. Even though the timing of human lung development has in general been characterized from clinical assessments [i.e. amniotic fluid phospholipid studies related to gestational age (44) and epidemiologic surveys (38, 89) or autopsy specimens (2, 4)], the many uncontrollable variables in human pregnancy have hampered efforts to delineate biochemical and physiological patterns with precision. In 1959, Avery & Mead (4) observed that lungs of infants succumbing to RDS were deficient in pulmonary surfactant. Subsequently, others (2, 18, 22) have noted specific decreases in PC and disaturated PC concentrations in fetal lungs associated with gestational age and in neonates dying from RDS.

Biochemical and physiological maturational changes in fetal nonhuman primate lung tissue as gestation progresses, almost certainly parallels human development (30, 30a, 37, 67). Of particular relevance is the pattern of surge in amniotic fluid PC to sphingomyelin ratio. As noted by Epstein et al (30), this increase occurs at 145–150 days in *Macacca mulatta* (term = 165 days) which corresponds to 34–36 weeks of human gestation. Although others (see 33 and 35 for review) have surveyed macaque fetuses over a broad gestational age range to distinguish interrelationships between biochemical and physiological aspects of lung development, recent observations in *Macaca mulatta* by Perelman et al (88) provide temporally linked data that allows statistical evaluation among gestational ages at which key fetal lung maturational events occur. These data reveal a sequential rise in lung PC concentration due to elevations in both disaturated and unsaturated constituents. The percent disaturated PC in lung tissue was noted to climb abruptly at 145 days of gestation prior to significant increases in PC or disaturated PC concentration but in association with improved lung deflation stability. The later suggests that the disaturated PC-to-total-PC ratio may be a sensitive biochemical indicator of surfactant phospholipid production in lung parenchyma. Phosphatidylglycerol content was not noted to increase significantly until after 155 days gestation, which was coincident with maximizing pulmonary distensibility. Declining levels of phosphatidylethanolamine and sphingomyelin in lung tissue at 162 days supported the hypothesis that preferential synthesis of PC occurs during late gestation. A serial decline in lung glycogen content with advancing gestational age was thought to reflect glycogen utilization as a substrate for lung phospholipid production.

In addition to delivery prior to term, fetal sex, endogenous hormones, and abnormal maternal metabolic states such as diabetes mellitus may affect the normal fetal lung developmental process.

Fetal Sex and Androgens

Epidemiologic surveys in human preterm neonates have noted increased morbidity and mortality from RDS in males as compared to females (32, 34, 35, 75). For example, Perelman & Farrell (89), in a review of US mortality statistics between 1968 and 1978, noted a striking discrepancy in the sex distribution for neonatal deaths attributable to RDS, such that the male:female ratio was higher (range = 1.47 to 1.76) than that observed for any other major category of fatal newborn disease. In contrast to the gradual decline in male:female ratio for total neonatal deaths, from 1.40 in 1968 to 1.32 in 1978, the disproportionately high number of RDS fatalities was found throughout the years surveyed. The reason for greater severity and mortality of RDS in male infants has not been examined until recently.

Because lung surfactant is involved in the pathobiology of RDS, a logical place to assess potential variations in the occurrence of the disease in premature male and females is the surfactant phospholipid biosynthetic system. In a study reported in 1981, Torday et al (112) demonstrated that human male fetuses had lower amniotic fluid L/S ratios than female fetuses. The lower L/S ratio was evident throughout the third trimester. The finding of delayed fetal lung maturation in the male fetus was supported by the work of Kotas & Avery (66). They found that premature male rabbit fetuses had less stable lungs than their female litter mates. Furthermore, although both sexes responded to glucocorticoid treatment, the lungs of female fetuses showed greater maturity as demonstrated by a higher proportion of airspaces and thinner airspace walls. Nielson & Torday (81) have suggested that the relationship between fetal sex and the occurrance of RDS is related to a delayed surge in pulmonary surfactant production in the male fetus. Data obtained from rabbits revealed higher ratios of saturated PC/sphingomyelin and total PC/sphingomyelin ratios in fetal female lung lavage fluid at 26 and 28 days gestation (term = 31 days) and in amniotic fluid at 28 days. Significant differences were not noted in very premature or in term fetuses. Although most studies have concentrated on developmental phospholipid biochemistry, Adamson & King (2a) have observed sex-related differences in rat lung structure that include more rapid increase in epithelial cells, lamellar body formation, and saturated PC content in female fetuses as compared to their male littermates. These investigations seem to indicate that fetal sex may be an important consideration in the development of neonatal RDS and could perhaps be attributed to hormonal control.

Some data support the contention that androgens may inhibit fetal pulmonary surfactant production. After assessment of androgen receptors in fetal rabbit lungs, Giannopoulos & Smith (40) hypothesized that the male disadvantage as regards fetal lung development does not appear to be related to a difference in the concentration of pulmonary androgen receptors but may be due in part to increased levels of circulating androgens. It should be noted, however, that others (39, 63) have been unable to detect differences in the biosynthesis of lung phospholipids between male and female fetuses and suggest that the sex-related disparity in pulmonary development may be accounted for by as yet undelineated differences in intracellular transport or secretion of surfactant. Additionally, in a nonhuman primate model of RDS, Truog and associates (113) reported that newborn female *Macaca nemistrena* had more severe clinical indices of respiratory distress, lower lung lavage fluid phospholipids, lower lavage fluid/whole lung homogenate phospholipid ratios, and less surface activity of lavage fluid than their male counterparts.

Recent studies (82) involving the administration of dihydrotestosterone (DHT) to pregnant rabbits revealed a dose-related blunting of sex-associated differences in indices of fetal surfactant production when compared to controls. The later findings resulted from a lowering of disaturated PC/sphingomyelin ratio in lung lavage fluid of females to the male level. When the anti-androgen flutamide was substituted for DHT and the experiments repeated, the investigators noted elimination of the sex-related differences in lung lavage disaturated PC/sphingomyelin ratio by elevation of the male ratios to that of the females.

Other Hormones

Although numerous other endogenous hormones have been implicated as affecting pulmonary phospholipid metabolism, the mechanisms by which these hormones act have for the most part not been elucidated, and therefore only the three most comprehensively studied to date will be mentioned.

Abundant evidence has been accumulated indicating that pulmonary phospholipid metabolism is affected by glucocorticoid hormones. In 1969, Liggins (68) found that dexamethasone injected into the fetus caused premature delivery in fetal lambs. He noted that lungs of vaginally delivered lambs were partially aerated, indicating advanced lung maturation and accelerated surfactant production. Further, injection of 9-fluoroprednisolone (119) or cortisol (64) caused an acceleration of fetal rabbit lung maturation such that electron microscopy revealed more numerous lamellar bodies and generally more mature cells of the alveolus than was noted in control littermates. As reviewed by Ballard (7), other morphologic indices of fetal lung development influenced by corticosteroids include flattening of epithelial cells, thinning of mesenchyme, and decreased glycogen content, whereas the content of rough endoplasmic reticulum and lamellar bodies are increased in type II pneumocytes.

Although not uniformly accepted, on the whole, data from numerous animal species support the hypothesis that the affects of antenatal glucocorticoid treatment represents acceleration of normal developmental events rather than alteration of the basic nature of fetal lung development (11, 12, 30, 31, 56, 57, 62, 79, 80). If true, this hypothesis is consistent with reported corticosteroid effects on differentiation of other developing tissues (6) and suggests that endogenous corticosteroids may influence the normal lung developmental process. Further rationales for the role of endogenous corticosteroids have been recently discussed in detail (6, 7) and involve temporal associations of plasma hormone levels with lung maturation, clinical correlations, and supportive yet tangential animal studies.

Wu et al (124) and Redding and associates (93a) have documented that thyroxine can affect lung maturation, by showing that administration of thyroid hormone caused an increase in type II pneumocyte size, an increase in the number and size of lamellar bodies, and depletion of type II cell glycogen. Further, thyroidectomy produced opposite results. Considering the aforementioned and because endogenous thyroid hormones measured in serum increase during late gestation in humans and other mammalian species as lung development is maximizing, thyroxine might be an important hormone for pulmonary maturation. Although some in vivo and in vitro (8, 107, 109) experiments have shown that thyroxine or its analogs can stimulate surfactant phospholipid synthesis and choline incorporation into PC, others (72, 93) had failed to demonstrate a significant effect. Although no definitive conclusions can at present be ascertained, further study is warranted on the role of thyroid hormone in the regulation of fetal lung development.

Because glucose can provide a substrate for pulmonary lipid synthesis, it is not surprising that insulin as a regulator of carbohydrate metabolism might have an effect in lung phospholipid biosynthesis. However, most studies to date have examined the effects of insulin on utilization of exogenously supplied substrate and have produced conflicting results (see 19 for review). The fetal lung, however, also contains a significant amount of endogenous or intracellular substrates stored as glycogen. The glucose stored in fetal lung glycogen may play a pivotal role in the synthesis of surfactant phospholipids. Surfactant phospholipid synthesis is increased dramatically during the last 10–15% of gestation, and coincident with this increase is a concomitant decrease in the amount of glycogen. Gross et al (46, 47) hypothesized that the utilization of glycogen by the fetal lung may be controlled by insulin, because high insulin levels delay glycogen breakdown in fetal lung explants. These results would indicate that pulmonary carbohydrate utilization in lipid metabolism is regulated, at least partially, by the action of insulin.

Abnormal Maternal Metabolism

Diabetes mellitus is perhaps the classic example of the interaction between an abnormal maternal metabolic state and fetal development. In instances of maternal hyperglycemia, the fetus also tends to be hyperglycemic and the fetal pancreas responds by increasing secretion of insulin. Fetal hyperinsulinemia resulting from chronic exposure to elevated glucose has been postulated to account for the often-reviewed abnormalities in growth and development that characterize infants of diabetic mothers (IDM) (87). One major concern is the relatively high incidence of RDS in infants of poorly controlled diabetic mothers. The study of Robert et al (100), for instance, revealed a six-fold higher incidence of RDS in IDM when adjustments for gestational age and other perinatal factors were made. This retrospective study, as well as others discussed by Farrell & Avery (35), support the concept that the increased incidence of RDS in progeny of inadequately controlled diabetics is fundamentally a consequence of impaired maturation of fetal lung as opposed to perinatal factors such as prematurity or delivery by cesarean section. The question remains, however, as to why the fetal milieu accompanying maternal diabetes leads to a defect in the nature or timing of fetal lung maturational process. Although a brief overview follows, the topic has been recently analyzed extensively by Bourbon & Farrell (19).

Numerous studies have demonstrated that Streptozotocin (STZ) may be used to produce glucose intolerance in *Macaca mulatta* (26, 58–60). STZ-treated monkeys when pregnant resemble human diabetic pregnancies with respect to abnormalities such as placental hypertrophy, polyhydramnios, fetal hyperinsulinemia, fetal macrosomia, and organomegaly (59, 60).

In the first studies performed using chemically induced glucose-intolerant macaques, Gluck and coworkers (43) found elevated amniotic fluid L/S ratios in diabetic rhesus pregnancies compared to matched controls. Epstein et al (30b) observed no change in lung PC concentration but an increase in ^{14}C-choline incorporation into PC in lung slices prepared from fetuses of STZ-treated mothers as compared to control fetuses. Recently, Kemnitz et al (39) reported the occurence of fetal macrosomia, hyperglycemia, and hyperinsulinemia in rhesus fetuses delivered at 145 days of gestation to females rendered glucose-intolerant with STZ prior to mating. Because only a small number of fetal animals were studied, observations on lung biochemistry and physiology remain inconclusive thus far. However, fetal lung glycogen concentrations were 28% higher in diabetic animals compared to euglycemic controls. Other investigators have induced hyperinsulinemia with euglycemia in the fetal rhesus monkey by the implantation of osmotically driven insulin minipumps (36, 73, 110). Lungs from these animals revealed no effect of chronic hyperinsulinemia on morphologic development or phospholipid content despite the fact that fetal macrosomia was produced by the treatment. The aforementioned results in monkeys are as yet quite incomplete and further investigation will be necessary to delineate the possible abnormalities in the process of fetal lung maturation in this model.

SUMMARY

From this review, it is evident that multiple maternal/fetal endogenous or completely exogenous factors have been associated with the complex process regulating fetal lung development. Recent in vitro experiments with human fetal lung explants are especially noteworthy and may establish a perspective for future research. Snyder et al (108) and Medelson et al (74) have found that lung explants from 16–22-week abortuses show differentiated type II cells and augmented PC synthesis within 4 days of culture, rather than the minimum 10- to 15-week period expected in utero. Such a phenomenon is reminiscent of the usual time for clinical recovery from uncomplicated RDS (34). Thus, although expression of the genes influencing lung surfactant phospholipid synthesis and related biochemical processes normally occurs relatively late in gestation, the potential for biochemical differentiation is clearly present in earlier stages. It appears then that the "programming" of the fetal lung for maturation is not absolute but may be altered under certain influences. Whether the advent of lung biochemical maturation occurs as a result of release from inhibition, as the human lung explant data imply, or occurs in response to stimuli, as suggested by exogenous corticosteroid effects, remains to be clarified and is a very challenging scientific problem. It will also be of great interest to define further other biochemical regulators, such as fibroblast pneumocyte factor, that may play an important role in fetal lung maturation.

Acknowledgments

The authors were supported by National Institutes of Health grants HD11429, SCOR P-50-HL-27358, RR00167, and KD4-HD-00350 (RCDA to M. J. Engle).

Literature Cited

1. Abramovich, D. R., Rowe, P. 1973. Foetal plasma testosterone levels at mid-pregnancy and at term: Relationship to foetal sex. *J. Endocrinol.* 56:621–22
2. Adams, F. H., Fujiwara, T., Emmanouilides, G. C., Raiha, N. 1970. Lung phospholipids of human fetuses and infants with and without hyaline membrane disease. *J. Pediatr.* 77:833–41
2a. Adamson, I. Y. R., King, G. M. 1984. Sex-related differences in cellular composition and surfactant synthesis of developing fetal rat lung. *Am. Rev. Respir. Dis.* 129:130–34
3. Atkinson, L. E., Hotchkiss, J., Fritz, G. R., Surve, A. H., Neill, J. D., Knobil, E. 1975. Circulating levels of steroids and chorionic gonadotropin during pregnancy in the rhesus monkey, with special attention to the rescue of the corpus luteum in early pregnancy. *Biol. Reprod.* 12:335–45
4. Avery, M. E., Mead, J. 1959. Surface properties in relation to atelactasis and hyaline membrane disease. *Am. J. Dis. Child.* 97:517–23
5. Bachrach, L. K., DiBattista, D., Burrow, G. N., Holland, F. J. 1983. Transplacental effects of 3,5-dimethyl-3'-isopropyl-1-thyronine on fetal hypothyroidism in primates. *Endocrinol.* 112:2021–24
6. Ballard, P. L. 1979. Glucocorticoids and differentiation. *Monogr. Endocrinol.* 12:493–515
7. Ballard, P. L. 1982. Hormonal aspects of fetal lung development. In *Lung Development: Biological and Clinical Perspectives,* ed. P. M. Farrell, 2:205–53. New York: Academic
8. Ballard, P. L., Benson, B. J., Brehier, A., Carter, J. P., Kriz, B. M., Jorgensen, E. C. 1980. Transplacental stimulation of lung development in the fetal rabbit by 3,5-dimethyl-3-isopropyl-L-thyronine. *J. Clin. Invest.* 65:1407–17
9. Batenburg, J. J., Longmore, W. J., Klazinga, W., van Golde, L. M. G. 1979. Lysolecithin acyltransferase and lysolecithin: lysolecithin acyltransferase in adult rat lung alveolar type II epithelial cells. *Biochim. Biophys. Acta* 573:136–44
10. Beamer, N., Hagemenas, F., Kittinger, G. W. 1972. Protein binding of cortisol in the rhesus monkey (Macaca mulatta). *Endocrinol.* 90:325–27
11. Beck, J. C., Johnson, J. W. C., Mitzner, W., Lee, P. A., London, W. T., et al. 1981. Glucocorticoids, hyperinsulinemia, and fetal lung maturation. *Am. J. Obstet. Gynecol.* 139:465–70
12. Beck, J. C., Mitzner, W., Johnson, J. W. C., Hutchins, G. M., Foldart, J. M., et al. 1981. Betamethasone and the rhesus fetus: Effect on lung morphology and connective tissue. *Pediatr. Res.* 15:235–40
13. Gail, D. B., Farrell, P. M. 1978. Measurement of phosphatidylcholine precursors-choline, ethanolamine and methionine in fetal and adult rat lung. *Lung* 155:255–63
14. Bhavnani, B. R. 1983. Ontogeny of some enzymes of glycogen metabolism in rabbit fetal heart, lungs, and liver. *Can. J. Biochem. Cell Biol.* 61:191–97
15. Bielert, C., Czaja, J. A., Eisele, S., Scheffler, G., Robinson, J. A., et al. 1976. Mating in the rhesus monkey (Macaca mulatta) after conception and its relationship to oestradiol and progesterone levels throughout pregnancy. *J. Reprod. Fertil.* 46:179–87
16. Bosu, W. T. K., Johansson, E. D. B., Gemzell, C. 1973. Peripheral plasma levels of oestrogen and progesterone in pregnant rhesus monkeys in early pregnancy. *Fertil. Steril.* 25:443–52
17. Bosu, W. T. K., Johnasson, E. D. B., Gemzell, C. 1973. Peripheral plasma levels of oestrogen and progesterone in pregnant rhesus monkeys treated with dexamethasone. *Acta Endocrinol.* 74:338–47
18. Boughton, K., Gandy, G., Gardner, D. 1970. Hyaline membrane disease. II Lung lecithin. *Arch. Dis. Child.* 145:311–20
19. Bourbon, J. R., Farrell, P. M. 1984. Fetal lung development in the diabetic pregnancy. *Pediatr. Res.* In press
20. Bourbon, J., Jost, A. 1982. Control of glycogen metabolism in the developing fetal lung. *Pediatr. Res.* 16:50–56
21. Bourbon, J. R., Rieutort, M., Engle, M. J., Farrell, P. M. 1982. Utilization of glycogen for phospholipid synthesis in fetal rat lung. *Biochim. Biophys. Acta* 712:382–89
22. Brumley, G. W., Hodson, W. A., Avery, M. E. 1967. Lung phospholipids and surface tension correlations in infants with and without haline membrane disease and in adults. *Pediatrics* 40:13–19
23. Challis, J. R. G., Davies, I. J., Benirschke, K., Hendricks, A. G., Ryan, K. J. The effects of dexamethasone on plasma steroid levels and fetal adrenal histology in the pregnant rhesus monkey. *Endocrinol.* 95:1300–05
24. Challis, J. R. G., Socol, M., Murata, Y., Manning, F. A., Martin, C. B. Jr. 1980.

Diurnal variations in maternal and fetal steroids in pregnant rhesus monkeys. *Endocrinology* 106:1283–88

25. Chez, R. A., Mintz, D. H., Horger, E. O. III, Hutchinson, D. L. 1970. Factors affecting the response to insulin in the normal subhuman pregnant primate. *J. Clin. Invest.* 49:1517–27

26. Chez, R. A., Mintz, D. H., Reynolds, W. A., Hutchinson, D. L. 1975. Maternal-fetal plasma glucose relationships in late monkey pregnancy. *Am. J. Obstet. Gynecol.* 121:938–40

27. Ellinwood, W. E., Baughman, W. L., Resko, J. A. 1982. The effects of gonadectomy and testosterone treatment on luteinizing hormone secretion in fetal rhesus monkeys. *Endocrinol.* 110:183–89

28. Ellinwood, W. E., Brennan, R. M., Hess, D. L., Resko, J. A. 1980. Testosterone synthesis in rhesus fetal testes: Comparison between middle and late gestation. *Biol. Reprod.* 22:955–63

29. Engle, M. J., Langan, S. M., Sanders, R. L. 1983. Effects of insulin and hyperglycemia on surfactant phospholipid synthesis in organotypic type II cells. *Biochim. Biophys. Acta* 753:6–13

30. Epstein, M. F., Farrell, P. M. 1975. The choline incorporation pathway: Primary mechanisms for *de novo* lecithin synthesis in fetal primate lung. *Pediatr. Res.* 9:658–65

30a. Epstein, M. F., Farrell, P. M., Sparks, J. W., Pepe, G., Driscoll, S. G., Chez, R. A. 1977. Maternal betamethasone and fetal growth and development in the monkey. *Am. J. Obstet. Gynecol.* 127:261–63

30b. Epstein, M. F., Farrell, P. M., Chez, R. A. 1976. Fetal lung lecithin metabolism in the glucose-intolerant rhesus monkey pregnancy. *Pediatrics* 57:722–28

31. Farrell, P. M. 1977. Fetal lung development and the influence of glucocorticoids on pulmonary surfactant. *J. Steroid Biochem.* 8:463–70

32. Farrell, P. M. 1982. Overview of hyaline membrane disease. In *Lung Development: Biological and Clinical Perspectives, Vol. II, Neonatal Respiratory Distress*, ed. P. Farrell, pp. 23–46. New York: Academic

33. Farrell, P. M. 1982. General features of phospholipid metabolism in the developing lung. See Ref. 32, pp. 391–97

34. Farrell, P. M. 1983. RDS today: Advances in treatment and prevention. *J. Res. Dis.* Nov:80–102

35. Farrell, P. M., Avery, M. E. 1975. State of the art—hyaline membrane disease. *Am. Rev. Resp. Dis.* 111:657–88

35a. Farrell, P. M., Blackburn, G. K., Cefalo, R. C. 1979. Familial respiratory distress syndrome in three consecutive full-term infants: Case reports and documentation of lung enzyme activities. *J. Reprod. Med.* 22:255–58

36. Farrell, P. M., Engle, M. J., Frantz, J. D., Goldman, A. S., Kalkhoff, R., et al. 1982. Complications of pregnancy and fetal development. *Diabetes* 31: (Suppl.1):89–94

37. Farrell, P. M., Epstein, M. F., Fleischman, A. R., Oakes, G. K., Chez, R. A. 1976. Lung lecithin biosynthesis in the nonhuman primate fetus: Determination of the primary pathway in vivo. *Biol. Neonate* 29:238–46

38. Farrell, P. M., Wood, R. E. 1976. Epidemiology of hyaline membrane disease in the United States. *Pediatrics* 58:167–76

39. Freese, W. B., Hallman, M. 1983. The effect of betamethasone and fetal sex on the synthesis and maturation of lung surfactant phospholipids in rabbits. *Biochim. Biophys. Acta* 750:47–59

40. Giannopoulos, G., Smith, S. K. S. 1982. Androgen receptors in fetal rabbit lung and the effect of circulating hormones and pulmonary hormone receptors. *J. Steroid Biochem.* 17:461–65

41. Gilden, C., Sevanian, A., Tierney, D. F., Kaplan, S. A., Barrett, C. T. 1977. Regulation of fetal lung phosphatidyl choline synthesis by cortisol: Role of glycogen and glucose. *Pediat. Res.* 11:845–48

42. Girard, J. R., Cuendet, G. S., Marliss, E. B., Kervran, A., Rieutort, M., Assan, R. 1973. Fuels, hormones, and liver metabolism at term and during the early postnatal period in the rat. *J. Clin. Invest.* 52:3190–200

43. Gluck, L., Chez, R. A., Kulovich, M. V., Hutchinson. D. L., Niemann, W. H. 1974. Comparison of phospholipid indicators of fetal lung maturity in the amniotic fluid of the monkey (Macaca mulatta) and baboon (Papio papio). *Am. J. Obstet. Gynecol.* 120:524–30

44. Gluck, L., Kulovich, M. V., Borer, R. C., Keidel, W. N. 1974. The interpretation and significance of the lecithin/sphingomyelin ratio in amniotic fluid. *Am. J. Obstet. Gynecol.* 120:142–55

45. Gluck, L., Sribney, M., Kulovich, M. V. 1967. The biochemical development of surface activity in mammalian lung. II. The biosynthesis of phospholipids in the lung of the developing rabbit fetus and newborn. *Pediatr. Res.* 1:247–65

45a. Graven, S. N., Misenheimer, H. R. 1965. Respiratory distress syndrome and the high risk mother. *Am. J. Dis. Child.* 109:489–94

46. Gross, I., Smith, G. J. W. 1977. Insulin delays the morphologic maturation of fetal rat lung in vitro. *Pediatr. Res.* 11:515 (Abstr.)

47. Gross, I., Smith, G. J. W., Wilson, C. M., Maniscalco, W. M., Ingleson, L. D., et al. 1980. The influence of hormones on the biochemical development of fetal rat lung in organ culture II insulin. *Pediatr. Res.* 14:834–38

48. Gross, I., Warshaw, J. B. 1974. Enzyme activities related to fatty acid synthesis in developing mammalian lung. *Pediat. Res.* 8:193–99

49. Hagemenas, F. C., Kittenger, G. W. 1972. The influence of fetal sex on plasma progesterone levels. *Endocrinol.* 91: 253–56

50. Hagemenas, F. C., Kittenger, G. W. 1973. The influence of fetal sex on the levels of plasma progesterone in the human fetus. *J. Clin. Endo. Metab.* 36:389–91

51. Hamosh, M., Shechter, Y., Hamosh, P. 1978. Metabolic activity of developing rabbit lung. *Pediat. Res.* 12:95–100

52. Hamosh, M., Simon, M. R., Canter, H. Jr., Hamosh, P. 1978. Lipoprotein lipase activity and blood triglyceride levels in fetal and newborn rats. *Pediat. Res.* 12:1132–36

53. Hodgen, G. D., Dufan, M. L., Catt, K. J., Tullner, W. W. 1982. Estrogens, progesterone and chorionic gonadotropin in pregnant rhesus monkeys. *Endocrinol.* 91:896–900

54. Hodgen, G. D., Gulyas, B. J., Tullner, W. W. 1975. Role of the primate placenta in cortisol secretion by the maternal adrenals. *Steroids* 26:233–40

55. Hodgen, G. D., Tullner, W. W. 1975. Plasma estrogens, progesterone and chorionic gonadotropin in pregnant rhesus monkeys (Macaca mulatta) after ovariectomy. *Steroids* 25:275–84

56. Johnson, J. W. C., Mitzner, W., Beck, J. C., London, W. T., Sly, D. L., et al. 1981. Long-term effects of betamethasone on fetal development. *Am. J. Obstet. Gynecol.* 141:1053–64

57. Johnson, J. W. C., Mitzner, W., London, W. T., Palmer, A. E., Scott, R., Kearney, K. 1978. Glucocorticoids and the rhesus fetal lung. *Am. J. Obstet. Gynecol.* 130:905–14

58. Jones, C. S., Reynolds, W. A., Hoganson, G. E. 1980. Streptozotocin diabetes in the monkey: Plasma levels of glucose, insulin, glucagon, and somatostatin with corresponding morphometric analysis of islet endocrine cells. *Diabetes* 29:536–46

59. Kemnitz, J. W., Perelman, R. H., Engle, M. J., Farrell, P. M. 1984. An experimental model for studies of fetal maldevelopment in the diabetic pregnancy. *Pediatr. Pulmonol.* In press

60. Kemnitz, J. W., Eisele, S. G., Lindsay, K. A., Engle, M. J., Perelman, R. H., Farrell, P. M. 1984. Changes in food intake during menstrual cycles and pregnancy of normal and diabetic rhesus monkeys. *Diabetologia* 26:60–64

60a. Kemnitz, J. W., Houser, W. D., Eisele, S. G., Engle, M. J., Perelman, R. H., Farrell, P. M. 1984. Pregnancy and fetal development in the rhesus monkey. I. Maternal metabolism and fetal growth. In *Animal Models in Fetal Medicine*, ed. P. W. Nathanielsz, J. T. Parer, in press. New York: Perinatology Press

61. Kerr, G. R., Tysou, I. B., Allen, J. R., Wallace, J. H., Scheffler, G. 1972. Deficiency of thyroid hormone and development of the fetal rhesus monkey. *Biol. Neonate.* 21:282–95

62. Kessler, D. L., Truog, W. E., Murphy, J. H., Palmer, S., Standaert, T. A., et al. 1982. Experimental hyaline membrane disease in the premature monkey. Effects of antenatal dexamethasone. *Am. Rev. Respir. Dis.* 126:62–69

63. Khosla, S. S., Brehier, A., Eisenfeld, A. J., Ingleson, L. D., Parks, P. A., Rooney, S. A. 1983. Influence of sex hormones on lung maturation in the fetal rabbit. *Biochim. Biophys. Acta* 750:112–26

64. Kikkawa, Y., Kaibara, M., Motoyama, E. K., Orzalesi, M. M., Cook, C. D. 1971. Morphologic development of fetal rabbit lung and its acceleration with cortisol. *Am. J. Pathol.* 64:423–42

65. Kittinger, G. W. 1974. Feto-maternal production and transfer of cortisol in the rhesus (Macaca mulatta). *Steroids* 23: 229–43

66. Kotas, R. V., Avery, M. E. 1980. The influence of sex on fetal rabbit lung maturation and on response to glucocorticoid. *Am. Rev. Respir. Dis.* 121:377–80

67. Kotas, R. K., Farrell, P. M., Ulane, R. E., Chez, R. A. 1977. Fetal rhesus monkey lung development: Lobar differences and discordances between stability and distensibility. *J. Appl. Physiol.* 43:92–98

67a. Lankenau, H. M. 1976. A genetic and statistical study of the respiratory distress syndrome. *Europ. J. Pediatr.* 123:167–77

68. Liggins, G. C. 1969. Premature delivery of foetal lambs infused with glucocorticoids. *J. Endocrinol.* 45:515–23

69. Liggins, G. C., Howie, R. N. 1972. A

controlled trial of antepartum glucocorticoid treatment for prevention of the respiratory distress syndrome in premature infants. *Pediatrics* 50:515

70. Liskowski, L., Wolf, R. C. 1972. Urinary excretion of progesterone metabolites in pregnant rhesus monkeys. *Proc. Soc. Exp. Biol. Med.* 139:1123–26

71. Maniscalco, W. M., Wilson, C. M., Gross, I., Gobran, L., Rooney, S. A., Warshaw, J. B. 1978. Development of glycogen and phospholipid metabolism in fetal and newborn rat lung. *Biochim. Biophys. Acta* 530:333–46

72. Mason, R. J., Manganiello, V., Vaughan, M. 1972. Effect of thyroxine on the disaturated lecithin content of lung. *Am. Rev. Respir. Dis.* 106:767–68

73. McCormick, K. L., Susa, J. B., Widness, J. A., Singer, D. B., Adamsons, K., Schwartz, R. 1979. Chronic hyperinsulinemia in the fetal rhesus monkey: Effects on hepatic enzymes, lipogenesis, and carbohydrate metabolism. *Diabetes* 28:1064–68

74. Mendelson, C. R., Johnston, M. J., MacDonald, P. C., Snyder, J. M. 1981. Multihormonal regulation of surfactant synthesis by human fetal lung in vitro. *J. Clin. Endocrinol. Metab.* 53:307–17

75. Miller, H. C., Futrakul, P. 1968. Birthweight, gestational age, and sex as determining factors in the incidence of respiratory distress syndrome of prematurely born infants. *J. Pediatr.* 72:628–35

76. Mims, L. C., Mazzuckelli, L. F., Kotas, R. V. 1975. The significance of circulating glycerol as a precursor of pulmonary phosphatidylcholine in the developing mammalian lung. *Pediat. Res.* 9:165–67

76a. Mintz, D. H., Chez, R. A., Horger, E. O. III. 1969. Fetal insulin and growth hormone metabolism in the subhuman primate. *J. Clin. Invest.* 48:176–86

77. Mitchell, B. F., Seron-Ferre, M., Hess, D. L., Jaffe, R. B. 1981. Cortisol production and metabolism in the late gestation rhesus monkey fetus. *Endocrinol.* 108:916–24

78. Mitchell, B. F., Seron-Ferre, M., Jaffee, R. B. 1982. Cortisol-cortisone interrelationship in the late gestation rhesus monkey fetus *in utero*. *Endocrinol.* 111:1837–42

79. Mitzner, W., Johnson, J. W. C., London, W., Sly, D. 1982. Influence of betamethasone on the development of mechanical properties in the fetal rhesus monkey lung. *Am. Rev. Respir. Dis.* 125:233–38

80. Mitzner, W., Johnson, J. W. C., Scott, R., London, W. T., Palmer, A. E. 1979. Effect of beta methasone on pressure-volume relationship of fetal rhesus monkey lung. *J. Appl. Physiol.* 47:377–82

81. Nielson, H. C., Torday, J. S. 1981. Sex differences in fetal rabbit pulmonary surfactant production. *Pediatr. Res.* 15:1245–47

82. Nielson, H. C., Zinman, H. M., Torday, J. S. 1982. Dihydrotestosterone inhibits fetal rabbit pulmonary surfactant production. *J. Clin. Invest.* 69:611–16

83. Novy, M. J., Walsh, S. W. 1983. Dexamethasone and estradiol treatment in pregnant rhesus macaques: Effects on gestational length, maternal plasma hormones, and fetal growth. *Am. J. Obstet. Gynecol.* 145:920–31

84. Oldenborg, V., van Golde, L. M. G. 1977. The enzymes of phosphatidylcholine biosynthesis in the fetal mouse lung: Effects of dexamethasone. *Biochim. Biophys. Acta* 489:454–65

85. Olson, E. B. Jr., Rankin, J. 1983. Isolated, perfused fetal rabbit lungs: preparation and flow relationships. *Lung* 161:87–98

86. Patrick, J. E., Challis, J. R. G., Johnson, P., Robinson, J. S., Thorbarn, G. D. 1976. Cortisol in amniotic fluid of rhesus monkeys. *J. Endocrinol.* 68:161–62

87. Perelman, R. H. 1983. The infant of the diabetic mother: Pathophysiology and management. *Primary Care* 10:751–60

88. Perelman, R. H., Engle, M. J., Kemnitz, J. W., Kotas, R. V., Farrell, P. M. 1982. Biochemical and physiological development of fetal rhesus lung. *J. Appl. Physiol.* 53:230–35

89. Perelman, R. H., Farrell, P. M. 1982. Analysis of causes of neonatal death in the United States with specific emphasis on fetal hyaline membrane disease. *Pediatrics* 70:570–75

90. Persson, B., Gentz, J. 1966. The pattern of blood lipids, glycerol, and ketone bodies during the neonatal period, infancy, and childhood. *Acta Paediatr. Scand.* 55:353–62

91. Pickering, D. E. 1968. Thyroid physiology in the developing monkey fetus (Macaca mulatta). *Gen. Comp. Endocrinol.* 10:182–90

92. Pickering, D. E., Kontaxis, N. E. 1961. Thyroid function in the foetus of the macaque monkey (Macaca mulatta). Chemical and morphological characteristics of the foetal thyroid gland. *J. Endocrinol.* 23:267–75

92a. Pitkin, R. M., VanOrden, D. E., Reynolds, W. A. 1970. Plasma insulin response and glucose tolerance in pregnant rhesus monkeys. *Endocrinology* 86:435–37

93. Post, M., Batenburg, J. J., van Golde, L. M. G. 1980. Effects of cortisol and thyroxine on phosphatidylcholine and phosphatidylglycerol by adult rat lung type II cells in primary culture. *Biochim. Biophys. Acta* 618:308–17

93a. Redding, R. A., Douglas, W. H. J., Stein, M. 1972. Thyroid hormone influence upon lung surfactant metabolism. *Science* 175:994–96

94. Resko, J. A., Ellinwood, W. E., Pasztor, L. M., Buhl, A. E. 1980. Sex steroids in the unbilical circulation of fetal rhesus monkeys from the time of gonadal differentiation. *J. Clin. Endocrinol. Metab.* 50:900–05

95. Resko, J. A. 1975. Fetal hormones and their effect on the differentiation of the central nervous system in primates. *Fed. Proc.* 34:1650–55

96. Resko, J. A., Malley, A., Begley, D., Hess, D. L. 1973. Radioimmonoassay of testosterone during fetal development of the rhesus monkey. *Endocrinol.* 93:156–60

97. Resko, J. A., Ploen, J. G., Stadelman, H. L. 1975. Estrogens in fetal and maternal plasma of the rhesus monkey. *Endocrinol.* 97:425–30

98. Reyes, F. I., Boroditsky, R. S., Winter, J. S. D., Faiman, C. 1974. Studies on human sexual development. II. Fetal and maternal serum gonadotropin and sex steroid concentrations. *J. Clin. Endocrinol. Metab.* 38:612–17

99. Rhoades, R. A., Shaw, M. E., Eskew, M. L., Wali, S. 1978. Lactate metabolism in perfused rat lung. *Am. J. Physiol.* 235:E619–23

100. Robert, M. F., Neff, R. K., Hubbell, J. P., Taeusch, H. W., Avery, M. E. 1976. Association between maternal diabetes and the respiratory distress syndrome in the newborn. *N. Engl. J. Med.* 294:357–60

101. Rooney, S. A., Gobran, L. I., Marino, P. A., Maniscalco, W. M., Gross, I. 1979. Effects of betamethasone on phospholipid content, composition, and biosynthesis in the fetal rabbit lung. *Biochim. Biophys. Acta* 572:64–76

102. Rooney, S. A., Wai-Lee, T. S., Gobran, L., Motoyama, E. K. 1976. Phospholipid content, composition, and biosynthesis during fetal lung development in the rabbit. *Biochim. Biophys. Acta* 431:447–58

103. Seron-Ferre, M., Taylor, N. F., Rotten, D., Koritnik, D. R., Jaffe, R. B. 1983. Changes in fetal rhesus monkey plasma dehydroepiandrosterone sulphate: Relationship to gestational age, adrenal weight, and preterm delivery. *J. Clin. Endocrinol. Metab.* 57:1173–78

104. Sheehan, P. M., Yeh, Y.-Y. 1983. Lung lipid synthesis from acetoacetate and glucose in developing rats in vitro. *Lipids* 18:295–301

105. Sholl, S. A., Robinson, J. A., Wolf, R. C. 1979. Estrone, 17-estradiol, and cortisol in serum of perimartum rhesus monkeys. *Endocronol.* 104:1274–78

106. Sholl, S. A., Robinson, J. A., Wolf, R. C. 1979. Progesterone and 5-pregnane-3, 20-dione in serum in peripartum rhesus monkeys. *Endorcinol.* 104:329–32

107. Smith, B. T., Torday, J. S. 1974. Factors affecting lecithin synthesis by fetal lung cells in culture. *Pediatr. Res.* 8:848–51

108. Snyder, J. M., Mendelson, C. F., Johnston, J. M. 1981. The effect of cortisol on rabbit fetal lung maturation in vitro. *Dev. Biol.* 85:129–40

109. Sommers, S. K., Sanders, R. L., Hitchcock, K. R. 1980. Effect of triiodothyronine (T₃) on organotypic cultures of alveolar type II cells. *Fed. Proc.* 80:4189 (Abstr.)

110. Susa, J. B., McCormick, K. L., Widness, J. A., Singer, D. B., Oh, W., et al. 1979. Chronic hyperinsulinemia in the fetal rhesus monkey. Effects on fetal growth and composition. *Diabetes* 28:1058–63

111. Tokmakjian, S., Possmayer, F. 1981. Pool sizes of the precursors for phosphatidylcholine synthesis in developing rat lung. *Biochim. Biophys. Acta* 666:176–80

112. Torday, J. S., Nielson, H. C., Fenel, M., Avery, M. E. 1981. Sex differences in human fetal lung maturation. *Am. Rev. Respir. Dis.* 123:201–8

113. Truog, W. E., Kessler, D. L., Palmer, S., Murphy, J., Woodrum, D. E., Hodson, W. A. 1981. Differential effect of sex in experimental hyaline membrane disease in newborn monkeys. *Am. Rev. Respir. Dis.* 124:435–39

114. Tsao, F. H. C., Zachman, R. D. 1982. Prenatal assessment of fetal lung maturation: A critical review of amniotic fluid phospholipid test. See Ref. 32, pp. 167–203

115. Tullner, W. W., Gulyas, B. J., Hodgen, G. D. 1975. Maternal estrogen and progesterone levels after hypophysectomy in early pregnancy and in term fetuses or newborn monkeys. *Steroids* 26:625–33

116. Tullner, W. W., Hodgen, G. D. 1974. Effects of fetectomy on plasma estrogens and progesterone in monkeys (Macaca mulatta). *Steroids* 24:887–97

117. Walsh, S. W., Kittinger, G. W., Novy, M. J. 1979. Maternal peripheral concentrations of estradiol, estrone, cortisol, and progesterone during late pregnancy in rhesus monkeys (Macaca mulatta) and

after experimental fetal anencephaly and fetal death. *Am. J. Obstet. Gynecol.* 135:37–42

118. Walsh, S. W., McCarthy, M. S. 1981. Selective placental secretions of estrogens into fetal and maternal circulations. *Endocrinol.* 109:2152–59

119. Wang, N. S., Kotas, R. V., Avery, M. E., Thurlbeck, W. M. 1971. Accelerated appearance of osmiophilic bodies in fetal lungs following steroid injection. *J. Appl. Physiol.* 30:362–65

120. Warshaw, J. B., Terry, M. L., Ranis, M. B. 1980. Metabolic adaptation in developing lung. *Pediatr. Res.* 14:296–99

121. Williams, M. C. 1977. Development of the alveolar structure of the fetal rat in late gestation. *Fed. Proc.* 36:2653–59

122. Williams, M. C., Mason, R. J. 1977. Development of the type II cell in the fetal rat lung. *Am. Rev. Resp. Dis.* 115:37–47

123. Wolf, R. C., Bowman, R. E. 1966. Adrenocortical function during pregnancy in the rhesus monkey. *Proc. Soc. Exp. Bio. Med.* 121:986–88

124. Wu, B., Kikkawa, Y., Orzales, M. M., Motoyama, E. K., Kaibara, M., et al. 1973. The effect of thyroxine on the maturation of fetal rabbit lungs. *Biol. Neonate.* 22:161–68

125. Zeisel, S. H., Epstein, M. F., Wurtman, R. J. 1980. Elevated choline concentration in neonatal plasma. *Life Sci.* 26:1827–31

SUBJECT INDEX

A

Absorption
  and function of enterocytes,
    253-56
Absorptive function
  see Digestive and absorptive
    function
Acanthosis nigricans
  and insulin receptors and reg-
    ulation, 367
Acetylcholine
  and the adrenergic-blockade
    in nucleotide transport, 612
  and gastric development, 199
Acetylcholinesterase activity
  and insulin-like growth fac-
    tors, 458
Acetylsalicyclic acid
  early clinical research, 12
Acid
  and gastric development, 200-
    4
Acid-base balance
  and the kidney, 156-57
Acidic amino acids
  and metabolic substrate trans-
    port, 111-12
Acidosis
  inotropic response of cardiac
    muscle to, 564
Acid phosphatase
  and ligand internalization, 385
  and lung surfactant recycling,
    793
Acid secretion
  early research, 10-11
Acromegaly
  and IGF levels, 454
Actin-activated myosin ATPase
  activity
  and isometric force develop-
    ment, 640
Actin-bound nucleotide pools
  and metabolic blockers, 680
A-current channels
  involvement in rhythmic be-
    havior, 18
Acyl-CoA
  and PDH enzyme complex,
    650
Acyl CoA compounds
  and cardiac mitochondrial
    functioning, 656
Adenine
  metabolism of
    and purine salvage, 695-96

production of
  and purine nucleoside phos-
    phorylase, 698
Adenine derivatives
  and kidney mitochondrial
    transport, 149
Adenine nucleotide catabolites
  and cellular damage, 732
Adenine nucleotide control
  of respiration, 709-15
Adenine nucleotide degradation
  and irreversible ischemic in-
    jury
  changes associated with,
    737-43
  pathways of, 729-33
Adenine nucleotide-derived adenosine
  extracellular metabolism of
    single carrier for, 608
Adenine nucleotide translocase
  and cardiac mitochondrial
    function, 652-53
  as rate-limiting step, 655-57
Adenine nucleotide translocator
  and kidney mitochondrial
    transport, 154
Adenine nucleotide uptake
  and ATP-induced contraction,
    606
Adenine nucleotides
  in heart and blood vessels,
    665
  see also Myocardial nucleotide
    transport
Adenine phosphoribosyltransferase (APRT)
  in purine salvage, 695
Adenosine
  intracellular source of
    and cardiac mitochondrial
      function, 657-59
  metabolism of
    and purine salvage, 696
    and myocardial nucleotide
      transport, 605
  as potent cerebral vasodilator
    and cardiovascular nuc-
      leotide function, 672
  production of
    by S-adenosylhomocysteine
      (SAH) hydrolase, 698
  single carrier for
    and extracellular metabol-
      ism of, 608
  and vasodilation in cardiac
    muscle function, 666

Adenosine hypothesis
  in cardiovascular nucleotide
    functions, 666
  and oxygen deficient
    myocytes, 730
Adenosine kinase
  and purine salvage, 696
Adenosine transport
  inhibition of, 609
Adenosine uptake
  and endothelial nucleotide
    metabolism, 618-19
Adenylate cyclase
  hormone activation of
    and junctional physiology,
      345
  hormone-stimulated
    insulin mediator to depress,
      411
  inhibition of
    and cardiovascular nuc-
      leotide functions, 668
    and direct actions of GH,
      494
  oocyte
    and gap junctions in de-
      velopment, 323
Adenylate kinase equilibrium
  and platelet nucleotide meta-
    bolism, 687
Adenylosuccinate synthetase
  and conversion of IMP
    to adenylosuccinate, 700
  and metabolism of IMP, 699-
    700
Adipocytes
  and elevation of AMP
    in insulin receptor kinase,
      374
  insulin binding to, 358
  and receptor function, 470
Adipose cell glucose metabolism
  and IGF receptors, 425
Adipose conversion
  and effects of GH
    on cell differentiation,
      490
Adipose tissue
  and glucose metabolism
    insulin-like effects of IGF,
      449
ADO deaminase
  inhibition of
    hypoxia, 730
ADP
  as a potent activator of
    platelet response, 678

823

CUMULATIVE INDEXES

CONTRIBUTING AUTHORS, VOLUMES 43–47

CHAPTER TITLES, VOLUMES 43-47

NEW BOOKS
FROM
ANNUAL REVIEWS INC.

NOW YOU CAN
CHARGE THEM
TO

ORDER FORM

Annual Reviews Inc.

A NONPROFIT SCIENTIFIC PUBLISHER

4139 EL CAMINO WAY • PALO ALTO, CA 94306-9981 • (415) 493-4400

Orders for Annual Reviews Inc. publications may be placed through your bookstore; subscription agent; participating professional societies; or directly from Annual Reviews Inc. by mail or telephone (paid by credit card or purchase order). Prices subject to change without notice.

Individuals: Prepayment required in U.S. funds or charged to American Express, MasterCard, or Visa.
Institutional Buyers: Please include purchase order.
Students: Special rates are available to qualified students. Refer to Annual Reviews *Prospectus* or contact Annual Reviews Inc. office for information.
Professional Society Members: Members whose professional societies have a contractural arrangement with Annual Reviews may order books through their society at a special discount. Check with your society for information.

Regular orders: When ordering current or back volumes, please list the volumes you wish by volume number.
Standing orders: (New volume in the series will be sent to you automatically each year upon publication. Cancellation may be made at any time.) Please indicate volume number to begin standing order.
Prepublication orders: Volumes not yet published will be shipped in month and year indicated.
California orders: Add applicable sales tax.
Postage paid (4th class bookrate / surface mail) by Annual Reviews Inc.

ANNUAL REVIEWS SERIES		Prices Postpaid per volume USA/elsewhere	Regular Order Please send:	Standing Order Begin with:
			Vol. number	Vol. number
Annual Review of ANTHROPOLOGY				
Vols. 1-10	(1972-1981)	$20.00/$21.00		
Vol. 11	(1982).............................	$22.00/$25.00		
Vols. 12-13	(1983-1984)	$27.00/$30.00		
Vol. 14	(avail. Oct. 1985).................	$27.00/$30.00	Vol(s)._____	Vol._____
Annual Review of ASTRONOMY AND ASTROPHYSICS				
Vols. 1-19	(1963-1981)	$20.00/$21.00		
Vol. 20	(1982).............................	$22.00/$25.00		
Vols. 21-22	(1983-1984)	$44.00/$47.00		
Vol. 23	(avail. Sept. 1985)	$44.00/$47.00	Vol(s)._____	Vol._____
Annual Review of BIOCHEMISTRY				
Vols. 29-34, 36-50	(1960-1965; 1967-1981)	$21.00/$22.00		
Vol. 51	(1982).............................	$23.00/$26.00		
Vols. 52-53	(1983-1984)	$29.00/$32.00		
Vol. 54	(avail. July 1985).................	$29.00/$32.00	Vol(s)._____	Vol._____
Annual Review of BIOPHYSICS				
Vols. 1-10	(1972-1981)	$20.00/$21.00		
Vol. 11	(1982).............................	$22.00/$25.00		
Vols. 12-13	(1983-1984)	$47.00/$50.00		
Vol. 14	(avail. June 1985)	$47.00/$50.00	Vol(s)._____	Vol._____
Annual Review of CELL BIOLOGY				
Vol. 1	(avail. Nov. 1985) ....est.	$27.00/$30.00	Vol. _____	Vol._____
Annual Review of EARTH AND PLANETARY SCIENCES				
Vols. 1-9	(1973-1981)	$20.00/$21.00		
Vol. 10	(1982).............................	$22.00/$25.00		
Vols. 11-12	(1983-1984)	$44.00/$47.00		
Vol. 13	(avail. May 1985)	$44.00/$47.00	Vol(s)._____	Vol._____
Annual Review of ECOLOGY AND SYSTEMATICS				
Vols. 1-12	(1970-1981)	$20.00/$21.00		
Vol. 13	(1982).............................	$22.00/$25.00		
Vols. 14-15	(1983-1984)	$27.00/$30.00		
Vol. 16	(avail. Nov. 1985)	$27.00/$30.00	Vol(s)._____	Vol._____

1

SEE ORDERING INFORMATION ON PAGE 4

	Prices Postpaid per volume USA/elsewhere	Regular Order Please send: Vol. number	Standing Order Begin with: Vol. number

Annual Review of ENERGY

Vols. 1-6	(1976-1981)	$20.00/$21.00
Vol. 7	(1982)........................	$22.00/$25.00
Vols. 8-9	(1983-1984)	$56.00/$59.00
Vol. 10	(avail. Oct. 1985)...........	$56.00/$59.00 Vol(s)._____ Vol._____

Annual Review of ENTOMOLOGY

Vols. 8-16, 18-26	(1963-1971; 1973-1981)	$20.00/$21.00
Vol. 27	(1982)........................	$22.00/$25.00
Vols. 28-29	(1983-1984)	$27.00/$30.00
Vol. 30	(avail. Jan. 1985)...........	$27.00/$30.00 Vol(s)._____ Vol._____

Annual Review of FLUID MECHANICS

Vols. 1-5, 7-13	(1969-1973; 1975-1981)	$20.00/$21.00
Vol. 14	(1982)........................	$22.00/$25.00
Vols. 15-16	(1983-1984)	$28.00/$31.00
Vol. 17	(avail. Jan. 1985)...........	$28.00/$31.00 Vol(s)._____ Vol._____

Annual Review of GENETICS

Vols. 1-15	(1967-1981)	$20.00/$21.00
Vol. 16	(1982)........................	$22.00/$25.00
Vols. 17-18	(1983-1984)	$27.00/$30.00
Vol. 19	(avail. Dec. 1985)	$27.00/$30.00 Vol(s)._____ Vol._____

Annual Review of IMMUNOLOGY

Vols. 1-2	(1983-1984)	$27.00/$30.00
Vol. 3	(avail. April 1985)	$27.00/$30.00 Vol(s)._____ Vol._____

Annual Review of MATERIALS SCIENCE

Vols. 1-11	(1971-1981)	$20.00/$21.00
Vol. 12	(1982)........................	$22.00/$25.00
Vols. 13-14	(1983-1984)	$64.00/$67.00
Vol. 15	(avail. Aug. 1985)	$64.00/$67.00 Vol(s)._____ Vol._____

Annual Review of MEDICINE: Selected Topics in the Clinical Sciences

Vols. 1-3, 5-15	(1950-1952; 1954-1964)	$20.00/$21.00
Vols. 17-32	(1966-1981)	$20.00/$21.00
Vol. 33	(1982)........................	$22.00/$25.00
Vols. 34-35	(1983-1984)	$27.00/$30.00
Vol. 36	(avail. April 1985)	$27.00/$30.00 Vol(s)._____ Vol._____

Annual Review of MICROBIOLOGY

Vols. 17-35	(1963-1981)	$20.00/$21.00
Vol. 36	(1982)........................	$22.00/$25.00
Vols. 37-38	(1983-1984)	$27.00/$30.00
Vol. 39	(avail. Oct. 1985)...........	$27.00/$30.00 Vol(s)._____ Vol._____

Annual Review of NEUROSCIENCE

Vols. 1-4	(1978-1981)	$20.00/$21.00
Vol. 5	(1982)........................	$22.00/$25.00
Vols. 6-7	(1983-1984)	$27.00/$30.00
Vol. 8	(avail. March 1985)..........	$27.00/$30.00 Vol(s)._____ Vol._____

Annual Review of NUCLEAR AND PARTICLE SCIENCE

Vols. 12-31	(1962-1981)	$22.50/$23.50
Vol. 32	(1982)........................	$25.00/$28.00
Vols. 33-34	(1983-1984)	$30.00/$33.00
Vol. 35	(avail. Dec. 1985)	$30.00/$33.00 Vol(s)._____ Vol._____

SEE ORDERING INFORMATION ON PAGE 4